# Environmental Effects on Polymeric Materials

(In Two Volumes)

VOL. II: Materials

## POLYMER ENGINEERING AND TECHNOLOGY

*Executive Editor:* **D. V. Rosato**

*Editors:* **R. B. Akin, H. F. Mark, J. J. Scavuzzo, S. S. Stivala, L. J. Zukor**

---

# Environmental Effects on Polymeric Materials

**Edited by DOMINICK V. ROSATO**

Technical Editor, *Plastics World*
and Engineering Consultant

**and ROBERT T. SCHWARTZ**

Chief, Nonmetallic Materials Division,
Air Force Materials Laboratory, Dayton, Ohio

**VOLUME II: Materials**

**Interscience Publishers**

a division of John Wiley & Sons   New York • London • Sydney

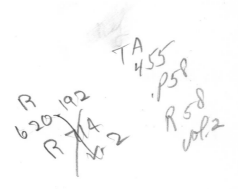

Practically all plastic material suppliers have contributed in the preparation of this book, also many fabricators, trade publications (particularly *Plastics World* and *Reinforced Plastics and Composites World*), and technical societies (particularly SPI and SPE).

Photographs of the editors and authors appear on the following pages.

*D. V. Rosato*
*R. T. Schwartz*

# Editors

DOMINICK V. ROSATO
*Technical Editor,* Plastics World
*and Engineering Consultant*
*Boston, Mass.*

ROBERT T. SCHWARTZ
*Chief, Nonmetallic Materials Division*
*Air Force Materials Laboratory*
*Dayton, Ohio*

# *Authors*

JACK H. ROSS, Chap. 10
*Air Force Materials Laboratory*
*Wright-Patterson Air Force Base,*
*Ohio*

MARGARET B. HAYS, Chap. 11
*Naval Air Development Center*
*Johnsville, Pa.*

CHARLES A. CASSOLA, Chap. 11
*Naval Air Development Center*
*Johnsville, Pa.*

MARTIN J. DEVINE, Chap. 12
*Naval Air Development Center*
*Johnsville, Warminster, Pa.*

PHILIP A. DiMATTIA, Chap. 13
*Supervisor in Education, Research,*
*    and Development*
*Massachusetts State Department of*
*    Education*
*Boston, Mass.*

JERRY K. SIERON, Chap. 14
*Air Force Materials Laboratory*
*Wright-Patterson Air Force Base,*
*    Ohio*

RAYMOND G. SPAIN, Chap. 14
*Air Force Materials Laboratory*
*Wright-Patterson Air Force Base,*
*Ohio*

ALBERT G. H. DIETZ, Chap. 15
*Massachusetts Institute of Technology*
*Cambridge, Mass.*

HERBERT S. SCHWARTZ,
Chap. 15
*Air Force Materials Laboratory*
*Wright-Patterson Air Force Base,*
*Ohio*

FRANK J. RIEL, Chap. 16
*Whittaker Corp.*
*San Diego, Calif.*

DONALD V. ROSATO, Chaps. 15
and 16
*Boston College*
*Chestnut Hill, Mass.*

# *Preface*

The age-old problem of damage due to environment will always be with mankind. However, with polymers or plastics major advances have been achieved in resisting or reducing deterioration. Practically all the available plastics contribute different characteristics which improve resistance to environmental damage when compared to other materials. As reviewed in this book, plastics are used successfully and required in myriad applications such as those in packaging, housewares, building, highway construction, electronics, appliances, medical, biological, chemical, adhesives, coatings, lubricants, reinforced plastics, elastomers, clothing, transportation, hydrospace, and aerospace. Significant improvements have been made with plastics in the past thirty years, with the future improvements to be even more spectacular based on new polymers in the test tubes.

Plastics vitally concern almost every facet of mankind. They occupy the attention of a large fraction of the research, development, design, production, sales, marketing, and consumer efforts in diverse industry operations, each basically with its own product, approach, and purpose.

Of the 25% of all the plastics exposed to the effects of weather, 8% goes into the building and construction market, mainly as outside coating, paneling, roofing, glazing, and gutters. The 4% used for packaging and containers involves the use of film for covering products in shipment and molded industrial or domestic outdoor storage containers. Wire and cable insulation use most of the 2% for electronics. The 2% for transportation provides an outlet for different plastics being used on the exterior of automobiles, trucks, and boats. Most of the 2% going into pipe involves underground applications. Practically all of the 2% for agriculture requires film or sheet. The remaining 7% has a variety of applications, from rainwear to playground products, picnic facilities, and beach housing. In addition to these weather environments, the other environments reviewed include those listed in the Table of Contents.

This review fulfills the important and growing need which industrial, commercial, and Federal Government personnel identify as the most critical; namely, more information about the degradation of materials. In order to understand the present related problems, there has been a tremendous demand for knowledge on the effects of environments. A considerable amount of information on plastics has been generated from different sources in the last few years. Industry experts have participated in the preparation of this book based on personal and co-workers' experience. Data and conclusions have been assembled, as well as condensed reviews. References are considered very complete.

In the two volumes of this book the most important new developments and meaningful data are reported. Most of these chapters have been prepared so that they can be classified as "technical works of art." As shown in the Table of Contents and Subject Index of these reviews many different environments, materials, products, processing, testing, service life, fundamentals of degradation, rheology, design criteria, material selection, and technical business decisions related to the overall subject are considered.

The business aspect has played an important part in expanding the use of plastics to resist environmental damage. Decisions to expand profitably the national economy has in many cases been possible through the use of plastics to reduce the overall capital investment or maintenance. This condition has been one of the major reasons for developing the present multibillion dollar industries which use plastics. The steady flow of new plastics, new production processes, and new market demands have caused this tremendous growth. Production in pounds is increasing at a rate in excess of ten times that of metals production; it is already greater than the total production of all non-ferrous metal and is about a fifth of that of steel. From a 1957–1959 base, plastics sales grew 286% by 1964 as compared to a growth of 170% for all chemicals and 143% for all manufacturing. Predictions indicate that by the early 1980's more volume of plastics will be used than steel; by the year 2000, more weight of plastics will be used.

We hope that this book will aid in stimulating further research on plastics, development of the very important and necessary new equipment, and more sound use of plastics. The use of plastics is limited only by the ingenuity and imagination of the people in research, engineering, marketing, buying, and management.

D. V. ROSATO
R. T. SCHWARTZ

# Contents

VOLUME II: MATERIALS

# Contents of Volume I: Environments

# 10

# *Fibers*

## Jack H. Ross

*Air Force Materials Laboratory,*
*Wright-Patterson Air Force Base, Ohio*

## CONTENTS

## I. POLYMERIC FIBERS: HISTORY, FORMATION, AND UTILIZATION

### A. Formation and Utilization

The emergence of fibers formed from polymeric substances have in recent years come about as a result of tremendous strides in the synthesis of entirely new and unique polymers. From the appearance in the late 1930's of nylon 6-6, the flow of new polymers and fibers formed from them has resulted in many new classes of fibers. Included in this flow of new fibers have been many new types of cellulosic fibers. So that a better understanding can be gained of these new fiber types a brief description of how fibers are formed is presented along with basic fiber data. The evolvement of these many new fibers is so broad that it is impossible to describe how each is formed and there are so many trade names and generic terms in common usage that it is quite possible that some will be inadvertently omitted. Table 10-1 shows a breakdown by polymer class of some of the well-known fibers available, either commercially or experimentally. The fibers to be presented and discussed are those primarily used in military and industrial applications.

## 1. Formation and Properties

Essentially there are three basic techniques that are utilized in the forming of polymeric fibers. These are described as "wet," "dry," and "melt" spinning. In the case of melt spinning the polymer is, with the use of elevated temperatures, converted to a viscous liquid, then extruded through a spinnerette under pressure into an atmosphere at a lower temperature where it is reconverted into a solid material, i.e., a fiber. Fibers formed by the dry spinning technique are achieved by the

TABLE 10-1.   Fiber Types by Polymer Systems

| Cellulosics | Polyamides |
|---|---|
| Rayon | Nylon 6 |
| High wet modulus rayon | Nylon 66 |
| Saponified acetate | Nomex (Aromatic) |
| Acetate | |
| Cellulose triacetate | Polyester |
| | Dacron |
| Acrylics | Kodel |
| Orlon | Vycron |
| Creslan | Fortrel |
| Acrilan | |
| Zefran | Heterocyclic Polymers |
| Dynel | Polyimides |
| | Polybenzimidazoles |
| Olefins | Polytrafluoroethylene |
| Polyethylene | |
| Polypropylene | |

dissolving of the polymer in a highly volatile solvent, then extruding through a spinerette into a warm air or heated chamber, causing evaporation of the solvent leaving the solid fiber ready for stretching. The last of the commonly used spinning techniques, wet spinning, necessitates the dissolving of the polymer in a chemical solution, followed by extrusion into a coagulating bath where the polymer is changed into an insoluble fiber form. There are variations to the three techniques described, but for all practical purposes the fibers described herein are formed by one of these three techniques. In Table 10-2, the fibers shown in Table 10-1, are tabulated by spinning system. It is not the intention here to describe the specifics of how each fiber is formed since Kaswell (1) and Press (2) have well documented these procedures. The formation of a polymeric fiber is the first of two major steps that must be carried out to achieve maximum fiber properties. The fiber when first formed is is most cases highly extensible, has a large diameter, and low strength. The molecules in the structure are considered unoriented and the fiber has no elastic recovery. The second step is to draw or stretch the fibers to essentially straighten out the molecules, and orient them so that high strength is achieved through molecule crystallinity. This drawing or stretching is generally carried out in the presence of steam or over a heated metal shoe or using both. This second step effectively creates a fiber with such properties, as in the case of nylon, of high strength, elasticity, resiliance, and excellent energy absorption.

These fibers are available in many forms and configurations. The most common form (when considering industrial and military uses) is continuous filament yarn, in which the yarn, composed of a few or

TABLE 10-2.  Spinning Techniques

| Melt spinning | Wet spinning | Dry spinning |
|---|---|---|
| Nylon 6 | Rayon | Acetate |
| Nylon 66 | High wet modulus rayon | Saponified acetate |
| Dacron | Orlon [a] | Cellulose triacetate |
| Kodel | Creslan [a] | Polyimides [b] |
| Vycron | Acrilan [a] | Polybenzimidazoles [b] |
| Fortrel | Zefran [a] | |
| Polyethylene | Dynel [a] | |
| Polypropylene | | |

[a] Can also be dry spun.
[b] These classes of polymers are still experimental and specifics on fiber forming have not been made public, but it is assumed they are dry spun based on polymer properties.

many fibers, is wound, after spinning and drawing, on a pirn, cone, bobbin, or warp beam, depending on the intended use. Other forms of these fibers include staple fibers (synthetic), cut to given lengths for processing on the cotton or woolen spinning systems, and tow, which is sometimes described as a heavy continuous multifilament strand of fibers suitable for cutting into staple or using as a heavy yarn after twisting. The size of the synthetic fiber is known as denier. Denier is defined as the weight in grams of 9000 m of a fiber or yarn; the higher the denier the coarser the yarn. It has been shown in Table 10-1, that each polymer system has spawned a number of commercial fibers, each of which was created through slight modification of the polymer system or the spinning system. This is especially true in the case of the acrylics and modacrylics. Polyacrylonitrile can be formed into a fiber which probably has as an only advantage, its ability to be pyrolyzed into a high modulus carbon fiber. To achieve a dyeable, medium strength, processable, and resilient fiber, each of the acrylic fibers contain from 5 to 10% of a polymer which assists in creating a commercially profitable product. The modacrylics normally contain as much as 55% of another monomer. As the industrial and military uses of polymeric fibers have increased, it has become apparent that modifications or additives would be necessary to provide specific forms of a fiber for specific uses. In Table 10-3, some variations for each polymer class are shown. These are only a few, as the two Nylon 6-6 producers show 20–25 yarn variations apiece, Nylon 6 producers have 5–10 yarn variations, polyester producers have up to 6 yarn variations to supply, Olefin producers have 4-6 yarn variations and acrylic producers have up to 11 variations in their yarns available, and none of these variations reflect the many yarn sizes available in continuous filament and monofilament, staple and tow forms (3). The cellullosic fibers are available in so many forms (sizes), variations (chemical), and shapes (cross sections) that the only source of information must be the fiber producers.

The mechanical properties of these fibers can be made to vary depending on polymer variations, degree of draw, finish applied to the fiber, etc. In Table 10-4, a number of fibers from each polymer class are shown with their tenacity (grams per denier) and elongation (in percent). From this table it is seen that any strength or elongation can be obtained and, although not shown, energy absorption can be varied through control of strength and elongation. Data are given for some Russian fibers to demonstrate their capabilities in the fiber-forming area. Further, data on glass and superalloy fibers are presented to

TABLE 10-3. Some Variations in Synthetic Fibers

| Polyamides | Polyesters | Acrylics | Olefins |
|---|---|---|---|
| Normal tenacity | Bright, high tenacity | Bright | Heat stabilized |
| High tenacity | Bright, normal tenacity | Semidull | Heat and light stabilized |
| Crimped textured bulked | Modified cross section | Carpet staple | Pigmented or clear |
| Semibright | Semidull regular tenacity | High bulk | Carpet fibers |
| Bright | Dull, normal tenacity | High shrink | Bulked continuous fibers |
| Modified cross section | | Solution dyed | Solution dyed |
| Dull | | | High tenacity |
| Semidull | | | Low tenacity |
| Heat stabilized | | | |
| Light resistant | | | |
| Heat and light resistant | | | |
| Light resistant–deep dyeing | | | |
| Normal tenacity, high elongation, low finish, light resistant | | | |
| Bright, high tenacity | | | |

TABLE 10-4. Mechanical Properties of Fibers (2,4,5,9)

| Polymer type and fiber trade or generic name | Tenacity, g/denier | Elongation, % | Tensile strength, $10^{-3}$ psi |
|---|---|---|---|
| Cellulosic | | | |
| Avisco RD-101 | 4.07 | 30.2 | |
| Avisco U-22 | 2.96 | 19.3 | |
| Avisco Fiber 40 | 5.00 | 18.0 | 96.0 |
| Super Cordura | 3.38 | 17.4 | |
| Acetate | 1.23 | 24.3 | 20.5–26.0 |
| Polyamide | | | |
| Nylon 66, | | | |
| DuPont | | | |
| high tenacity | 6.9–9.2 | 17–21 | 86–134 |
| Chemstrand | | | |
| high tenacity | 6.1–9.0 | 17–24 | 86–134 |
| Nylon 6 | | | |
| Enka | 7.6 | 18.6 | 99–125 |
| Caprolan | 5.5–9.0 | 17–33 | 99–125 |
| Lilion | 4.5–6.0 | 30–35 | 99–125 |
| Kapron | 7.6 | 18.5 | |
| Nylon 7 | | | |
| Enant | 7.2 | 18.7 | |
| Nomex | 5.5 | 17.0 | 84 |
| Polybenzimidazole | 4.5–6.0 | 20–25 | 68 |

| Polymer type and fiber trade or generic name | Tenacity, g/denier | Elongation, % | Tensile strength, $10^{-3}$ psi |
|---|---|---|---|
| Polyester | | | |
| Dacron, Ty 68 | 9.5 | 13.7 | 111–138 |
| Vicron | 5.3–5.4 | 32–36 | 97.5–110.0 |
| Kodel | 2.7 | 27 | 39–47 |
| Fortrel | 4.0–4.3 | 40 | 71–76 |
| Lavsan | 2.5–4.7 | 30.0–40.0 | |
| Acrylic | | | |
| Acrilan | 2.5 | 36 | 30–40 |
| Orlon | 2.4 | 27 | 32–39 |
| Creslan | 2.7 | 33 | 38 |
| Zefran | 3.5 | 33 | 53 |
| Dynel | 3.5 | 30 | 50 |
| Nitron | 5.5 | 15 | |
| Olefin | | | |
| Polypropylene | 5.0–7.0 | 10–20 | 55–98 |
| Polyethylene | 4.5–8.5 | 20–35 | 46–81 |
| Fluorocarbon | | | |
| Teflon | 1.6 | 13 | |
| Ftorlon | 5.2–6.7 | 8–10 | 50 |
| Glass | 6.0–7.3 | 3–4 | 195–237 |
| Superalloys (Chromel A) | 1.6 | 8.5 | 162 |

allow one to realize the penalties in strength and elongation that must be endured, in addition to problems of abrasion and flexibility, if these two fiber classes are to be used in flexible fabric applications.

Because so many classes of polymers are available, it is extremely important to be able to distinguish between them in the yarn form as well as in fabric. Techniques used to define a specific fiber include: (*1*) burning test, (*2*) density, (*3*) microscopy (longitudinal and cross section), (*4*) staining with dyes and reagents, and (*5*) solubility in chemicals. These have been described by many others (1,2,6,7). Since most of these techniques require equipment not always available, only the first technique is best suited for the layman's use. This test involves exposure of a sample to a small flame and recording of the reaction that takes place. The test specimen can consist of groups or "wads" of fiber, short lengths of yarn, or small pieces of cloth. The specimen is pushed slowly into the flame and effect, odor, and characteristic of residue is noted. Table 10-5, shows how one fiber type chosen from each polymer class reacts to this test. It is obvious that this test is very effective in making a preliminary analysis of fiber type. The bulk of the technical material to be discussed herein will be limited to only a few of the fibers reviewed in this section. Specifically fibers from polyamides, polyesters, olefins, and heterocyclic polymers will be the most interesting, as they have the most potential for the military and industrial applications to be discussed.

## 2. Uses for Polymeric Fibers

Polymeric fibers in woven form have found their way into an ever-growing field that requires high strength and flexibility as a prerequisite. The ability to transform a bundle of extremely fine filaments (fiber diameter as fine as 2–3 $\mu$) into a plied and cabled yarn which can withstand tremendous impact loads such as experienced by tires or aircraft overrun barriers is in itself quite a fascinating goal to achieve. The way that polymeric fibers have superceded natural fibers is a story in itself, while the main goal here is to acquaint one with the uses of polymeric fibers, the environments to which the woven materials can be exposed to and degraded to a point of failure if not adequately protected. Polymeric fibers have found wide acceptance in (*1*) the woven state where the fabric structure provides the properties desired in a specific end use, and (*2*) the woven state with an elastomeric or resinous coating added to provide protection to the polymeric base fiber as well as providing protection from environments and im-

TABLE 10-5.   Reaction of Fibers to Burning

| Fiber (by polymer class) | Behavior during test | | | Odor of reaction product | Residue |
|---|---|---|---|---|---|
| | Approaching flame | In flame | Removal from flame | | |
| Cellulosic, rayon | Does not fuse or shrink | Burns | Continues to burn | Burnt paper | No ash, unless a dull or semidull fiber |
| Acrylic (Acrilan)[a] | Fuses away from flame | Burns with melting | Continues to burn with sputtering | Burnt red meat | Hard, black, irregular ash |
| Polyamides, Nylon 66 | Fuses away from flame | Melts as it burns | Self-extinguishing | Celery | Hard, round, gray, bead |
| Polyester, Kodel | Fuses away from flame | Melts as it burns | Continues to burn | Faintly sweet | Hard, irregular, black bead |
| Olefins, polypropylene | Fuses rapidly from flame | Melts as it burns | Continues to burn slowly | Burning tar | Hard, tan, round bead |
| Glass | No reaction | Glows orange to red and smokes | No reaction | None | Fibers are intact but brittle |
| Metal | No reaction | Glows red | No reaction | None | Fibers are intact and flexible |

[a] So called modacrylics differ in that they are self-extinguishing.

prove mechanical properties. The uses of polymeric fibers to be discussed have been arranged in two categories, military and industrial. There is some overlapping of end uses between these two groups, however this is an accepted fact, since many military uses are translated to similar industrial applications after military prove out. Since clothing materials are being covered in another chapter, uses and environmental effects are not discussed.

**a. Military Uses.** The utilization of woven polymeric fibers have become extremely widespread in the military scheme. In Fig. 10-1, many of the present and proposed future uses for both uncoated and coated woven materials are listed by general categories.

*(1) Deceleration Systems.* A major use for woven polymeric fibers, where the fabric does not require a coating, is in self inflating parachutes. Prior to World War II, silk was used in personnel type parachutes, with cotton and rayon used for cargo and other parachutes. Since that time nylon 6-6 has taken over in all categories of parachutes, except for expendable or one use parachutes which are still made of flame-proofed cotton or rayon. Polyester(Dacron) fibers were the subject of extensive research to utilize their improved thermal stability over nylon 6-6 up to 425°F, but due to inability of weavers to duplicate research results, polyester fiber fabrics were not stable at temperatures above 250°F and therefore have never been extensively used. Nylon 6 fibers have not been considered due to low melting temperature where a major requirement calls for nonmelting fibers. Acrylic fibers are too weak or too elastic in addition to being available only in staple form, to make the high strength yarns and fabric required in any form of parachute. Figure 10-2 shows the latest in personnel type parachutes. In addition to high strength, parachute fabrics are woven to have a specific range of air flow or permeability (in cubic feet per minute per square foot) which will have a direct effect on the opening shock imposed when the parachute deploys or opens and on the rate of descent. This control of permeability is essential in all parachute fabrics regardless of the intended use. This is one reason why the fabrics must be heat set during finishing to set the yarns in the fabric so that permeability can be maintained regardless how the parachute is packed and stored. The ultimate in cargo involves the use of six parachutes, 100 ft nominal diameter (Fig. 10-3) and can successfully lower bulldozers, howitzers, and heavy trucks to the ground. As aircraft were built with landing speeds in excess of 140 knots and of heavier weights, some means of slowing them down had to be devised. Because

## Decelerators

Personnel recovery
Aircraft brake
Reentry capsule
Booster recovery
Capsule recovery
Weapons delivery
Cargo
Subsonic
  Solid canopy
  Ringslot
  Ribbon
  Parawing
Supersonic
  Solid Canopy
  Ribbon (Hemisflo)
  Balloon
  Flexible rotor
Hypersonic
  (Hyperflo)
  Balloon
  Inverted Umbrella

## Fiber Optics

Instrument review
Area scanning
Remote photography

## Pressurized Containers

Pressure suits
Tires
Hose
Ducting
Fluid storage
Fuel expulsion bladders
Collapsible landing bags
Inflated survival gear

## Insulation Systems

Aerospace vehicles
Airbreathing vehicles
Chaff
Gaskets
Orbital systems
Personnel protection development
Rocket motor cases

## Protective Systems

Thermal curtains
Flexible radomes
Exposure shields
Missile shelters
Personnel shelters
Overrun barriers
Personnel restraint

## Expanded Structures

Aerospace vehicles
Manned orbital system
Solar collectors
Antennas
Orbital gliders
Personnel protection development
Inflatable rotors
Parawing
Orbital
  Rigidizable
  Flexible filament wound
  Multiwall
Superorbital
  Rigidizable
  Flexible filament wound
  Multiwall
Reentry
  Airmat
  Multiwall

## Rigid Structures

Filament wound cases
Rocket nozzles
Nose cones
Radomes

Fig. 10-1.  Potential uses of fibrous materials.

Fig. 10-2. Personnel type parachute.

thrust reversers on jet engines cause a loss in forward speed during normal flight, parachutes were chosen as the most efficient means of slowing the aircraft. All of the Century series aircraft use ring-slot parachutes (Figs. 10-4 and 10-5) as a means of slowing down. A ring-slot parachute is made by incorporating 8, 12, or 15-in. wide ribbons (woven as such or cut from broad goods) in the canopy in lieu of fabric. The larger bomber aircraft are also slowed down by parachute (Fig. 10-6) which in this case is called a ribbon parachute, since the canopy is fabricated from 2-in. wide woven ribbons having an ultimate breaking strength of 300 lb. Another type of ribbon parachute is used for the delivery of heavy bomb type devices and because of the low altitude, high speed, high weight combination, ribbons of 2-in. width having ultimate strengths to 5000 lb are used as shown in Figs. 10-7 and 10-8. Since the first space shots, parachutes have been used to recover the load, whether instrument or man, after reentry. Recent developments in the

Fig. 10-3.  Cluster of six 100 ft diameter cargo parachutes.

Fig. 10-4.  Ringslot brake parachute on F-101 aircraft.

Fig. 10-5. B-58 using 28 ft diameter nylon 6-6 brake parachute.

parachute field has been the Rabbit Ear type (Fig. 10-9) which is a parachute that can be picked up by an aircraft while in descent thru the use of a hook to snag the line between the ears. Parachutes are used extensively to lower flares during the night, to recover detachable fuel tanks from aircraft, to create initial drag and to stabilize loads before deployment of paragliders (parawings, Rogallo Wings, etc.) to name only a few. The deployment speed of parachutes described to this point have been primarily subsonic (Mach 1 or lower) making possible the use of nylon 6-6. Recent research has resulted in parachutes capable of operating up to Mach 4.0. Even at altitudes in excess of 100,000 ft, nylon monofilaments in the top of parachutes melted, re-

Fig. 10-6. Ribbon parachute for heavy bomber.

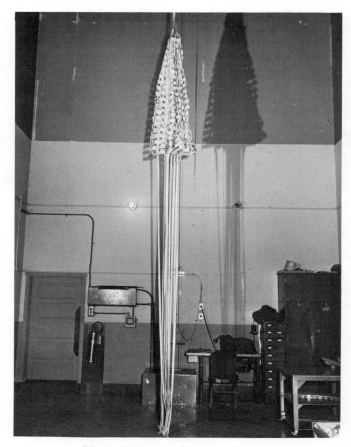

Fig. 10-7. Nomex ribbon parachute.

quiring the use of Nomex (aromatic polyamide) fibers. Extensive wind tunnel and flight tests have shown that Nomex fibers in a unique, new deceleration configuration can be deployed and recovered from speeds up to Mach 4.0. Flight tests of two of these new configurations, the Hemisflo (Fig. 10-10) and the Hyperflo (Fig. 10-11) using Nomex fibers were deployed at Mach 3.4 and 4.0, respectively (8). Even ultra-fine fibers (0.0005 in. diameter) drawn from superalloys such as Chromel R and Rene 41 are being woven into fabrics for use in these new decelerator configurations. Future deployable decelerators will take on even more unique shapes (Fig. 10-12).

**(2) *Flexible Wing Devices.*** In recent years a new concept of deceleration and recovery has come into being. Originally known as the

Fig. 10-8. Heavy bomb device with drag parachute.

Rogallo Wing (after its inventor, F. M. Rogallo), it is now known as the paraglider or parawing. Made of three inflatable coated fabric booms which come to an apex at the front, with a nonporous sail between the booms, the paraglider can be packaged in small containers and inflated manually or automatically by barometric devices or telemetered from remote stations. An example of a practical use for this device is a cargo delivery system (Fig. 10-13*a*) which can be controlled from the ground and flown to a pin point landing. In addition micrometeoroid sensing has been accomplished using a paraglider made of glass fabric coated with ablating silicone rubber (Fig. 10-13*b*) as the means for descent and final recovery of the sensor. Consideration is being given to the use of this device as an escape mode from manned orbiting vehicles (Fig. 10-13*b*). Wind tunnel tests have shown that a retractable form of this device mounted on an aircraft can increase lift during takeoff and landing.

Fig. 10-9. Rabbit-ear parachute for mid-air pickup of capsule.

**(3) Expandable Systems.** It would be very advantageous to be able to carry a means of transportation or recovery in a small package ready for instant use. A device of this type is being given serious consideration at present. Fabricated from two layers high strength fabric woven intergrally together with tie threads and coated with an elastomer to provide impermeability, devices of this type can be inflated quickly from compressed air or $CO_2$ bottles. The first of these devices was Goodyear's Inflatoplane (Fig. 10-14). From this initial vehicle have come many concepts utilizing this two layer fabric. One of these is the recovery of missile boosters. Through the use of expandable wings (Fig. 10-15) and fins that would be packaged during the initial stages of flight and deployed as the booster reentered the earth's atmosphere, a navigable, recoverable booster could be achieved. In a wing of this type, the fibers used would have to be a polymeric substance or an ultrafine (0.0005 in.) diameter superalloy woven into a double wall fabric with tie threads (connecting the face and back fabrics) 6–9 ft in length. Another concept under consideration is Douglas Aircraft's Paracone which could also be made from this double woven fabric. When woven of high temperature fibers it could be used as an astronaut emergency escape system, that is expanded by gas into an inverted cone that envelopes the escapee, protects him through reentry and carries him safely to the ground, where he is pro-

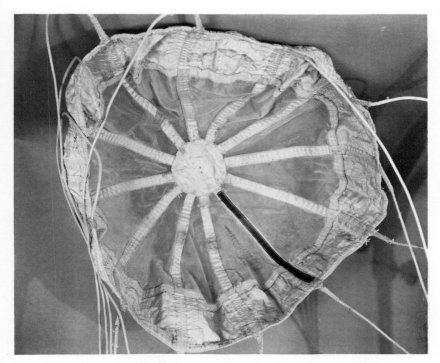

Fig. 10-10. One form of supersonic parachute (Hemisflo) made of metal fabric.

tected from high speed impact by collapse of the point of the cone which absorbs the energy of impact. A technique similar to this (Fig. 10-16) can be used for delivering troops, cargo, or can be used as emergency escape from aircraft. Larger Paracones could carry large numbers of men or even vehicles. Further use for the double wall fabric held together with tie threads is an easily inflatable fabric structure for housing electronic gear and its operators. This type of portable shelter (Fig. 10-17) can be erected in less than an hour from a package 10 ft × 6 ft × 3 ft weighing 1300 lb.

*(4) Inflatable Devices.* Yet another form of inflatable structure involves simple inflation of a tube of coated high strength fabric. One concept of this form of structure would be the ring of a circular shaped space station having a metal hub (Fig. 10-18) which could be inflated from an empty booster. The hub would remain at zero G, while rotation of the system would provide artificial gravity in the torous section. Still another form of the inflated tube concept is a tunnel for use by astronauts in moving from one vehicle to another, or between

Fig. 10-11. Hyperflo parachute of Nomex with ribbon cap.

two areas of a single vehicle in space (Fig. 10-19). This tunnel would be packaged and covered by a deployable cover during launch and injection into orbit. Made of a coated fabric and a foam which is self-erecting due to the elastic recovery characteristics of the materials. Yet another potential use for this type of structure is as shock absorbing devices for both cargo (Fig. 10-20) and soft landing on the moon or other planets (Fig. 10-21). Similar to the latter is a proposed inflatable torous landing gear for the Apollo Lunar Excursion Module made of fabric woven of 0.0007-in. diameter superalloy fiber and covered with an elastomeric coating to provide necessary sealing characteristics. A major use today of the inflated tube concept is to provide emergency

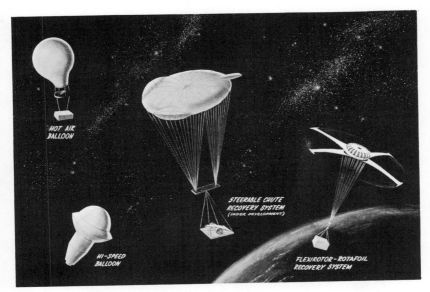

Fig. 10-12. Future deployable aerodynamic decelerators.

flotation to aircrew personnel who must parachute into water. In Fig. 10-22, a multi-man life raft with sea anchor, boarding ramp, and sun shield demonstrates how various elastomeric (natural and synthetic) coatings on polymeric and polyester fiber fabrics are effectively utilized. The individual is also provided with his own flotation gear (Fig. 10-23) consisting of $CO_2$ inflated life vest and one man life raft with shield.

**(5) *Air Supported Structures.*** The major use of fibers in air supported structures are for inflated shelters for radar equipment, and satellite communications equipment. Radomes play a large part in the successful operation of radar units over a long period of time under adverse weather conditions. Initial radomes (Fig. 10-24) were 50–60 ft in diameter and have grown to a diameter of 210 ft diameter as achieved in the structure (Fig. 10-25) built to house the Telstar antenna system. Important here has been the need for holding to critical tolerances during construction and use to avoid distortion of the signals being transmitted and received.

**(6) *Fuel and Liquid Containers.*** Elastomeric coated polyamide and polyester fibers in fabrics have been fabricated into tanks capable of storing up to 50,000 gallons of fuel or other liquids. One airtransportable refueling system (Fig. 10-26) has been extensively evaluated by

(a)

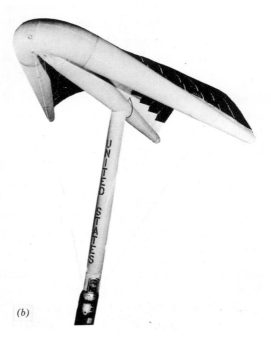

(b)

Fig. 10-13(*a*). Cargo type paraglider. (Courtesy of Ryan Aeronautical Co.); (*b*). paraglider for recovery of micrometeoroid sensor. (Courtesy of Space-General Corp.); (*c*) paraglider for recovery of man from space orbit. (Courtesy of Space-General Corp.)

Fig. 10-14. Fabric Inflatoplane. (Courtesy of Goodyear Aerospace Corp.)

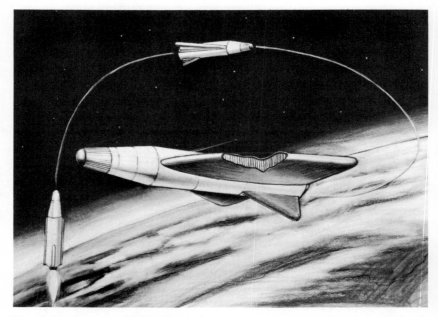

Fig. 10-15. Concept of inflatable device for booster recovery. (Courtesy of Goodyear Aerospace Corp.)

the Air Force for use at advanced, unimproved, forward area air strips.
The collapsible containers can be deployed quickly when empty, and
are easily camouflaged due to their low, flat profile. Fuel tanks capable
of use in armoured carriers and trucks are also being developed. Fuel
cells designed to fit into KC-135 Jet Tankers will provide additional
refueling capability.

*(7) Flexible Covers.* Aircraft as well as personnel must be protected from environments, especially the ice and snow of the Arctic
and Antarctic regions. Previously cotton was the material used in
most cases; however, resin or elastomeric-coated polyamide and
polyester fabrics (Fig. 10-27) are used to provide the protection to the
wing and tail surfaces of the aircraft as well as to the clear plastic
canopy.

*(8) Aircraft Arresting Gear.* Jet aircraft deceleration has always
been a problem especially if both the hydraulic system (which operates
the brakes) and the drag parachute fail to operate. Many forms of
arresting gear have been used for ground based aircraft. The latest and
most efficient system (Fig. 10-28) utilizes a 120,000 lb ultimate strength

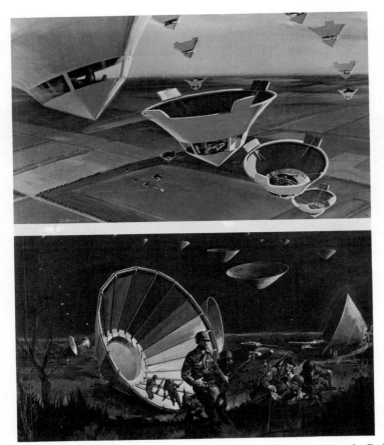

Fig. 10-16. Inflatable fabric paracone. (Courtesy of Douglas Aircraft Co.)

webbing 8 in. wide and 1250–1450 ft long. This webbing (Fig. 10-29) is used to absorb, through the elongation of the nylon webbing in conjunction with a hydraulic brake system, the kinetic energy which is generated during the aircraft's deceleration.

*(9) Safety Harnesses.* When aircraft designers first considered belts to hold the pilot in a stable position during normal flight and emergency conditions, they had an ideal material, cotton, available. Cotton when woven into webbing, provided fair strength and low elongation which would prevent forward motion of the pilot during rapid decelerations. When nylon became available it was used in the same application, safety harnesses. The higher rupture elongation of

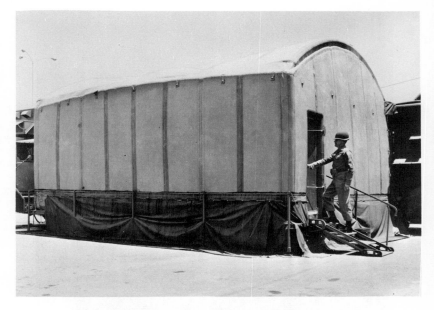

Fig. 10-17. Inflatable rubber fabric shelter.
(Courtesy of Goodyear Aerospace Corp.)

nylon over cotton was translated into the safety harnesses causing an increase in injuries due to the nylon stretching during rapid deceleration (upper part of Fig. 10-30). Where nylon could not be hot stretched and stabilized it was found that a polyester fiber, Dacron could be so treated. When woven into webbing, ultimate elongation could be reduced by 20–25% effectively holding the aircrew member in a stable position, lower part of Fig. 10-30.

*(10) Parachute Harnesses.* Whether a parachute is being used to lower a man, or cargo, or stop an aircraft, a harness or riser or both of single or multiple layers of webbing must be used to carry the load. Many widths and thicknesses of webbing can be used (Fig. 10-31). Examples of present day harnesses and risers are shown in Figs. 10-32 and 10-33.

**b. Industrial Uses.** It is sometimes extremely difficult to determine whether a military use breeds an industrial application for a new fiber or its woven form, or the opposite. Regardless of this consideration it will be seen that a definite relationship exists between military

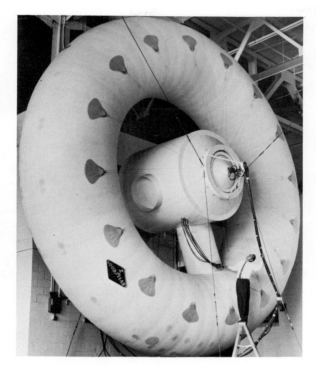

Fig. 10-18. Dacron torous shaped space station.
(Courtesy of Goodyear Aerospace Corp.)

and industrial applications of polymeric fibers. It is the intention here to describe those more unique industrial uses of polymeric fibers that can be considered an outgrowth of military conceived systems.

*(1)* *Expandable Systems.* An interesting outgrowth of the development of a double wall fabric held together with tie threads is the expandable ladder. Originally developed for inflation and use in the small confines of a missile tank where small openings prevent insertion of normal ladders, this unconventional ladder (Fig. 10-34) should find many uses in factories where narrow spaces prevent use of standard ladders.

*(2)* *Fuel and Liquid Containers.* As in the case of the military, rubber coated nylon fabrics are used extensively in the storage and shipment of liquid chemicals and fuels. The ability to fabricate these containers in various sizes (Fig. 10-35) makes them an extremely efficient means of handling liquids, along with their ability to be col-

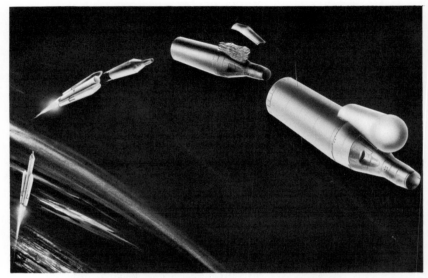

Fig. 10-19. Transfer tunnel concept of coated fabric.
(Courtesy of Goodyear Aerospace Corp.)

Fig. 10-20. Coated fabric self-inflating landing bags.

Fig. 10-21. Artist's concept of pneumatic decelerator for lunar vehicle. (Courtesy of Goodyear Aerospace Corp.)

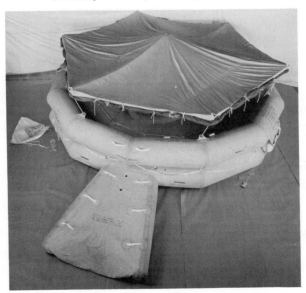

Fig. 10-22. Rubber coated nylon 6-6 multi-man life raft.

Fig. 10-23. One man life raft and life vest.

lapsed for storage and shipment after use they are gaining more wide spread usage. A unique application of this type container utilizes an entirely new fuel tank concept in the automotive field. The recent design by the Ford Motor Co. of the "GT" necessitated placing the fuel tank in an unusual position in the vehicle (Fig. 10-36) (tanks are superimposed in the photo). A metal tank would not fit due to body members causing obstructions and would be highly susceptible to collision damage. The end result was a flexible, bladder-type tank fabricated using the same spray urethane technique utilized in fabric fuel cells for aircraft.

*(3) Inflatable Structures.* Originally designed for carrying scientific instruments to very high altitudes and providing a stable platform, the Vee-Balloon is also capable of applications where heavy loads must be moved over varied terrain. Fabric of either polyamide or polyester fibers elastomeric coated are fabricated into two cigar shaped balloons joined at the nose, with a horizontal tail fin joining the two balloons at the back (Fig. 10-37) this device could make it possible to reduce the

Fig. 10-24. Transportable radomes. (Courtesy of Westinghouse Corp.)

Fig. 10-25. Flexible antenna cover. (Courtesy of Birdair Structures, Inc.)

Fig. 10-26. Rubberized fabric fuel tank.
(Courtesy of Goodyear Tire and Rubber Co.)

Fig. 10-27. Vinyl resin coated nylon 6-6 fabric aircraft cover.

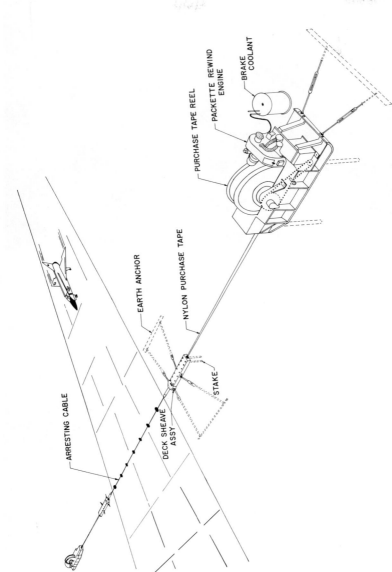

ARRESTING CABLE

DECK SHEAVE ASSY

EARTH ANCHOR

NYLON PURCHASE TAPE

STAKE

PURCHASE TAPE REEL

PACKETTE REWIND ENGINE

BRAKE COOLANT

Fig. 10-28. Schematic of system for arresting aircraft.

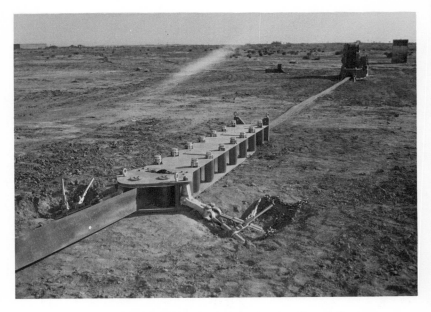

Fig. 10-29. Eight inch nylon 6-6 webbing for aircraft arresting gear.

cost of logging or make it feasible to move heavy difficult to handle loads to their destination.

*(4) Flexible Covers.* Materials used to provide protection from weather, chemicals (liquid or fumes), abrasion, etc., must be light in weight and highly flexible to provide easy handling and movement. Polyamide and polyester fibers in woven form with either resin or elastomer coatings are considerably lighter in weight then equal strength cotton materials. Their use as cargo covers (for trucks, boats, trailers, etc.) inflated shelters, in warehouses and temporary protection over building sites and water resistant ground cover (Fig. 10-38) has largely supplemented cotton where long service life is desired.

*(5) Seat Belts.* A direct outgrowth of webbing designed for aircraft safety harnesses and parachute harnesses has been the automobile seat belt. Proven to be an important factor in saving lives in automobile crashes, if woven properly, their wide spread acceptance has resulted in their being made standard on most new cars delivered. From the simple herringbone weave of nylon 6-6 yarn used by the military, present belts are made of nylon 6 as well and Dacron, and are available in a number of weave variations and in a multitude of colors (Fig. 10-

Fig. 10-30. Artist's concept of advantage of Dacron safety harness webbing.

39). Proper installation (Fig. 10-40) of belts is essential to effective use.

**(6) Marine Uses.** Many fibers, especially natural fibers such as hemp, sisal, etc., are used in rope making, however in marine use the synthetic fibers have been making steady inroads toward replacing the natural fibers. It is possible to make synthetic fibers into all rope forms and sizes each having superior strength to weight ratio than the natural fiber ropes (Fig. 10-41). The synthetic fiber ropes of either polyamide or polyester have found wide spread acceptance in the marine industry (Fig. 10-42). They resist rot, mildew, marine growths and because of greater strength, smaller bulk can be carried in greater

Fig. 10-31. Variations of nylon webbing. (Courtesy of Allied Chemical Co.)

lengths. The sails (Fig. 10-43) used in many sizes of sailboats are also made of synthetic fibers, especially polyesters. Having higher strength to weight ratios over cotton, they in the case of racing boats, can be changed faster, with greater ease, and require less storage space.

*(7)  Hose.* Many forms of hosing are now made of polymeric fibers. These have evolved from the need for materials that are stronger, more resistant to chemicals and heat, and more compatible with the coatings used in the hose. In the case of fire hose, polyester fibers (Fig. 10-44) are being used because of lighter weight, handleability, and lower maintenance. Recently a new nonmelting fiber, Nomex, has become available that because of its greater thermal stability to 500°F. should be a vast improvement over the polyesters and be a factor in reducing hose damage due to exposure to fire.

*(8)  Tires.* Automobile tires consume a tremendous quantity of polymeric fibers ranging from rayon to polyamide to polyester and even

Fig. 10-32. Harness of personnel parachute made of **3600** and **7000** lb nylon webbing.

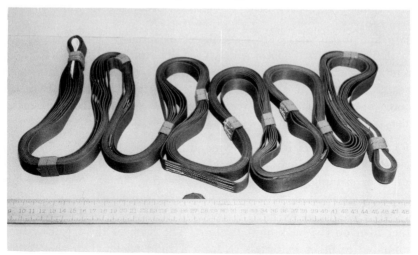

Fig. 10-33. Riser for cargo parachute made of 8 layers of **7800** lb nylon webbing.

Fig. 10-34. Expandable ladder. (Courtesy of Goodyear Aerospace Corp.)

glass and metal fibers are the subject of intensive research. Nylon (both 6 and 6-6) is the most widely used fiber in tires. (Fig. 10-45) only in recent years having topped the rayon fibers. The need for tires with greater resistance to the heat generated during flexure has been the source of research on adhesive systems for Nomex, glass and metal fibers.

*(9) Miscellaneous Uses.* Polymeric fibers are found in many supposedly unique applications, yet fibers were ultimately the only solution. For example, Teflon is used as a bearing surface due to its low coefficient of friction, with the Teflon being woven with another fiber in such a manner as to have the Teflon on the face of the fabric and the other fiber on the back of the fabric. The back of the fabric is then laminated to other materials to form a rigid backing for the Teflon. Braided packing (Fig. 10-46) of this same fiber is also used on acid

Fig. 10-35.  Portable fuel tanks.  (Courtesy of U.S. Rubber Co.)

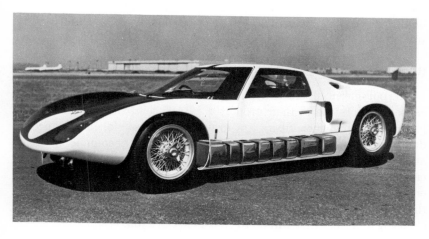

Fig. 10-36.  Concept of automobile fuel tank.
(Courtesy of Goodyear Aerospace Corp.)

Fig. 10-37. Inflatable skyhook. (Courtesy of Goodyear Aerospace Corp.)

pump valve shafts since the fiber is extremely resistant to corrosive liquids and fumes, even the most vigorous acids, alkalis, and organic solvents.

## B. Susceptibility to Environmental Degradation

All polymeric fibers are susceptible to environments which can cause deterioration of their properties. Because of the many classes of polymers from which fibers are drawn, it is possible, in advance, to determine those environments a specific use will encounter or create and through judicial choice, the most resistant fiber forming polymer can be used in preparing an optimum material. However there are some environments which effect all polymers and their fibers to some degree, thus placing squarely on the shoulders of the end item designer the choosing of a fiber that will do the most effective job.

### 1. *Environments Which Degrade Polymeric Fibers*

Since polymers are created through reactions which involve either heat, cold, other chemicals as reactants or catalysts, pressure, gases, or

Fig. 10-38. Coated nylon 6 fabric as a ground cover.
(Courtesy of Allied Chemical Co.)

more than one of these in combination, it becomes obvious that these polymeric fibers can be degraded by exposure to similar or related conditions, depending on the actual polymeric fiber. As will be seen, heat is the most critical environment (if one can be so indicated) that will effect the fibers. The manner in which the fiber (or polymer) sees the heat has a great deal to do with how it is degraded. For example, polyamides are degraded far more by heat and oxygen then by heat and nitrogen, which allows one to conclude that the polyamides oxidize during heating; whereas a polyester is degraded equally by heat in oxygen and nitrogen showing that it is truly heat sensitive. Further, the heat might be in the form of flame, or it might strike the fiber moving at a high velocity. As in exposure to other environments, the form the fiber is in has a great deal to do with how resistant it will be to the environment, for example; a thin fabric will fail in a much shorter time when exposed to a high intensity heat pulse than a thick, high strength webbing. In Section II, this will be shown most graphically. Heat in its many forms can effect polymeric fibers in many of their

Fig. 10-39. Styles of seat belt webbing. (Courtesy of Allied Chemical Co.)

uses, however heat as an environment is much more apparent in military uses.

Another of the more critical environments is radiation, which is divided in ultraviolet radiation (such as from sunlight) and ionizing radiation as experienced with nuclear sources or from the various radiation belts that surround our planet. It is further known that this latter form of radiation is in various forms, i.e., alpha, beta, gamma, and X-rays of which gamma is the most degrading and difficult to protect from (with respect to fibers and their woven forms). Sunlight is an environment that effects fibers (of all types) used in both industrial and military uses. Since many of the uses cited provide protection from the weather, sunlight is one environment that must be given special consideration in providing fibers with greater environmental resistance.

Since the polymerization process involves in many cases chemicals as catalysts or reactants, these chemicals (acids, alkalies, organic solvents) can also cause these polymers to degrade, dissolve, or even change structure depending on conditions. Time, concentration, and

Fig. 10-40. Nylon seat belt installation. (Courtesy of Seat Belt Council.)

pressure can magnify or slow the degradation of these fibers. The exposure to chemicals can occur at any point in the processing and use of the fibers.

Aging of fibrous materials formed from polymers is a determination of how storage or use in conditions other than weathering effects the polymer. Many materials are stored for long periods of time prior to actual use. How these storage conditions effect the polymeric fibers (and other fiber forms as well) can critically change their properties to such a degree as to reduce their intended service. Interrelated with ageing or storage is the moisture sensitivity of a polymeric system. Moisture can effect most critically such properties as shrinkage and strength. Equally important with the environment of aging is the effect of biological agents. As will be seen, it is not the polymeric fiber that is effected by bacteria or fungi, but the finish that is applied during forming or subsequently added coatings that are applied to provide protection from wholly different environments.

Fig. 10-41. Various nylon ropes. (Courtesy of Allied Chemical Co.)

The use of fibers in application that involve exposure to the environments of space have created new areas that can cause catistrophic degradation of the polymers. Ultraviolet radiation is unfiltered at altitudes above 100,000 ft and therefore will cause much more rapid breakdown of the polymeric fibers so exposed. The lack of any atmosphere (vacuum of $10^{-6}$ to $10^{-9}$ torr) might not in itself cause degradation to polymers. However, the outgassing of moisture and other volatile materials from the fiber, finish, or coating could well cause temporary and even permanent changes in the fiber or fabric properties. The effects of vacuum in fibers in any form irregardless of their substance, are little known at this time. Some effort has been initiated to establish effect of such environments as heat and vacuum, and UV and vacuum, and chemicals (rocket fuel residues) on woven fibrous materials either while still in the vacuum or immediately after removal from such an environment. In considering forthcoming space flight to planets such as Mars and Venus the time of exposure to these environments could exceed 90 days. Thus it is very important to establish how

Fig. 10-42. Nylon marine hawser. (Courtesy of du Pont.)

these new and unique conditions will degrade fibers in any form so that research can be initiated to achieve fibers that will withstand the these exposures.

## 2. Need for Protecting Polymeric Fibers

As can be seen from the many and varied uses for all forms of fibers and their selective susceptability to degradation by one or more environments some form of protection is required to extend the useful life of these flexible materials. Some properties of these materials cannot be given protection, except through the applying of heavy coatings. For example, most fibers when dry do not lose their flexibility at low temperatures, but as temperature increases become stiff and subsequently lose strength. The application of a coating of an elastomer such as neoprene or Viton will effectively increase the temperature at which flexibility is still retained. Obviously this route to provide protection is simply an ablative type protective that is dependent on the thick-

Fig. 10-43. Dacron sailcloth. (Courtesy of du Pont.)

ness of the coating and the exposure temperature. In reentry devices the rapid movement of the system tends to wipe (or ablate) the coating off. In an application where the system is stationary it will take longer for the coating to be burned off. Fibers can be protected from the degrading action of any environment simply by adding a coating of one form or another, but this is only a "crutch." The real need is for fibers with built-in resistance to degradation. The initial step in this direction has already been taken by many fiber producers. Both nylon 6 and 6-6 are available as a regular yarn or in a form that is resistant to both ultraviolet light and heat. Although the fiber retains the same melting point, strength retention and modulus are retained to temperatures closer to the melting point. Other polymeric fibers are being improved in the same manner. This is achieved through the addition of inhibitors to the polymer before spinning, making changes in the polymer structure through the attachment of other polymers to the main polymer backbone, addition of finishes to the fiber after formation which will react with the molecules on the surface of the fiber, and the use of some

Fig. 10-44. Fire hose woven of dacron fiber.
(Courtesy of du Pont.)

form of irradiation to change the molecules on the fiber surface or achieve linkage between a finish and the basic polymer structure.

Since each fiber has its own failings with regard to environmental degradation each must be treated as a separate entity. The ideal solution is the development of fibers with the capability of resisting the major or most critical environment anticipated for the specific use. This is not very practical and thus we find the present day system of achieving greater resistance to degradation involves, (1) adding an inhibitor to the polymer before spinning, (2) adding a second polymer to the initial polymer prior to spinning, or (3) adding a finish after the fiber has been formed.

## II. BEHAVIOR OF POLYMERIC FIBERS WHEN EXPOSED TO VARIOUS ENVIRONMENTS

Fibers are, throughout their processing, fabrication, and use, continually exposed to environments which can cause degradation of one or many of this fiber's properties. This degradation can occur in two general periods of the fiber's use life, namely, (1) during formation,

Fig. 10-45.  Example of nylon reinforced tire.
(Courtesy of Allied Chemical Co.)

weaving, and finishing, and (*2*) during the fibers use as an individual fiber or in some form of woven structure.

## A. Environments and Their Effect during Fiber Processing

In the forming of polymeric fibers and through the various stages of processing until they are in the final woven, braided, corded, knitted, or twisted form they can be degraded by three basic environments, (*1*) chemicals, (*2*) moisture, and (*3*) aging (heat and time).

### 1. Chemical Degradation

Throughout processing, chemicals continually impinge their reactive nature on polymeric fibers. Since many polymers such as rayon, acetate, acrylic, etc., are dissolved in chemicals to achieve a liquid that can be formed into a fiber form, their degradation can come about by the same chemicals that have been used to form them. For example, rayon which is formed by the coagulation of a xanthate solution in sulfuric

Fig. 10-46. Braided packing of Teflon fiber.
(Courtesy of du Pont.)

acid, will dissolve the same acid. In the finishing of fibers and fabrics they are exposed to salts, alkalies, bleaches, solvents, acids, and dyes which can, if improperly used, rapidly degrade the fibers. Table 10-6 to 10-9 summarize the effects that can be expected when fibers formed from various polymers are exposed to the conditions illustrated. Manufacturers of fibers publish extensive literature and data on the behavior of their fibers in these environments as do the fabricators of the end items (in many cases) and even the ultimate user (10). As can be seen, the degradation due to chemicals is greatly magnified by the presence of heat and it will be seen that heat by itself or in conjunction with moisture will seriously degrade some fibers, even at temperatures below 300°F.

## 2. Moisture Sensitivity

Polymeric fibers come in contact with moisture soon after formation (in that they receive a thorough rinse) to remove residue by-products.

TABLE 10-6. Effect of Acids Encountered in Formation and Finishing on Polymeric and Natural Fibers

| Acid | Loss in strength (%) | | | | | | | | | |
|---|---|---|---|---|---|---|---|---|---|---|
| | Polypropylene | Dacron | Nylon 66 | Cotton | Silk | Dynel modacrylic | Vycron 5 | Nylon 6 | Lilion | Acetate |
| **Acetic acid** | | | | | | | | | | |
| 10%, 72°F, 10 hr | None | | | | | | | | | 40 |
| 5%, 210°F, 10 hr | | None | 62 | 56 | 15 | | | | | |
| 25%, 212°F, 20 hr | | | | | | 6 | | | | |
| 5%, 210°F, 10 hr | | | | | | | 4 | | | |
| 3%, 210°F, 3 hr | | | | | | | | No sig. loss | | |
| 5%, 212°F, 2 hr | | | | | | | | | None | |
| 9.5%, 150°F, 4 mo | | 16.2 | 91.5 | | | | | | | |
| 4.9%, 150°F, 6 mo | | | | | | | | | | |
| **Formic acid** | | | | | | | | | | |
| 5%, 210°F, 10 hr | | 7 | 13 | 85 | 31 | | | | | 51 |
| 3%, 210°F, 3 hr | | | | | | | | None | | |
| 100%, 122°F, 20 hr | | | | | | No effect | | | | |
| 5%, 210°F, 10 hr | | | | | | | 0.9 | | | |
| 5%, 212°F, 2 hr | | | | | | | | | 9.0 | |
| 5.1%, 150°F, 6 mo | | 23.2 | | | | | | | | |
| 1.0%, 150°F, 6 mo | | | 26.2 | | | | | | | |

TABLE 10-7. Effect of Salts Encountered in Formation and Finishing on Polymeric and Natural Fibers

| Salt | Loss in strength (%) | | | | | | | | | |
|---|---|---|---|---|---|---|---|---|---|---|
| | Cotton | Silk | Nylon 66 | Orlon | Acetate | Rayon | Polypropylene | Vycron 5 | Lilion | Dynel, modacrylic |
| Sodium chloride | | | | | | | | | | |
| 3%, 210°F, 10 hr | 17 | 10 | 12 | 2 | 15 | 10 | | | | |
| 10%, 72°F, 10 hr | | | | | | | None | | | |
| 3%, 210°F, 10 hr | | | | | | | | None | | |
| 2%, 158°F, 3 hr | | | | | | | | | 9.1 | |
| 10%, 150°F, 6 mo | | | 2.8 | | | | | | | |
| Zinc chloride | | | | | | | | | | |
| 3%, 210°F, 10 hr | 6 | 38 | None | 1 | 21 | 9 | | | | |
| 3%, 210°F, 10 hr | | | | | | | | None | | None |
| 50%, 212°F, 20 hr | | | | | | | | | | |
| Copper sulfate | | | | | | | | | | |
| 3%, 210°F, 10 hr | Powders | 19 | 12 | 2 | 22 | 23 | | | | |
| 3%, 210°F, 10 hr | | | | | | | | 5.2 | | |

TABLE 10-8.  Effect of Bleaches Encountered in Finishing on Polymeric and Natural Fibers

| Bleach | Dacron | Nylon 66 | Orlon | Rayon | Cotton | Silk | Dynel, modacrylic | Vycron | Polypropylene |
|---|---|---|---|---|---|---|---|---|---|
| Hydrogen peroxide | | | | | | | | | |
| 3%, pH 6, 70°F, 10 hr | 8% | 3% | None | 20% | 12% | 7% | 15% | | |
| 90%, 68°F, 20 hr | | | | | | | | | |
| 3%, pH 6, 70°F, 10 hr | | | | | | | | | |
| 5%, 72°F, 10 hr | | | | | | | | None | None |
| Sodium hypochlorite | | | | | | | | | |
| 0.4%, pH 11, 160°F, 10 hr | None | 93% | 17% | Brittle | Brittle | Dissolved | | | |
| 5.2%, 122°F, 20 hr | | | | | | | None | None | None |
| 0.4%, pH 11, 160°F, 10 hr | | | | | | | | | |
| 10%, 72°F, 10 hr | | 76.5% | | | | | | | |
| 0.6%, 150°F, 6 mo | | | | | | | | | |
| 0.9%, 150°F, 6 mo | 7.4% | | | | | | | | |

TABLE 10-9.  Effect of an Alkali Encountered in Finishing of Polymeric and Natural Fibers

| | Loss in strength (%) | | | | | | | | | | |
|---|---|---|---|---|---|---|---|---|---|---|---|
| | Dacron | Nylon | Rayon | Cotton | Silk | Acetate | Orlon | Lilion | Dynel, modacrylic | Vycron | Nylon 6 |
| Sodium Hydroxide | | | | | | | | | | | |
| 1%, 210°F, 1 hr | None | 1 | 13 | None | Dissolved | 68 | 13 | | | | |
| 1%, 210°F, 10 hr | 16 | 10 | 42 | 17 | Dissolved | 69 | 54 | | | | |
| 10%, 210°F, 1 hr | 29 | | | | | Dissolved | 49 | | | | |
| 10%, 210°F, 10 hr | Dissolved | 6 | | | Dissolved | Dissolved | Dissolved | | | | |
| 10%, 212°F, 2 hr | | | | | | | | None | | | |
| 25%, 212°F, 3 hr | | | | | | | | | 7 | | |
| 10%, 210°F, 1 hr | | | | | | | | | | 12.9 | |
| 10%, 185°F, 16 hr | | | | | | | | | | | No stg. loss |
| | | | | | | | | | | | |
| 0.9%, 150°F, 6 mo | 26.0 | 20.5 | | | | | | | | | |
| 9.6%, 150°F, 6 mo | | No stg. | | | | | | | | | |
| 0.9%, 150°F, 6 mo | 26.0 | | | | | | | | | | |
| 9.6%, 150°F, 6 mo | Dissolved | | | | | | | | | | |

Through the various finishing operations moisture as a liquid and a vapor (steam) is used as an aid in processing. The moisture regain is thus an important characteristic, and is shown in Table 10-10. Moisture content versus relative humidity is plotted for a number of fibers in Fig. 10-47. The amount of moisture in the fiber will effect shrinkage in fibers and thus can cause changes in such fabric properties as air permeability and breaking strength. Unrestrained shrinkage of some fibers are shown in Table 10-11. Thus careful control must be maintained during fabric finishing operations to insure that desired dimensions are maintained. In addition, as moisture is absorbed a fiber will swell. This swelling, again, can cause changes in properties that are undesirable and is dependent on the size of crystallites, quantity of amorphous material and the availability of polar groups. Nylon will increase in length by 1.2% and diameter by 5%, while silk increases in length by 1.7% and diameter by 18% (11). The effect of moisture on the mechanical properties of fibers varies with polymer class. Stress–strain curves for nylon, acrylic, polyester, and modacrylic show little or no change because they absorb little or no water. On the other hand, the cellulosics, and natural fibers absorb large quantities of water and therefore the stress–strain behavior is effected.

## 3. Aging

In the finishing of fibers and fabrics in any form, heat setting or heating aging singly or in combination with steam, calendering, resins, or dyes are utilized. Because of the sensitivity of polymeric fibers to heat accurate control of all heat setting conditions is a necessity. Table 10-12, shows the initial shrinkage, sticking, and melting, decomposition

TABLE 10-10. Moisture Regain of Fiber Classes

| Fiber type | % Regain |
|---|---|
| Acetate | 6 |
| Acrylic | 4 |
| Nylon 6 | 4 |
| Nylon 66 | 4 |
| Polyester | >1 |
| Polypropylene | >1 |
| Rayon | 13 |
| Silk | 11 |
| Nomex | 7 |
| Polybenzimidazole | 13 |

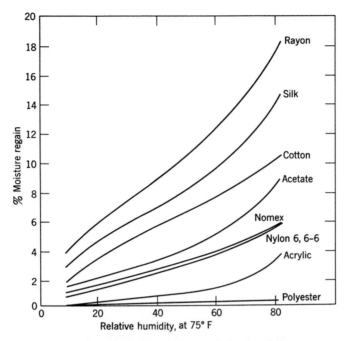

Fig. 10-47. Moisture regain vs relative humidity.

or char temperatures for various polymeric fibers and some natural fibers. In the finishing operation excess heat, even though lower than the temperatures indicated in Table 10-12, can create unusable fabrics because the heat has stiffened the fabric due to reaction within the

TABLE 10-11. Unrestrained Shrinkage of Fibers

| Fiber type | Boil-off shrinkage, % [a] |
|---|---|
| Polyester | |
| High tenacity | 4.0–9.5 |
| Low tenacity | 8.0 |
| Nylon 6 | 2–15 |
| Nylon 66 | |
| High tenacity | 9.5–12.4 |
| Polypropylene | |
| High tenacity | 5.5–6.5 |
| Normal tenacity | 4.0–5.0 |
| Nomex | 1.25 |

[a] Obtained by measuring the length of conditioned lengths of yarn before and after immersion in water at 212°F for 3–60 min with no tension.

TABLE 10-12.   Heat Sensitivity of Various Fibers

| Fiber | Shrinks, °F | Sticks or softens, °F | Melts, °F | Decomposes, °F | Chars, °F |
|---|---|---|---|---|---|
| Rayon | | | | 350–400 | |
| Acetate | | 400–445 | | | |
| Nylon 6 | | 356 | 419 | | |
| Nylon 6-6 | | 356 | 482 | | |
| Polyethylene | 165 | | 230–250 | | |
| Polypropylene | | 300–310 | 325–335 | | |
| Orlon | | 455 | | | |
| Acrilan | | 455 | | | |
| Dynel | 275 | | 480 | | |
| Vycron | | | 490–500 | | |
| Vinyon | 150 | 170 | 260 | | |
| Nomex | | | | | 840 |
| Polybenzimidazole | | | | | 1000 |
| Cotton | | | | 302 | |
| Teflon | | | 621 [a] | | |

[a] Gel temperature.

polymer or discolored dyed fabrics to the point that renders further dyeing useless. Heat setting of polymeric fibers and fabrics is done to achieve one or more of the following:

(1)  Stabilize twist
(2)  Remove residual shrinkage
(3)  Increase resistance to wrinkling and further shrinkage
(4)  To obtain variations in feel or drape
(5)  To form contours or shapes
(6)  To set or fix the air permeability if required
(7)  To cure resins which are added to provide protection to the woven material

Each new fiber that becomes available must be thoroughly evaluated to establish procedures for finishing which will not degrade its properties. As an example, nylon 6 was in its infancy, evaluated as a supplemental fiber for heavy webbings. Heat in finishing created two problem areas, (1) where nylon 6-6 is used for webbing an abrasion resistance finish is applied and cured at 340°F. The same webbing made of nylon 6, treated with the same resin and cured at 340°F lost considerable strength. However by reducing the curing temperature to 240°F, the strength remained uneffected; (2) Yarn dyeing of nylon 6 prior to weaving created a product that had high elongation and low shrinkage indicating that the yarn dyed webbing possessed a large amount of elongation at the low load levels which resulted in loss of shrinkage as a result of the tension used in the resin treating process (12). Obviously, similar problems can and do occur with other new polymeric fibers. In the majority of the new fibers, the producers conduct exhaustive studies prior to commercial production to insure that all problems relating to effect of heat ageing or heat setting have been resolved.

## B. Environments and Their Effects on Fibers and Woven Structures

Regardless of where polymeric fibers are used their exposure to environments which can cause degradation is an accepted fact. Such environments as heat, or flames, oxidation, sunlight, aging, chemicals, moisture, radiation, and biological will be encountered by fibers whether as a fiber, fabric, webbing, tape, ribbon, cord, or thread. The goal of every fiber producer is to achieve a fiber that will be resistant to all of these environments, and have high tenacity, good abrasion resistance, work to break and dyeability; however, as will be seen this has not as yet been accomplished. In this section, a review will be made of the above environments and how various mechanical properties of polymeric and other fibers in their many forms will be effected.

## 1. Thermal Degradation and Heat Resistance

Fibers in any number of forms can be exposed to heat through a wide range of conditions. The most common forms of heat would be exposure of a woven material to thermal energy while in a storage container, or exposure to actual fire during use. But heat can occur by other routes such as (1) heat released during detonation of a nuclear weapon, (2) heat encountered during reentry into a dense atmosphere such as the earth, (3) heat built up as a result of the frictional action between a fiber or fabric and itself or another object, (4) heat buildup due to the absorbing of energy by fibers within elastomeric matreces (such as tires), and (5) heat that will occur as a result of high velocity motion through a dense atmosphere. In considering these environments and their effect on the mechanical properties of a fiber or fabric structure, care must be taken to determine whether the properties *at* or *after* exposure to heat (in any form) are of major importance.

It is logical to start with the basic fiber in establishing its stability to elevated temperatures. From Table 10-12, it is quite apparent that most of the fibers available today cannot withstand the rigors of thermal exposure. In Table 10-13, a number of polymer types in single filament form are summarized over a broad temperature range (9), for effect on strength. As far back as 1950, data on the effect of temperature on synthetic yarns have been obtained. In Tables 10-14 and 10-15, some of Coplan's work (13) is presented. Data on initial modulus, work to rupture, and shrinkage was also obtained on these same yarns. Improvement in mechanical properties of many of these yarns have been attained since then and are shown chronologically in Tables 10-16 and 10-17. However, improvement of mechanical properties has not effected these fibers susceptability to shrinkage at elevated temperatures, even dry heat. Since such fibers as nylons, polyesters, etc., are thermoplastic; once their heat setting temperature has been reached they will shrink as shown in Table 10-18.

The use of fabrics in such applications as parachutes, creates situations, where the thermal limits are exceeded as a result of heat from aircraft fire. To more thoroughly study this effect, a device was built to impinge heated air at given velocities on a fabric and record the

TABLE 10-13.  Fiber Strength after 10 Minutes Exposure to Temperature

| Temp., °F | Fiber type, tenacity in grams/denier | | | | | |
|---|---|---|---|---|---|---|
| | Nylon 6-6 | Nomex | PBI [b] | "E" Glass | Fused Silica | René 41 |
| Room temp. | 6.5 | 6.6 | 4.0 | 13.8 | 15.0 | 3.2 |
| 260 | 4.6 | 6.5 | | | 15.6 | |
| 300 | | | 4.4 | | | |
| 360 | 3.8 | 4.8 | | | | |
| 450 | N.S.[a] | | 3.2 | | | |
| 460 | | 3.8 | | 13.7 | 16.3 | |
| 560 | | 2.8 | | | | 2.9 |
| 600 | | | 2.6 | | | |
| 660 | | 1.1 | | 9.9 | 9.3 | |
| 750 | | | 1.0 | | | |
| 760 | N.S.[a] | | | | | |
| 800 | | | 0.4 | | | |
| 860 | | | | 8.6 | 8.9 | 2.9 |
| 1000 | | | | 7.6 | 8.8 | |
| 1100 | | | | 6.5 | 8.2 | 2.8 |
| 1200 | | | | 4.2 | 6.3 | 2.5 |
| 1400 | | | | N.S.[a] | 5.2 | 1.7 |

[a] No strength.
[b] Poly 1,3,4-benzimidazole.

TABLE 10-14. Strength and Elongation of Yarns at Specific Temperatures

| Yarns | −70°F | | 70°F | | 210°F | | 350°F | |
|---|---|---|---|---|---|---|---|---|
| | Tenacity, G/D | Elongation, % | Tenacity, G/D | Elongation, % | Tenacity, G/D | Elongation, % | Tenacity, G/D | Elongation, % |
| Multifilament | | | | | | | | |
| Nylon 6–6, 30 den. semidull | 8.0 | 11.4 | 4.7 | 18.9 | 3.1 | 13.8 | 2.3 | 26.0 |
| Nylon 6–6, bright, 210 den. | 8.7 | 11.1 | 7.2 | 13.1 | 5.1 | 14.2 | 2.9 | 29.4 |
| Orlon, 200 den. | 5.5 | 11.4 | 3.9 | 15.3 | 2.5 | 19.1 | 0.3 | 16.7 |
| Dacron, 210 den. | 8.8 | 7.6 | 6.4 | 8.9 | 4.2 | 11.5 | 2.8 | 29.9 |
| Fortisan, 270 den. | 7.9 | 5.2 | 6.3 | 5.8 | 4.2 | 3.6 | 2.6 | 3.0 |
| Rayon, 300 den. | 3.9 | 12.4 | 2.4 | 20.0 | 2.3 | 8.1 | 1.9 | 14.4 |
| Vinyon, 270 den. | | | 3.5 | 29.9 | 1.7 | 37.4 | 1.2[a] | 42.3[a] |
| Silk, 5 thd. | 4.4 | 8.0 | 3.5 | 18.7 | 2.8 | 9.2 | 2.2 | 10.2 |
| Glass, 450/1 | | | 5.8 | 2.5–3.0 | | | | |
| Staple | | | | | | | | |
| Acrilan, 24/1 | 2.1 | 4.3 | 1.4 | 11.2 | 1.1 | 15.7 | 0.1 | 17.4 |
| Dynel, 20/1 | | | 1.4 | 27.8 | 0.8 | 46.9 | | |
| Cotton, 20/4 | 2.9 | 6.0 | 2.1 | 7.7 | 1.6 | 5.2 | 1.2 | 6.3 |

[a] At 215–220°F.

TABLE 10-15. Strength and Elongation after 24 Hours of Specific Temperatures

| Yarns | Denier or count | −70°F | | 70°F | | 210°F | | 350°F | |
|---|---|---|---|---|---|---|---|---|---|
| | | Tenacity, G/D | Elongation, % | Tenacity, G/D | Elongation, % | Tenacity, G/D | Elongation, % | Tenacity, G/D | Elongation, % |
| Multifilament | | | | | | | | | |
| Nylon 66, semidull | 30 | 4.3 | 18.4 | 4.7 | 19.0 | 4.5 | 17.8 | | |
| Nylon 6-6, bright | 210 | 6.9 | 17.2 | 7.2 | 13.0 | 7.0 | 18.1 | 1.8 | 6.6 |
| Orlon | 200 | 3.9 | 14.6 | 3.9 | 15.0 | 4.2 | 16.5 | 3.1 | 13.3 |
| Dacron | 210 | 6.1 | 9.0 | 6.4 | 9.0 | 6.2 | 15.1 | 5.5 | 34.1 |
| Fortisan | 270 | 5.8 | 5.9 | 6.3 | 6.0 | 5.8 | 5.6 | 1.1 | 1.2 |
| Rayon | 300 | 2.4 | 18.6 | 2.4 | 20.0 | 2.4 | 19.9 | 1.0 | 8.6 |
| Vinyon | 270 | 2.8 | 30.6 | 2.7 | 31.0 | 2.9 | 31.8 | | |
| Silk | 5 thd. | 3.2 | 18.1 | 3.5 | | 3.1 | 14.7 | 0.5 | 0.8 |
| Glass | 450/1 | | | 6.0 | 3.0 | | | 5.3 | 2.1 |
| Staple | | | | | | | | | |
| Acrilan | 24/1 | 1.8 | 11.5 | 1.4 | 11.0 | 1.7 | 10.4 | 1.3 | 7.9 |
| Dynel | 20/1 | | | 1.4 | 28.0 | 1.4 | 30.5 | | |
| Cotton | 20/4 | 2.0 | 7.5 | 2.1 | 8.0 | 2.1 | 8.3 | 1.0 | 4.8 |

TABLE 10-16. Breaking Strength Retention (%) after Exposure to Various Temperatures and Time [a]

| Time and temperature | Dacron, 220 denier, type 5100 | Nylon 6-6, 840 denier, type 300 | Orlon, 100 denier, type 81 | Rayon, 1650 denier, type 258 | Silk, 13/15 |
|---|---|---|---|---|---|
| Air | | | | | |
| 250°F, 1 hr | 108 | 102 | 102 | 97 | 87 |
| 300°F, 1 hr | 92 | 91 | 94 | 80 | 98 |
| 350°F, 1 hr | 106 | 61 | 99 | 50 | 72 |
| 380°F, 1 hr | 100 | 42 | 91 | 32 | 43 |
| 400°F, 1 hr | 92 | 38 | 87 | 30 | Degraded |
| Water | | | | | |
| 310°F 1 hr | 108 | 101 | 94 | 94 | 95 |
| 225°F, 1 hr | 108 | 98 | 94 | 93 | 95 |
| 250°F, 1 hr | 105 | 100 | 104 | 87 | 89 |
| 300°F, 1 hr | 116 | 96 | 109 | 90 | 68 |

[a] From duPont Technical Bulletin X-56, Sept. 1956.

fabric back-side temperature to equilibrium. A cross section of the fabrics evaluated are summarized in Table 10-19, using an air (heated) velocity of 225 ft/min (14). The nonmelting fibers such as Nomex, graphite, and cotton are outstanding in such an exposure and graphically reveal their potential over fibers that will melt. Following this laboratory investigation, Ross and Little (15) exposed entire parachutes (in standard and experimental packs) to simulated aircraft fires using jet fuel (high octane aviation gasoline releases considerably more heat in burning, thus would cloud any results). Comparison of nylon and Nomex packs and harnesses (canopy inside the pack was nylon 6-6) was made by this procedure, Table 10-20, and the advantage of the nonmelting fiber, Nomex, was again verified. In Fig. 10-48, a multisequence photo description of a simulated fire test is shown. Others have investigated this same phenomena. In designing the emergency escape system for the Gemini, a study was made in the laboratory similar to that described in Ref. 14, but with the air moving against one side of the fabric and heat against the other side (16). Some results are shown in Table 10-21. These results, however, are somewhat questionable since temperatures above the melting point of nylon 6-6 were obtained over 10 sec periods which would have caused major damage. The points 1–5 on Table 10-21 are thermocouple locations at equidistant across the sample.

There are a variety of heating conditions to which fibers in their many forms can be exposed as a result of the applications for which

TABLE 10-17. Breaking Strength and Elongation of Selected Yarns after Exposure to Various Temperatures

| Temp. at 100 hr | Type 51 Dacron, 1100 den. | | Glass fiber 450-3/5 | | Type 300 nylon 6-6, 210 den. | | Type 330 nylon 6-6, 210 den. | | Type 700 nylon 6-6, 840 den. | | Type 272 rayon, 1650 den. | | Teflon, 400 den. | |
|---|---|---|---|---|---|---|---|---|---|---|---|---|---|---|
| | Ten. | Elong.[a] | Ten. | Elong. | Ten. | Elong. | Ten. | Elong. | Ten. | Elong. | Ten. | Elong. | Ten. | Elong. |
| 175°F | 6.7 | 14.0 | | | 7.6 | 18.6 | 7.1 | 20.0 | 7.8 | 17.2 | 4.4 | 10.1 | | |
| 250°F | 6.7 | 20.4 | | | 6.7 | 19.6 | 7.1 | 21.9 | 8.2 | 19.6 | 4.0 | 10.0 | | |
| 350°F | 4.7 | 29.1 | 5.9 | 2.7 | 0.7 | 2.5 | 2.3 | 8.5 | 2.6 | 8.8 | 0.7 | 2.7 | 1.7 | 18.3 |
| 425°F (1 hr) | 5.8 | 37.5 | | | 1.5 | 6.8 | 5.3 | 24.5 | 6.9 | 25.3 | 2.4 | 8.2 | 1.7 | 19.2 |
| 550°F | | | 2.5 | 1.0 | | | | | | | | | 1.6 | 38.8 |
| 720°F | | | 1.4 | 0.9 | | | | | | | | | | |

[a] Tenacity: grams per denier; elongation: %.

TABLE 10-18.  Effect of Elevated Temperature on the Shrinkage of Yarns

| Temperature °F, 1 hr | Type 5100 Dacron 220 denier | Type 300 Nylon 6-6 840 denier | Type 81 Orlon 100 denier | Type 258 Rayon 1650 denier | Silk 13/15 |
|---|---|---|---|---|---|
| Air | | | | | |
| 250 | 0.5 | 0.5 | 0.3 | 0.9 | 0.0 |
| 300 | 4.7 | 0.5 | 1.1 | 1.3 | 0.0 |
| 350 | 7.2 | 0.9 | 1.9 | 1.0 | 0.1 |
| 380 | 10.8 | 2.7 | 2.4 | 0.9 | 0.1 |
| Water | | | | | |
| 210 | —0.3 | —0.7 | —0.2 | 0.0 | 0.0 |
| 225 | 2.6 | 0.5 | 0.9 | 0.2 | 0.4 |
| 250 | 3.3 | 1.4 | 1.6 | 0.4 | 0.0 |
| 300 | 7.9 | 5.8 | 4.8 | 4.2 | —0.4 |
| Steam Sat. | | | | | |
| 250 | 3.2 | 1.4 | 2.2 | —0.2 | —0.1 |

Fig. 10-48.  Before, during, and after scenes of Nomex parachute exposed to simulated aircraft fire.

TABLE 10-19. Effect of Air at 1200°F on Fibrous Materials

| Materials description: specimens 1–6 are two-layer configuration with the fabric facing the hot air being a Nomex fabric, 7.25 oz/yd²; description is of back layer | Time to 300°F (sec) | Time to 400°F (sec) | Time to equilibrium (sec) | Equilibrium temp. (°F) |
|---|---|---|---|---|
| 1. Nomex paper—2.90 oz/yd², 0.013 in. thick | 6 | 8 | 30½ | 630 |
| 2. Nomex Fabric—2.25 oz/yd², 0.005 in. thick, dobby weave | 4½ | 6 | 25½ | 640 |
| 3. Nomex fabric—3.5 oz/yd², 0.014 in. thick | 5¾ | 7½ | 28½ | 640 |
| 4. Nomex fabric, 2.25 oz/yd², 0.005 in. thick, dobby weave; vacuum deposition of aluminum on fabric, facing heat | 5¼ | 8¼ | 22¾ | 620 |
| 5. Nomex fabric, 3.5 oz/yd²; vacuum deposition of aluminum on fabric, facing heat | 8 | 12¼ | 21½ | 550 |
| 6. Nomex fabric, 7.25 oz/yd², plain weave | 9¼ | 12¾ | 37 | 580 |
| 7. Experimental two-ply cotton (poplin-duck) bonded together with flame resistant neoprene, 21.70 oz/yd²; poplin facing heat [a] | 15 | 21 | 36½ | 1075 |
| 8. Same as above except duck facing heat [a] | 14½ | 25 | 31½ | 1075 |
| 9. Nylon fabric, 7.25 oz/yd², plain weave [a] | 4¼ | 6¼ | Melted 6¼ | — |
| 10. Dacron fabric, 7.25 oz/yd², plain weave [a] | 2 | — | Melted 2½ | — |

[a] Single layer.

TABLE 10-20. Summary of Parachute Fire Tests at 1200–1400°F

| Pack construction | Exposure time, sec | Condition of[a] | | | | Opened satisfactorily | | Remarks |
|---|---|---|---|---|---|---|---|---|
| | | Outer fabric | Inner fabric | Canopy | Suspension lines | Pilot chute | Canopy | |
| Standard Air Force parachute pack of nylon 6-6, one layer, plain weave 7.25 oz/yd² | 11 | 5 | None | 5 | 5 | No | No | |
| Cotton pack, of 14.77 oz/yd² duck, plain weave | 11 | 5 | None | 5 | 5 | No | No | |
| Nomex fabric used in lieu of nylon; plain weave, 7.25 oz/yd² | 11 | 4 | None | 3 | 1 | Yes | Yes | |
| Nomex fabric, double layer configuration, outer layer-plain weave, 7.25 oz/yd² | 12 | 5 | 4 | 4 | 1 | Yes | No | Second layer aluminized Nomex, 2.25 oz/yd², dobby weave |
| Nomex fabric, double layer configuration, outer layer-plain weave, 7.25 oz/yd² | 12 | 5 | 4 | 4 | 1 | Yes | Partially | Second layer aluminized Nomex, 3.50 oz/yd², dobby weave |
| Nomex fabric, double layer configuration; both layers-plain weave, 7.25 oz/yd² | 12 | 4–5 | 1 | 1 | 1 | Yes | Yes | Between the two fabrics is a layer of aluminum foil |

[a] 1, no damage; 2, darkened areas indicating presence of high heat; 3, melt spots and weak areas caused by high heat; 4, large melt spots and fusion indicating high heat; 5, destroyed.

Table 10-21.  Determination of Heat Buildup on Parachute Fabrics at Various Points across a Heat Source

| Material | ΔP in. of water | Air Flow, ft³/min-ft² | Temperature, °F, at points | | | | | Flux Btu/sec ft² | Exposure time, sec | Remarks |
|---|---|---|---|---|---|---|---|---|---|---|
| | | | 1 | 2 | 3 | 4 | 5 | | | |
| Nylon 6-6, Ripstop Weave, 1.1 oz/yd² | 0.08 | 16.8 | 626.8 | 512.5 | 447.7 | 561.3 | 626.8 | 22.3 | 10.0 | No damage |
| | 3.96 | 267.5 | 219.7 | 186.3 | 236.3 | 236.3 | 203.0 | 38.9 | 10.0 | Started to melt |
| Nylon 6-6, Dobby weave 2.25 oz/yd² | 20.21 | 39.8 | 577.7 | 545.0 | 659.1 | 496.3 | 480.0 | 35.1 | 10.0 | No damage |
| | 2.08 | 214.5 | 285.6 | 219.7 | 318.1 | 252.7 | 252.7 | 38.9 | 10.0 | Started to melt |
| Nylon 6-6, Dobby weave 3.50 oz/yd² | 0.08 | 15.8 | 789.7 | 691.7 | 561.3 | 463.8 | 691.7 | 31.7 | 10.0 | No damage |
| | 0.97 | 131.5 | 366.7 | 269.1 | 252.7 | 269.1 | 285.6 | 38.9 | 10.0 | Started to melt |
| Nylon 6-6, 2/2 twill weave, 4.75 oz/yd² | 0.08 | 6.0 | 756.9 | 724.3 | 675.3 | 691.7 | 773.3 | 19.4 | 10.0 | No damage |
| | 3.60 | 195.5 | 203.0 | 219.7 | 236.3 | 236.3 | 252.7 | 38.9 | 38.9 | Began burning |

they are intended. These can include cycling at various temperatures (Table 10-22) to establish the effect of these cycles on the strength of various forms. This work by Muse (17) was made necessary when certain types of parachutes had to endure repeated 2 hr cycles of elevated temperatures. Because of storage environments that would occur in various atmospheres and at temperature, Muse also studied the effect of air, oxygen, and nitrogen at two temperatures with two fibers (Table 10-23). In another instance, the effects of compression at elevated temperatures had to be known since most textile materials used in today's parachutes and space systems must be packaged under pressure in as much as most systems are severely limited as to space. A number of fibers were exposed to 350°F at packing pressures of 50–250 psi. As shown in Tables 10-24 and 10-25, nylon is most seriously effected while Dacron, Nomex, and glass are largely uneffected except where the materials were folded. This work by Abbott (18) showed that when entire parachutes were packed under pressure and exposed to elevated temperatures, elimination of oxygen from the container (having been squeezed out) prevented damage to nylon even at temperatures above its melting point (originally noted by Muse, Table 10-23, in the exposures to nitrogen). Much effort has been carried out to establish the behavior of fibers in woven forms *at* and *after* exposure to high temperatures. In the development of Dacron materials for use in parachutes (19,20) Nomex materials (21) and glass fiber materials (22) specimens were oven-aged at high temperatures for various times (Table 10-26). Data have also been assembled showing the *at* temperature behavior of some of these same fibers and fused silica in woven forms. Work by Chu et al. (23) and Barish et al. (24) are briefly reviewed in Tables 10-27 and 10-28, and if compared to data obtained *after* exposure to temperature reveals that the former condition is much more degrading to the fiber types studied. In the case of the fused silica fiber (quartz), finish is shown to be quite important for retention of strength.

Much has been made of atomic and nuclear weapons and the heat damage that can be caused. The use of fibers in many forms for clothing, parachutes, etc., resulted in a great deal of study of the effect this short time, high intensity thermal will have on fibers. McQuade et al. (25) has shown that blends of cotton/nylon are better than all-nylon and approaches being as good as all-cotton at fluxes between 3 and 21 cal/cm²-sec. Other fiber blends are being studied as well as finishes to achieve even better properties using synthetic fibers. Study of how color and cleanliness can effect thermal resistance have also been

TABLE 10-22.  Effect of Cycling vs Continuous Exposure to Temperature of Two Fibers in Woven Forms

| Material | Strength change, % | | | |
| --- | --- | --- | --- | --- |
| | 250°F | | 300°F | |
| | Cycling, 2 hr soaks, 3 soaks | 6 hr, continuous | Cycling, 2 hr soaks, 3 soaks | 6 hr, continuous |
| Nylon 6-6 | | | | |
| Fabric, 1.6 oz/yd$^2$, 3/1 twill, warp | −6.7 | +1.4 | −21.0 | −20.7 |
| Fabric, 2.25 oz/yd$^2$, dobby weave, warp | −0.5 | +0.6 | −21.9 | −14.7 |
| Fabric, 4.75 oz/yd$^2$, 2/2 twill, warp | +5.6 | +4.4 | −24.3 | −14.5 |
| Webbing, untreated, 8700 lb min stg. | −1.5 | −2.7 | −33.4 | −36.8 |
| Webbing, treated, 8700 lb min stg. | −23.5 | −25.0 | −52.2 | −52.4 |
| Dacron | | | | |
| Sewing thread, size E, natural | +0.3 | 0 | −1.3 | −0.9 |
| Sewing thread, size E, sage green | +1.3 | +1.0 | +3.5 | −2.1 |

TABLE 10-23.  Nylon and Dacron Strength Retention (%) after Exposure to Various Atmospheres and Temperatures

| Atmosphere | 212°F | | | | | | 284°F | | | | | |
|---|---|---|---|---|---|---|---|---|---|---|---|---|
| | 2 hr | | 4 hr | | 8 hr | | 2 hr | | 4 hr | | 8 hr | |
| | Nylon | Dacron | Nylon | Dacron | Nylon | Dacron | Nylon | Dacron | Nylon | Dacron | Nylon | Dacron |
| Compressed air, 300 psi | 97.8 | 96.6 | 97.1 | 95.0 | 94.6 | 95.1 | 39.9 | 89.8 | 27.2 | 91.5 | 22.6 | 90.7 |
| Oxygen, 300 psi | 97.4 | 95.5 | 91.4 | 96.7 | 78.2 | 96.2 | 18.4 | 90.8 | 8.1 | 91.5 | 3.4 | 90.3 |
| Nitrogen, 30 psi | 100.0 | 98.1 | 100.0 | 98.4 | 100.0 | 96.9 | 98.9 | 92.2 | 93.5 | 90.8 | 91.4 | 92.2 |

TABLE 10-24.  Effect of Time, Temperature, and Pressure on the Strength of Fabrics and Ribbons

| Materials | Original strength | Time and pressure: exposed at 350°F | | | | |
|---|---|---|---|---|---|---|
| | | 2 hr, 250 psi | 0 psi | 6 hr, 50 psi | 250 psi | 24 hr, 250 psi |
| **Fabric, breaking stg., lb/in.** | | | | | | |
| Nylon 6–6, 3.5 oz/yd² | 158 | 141 | 89 | 80 | 87 | |
| Nylon 6–6, 7.0 oz/yd² | 335 | 294 | 101 | 131 | 137 | |
| Nylon 6–6, 14.0 oz/yd² | 720 | 550 | 384 | 395 | 377 | |
| Dacron 3.5 oz/yd² | 146 | | 143 | 141 | 141 | |
| Nomex, 3.7 oz/yd² | 138 | 135 | 135 | 134 | 133 | 139 |
| Glass, 9.0 oz/yd² | 387 | | 430 | 390 | 430 | |
| Glass, 19.0 oz/yd² | 664 | | 628 | 680 | 634 | |
| **Ribbon, breaking stg., lb** | | | | | | |
| Nylon 6–6, 30 yd/lb | 1210 | 679 | 374 | 443 | 574 | |
| Nylon 6–6, 17 yd/lb | 2320 | 1830 | 660 | 740 | 840 | |
| Dacron, 30 yd/lb | 1070 | 1060 | 970 | 1040 | 1030 | |

investigated by Ross (26) and Glaser (27). In the former, olive drab and natural color nylon sewing threads were used in seaming natural color nylon 6-6 ribbon. The strength of the seams after exposure to three (3) flux levels, Table 10-29, is quite apparent and has caused a change to all natural color parachute systems for certain applications. In Fig. 10-49, a graphic example of how flash thermal effects dark numbers (ink in this case) on light colored fabric. Cleanliness of the material used must also be considered and whether clothing, shelters, or parachutes, if exposure to flash thermal is a possibility extreme care should be taken to maintain cleanliness or the results shown in Table 10-30, can occur. However, as is also shown, if there is a high wind factor, the damage due to dirt is not as great.

In considering the use of woven fibers in space, thermal properties at ambient as well as in a vacuum must be known. These are extremely difficult to establish due to variations in fabric structure, fiber and yarn cross section, and density of the material. Some initial research (28) has given the data shown in Table 10-31. As attempts have been made to recover instruments from space, parachute failures have occurred due to aerodynamic heating. Wind tunnel studies were made to establish temperature vs time during simulated reentry cycles. The first work in this area by Block (29) showed that with thermocouples woven into ribbon, temperature change could be measured. In Figs. 10-50 and 10-51, a nylon 6-6 and Dacron ribbon are plotted at an altitude

TABLE 10-25.  Effect of Time, Temperature, and Pressure on the Strength Flat and Folded Specimens

| Materials | Original strength | Exposed at 350°F | | | | | | |
| --- | --- | --- | --- | --- | --- | --- | --- | --- |
| | | Flat | | | Folded | | | |
| | | 2 hr | 6 hr | | 2 hr | 6 hr | | |
| | | 250 psi | 50 psi | 250 psi | 250 psi | 50 psi | 250 psi | |
| Fabric, breaking stg., lb/in. | | | | | | | | |
| Nylon 6-6, 3.5 oz/yd² | 158 | 141 | | | 140 | | | |
| Nylon 6-6, 7.0 oz/yd² | 335 | 294 | 131 | 137 | 228 | 115 | 89 | |
| Nylon 6-6, 14.0 oz/yd² | 493 | 498 | | | 502 | | | |
| Nomex, 3.7 oz/yd² | 138 | 135 | | | 139 | | | |
| Glass, 9.0 oz/yd² | 387 | | | 295[a] | | | 290[a] | |
| Glass, 19.0 oz/yd² | 664 | | | 454[a] | | | 380[a] | |
| Ribbon, breaking stg. (lb) | | | | | | | | |
| Nylon 6-6, 17 yd/lb | 2320 | | 743 | 840 | | 655 | 835 | |

[a] 500°F.

TABLE 10-26. Comparison of Strength after Oven Aging for Webbings and Ribbons of Three Fibers

| Fiber type and webbing description | 70°F lb | 24 hr, 350°F, lb | 5 hr, 500°F, lb | 6 hr, 500°F, lb | 6 hr, 600°F, lb |
|---|---|---|---|---|---|
| Dacron | | | | | |
| $\frac{9}{16}$ in. width, tubular | 1500 | 1416 | | | |
| $1\frac{3}{4}$ in. width, twill | 10000+ | 8427 | | | |
| $\frac{9}{16}$ in. width, twill | 528 | 450 | | | |
| 2 in. width, twill | 1288 | 919 | | | |
| Nomex | | | | | |
| 1 in. width, plain weave | 1115.0 | | | 1147.3 | 614.0 |
| $\frac{9}{16}$ in. width, tubular | 1518.0 | | | 1260.0 | 659.3 |
| Glass Fibers | | | | | |
| $\frac{5}{8}$ in width, DE fiber | 634 | | 620 | | |
| $\frac{7}{8}$ in. width, DE fiber | 3419 | | 3987 | | |
| 2 in. width, DE fiber | 1558 | | 1755 | | |

equivalent of 100,000 ft. Recordor No. 1 was on the ribbon leading edge, No. 2. toward the center, and No. 3. on the trailing edge of the ribbon. Additional effort (30,31) revealed that treating the ribbons with chemicals having a high rate of sublimation was possible but storage problems with the treated ribbons precluded their use.

Obviously seams must be capable of withstanding elevated temperatures as well as the base materials used in the seams. Table 10-32 shows some data to this end. However, this work by Coplan and Singer (32) has been to little and the many facets of how seams react during shrinkage during heating are still little known.

TABLE 10-27. Strength Comparison at Temperature for Fabrics of Two Fibers (Warp Specimens)

| Fiber type and fabric description | 70°F lb/in. | 300°F lb/in. | 450°F lb/in. | 600°F lb/in. | 1200°F lb/in. | 1800°F lb/in. |
|---|---|---|---|---|---|---|
| Nomex | | | | | | |
| 4.3 oz/yd² | 188.0 | 138.4 | 107.6 | 65.7 | | |
| 10.3 oz/yd² | 492.0 | 326.0 | 237.0 | 148.0 | | |
| Fused Silica | | | | | | |
| 9.61 oz/yd² aluminum chelate finish | 398.0 | | | 388.0 | 87.0 | 56.0 |
| 9.56 oz/yd² magnesium acetate finish | 242.0 | | | 129.6 | 36.0 | 25.4 |

TABLE 10-28. Comparison of Strength at Temperature for Webbings of Two Fibers

| Fiber type and webbing width | 70°F lb | 300°F lb | 450°F lb | 500°F lb | 600°F lb | 750°F lb |
|---|---|---|---|---|---|---|
| Nomex | | | | | | |
| 1 inch webbing | 7145 | 5141 | 3816 | | 1285 | |
| $\frac{9}{16}$ inch webbing | 1482 | 1157 | 708 | | 374 | |
| Glass fibers | | | | | | |
| $\frac{5}{8}$ inch webbing | | | | | | |
| DE fiber | 784 | | | 857 | | 523 |
| Beta fiber | 714 | | | 721 | | 549 |

A great deal of research has been expended to achieve tires (both commercial and military) that will endure higher temperatures than the present 300–350°F. Many fibers and elastomers have been considered to no major effect. Some gain has been made using Nomex and resin cured butyl (33). In Table 10-33, Nomex and nylon 6-6 cord construction are compared at various temperatures while adhesion properties on the two fibers and steel tire cord are shown in Table 10-34. Finally it was possible to calculate the cord loads and time to failure at elevated temperatures using the room temperature burst strength of the tire (Table 10-35). However, even though the Nomex tire can take the high temperature soak and perform in a landing test, tread separation during taxi takeoff is still a problem. Wire on the other hand, failed due to insufficient adhesion, while nylon can take the taxi takeoff cycle, but fails in long term flight heat soak.

TABLE 10-29. Effect of Color on Strength of Seams Exposed to Flash Thermal

| Flux, cal/cm²-sec | Olive drab sewing thread | | Natural sewing thread | |
|---|---|---|---|---|
| | Total exposure, cal/cm² | Breaking strength, lb | Total exposure, cal/cm² | Breaking strength, lb |
| 5 | 25 | 126 | 25 | 172 |
| | 15 | 201 | 15 | 218 |
| | 5 | 217 | 5 | 210 |
| 15 | 25 | 127 | 25 | 152 |
| | 15 | 137 | 15 | 158 |
| | 5 | 212 | 5 | 198 |
| | Control | 215 | | 200 |

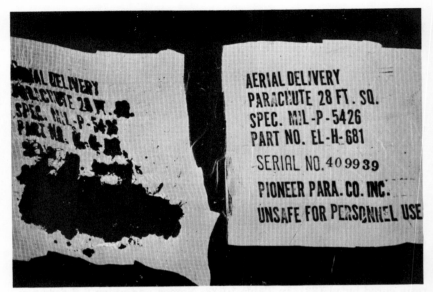

Fig. 10-49. Stenciled nylon 6-6 parachute fabric before and after exposure to flash thermal.

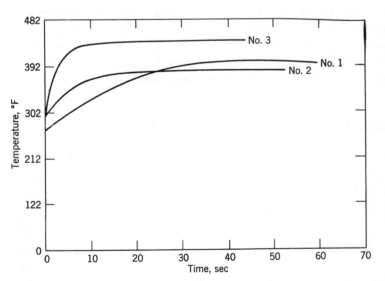

Fig. 10-50. Temperature rise vs time for wind tunnel test of 2 in. nylon ribbon 0.42 oz/yd.

TABLE 10-30. Effect of Flash Thermal at Varying Conditions on the Strength of Webbing

| Material and condition | Exposure, cal/cm² | Static load, lb | Air velocity, fps | | | Static load, lb | Air velocity, fps | | |
|---|---|---|---|---|---|---|---|---|---|
| | | | 0 | 100 | 500 | | 0 | 100 | 500 |
| Nylon webbing, clean, 4000 lb | 21.3 | 0 | 3960 | 3900 | 3850 | 75 | 3740 | 3850 | — |
| | 64.5 | 0 | 1475 | 3920 | 3960 | 75 | 4000 | 3850 | 4070 |
| Nylon webbing, soiled, 4000 lb | 21.3 | 0 | 1695 | 3120 | 3300 | 75 | 1870 | 2040 | 3250 |
| | 64.5 | 0 | 0 | 1915 | 2190 | 75 | 0 | 1980 | 3480 |
| Nylon webbing, clean, 8700 lb | 21.3 | 0 | 9300 | 9460 | 9460 | 75 | 9850 | 9400 | 9460 |
| | 64.5 | 0 | 9570 | 9450 | 9080 | 75 | 9540 | 9390 | 9400 |
| Nylon webbing, soiled, 8700 lb | 21.3 | 0 | 4800 | 6950 | 8580 | 75 | 5210 | 7610 | 8940 |
| | 64.5 | 0 | 880 | 2311 | 9200 | 75 | 308 | 2600 | 9190 |

TABLE 10-31.   Thermal Properties of Fabrics Woven of Various Fibers

| Fiber and fabric | Atmospheric conditions | Temp. °F | Avg. thermal conductance Btu/hr, ft°F | Specific heat, Btu/lb, °F | Wt/unit area, lb/ft² | Thickness under load, ft | Density, lb/ft³ | Thermal diffusivity, ft²/hr |
|---|---|---|---|---|---|---|---|---|
| Nylon, 2.25 oz/yd² 2/1 Twill | 17.0 psia Ambient | 400 | 0.022 | 0.57 | 0.0146 | 0.00038 | 38.2 | 0.0012 |
| | 15.3 mm Hg Vacuum | 400 | 0.015 | 0.57 | 0.0146 | 0.00038 | 38.2 | 0.00069 |
| Nomex, 1.95 oz/yd² Dobby Weave | 17.0 psia Ambient | 400 | 0.021 | 0.35 | 0.0135 | 0.000479 | 28.3 | 0.0038 |
| | 15.3 mm Hg Vacuum | 400 | 0.008 | 0.35 | 0.0135 | 0.000479 | 28.3 | 0.0014 |
| | 17.0 psia Ambient | 600 | 0.025 | 0.35 | 0.0135 | 0.000479 | 28.3 | 0.0045 |
| | 15.3 mm Hg Vacuum | 600 | 0.010 | 0.35 | 0.0135 | 0.000479 | 28.3 | 0.0018 |
| Glass fibers, 8.9 oz/yd², Satin weave | 17.0 psia Ambient | 600 | 0.038 | 0.26 | 0.0618 | 0.00110 | 56.3 | 0.0026 |
| | 15.3 mm Hg Vacuum | 600 | 0.022 | 0.26 | 0.0618 | 0.00110 | 57.9 | 0.0015 |
| Fused silica 8.9 oz/yd², Satin weave | 17.0 psia Ambient | 600 | 0.042 | 0.25 | 0.0664 | 0.00129 | 51.5 | 0.0033 |
| | 4.2 mm Hg Vacuum | 600 | 0.025 | 0.25 | 0.0664 | 0.00129 | 51.5 | 0.0020 |
| | 17.6 psia Ambient | 1200 | 0.060 | 0.26 | 0.0664 | 0.00129 | 51.5 | 0.0045 |
| | 4.2 mm Hg Vacuum | 1200 | 0.033 | 0.26 | 0.0664 | 0.00129 | 51.5 | 0.0025 |
| Graphite | 17.4 psia Ambient | 1200 | 0.166 | 0.40 | 0.053 | 0.00172 | 30.9 | 0.0034 |
| | 16.2 mm Hg Vacuum | 1200 | 0.120 | 0.40 | 0.053 | 0.00168 | 31.6 | 0.0095 |

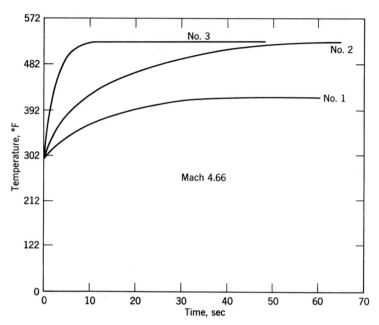

Fig. 10-51. Temperature rise vs time for wind tunnel test of 2 in. Dacron ribbon, 0.46 oz/yd.

TABLE 10-32. Strength of Fabric, Sewing Thread, and Seams at Specific Temperatures

| | Breaking strength, lb | | | |
|---|---|---|---|---|
| | −70°F | 70°F | 210°F | 350°F |
| Thread | | | | |
| Cotton, 3 cord | 22.0 | 16.00 | 10.2 | 7.3 |
| Nylon 6–6, 5 cord | 62.5 | 48.6 | 31.1 | 17.3 |
| Fabric | | | | |
| Nylon 6–6, 1.1 oz/yd², ripstop warp/in. | 51.2 | 41.4 | 29.8 | 21.4 |
| Nylon 6–6, 1.6 oz/yd², 33/1 twill, warp/in. | 66.0 | 55.2 | 37.0 | 28.6 |
| Nylon 6–6, ribbon, 2/2 twill, 2 in. wide | 152.0 | 123.0 | 87.0 | 64.0 |
| Cotton, duck, 9.85 oz/yd², plain weave, warp/in. | 108.0 | 188.0 | 121.0 | 93.0 |
| Seams | | | | |
| Nylon 6–6, 1.1 oz/yd², warp to warp, 1 in. | 45.0 | 36.0 | — | 22.0 |
| Nylon 6–6, 1.6 oz/yd², warp to warp, 1 in. | 70.0 | 49.0 | 33.0 | 31.0 |
| Nylon 6–6, ribbon, seam parallel to fill | 70.0 | 47.0 | 36.0 | 32.0 |

TABLE 10-33. Strength of Tire Cord at Various Temperature

| Temp., °F | Nomex 200/4/2 | | Nylon 6–6, 840/2, type 300 | |
|---|---|---|---|---|
| | Strength, lb | % Retention | Strength, lb | % Retention |
| 75 | 25.2 | | 27.0 | |
| 200 | 21.7 | 86.1 | 20.8 | 77.1 |
| 300 | 18.9 | 75.0 | 16.6 | 61.5 |
| 350 | 17.2 | 68.2 | 14.4 | 53.3 |
| 400 | 15.2 | 60.5 | 12.3 | 45.5 |
| 450 | 13.0 | 51.6 | 8.7 | 32.2 |
| 500 | 10.8 | 42.9 | | |

TABLE 10-34. Adhesion of Resin Cured Butyl to Cord of Three Fibers

| Exposed to | "H" Adhesion, lb | | |
|---|---|---|---|
| | Nylon 6–6 | Nomex | Steel cable |
| 75°F | 16.4 | 13.8 | 16.7 |
| 250°F | 11.4 | 11.7 | 8.2 |
| 400°F | 8.8 | 7.8 | 8.0 |
| Aged in metal bath, 8 hr at 400°F | | | |
| 75°F | 14.1 | 12.8 | 10.7 |
| 400°F | 7.5 | 8.4 | 2.5 |
| Aged in air, 8 hr at 400°F | | | |
| 75°F | 8.3 | 8.7 | 7.7 |
| 400°F | 6.7 | 6.9 | 1.5 |

TABLE 10-35. Calculated Properties of Two Fibers in an Aircraft-Type Tire

| Fiber | Burst strength, R.T. | Load/cord | | | | Time to Failure, hr | | |
|---|---|---|---|---|---|---|---|---|
| | | R.T. | 350°F | 400°F | 450°F | 350°F | 400°F | 450°F |
| Nylon 6–6 | 2020 | 3.7 | 5.6 | 5.9 | 6.3 | 650 | 50 | 1.3 |
| Nomex | 2030 | 3.4 | 5.2 | 5.5 | 5.8 | 500 | 150 | 45 |

## 2. *Oxidation Degradation*

Fibers in any form and regardless of substance must be capable of resisting oxidation attack. As has been shown by Muse (17), nylon degradation increases as the oxygen content of the atmosphere increases, while polyesters are not so effected. Since oxygen is present in the earth's atmosphere it can be concluded that in essentially all uses of fibers oxidation can be a cause of degradation. However, this one gas is so prevelent it is almost impossible to assume that if degradation occurs it is caused by just the oxygen. There must be a cause for the oxidation to take place, for example: the ignition of fire creates an oxidizing atmosphere, thus in such environments as thermal degradation, weathering, aging, chemical degradation, moisture, etc., the oxidation reaction occurs at some point in the deterioration of the fiber's properties. In such polymers as polyesters, aromatic polyamides, etc., this might well be a very subtle and little noticed reaction, thoroughly overshadowed by the major cause of degradation. With this in mind, the data presented in other sections should be reviewed with the consideration that oxidation is part of the overall degradation that occurs, but cannot be quantitatively established except as accomplished by Muse.

## 3. *Weathering*

The exposure of fibers in their various forms to weathering which includes sunlight (ultraviolet radiation) creates rapid degradation in most natural and some polymeric fibers while effecting others only very slightly. To overcome this form of degradation, finishes have been developed which absorb UV radiation, dyes have also been developed to provide the same protection and in many cases the polymer from which the fiber is formed has been modified to prevent degradation. An example of the latter is shown in Table 10-36, where polypropylene fibers with and without a UV inhibitor have been exposed to sunlight. The data also shows how nylon 6 is effected by sunlight and also is an example of how discrepancies occur when one producer evaluates various forms of other producers fibers. In the development of new polymers, UV degradation is one of the first properties characterized. Comparative studies, such as shown in Table 10-37, are conducted by the yarn producers as a means of demonstrating the superiority of their fiber(s) or to become fully aware of the capability of other producer's fibers. Effect of UV radiation at various wavelengths is important

TABLE 10-36.  Comparison of Polypropylene (Two manufacturers) and Nylon 6 Strength Retention after Exposure to Sunlight [a]

| Fiber designation | Strength retention, % | | | | | | |
|---|---|---|---|---|---|---|---|
| | Hours of exposure (rounded off) | | | | | | |
| | 20 | 65 | 120 | 175 | 205 | 250 | 300 |
| Mfg. No. 1 Polypropylene, with UV stabilizer | (2940) 102.4 | (2940) 102.8 | (2940) 102.4 | (848) 92.1 | (2940) 101.5 | (848) 81.3 | (848) 63.7 |
| Mfg. No. 1 Polypropylene, w/o UV stabilizer | | | | (1018) 97.2 | (1018) 95.2 | (1018) 96.3 | (1018) 98.7 |
| Mfg. No. 2 Polypropylene | (3508) 96.9 | (3508) 88.8 | (3508) 71.7 | | (3508) 52.1 | | |
| Nylon 6 | (2055) 96.3 | (2055) 89.6 | (2055) 81.3 | (3453) 28.0 | (2055) 66.2 | (3453) 23.4 | (3453) 19.2 |

[a] Yarn denier is shown in parentheses for each exposure.

in establishing a fiber's basic characteristics. Stephenson et al. (34,35) have done just this on a number of fibers at 244, 314, and 360 m$\mu$. Both organic and inorganic fibers were studied. In Table 10-38, data on yarns irradiated at 369 $\mu$ is summarized.

When it first became apparent that sunlight degraded fibers and outdoor exposures were to establish the time to achieve specific breakdown in properties exposure time was measured in hours, days, weeks, etc., while indoor exposure in fade-o-meter and weather-o-meter were measured in hours. Some studies of this type are graphically shown for yarns in Figs. 10-52 and 10-53. Attempts to correlate indoor tests to outdoor weathering data have never been found to be practical. The curves for nylon 6-6 and cotton fabric presented in Fig. 10-54 reveal this fact.

The lack of ability to correlate indoor (artificial) tests and outdoor exposure led to the use of the pyroheliometer to measure the light energy emitted by the sun. In Table 10-39, this energy (langleys-gram calories/square centimeter) is shown for various number of days at six locations where outdoor tests have been conducted. Since 1950, considerable data has been obtained for fibers in many forms and using many finishes and dyes. These are tabulated in Tables 10-40 to 10-43, and graphically presented in Figs. 10-55 to 10-58. Although the fiber producers generated data on yarn and some woven materials,

TABLE 10-37.  Comparative Strength Retention of Yarns after Exposure Outdoors in Florida

| Fiber, designation | Time of year | Original tenacity, g/den. | Strength retention, % | | | | | |
|---|---|---|---|---|---|---|---|---|
| | | | 1 mo | 2 mo | 4 mo | 8 mo | 18 mo | 36 mo |
| Acetate, bright, 70° den. | Winter | 1.1 | 75.0 | 57.0 | 47.0 | 13.0 | | |
| | Summer | 1.0 | 68.0 | 57.0 | 32.0 | B.E. | | |
| Polyester, bright, 70° den. | Winter | 4.1 | 83.0 | 72.0 | 64.0 | 28.0 | | |
| | Summer | 3.8 | 80.0 | 70.0 | 38.0 | 15.0 | | |
| Nylon 6-6, bright, 70° den. | Winter | 5.8 | 75.0 | 71.0 | 56.0 | 38.0 | | |
| | Summer | 5.5 | 85.0 | 55.0 | 29.0 | 7.0 | | |
| Nylon 6-6, bright, black, 200 den. | Winter | 4.8 | 90.0 | 87.0 | 83.0 | 94.0 | 62.0 | 37.0 |
| | Summer | 4.6 | 102.0 | 93.0 | 82.0 | 66.0 | 49.0 | 33.0 |
| Rayon, high tenacity, bright, 1650 den. | Winter | 3.5 | 55.0 | 36.0 | 26.0 | 16.0 | B.E.[a] | |
| | Summer | 3.5 | 41.0 | 32.0 | 19.0 | 13.0 | B.E.[a] | |
| Teflon, 1200 den. | Winter | 1.6 | | | | 104.0 | 100.0 | 98.0 |
| | Summer | | | | | | | |
| Cotton, 177 den. | Winter | 1.6 | 93.0 | 70.0 | 42.0 | B.E.[a] | B.E.[a] | |
| | Summer | 1.4 | 51.0 | 26.0 | B.E.[a] | B.E.[a] | B.E.[a] | |
| Glass, 101 den. | Winter | 5.4 | 64.0 | | | | 36.0[b] | |
| | Summer | 5.2 | | | | 79.0 | | |

[a] B.E. = broke during exposure.
[b] 21 months.

TABLE 10-38.  Yarns Irradiated at 369 M in Nitrogen

| Fiber and incident energy, joules/cm² | | Tensile strength, 10³ psi | Elongation % |
|---|---|---|---|
| Glass fibers | No exposure | 278.0 | 4.6 |
| | 830 | 202.0 | 4.0 |
| | 1780 | 204.0 | 3.8 |
| Fused silica | No exposure | 103.0 | 2.3 |
| | 440 | 159.0 | 3.6 |
| | 1730 | 147.0 | 3.4 |
| Nomex | No exposure | 114.0 | 32.1 |
| | 485 | 86.0 | 12.1 |
| | 1840 | 56.0 | 4.6 |
| Teflon | No exposure | 59.5 | 26.7 |
| | 440 | 58.5 | 27.8 |
| | 1570 | 57.1 | 26.1 |
| Nylon 6–6 | No exposure | 80.0 | 37.8 |
| | 470 | 78.7 | 38.6 |
| | 1330 | 73.3 | 36.6 |
| Dacron | No exposure | 145.0 | 21.5 |
| | 596 | 135.0 | 17.5 |
| | 1910 | 119.0 | 14.7 |
| Polybenzimidazole | No exposure | 23.5 | 19.4 |
| | 640 | 21.7 | 15.9 |
| | 1180 | 19.2 | 10.7 |

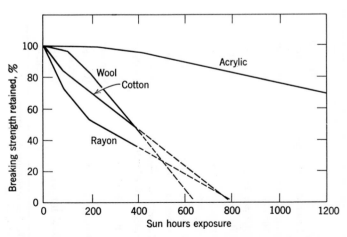

Fig. 10-52. Sunlight exposure of natural, cellulose, acrylic fibers.

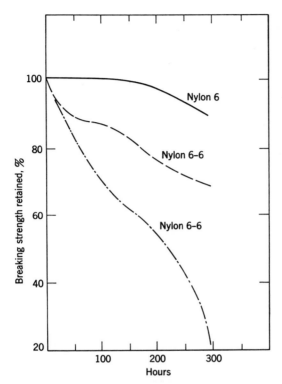

Fig. 10-53. Strength retention of nylon 6 and 6-6 (two manufacturers) exposed to Fade-O-Meter at 140°F.

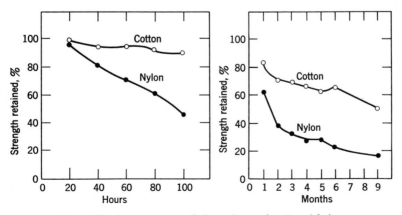

Fig. 10-54. Average strength for nylon and cotton fabrics.

TABLE 10-39. Comparison of Langleys Measured at Various Test Sites

| Days | Site and Langleys, g/Cal-cm² | | | | | |
|---|---|---|---|---|---|---|
| | Massachusetts | W-P AFB, O.[a] | Las Cruces, N. Mexico | Phoenix, Arizona | El Centro, Calif. | College, Alaska |
| 5 | 2,495 | | | 2,495 | | |
| 7 | 4,410 | | | | 4,226 | |
| 10 | | | | 4,947 | | |
| 14 | | | | | 8,586 | 1,546 |
| 15 | 8,919 | 5,148 | 9,728 | | | |
| 20 | 8,919 | | | 10,429 | | |
| 21 | | | | | 12,616 | |
| 28 | | | | | 16,101 | |
| 30 | 15,105 | 9,975 | 19,452 | | | 3,093 |
| 35 | 15,105 | | | 18,427 | 19,979 | |
| 42 | | | | | 23,824 | |
| 45 | | 14,486 | 28,930 | | | 5,042 |
| 55 | 23,445 | | | 29,374 | | |
| 60 | | 18,435 | 35,712 | | | 5,900 |
| 90 | | 25,475 | 52,620 | | | 6,271 |
| 120 | | 30,833 | 65,720 | | | 7,897 |
| 180 | | 37,859 | 81,930 | | | 11,730 |
| 360 | | 127,430 | 211,778 | | | 112,979 |
| Starting | July 1960 | Oct. 1955 | Oct. 1955 | July 1960 | July 1962 | Oct. 1955 |

[a] Wright-Patterson Air Force Base, Ohio.

TABLE 10-40. Strength of Fabrics Exposed in Weather-O-Meter and Outdoors (New Mexico)

| | | White silk | White nylon | Yellow cotton | White acetate satin | Yellow saran | White fortisan | White cuprammonium rayon (German) |
|---|---|---|---|---|---|---|---|---|
| Weave | | Plain | Plain | 2/2 Twill | Crowfoot | Satin | Oxford | Unknown |
| Thread, count/in. | | 142×84 | 120×98 | 164×84 | 56×45 | 211×155 | 196×94 | 130×104 |
| Weight, oz/sq yd | | 1.17 | 1.03 | 5.56 | 4.20 | 16.52 | 1.45 | 1.61 |
| Original breaking strength, lb/in.W.X.F. | | 39×39 | 41×44 | 140×64 | 41×40 | 211×155 | 66×58 | 20×16 |
| Weather-O-Meter XIA unit no water spray | 20 hr | 31×31 | 36×36 | 140×63 | 36×40 | 213×150 | 60×57 | 18×16 |
| | 40 hr | 11×11 | 16×23 | 134×60 | 38×32 | 214×139 | 62×56 | 16×10 |
| | 60 hr | 11×9 | 13×10 | 123×59 | 37×34 | 215×135 | 60×57 | 18×17 |
| | 80 hr | 8×3 | 14×12 | 123×61 | 29×31 | 207×133 | 59×57 | 19×17 |
| | 100 hr | 6×5 | 8×3 | 125×55 | 26×22 | 205×130 | 53×50 | 15×13 |
| Outdoors, New Mexico 45° angle facing south | 1 mo | 3×2 | 20×18 | 103×52 | 31×32 | 185×127 | 44×34 | 12×12 |
| | 2 mo | N.S. | 12×11 | 82×39 | 27×21 | 199×124 | 32×27 | 10×10 |
| | 3 mo | N.S. | 11×7 | 77×39 | 26×25 | 210×124 | 26×17 | 10×8 |
| | 4 mo | N.S. | N.S. | 73×37 | 24×22 | 190×144 | —[a] | N.S. |
| | 5 mo | N.S. | N.S. | 57×35 | —[a] | 198×127 | 21×14 | N.S. |
| | 6 mo | N.S. | N.S. | 73×37 | —[a] | 184×134 | 10×12 | N.S. |
| | 9 mo | N.S. | N.S. | 57×35 | 13×6 | 194×120 | 11×10 | N.S. |

[a] Samples lost.

TABLE 10-41. Strength Retained after Outdoor Exposure in Imperial Valley, California

| Fabric description and yarn designation | Original strength, lb/in. | Strength retained, %; exposure in weeks | | | | | |
|---|---|---|---|---|---|---|---|
| | | 1 | 2 | 3 | 4 | 5 | 6 |
| Nylon 6-6, ripstop weave type 300, natural | | | | | | | |
| Warp | 50.0 | 77.2 | 68.0 | 51.2 | 49.0 | 42.6 | 33.4 |
| Filling | 50.6 | 84.8 | 65.8 | 53.9 | 51.4 | 53.1 | 37.9 |
| Nylon 6-6, ripstop weave type 330, natural | | | | | | | |
| Warp | 47.0 | 89.4 | 88.9 | 81.7 | 78.5 | 77.7 | 68.5 |
| Filling | 47.0 | 85.9 | 91.1 | 88.5 | 85.7 | 77.7 | 76.2 |
| Nylon 6-6, ripstop weave type 330, orange | | | | | | | |
| Warp | 43.6 | 72.5 | 55.3 | 45.6 | 30.7 | 23.2 | 18.3 |
| Filling | 42.3 | 84.4 | 63.1 | 45.6 | 38.1 | 26.1 | 24.1 |
| Nylon 6-6, ripstop weave type 300, orange | | | | | | | |
| Warp | 48.3 | 91.7 | 79.3 | 59.2 | 49.1 | 48.9 | 38.9 |
| Filling | 43.8 | 96.1 | 87.7 | 67.1 | 62.1 | 44.7 | 34.9 |

TABLE 10-42. Strength of 1.10 oz/sq yd Nylon 6-6 Fabric Exposed Outdoors in Arizona and Massachusetts

| Identification | | Control | Strength lb/in. | | | | |
|---|---|---|---|---|---|---|---|
| | | | 5 Days | 10 Days | 20 Days | 35 Days | 55 Days |
| Griege (as woven) | Mass. | 46.2 | 39.2 | 33.8 | 22.3 | 14.6 | 8.4 |
| | Ariz. | 46.2 | 34.8 | 28.7 | 21.3 | 15.7 | 11.5 |
| Scoured | Mass. | 49.7 | 46.6 | 43.9 | 33.9 | 22.9 | 12.5 |
| | Ariz. | 49.7 | 43.1 | 37.6 | 26.3 | 21.0 | 15.0 |
| Green | Mass. | 49.6 | 48.5 | 46.8 | 40.0 | 31.1 | 19.4 |
| | Ariz. | 49.6 | 46.7 | 43.2 | 29.2 | 21.9 | 15.7 |
| Orange | Mass. | 49.3 | 47.8 | 46.7 | 37.6 | 27.1 | 15.5 |
| | Ariz. | 49.3 | 46.4 | 42.3 | 30.2 | 20.1 | 13.5 |
| Silicone oil finished | Mass. | 49.2 | 46.6 | 45.4 | 33.9 | 23.2 | 12.4 |
| | Ariz. | 49.2 | 43.1 | 37.0 | 27.3 | 18.8 | 14.6 |
| Antistatic agent | Mass. | 49.1 | 46.7 | 44.7 | 35.2 | 25.4 | 13.6 |
| | Ariz. | 49.1 | 43.0 | 39.0 | 29.2 | 20.4 | 17.9 |
| UV filtering finish | Mass. | 49.5 | 47.8 | 45.3 | 37.1 | 26.8 | 14.6 |
| | Ariz. | 49.5 | 44.1 | 41.1 | 33.4 | 27.2 | 22.4 |
| All oils extracted | Mass. | 48.6 | 45.4 | 42.2 | 32.5 | 22.2 | 11.8 |
| | Ariz. | 48.6 | 25.4 | 13.8 | 8.0 | 6.1 | 5.7 |

TABLE 10-43. Breaking Strength of Tapes and Cords of Nomex Exposed Outdoors and in Weather-O-Meter

| Exposure condition and time of exposure | | Breaking strength, lb | | | | |
|---|---|---|---|---|---|---|
| | | $\frac{9}{16}$ in. Tape herringbone twill | 1 in. Tape plain weave | 1 in. Webbing tubular weave | 2 in. Ribbon twill weave | Core and sleeve braid |
| Control | | 429.8 | 1115.0 | 2500.0 | 1501.0 | 574.0 |
| Weather-O-Meter | 20 hr | 418.0 | 1085.0 | 2482.0 | 1555.0 | 552.0 |
| | 40 hr | 369.0 | 974.0 | 2277.0 | 1510.0 | 507.4 |
| | 60 hr | 376.8 | 945.0 | 2222.0 | 1453.0 | 492.0 |
| | 80 hr | 312.4 | 918.0 | 2190.0 | 1395.0 | 477.0 |
| | 100 hr | 336.0 | 902.0 | —[a] | 1274.0 | 448.4 |
| | 150 hr | 323.0 | 862.0 | —[a] | 1200.0 | 415.8 |
| Outdoor exposure, El Centro, Calif. | 1 wk | 307.0 | 1009.0 | 2390.0 | 1343.0 | 515.6 |
| | 2 wk | 367.0 | 1005.2 | 2320.0 | 1405.0 | 496.8 |
| | 3 wk | 363.4 | 974.0 | 2184.0 | 1315.0 | 483.6 |
| | 4 wk | 348.0 | 920.2 | 2064.0 | 1232.0 | 470.0 |
| | 5 wk | —[a] | 880.4 | 1976.0 | 1192.5 | 458.8 |
| | 6 wk | 325.4 | 856.4 | 1922.0 | 1112.0 | 434.4 |

[a] Sample lost.

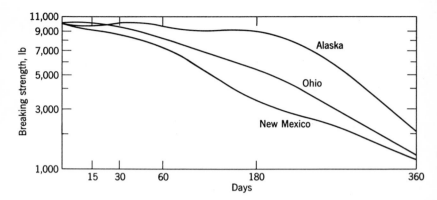

Fig. 10-55. Strength of natural nylon 6-6 webbing after exposure at three sites.

the end item users are the prime source of data on specific woven forms. McGrath (21,36,37) has been one of the more prolific workers in this area along with Wilkinson (38). When parachutes were put into use as brakes for aircraft, they were exposed to sunlight during use and while they lay on the ground for indeterminate times after release from the aircraft. An attempt was made to relate strength lost to UV reflectance (39). As shown in Table 10-44, the reflectance is greatly effected by the finish on the fabric. Obviously this is a problem that needs considerable further study using not only ultraviolet reflectance but in addition infrared reflectance as a means of relating deterioration of strength to sunlight exposure.

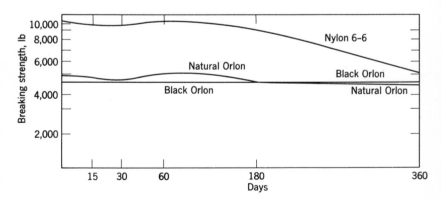

Fig. 10-56. Strength of natural nylon 6-6 (UV resistant) and Orlon (natural and black) webbing after exposure in New Mexico.

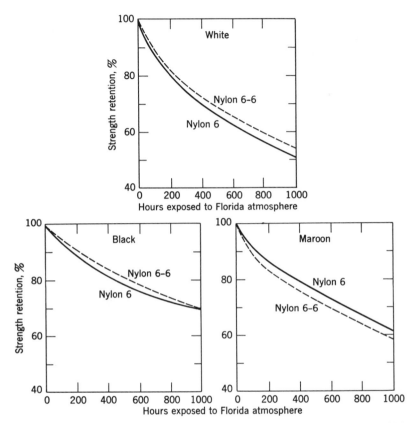

Fig. 10-57. Strength retention of three colors of "3 panel herringbone" webbing of two fibers after exposure to sunlight.

## 4. Chemical Degradation

As discussed earlier in this chapter, the chemical structure of both natural and synthetic fibers are highly susceptable to degradation by chemicals, from the time of their formation throughout processing, fabrication, and use. The fiber producers have spent a great deal of effort to establish how the chemicals used in the formation and processing of polymers into fibers, can be detrimental and how this detrimental effect can be prevented. After a fiber is formed studies are conducted on the yarn to establish how acids, solvents, etc., will effect such properties as strength, elongation, initial length, flexibility, and elastic recovery. These exposures are generally limited to short times with concentrations of 0.1–95% for acids and to 100% for other

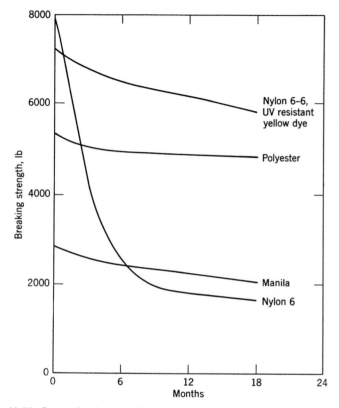

Fig. 10-58. Strength of ropes after various exposures to sunlight in Florida.

chemicals. Some exposures up to 1000 hr are used but only for chemicals that do not cause serious degradation of the polymers. How chemicals effect the woven forms of fibers for longer periods of time and in conjunction with other environments such as heat and ultraviolet light are also investigated.

The fiber producers report the effect of degradation via many techniques. The most simple routine is to qualitatively show the effects of laboratory exposure of fibers, as shown in Table 10-45. As a fiber achieves widespread usage, problems must be solved, especially where chemical degradation occurs. Then very complete comparative and exhaustive studies are conducted. Time of exposure, concentration of solution, temperature of solution are varied and reams of data are obtained which are published in technical bulletins. Some of this type of data is tabulated in Tables 10-46 and 10-47.

TABLE 10-44. Change in Strength and Ultraviolet Reflectance of Three Fabrics Exposed in Weather-O-Meter (Percent)

| Samples exposed for 100 hr with water spray | 1.1 oz/yd² nylon 6–6, 30 den. | | 2.25 oz/yd² nylon 6–6, 100 den. | | 4.75 oz/yd² nylon 6–6, 210 den. | |
|---|---|---|---|---|---|---|
| | Strength loss | Reflectance change | Strength loss | Reflectance change | Strength loss | Reflectance change |
| Griege | 19.5 | 54.8 | 15.2 | 62.1 | 23.7 | 48.8 |
| Scoured | 12.9 | 39.7 | 9.4 | 49.6 | 12.7 | 44.9 |
| Silicone oil finished | 10.6 | 49.3 | 10.9 | 48.4 | 7.1 | 47.2 |
| Antistatic agent | 9.8 | 42.3 | 11.7 | 45.0 | 10.2 | 37.2 |
| Ultraviolet filter | 8.7 | 50.4 | 9.0 | 31.9 | 4.9 | 33.9 |
| Extracted | 8.2 | 47.0 | 18.4 | 30.9 | 18.3 | 17.8 |

TABLE 10-45.  Qualitative Effect of Various Chemicals on Yarns

| Chemical, Concentration, Time, Temperature | Effect of Exposure on | | | | | | |
|---|---|---|---|---|---|---|---|
| | Rayon | Polypropylene | Nomex | Teflon | Nylon 6-6 | Dacron | Dynel |
| Ethyl alcohol | Excellent | | | | | | |
| Sulfuric acid | | | | | | | |
| 10%, 10 hr, 72°F | | None | | None | | | |
| 10%, 100 hr, 70°F | | | | | | | |
| Seawater | Good | None | None | None | None | None | |
| Jet fuel | Excellent | Excellent | None | | | | |
| Benzene | Excellent | None | None | None | | Moderate | None |
| Xylene | Excellent | | None | | None | Moderate | |
| Stoddard solvent | Excellent | | None | | None | Moderate | |

TABLE 10-46. Effect of Mineral Acids on the Strength Retention of Yarns

| Acid, conc. time, temp. | Strength retained, % | | | | | | | | |
|---|---|---|---|---|---|---|---|---|---|
| | Acetate | Dacron | Nylon 6-6 | Orlon 81 | Rayon | Cotton | Dynel | Lilion | Vycron 5 |
| H₂SO₄ | | | | | | | | | |
| 10%, 10 hr, 70°F | 93 | 103 | 57 | 87 | 59 | 59 | | | |
| 70%, 10 hr, 70°F | | 102 | | 88 | | | | | |
| 70%, 20 hr, 120°F | | | | | | | 100 | | |
| 10%, 1 hr, 104°F | | | | | | | | 82 | |
| 10%, 1 hr, 104°F | | | | | | | | | 106 |
| HCL | | | | | | | | | |
| 10%, 10 hr, 70°F | 72 | 100 | 82 | 101 | 69 | 74 | | | |
| 37%, 10 hr, 70°F | | 107 | | 92 | | | | | |
| 38%, 20 hr, 212°F | | | | | | | 86 | | |
| 10%, 1 hr, 104°F | | | | | | | | 100 | |
| 10%, 10 hr, 70°F | | | | | | | | | 106 |
| HNO₃ | | | | | | | | | |
| 10%, 10 hr, 70°F | 76 | 105 | 91 | 92 | 91 | 85 | | | |
| 20%, 20 hr, 212°F | | | | | | | 92 | | |
| 10%, 1 hr, 70°F | | | | | | | | 100 | |
| 10%, 10 hr, 70°F | | | | | | | | | 101 |

TABLE 10-47.  Effect of Various Chemicals on the Strength Retention of Yarns

| Chemical, conc., time, temp. | Strength retained, % | | | | | | | |
|---|---|---|---|---|---|---|---|---|
| | Acetate | Dacron | Nylon 6-6 | Orlon 81 | Rayon | Cotton | Vycron 5 | Dynel |
| Carbon disulfide | | | | | | | | |
| 100%, 1000 hr, 70°F | 90 | 91 | 91 | 84 | 87 | 91 | | |
| 100%, 1000 hr, 70°F | | | | | | | 109 | |
| Perchlorethylene | | | | | | | | |
| 100%, 10 hr, 210°F | 89 | 104 | 99 | 97 | 91 | 84 | | |
| 90%, 20 hr, 167°F | | | | | | | 99 | 95 |
| 100%, 10 hr, 210°F | | | | | | | | |
| Phenol | | | | | | | | |
| 5%, 10 hr, 70°F | Dissolved | 107 | 43 | 93 | 94 | 89 | | |
| 100%, 0.1 hr, 210°F | Dissolved | Dissolved | Dissolved | 94 | 89 | 88 | | |
| 5%, 20 hr, 72°F | | | | | | | 109 | 53 |
| 5%, 10 hr, 70°F | | | | | | | | |
| Ethyl alcohol | | | | | | | | |
| 100%, 1000 hr, 70°F | 98 | 95 | 87 | 95 | 91 | 98 | | |
| 100%, 1000 hr, 70°F | | | | | | | 110 | |
| 100%, 20 hr, 122°F | | | | | | | | 91 |
| Hydrazine | | | | | | | | |
| 25%, 20 hr, 122°F | | | | | | | | 100 |

When the fiber is woven and fabricated for use in military or industrial systems, the possibility of exposure to a chemical environment during use must be taken into consideration. These woven structures come in contact with battery acid, motor exhaust gases, reaction products of chemicals being processed, fuel from aircraft, rocket motor exhaust gases as well as the rocket fuel, to name only a few degrading factors, and this exposure can be quite a long one at either low or high humidity (in the case of the latter as the moisture concentration decreases after exposure the chemical concentration will increase). An excellent example of this type of situation is in the military use of parachutes. Because the fibers (in woven form) that can be used in recovery of personnel and loads must be repacked at intervals the possibility of coming into contact with fumes and liquids of varying concentrations, rate of deterioration had to be established. Cates (10) and Templeton (40) made a broad study of nylon 6-6 and Dacron, in fabric form, exposing them to mineral and organic acids, and a broad spectrum of alkalis, salts, organic solvents, alcohols, and esters. Tables 10-48 and 10-49, summarize a minute part of the data obtained. Since these fabrics would also see sunlight at some point in their history, Templeton (40) exposed fabrics soaked in acids, to ultraviolet light in a Fade-O-Meter (Table 10-50) which appreciably increased their rate of degradation.

Others have also studied how various chemicals, either pure or as a finished fluid (such as a lubricant or hydraulic fluid) effect the properties of the woven fibers. Hall of the U.S. Army QM (41) has established how chemicals used to simulate biological agents affected the cords used in the seams of protective garments. The shrinkage after exposure to water and three simulator chemicals is shown in Table 10-51. Other factors studied included rate of liquid migration through the cord, as well as penetration through the seam using the cords as is and after seaming. In another investigation, Sublette (42), evaluated the effect of lubricants on various fibers in fabric forms as would be used in military applications. These lubricants were (*1*) a chlorinated silicone, (*2*) two silicate base fluids, (*3*) a disiloxane base fluid and (*4*) an ester base oil. As shown in Table 10-52, strength before and after soaking in the fluid followed by dry cleaning or laundering was obtained (in this table only one fluid is summarized).

In every application that fibers in any form are used, the potential of coming in contact with fumes or liquid chemicals must be considered and the proper choice of fiber made to insure that adequate protection can be attained.

TABLE 10-48.  Loss in Strength of Nylon and Dacron Fabric When Aged in Acid Solutions for Two and Four Weeks

Strength loss, %

| Acid and fiber type | Two weeks | | | | | | Four weeks | | | | | |
|---|---|---|---|---|---|---|---|---|---|---|---|---|
| | 0.1N | | 1.0N | | 5.0N | | 0.1N | | 1.0N | | 5.0N | |
| | Room temp. | 150°F | Room temp. | 150°F | Room temp. | 150°F | Room temp. | 150°F | Room temp. | 150°F | Room temp. | 150°F |
| $H_2SO_4$ | | | | | | | | | | | | |
| Nylon | 5.6 | 37.2 | 0.6 | 90.1 | 12.0 | 100.0 | 1.2 | 66.8 | 10.01 | 100.0 | 3.48 | 100.0 |
| Dacron | 1.4 | +1.4 | 0.0 | 0.0 | +0.7 | 2.7 | +0.7 | 1.4 | +1.3 | 0.7 | +0.7 | 2.8 |
| HCL | | | | | | | | | | | | |
| Nylon | +0.2 | 32.0 | 2.1 | 100.0 | 100.0 | 100.0 | +3.4 | 64.6 | 21.9 | 100.0 | 100.0 | 100.0 |
| Dacron | 0.7 | +2.7 | 2.0 | +2.7 | 0.7 | 45.9 | 0.7 | 0.7 | 0.0 | +0.4 | 0.7 | 95.2 |
| $HNO_3$ | | | | | | | | | | | | |
| Nylon | +5.3 | 66.9 | 7.1 | 100.0 | 100.0 | 100.0 | 3.1 | 77.6 | 21.7 | 100.0 | 100.0 | 100.0 |
| Dacron | 0.7 | 0.7 | +3.4 | 100.0 | 25.4 | 100.0 | 0.7 | 0.8 | 0.0 | 100.0 | 55.4 | 100.0 |

TABLE 10-49.  Effect of Aging in Solution and at Various RH on Nylon 6-6 for Some Organic Chemicals

| Chemical conc. g/100 ml; Temp., °F | Strength loss, % | | | | | |
|---|---|---|---|---|---|---|
| | 1 Month | | | 6 Months | | |
| | In solution | Low RH | High RH | In solution | Low RH | High RH |
| Phenol | | | | | | |
| 1.0,  70° | +1.01 | 0.19 | 1.85 | +0.12 | 0.27 | +0.93 |
| 5.0,  70° | 6.37 | 1.16 | +0.14 | 19.66 | 1.67 | 0.09 |
| 1.0, 150° | 1.23 | 2.02 | 2.00 | 4.05 | 19.33 | 5.38 |
| 5.0, 150° | 9.77 | 1.48 | 1.25 | 18.55 | 4.79 | 2.17 |
| Perchloroethylene | | | | | | |
| 70° | 0.02 | | 1.87 | 1.83 | | +0.64 |
| 150° | 2.59 | | 5.45 | 16.79 | | 38.91 |
| Ethyl alcohol | | | | | | |
| 70° | +0.32 | | 1.23 | 0.50 | | 0.86 |
| 150° | 3.58 | | 2.17 | 5.71 | | 2.54 |
| Carbon tetrachloride | | | | | | |
| 70° | +0.39 | | 3.11 | 5.41 | | 15.99 |
| 150° | 40.76 | | 56.07 | —[a] | | —[a] |

[a] Completely degraded.

## 5. Aging

From the time that a fiber is formed, even natural fibers, an aging process is initiated which continues at varying rates (depending on the molecular structure of the fiber) until the fiber has outlived its usefullness.  This aging can include many considerations, from storage

TABLE 10-50.  Loss in Strength of Two Fabrics When Treated in Different Solutions and Exposed in Fade-O-Meter

| Solution | Fiber | Strength loss, % | | | | |
|---|---|---|---|---|---|---|
| | | Hours exposure in Fade-o-Meter | | | | |
| | | 20 | 40 | 80 | 160 | 320 |
| Water | Nylon | 44.0 | 63.9 | 75.4 | | |
| | Dacron | | 13.4 | 12.1 | 17.0 | 14.6 |
| H₂SO₄ | Nylon | 72.2 | 76.2 | 83.0 | | |
| 1.0N | Dacron | | 49.5 | 37.6 | 72.0 | 100.0 |
| HCL | Nylon | 90.2 | 92.9 | 100.0 | | |
| 1.0N | Dacron | | 11.6 | 21.0 | 57.1 | 26.7 |
| HNO₃ | Nylon | 78.1 | 86.0 | 97.1 | | |
| 1.0N | Dacron | | 9.4 | 16.8 | 32.6 | 21.5 |

TABLE 10-51.  Shrinkage of Unsewn Cords after Soaking in Fluids

| Fluid and description of exposure | % Shrinkage | | |
|---|---|---|---|
| | Cotton sewing cord | Rayon parachute cord | Polyester tentage cord |
| Water: | | | |
| Immediately after | 7.0 | 17.0 | 0.0 |
| 4 hr after | 5.0 | 17.0 | 0.0 |
| Dimethyl hydrogen phosphite: | | | |
| Immediately after | 1.0 | 0.0 | 0.0 |
| 4 hr after | 4.0 | 0.0 | 0.0 |
| Diethyl phthalate: | | | |
| Immediately after | 0.0 | 0.0 | 0.0 |
| 4 hr after | 0.0 | 0.0 | 0.0 |
| Bis(2-ethylhexyl)hydrogen phosphite: | | | |
| Immediately after | 0.0 | 1.0 | 0.0 |
| 4 hr after | 0.0 | 0.0 | 0.0 |

intermittently in a container or a dark room, to repeated or cyclic loading outdoors to, as in the case of materials being used in aerospace applications, exposure to vacuum in combination with heat or ultraviolet light. Aging of this type is very rarely explored by the fiber producer, primarily because they cannot predict how an application utilizing their fiber will be aged, using as a definition of aging, the following: The exposure of a fiber or its fabricated form to a combination of environments such as storage indoors or in containers, with or without ultraviolet light, heat, vacuum for various times in conjunction with (in some cases) repeated usage. Indoor aging, under various conditions, of nylon 6-6 has been conducted by the U.S. Navy as a means of establishing personnel parachute service life. Boone (43), has compared fabric exposed to, and stored in nylon 6-6 packs (composed of 7.25 oz./sq yd Zelan treated fabric) while exposed to fluorescent lighted laboratory at Standard Textile Conditions, as well as in an unheated, nonconditioned room. Over a one year period, little change was evidenced in the strength of the fabric (Table 10-53). Others have stored both cotton and nylon 6-6 outdoors, Table 10-54, in narrow fabric form, again with little change in strength (44) even though the exposure took place between April and September in a hot moist climate (the relative humidity exceed 80% for 25% of the exposure period). Over the many years that aircraft have been used, parachutes have also been used. To provide maximum safety to flight per-

TABLE 10-52. Strength of Fabrics Exposed to a Silicate Base Fluid

| Fibers and fabric descrip. | Cleaning method | 72 hr at room temp. | | 72 hr at 160°F | |
|---|---|---|---|---|---|
| | | No lubricant, lb | Silicate base lub., lb | No lubricant, lb | Silicate base lub., lb |
| Cotton | None | 161 | 143 | 136 | 153 |
| 2×2 Basket weave | Dry cleaned | 145 | 154 | 146 | 151 |
| 4.75 oz/sq yd | Laundered | 144 | 142 | 135 | 133 |
| Dacron | None | 151 | 150 | 144 | 148 |
| Twill weave | Dry cleaned | 142 | 149 | 138 | 147 |
| 1.6 oz/sq yd | Laundered | 150 | 148 | 151 | 148 |
| Orlon | None | 319 | 337 | 314 | 320 |
| Dobby weave | Dry cleaned | 318 | 332 | 314 | 303 |
| 5 oz/sq yd | Laundered | 316 | 326 | 316 | 307 |
| Nylon 6-6 | None | 141 | 142 | 130 | 141 |
| Twill weave | Dry cleaned | 142 | 144 | 135 | 138 |
| 1.6 oz/sq yd | Laundered | 149 | 140 | 139 | 143 |
| Rayon | None | 169 | 164 | 139 | 163 |
| Plain weave | Dry cleaned | 148 | 155 | 153 | 159 |
| 3-5 oz/sq yd | Laundered | 158 | 161 | 152 | 156 |

TABLE 10-53.  Strength of Nylon 6-6 Fabric after Aging  Indoors

| Months aged beginning 1 Jan 60 | In laboratory at std. cond. (65% RH, 72°F), under fluorescent lights: strength, lb/in. | | At std. cond. (65% RH, 72°F), in package: strength, lb/in. | | In unheated, nonconditioned room in package: strength, lb/in. | |
|---|---|---|---|---|---|---|
| | Warp | Filling | Warp | Filling | Warp | Filling |
| Control | 54 | 68 | 54 | 68 | 54 | 68 |
| 1 | 52 | 69 | 51 | 67 | 52 | 69 |
| 2 | 52 | 68 | 52 | 71 | 50 | 68 |
| 3 | 53 | 69 | 52 | 70 | 52 | 70 |
| 4 | 50 | 65 | 53 | 62 | 52 | 78 |
| 5 | 49 | 65 | 53 | 69 | 54 | 70 |
| 6 | 49 | 66 | 52 | 68 | 57 | 69 |
| 7 | 49 | 65 | 49 | 65 | 53 | 67 |
| 8 | 51 | 67 | 51 | 67 | 54 | 70 |
| 9 | 52 | 64 | 52 | 64 | 50 | 69 |
| 10 | 53 | 65 | 53 | 65 | 58 | 72 |
| 11 | 48 | 65 | 52 | 63 | 51 | 66 |
| 12 | 48 | 63 | 51 | 66 | 51 | 66 |

sonnel, a service life has been established for personnel parachutes. Extensive evaluation of fabrics of many fiber types (as they have been used in parachutes) have been conducted (44). An example of the data obtained from 15-year old fabrics is shown in Table 10-55. As a result of these extensive studies it has been possible to increase personnel parachute service life from 7 to $7\frac{1}{2}$, and recently, to 10 years or in the case of paratrooper parachutes, 100 actual uses. The life of parachutes used to decelerate aircraft and other aeronautical systems is based on the number of uses rather than the number of years. In parachutes that use a porous fabric, airflow is very critical, too high an airflow prevents a parachute from opening, while to low an airflow creates high "Q" (loads) in the parachute and possible failure. Fabric taken from recovery systems and evaluated for air permeability, Table 10-56, showed that the lower the initial airflow the greater the increase after use. Strength is just as important in establishing the number of uses as in airflow. In the case of bomber aircraft, a series of use tests were conducted and the parachutes torn down for complete materials evaluation. As shown in Table 10-57, the results are erratic which might be attributable to the fact that some materials were dirtier or oil soaked than others, even within the same entity.

The use of fibers in aerospace applications has created concern as to

TABLE 10-54.  Effect of Protected Outdoor Storage on the Breaking Strength of Webbing and Ribbon

| Material description | Original minimum required stg. lb | Strength, lb | | | Condition of storage |
|---|---|---|---|---|---|
| | | Minimum | Average | Maximum | |
| Cotton, $\frac{9}{16}$ in. wide, herringbone twill | 350 | 398 | 411 | 418 | Stored outdoors in a can and covered with canvas which was supposedly waterproof |
| Nylon 6-6, 2 in wide, twill weave | 1000 | 1048 | 1106 | 1160 | |
| Nylon 6-6, $\frac{5}{8}$ in. wide, twill weave [a] | 180 | 207 | 221 | 235 | |
| Nylon 6-6, 1 in wide, plain tubular weave | 3000 | 3830 | 3848 | 3910 | |
| Cotton, $\frac{9}{16}$ in. wide, herringbone twill | 350 | 420 | 423 | 430 | Stored outdoors in an uncovered shipping container |
| Nylon 6-6, 2 in wide, twill weave | 1000 | 1160 | 1182 | 1210 | |
| Nylon 6-6, $\frac{5}{8}$ in. wide, twill weave [a] | 180 | 220 | 227 | 231 | |

[a] Used as a double layer stitched together.

TABLE 10-55.  Strength of Fabrics Taken from 15-Year-Old Parachutes

| Mechanical properties | Nylon 6–6 | Rayon | Cotton | Silk |
|---|---|---|---|---|
| Weight, oz/sq yd | 1.45 | | 4.3 | 1.36–1.55 |
| Breaking strength, lb/in. | | | | |
| Warp | 57.5 | 85.8 | 102.5 | 41.0–50.0 |
| Filling | 52.6 | 85.4 | 102.2 | 40.0–55.8 |
| Elongation, % | | | | |
| Warp | 23.7 | 16.6 | 17.0 | 16.7–21.7 |
| Filling | 27.7 | 19.4 | 16.5 | 15.0–18.3 |
| Air permeability, ft$^3$/min-ft$^2$ | 142.4 | 141.6 | 25.6 | 100–137.5 |
| Tear Strength, lb | | | | |
| Warp | 4.9 | 26.8 | 8.1 | 4.4–5.6 |
| Filling | 4.5 | 27.2 | 7.9 | 4.0–6.0 |

how vacuum singely and with other environments will effect fibers. Stephenson (34) in addition to studying ultraviolet deterioration in air and nitrogen also investigated this same degradation at various vacua. In Table 10-58, results are shown that were obtained using a G30T8 light source (that emitted a major portion of its energy at 253.7 m$\mu$. It can be expected that some materials will give up some of their constituents (primarily moisture and unattached gases) in a vacuum as shown in Table 10-59. This data, reported by Pettus (45) and that shown in Table 10-60, is only the first of a magnitude of data that must be generated to adequately describe the reaction that occurs in fibrous materials when in space. Witte (46), has taken another step toward achieving the same goal. The effect of exposing nylon 6-6 to a vacuum and heat is shown in Fig. 10-59. Thus, although preliminary

TABLE 10-56.  Effect of Repeated Usage on Nylon 6–6 Fabric Permeability

| | Permeability, ft$^3$/min-ft$^2$ [a] | |
|---|---|---|
| No. of uses | Before use | After use |
| Control | 134.0 | |
| 5 | 139.3 | 175.8 |
| 10 | 141.0 | 155.8 |
| 15 | 149.2 | 173.1 |
| 20 | 165.8 | 175.8 |
| 25 | 139.5 | 179.0 |
| 30 | 158.8 | 144.9 |
| 35 | 164.0 | 176.5 |

[a] Requirement for new fabric is 100–150 ft$^3$/min-ft$^2$.

TABLE 10-57.  Strength Loss (%) of Nylon 6-6 Materials after Repeated Use in Parachutes for Decelerating Bomber Aircraft

| Material evaluated | After 5 uses | After 10 uses | After 15 uses | After 20 uses | After 25 uses | After 30 uses | After 40 uses | After 50 uses | After 60 uses [b] |
|---|---|---|---|---|---|---|---|---|---|
| First test series: | | | | | | | | | |
| Nylon 6-6, 2 in. wide, 300 lb min. | 3.2 | 36.8 | 34.7 | 39.3 | 38.7 | | | | |
| Nylon 6-6, 1 in. wide, 2250 lb min. | 4.7 | 6.1 | 11.1 | 6.4 | 6.7 | | | | |
| Nylon 6-6 [a] 1¾ in. wide, 1800 lb min. | +11.3 | 6.1 | 20.8 | 12.1 | 14.3 | | | | |
| Nylon 6-6, [a] 1½ in. wide, 1500 lb min. | +7.1 | v+2.3 | 12.6 | 11.9 | 4.4 | | | | |
| Second test series: | | | | | | | | | |
| Nylon 6-6, 2 in. wide, 300 lb min. | | 46.4 | | 31.4 | | 28.9 | 33.4 | 26.9 | 27.1 |
| Nylon 6-6, 1 in. wide, 2250 lb min. | | 4.5 | | 10.7 | | 3.3 | 11.4 | 8.8 | 14.3 |
| Nylon 6-6 [a] 1¾ in. wide, 1800 lb min. | | 3.6 | | 25.5 | | 21.3 | 35.4 | 13.6 | 29.1 |
| Nylon 6-6, [a] 1½ in. wide, 1500 lb min. | | 0.8 | | 15.2 | | 14.8 | 12.5 | 2.2 | 15.8 |

[a] Lost overseas for over 1 year.
[b] This is the inner layer of a 3-layer configuration; stitches may have caused erratic data.

TABLE 10-58.  Yarns Irradiated in Various Vacua

| Fiber | Vacuum, mm Hg | Hours exposed | Tensile Stg., $10^3$ psi | Elongation, % |
|---|---|---|---|---|
| Teflon | | No exposure | 59.5 | 26.7 |
| | $5\times10^{-2}$ | 24 | 69.1 | 30.5 |
| | | 72 | 52.4 | 22.4 |
| Acrilan | | No exposure | 34.9 | 25.5 |
| | $5\times10^{-2}$ | 24 | 34.5 | 24.0 |
| | | 72 | 32.2 | 17.0 |
| | $1\times10^{-6}$ | 24 | 32.0 | 24.1 |
| | | 63 | 28.2 | 14.6 |
| Nomex | | No exposure | 113.0 | 29.5 |
| | $1\times10^{-3}$ | 24 | 104.0 | 24.4 |
| | | 72 | 100.0 | 20.9 |
| | $1\times10^{-6}$ | 24 | 107.0 | 24.9 |
| | | 72 | 102.0 | 24.0 |
| Polybenzimidazole | | No exposure | 23.5 | 19.4 |
| | $1\times10^{-3}$ | 24 | 22.9 | 20.2 |
| | | 72 | 22.5 | 24.5 |
| | $1\times10^{-6}$ | 24 | 23.5 | 20.7 |
| | | 72 | 22.4 | 20.3 |

results have shown that some materials are effected by vacuum and temperature, vacuum itself (based on data available) does not seriously change the strength, but as expected does cause some weight loss.

It will be seen in the future that other combinations of environments will occur, which will be labeled aging, however it will be essentially

TABLE 10-59.  Percent Loss in Weight of Woven Materials After Exposure to Vacuum and Heat

| Fiber and woven form | Control wt, g | Wt after exposure to $2.9\times10^{-9}$ torr and 743°F g | Weight loss, % |
|---|---|---|---|
| Cotton–sateen weave | 16.21 | 15.64 | 3.5 |
| Nomex ribbon–twill weave | 36.28 | 35.38 | 2.5 |
| Nomex ribbon, rubber coated | 15.21 | 14.87 | 2.2 |
| Dacron webbing | 225.20 | 225.2 | 0.0 |
| Nylon 6–6 tape | 41.69 | 37.90 | 9.1 |

TABLE 10-60. Effect of Vacuum and Temperature on Strength of Fibers in Various Forms

| Description of materials | Exposed to | | Tested at °F | Strength, lb/in. for fabric | Control strength |
|---|---|---|---|---|---|
| | Vacuum $\times 10^{-6}$ torr | Temp. °F | | | |
| Nylon 6–6, tape | 3.5–6.7 | 72 | 72 | 298 | 310 |
| | 3.5–6.7 | 112–122 | 200 | 247 | 310 |
| | 3.5–6.7 | 112–122 | 200 | 244 | 310 |
| | 3.5–6.7 | 116–122 | 200 | 247.5 | 310 |
| Nylon 6–6, cloth | 1.2–4.4 | 72 | 72 | 164 | 167 |
| | 1.2–4.4 | 72 | 72 | 173 | 167 |
| | 2.5–4.3 | 118–123 | 200 | 100 | 167 |
| | 2.5–4.3 | 118–123 | 200 | 157 | 167 |
| Nylon 6–6, braided cord | 1.2–4.4 | 118–123 | 195–201 | 473 | 590 |
| | 3.5–6.7 | 115–122 | 150–190 | 540 | 590 |
| Dacron, tape | 2.5–4.3 | 112–124 | 200 | 474 | 621 |
| | 2.5–4.3 | 110–122 | 81 | 526 | 621 |
| Nomex, ribbon | 2.5–4.3 | 115–121 | 200 | 56 | 67 |

the application or use of the fiber is put to, that will establish an aging cycle that will require evaluation.

## 6. Moisture Sensitivity

As during processing, fibers in their many forms face intermittant and continuous exposure to moisture in both liquid and vapor form. When the fiber form is used without protective finishes, moisture can penetrate the fiber and depending on its absorption characteristics (Table 10-10) can under the proper conditions trigger reactions which will cause degradation of the polymer structure with subsequent property change. Some of the newer high temperature inorganic fibers, which are being given serious consideration as replacements for polymeric fibers, are also effected by moisture but in a far different manner. In the case of vitreous fibers, moisture invades surface cracks or striations causing stress concentrations which will fail when the fiber is statically loaded. Metal fibers, because of their high ratio of surface area to cross-sectional area, corrode very rapidly when exposed to moisture causing rapid strength loss.

Based on the moisture regain data shown in Table 10, it would be expected that fibers of cellulose or regenerated cellulose should be drastically effected by moisture. As shown in Table 10-61, elongation retention is more effected in the cellulose base fibers than in other

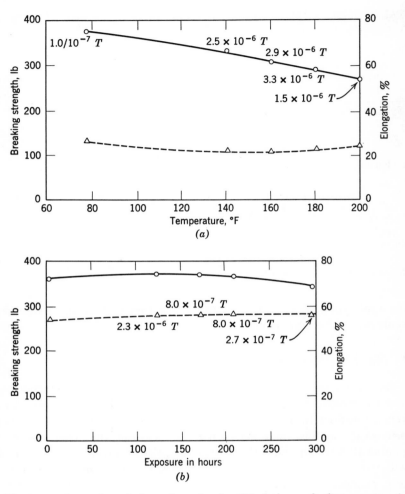

Fig. 10-59. Strength and elongation of nylon 6-6 during and after exposure to Vacuum; *a*, during exposure to vacuum and temperature; *b*, after exposure to vacuum, ○, strength; △, elongation.

fibers. Kaswell (1) shows the stress-strain behavior of many fibers in air and water at various temperatures. From these data it can be concluded that the regenerated hydroscopic fibers in general, have poor recovery properties, while the hydrophobic synthetic fibers, which are generally insensitive to water, are not effected.

Fabric structures have found use in many applications which require their continual exposure to moisture vapor or water over long periods

TABLE 10–61. Retention of Properties (in %) after Exposure to
Salt Solutions (NaCl)

| Conc., time, temp, | Fiber types | | | | | |
|---|---|---|---|---|---|---|
| | Acetate | Dacron | Nylon 6–6 | Orlon (81) | Rayon | Cotton |
| Strength retention, % [a] | | | | | | |
| 1.0 g/100 ml, 3 mo, 70°F | | 99.2 | 98.3 | | | |
| 20.0 g/100 ml, 3 mo, 70°F | | 98.9 | 98.4 | | | |
| 1.0 g/100 ml, 3 mo, 150°F | | 93.8 | 99.9 | | | |
| 20.0 g/100 ml, 3 mo, 150°F | | 96.9 | 98.9 | | | |
| Elongation retained, % [b] | | | | | | |
| 3%, 1000 hr, 70°F | 87.0 | 82.0 | 92.0 | 100.0 | 75.0 | 96.0 |
| 3%, 10 hr, 210°F | 76.0 | 97.0 | 87.0 | 103.0 | 81.0 | 79.0 |

[a] In fabric form.
[b] In yarn form.

of time. For example: coated fabric covers for supplies, vehicles, aircraft, etc., are exposed to intermittant rain and varying humidities.
Even though protected by a coating, moisture does penetrate to the
fiber, and subsequent fiber property change depending on the fiber.
In other cases, bare tightly woven fabrics are used as protective covers,
and finally certain types of clothing and parachutes are accidently
exposed to water and water vapor during use. In Table 10-62, the effect
of this type exposure on nylon 6-6 and Dacron is shown for periods
up to 6 months. The only conclusion that can be drawn from this
data is that low humidity is much more degrading (in this instance)
to nylon 6-6 than to Dacron, especially at 150°F.

## 7. Radiation Effects

The behavior of fibrous materials in an atmosphere (or lack of
atmosphere) containing ionizing radiation is quite different than when
exposed to ultraviolet radiation. Let us consider the case of ionizing
radiation first in air and then in a vacuum (space) environment. There
are instances when fibers, yarns, or fabrics will be exposed primarily to
gamma radiation emitting from a nuclear source. As in the case of
ultra-violet radiation, the degree of degradation is dependent on the
polymer structure, regardless of whether the fiber is natural or
synthetic. In early studies, McGrath and Johnson (47), a cobalt-60
source (aluminum clad 1500 Ci cobalt pipe 15 in. long with a
1.7 in. inside diam) with a flux of $4.6 \times 10^5$ R/hr was used. Since at

TABLE 10-62.  Loss in Strength of Two Fibers When Exposed in Water at Various Temperatures

| Aging conditions | Strength loss, % | | | | | | | |
|---|---|---|---|---|---|---|---|---|
| | 1 mo | | 2 mo | | 4 mo | | 6 mo | |
| | Nylon 6-6 | Dacron | Nylon 6-6 | Dacron | Nylon 6-6 | Dacron | Nylon 6-6 | Dacron |
| In solution at | | | | | | | | |
| Room temp. | 1.0 | 4.2 | 1.5 | 2.5 | +1.2 | 6.9 | 1.5 | +2.7 |
| 100°F | 1.2 | +3.2 | 2.9 | 0.0 | +1.2 | 7.7 | 2.0 | +4.7 |
| 120°F | 1.0 | 17.0 | 2.9 | 1.7 | 0.7 | 11.1 | 0.9 | +2.7 |
| 150°F | 5.4 | 13.6 | 10.0 | 3.0 | 12.5 | 17.8 | 13.5 | +0.2 |
| Low RH at | | | | | | | | |
| Room temp. | 0.9 | 0.5 | +1.2 | +1.5 | 12.3 | 4.4 | 18.9 | 1.5 |
| 100°F | +0.7 | +2.0 | +2.7 | 0.4 | 15.2 | 7.4 | 17.1 | 1.2 |
| 120°F | 0.7 | +2.2 | 0.0 | +0.8 | 7.1 | 10.1 | 7.4 | 12.4 |
| 150°F | 1.2 | +1.0 | 4.9 | 0.8 | 31.0 | 12.6 | 45.9 | 9.9 |
| High RH at | | | | | | | | |
| Room temp. | +0.5 | 3.2 | +1.2 | 4.4 | 0.7 | +1.2 | +0.7 | +3.9 |
| 100°F | 3.4 | 7.4 | +0.2 | 1.9 | 0.2 | 4.0 | 2.0 | +4.9 |
| 120°F | 7.6 | 2.7 | +1.2 | 4.4 | 1.7 | 1.2 | 3.4 | +3.2 |
| 150°F | 3.9 | 8.4 | 0.5 | 0.9 | 2.0 | 4.7 | 0.2 | 6.2 |

that time little or no data was available as to how fibrous materials would be effected arbitrary exposures were made with 1 day as the shortest. As seen in Table 10-63, some of the materials deteriorated extremely fast, therefore a second study was conducted using exposures from 1 to 16 hr, Table 10-64. From these exposures it was found that the more complex polymers (Orlon and Dacron) were leasted affected. Pezdirtz (48), has concluded in the case of Mylar (which is a film formed from the same polyester polymer as Dacron is drawn from) that the presence of benzene rings makes the polymer more radiation resistant because the unsaturated ring absorbs energy (acting as an energy sink) without degrading the polymer. More recently, Nomex (an aromatic polyamide) has been thoroughly evaluated in the same Gamma source used by McGrath and Johnson (47) with one added feature, that of being able to provide heat during irradiation. The results of this study (Little, 49) summarized in Table 10-65, (% strength retention) and Table 10-66 (actual elongation %). A close review of this data reveals that through proper post fiber formation treatment, Nomex could be made more thermally stable (after heat and gamma radiation plus 600°F up to 30% more strength is retained than for the same radiation and no heat). The handicap to overcome in this instance is a feasible technique to achieve large scale production capability. As other fibers become available, it is normal practice to establish their resistance to ionizing radiation. Recently fibers formed from poly-1,3,4 benzimidazole have been irradiated in the same manner as already described, and as can be seen in Table 10-67, are more seriously degraded than Nomex under the same exposure conditions, even though the PBI is less effected by elevated temperatures. It can be seen that each fiber should be thoroughly evaluated to adequately establish advantages (or potential) and deficiencies. Recent exposures of PBI to gamma and heat have revealed that improvements in polymer structure, IV, and spinning dope results in fibers with greatly improved strength retention at elevated temperatures.

In the case of space and use of polymeric fibers, exposure to the ionizing radiation from the Van Allen Belt (and other radiation sources) constitutes serious problems. Many others have described the magnitude, range, and spectrum of this and other radiation belts (50, i.e., this reference further references a large number of sources on the intensity of aerospace radiation). For polymeric fibers, little data has been made available if even obtained, due undoubtedly to a lack of interest in flexible fibers for aerospace applications. In the case of related plastics such as tetrafluoroethylene both mechanical and

TABLE 10-63. Strength of Fabrics Exposed to Gamma Radiation

| Fiber type, weight, weave, and color | | Breaking strength, lb/in. | | | | |
|---|---|---|---|---|---|---|
| | Control | 1 Day 1.1×10⁷ R | 2 Days 2.3×10⁷ R | 4 Days 4.5×10⁷ R | 8 Days 9.0×10⁷ R | 16 Days 1.8×10⁸ R |
| Nylon, 6–6 1.1 oz/sq yd plain weave, white | 42.8 | 16.7 | 11.4 | | | |
| Nylon 6–6, 1.1 oz/sq yd plain weave, orange | 40.0 | 26.5 | 17.3 | 9.8 | | |
| Nylon 6–6, 1.6 oz/sq yd twill weave, white | 53.0 | 19.9 | 17.1 | 5.2 | | |
| Dacron, 1.6 oz/sq yd twill weave, white | 55.1 | 52.7 | 50.6 | 44.4 | 37.3 | 28.7 |
| Cotton, 4.5 oz/sq yd plain weave, natural | 86.4 | 59.4 | 43.5 | 11.2 | | |
| Acetate, plain weave, white | 27.5 | 20.0 | 16.0 | 9.5 | | |
| Rayon, plain weave, yellow | 67.1 | 43.4 | 34.1 | 20.8 | | |
| Orlon 4–5 oz/sq yd dobby weave, natural | 147.8 | 129.8 | 117.7 | 94.4 | 71.2 | 52.2 |

TABLE 10-64.  Strength of Fabrics Exposed to Gamma Radiation

| Fiber type, weight weave and color | Control | Breaking strength, lb/in. | | | | |
|---|---|---|---|---|---|---|
| | | $4.6\times10^5$ R | $9.2\times10^5$ R | $1.8\times10^6$ R | $3.7\times10^6$ R | $7.4\times10^6$ R |
| Nylon 6–6, 1.1 oz/sq yd plain weave, white | 42.8 | 41.7 | 41.1 | 38.8 | 37.2 | 26.3 |
| Nylon 6–6, 1.1 oz/sq yd plain weave, orange | 40.0 | 41.1 | 40.8 | 40.6 | 39.2 | 34.1 |
| Nylon 6–6, 1.6 oz/sq yd twill weave, white | 5.3 | 52.0 | 51.8 | 49.6 | 46.9 | 34.0 |
| Dacron, 1.6 oz/sq yd twill weave, white | 55.1 | 54.5 | 55 | 52.9 | 51.7 | 51.8 |
| Orlon, 4–5 oz/sq yd dobby weave, natural | 147.8 | 146.2 | 143.0 | 140.8 | 139.6 | 133.8 |
| Rayon, 4–5 oz/sq yd plain weave, white | 80.8 | 83.0 | 82.0 | 77.6 | 73.4 | 64.5 |
| Dynel plain weave, natural | 72.6 | 65.0 | 65.0 | 64.0 | 63.0 | 58.0 |
| Nylon/cotton, 5–6 oz/sq yd satin weave, sage green | 131.2 | 125.0 | 121.0 | 122.0 | 115.0 | 106.0 |

TABLE 10-65. Strength Retention of Nomex at Temperature Before and After Various Radiation Doses

| Temp. | Radiation | Strength retained, % | | | | |
|---|---|---|---|---|---|---|
| | | Time increments and dosages | | | | |
| | | 2 hr 12 min $9.0 \times 10^5$ R | 5 hr 18 min $2.17 \times 10^6$ R | 9 hr 36 min $4.01 \times 10^6$ R | 19 hr 30 min $8.01 \times 10^6$ R | 39 hr $1.61 \times 10^7$ R |
| Room temp. | After | 98.8 | 97.0 | 96.8 | 98.0 | 99.7 |
| 300°F | Before | 96.4 | 95.1 | 94.8 | 96.1 | 96.9 |
| | After | 99.0 | 98.0 | 97.8 | 96.3 | 94.9 |
| 400°F | Before | 92.1 | 91.7 | 93.2 | 92.1 | 93.1 |
| | After | 99.5 | 97.0 | 98.1 | 97.5 | 94.9 |
| 500°F | Before | 95.9 | 91.5 | 91.0 | 89.5 | 84.8 |
| | After | 98.3 | 93.1 | 92.6 | 86.7 | 82.1 |
| 600°F | Before | 78.0 | 69.8 | 64.2 | 58.6 | 52.2 |
| | After | 80.2 | 89.5 | 88.9 | 92.1 | 84.3 |
| 700°F | Before | 42.7 | 21.6 | 4.1 | 0 | 0 |
| | After | 42.3 | 47.3 | 30.7 | 7.4 | 0 |

TABLE 10-66. Elongation of Nomex at Temperatures Before and After Radiation

| Temp. | Radiation | Elongation, % | | | | |
|---|---|---|---|---|---|---|
| | | Time increments and dosages | | | | |
| | | 2 hr 12 min 9.0×10⁵ R | 5 hr 18 min 2.17×10⁶ R | 9 hr 36 min 4.01×10⁶ R | 19 hr 30 min 8.01×10⁶ R | 39 hr 1.61×10⁷ R |
| Room temp. | After | 12.5 | 12.1 | 11.1 | 10.7 | 11.7 |
| 300°F | Before | 13.3 | 13.1 | 13.6 | 14.4 | 14.1 |
| | After | 12.3 | 12.9 | 12.5 | 12.2 | 11.6 |
| 400°F | Before | 11.4 | 10.9 | 11.3 | 11.0 | 11.1 |
| | After | 12.7 | 12.4 | 13.3 | 13.0 | 11.7 |
| 500°F | Before | 12.5 | 12.4 | 12.7 | 12.4 | 11.3 |
| | After | 13.4 | 11.3 | 10.8 | 9.3 | 8.9 |
| 600°F | Before | 11.4 | 9.8 | 9.0 | 8.2 | 6.1 |
| | After | 7.6 | 11.1 | 10.5 | 11.9 | 10.6 |
| 700°F | Before | 6.0 | 2.4 | 2.0 | 0 | 0 |
| | After | 5.4 | 6.0 | 3.2 | 1.5 | 0 |

$$9.0\times10^5 \text{ R}$$

TABLE 10-67.  Effect of Gamma Radiation on the Strength of Two Thermally Stable Fibers

| | Loss in strength, %[a] | | | | | | | | | |
|---|---|---|---|---|---|---|---|---|---|---|
| | No Exposure | | 2.04×10⁶ R | | 4.1×10⁶ R | | 8.1×10⁶ R | | 1.65×10⁷ R | |
| Exposure conditions | PBI | Nomex | PBI | Nomex | PBI | Nomex | PBI | Nomex | PBI | Nomex |
| Standard textile conditions | | | 15.7 | 3.0 | 18.2 | 3.2 | 16.5 | 2.0 | 11.9 | 0.3 |
| 300°F | 15.6 | 29.3 | 15.9 | 2.0 | 16.3 | 2.2 | 20.6 | 3.7 | 14.5 | 5.1 |
| 450°F | 30.1 | 31.4 | 28.9 | 6.9 | 28.7 | 7.4 | 28.0 | 13.3 | 27.7 | 17.9 |
| 600°F | 45.6 | 57.6 | 42.7 | 10.5 | 43.0 | 11.1 | 47.4 | 7.9 | 47.4 | 15.7 |

[a] PBI, 15 min; Nomex, 5 min.

electrical properties have been degraded by exposure to $10^6$–$10^7$ ergs/g. Elastomers, such as those that would be used for coatings on fabrics, appreciable mechanical breakdown would occur at $10^8$–$10^{10}$ ergs/g. Thus little can be said on the effect of this type of radiation on fibers, instead it is best to emphasize the need for establishing to what degree ionizing radiation in vacuum will degrade fibers.

## 8. Biological Degradation

One of the most important advantages of polymeric fibers has been their ability to resist the attack of insects and microorganisms. Their are those polymeric fibers, the cellulosics such as rayon, Fortisan, and acetate which are susceptible to this type of attack and must be protected by the addition of finishes. These are well documented in the fiber producers technical bulletins and will not be discussed here. With respect to the fibers formed from the high polymers microorganism growth has been found to occur through out the yarn structure (on the surface), however no change in properties has been evidenced, indicating that the growth is feeding on the oils and other agents used as lubricants in the processing of the fiber. Studies using thoroughly scoured fibers and fabrics have revealed little or no growth. In the case of insects, it has been found that only when entrapped in the folds of materials will they cut or eat through the materials to gain their freedom.

When considering the exploration of space and other planets, which must occur at some time soon, extreme care will have to be taken to insure that insects and microorganisms are not taken to these other planets as they would multiply at rather fantastic rates. It will therefore be necessary to sterilize all materials intended for these explorations. Since it will be imperative to land these exploratory devices without damage, parachutes are presently being considered. To this end the effect that both thermal and chemical sterilization followed by exposure to the environments to be encountered in a long space mission were investigated. The thermal sterilization consisted of three cycles of 36 hr at 294°F in dry nitrogen. Chemical sterilization was achieved using a mixture of 12% ethylene oxide, 88% Freon 12 with one test run at 75°F and another at 104°F, both for 24 hr. These were followed by exposure to $10^{-6}$ torr and 160°F for 5, 10, and 30 days. Fibers evaluated included silk, nylon 6-6, Dacron, and Nomex. The silk was completely degraded in preliminary tests while the thermal sterilization was to much for the nylon 6-6 (caused stiffness and loss of strength). Of the two remaining fibers, Nomex average strength loss did not exceed 5% although large variations in strength were observed, while the Dacron had less variation in strength, larger—about 20%—strength loss was recorded. Finally, Anderson (51), shows that the latter two fibers in woven form were not appreciably effected by folding and compacting as experienced in parachutes.

## C. Protective Coatings

It has already been shown that some polymers in fiber form are seriously degraded by such environments as chemical exposure, ultraviolet light, moisture, and heat (primarily in the form of fire). The use of both elastomeric and plastic coatings to provide protection to these fibers has been well exploited. Ranging from natural rubber to synthetic rubber to flexible plastic formulations, these coatings are used to provide abrasion resistance, stability to elevated temperatures, resistance to burning, resistance to microorganisms, weatherability, and low temperature flexibility. To further promote the utilization of the proper coatings the National Academy of Sciences has furnished scientific and technical advice to the various Department of Defense agencies which culminated in at least one document (52) describing the more recent advances in coatings for fabrics. Even though labeled as for military applications, utilization of these coatings in industrial applications has been one of the unexpected dividends. More recent technical advances have been the development of thermally stable, fluid resistant coatings. In Table 10-68, the qualitative (and some quantitative) capabilities are shown. From this it can be seen that not all coatings have the capability of utilization across a broad spectrum of applications.

The protection of fibers from weathering has always been one of the most important needs for coatings. In Ref. 52, the need for better coatings to provide this type of protection is described. The most commonly used coatings have been the chloroprenes (generic term) with various antioxidants, flame inhibitors, colorants, etc., and vinyl (polyvinyl chloride and suitable plasticizer). Other coatings such as the urethanes, polyesters, hypalons, each have their own specific characteristics which make them useful for applications involving weathering, or chemical protection, or heat. Attempts to establish reproducible methods of predicting the weathering life of coated fabrics led to one study the data of which is shown in Table 10-69. Various coating weights, colors, and inhibitors in the coating were investigated as

TABLE 10-68. Thermal and Fluid Resistant Coatings

| Chemical description | Common (sales) name | Tensile Stg. Max. psi | Thermal resistance max. temp. | Fuel resistance | Chemical resistance | Low temp. |
|---|---|---|---|---|---|---|
| Acrylic acid ester copolymer with halogen-containing derivative | Silicones | 1500 | 600 | Poor | Fair | Excellent |
| Polytetrafluoroethylene | Hycar PA | 1800 | 350 | Good | Poor | Poor |
| Vinylidene fluoride-hexafluoro- propylene copoylmer | Teflon | 4100 | 600 | Excellent | Excellent | Poor |
| Trifluorochloroethylene-vinylidene fluoride copolymer | Viton | 2500 | 600 | Very good | Very good | Fair |
| | Kel F (3700) | 2700 | 450 | Good | Very good | Fair |

TABLE 10-69.  Retention of Strength of Coated Fabrics after Weathering (Weather-O-Meter)

| Fabric and coating description | Strength retention, % | | |
|---|---|---|---|
| | 50 hr | 100 hr | 150 hr |
| *1.* Coated fabrics less than 8 oz/sq yd | | | |
| 6.5 oz/sq yd chloroprene, olive drab | 82.6 | 48.4 | 44.9 |
| 6.5 oz/sq yd chloroprene, black | 60.2 | 41.1 | 42.3 |
| 5.0 oz/sq yd vinyl, olive drab | 105.7 | 76.0 | 75.8 |
| *2.* Coated fabrics 9–11 oz/sq yd | | | |
| 9.0 oz/sq yd vinyl, olive drab | 89.3 | 83.3 | 72.5 |
| 9.5 oz/sq yd chloroprene, black | 99.4 | 84.2 | 70.4 |
| 9.0 oz/sq yd chloroprene, black | 103.3 | 84.4 | 87.7 |
| *3.* Coated Fabrics 12–15 oz/sq yd | | | |
| 15.0 oz/sq yd chloroprene, black | 131.2 | 99.2 | 32.2 |
| 14.0 oz/sq yd chloroprene, olive drab | 102.7 | 85.6 | 82.8 |
| 14.0 oz/sq yd chloroprene, black | 100.2 | 89.6 | 88.7 |
| 13.0 oz/sq yd chloroprene, black | 98.0 | 74.3 | 85.9 |
| *4.* Coated fabrics 16–20 oz/sq yd | | | |
| 16.0 oz/sq yd vinyl, olive drab | 100.8 | 109.3 | 99.9 |
| 16.0 oz/sq yd vinyl, olive drab | 96.7 | 74.9 | 66.8 |
| 18.0 oz/sq yd vinyl, olive drab | 99.7 | 93.2 | 91.5 |
| 17.8 oz/sq yd vinyl, white | 94.7 | 77.6 | 56.1 |
| 19.5 oz/sq yd chloroprene, black | 95.5 | 73.5 | 84.9 |

well as using two weights of base fabric (nylon 6-6) namely 2.5 oz/yd$^2$ and 5.0 oz/yd$^2$. The vinyls were found to have superior strength retention in the lighter weights, but are inferior to chloroprene in the heavier weights. The sample with the flame inhibitor added to the chloroprene (15 oz/yd$^2$ fabric) showed up very poorly after 150 hr of weathering revealing the problems that can occur when inhibitors are added to the basic coatings. This work, by Todd (53) is only a preliminary investigation and has been duplicated since then without achieving an adequate reproducible weathering test.

The use of coatings to protect aerospace vehicles opens an entirely new field for flexible coatings. This concept involves the use of high strength coated fabrics to form the structural part of a vehicle that will be used to reenter the atmosphere of earth or other planets. However, due to the speeds at which vehicles or systems will reenter an atmosphere, consideration must be given to what happens to the coating during this action. Many thermal analysis have been conducted to establish whether ablative or radiation-insulation or both should be used. A more recent study of this type (54) has shown that in the case of expandable structures ablative coatings would be far to thick and heavy (229 oz/yd$^2$) while radiation-insulation coatings would be feasible for a light wing loading vehicle where temperatures up to 1500°F are expected using only 5–10% of the weight required for a ablation material, (assuming an emittance of 1.0). However it must be emphasized that little useful information exists on the performance of ablative materials under low heat transfer rates. Only silicone rubber has been sufficiently investigated to permit an analysis of char-forming for the protection of lifting (glide type) reentry vehicles. Since silicone rubber did have good thermal stability, it has been used as a base for radiation-insulation coatings with ceramic frit added to increase the temperature capability of the coating between the thermal degradation temperature of the silicone and the desired operating temperature (55). This concept works in such a manner that as the temperature rises, a thermal decomposition of the silicone will occur, and the ceramic (or inorganic) frit will change into a very viscous fluid which would have a high surface tension and would hold the residue of the elastomer in suspension. Upon cooling, a solid surface would form which would have some degree of flexibility (but not as good as the unexposed coating). Preliminary studies used ceramic frit with a melting range from 1100°F up, and when blended with the silicone rubber yielded coatings usable to 1200°F, by using frit with lower melting temperature (800°F) greater resistance to gas permeability might be achieved. With this broader melting range of frits incorporated into the silicone elastomer it became apparent that the gas leak rate could be lowered and a more rubbery compound (at room temperature) achieved. The substrate fabric in this case was metal and it became apparent that a multifilament fabric (yarns composed of 100 fibers of 0.0005 in. diam (Chromel A) provided a better base than a monofilament wire (0.003 or 0.005 in diam) from stainless steel or René 41. This same coating has been applied to Nomex fabric and the combination evaluated at temperatures of 750, 1000, and 1250°F using a moving air blast for 30 sec and 1 min. Strength retention at 1000°F exceeded 50%, however at 1200°F the material had little or no strength. The specimens with strength at a temperature of 1000°F was of course above the fiber's carbonization temperature, making it possible to achieve greater utilization from the fiber itself. The next step is then to establish uses in which these materials can be employed. Future utilization of inorganic frits and finely divided particles in wholly new elastomeric substances should provide even greater thermal stability to both polymeric and inorganic fiber substrates.

## III. THE NEED FOR POLYMERIC FIBERS IN PRESENT AND FUTURE UNIQUE ENVIRONMENTS

The sensitivity of polymeric fibers to one or more environments has been graphically demonstrated with today's production type fibers in many forms. The use of strength and elongation as the prime means of presenting the degree of degradation was purely an arbitrary choice. Other mechanical properties of the fiber, yarn, or fabric, or properties of the basic polymers, such as fluidity, viscosity, molecular weight, and orientation, to name a few, could just as well have been the means of showing the degree of degradation that can occur. To a certain degree it can be concluded that certain polymers (in fiber form) are more suitable for use where specific environments are to be encountered. It is obvious that Nomex is excellent where thermal stability and nonmelting (up to carbonization temperature of 840°F), is desired but because of the difficulty encountered when applying surface finishes and dyes to the fiber surface, its ability to resist environments such as ultraviolet radiation is just average. This is not to preclude technological breakthroughs in the future that will overcome this deficiency. Reviewing other polymeric fibers has shown that those types with good ultraviolet radiation resistance also have fair to good resistance to ionizing radiation (polyesters and acrylics), the contradiction being Nomex (an aromatic polyamide) which has the best resistance to ionizing radiation of any polymeric fiber seen to this time. To the contrary, cellulosics (acetate, rayon, etc.) are not outstandingly resistant to either ultraviolet or ionizing radiation. Whether this situation will occur with some of the newer polymers such as the polyolefins (polypropylene or high density polyethylene) is as yet not defined.

Presently, entirely new classes of polymeric fibers (heterocyclics specifically) drawn from polyimides, polyoxadiazoles, polybenzimidazoles, and triazoles are becoming available in limited quantities. Generally they all have good thermal stability in the range of 700–1000°F. No other mechanical properties are as yet available since the small quantities of fiber produced have been inconsistant and in some cases have not been reproducible. An interesting point with these new polymers is the method used in fiber formation. Because of extremely high melting temperature (above 700°F) or nonmelting characteristic, dry spinning is required (and in the case of the polyoxadiazoles a thermal after-treatment). The technical scheme in dry spinning requires rapid evolution of the solvent in which the polymer is dissolved. To accomplish this, very fine (low denier 1–2) per filament yarns are drawn to provide greater surface area for the solvent to escape from (in vapor form). It has been shown that yarns with low denier per filament (acetate, Nomex) will have poor ultraviolet and abrasion resistance. One of the technical areas of improvement that will bear particular interest involves formation of yarns having greater denier per filament (at least 6–8 per filament. Ultimately wholly new techniques of fiber formation may be required to achieve the most optimum fiber forms. These new thermally stable polymer classes are susceptible to other than ultraviolet radiation. It is known that polyimides have poor resistance to bases although good resistance to acids.

The future of fibrous materials in flexible applications is one of continuous growth and expansion into new areas. Utilization of polymeric fibers in woven, knitted, braided, and nonwoven matting (oriented and bonded) will be limited only by the availability of fibers with the characteristics required for specific uses. The utilization of coated fabrics as protective covers for missile sites, buildings under construction, aircraft protection, space vehicles, and liquid storage will grow with technological advances leading to more light resistant fibers. Present polymeric fibers are limited to 600–800°F due to loss of thermal stability. However, even at 800°F, Nomex will endure 800 cycles of folding while 0.0005 in. diam superalloy fibers will endure only 120 cycles of folding at 1000°F. Thus future technological breakthroughs in the synthesis of fiberizable polymers having thermal stability to at least 1500°F (with little weight loss or structure change) would make possible high strength to weight flexible materials for expandable aerospace reentry vehicles, protective garments for use in industrial facilities, more efficient filtering and insulation systems, and hypersonic deceleration devices. Emphasis must therefore be two fold, first, the synthesis of fiberizable polymers having characteristics individual to specific applications, and second, the establishment of unique methods of forming these polymers into fibers.

## REFERENCES

1. E. R. Kaswell, *Wellington Sears Handbook of Industrial Textiles,* 1963.
2. J. J. Press, *Man-Made Textile Encyclopedia,* Interscience, New York, 1959.
3. Anon., *Modern Textiles,* December 1964.
4. Anon., *Soviet Bloc Development of Snythetic Fibers,* Q.M. Series Report No. 117, April 1961.

5. F. S. Dawn and J. H. Ross, "Investigation of Polybenzimidazole Fibers at High Temperatures," ASD TDR 62-435, July 1962.
6. Matthews, *Textile Fibers,* 5th ed., 1948.
7. W. Von Bergen and J. M. Krauss, *Textile Fiber Atlas,* 1949.
8. W. E. Nickel and L. W. Sims, "Study and Exploratory Free-Flight Investigation of Deployable Aerodynamic Decelerators Operating at High Altitudes and at High Mach Numbers," FDL TDR 64-35. July 1964.
9. S. Schulman, "Elevated Temperature Behavior of Fibers," ASD TDR 63-62, April 1963.
10. D. M. Cates, "A Study of the Effect of Chemicals on the Strength of Nylon and Dacron Parachute Fabrics," WADC TR 56-288, Nov. 1956.
11. R. Meredith, "Properties Depending on the Amorphous Regions of Fibers," Chap. XII, in Preston, Ed., *Fiber Science,* The Textile Institute, 1949.
12. R. Neff, "Development and Evaluation of Webbing Made from Nylon 6," WADC 57-538, March 1958.
13. M. J. Coplan, "A Study of the Effect of Temperature on Textile Materials," WADC TR 53-21, March 1953.
14. J. H. Ross and C. O. Little, "Thermal Stability of Flexible Fibrous Materials," RTD TDR 63-4031, Oct. 1964.
15. C. O. Little and J. H. Ross, "Fire Resistant Materials for Personnel Parachute Packs," ASD TDR 61-515, Dec. 1961.
16. D. L. Lunaford, "Determination of Maximum Allowable Heat Fluxes on Gemini Ejection Seat Parachute," McDonnell A/C Co. Rpt. No. 052-060.02.01, April 1963.
17. J. W. Muse, Jr., "A Study of the Effect of Temperature on Parachute Textile Materials," WADC TR 54-117, July 1954.
18. N. J. Abbott, "Some Effects of Compression and Heat on Decelerator Materials," WADC TR 55-135, Sep. 1956.
19. E. R. Kaswell and M. J. Coplan, "Development of Dacron Parachute Materials," WADC TR 55-135, September 1956.
20. C. Chu, E. R. Kaswell, and J. D. Doull, "Development of High Tenacity, Heat Stable Dacron Parachute Items," WADC TR 57-765, May 1958.
21. J. C. McGrath, "Study of Environmental Effects on High Temperature Organic Materials," ASD TDR 63-61, April 1963.
22. E. S. Cobb, Jr., "High Strength Glass Fiber Webbings, Tapes, and Ribbons for High Temperature Pressure Packaged Decelerators," ASD TDR 62-518, July 1962.
23. C. Chu, J. W. Gardella and E. R. Kaswell, "Research Leading to Optimum Fibrous Structures of HT-1 Yarn." ML TDR 64-78, Jan. 1964.
24. L. Barish, D. H. Powers, C. C. Chu, E. Cilley, and E. R. Kaswell, "Mechanical and Thermal Degradation Mechanisms of Quartz Fibers, and The Development of Experimental Quartz Fabrics with Improved Finishes," ASD TDR 63-802, Sep. 1963.
25. A. J. McQuade, E. T. Waldron and B. S. Farquhar, "Response of Fibers to Intense Thermal Radiation," *Ann. N.Y. Acad. Sci.,* **82,** Art. 3, 7 Oct. 1959.
26. J. H. Ross, "Thermal Requirements for Functional Textiles," *Ann. N.Y. Acad. Sci.,* **82,** Art. 3, 7 Oct. 1959.
27. P. E. Glaser and S. Merra, "Thermal Radiation Effects on Decelerator Materials," ASD TDR 62-185, Feb. 1962.

28. G. Engholm, S. J. Lis and R. J. Baschiere, "Thermal Transport and Radiative Properties of Fabrous Materials," ASD TDR 62-810, Nov. 1962.
29. L. C. Block, "Aerodynamic Heating of Parachute Ribbons," WADC TR 54-572, Nov. 1955.
30. A. L. Ruoff, S. W. Liu and F. Frank, "Aerodynamic Heating of Parachutes," WADC TR 57-157, Dec. 1957.
31. R. H. Cornish, F. J. Akiway, C. W. Beadle and J. K. Foster, "Mass Transfer Cooling of Parachute Materials," WADC TR 58-684, September 1959.
32. M. J. Coplan and E. Singer, "A Study of the Effect of Temperature on Textile Materials," WADC TR 53-21, Pt. 2, July 1953.
33. S. Van der Burg and J. G. Manchetti, "Resin Cured Butyl Aircraft Tires," to the American Chemical Society, Fall 1963.
34. C. V. Stephenson, W. S. Wilcox, B. C. Moses and H. T. Crenshaw, "Deterioration of Fibrous Materials by Ultraviolet Light," ASD TDR 61-730, Dec. 1961.
35. C. V. Stephenson, W. S. Wilcox, H. T. Crenshaw, H. L. Hancock and E. B. Dismukes, "Deterioration of Fibrous Materials by Ultraviolet Light," ASD TDR 63-57, Feb. 1963.
36. J. C. McGrath, "Textiles: Accelerater Weathering Versus Outdoor Exposure Tests," AFTR No. 5894, Oct. 1950.
37. J. C. McGrath, "Ultra Violet Radiation Resistant Materials for Decelerators," WADD TN 60-253, Dec. 1960.
38. R. A. Wilkinson, "The Effect of Solar Radiation on the Breaking Strength of Outdoor Exposed Webbings," WADC TR 58-201, Nov. 1958.
39. C. Chu, R. A. Kerry, E. R. Kaswell and E. J. Stavrakas, "The Measurement of Ultraviolet Reflectance as a Criterion of Nylon Fabric Deterioration," ASD TDR 61-560, Nov. 1961.
40. J. G. Templeton, "A Study of the Effects of Chemicals on the Properties of Parachute Fabrics," WADC TR 55-340, Sep. 1956.
41. P. P. Hall, "Behavior of Liquids on Various Cords for Seams of Chemical and Biological Protective Overgarments," U.S. Army Natick Laboratories TR TS-127, Oct. 1963.
42. R. A. Sublette, "The Effect of Five Lubricants on USAF Fabrics," WADC TR 55-379, May 1956.
43. J. D. Boone, "Actual Extent of Useful Life of Parachute Canopies," U.S. Naval Parachute Facility Technical Report 2-61, April 1961.
44. W. S. Baker, "Handbook of Fibrous Materials," WADD TR 60-584, Pt. II, Oct. 1961.
45. H. E. Pettus, "The Effect of Space Environment on Textile Materials," FTC TDR 64-12, Sep. 1964.
46. F. S. Witte, "Exposure of Fabric to High Temperature High Vacuum Environment," NAA Report NA-62-800, August 1962.
47. J. C. McGrath and R. H. Johnson, USAF, "The Effects of Gamma Radiation on Textile Materials," WADC TR 56-15, Feb. 1956.
48. G. F. Pezdirtz, "Nonmetallic Materials for Spacecraft," NASA SP-27, *Materials for Space Operations,* Dec. 1962.
49. C. D. Little, Jr., "Thermal and Gamma Radiation Behavior of a New High Temperature Organic Fiber," WADD TN 60-299, June 1961.
50. L. D. Jaffee and J. B. Rittenhouse, "Behavior of Materials in Space Environments," *J. Am. Rocket Soc.,* March 1962.

51. A. R. Anderson, "Effect of Biological Sterilization and Vacuum on Certain Parachute Retardation System Components," Final Report 4324, Aug. 1964, for Jet Propulsion Laboratory.
52. F. R. Fisher and S. Backer, Editors, "Fabrics for Coating, Military Applications," Proceedings of a conference, National Academy of Sciences-National Research Council, 1959.
53. L. O. Todd, "Determination of a Standard Accelerated Weathering Test for Vinyl and Neoprene Coated Nylon Fabrics," WADC TN 56-133, June 1956.
54. R. V. Kolarik and D. M. Marco, "New and Improved Materials for Expandable Structures, Phase IV, High Temperature Protective Study," ASD TDR 62-542, Pt. V, Feb. 1963.
55. W. B. Cross, D. M. Marco, and F. Nass, "New and Improved Materials for Expandable Structures, Phase III, Re-entry Coatings," ASD TDR 62-542, Pt. IV, Oct. 1963.

# 11

# Protective Flight Clothing and Sea Survival Equipment

Margaret B. Hays and Charles A. Cassola

*Naval Air Engineering Center,*
*Philadelphia, Pennsylvania*

## CONTENTS

## I. INTRODUCTION

Early carriers of air mail wanted clothing for protection against wind, sleet, and snow. This meant water repellent and wind resistant cotton jackets, leather jackets, and sheepskins. The dust cover of *Spirit of St. Louis* (1) shows the "Lone Eagle" wearing slacks, white shirt, and tie with a summer flight jacket. His thirty pounds of emergency equipment consisted of a rubber boat, red flares, emergency rations, and water. As planes and missions changed so did the requirements for special clothing and survival equipment. Early in World War II reports came in stating that flyers downed in Alaskan waters were sinking because of the weight of their clothing. The traditional pilot's cold weather sheepskin clothing was found to absorb 300–400% water. This led to the development of special protective clothing and sea survival equipment.

Various factors in environment will be considered as they affect the durability and suitability of material to protect the man in a given environment. Omnienvironmental protection is the goal of end-item designers and logisticians but at the present stage of development, available clothing and equipment are mission oriented.

## II. FLIGHT CLOTHING

Basically all flight clothing must be as light in weight as is compatible with other serviceability requirements. Furthermore, it must be comfortable and not restrict movement in a confined cockpit on long missions. Streamlining (see Fig. 11-1) to reduce chances of catching a sleeve, pocket, or any part of garment on a control knob reduces the normal "flap cooling" produced by movement in conventional clothing. As a result, air permeability is an important characteristic for any material used in summer flying coveralls (2).

Fig. 11-1. Single layer HT-1 coverall (U.S. Navy).

Colorfastness is a requisite. Dyestuffs react differently to sunlight as the cloth substrate varies. Certain dyestuffs act as catalysts or sensitizors in accelerating deterioration of cloth in sunlight. The dyed cloth must exhibit good fastness to sunlight, saltwater, crocking (rubbing), perspiration, and to washing or dry cleaning.

Winter flight suits (3), are composed of three layers of material and are designed to conserve body heat in cold climates. The outer layer of the suit in Fig. 11-2 has low air permeability to reduce heat loss which can be significant in winds as low as 10 mph. The middle layer provides entrapped air to yield insulation with dead air space and the third layer is a lining.

The anti-G coverall (4) is intended to prevent blackout during high speed maneuvers or high altitude flights. The cutaway suit shown

Fig. 11-2. Winter flight suit (U.S. Navy).

in Fig. 11-3 is designed to be worn in conjunction with other items of protective clothing, e.g., winter suit. The coverall or suit must inflate to 6 psi in not more than 2.5 sec. The outer fabric shell serves as a restraint to prevent the inflated bladders from ballooning. Because a high strength is required in both warp and filling directions and high seam strength is needed, a 3-oz nylon fabric is utilized in spite of its adverse characteristic known as "melt drop." Nylon is one of the synthetic fibers that does not support combustion and the flame is extinguished when the heat source is removed. However, in a flame the nylon melts and drops away. If the molten nylon touches the skin, a very severe burn results. It should be noted that nylon melts at 482°F.

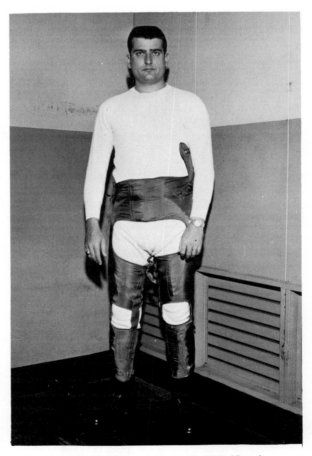

Fig. 11-3. Cut-away anti-G suit (U.S. Navy).

This led to an extensive search for a material with "no melt" drop and with sufficient strength for the anti-G coverall. The fire retardent treated lightweight cotton (5) used for years in the summer coverall and as a lining in winter flight suit gave a degree of flame resistance to those garments but seam strength is too low in this fabric for the anti-G coverall. During the interim, flight personnel are instructed to use the nylon anti-G coverall or suit in conjunction with fire retardent flight clothing, either over or under.

An experimental synthetic filament fiber with the laboratory designation of HT-1 was found that did not show "melt-drop." This lead to the development of a 3-oz fabric for the anti-G coverall (6). Initially the same fabric was used experimentally in summer coveralls and as the outer shell of winter suits. The first coverall is shown in Fig. 11-1. Thermal protection afforded by various garment assemblies is given in Table 11-1. Two layers of 3-oz HT-1 gave adequate protection. The protection afforded by only one layer is less as reported in Table 11-1 but is still considerable as shown in a crash report (7). The pilot wore an experimental coverall over regulation underwear whereas the copilot and crewchief wore regulation utility shirt and trousers over their underwear. All suffered second degree burns but the pilot returned to duty next day while the copilot and crewchief were hospitalized for prolonged periods. Thus, this new material afforded significantly more

TABLE 11-1. Flame Contact Evaluation of Thermal Protection Afforded by Garment Assemblies (6)

| Fabric | Weight, oz/yd$^2$ | Assembly | Time flames, sec | Skin burn effect, % surface area | | |
|--------|--------|----------|------|------|--------|--------|
| | | | | None | Slight | Severe |
| HT–1 | 3 | Single-layer coverall over HT–1 Z–3 and cotton underwear | 4 | 32.6 | 3.5 | 45.5 |
| HT–1 | 3 | Double-layer coverall over HT–1 Z–3 and cotton underwear | 4 | 48.7 | 24.2 | 8.0 |
| Cotton | 5+ | Standard fire-retarded, orange coverall over nylon Z–3 and cotton underwear | 4 | 7.0 | 6.5 | 67.5 |
| Nylon | 3 | Standard Z–2 over cotton underwear | 3 | 20.5 | 3.5 | 57.0 |
| HT–1 | 3 | Double layer HT–1 Z–2 over cotton underwear | 3 | 51.5 | 27.8 | 1.6 |

thermal protection to aviators. And after 10 years it may be considered a breakthrough in material capability for the anti-G coverall. Although not essential for this application this material has good resistance to gamma radiation. (See Chapter 7.)

The HT-1 fiber is an aromatic polyamide (see chapter 7). HT-1 is in the generic class of nylon and it is being offered on the commercial market as Nomex nylon. Fabric requirements are given in a current specification (8). Other fabric specifications will be prepared as optimum constructions are developed for summer flight coveralls and winter suits. Various opposing characteristics must be considered. For example, an open weave would be more comfortable in flight during hot weather but in the event of fire such a weave would transmit heat to the skin. Similarly, a filament yarn fabric offers more resistance to abrasion than a staple fiber fabric but its high reflectivity (6) may produce undesirable reflections on the instrument panel while offering advantages to search and rescue teams.

For intermediate temperature zone, two flight jackets are available. The light jacket (9) currently is made from fire retardent treated cotton cloth (5) and the intermediate jacket (10) is made from goatskin leather. Durability, including resistance to abrasion are important characteristics for these garments.

The hands are the most difficult area to provide adequate environmental protection and still maintain manual dexterity. Currently gloves for temperate zones (11) are made of sheepskin leather. When the gloves become wet, gripping ability is lost and aviators are unable to operate safety equipment. Various treatments for water repellency and antislip characteristics were evaluated. From these studies (12) recommendations were made for treatment of glove leather by the tanner with a chrome complex, a polysulfide rubber, Thiokol, or a silicone. The first two treatments also improved the tear resistance of leather. On the other hand, a silicone finish reduced the flame resistance (13). When required, wool knit inserts may be used with leather gloves.

The safety boot (14) is a chrome-tanned calfskin leather with a closed cell chloroprene crepe synthetic rubber sole and a rubber midsole. The grid type pattern for the sole is shown as insert in Fig. 11-4.

## III. SPECIAL PROTECTVE CLOTHING

### A. Exposure Suits

When flying over water when the water temperature is below 45°F, flight personnel require protection in the event of ditching. Such cloth-

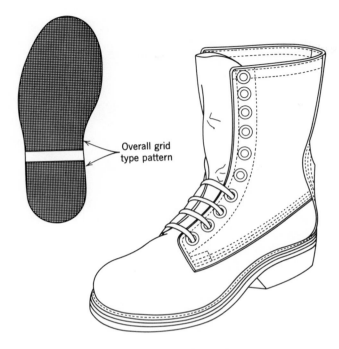

Overall grid type pattern

Fig. 11-4. Boot flying, safety.

ing is designed on the basis of sealed insulation protection. To have a man survive more than a few minutes, his clothing must be kept dry. Even retained moisture or perspiration in articles of clothing will freeze and consume body heat. Two types of exposure garments are used, namely, continuous-wear and quick-donning.

The continuous-wear antiexposure coverall (15) is a waterproof garment with attached socks and is worn with an insulating and ventilating liner. It may have an anti-G coverall fitting applied as shown in Fig. 11-5. The diagonal entrance shown in Fig. 11-6 is a watertight slide fastener with outer rubber lip and a Teflon coated slider (see Fig. 11-6 insert).

The antiexposure coverall in Fig. 11-7 is fabricated from knitted stretch nylon coated cloth (16) developed specifically for this application. Since the coverall is streamlined, stretch is inherent in the base fabric and coated cloth. The type I cloth shown in Table 11-2 is utilized in the body of the coverall and type II is used for neck and wrist seals. To insure comfort, modulus at 75% elongation in the courses direction requirements were established. Since the coverall is flexed during wear, the cloth is repeatedly flexed as shown in Fig. 11-8, then tested for

Fig. 11-5. Insulating ventilating liner (U.S. Navy).

water leakage and examined for tears in coating or separation of coating from base cloth to evaluate serviceability as well as control quality during production.

The liner in Fig. 11-5 is intended for use under the Mk 5 antiexposure suit. For its fabrication, Mk 5 (17) requires a bonded batt of polyester fibers, $3.5 \pm 0.5$ oz/yd² with at least 10% resin content, covered with an outer shell of 3 oz/yd² nylon and quilted onto the inner lining of fire retardent treated cotton (5). A bladder and duct system is installed between outer shell and the quilted lining. The duct casing is secured to the leg and arm lining outseams, respectively.

Another antiexposure garment (18) is intended for donning in ap-

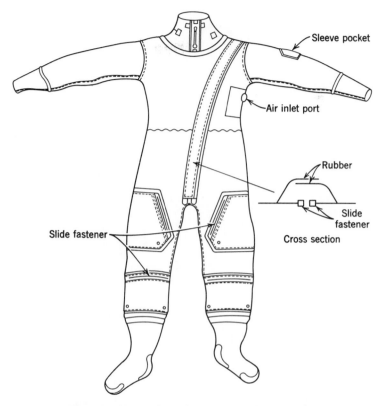

Fig. 11-6. Front of continuous wear exposure suit.

proximately 1 min by crew members of heavy bombers and cargo aircraft prior to emergency ditching at sea. Its purpose is to protect the wearer from exposure while swimming in cold water, and from exposure to wind, spray, and rain when marooned on a liferaft.

## B. Life Preservers

Inflatable life preservers (Fig. 11-9) provide more buoyancy and for a longer period of time than does the air entrapped in clothing as used in abandon ship instructions. The Mark 2 vest (19) consists of three independent inflatable compartments, each with its own means of inflation. The upper and lower compartments of the preserver are mechanically inflated with carbon dioxide and the center is orally inflated. When one compartment is inflated to 2.0 psi, at the end of 24 hr

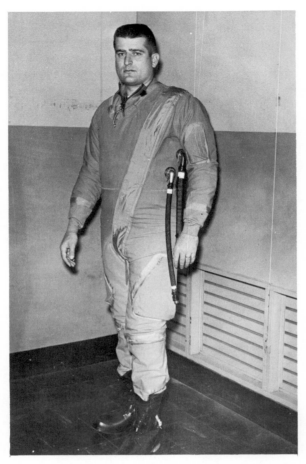

Fig. 11-7. Front of continuous wear exposure suit (U.S. Navy).

the pressure should be at least 1.5 psi. The buoyancy requirement is that when inflated to 1.5 psi in the oral compartment the vest should support a 30-lb steel weight in clean fresh water at $73 \pm 5 °F$. Some of the emergency equipment such as dye marker, shark chaser, whistle, signaling mirror, and flashlight are shown with the life preserver in Fig. 11-2.

The Mark 2 vest is susceptible to ultraviolet light degradation. The coated cloth (20), nylon with chloroprene coating, is used with the nylon side exposed to sunlight. It in turn screens the chloroprene coating. For good weather and gas retention the coating weight must be at least 4 oz/yd². The newer sunlight resistant nylon yarns (Fig. 11-10) which are coming onto the market in the proper yarn numbers

TABLE 11-2. Properties of Coated Cloth and Laminated Cloth [a]

| Characteristic | Spec. CCC-T-191 method no. | Requirements | |
| --- | --- | --- | --- |
| | | Type I coated cloth [b] | Type II laminated cloth [b] |
| Weight, oz/sq yd, max. | 5041 | 19.0 | 24.0 |
| Breaking strength, 2-in. wide strip, lb, min | 5102.1 | | |
| Wales | | 90 | 90 |
| Courses | | 45 | 45 |
| Elongation at break, 2-in. wide strip, %, min | 5102.1 | | |
| Wales | | 100 | 100 |
| Courses | | 250 | 250 |

[a] From MIL-C-23926 (Weps).

[b] Resistance to flexing: The type I cloth shall be subjected to 1000 flexing cycles at 50% stretch in the course direction and type II cloth shall be subjected to 500 flexing cycles at 100% stretch in the course direction. After flexing, the specimen of each type of cloth shall have no tears in the coating, no separation of coating from the cloth, nor shall it leak water.

Fig. 11-8. Repeated flex tester (U.S. Navy).

Fig. 11-9. Inflated life preserver (U.S. Navy).

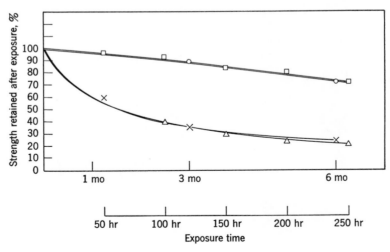

Fig. 11-10. Effect of ultraviolet exposure on nylon yarn.

for fabrication of the base cloth offer the possibility for developments to yield life vests with longer service lives.

A pneumatic life preserver (21) of different configuration is used with the high altitude suit, see Section III-C.

These life preservers have one characteristic in common with all inflatible sea survival equipment. $CO_2$ provides a quick means of inflating as required but the coated fabrics are permeable to $CO_2$ gas. When the pressure drops, the preserver may be inflated orally, and life rafts carry hand pumps to reinflate to provide required buoyancy.

## C. Pressure Suits

The high altitude full pressure suit (22) is intended to be worn in all flights above 45,000 ft to protect airmen from effects of low ambient pressures and of explosive, rapid, or slow decompression. In event of emergency ditching at sea or on land the suit (Fig. 11-11) also protects wearer from exposure to low, ambient temperature, cold water, wind and spray.

The basic design is an inner gas retaining layer (20) and an outer restraining layer of uncoated nylon fabric (3 oz/yd²). The entrance and relief slide fasteners are of the type described in Section III-A for use on the exposure suit. This suit also requires ventilation for comfort.

Since this full pressure suit will be worn in an oxygen-rich atmosphere for long periods, the effect of oxygen aging on textile components is under study. The first phase of this study on yarns (23) showed that oxygen bomb exposure of 96 hr at 300 psi and 158°F reduced the breaking strength of type 300, 305, and 380 nylon yarns in the greige approximately 10%. Type 330 nylon, a sunlight resistant type, and type 55 Dacron yarns exposed in the greige under the same conditions were not deteriorated. In the presence of dyes, all four types of nylon yarns lost strength during oxygen aging (see Fig. 11-12). Fabrics and coated cloths are under investigation for effects of oxygen aging.

The glove for the pressure suit (24) consists of a seamless flocked rubber inner shell and a 3 oz/yd² nylon cloth outer shell, except that the palm and front of fingers and thumb is a continuous piece of leather. The gauntlet end of the glove is cemented to a disconnect with an "O" ring and the pin portion of the slide fastener. These in turn mate with the torso assembly disconnect ring and slide fastener to form a continuous specified airtight assembly. In this design an expansion fold is provided on the back of the fingers at the second joint.

The oxygen mask (Fig. 11-13) is used for dispensing gaseous oxygen

Fig. 11-11. High altitude full pressure suit (U.S. Navy).

from demand regulators to aircrew members. The elastomeric mask (25) must retain pliability after 1 hr at $-65°F$, and must be operable for 3 hr at $-40°F$ and a wind velocity of at least 15 mph. In addition, it must retain its suitability for use after 8 hr exposure at $160°F$, and must not become sticky or tacky after storage for 72 hr at $212°F$.

## D. Protective Helmets

A protective helmet may be defined as a device for protection of personnel engaged in the operation of helicopters, trainer aircraft, and operational aircraft. The helmet will afford protection against head

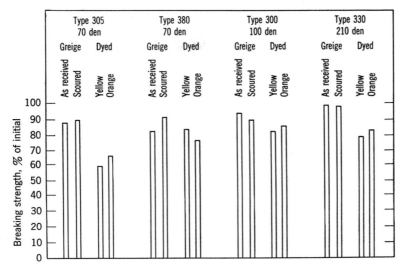

Fig. 11-12. Effect of 96 hr oxygen aging on nylon breaking strength.

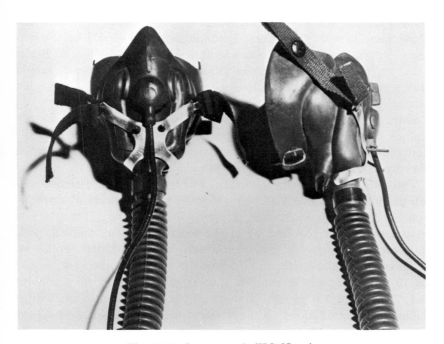

Fig. 11-13. Oxygen mask (U.S. Navy).

injuries and buffeting and will further act as a sound protection device to reduce pilot discomfort due to noise encountered during aircraft operation.

A protective helmet may consist of two or more of the following component parts: shell, edge roll, chafing strip, earphone cushion pads, microphone plug holder, accessory fasteners, inner foam liner, cloth liner fasteners, cloth liner, chin strap assembly, and miscellaneous materials. The construction of helmets are varied and some of the helmets currently in use are constructed as defined in Refs. 26–28. It must be remembered that these references typify some Navy pilot protective helmets and are not all-inclusive. Drawings generally are available which detail the construction of helmets.

A survey of literature of crash data on naval aircraft failed to reveal a breakdown of the type of blow which causes head injuries. It would seem obvious that a dynamic blow is more prevalent than a dead load such as when a pilot's head would be pinned underneath wreckage (simulated by static tests). The literature survey shows that generally dynamic type blows are sustained by helmets during the aircraft accidents. Thus, it seems safe to conclude that if an accident occurred which resulted in a pilot's head being pinned under a wreckage, the helmet would probably be subjected to severe buffeting before the plane came to rest. Therefore, dynamic test data should be the primary criteria upon which helmet shell design should be based. Static data, while of academic interest from a material standpoint, should play a minor role in applications where the end-use item is subjected primarily to dynamic loads.

Since dynamic impact loading is of major importance, laboratory studies were undertaken to develop a test that would simulate a condition under which a pilot might be struck a heavy, sudden, concentrated blow by a rounded object during a crash.

The impact test apparatus shown on Fig. 11-14 was designed and fabricated at the Naval Air Engineering Center. It consists of a pendulum approximately 5½ ft long, supported on a stand. It has a low resistance annular ball bearing at the fixed point, 1-in. diameter rod, and two interchangeable balls at the end. The smaller ball is 3.28 in. in diameter, weighing 5 lb, and the larger is 4.09 in. in diameter, weighing 10 lb. The release mechanism is so arranged to drop the pendulum at 1, 2, 3, 4, and 5 ft of vertical distance from the center of the ball to the lowest point of travel. A universally adjustable base was designed to support the head form.

A head form was prepared to stimulate the human head (see Fig.

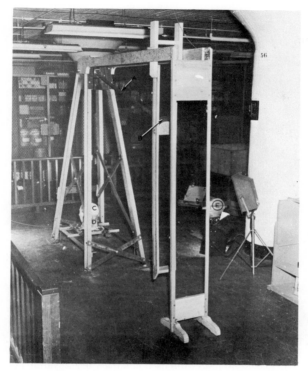

Fig. 11-14. Test setup for impact test (U.S. Navy): *A*, pendulum; *B*, ball; *C*, shell; *D*, head form; *E*, high speed camera.

11-15). It was fabricated using ten layers of glass fabric and a polyester resin. A special mold and pressure bag were used to give the exact size and contour of the inside of the shells. The outside of the head form was dipped in natural-rubber latex, and cured to give approximately a $\frac{1}{16}$-in. layer of cured latex "skin." The inside was entirely filled, layer after layer, with coagulated latex to give a semifluid "brain." One head form was used for all impact tests.

An ultrahigh speed motion picture camera was used to record the results of the impact test. The developed exposed film was projected on a screen equipped with a horizontal graded scale which permitted a determination of the actual deflection produced by each helmet impact. Figure 11-16 is a section of slow motion film and shows a noduled helmet shell being impacted and the associated deflection.

In order to report deflection produced with impact applied, it was necessary to determine the impact energy for each test. Therefore, it

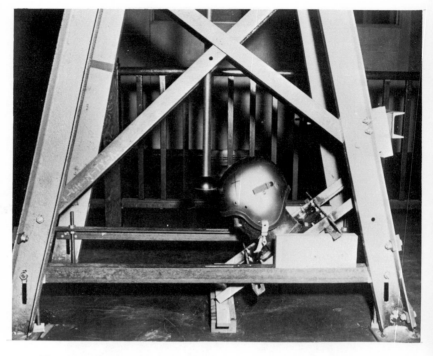

Fig. 11-15. Detail of head form used in impact test apparatus (U.S. Navy).

was required to determine angular velocity using the formula $W = v/r$, where $W$ = angular velocity, rad/sec, $v$ = linear velocity, ft/sec, $r$ = radius of rotation (determined by measuring the distance between the center of the rotation bearing and the center of the impact ball), ft. For example (for 10# ball):

$$W = \frac{17.09 \text{ ft/sec}}{5.51 \text{ ft}}$$

$$W = 3.1 \text{ radians/sec}$$

The moment of inertia can be determined from the formula

$$f = 1/2\pi \sqrt{wlg/I}$$

where $f$ = frequency, ft/sec, $w$ = mass at center of gravity, lb, $l$ = distance from center of gravity to the center of rotation, ft, $g$ = acceleration due to gravity in ft/sec$^2$ = 32.16, $I$ = moment of inertia in ft$^2$-lb. Solving for $I$:

$$I = wlg/4\pi^2 f^2$$

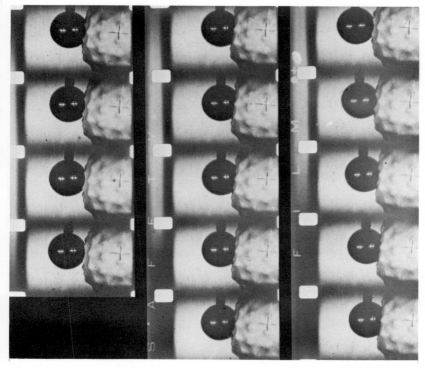

Fig. 11-16. Section of film showing impact (U.S. Navy).

For example (for 10# ball):

$$I = \frac{(98.56)\,(32.16)}{(39.44)\,(0.174)}\ \frac{(\text{ft-lb})\,(\text{ft/sec}^2)}{1/\text{sec}^2}$$

$$= 462.30\ \text{ft}^2\text{-lb}$$

Finally, the impact energy (kinetic energy) is obtained from the formula

$$KE = \tfrac{1}{2}(IW^2/g)$$

where $KE$ = kinetic energy, ft-lb, $I$ = movement of inertia, ft²-lb, $W$ = angular velocity, rad/sec, $g$ = acceleration due to gravity, ft/sec² = 32.16.

For example (for 10# ball):

$$KE = \frac{1}{2}\left(\frac{462.30 \times (3.1)^2}{32.16}\right)$$

$$= 67\ \text{ft-lb}$$

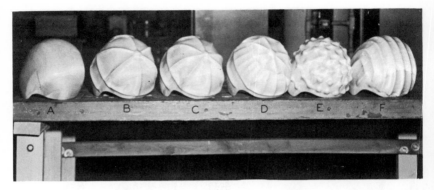

Fig. 11-17. Helmet shell ridge patterns (U.S. Navy): *A*, plain; *B*, 60° radial ridge; *C*, 45° radial ridge; *D*, 15° radial ridge; *E*, noduled; *F*, parallel ridge.

It was concluded that (29,30):

(*1*) The plain helmet shell in comparison to other type shells shown in Fig. 11-17 is superior to all other types tested with respect to dynamic energy service and deflection characteristics. The typical curve depicting this type of analysis is shown by Fig. 11-18.

(*2*) Data for pilot's protective helmets should primarily be based upon results of dynamic impact tests.

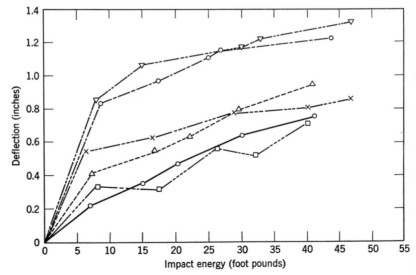

Fig. 11-18. Pendulum-impact (energy vs deflection). Data on helmet shells struck on side (off ridge).

## E. Body Armor

Body armor (31) and flak protective curtains (32) are classed as soft armor as distinguished from bulletproof vests. The vests utilize multilayers of high tenacity nylon fabrics as energy absorbers to afford protection against low velocity fragments and secondary missiles. They are more effective with higher tenacity yarn or fabric. Therefore prolonged exposure to ultraviolet light or a wet condition will reduce the effective stopping range for missiles.

## IV. SEA SURVIVAL EQUIPMENT

Emergency equipment for one man forced down at sea consists of an inflatible raft (see Fig. 11-19) and various components including signaling devices, poncho, desalting tablets and still for survival (33). Current specifications utilize natural rubber coated on cotton and on nylon base cloths for the raft. A nylon sea anchor and nylon securing lines and a lanyard for attaching raft to the life preserver are provided. One model has a weather shield made from type S cloth (34) (see Table 11-3). The red side of the shield fabric is dyed with a fluorescent red dyestuff to facilitate location by search and rescue parties during dawn or twilight hours. In addition to deterioration resulting from weathering, the red dyestuff is subject to change under light intensities of the level of fluorescent lamps. Another model raft is furnished with a survival kit containing a poncho made from the heavy type P cloth, Table 11-3. The coated cloth side of the poncho serves to collect rain for storage in a 5-qt water storage bag as well as protect the man against the weather.

Four and seven man rafts (35) serve as emergency and life support equipment for personnel forced down at sea. These carry paulins (36) of the appropriate size fabricated from the same variety P materials as the one-man poncho. A larger raft (37) has a carrying capacity of 12 men. The 20-man raft (38) is equipped with a reversible type canopy made of variety P fabric.

Some rafts have an inflatable floor for insulation against cold seawater (39). The key to the floor construction is a pilecloth which consists of two nylon cloths joined by a minimum of 30 pile yarns per square inch so that the cloths are spaced a minimum of 1 in. apart after heat setting. The construction is shown in Table 11-4 and Fig. 11-20.

Rafts of somewhat different design (40) are intended to be dropped from military aircraft to survivors at sea. The main tube is auto-

TABLE 11-3.  Properties of Rubber Coated Nylon Cloth [a]

| Characteristic cloth variety | Requirement | | | |
|---|---|---|---|---|
| | S | | P | |
| Weight, oz/yd², max. | 3.0 | | 6.75 | |
| Breaking strength, grab, lb/min. | | | | |
| Warp | 50 | | 200 | |
| Filling | 50 | | 150 | |
| Tearing strength, pendulum, g/min. | | | | |
| Warp | 450 | | 2000 | |
| Filling | 350 | | 1000 | |
| Water resistance, psi, min. | | | | |
| As received | 15 | | 15 | |
| After cold effect test | 12 | | 12 | |
| After abrasion | — | | 12 | |
| Adhesion in warp direction, lb/in. | | | | |
| of width, min. | 1.5 | | 3.0 | |
| Acidity, pH | 6.5–8.0 | | 6.5–8.0 | |
| Reflectance, % | | | | |
| Wavelength, mμ | min. | max. | min. | max. |
| 440 | 15 | 30 | 25 | 55 |
| 450 | 15 | 30 | 30 | 60 |
| 460 | 15 | 30 | 30 | 55 |
| 540 | — | 8 | — | 8 |
| 550 | — | 8 | — | 8 |
| 560 | — | 8 | — | 8 |
| 630 | 60 | — | 120 | — |
| 640 | 60 | — | 120 | — |
| 650 | 60 | — | 120 | — |

[a] From MIL-C-7966A.

matically inflated with $CO_2$. The raft has an outer life line, a sail, and means of attaching an outboard motor. It also has a canopy and inflatible floor to protect survivors against the environment.

A solar, seawater, distillation kit is a standard item packaged with life rafts for sea survival. Figure 11-21 shows a life raft with a series of solar distillation kits. The construction of a solar distillation kit which provides drinking water for survivors on life rafts is defined in the specification (41) and Fig. 11-22.

The operation of a solar still is relatively simple. The vinyl still is inflated orally or by means of a hand pump attached to the distilled water drain after wetting the seawater drain cloth. Seawater is poured in the seawater reservoir, which fills the ballast tube through the ballast tube feed line. Seawater drips from the seawater reservoir through

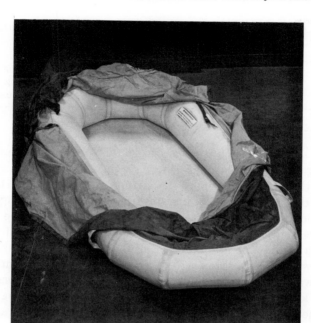

Fig. 11-19. One man raft with weather shield (U.S. Navy).

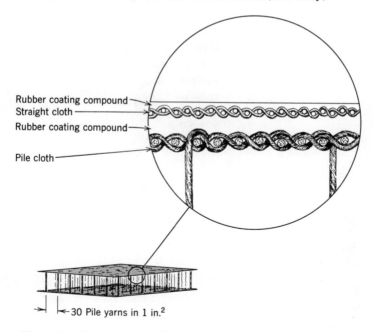

Rubber coating compound
Straight cloth
Rubber coating compound

Pile cloth

←30 Pile yarns in 1 in.²

Fig. 11-20. Construction of fabric for inflatable rubber mattresses.

TABLE 11-4.   Construction and Weight Distribution of Inflatable Mattress Cloth
(ounces per square yard) (39)

| Rubber coating compound | Weight of cloth | Rubber coating compound | Weight of cloth | Rubber coating compound | Weight of cloth | Rubber coating compound | Total weight |
|---|---|---|---|---|---|---|---|
| 1.5 | 1.0 | 9.5 | 7.0 | 9.5 | 1.0 | 1.5 | 30–32 |

an orifice at the bottom of the reservoir onto the black evaporator bag, saturating it. Excess seawater drips onto the seawater drain cloth and is forced through the fabric by the air pressure in the still. Upon exposure to the sun, seawater evaporates from the evaporator bag, and the water condenses on the inside of the plastic envelope. The distilled water runs down the inside of the envelope to the junction of the skirt and the ballast tube. From there it runs through holes in the skirt to the space between the skirt and the envelope and is drawn off through the distilled water drain. The materials currently utilized in constructing the solar kits are reasonably durable. However, the mending tape for use in emergency repairs will deteriorate with long-time storage. Currently, some consideration is being given to use of polyethylene in the construction of the still rather than vinyl. Polyethylene offers advantages in that it remains flexible at low temperatures, requires no special

Fig. 11-21. Sea test arrangement for still operation (U.S. Navy).

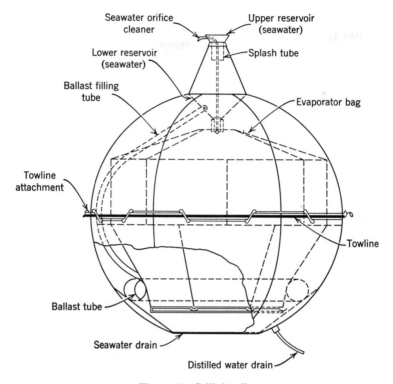

Fig. 11-22. Still details.

handling and could be less expensive in comparison to the currently used vinyl material.

## V. LOOKING AHEAD

In general, this protective clothing and sea survival equipment discussed in this section are designed for in-flight protection and emergencies encountered in flights below the stratosphere. There will be improvements in fabric construction to reduce weight, to reduce packing space, to increase durability under various service conditions, to facilitate fabrication, to provide comfort at high temperatures or insulation at low end of the temperature scale, and to provide improved visibility or camouflage characteristics to survivors of ditching at sea or on land. New material developments that will offer protection against thermal blast and finishes to protect against bacteria and microbes are on the horizon. Design developments are directed toward a solution for multi- and omnienvironmental protection.

Flights into and above the stratosphere bring the heat problem of reentry. The aromatic polyamide known as Nomex nylon has no definite melting point but does deteriorate at 700°F. Development work is in progress to extend the temperature capability by new polymers or by incorporating ceramics in spinning solutions. The flexibility associated with textile products is desirable so interim work has been directed to development of woven fine metal filaments (42,43) in order to attain the required high temperature resistance.

## VI. GLOSSARY

A limited number of terms are defined below. Additional definitions are given in "Standard Definitions of Terms Relating to Textile Materials," ASTM Designation D123-64, in *ASTM Standards,* 1964, Pt. 24, and "Tentative Nomenclature Relating to Plastics" ASTM Designation D883-61T, in *ASTM Standards,* 1961, Pt. 9.

*Air permeability.* The ability of air to pass through the openings or interstices of a fabric. For test method see Fed. Spec. CCC-T-191b method 5450.

*Blackout (aviation).* To suffer loss of vision, often also consciousness, for an interval of seconds, in a steeply banked turn, or steep pullout from a dive because of the increased weight of the blood due to centrifugal force, often 5 or more times gravity.

*Buffeting.* To strike repeatedly such as may occur when an object, traveling with significant velocity, hits a surface then hits again and again until the object comes to rest.

*Cast film.* A film made by depositing a layer of plastic, molten, in solution, or in a dispersion, onto a surface, stabilizing this form, and removing the film from the surface.

*Cellular plastic.* A plastic the apparent density of which is decreased substantially by the presence of numerous cells disposed throughout its mass. The term *foamed plastic* is sometimes used.

*Colorfastness.* The ability of a color to meet the standard requirements and specifications of some specific test on yarn or material. Some colorfastness tests are: fastness to washing and laundering, drycleaning, crocking, pressing or ironing, sunlight, perspiration—whether the color will fade or stain.

*Count (Fabric).* The number of warp yarns (ends) and filling yarns (picks) per inch. For example: A fabric count of 68 × 52 means 68 ends in the warp and 52 picks in the filling.

*Denier* (abbrev. d or den). The number of unit weights of 0.05 g per 450-m length. Note: Denier is equal numerically to the number of grams per 9000 m.

*E-Glass.* Electrical grade glass.

*Fabric, bonded.* A structure consisting of a web of fibers held together with a cementing medium which does not form a continuous sheet of adhesive material.

*Fabric, braided.* A structure produced by interlacing several ends of yarns in a manner such that the paths of the yarns are not parallel to the fabric axis.

*Fabric, knitted.* A structure produced by interlooping one or more ends of yarn or comparable material.

*Fabric, textile.* A planar structure produced by interlacing yarns, fibers, or filaments.

*Fabric, woven.* A planar structure produced by interlacing two or more sets of yarns, fibers, rovings or filaments where the elements pass each other essentially at right angles and one set of elements is parallel to the fabric axis.

*Fiber* (Specific). A unit of matter characterized by having a length at least 100 times its diameter or width, and with the exception of noncrystalline glass fiber, having a definitely preferred orientation of its crystal unit cells with respect to a specific axis.

(Textile). Fibers that can be spun into a yarn or made into a fabric by interlacing in a variety of methods, including weaving, knitting, braiding, felting, and twisting.

*Filament.* A variety of fiber having an extreme length, not readily measured. Note *1:* The extreme length of filaments permits their use as yarns with little or no additional twist and without the spinning operation required to convert fibers to yarn. Note *2:* Typical commercial filaments include silk from undamaged cocoons and a number of man-made filaments, including esterified cellulose, polyamides, polyacrylics, polyesters, polyvinyls, regenerated cellulose, regenerated proteins and glass.

*Filling.* *1.* Yarn running from selvage to selvage at right angles to the warp in a woven fabric. *2.* Yarn to be used as filling in weaving.

*Finish.* See Finishing.

*Finishing.* General term for variety of processes by which fabrics from the loom or knitting machine are converted into finished goods. Bleaching, mercerizing, application of resins, printing, calendering, singeing, shearing, and dyeing are some of the finishing processes. The term includes application of additive materials to increase serviceability or to impart specific properties.

*Flocked.* Very short fibers were applied to cloth surfaces. The flock may be contained in the adhesive paste, dusted on, or applied by means of an electrostatic field.

*Gray goods.* Woven or knitted fabrics which have received no bleaching, dyeing, or finishing treatment.

*Greige.* See Gray goods.

*Lamination.* A general term for the processes of combining two or more layers of reinforcing material with resin or rubber compounds, and bonding with heat and pressure to form a single piece.

*Monofilament.* Any single filament of sufficient size to function as a yarn in normal textile operations.

*Multifilament.* A trade term loosely used to describe filament yarns having more than the normal number of individual filaments for a particular fabric or in a given style season.

*Plastic.* A material that contains as an essential ingredient an inorganic substance of large molecular weight, is solid in its finished state, and at some stage in its manufacture or its processing into finished articles, can be shaped by flow.

*Resin.* A solid, semisolid, or pseudosolid organic material which has an indefinite and often high molecular weight, exhibits a tendency to flow when subjected to stress, usually has a softening or melting range, and usually fractures conchoidally.

*Rubber.* A natural or synthetic material that can be or is already vulcanized to a state in which it has high extensibility and forcible quick retraction.

*Sizing.* A generic term for compounds which, when applied to yarn or fabric form a more or less continuous solid film around the yarn and individual fibers.

*Tenacity.* The tensile stress when expressed as force per unit linear density of the unstrained specimen; for example grams per tex or grams per denier.

*Warp 1.* The yarn running lengthwise in a woven fabric. *2.* A group of yarns in long lengths, put on beams or warp reels for further textile processing including weaving, knitting, twisting, dyeing, etc.

*Yarn.* A generic term for a continuous strand of textile fibers, filaments or material in a form suitable for knitting, weaving or otherwise intertwining to form a textile fabric.

# REFERENCES

1. C. A. Lindberg, *The Spirit of St. Louis,* Scribner's, New York, 1953.
2. Coveralls, Flying, Men's, Summer MIL-C-5390G (Weps) of 22 Mar 1964.
3. Suits, Flying, Winter (Jackets and Trousers) MIL-S-18342C (Wep) of 18 Apr 1963.
4. Coveralls, Anti-G MIL-C-5083B (Wep) of 23 Mar 1961.
5. Cloth, Cotton, Twill, Fire Retardent Treated MIL-C-18387D (Wep) of 1 Feb 1962.
6. M. B. Hays and A. M. Stoll, *Amer. Dyestuff Rptr,* **50,** 872, 908 (1961).
7. A. M. Stoll, Report No. NADC-ML-L-6415 of 18 Nov 1964.
8. Cloth, Synthetic, Twill MIL-C-23882 (Wep)-1 of 4 May 1964.
9. Jackets, Flying, Man's, Very Light MIL-J-7758B (Aer) of 6 Nov 1959.
10. Jacket, Flying, Man's Intermediate, Type G-1 MIL-J-7823C (Wep)-1 of 3 Sep 1963.
11. Gloves, Flying, Leather, Summer, Type B-3A MIL-G-9087A (ASG)-2 of 5 Nov 1957.
12. G. Hargreaves, NAMC Report No. NAM AE 1081 of 8 Jan 1958.
13. M. B. Hays, Report No. NAEC-AML-1995 of 21 Jul 1964.
14. Boot, Flying, Safety MIL-B-21408A (Navy) of 29 Mar 1963.
15. Coveralls, Flying, Anti-exposure, Mk 5A MIL-C-23484B (Weps) of 2 Dec 1963.
16. Cloth, Coated and Laminated; Polychloroprene on Nylon, and Tape, Polychloroprene, Unsupported MIL-C-23926 of 2 Dec 1963.
17. Liners, Coverall, Anti-exposure Mk 5A insulating and ventilating MIL-C-23485A (Weps) of 2 Dec 1963.
18. Coverall, Flying, Antiexposure, Quick Donning, Type QD-1 MIL-C-005808H (Weps) of 1 Oct 1964.
19. Life Preserver, Vest, Inflatable Mark 2 MIL-L-6077G of 24 Sep 1963.
20. Cloth, Coated; and Tape, Coated Cloth-Chloroprene on Nylon, Pneumatic Life Preserver MIL-C-19002B-1 of 28 Apr 1959.

21. Life Preserver Mk IV, Vest; Pneumatic, Full Pressure Suits MIL-L-22208B (Wep)-1 of 20 Apr 1960.
22. Torsos, Mk IV, High Altitude Full Pressure Suit MIL-T-21395B (Weps) of 6 Jan 1964.
23. W. T. Kelly, Report No. NAEC-AML-1897 of 4 Mar 1964.
24. Gloves, Mark IV, High Altitude Full Pressure Suit MIL-G-23978 (Wep) of 9 Jan 1964.
25. Mask Oxygen, Type A-14B MIL-M-7585C (ASG)-1 of 22 Jan 1958.
26. Helmet, Pilot's Protective, Type SPH-1 MIL-H-22059 (Wep)-1 of 27 Jul 1961.
27. Helmet, Pilot's Protective, Type APH-5 MIL-H-19366B (Wep) of 2 Dec 1959.
28. Helmet, Pilot's Protective, Type APH-6 MIL-H-22995 (Wep)-1 of 14 Dec 1961.
29. F. H. Bair and L. J. Petti, NAMC Report No. AML NAM AE 4407, Part I of 9 Dec 1953.
30. S. Polis, NAMC Report No. AML NAM AE 4407, Part II of 17 Nov 1955.
31. Armor, Body, Fragmentation Protective MIL-A-18628B (Aer) of 12 May 1958.
32. Curtain, Flak Protective MIL-C-18491 of 3 Mar 1955.
33. Life Raft, Inflatable, One Man, for Aircraft Use MIL-L-8664A (Aer) of 16 Jun 1959.
34. Cloth, Coated, Rubber, Nylon Base MIL-C-7966A-1 of 19 Nov 1962.
35. Life Rafts, Inflatable-4 and 7 Man—for Aircraft Use MIL-L-5567D of 17 Dec 1963.
36. Paulins, Life Saving MIL-P-7967A (Navy) of 16 Jun 1955.
37. Life Raft, Inflatable, Mark 12A-1 MIL-L-18494B (Wep) of 21 Feb 1963.
38. Life Rafts, Inflatable, Twenty Man MIL-L-009131E (Wep) of 15 Apr 1963.
39. Cloth, Laminated, Rubber on Nylon, Inflatable Floor MIL-C-22427 (Wep) of 17 Feb 1960.
40. Life Raft, Inflatable, AR-4, for Aircraft Use MIL-5012C (Wep) of 2 May 1962.
41. Distillation Kits, Sea Water, Solar MIL-D-5850D of 31 Jul 1964.
42. M. J. Coplan, W. D. Freeston, Jr., and D. H. Power, Jr., ASD Tech. Rept. 61-677 Wright-Patterson Air Force Base, Ohio, Nov. 1961.
43. E. H. Newton and D. E. Johnson, ML-TDR-64-92, Wright-Patterson Air Force Base, Ohio, Feb. 1964.

# 12

# *Solid Lubricants*

**Martin J. Devine**
*Naval Air Development Center,*
*Johnsville, Warminster, Pennsylvania*

## CONTENTS

## I. INTRODUCTION

The phenomenon of solid lubrication involves a means for reducing friction and wear between surfaces in rolling and sliding contact without employing hydrodynamic effects. Low shear characteristics may result from crystal structure, interstitial matter, bond strength, or chemical interaction of the metal surface and constituents of the solid lubricant. The mechanism of solid lubrication cannot be described on the basis of a single property of the lubricant. The interdependence of the surface and lubricant composition, geometry of the bearing, and the nature of the processes occurring at or near the surface represents a major concept in analyzing lubrication by solids. In view of the many engineering possibilities extended by solid lubricants, several aspects of this area of lubrication science will be presented. The discussion will include a general classification of solid lubricants, methods of preparation, techniques for studying solid lubricant properties, and a review of several factors which characterize important parameters basic to solid lubrication.

## II. CLASSIFICATION

A solid lubricant may be defined as a material comprised entirely of solids and maintained between two relatively moving surfaces to reduce friction and wear. Numerous solid inorganic and organic compounds, as well as certain metals and composite materials, may be classified as solid lubricants: e.g., inorganic compounds: $MoS_2$, graphite, PbO, $Na_2MoO_4$; organic compounds: polytetrafluoroethylene, phthalocyanine, polyhexamethylene adipamide; metals: Ag, Au, Pb, In, Ba; composites: WB–Ag–Ni, Mo–MoS$^2$, Ag–PTFE–WSe$_2$. Several hundred different compounds and mixtures, possessing a range of chemical and physical properties, have been described as potential solid lubricants.

In order to provide more detailed understanding of the material types encompassed by this technical area, examples of three lubricating solids will be discussed in detail. First, self-lubricating solid sections possessing structural properties will be considered.

## III. SOLID SECTIONS—AROMATIC POLYIMIDE

A number of organic polymers, i.e., fluorocarbons, amides and acetals, possess properties advantageous for lubricant-bearing applications.

These advantages include light weight, corrosion resistance and inherent lubricating properties. Recently, research quantities of a new organic solid based on aromatic polyimides became available and were studied to investigate potential lubricating properties for high speed, high temperature antifriction bearings. In this section we shall describe the results of exploratory studies. The first portion describes the new material in terms of its mechanical and electrical properties, followed by a description of its lubricant properties in an antifriction bearing.

In an effort to increase the useful temperature range of plastics, the field of polyimide chemistry has been under investigation for many years (1,2,3). More recently laboratory studies have shown that certain aromatic polyimides offered a real advance in high temperature properties (4,5). One of the most promising polyimide compositions is now under field evaluation. Chemically, this polymer is an aromatic polyimide resulting from the polycondensation reaction between pyromellitic dianhydride and an aromatic diamine as shown in Fig. 12-1.

The properties of the aromatic polyimide are described below. In general the polymer may be described as a strong, rigid material which maintains its strength at temperatures well above most plastics. Other useful properties include good resistance to abrasive and frictional wear, oxidation, radiation, and outgassing in high vacuum and good electrical properties. It is resistant to most common chemicals

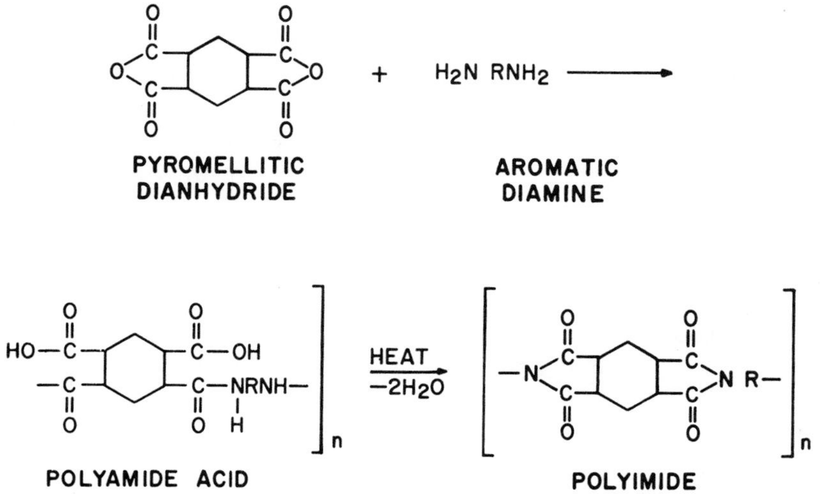

PYROMELLITIC
DIANHYDRIDE

AROMATIC
DIAMINE

POLYAMIDE ACID

POLYIMIDE

Fig. 12-1. Condensation reaction of pyromellitic dianhydride and an aromatic diamine.

and solvents but is attacked by alkalis. Further, the polymer does not melt but exhibits charring at elevated temperatures in air.

A graphite filled polyimide composition has also been developed. This material has a lower wear rate and lower friction coefficient than unfilled polymer. However, the mechanical strength is lower than the unfilled polymer. Other properties of the graphite filled material are given below.

The aromatic polyimide is now undergoing intensive investigation for many field applications. This polymer should be useful in applications where other organic materials are ruled out; for example, where temperatures exceed 400°F, where atomic radiation is severe and where high vacuums are involved.

This aromatic polyimide is one of the strongest of known plastics. At room temperature a tensile strength in excess of 13,000 psi was measured with no true yield point. The graphite filled composition is somewhat weaker with a room temperature tensile strength of 9100 psi. Stress–strain curves for the unfilled and the graphite filled aromatic polyimide at various temperatures are shown in Figs. 12-2 and 12-3.

The effect of temperature on the ultimate tensile strength of the aromatic polyimides together with aluminum alloys 1100 and 2024 are shown in Fig. 12-4. It can be seen that the strength of the aromatic polyimide changes slowly with temperature and above 500°F changes even more slowly than aluminum.

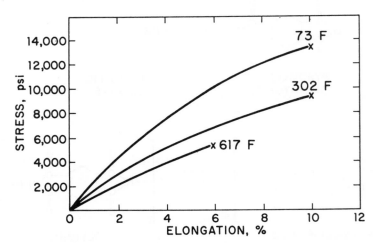

Fig. 12-2. Polyimide stress–strain curves based on original cross section using a strain rate of 0.2 in./min.

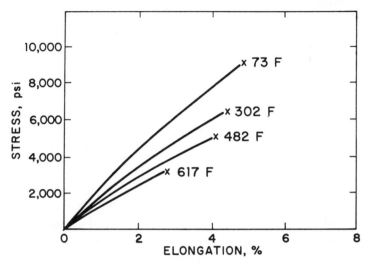

Fig. 12-3. Polyimide (graphite filled) stress–strain curves based on original cross section using a strain rate of 0.2 in./min.

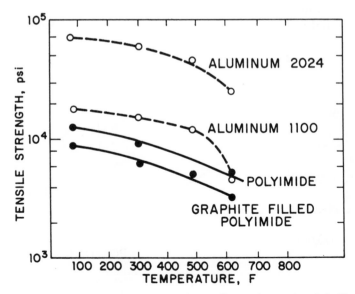

Fig. 12-4. Tensile strength vs temperature. Comparison of polyimides with aluminum.

Although the high stiffness of plastics is an important design property, even more important is the retention of high modulus at elevated temperatures. The effect of temperature on the flex modulus of unfilled and graphite filled polyimides is shown in Fig. 12-5. The inherent stiffness of the polyimides coupled with high strength provides resistance to heavy loads without bending.

Creep or deformation with time under a continuously applied load occurs with all plastics. The polyimide has outstanding resistance to creep when compared to other plastics and at higher temperatures has a lower creep rate than aluminum alloy 2024. Apparent modulus–time curves are shown in Fig. 12-6.

Izod impact strength of the polyimide unnotched is 9.6 ft-lb/in. while the notched value drops to 0.70 ft-lb/in. This difference between the notched and unnotched impact strength emphasizes the importance of eliminating all sharp corners (stress concentrations) in design of any parts by using fillets and radii. Table 12-1 shows a comparison of unnotched and notched polyimides and grey cast iron at two temperature levels.

The coefficient of linear thermal expansion for the polyimide is relatively low for plastics. The thermal expansion of the polyimide is about twice that of aluminum and about four times that of carbon steel. The values are shown in Table 12-2.

The unlubricated dynamic coefficient of friction of unfilled poly-

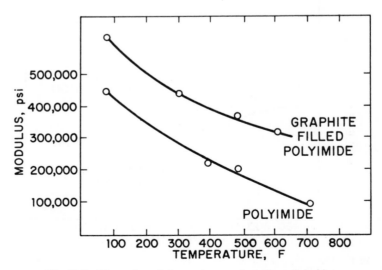

Fig. 12-5. Flexural modulus vs temperature for polyimides.

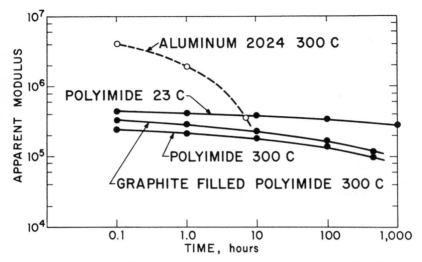

Fig. 12-6. Apparent modulus in flexural creep vs creep time for polyimides and aluminum.

imide against steel is low and the graphite filled material is even lower. When run in contact with polished SAE 1025 mild steel at a relative velocity of 834 fpm (30 psi) the coefficient of friction for unfilled polyimide varies from 0.08–0.15 and for filled material under the same conditions the value varies from 0.05–0.08.

Samples irradiated under a variety of conditions and types of radiation clearly indicate that the polyimide has outstanding radiation resistance. Polyimide samples have been exposed to doses of $10^{11}$ rads in Brookhaven pile at 175°C and $7 \times 10^9$ rads in Van de Graaff generator (high speed electrons) and were still form stable and

TABLE 12-1.  Impact Tests Comparing Polyimides with Cast Iron [a]

|  | Unnotched (ft lb/in.) | | Notched (ft lb/in.) | |
|---|---|---|---|---|
|  | 73°F | 482°F | 73°F | 482°F |
| Polyimide | 9.6 | 11.8 | 0.70 | 0.90 |
| Graphite filled polyimide | 1.8 | 2.8 | 0.23 | 0.47 |
| Grey cast iron | 6.5 | 7.3 | 2.8 | 3.4 |

[a] Both the grey iron and polyimide samples were tested according to D-256-56 ASTM Standards on Plastics (D-20).

TABLE 12-2.  Coefficient of Linear Thermal Expansion [a]

| Polyimide | $\mu$in./in. °F |
|---|---|
| (73–212°F) 23–100°C | 24.2 |
| (73–392°F) 23–200°C | 26.5 |
| (73–572°F) 23–300°C | 27.4 |
| (73–752°F) 23–400°C | 30.0 |
| Graphite filled polyimide | |
| (73–482°F) 23–250°C | 21.6 |
| (73–752°F) 23–400°C | 22.5 |

[a] Values given here are for one direction. This property is anisotropic and values in the other direction are 15–25% higher for unfilled polyimide and 40–50% higher for graphite filled polyimide.

flexible after several weeks. Under similar conditions of exposure, most plastic materials embrittle in seconds.

A complete summary of properties measured to date is given in Tables 12-3 and 12-4.

Initial experiments were aimed at establishing the degree of self-lubrication and the nature of bearing failure. Since the results of previous work with other lubricant types for ball bearings showed that the retainer can serve as a source of lubricant, solid sections of polyimide were prepared for use as the retainer component. The test specimen consisted of a 204 size ball bearing having a two-piece machined retainer (O. D.=1.420 in., I. D.=1.078 in.) fabricated from unannealed polyimide solid having no filler. Tests were conducted at 10,000 rpm and 450 F with a 5 lb thrust load and a 3 lb radial load. Failure criteria included a 50% increase in power or a 20°F temperature rise in the outer race of the test bearing. Bearing performance was determined using a high speed spindle (6). The design employs inner race rotation with a stationary outer race. The running time to failure was 8 hr. Examination of the bearing after completion of the test showed that retainer breakage limited operating time for the test specimen. An annealing treatment was introduced in the processing of the retainer test specimens fabricated from the polyimide to improve dimensional stability. An evaluation of the effect of annealing was conducted on bearing test specimens of the same design and under the aforementioned test conditions. The performance life was advanced to 51 hr. Although the percentage increase was significant showing the advantages resulting from annealing, the total running time was short when compared to grease or solid film lubrication. It was considered that retainer dimensions for the polyimide represented a critical wear life factor. Several variations of the retainer dimensions covering inside and outside diameter as well as ball pocket diameter were investigated to determine suitable requirements. Three determinations for bearing specimens with polyimide retainers having the design and dimensions shown in Fig. 12-7 were conducted at 10,000 rpm and 450°F. The bearing operating time averaged 154 hr. Polymer modification was then investigated to determine the effect of additives such as graphite and molybdenum disulfide. The results obtained at 450°F for the bearing utilizing graphite modified polyimide retainers was 473 hr. Test runs conducted at 600°F showed running times between 183 and 341 hours. It should be noted that the ball-race composition for the bearings utilized as test specimens was Cr–Mo–V alloy steel (AISI-M10). Test bearings having a ball race composition of stainless steel (AISI-440C) equipped with retainers having the graphite modified polyimide composition showed a running time essentially of the same range, i.e., 200 hr at 600°F.

$WSe_2$,$MoS_2$/graphite mixture and $MoS_2$ were also evaluated as additives to the polymer. Tests were conducted at 600°F using the Cr–Mo–V alloy bearings. The retainer dimensions are shown on Fig. 12-7. The respective running times were 79, 90, and 122 hr Hardness measurements conducted on the retainer specimens prior to test showed that differences existed for each of the different additive modified polyimide specimens. Accordingly, a comparison of the effectiveness for the different additives is limited.

Results of two runs conducted at 700°F for the graphite modified polyimide showed running times of 95 and 81 hr, respectively. It should be noted that test runs were also conducted at 700°F in a nitrogen atmosphere. It was observed that the running time to failure was increased to 418 hr. Further, a significant decrease was shown in polyimide retainer wear. A summary of bearing performance life determinations for the polyimide compositions in air is shown on Table 12-5. These data include the results of individual runs for tests employing radial type bearings.

A graphical presentation comparing the performance life in air versus temperature in the elevated temperature region for the modified polyimide and a silicone grease lubricant designed for high temperature operation is given in Fig. 12-8. The test bearings were 20 mm radial ball bearings fabricated from AISI-M10 steel. Silver-plated beryllium copper retainers were employed for the bearings lubricated with the silicone grease. Failure criteria included a 50% increase in power or

TABLE 12-3. Summary of Polyimide Properties

| Property | ASTM No. | Polyimide | Graphite filled polyimide |
|---|---|---|---|
| Sp. grav. | | 1.41-1.43 | 1.49 |
| Ten. str., psi at | D 638 | | |
| 73°F | | 13,400 | 9,120 |
| 302°F | | 9,410 | 6,530 |
| 482°F | | — | 5,200 |
| 617°F | | 5,370 | 3,390 |
| Elong., % at | D 638 | | |
| 73°F | | 10 | 4.9 |
| 302°F | | 10 | 4.4 |
| 482°F | | — | 4.1 |
| 617°F | | 6 | 2.7 |
| Flex. mod., psi at | D 790 | | |
| −310 | | 515,000 | — |
| 73°F | | 450,000 | 627,000 |
| 392°F | | 225,000(302°F) | 448,000 |
| 482°F | | 210,000 | 376,000 |
| 707°F | | 100,000(608°F) | 325,000 |
| Flex. str., psi at | D 790 | | |
| 73°F | | 14,700 | 12,500 |
| 509°F | | 8,000(482°F) | 7,520 |
| Shear str., psi at | D 732 | | |
| | | 11,400 | 6,265 |

| | Test | Notched | Unnotched | Notched | Unnotched |
|---|---|---|---|---|---|
| Impact str., izod ft-lb/in. at | D 256–56 | | | | |
| −112°F | | 0.50 | — | — | — |
| 73°F | | 0.70 | 9.6 | 0.23 | 1.8 |
| 482°F | | 0.90 | 11.8 | 0.47 | 2.8 |
| Deformation under load, % at 2000 psi and 122°F | D 621 | | 0.13 | | 0.14 |
| Comp. str., psi | D 695 | | 24,400 | | 19,000 |
| Heat dist. temp. °F at 264 psi | D 648 | | >473°F | | >464°F |
| Sp. heat, Btu lb/°F | D 648 | | 0.27 | | — |
| Thermal conductivity, Btu/hr-ft²-°F-in. | | | 2.20 | | — |
| Rockwell hardness | | | H 83–89 | | H 73–75 |
| Coefficient of linear thermal exp. per °F (73–752°F) | | | $30 \times 10^{-6}$ | | $22.5 \times 10^{-6}$ |
| Taber abrasion (1000 g load, CS-17 wheel) mg/1000 cycles | D1044–56 | | 6.3 | | 7.8 |

TABLE 12-4.  Electrical Properties of Polyimide

| | |
|---|---|
| Dielectric strength | |
| Short time (80 mils) | 570 V/mil |
| (3 mils) | 4100 V/mil |
| Volume resistivity | $1.6 \times 10^{15}$ ohm-cm |
| Arc resistance | 185 sec (tracks) |
| Dielectric constant, dry, $10^6$ cps at | |
| 73°F | 3.4 |
| 347°F | 3.4 |
| 437°F | 3.4 |
| 527°F | 3.4 |
| 572°F | 3.4 |
| Dissipation factor, dry, $10^6$ cps at | |
| 73°F | .003 |
| 347°F | .003 |
| 437°F | .003 |
| 527°F | .003 |
| 572°F | .003 |

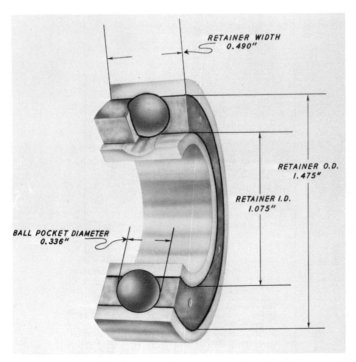

Fig. 12-7.  Ball bearing design.  Aromatic polyimide plastic retainer.  Two-piece, inner land guided.

TABLE 12-5.  Comparison of Bearing Performance Life

Apparatus: High temperature performance test apparatus
Specimen: 20 mm radial ball bearing
Load: 5 lb thrust, 3 lb radial
Speed: 10,000 rpm
Lubricant: Self lubricating aromatic polyimide retainer (as shown)

| Bearing | Retainer | Temp., °F | Performance life (hr) |
|---|---|---|---|
| AISI–M10 | Polyimide | 450 | 151, 153, 159 |
| AISI–M10 | Polyimide-graphite | 450 | 473 |
| AISI–M10 | Polyimide-graphite | 600 | 183, 205, 341 |
| AISI–440C | Polyimide-graphite | 600 | 200, 238 |
| AISI–M10 | Polyimide-WSe$_2$ | 600 | 79 |
| AISI–M10 | Polyimide-MoS$_2$/graphite | 600 | 90 |
| AISI–M10 | Polyimide-MoS$_2$ | 600 | 122 |
| AISI–M10 | Polyimide-graphite | 650 | 180, 155 |
| AISI–M10 | Polyimide-graphite | 700 | 95, 81 |

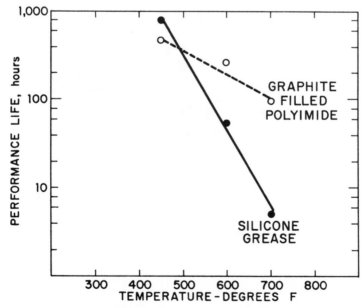

Fig. 12-8.  Performance life vs temperature for silicone grease and polyimide lubricated ball bearings.

a 20°F temperature rise for the test bearing. The data show the effective lubricating properties of the polyimide solid section under temperature conditions where most organic based materials are severely limited.

In each of the runs described above covering polyimide materials, the sole source of lubricant was the self-lubricating retainer. Examination of the ball components indicated that polymer transfer was accomplished by continual contact between ball and retainer so that each ball was coated with a thin film. The same degree of film deposition was not observed on the land areas in sliding contact with the retainer. In order to provide the self-lubricating substance on the land, a portion of the steel composition was removed and replaced with an insert of the polyimide material. The design is shown in Fig. 12-9. The retainer dimensions were modified to allow for the differences in expansion characteristics. Tests were conducted using Cr–Mo–V alloy bearings at 350°F and 10,000 rpm. A running time of 814 hr was obtained for the design employing polyimide retainers and lands. In comparison bearings having polyimide retainers of the same dimen-

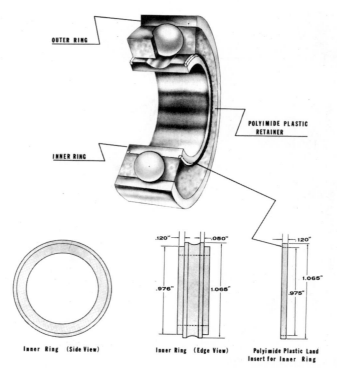

Fig. 12-9. Ball bearing design. Aromatic polyimide plastic retainers and lands.

sions (O. D.=1.454 in., I. D.=1.087 in.) and without land modification provided a running time of 294 hr.

These results show the importance of design considerations for the effective use of self-lubricating solid sections in bearing lubrication. Additional experiments were concerned with providing additional sources of lubricant to the bearing. For example, polyimide balls were substituted for some of the steel balls such that a polyimide ball was interposed between two steel balls. Test runs were conducted at 600°F using a test bearing with polyimide-graphite retainers. Duplicate determinations for performance life were 303 and 312 hr, respectively.

The next series of test runs utilized one-piece machined polyimide-graphite retainers designed for thrust bearings. The design of the bearing assembly is shown in Fig. 12-10. Initial tests were conducted at 600°F and 10,000 rpm for the one-piece outer land riding retainer having pockets to accommodate eight balls. Failure occurred after 130 hr of operation. Three additional tests provided running times of 133, 151, and 93 hr. It was observed that failure was associated with

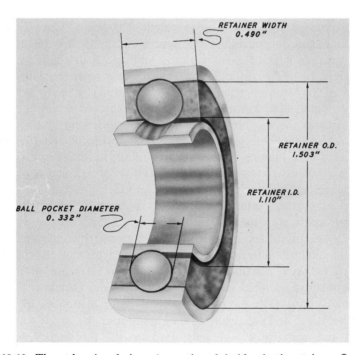

Fig. 12-10. Thrust bearing design. Aromatic polyimide plastic retainer. One piece, outer land guided.

the wear of the low retainer cross sections separating the balls. Increasing this cross section by reducing the number of ball pockets to six resulted in performance life of 228 hr.

Additional tests were conducted at 600°F using a one-piece, innerland riding polyimide-graphite retainer having pockets to accommodate eight balls. The average of two determinations for performance life was 139 hr. Retainer breakage at the low cross sections separating the balls indicated that reinforcement in this cross-section area may be required. Two-piece retainer assemblies using threaded bolts were prepared for the test bearing. Duplicate tests conducted at 600°F and 10,000 rpm showed running times of 256 and 307 hr, respectively.

## IV. SOLID FILM—INORGANIC

A second specific type of solid lubricant is the thin film normally composed of lubricating solids and binder solids. Generally, molybdenum disulfide and/or graphite constitute the lubricating solids and an organic resin acts as the binder solid. A sprayable consistency is obtained by the addition of a thinner. After being applied to the surface of a metal part, the film is cured by baking. Cure time and temperature are dependent on the nature of the organic resin as well as the metal to which the solid film is applied. A discussion of properties for a variety of solid film lubricants has been the subject of a number of paper and reports (7–10). Recently a new system of inorganic solid film lubricants has been achieved utilizing soluble metal silicates for the binder fraction. The following characteristics were exhibited by the inorganic binder: capability of being deposited in the form of a binding film, ability to retain hardness and chemical stability at elevated temperatures, capability of forming a tenacious bond at temperatures which would not produce dimensional changes in metal substrates, compatibility with a variety of lubricating solids and resistance to abrasion.

Since the resultant solid film is inorganic, greater stability under conditions of nuclear radiation, low pressure, and extreme temperatures might be expected for lubrication applications in high performance aircraft, nuclear powered rockets, and other space vehicles. Viscosity and density data (11) have been presented for a number of sodium silicate solutions and potassium silicate solutions.

$MoS_2$ and graphite were chiefly used for the lubricant fraction of the solid film environmental studies.

Techniques for sample preparation, bonding, and lubricating formulation were investigated. Molybdenum disulfide and sodium silicate (% ratio $Na_2O:SiO_2=1:2.90$) as lubricant fraction and binder fraction, respectively, were chosen for preliminary studies. It was found that poor wettability of the solid lubricant results from direct addition of $MoS_2$ to sodium silicate solution. Samples were prepared by first wetting the lubricant solid with water to obtain a slurry, adding the slurry to the solution of sodium silicate, and stirring to obtain a uniform mixture. This mixture can be applied in the form of a thin film by a spray application. The film contains water which must be removed to obtain effective bonding and reduce softness. The water was removed by heating with a gradual temperature increase over a period of 32–48 hr.

Recent work has shown that curing time may be substantially reduced. This sample preparation method was extended to a variety of solids and solid mixtures. It was observed that an immediate reaction occurred when PbO, PbI, PbS, ZrCl, or $CdI_2$ are added to the sodium silicate solution yielding a very thick fluid or a solid mass. A substitution of sodium phosphate and/or sodium borate for the sodium silicate binder eliminated the reaction, provided a means for solid lubricant-binder compatibility for PbO, $PbI_2$, PbS, ZrCl, and $CdI_2$, and extended the number and types of inorganic binders for solid film lubricants.

The results of lubricity studies conducted using a ball bearing life test apparatus (12) are shown in Table 12-6. These data represent the results of single runs on a number of combinations of solids or solid mixtures and binders. Significance is attributed to the results of single runs, since successive tests on a limited number of samples have produced a deviation from the average of less than 10%. A graphical presentation showing the effect of the ratio of graphite to $MoS_2$ in a sodium silicant binder ($Na_2O:SiO_2=1:2.90$) on wear life in terms of cycles is shown on Fig. 12-11. A molybdenum disulfide–graphite mixture with a sodium silicate binder has proved to be the most satisfactory lubricant film produced to date for high speed, light load, ball bearing applications wherein the bearings are fabricated from Cr alloy steel (AISI-C52100) for the races and balls and carbon steel (AISI-C1010) for the retainers. Accordingly, most of the experiments conducted to determine the effect of environment on the properties of the inorganic solid film have utilized films containing $MoS_2$, graphite, and sodium silicate.

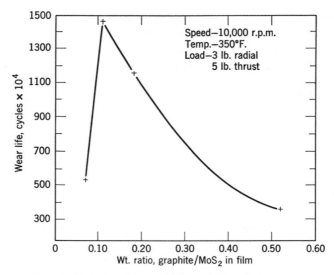

Fig. 12-11. Wear life vs graphite/MoS₂ weight ratio.

## A. Environment Studies

Experimental procedures were selected or devised to produce the extreme environments associated with the bearing systems of present and future space vehicles. The successful lubrication of such bearings requires lubricant performance over a wide range of temperature, resistance to nuclear radiation, and stability under reduced pressure. Lubrication with conventional oils and greases, if feasible, would demand a weight penalty in terms of accessory equipment such as pumps, tanks, heaters, etc.

Unless otherwise specified, the ball bearing test specimens were fabricated from AISI-C52100 steel for the races and balls and AISI-1010 for the retainers.

*Liquid Oxygen Detonation.* Essentially the apparatus consists of a plummet assembly weighing 20.0 lb, a striker pin, and a test sample cup. The cup containing the solid film is slowly cooled to liquid oxygen temperature by suspending in the gaseous oxygen followed by immersion in the liquid oxygen. The cup is filled with liquid oxygen and transferred to the test apparatus. A clean striker pin, precooled by immersion in liquid oxygen, was placed in contact with the sample surface and the cup was topped with liquid oxygen prior to impact. The plummet drop distance is 50 in.

***Lubricant Performance in Liquid Oxygen.*** Ball bearing lubrication in the presence of liquid oxygen was studied using the following experimental procedure: Liquid oxygen was contained in a 25-liter flask and pressurized gas was used to pump the liquid oxygen through copper tubing to an insulated stainless steel beaker containing the test bearing. The solid film lubricated bearing was attached to a shaft which can be rotated at 3600 rpm by means of a drill press motor. The ball bearing is encased in a bearing prior to being adapted to the test shaft. A 5-lb thrust load is applied and the drive motor is actuated.

***Nuclear Radiation.*** Solid film-lubricated ball bearing specimens were exposed to gamma radiation in the Materials Testing Reactor Gamma Irradiation Facility at Idaho Falls. The average dose rate was $4.21 \times 10^6$ rads/hr. The total dosage was $5 \times 10^9$ rads. Exposure time required to obtain this dosage was 1187 hr. Prior to exposure, the bearings were wrapped in aluminum foil and placed in an aluminum container, 3 in. in diameter and 8 in. in length. The lubricated bearings were irradiated while under a constant air pressure of approximately 9.5 psig. After irradiation, the performance life was evaluated using the standard test spindle (12). The test was conducted at 10,000 rpm and 350°F.

***Low Pressure.*** A vacuum evaporator (13) was utilized to provide pressures of less than 1 $\mu$. A cylindrical 18-8 stainless steel pin, 1.25 in. in length and 0.25 in. in diameter having a Rockwell hardness of Rc32, was selected for the bearing specimen. The solid film-lubricated specimen was placed in a combustion boat which was subsequently wrapped with resistance wire. The assembly was placed in the bell jar of the evaporator. A preliminary degassing was accomplished by heating to 500°F for 2 hr. The temperature was increased to 1020°F over a period of 3 hr, while maintaining a pressure of less than 15 $\mu$. The temperature was maintained at 1020°F. for 1 hr and 45 min. The pressure during this period was between 0.1 and 1.0 $\mu$ for two-thirds of the time period and between 2 and 7 $\mu$ for the remainder of the period. After this treatment the temperature was returned to 300°F and the pressure was raised to atmospheric.

***Thermal Stability.*** Steel panels, AISI-4130, $3 \times 6 \times 0.036$ in. were utilized as test specimens. Prior to application of the lubricant, the surface of the panel was subject to a vapor blast pretreatment. The coated panels were then placed in a forced draft oven at 700°F and allowed to remain at this temperature for 24 hr. The panels were then directly removed to a metal block to accelerate cooling to room temperature. The film was examined visually for color change, cracking, flaking, etc., and was scratched to determine, qualitatively, the adhesion characteristics.

*Low Temperature Torque.* The apparatus (14) used to evaluate the starting torque characteristics of the solid film consists essentially of a test bearing, a bearing housing, a side load, and a test shaft. The equipment is sufficiently compact so that it can be placed in a subzero cabinet, and tests can be conducted at controlled temperatures. Starting and running torque determinations were made at 77 and $-100°F$.

## B. Results of Environment Experiments

*Liquid Oxygen Detonation.* Twenty-five separate liquid oxygen detonation tests were conducted on the solid film lubricant composed of 71% molybdenum disulfide, 7% graphite, and 22% sodium silicate. The film thickness was approximately 0.002 in. No detonations were observed in any of the runs. The tentative safety limit of 350 ft-lb/sq in. was exceeded in all runs.

*Lubricant Performance in Liquid Oxygen.* The retainer surfaces and races of the ball bearing specimen were lubricated with a solid film composed of 66% molybdenum disulfide, 11% graphite, and 23% sodium silicate. A phosphate pretreatment (15) was applied to the retainer surfaces prior to application of the solid film. Approximately 35 min were required to reach a temperature of $-296°F$ at the bearing race. The run was continued for 1 hr with the bearing submerged in liquid oxygen. The run was arbitrarily stopped and the bearing brought back at room temperature. After the bearing was dried, a 10,000 rpm run at 350°F was conducted for 21 hr. A duplicate determination gave the same result. The running time for the same formulation not subjected to the liquid oxygen run, but only to the 10,000 rpm 350°F test was also 21 hr. No comparison with oils, greases, or solid films having organic binders is afforded, because of the possibility of detonation in making runs with these materials in liquid oxygen. A nonlubricated bearing failed in 1 min during the liquid oxygen test. In order to make runs at 750°F after the liquid oxygen run, bearings with races and balls fabricated from Cr–Mo–V tool steel (SAE M-10) and retainers of

302 stainless steel were used. A running time of 6 hr was obtained at 750°F, 5000 rpm, with no applied load. The phosphate pretreatment used with the AISI-C1010 steel retainers could not be used for the stainless steel retainers.

*Nuclear Radiation.* The races and retainers of the ball bearing specimens were lubricated with a solid film composed of 71% molybdenum disulfide, 7% graphite, and 22% sodium silicate. After irradiation, the bearing performance life (12) at 10,000 rpm and 350°F was determined. A running time of 17 hr was obtained. An unirradiated bearing lubricated with a film of the same composition, but stored for a time equivalent to that required for the radiation exposure experiment, lasted 19 hr. Since the differences in these two running times are within repeatability limits, it is considered that no damaging effects to the solid film were produced by a gamma dosage of $5 \times 10^9$ rads. Experiments are now in progress to determine the solid film stability at $1 \times 10^{10}$ rads.

*Low Pressures.* After being exposed to the conditions previously described for the low pressure experiment, the solid film (71% molybdenum disulfide, 7% graphite, and 22% sodium silicate) lubricated specimen was visually examined for evidence of deterioration and then subjected to a Falex endurance life test. Tests were conducted with an applied load of 500 lb at room temperature. The V-block components were AISI-1137 steel, Rockwell Rc20. The solid film lubricant was not applied to the V-blocks. An endurance life of 271 minutes was obtained. The endurance life for the same composition not subjected to vacuum-temperature conditions was 228 min.

*Thermal Stability.* A comparison of the thermal stability characteristics of the inorganic solid film (71% molybdenum disulfide, 7% graphite, and 22% sodium silicate), a commercial solid film containing molybdenum disulfide in a phenolic resin binder, and an extreme high temperature grease, MIL-G-25013A, was made. After 24 hr at 700°F, no breakdown of the experimental film was observed, while the two organic lubricants were degraded within several hours. An 800°F test was also conducted on the same inorganic film. No breakdown was observed after 24 hr at this temperature. At 900°F approximately 20% of the film surface was white indicating that $MoS_2$ was being converted to $MoO_3$.

*Low-Temperature Torque.* The retainer surfaces and races of the ball bearing specimen were lubricated with a solid film composed

TABLE 12-6.  Effect of Solid Film Composition on Bearing Performance Life [a]

Apparatus: High speed bearing performance apparatus
Specimen:  204 size ball bearing, AISI-C52100 steel balls and races, AISI-C1010
retainers
Load: 5-lb thrust, 3-lb radial
Test temp: 350°F

| Chemical composition of solid film, wt % | | | Test speed, rpm | Performance life, hr |
|---|---|---|---|---|
| $MoS_2$ | Graphite | Sodium silicate | | |
| 0 | 66 | 34 | 10,000 | 4 |
| 48 | 26 | 26 | 10,000 | 6 |
| 66 | 11 | 23 | 10,000 | 21 |
| 71 | 7 | 22 | 10,000 | 29 |
| 74 | 4 | 22 | 10,000 | 9 |
| 71 | 7 | 22 | 3,500 | 42 |
| 71 | 7 | 22 | 1,250 | 240 |
| PbO | Graphite | Sodium phosphate | | |
| 59 | 29 | 12 | 3,500 | 14 |
| 89 | 0 | 11 | 10,000 | 0.5 |
| $PbI_2$ | Graphite | Sodium phosphate | | |
| 83 | 0 | 17 | 10,000 | 4 |
| $MoS_2$ | Graphite | Sodium phosphate | | |
| 71 | 7 | 22 | 3,500 | 88 |
| $MoS_2$ | Graphite | Sodium borate | | |
| 71 | 7 | 22 | 3,500 | 14 |
| $MoS_2$ | Graphite | Potassium silicate | | |
| 71 | 7 | 22 | 1,250 | 207 |
| 71 | 7 | 22 | 10,000 | 22 |

[a] Solid film applied to races and retainers. Cure condition. Room temp. 0.5 hr;
180°F; 16–24 hr; 300°F; 16–24 hr. Retainer surfaces phosphated prior to solid
film deposition. Approximate film thickness: 0.0001 in. (races), 0.0009 in.
(retainers).

of 71% molybdenum disulfide, 7% graphite, and 22% sodium silicate.
The solid film produced a starting torque of 472 g-cm at −100°F
and of 118 g-cm at 77°F. Test results for a low temperature
grease designed for −100°F operation (MIL-G-7421 grease) showed

that the grease produced a starting torque of 4764 g-cm at $-100°F$ and 177 g-cm at $77°F$. Running torque characteristics were approximately the same for both lubricants.

## C. Mechanism Studies

*Solid Film Structure.* The typical solid film lubricant is composed of lubricating solids and binder solids. The lubricating solids and binder solids are each composed of one or more constituents. Figure 12-12 illustrates a cross section of a solid film lubricant bonded to a metal surface. The film thickness is exaggerated in order to show a probable gradient of lubricating solids in a continuous binder medium. The ratio of lubricating solids to binder solids is one of the factors determining lubricity for solid film lubricants. Experiments to study the comparative properties of potential lubricating solids should not be based on a direct weight substitution, since density and/or particle size differences exist. The more important volume factor should be considered. The work conducted in phase I was aimed at producing a satisfactory solution to the problem of substitution of lubricating solids in a binder such that the volume of the lubricating solids remains essentially constant.

The technique devised provides an adequate approximation for equal volume substitution. In the following outline of the procedure for a sample of given weight, the per cent by weight of lubricating

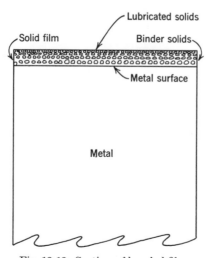

Fig. 12-12. Section of bonded film.

solid initially employed is selected on the basis of the maximum number of wear cycles obtainable by estimation from a curve of number of wear cycles vs per cent of lubricating solids.

The weighed solid is placed in a graduated cylinder and packed by tapping until a constant volume reading is obtained, and is centrifuged (1800 rpm, 7.5-in. radius) for 1 hr.

The final volume of the cylinder is noted.

The initial weight divided by the final volume represents the apparent density of the lubricating solid.

The weight of lubricating solid $B$ required to give a volume equal to lubricating solid $A$ was calculated on the basis of the following equation:

$$W_B = \frac{D_B \times W_A}{D_A}$$

where  $W_B =$ weight of solid $B$ (to be calculated)
  $W_A =$ weight of solid $A$ (in solid film formulation)
  $D_B =$ apparent density of solid $B$
  $D_A =$ apparent density of solid $A$

Table 12-7 presents apparent density data for a number of lubricating solids of interest for future research.

***Wear Life.*** The utilization of solid film lubricants in high speed ball bearing applications is a relatively recent advance in the science of lubrication. Accordingly, not enough is yet known about the wear pattern encountered with such lubricants in ball sliding and rolling. Oxidation or other chemical degradation of liquid lubricants is a frequent cause of failure of oils and greases; however, at equivalent

TABLE 12-7.  Apparent Density of Selected Inorganic Solids

| Solid, 5.5 g | Final volume, cc | Apparent density [a] |
|---|---|---|
| $MoS_2$, 5 g, graphite, 0.5 g [b] | 3.25 | 1.7 |
| $MoS_2$, 5 g, graphite, 0.5 g [c] | 5.35 | 1.0 |
| PbO | 1.5 | 3.6 |
| Pb | 1.1 | 5.0 |
| Ag | 2.2 | 2.5 |
| AgI | 2.05 | 2.7 |
| $PbI_2$ | 2.65 | 2.0 |
| Pb, 5 g, graphite, 0.5 g | 1.5 | 3.6 |
| Ag, 5 g, graphite, 0.5 g | 2.2 | 2.5 |

[a] Laboratory techniques for preparation of samples may affect apparent density.
[b] Avg. particle size, 7 $\mu$.
[c] Avg. particle size, $<1$ $\mu$.

temperature and operating times, the inorganic lubricating solid present in the solid film under investigation is, by comparison, more oxidation resistant and thermally stable. Therefore, it is hypothesized that ball bearing failure is due to the removal of the solid film by the continual rubbing action of the ball in contact with the lubricated surfaces. Table 12-8 presents the average results of initial runs covering the total wear cycles for two solid films at 10,000, 3500, and 1250 rpm. Experimental details and solid film constituents are contained in Table 12-8. These data indicate that the mechanism of failure under the conditions described is a mechanical removal of film by the rotating balls. Furthermore, it appears the bearing life (hours) may be directly related to speed for this wear process, provided that the conditions of loading and temperature, etc., are held constant.

**Wear Rate.** During wear experiments it was observed, although not measure, that the rate of removal was not constant, since the rate during the beginning of the wear process was higher than during the latter. Present work covers a study of wear rate of the solid film under dynamic conditions. During the wear process, the thickness of the solid film decreased, resulting in a loss of weight. These two factors can be utilized to measure the rate of wear. However, experimental techniques for measuring these factors are cumbersome and do not yield a continuous measurement of wear rate. The approach developed consisted of placing a ball which can be rotated in contact with fixed metal specimens lubricated with solid films.

TABLE 12-8. Comparison of Total Wear Life (Cycles) with the Rotary Speed

Apparatus: High speed bearing performance apparatus
Specimen: 204 size ball bearings, AISI-C 52100 steel balls and races, ASIS-C 1010 steel retainers, radial clearance 0.0003–0.0008 in.
Load: 5-lb thrust, 3-lb radial
Temp: 350°F

| Solid film lubricant | Wt % | Test speed, rpm | Total cycles $\times 10^4$ | % dev. from av. |
|---|---|---|---|---|
| $MoS_2$ | 71 | 10,000 | 1470 | +11 |
| Graphite | 7 | 3,500 | 1113 | —15 |
| Sodium silicate | 22 | 1,250 | 1373 | +4 |
| $MoS_2$ | 66 | 10,000 | 1170 | +17 |
| Graphite | 11 | 3,500 | 953 | —4 |
| Sodium silicate | 23 | 1,250 | 870 | —13 |

The specimen-ball combination is placed in an electrical circuit of a Weston Model 785 Type 4B ohmmeter. Since the resistance of the solid film will be high by comparison with a substrate, the rate of film removal can be obtained by measuring electrical resistance as a function of time, while the ball is rotating against the loading specimen coated with a solid film. The apparatus consisted of a Shell 4-ball lubricant apparatus with a modification permitting the substitution of three fixed flat metal specimens for the three fixed ball specimens. The bearing surfaces separated by the solid film were placed in the circuit of an ohmmeter.

A load of 80 kg was applied to the specimens in contact with the ball and the drive motor was actuated. Resistance readings in ohms were recorded prior to and during the run. The ball was M-10 tool steel and the flat specimens were 301 stainless steel. The solid film consisted of AgI (85 wt %), graphite (1 wt %), and sodium silicate (14 wt %).

The curve (Fig. 12-13) for an initial run shows that the wear rate is rapid during the first phases, indicating the removal of loosely held surface particles. The wear then decreases, approaching a nearly constant rate. Various factors—film thickness, increased contact area with increasing depth of ball penetration, and orientation of solid crystals—are considered important to the interpretation of the report data. Accordingly, no additional conclusions can be drawn without additional experiments.

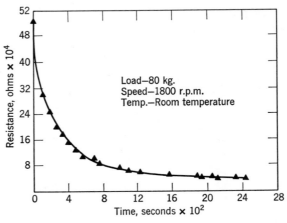

Fig. 12-13. Resistance vs time. Resistance reading at time zero > 1,000,000 ohms.

# V. SOLID LUBRICANT—GREASE CARRIER

The third example covers the effects produced by employing solid lubricant as an additive for lubricating grease. Although molybdenum disulfide was the compound of primary interest in the research outlined below, other solids i.e.; graphite, zinc oxide and talc have been used extensively as lubricating grease components.

Molybdenum disulfide powder has been found to be an effective additive for lubricating grease in numerous industrial, automotive and aeronautical applications (16,17). The improvements imparted to the properties of the grease by the addition of molybdenum disulfide include significant increases for:

*1.* Load carrying capacity

*2.* Friction reduction

*3.* Wear prevention

Molybdenum disulfide has exhibited compatibility with a variety of lubricating greases and chemical addition agents. Further, the thermal stability characteristics of $MoS_2$ can provide a reliability factor under conditions of marginal lubrication where the fluid film has ceased to exist. Under such conditions, the $MoS_2$ functions to maintain a film on the bearing surfaces thereby preventing immediate seizure or catastrophic failure.

In view of the aforementioned properties of $MoS_2$, a laboratory study sponsored by the Naval Air Systems Command was initiated to explore:

*1.* Effects of grade and concentration on extreme pressure and wear characteristics of lubricating grease

*2.* Stability of the lubricating grease

*3.* Means for regenerating lubricating film on metal surfaces

## A. Load Carrying Capacity

Initial experiments were concerned with the effect of $MoS_2$ concentration on grease load carrying properties and wear characteristics. A lithium base grease employing diester fluid and containing no extreme pressure additive was modified by the addition of $MoS_2$ (average particle size$=7$ $\mu$) to provide concentrations of 3, 5, 10, and 20 wt %. A constant soap oil ratio and worked penetration was shown for each of the grease samples. The chemical analysis and particle size for the molybdenum disulfide powder is shown in Table 12-9. The data show that the molybdenum disulfide is a grade suitable for purposes of lubricant additive (18).

TABLE 12-9. Chemical Analysis—Molybdenum Disulfide Powder

| | |
|---|---|
| Molybdenum disulfide | 99.0 |
| Moisture | 0.079 |
| pH | 5.7 |
| pH (change of aqueous extract from blank) | 1.2 |
| Water soluble matter | 0.24% |
| Oil content | 0.08% |
| Total insoluble matter | 0.72% |
| Particle size | 6–7 $\mu$ |

Load carrying capacity for the $MoS_2$ modified grease samples was measured in accordance with a technique (19) employing the Shell 4-Ball E. P. Tester. A graphical presentation of load versus wear scar diameter is shown in Fig. 12-14. It is apparent that increasing $MoS_2$ concentration increases wear resistance at the higher loads and

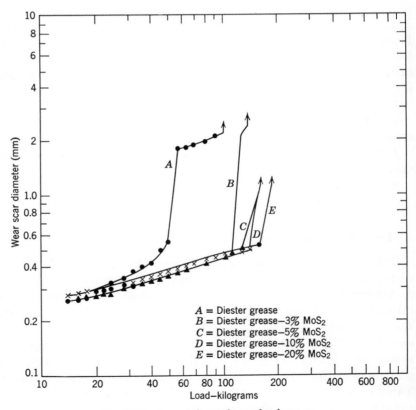

Fig. 12-14. Comparison of wear load curves.

increases the weld point load. The effect of $MoS_2$ concentration on the mean Hertz load value is shown in Fig. 12-15 which illustrates the marked effect of $MoS_2$ on this particular property. Comparative mean Hertz load values for the diester oil base grease modified with $WSe_2$, $WS_2$, graphite, and $MoS_2$ employing a 5 wt % concentration are shown on Table 12-10. The differences shown in mean Hertz load value are especially important when it is realized that there is little difference in wear results between any of the grease compositions at low loads. Further, it is characteristic of $MoS_2$ (18) grease to show a high load at weld coupled with low wear over the entire load spectrum.

## B. Gear Wear

The antiwear characteristics of the lithium base grease containing diester fluid with and without $MoS_2$ additive were studied by a technique (20) employing the Navy gear wear test apparatus. The test consists of measuring the loss in weight of the driving gear after a specified period of operation with the lubricant being evaluated. The gears were operated at a speed of 50 cpm at room temperature. The tests were run for 6000 and 3000 cycles at 5 and 10-lb loads, respectively. An initial break-in run of 1500 cycles at a 5-lb load

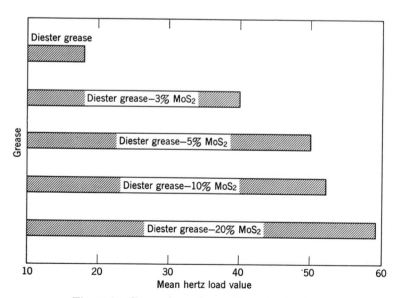

Fig. 12-15. Comparison of mean Hertz load values.

TABLE 12-10.   Comparison of Mean Hertz Load Values

Test Apparatus: Shell 4-Ball E. P. Tester
Specimens: AISI-C52100 steel balls
Speed: 1800 rpm
Temperature: 77°F
Lubricant: Diester oil base grease, additive—as shown (5 wt %)

| Additive | Particle size | Mean Hertz load |
|---|---|---|
| MoS₂ | 7μ | 50 |
| WSe₂ | 5μ | 36 |
| WS₂ | 1μ | 48 |
| Graphite (synthetic) | 5μ | 26 |

to determine suitability of the gears was conducted using di-2-ethyl-hexyl sebacate. Wear rates were studied for five metallic combinations, i.e., brass—stainless steel, SAE B-1112 steel—stainless steel, phosphor bronze—SAE 4130 steel, SAE 4130 steel—stainless steel and SAE 4130 steel—SAE 4130 steel. The results of tests comparing the characteristics of 3, 5, 10, and 20 wt % concentrations of $MoS_2$ in the diester grease are presented in Table 12-11. These results show that:

*1.* The addition of $MoS_2$ to the lubricating grease increases the amount of wear on the brass gear in the brass–stainless steel combination.

*2.* The effect of $MoS_2$ concentration appears minor under the five-pound load test condition, however, concentration shows a significant effect under 10-lb load.

*3.* The gear wear characteristics of the base grease are not changed by $MoS_2$ additive (3, 5, 10, and 20%) for the four additional gear combinations. It should be noted that the anti-wear properties of the base grease in this test are exceptionally good, and accordingly further reduction of wear by the addition of $MoS_2$ was not anticipated. The increased wear observed for the brass on stainless steel combination by the addition of $MoS_2$ is consistent with the fact that extreme pressure additives generally show such results for this gear combination. Brass on stainless steel combinations represent two of the poorer materials from the standpoint of ease of lubrication of gears in the Navy Gear Wear Tester.

## C. Grease Stability

The usefulness of an additive is related to the degree of improvement imparted to a specific property of a lubricant, compatibility

TABLE 12-11. Results of Gear Wear Tests Comparing $MoS_2$ Concentration and Wear Rate for Five Metallic Combinations

Apparatus: Navy Gear Wear Tester
Room temperature

| Gear combination: | Brass— | SAE B 1112 steel | Phosphor bronze | 4130 steel | 4130 steel |
|---|---|---|---|---|---|
| | | Wear rate (mg/1000 cycles)—5 lb load | | | |
| Lubricant | Stainless steel | Stainless steel | 4130 steel | Stainless steel | 4130 steel |
| Diester grease | 0.3 | 0.3 | 0.1 | 0.4 | <0.1 |
| Diester— 3% $MoS_2$ | 1.2 | — | — | — | — |
| Diester— 5% $MoS_2$ | 1.7 | 0.4 | 0.1 | 0.4 | <0.1 |
| Diester—10% $MoS_2$ | 1.7 | — | 0.2 | — | — |
| Diester—20% $MoS_2$ | 1.9 | 0.3 | 0.3 | 0.3 | <0.1 |

| Gear combination: | Brass— | SAE B 1112 steel | Phosphor bronze | 4130 steel | 4130 steel |
|---|---|---|---|---|---|
| | | Wear rate (mg/1000 cycles)—10 lb load | | | |
| Lubricant | Stainless steel | Stainless steel | 4130 steel | Stainless steel | 4130 steel |
| Diester grease | 0.7 | 0.8 | 0.3 | 0.9 | 0.2 |
| Diester— 3% $MoS_2$ | 3.3 | — | — | — | — |
| Diester— 5% $MoS_2$ | 4.6 | 1.1 | 0.2 | 0.9 | 0.2 |
| Diester—10% $MoS_2$ | 5.7 | — | 0.4 | — | — |
| Diester—20% $MoS_2$ | 6.2 | 0.8 | 0.3 | 0.6 | 0.1 |

with other additives and lubricant stability. In order to determine the effect of molybdenum disulfide (18) on the general characteristics of lubricating grease, three different lithium base greases employing diester fluid and each containing anti-oxidants, corrosion inhibitors and extreme pressure agents were evaluated for consistency, oil separation, oxidation stability, ball bearing performance, mechanical stability, rust-preventive properties, etc. A comparison of test results for the three greases with and without $MoS_2$ is shown on Table 12-12. It can be observed that $MoS_2$ substantially increases the load carrying capacity for each grease and produces no adverse effects on other grease properties. These data are in good agreement with field results for the same grease type containing $MoS_2$.

## D. Particle Size

Molybdenum disulfide is available in three average particle sizes, i.e., 0.3, 0.7 and 7 $\mu$. Since limited information is available on the effect of powder particle size for $MoS_2$ used in grease formulations, samples of $MoS_2$ for each of the aforementioned powder sizes were dispersed in lithium base grease employing diester fluid and evaluated for load carrying capacity. Particle size determinations were conducted using a Fisher Sub-Sieve Sizer. A comparison of test results showing the effect of particle size on mean Hertz load value is shown in Table 12-13. No significant differences in mean Hertz load value were obtained between grease samples containing 0.7 and 7 $\mu$ average particle size $MoS_2$. However, the load carrying capacity for the same grease modified with the 0.3 $\mu$ $MoS_2$ was significantly lower. It was noted that the worked penetration for the latter grease was 248 compared to 274 for the sample having the 7 $\mu$ particle size $MoS_2$.

Chemical analysis of the different particle size powders shows that differences exist with respect to purity, oil content, moisture and $MoO_3$ content. In view of the possibility that some of the impurities present in the smaller particle size powders as well as increased surface area may result in decreased stability, tests (21) were conducted on $MoS_2$ modified grease to compare the resistance of the samples to oxidation. The results of the oxidation tests are presented graphically in Fig. 12-16. It can be observed that 0.3 and 0.7 $\mu$ particle size $MoS_2$ decrease the oxidation resistance of the base grease during the 500 hr test period. Based on test repeatability, the differences in oxidation stability between the grease

TABLE 12-12. Comparison of the Properties: MoS₂ Grease vs Properties of Base Grease

| Test | Grease A | | Grease B | | Grease C | |
|---|---|---|---|---|---|---|
| | 0 MoS$_2$ | 5% MoS$_2$ | 0 MoS$_2$ | 5% MoS$_2$ | 0 MoS$_2$ | 5% MoS$_2$ |
| Drop pt., °F | 356 | 355 | 360 | 363 | 378 | 375 |
| Worked penetration | 286 | 275 | 278 | 285 | 286 | 274 |
| Bomb oxidation (psi drop) 100 hr | 4.0 | 4.0 | 0 | 0 | 2 | 4 |
| 500 hr | 10.0 | 13.0 | 4 | 3 | 8 | 9 |
| Oven Cu corrosion | No corrosion | No corrosion | No corrosion | No corrosion | No corrosion | No corrosion |
| H$_2$O resistance, % | 7.5 | 5.0 | 9.0 | 3.0 | 7.8 | 5.1 |
| Evaporation, % | 1.9 | 1.9 | 1.3 | 1.0 | 2.8 | 2.8 |
| Oil separation, % (212°F) | 3.9 | 3.2 | 2.6 | 3.9 | 3.5 | 3.4 |
| Apparent viscosity, poises (−65°F) | | | | | | |
| 20 sec$^{-1}$ | 3820 | 4575 | 2680 | 2190 | 5510 | 5610 |
| 50 sec$^{-1}$ | 5950 | 7550 | 5025 | 3910 | 8800 | 9800 |
| Low temp. torque, g cm (−65°F) | | | | | | |
| Starting | 4071 | 3422 | 3570 | 2198 | 3865 | 5163 |
| Running | 230 | 192 | 354 | 266 | 281 | 358 |
| High temp. performance, hr (250°F) | 1012+ | 1058+ | 1048+ | 1066+ | 1325 | 1047+ |
| Work stability | 353 | 343 | 361 | 325 | 336 | 331 |
| Rust preventive properties | No rust or corrosion | No rust or corrosion | No rust or corrosion | No rust or corrosion | No rust or corrosion | No rust or corrosion |
| 6 month storage stability (penetration) | 280 | 283 | 267 | 283 | 271 | 282 |
| Mean Hertz load | 32 | 52 | 42 | 62 | 38 | 61 |

Test results

TABLE 12-13.   Effect of Particle Size on Mean Hertz Load

Test apparatus:  Shell Four-Ball E. P. Tester
Specimens:  AISI-C52100 steel balls
Speed:  1800 rpm
Temperature:  77°F
Lubricant:  Inhibitor modified diester grease, S-compound as shown

| Additive | Particle size, $\mu$ | % | Mean Hertz load |
|---|---|---|---|
| MoS$_2$ | 7 | 5 | 59 |
| MoS$_2$ | 7 | 10 | 59 |
| MoS$_2$ | 0.7 | 5 | 61 |
| MoS$_2$ | 0.7 | 10 | 60 |
| MoS$_2$ | 0.3 | 5 | 41 |

containing the 7 $\mu$ particle size MoS$_2$ and the base grease are considered slight.

## E. Metal Surface Effects

In order to investigate the possibility for substantially increasing the performance life of a bearing assembly by considering chemical

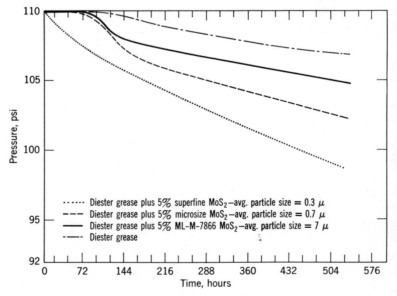

Fig. 12-16. Results of oxidation stability determinations for MoS$_2$–diester oil base grease.

influences of the metal bearing surface, molybdenum metal was selected for one of the bearing components in combination with grease containing molybdenum disulfide. Four different greases were prepared with and without $MoS_2$ to compare endurance life characteristics for steel–steel and steel–molybdenum bearing combinations. Endurance life tests were conducted using the Falex Lubricant Tester. The following procedure was employed:

*1.* The test specimens (V-blocks and pin) were cleaned with petroleum ether and then air-dried.

*2.* The test pin was mounted in the pin holder.

*3.* The grooves of the V-blocks were filled with lubricating grease and struck flush.

*4.* The V-blocks were set in their sockets.

*5.* The jaw loading assembly with load gauge was mounted on the lever arms.

*6.* The jaw load was brought up to 350 lb by hand turning the ratchet wheel, at which time the drive motor was started.

*7.* The time from start of test to failure was recorded as the endurance life of the grease.

*8.* Failure was determined by a torque rise of 5 in.-lb above a steady state value or breakage of the shear pin.

The effect of $MoS_2$ additive in combination with a molybdenum bearing surface is shown by the data presented in Table 12-14. It can be observed that although the steel–molybdenum bearing system provides a beneficial wear combination for grease having no $MoS_2$ additive, a significantly longer endurance life is produced by $MoS_2$ modified grease in contact with the bearing system having the molybdenum component. Further, it was projected that under extreme pressure conditions, additives based on sulfur compounds would be more susceptible to interaction with molybdenum resulting in increased endurance life. In addition, it was considered that increasing the applied load would magnify the differences based on the presence of the sulfur containing additive for the steel–molybdenum bearing combination. A variety of sulfur compounds were included as additive for a silica thickened petroleum oil base grease. Endurance life tests for the steel–steel and steel–molybdenum bearing combinations were conducted using the Falex lubricant tester according to the aforementioned wear test procedure except that the load was increased from 350 to 1000 lb. The results of comparative tests are shown on Table 12-15. These results further established the preferential lubricating effect resulting from sulfur compounds as

TABLE 12-14.   Effect of $MoS_2$ Additive on Steel-Molybdenum Metal Combination

Test Apparatus: Falex lubricant tester
Specimens: V-blocks—steel (AISI-C1137), $R_c20$ pin—as shown
Speed: 290 rpm
Temperature: 77°F
Load: 350 lb

| Lubricating grease | | | Running time (min) | |
|---|---|---|---|---|
| Thickener | Fluid | $MoS_2$ (wt %) Additive | Steel pin ($R_b85$) | Molybdenum pin ($R_b95$) |
| Li soap | Diester | 0 | 12 | 191 |
| Li soap | Diester | 5 | 39 | 390+ |
| Li soap | Petroleum | 0 | 20 | 141 |
| Li soap | Petroleum | 5 | 54 | 252 |
| Silica | Polyphenyl ether | 0 | 1 | 2 |
| Silica | Polyphenyl ether | 5 | 1 | 36 |
| Aryl urea | Silicone [a] | 0 | 0.5 | 6 |
| Aryl urea | Silicone [a] | 5 | 1.5 | 12 |

[a] Tests for the silicone grease conducted at 50 lb load.

TABLE 12-15.   Effect of Sulfur Compounds on Steel–Molybdenum Metal Combination

Test apparatus: Falex lubricant tester
Specimens: V-blocks—steel (AISI-C1137), $R_c20$ pin—as shown
Speed: 290 rpm
Temperature: 77°F
Load: 1000 lb
Lubricant: Silica thickened petroleum grease, additive as shown

| | | Running time (min) | |
|---|---|---|---|
| Additive | Wt % | Steel pin ($R_b85$) | Molybdenum pin ($R_b95$) |
| None | 0 | <1 | 4 |
| Sb-diamyl dithiocarbamate | 5 | <1 | 8 |
| Ba-diamyl phenolate sulfide | 5 | <1 | 31 |
| 2-Mercaptobenzothiazole | 5 | <1 | 33 |
| Sb-phosphorodithioate | 5 | <1 | 67 |
| Dibenzyl disulfide | 5 | 5 | 73 |
| Molybdenum disulfide | 5 | <1 | 140 |
| Pb-dinonyl naphthalene sulfonate | 5 | 21 | 144 |
| Ditertiary nonyl-polysulfide | 5 | 25 | 313 |

lubricating grease additives for bearing combinations having a molybdenum component. The Timken wear test configuration employing both steel and molybdenum wear blocks was also used to investigate the preferential lubricating effect displayed by lubricating grease containing a sulfur compound. A comparison of results for steel-steel and steel–molybdenum systems is presented on Table 12-16. The affinity of grease modified with the sulfur compound for molybdenum metal is further demonstrated by these data.

Laboratory experiments have shown that a lubricating grade of molybdenum disulfide as an additive to diester lubricating grease substantially increases carrying capacity and functions to reduce wear in the high load regions. Further, such molybdenum disulfide produces no adverse effect on other grease properties, e.g., storage stability, oil separation and rust preventive properties. It should be noted that field experience for the same grease type containing $MoS_2$ shows good performance, storage stability and corrosion protection and substantiates the laboratory findings. The results of additional studies covering microsize molybdenum disulfide show that no advantages are provided by smaller particle size $MoS_2$ powder over the lubricating grade $MoS_2$ as an additive for grease. In addition, the small particle size $MoS_2$ shows lower oxidation resistance. Several factors may account for the latter characteristic including larger surface area, oil content and the presence of impurities. Additional work was aimed at providing means for regenerating a lubricating

TABLE 12-16. Comparison of Endurance Life for Steel–Steel and Steel–Molybdenum Combinations

Test apparatus: LFW-1 test apparatus
Specimens: Test ring—SAE 4620, block—as shown
Speed: 72 rpm
Temperature: 77°F
Load: 54,000 psi

| Grease | Additive | % | Endurance life (cycles) | |
| --- | --- | --- | --- | --- |
| | | | Steel–steel | Steel–molybdenum |
| Silica-petroleum | None | 0 | 2,257 | 84,527 |
| Silica-petroleum | Dibenzyl disulfide | 1 | 23,408 | 405,700 |
| Silica-petroleum | Dibenzyl disulfide | 5 | 8,668 | 222,534 |
| Silica-petroleum | $MoS_2$ | 5 | 49,817 | 358,275 |
| Li-diester | $MoS_2$ | 5 | 2,753 | 188,250 |
| Silica-silicone | Ditertiary nonyl polysulfide | 10 | 358 | 2,900 |

film on metal surfaces based on the reaction of sulfur compounds and molybdenum metal. The results of endurance life tests conducted under conditions of sliding wear for greases containing $MoS_2$ and other sulfur compounds show the affinity of such compounds for molybdenum metal. Wear life increases in the range of 100% were realized for greases having a sulfur compound additive in bearings have a molybdenum component.

## VI. LUBRICANT PREPARATION

Outline of methods for the preparation of several powder forms, solid lubricant–binder mixtures, and solid sections is shown below. The production technology for solid lubricants ranges from purification of crude ore to organic synthesis. This information pertaining to some of the production methods is provided to emphasize the range of technology involved in the manufacture of solid lubricants. It should be noted that the method of preparation will vary with the class as well as the solid substance within a specific class. In addition, several alternate methods of preparation may be available for many of the solid materials.

### A. Methods of Preparation

#### 1. Powders

*Molybdenum Disulfide*

Ore→Grind→Separate (flotation)→Purification (solvent extraction, acid treat)→$MoS_2$

*Graphite*

Petroleum coke $\xrightarrow[\text{sizing}]{\text{calcining}}$ mix coke-coal tar pitch (165°C)
→extrude or mold→bake (750–1400°C)
→heat baked shapes (260–2000°C)→graphite

*Sodium Molybdate*

$$2Na + MoO_2 \xrightarrow[\Delta]{O_2} Na_2MoO_4 + Mo$$

*Mixed Sulfides*

$$Me_x(MS_4)_y \xrightarrow[500 \text{ C}]{N_2} Me_xS_y + yS\uparrow$$

(M = Mo or W, Me = heavy metal of group Ib, IIb, IVa, Va, VIb, VIIb)

## 2. Solid Lubricant–Binder Mixtures

*Graphite–Metal Powder–Resin*
Mix powders→grind (soln-resinous material)→spray
→cure (350–500°F)

*MoS₂–Silver Matrix*
$Ag_2O/MoS_2$→solvent immersion→electrophoretic bath
(Ti cathode—steel anode)→voltage applied→remove Ti
→heat (1400°F) He→$MoS_2/Ag$ matrix (codiffused to titanium)

*MoS₂–Graphite–Sodium Silicate*
Mix solid lubricants→wet ($H_2O$)→add sodium silicate soln→spray
→cure (180–300°F)

*PbO–SiO₂*
Mix powder→add thin layer ($\frac{1}{16}$ in.) to metal surface→heat (165°F/
8 min)→cool→grind

## 3. Solid Sections

*Metal–Graphite*
Mix powder→press (70,000 psi→sinter→machine

*MoS₂—Graphite*
Mix powder→wet ($Na_2SiO_3$)→press (1500 psi)—cure (180–300°F)
→machine

*MoS₂–Resin Molding Powder–Paraformaldehyde–CaO*
Mix powder→press (2000 psi)/170°C→machine

*Polytetrafluoroethylene*

$$CHCl_3 + HF \rightarrow CHF_2Cl \xrightarrow{\text{pyrolysis}} CF_2 = CF_2 \xrightarrow{\text{cat.}}$$
$(-CF_2 - CF_2 -)$→granulate→cold form (2000–10,000 psi)/77°F
→sinter (700–740°F)→cold coining die (2000 psi)
→anneal

## VII. APPLICATION

Solid lubricants have been used as thin films, structural sections
of bearing assemblies, reinforced laminates, and inserts. Figure 12-17
shows several bearing designs utilizing different means for solid lubrication: viz., a plain spherical bearing having polytetrafluoroethylene

(TFE) in a liner between the inner ring and outer ring, a rolling contact bearing having a solid film lubricant on the surfaces of the raceways and ball separator, and a journal bearing wherein an $MoS_2$ solid insert is incorporated in the housing and spring loaded to maintain a supply of lubricant to the shaft.

Methods for thin film deposition are gas or fluid carried particles, spraying solid lubricant–binder mixtures, vacuum evaporation, electroplating, and chemical reaction. Solid structural sections may be machined, cast, coined, molded, etc. Examples of specific solid lubricants and a resume covering some methods of application, bearing arrangement, operating conditions and literature reference for the study are shown in Table 12-17. Environment including temperature, load, speed, atmosphere (air, $N_2$, $CO_2$, $O_2$), pressure, radiation, etc., and type of motion are primary factors in the selection of lubricant type. Weight requirements, performance, lubrication interval, maintenance, and economics constitute additional limiting factors. Solid lubricants have

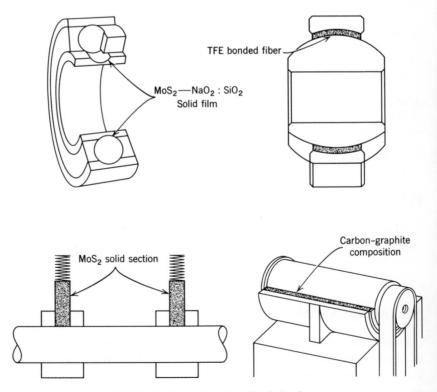

Fig. 12-17. Examples of solid lubrication.

been found suitable for many applications: e.g., rolling element, journal and plain bearings, control cables, threads, actuators, and gears. Several specific examples of devices employing solid lubricants, as well as bearing type and primary operating environment, are presented in Table 12-18. It should be noted that there are many conditions which exclude the use of conventional lubricants such as oils and greases on the basis of:

1. Increased volatility with increases in temperature or decreases in pressure.
2. Change in viscosity with change in temperature.
3. Reactivity with rocket fuels and oxidizers.
4. Susceptibility to chemical degradation when exposed to nuclear radiation or high temperature.

The solid film lubricant approach to friction and wear problems associated with a spatial environment was proposed on the basis of such limitations of lubricating oils and greases.

The findings for inorganic solid film lubrication in the very high-vacuum region at elevated temperatures are described below. The inorganic solid lubricant composition was $MoS_2$ (71 wt %), graphite (7 wt %) and sodium silicant (22 wt %).

## VIII. SOLID LUBRICATION EXPERIMENTS—VACUUM ENVIRONMENT

### A. Apparatus

A research technique and apparatus (64) for investigating the properties of conventional lubricating greases at atmospheric pressure and elevated temperature have resulted from extensive cooperative laboratory programs. Further, the technique affords pertinent technical information for practical bearing configurations. In view of the quantity of experimental work and associated knowledge, preliminary (65,66) and continuing solid film lubricant studies for wear life have included this procedure.

Accordingly, it was considered that a lubricant-bearing test apparatus of the same design having provisions for subjecting the rotating specimen to a vacuum environment would provide a consistent experimental pattern for the lubricant studies.

The design shown in Fig. 12-18 incorporates a vertically positioned Pope Manufacturing Company Model 7605B test spindle extending

TABLE 12-17. Examples of Solid Lubricants and Experimental Conditions

| Lubricant | Method of application | Test specimen | Test condition | Variables investigated | Ref. |
|---|---|---|---|---|---|
| MoS$_2$/Epoxy | Solid Section<br>1. Self-lubricating retainer | 1. 20 mm bearing (440C)<br>2. Outer land riding retainer | 1. 70–90°F<br>2. 1800 rpm<br>3. Very high vacuum | 1. Torque vs. temp.<br>2. Comparison of performance | (22) |
| PbS/B$_2$O$_3$ | Solid Film<br>1. PbS dispersed in a sat. soln. of B$_2$O$_3$ in 100% ETOH<br>2. Spray mixture<br>3. Cure at 1000°F for 15 min in N$_2$ atmosphere | 1. Timken test cup (T54148) vs. Rex AAA (R-60-65) test block (solid film applied to test cup) | 1. 1000°F<br>2. 200–300 rpm<br>3. 120 lbs<br>4. 10$^{-5}$–10$^{-6}$ mm Hg | 1. Effect of lubricant to binder ratio<br>2. Effect of reduced pressures<br>3. Effect of temp. | (23) |
| PbO | Solid Film<br>1. Metal evaporation onto disk specimen followed by oxidation<br>2. Layer of powder ($\frac{1}{4}$" thick) | 1. Cylindrical rider (cast Inconel) with hemispherical tip sliding on disk (Inconel X) | 1. 1000°F<br>2. 5.7 ft/min<br>3. 40 lbs | 1. Comparison of friction for PbO, Pb$_3$O$_4$, CdO, Bi$_2$O$_3$, WO$_3$, Sb$_2$O$_3$, PdO, BN, Talc | (24) |
| Au | Plating<br>1. Applied from acid gold depositing solution | 1. Miniature stainless steel ball bearing (balls and races plated) | 1. 77°F<br>2. 10,000 rpm<br>3. 10$^{-7}$ torr | 1. Effect of retainer material<br>2. Comparison of gold vs. gold +Ni, In, Co, platings | (25) |
| Ag$_2$Te, Bi$_2$Se$_3$, CdS, CdSe, Ce$_2$S$_3$, ZnSe, ZnTe | Gas (N$_2$, Air) Carried Powder<br>1. Flow rate: 0.2–8 gm/min | 1. Kentanium 163A1, Star J and Haynes 25 disks loaded together and rotated | 1. 1200°F (15 min)<br>2. 12,000 rpm<br>3. 40 lbs | 1. Comparison of various solid lubricants<br>2. Effect of disk material | (26) |
| PbS+MoS$_2$+B$_2$O$_3$ | Solid Film<br>1. Dispersed in ETOH water and cured at 1500°F in N$_2$<br>2. Spray mixture cured at 180 and 300°F<br>3. Sprayed and cured at 2000°F | 1. Inconel X test cups and Rex AAA blocks | 1. 128 ft/min<br>2. 110 lb | 1. Effect of nuclear radiation on the wear properties of solid film lubricants | (27) |
| MoS$_2$+Graphite+ sodium silicate CaF$_2$+metal oxides Chlorotrifluoro- ethylene+glass filler | Solid Section<br>1. Self-lubricating retainers | 1. 20 mm angular contact bearing | 1. 34–40°C<br>2. 600 to 6800 rpm<br>3. 10 to 280 lb<br>4. 760—1×10$^{-5}$ torr | 1. Effect of variable speed and temp., 10 lb load at atmospheric pressure<br>2. Effect of variable temp. at 1×10$^{-5}$ torr<br>3. Comparison of various self-lubricating plastics | (28) |
| Ag-Pd | Cladding<br>1. Sandblast surface<br>2. Clad-bonding by pressure and heat<br>3. Machine to .003-.005" thick | Plain journal and self-aligning bearing | 1. −90°-+1500°F<br>2. 31 cpm<br>3. 4400–12,000 psi<br>4. 10$^{-6}$ mm Hg | 1. Comparison of Ag-Pd, MoS$_2$, MoS$_2$/silicone resin<br>2. Effect of substrate material (Rene '41, F-48, LT-1B, LT-2) | (29) |
| Metal-free phthalocyanine | Gas (N$_2$) Carried Powder<br>1. Flow rate: 0.2-1.5 gm/min | TiC-Ni-Mo vs. TiC-Ni-Mo disks | 1. 1200°F<br>2. 10,000 ft/min<br>3. 100,000 psi | 1. Coefficient of friction<br>2. Comparison of various solid lubricants | (50) |

| Material | Form / Preparation | Test specimen | Conditions | Properties measured | Ref. |
|---|---|---|---|---|---|
| *(continued from previous row)* | 1. Powder compressed at 60,000 psi | Pellet (WS$_2$)—stainless steel disk—(disk lapped with 600 mesh carborundum) | 1. [illegible] 2. 310 cm/sec 3. 395 gms 4. 10$^{-6}$ mm Hg | 1. Coefficient of friction—data obtained after periods of standing at various temps. | (38) |
| MoO$_3$, WO$_3$, CoO$_3$, ZnO, CdO, CuO, SrO | Powder 1. Powder distributed on surface of flat plate ($\frac{1}{4}$" thick) | Hemispherical rider vs. flat plate | 1. 700°C 2. 0.3 inch/sec 3. 1880 g | 1. Comparison of coefficient of friction for metallic oxides 2. Paper also includes friction results for molybdates, tungstates and several metals | (39) |
| Impregnated Carbon | Solid Section | Rotating ring vs. stationary block | 1. 77–1000°F 2. 1600 sfpm 3. 5 lb radial | 1. Comparison of wear and friction for a variety of solid materials | (40) |
| Teflon/phenolic | Solid Section 1. Charge powder mixture into a compression mold and mold at 360°F for 20 min at 8,000 psi | $\frac{1}{2}$ sq in. section of solid section vs. rotating steel disk | 1. 77°–340°F 2. 25–625 fpm 3. 30–250 psi | 1. Effect of filler | (41) |
| Na$_2$MoO$_4$ | Solid Film 1. Deposition by vacuum evaporation | AISI 347 stainless steel flat specimen vs. molybdenum ball | 1. 77–1200°F 2. 9.2 mm/sec 3. 100,000 psi | 1. Coefficient of friction | (42) |
| PbI$_2$ | Solid Film 1. Dispersed in sodium phosphate soln. and deposited by spraying | 20 mm radial ball bearing (film applied to races and retainers) | 1. 350°F 2. 10,000 rpm 3. 5 lb thrust, 3 lb radial | 1. Comparison of wear life for various solids | (43) |
| Bi$_2$S$_3$, BiOCl, CuCl$_2$, MoS$_2$, Graphite, PbO | Gas (N$_2$) Carried Powder 1. Flow rate: 0.2–0.8 gm/min | Two disks loaded together and rotated | 1. 400–1200°F 2. 12,000 rpm 3. 100,000 psi | 1. Comparison of friction for PbS, CuCl$_2$, HgS, BiOCl, Bi$_2$Se$_3$, Bi$_2$S$_3$, CuO, PbO, CdO, BN, MoS$_2$, graphite 2. Effect of disk materials: TiC and cobalt-base alloy 3. Free energy relationships | (44) |
| Ti$_2$S$_3$, Cr$_2$S$_3$, HgS, TiS$_2$, Sb$_2$S$_3$, CaS | Solid Film 1. Dispersed in sodium silicate and water. Deposition by spray. Cure film slowly from 77°F–300°F | Molybdenum pin vs. steel V-blocks (film applied to phosphated V-blocks) | 1. 77°F 2. 290 rpm 3. 1000 lb gauge | 1. Comparison of alloy response | (34) |
| Me$_x$(MS$_4$)$_y$ M=Mo, W Me=Ni, Pb, Fe, Cd | Powder | $\frac{1}{4}$ in. diameter pin and conforming bearing shells | 1. 77°F 2. 200 rpm 3. 500–1500 kg | 1. Method of preparation 2. Load vs. friction | (60) |
| MoSe-SnS$_2$ | Solid Section 1. Pellet loaded against shaft by spring loading | $\frac{1}{4}$ in. diameter steel ball, lubricant pellet, $\frac{1}{2}$ in. steel shaft | 1. 77°F 2. 0–2000 rpm 3. 15 lb | 1. Coefficient of friction | (61) |
| TFE/(AlOOH) | Solid Film 1. Spray | $\frac{1}{2}$ in. steel ball and coated steel panel | 1. 70–550°F 2. 0.1 cm/sec 3. 800 g load | 1. Coefficient of friction | (62) |
| WB-Ag-Ni CrN-Ag-Ni | Solid Section | Solid section vs. Inconel | 1. 100–1200°F 2. 29,000 fpm 3. 14 psi | 1. Wear rate vs. temp. 2. Wear rate vs. solid section composition | (63) |

TABLE 12-18. Several Examples of Applications for Solid Lubricants

| Application | Primary environment | Operating requirements |
|---|---|---|
| Journal bearing | Nuclear radiation | No deterioration |
| Conveyor slide rail | Food processing | No contamination |
| Threaded tubing | Liquid oxygen | No detonation |
| Sliding die core | High pressure | No seizing |
| Miniature (R–2) bearing | Vacuum | Low torque |
| Plain spherical bearing | High load | Low torque |
| Thrust washer | High sliding speed | No abrasion |
| Rolling contact bearing | Vacuum | Low torque |
| Gears | Helium coolant | Reduce friction |
| Self locking nuts | High temperature | No galling |
| Governor pinion | Room temperature | No leakage |
| Turbine blade root | High temperature | No galling |
| Wire rope | High load | No scoring |
| Actuator | Low-high temperature | No evaporation |
| Arbor sleeve | High sliding speed | Low friction |
| Valve | Cryogenic fluid | No reactivity |
| Fastener | Water | No corrosion |
| Press fit parts | High load | Smooth assembly |
| Spacer | Room temperature | No leakage |
| Compressor nozzle | High temperature | No evaporation |

into an 18-inch diameter steel vacuum test chamber. The support bearings of the test spindle are mounted external to the vacuum chamber. Water cooling is provided for the "O" ring chamber seals. The vacuum pumping system consists of a mechanical forepump capable of maintaining the system at approximately 15 microns, a 6-inch oil diffusion pump and liquid nitrogen cold trap providing a pressure in the range of $5 \times 10^{-6}$ mm Hg in the test chamber. Pressure measuring devices include an ionization gauge and thermocouple gauge. Resistance heaters contained in the test specimen housing, permit an operating temperature range from 77 to 1000°F. Electrical feed-throughs in the steel base plate allow for continuous measurement of test specimen and housing temperature. A power recorder is employed to provide a record of test spindle drive motor wattage. A magnetic circuit breaker allows for instantaneous drive motor cut off when a preselected motor power draw is exceeded.

Essentially the lubricant vacuum equipment described above facilitates the study of solid lubricants in 20 mm bearings at 1250 rpm and pressures in the range of $5 \times 10^{-6}$ mm Hg throughout a temperature range from 77 to 1000°F.

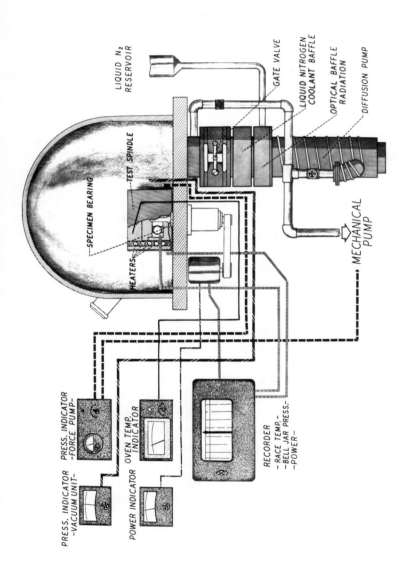

Fig. 12-18. Lubricant vacuum environment apparatus.

## B. Results—Vacuum versus One Atmosphere

A number of runs were made to measure performance of the solid film lubricant in vacuum and compare with results at one atmosphere. Some of the data are summarized in Table 12-19, as discussed below.

Initial experiments were conducted to determine the wear life of non-lubricated Cr alloy steel (AISI-C52100) bearing specimens having carbon steel (AISI-C1010) retainers at pressures of 760 and $2 \times 10^{-5}$ mm Hg. The test temperature was approximately 77°F. Specimen failure occurred within 3 hr in duplicate runs at each pressure condition. Duplicate determinations were then conducted on bearings of the same design and metallurgy having the solid film lubricant deposited on the races and retainers. The test conditions included a pressure of $1 \times 10^{-6}$ mm Hg and a temperature of 77°F. These runs were terminated after a period of 80 hr to allow for comparisons of the effect of reduced pressure-elevated temperature versus atmospheric pressure-elevated temperature for the aforementioned solid film composition.

Prior to this time, a series of laboratory runs had been completed at 750°F, 10,000 rpm at atmospheric pressure for solid film lubricated bearings with races and balls fabricated from Cr–Mo–V tool steel (SAE M-10) and machined retainers of the same composition. The first run conducted with the solid film lubricated bearing specimen of identical composition in vacuum at a pressure of $5 \times 10^{-5}$ mm Hg at 750°F was subjected to a cyclic operation of 6 hr on and 18 hr off. No differences were shown for torque and race temperature characteristics from results of tests at 750°F and atmospheric pressure. After four cycles, the run was discontinued to allow for a visual examination of the bearing. Rotation by hand showed no roughness of the test specimen. Further, the surface of the solid film and bearing metal were essentially unchanged. A second run was conducted at pressures ranging from $1 \times 10^{-5}$ to $5 \times 10^{-6}$ mm Rg at a temperature of 1000°F. The test specimen was smooth turning and showed no evidence of deterioration after 5 cycles of operation.

Figure 12-19 shows a comparison of solid film lubricated bearing retainer components for a specimen subjected to 1000°F and 100 hr running time at a reduced pressure of approximately $5 \times 10^{-6}$ mm Hg and solid film lubricated retainers not subjected to the test conditions. It can be observed that solid film wear was negligible and no deterioration is evident for the lubricant or bearing alloy.

Further data have been reported for the same solid film lubricant

TABLE 12-19. Performance of Solid Film Lubricant in Vacuum versus One Atmosphere
(20 mm Bearings in Pope Model 7605B Test Spindle)

| Run | Materials | | Lubricant | Temp., °F | Pressure, mm/Hg | Speed, rpm | Cycle | Results |
|---|---|---|---|---|---|---|---|---|
| | Bearing | Retainers | | | | | | |
| A-1 | 52100 | 1010 | None | 77 | 760 | 1,250 | Continuous run | Failure <4 hr |
| A-2 | 52100 | 1010 | None | 77 | $2\times10^{-5}$ | 1,250 | Continuous run | Failure <4 hr |
| B-1 | 52100 | 1010 | 71% MoS$_2$, 7% graphite 22% sodium silicate | 77 | 760 | 1,250 | Continuous run | Still running—80 hr [a] |
| B-2 | 52100 | 1010 | 71% MoS$_2$, 7% graphite 22% sodium silicate | 77 | $1\times10^{-6}$ | 1,250 | Continuous run | Still running—80 hr [a] |
| C-1 | M-10 | M-10 | 71% MoS$_2$, 7% graphite 22% sodium silicate | 750 | 760 | 10,000 | 6 hr on, 18 hr off | Rotation smooth, no damage for solid film lubricant, 4 cycles [a] |
| C-2 | M-10 | M-10 | 71% MoS$_2$, 7% graphite 22% sodium silicate | 750 | $5\times10^{-5}$ | 1,250 | 6 hr on, 18 hr off | Same as run C-1 |
| D-1 | M-10 | M-10 | 71% MoS$_2$, 7% graphite 22% sodium silicate | 1000 | $1\times10^{-5}$ to $5\times10^{-6}$ | 1,250 | 6 hr on, 18 hr off | Same as run C-1, 5 cycles [a] |
| E-1 | M-10 | M-10 | 71% MoS$_2$, 7% graphite 22% sodium silicate | 1000 | $1\times10^{-6}$ | 1,250 | 6 hr on, 18 hr off | Same as run C-1, 17 cycles [a] |

[a] No evidence of failure, test discontinued.

BEFORE VACUUM RUN

AFTER VACUUM RUN

Fig. 12-19. MoS₂, graphite, sodium silicate solid film lubricated bearing components before and after 100 hr vacuum run at 1000°F, $1 \times 10^{-6}$ mm Hg.

and reported in the references listed in the following brief summary. Forty bearing specimens were lubricated with the solid film lubricant for additional vacuum experiments conducted at temperatures ranging from $-100$ to $+400°F$ at pressures in the range of $1 \times 10^{-9}$ mm Hg. The results of the test runs (67) under conditions of rotary and oscillatory motion showed satisfactory performance of the solid film lubricant. Further, the capability of the same lubricant formulation to function for extended periods has been demonstrated in recent applications for stainless steel bearings subjected to $1 \times 10^{-7}$ mm Hg, 160°F at a speed of 8000 rpm for periods of 2000 hr (68); chromium steel ball bearings equipped with machined bronze retainers operating at 3600 rpm, 300°F at a reduced pressure of $5 \times 10^{-8}$ mm Hg for periods of several hundred hours (69), and sliding friction studies (70) conducted at 900 rpm, in a temperature range from 77 to 400°F and pressures of approximately $1 \times 10^{-6}$ mm Hg.

Results of other vacuum studies (71) at $1 \times 10^{-7}$ mm Hg describe the use of the $MoS_2$, graphite, sodium silicate solid film in high speed drives.

The overall conclusion from the work at high vacuum is that this solid film lubricant functions as well in vacuum as at 1/atm pressure.

A number of advanced considerations and approaches to lubrication under extreme conditions involving solid lubricant material together with design criteria are provided in several publications (72,73).

## IX. PROPERTY MEASUREMENTS

The investigation of the friction and antiwear characteristics of solid lubricants has been a primary objective of many laboratory studies. A number of techniques and test machines have been developed specifically to measure the wear properties of solids. In addition, wear machines common to the study of lubricating oils and greases, such as, the Falex Lubricant Tester, Timken Wear Tester, and Shell 4-Ball Wear Tester have been applied to wear research involving solid lubricants. Table 12-20 provides a partial list of wear and friction test equipment, examples of operating conditions, test specimen components, and literature references. The number of different test machines reflect the variety of applications and environments examined for solid lubrication. In addition, information for projecting the ability of a lubricant to function in a new or different application should be based on laboratory experiments that very closely approximate field conditions. The laboratory test method should simulate: (1) bearing configuration, composition, pretreatment, surface finish, and hardness, (2) type of motion (rotary, oscillatory, or sliding), and (3) environment (load, speed, temperature, pressure, etc.). Lubricant processing requirements and film thickness may also represent important factors where critical clearances are imposed on the bearing system. Exploratory programs aimed at developing approaches or trends may not warrant the expenditures required for apparatus designed to correlate with a particular field condition. Accordingly, caution should be exercised in extrapolating data from such programs to anticipated or existing lubrication problems.

Solid lubricants are also studied to determine a wide range of chemical and physical properties. For example, powder forms may be examined for purity, type and percent of contaminants, particle size,

TABLE 12-20. Examples of Friction and Wear Test Apparatus for Solid Lubricants

| Test apparatus | Conditions | Specimen | Reference |
| --- | --- | --- | --- |
| Plain bearing tester | 1. 630°F<br>2. 10 cpm<br>3. ±32°/cycle<br>4. 10,000 psi | H-11 test shaft, M-2 steel bushing | (30) |
| Friction tester | 1. 77°F<br>2. 65 cm/sec<br>3. Variable load | Metal disk and rider | (31) |
| High temperature, high speed bearing performance apparatus | 1. 750°F<br>2. 10,000 rpm<br>3. 5 lb thrust load, 3 lb radial load | 20 mm rolling contact bearing | (32) |
| Vacuum friction and wear apparatus | 1. 77°F<br>2. 390 fpm<br>3. 1000 g<br>4. $10^{-6}$ to $10^{-7}$ mm Hg | Metal disk and rider | (33) |
| Lubricant vacuum environment apparatus | 1. 77 to 1000°F<br>2. 1250 rpm<br>3. 5 lb thrust load, 3 lb radial load<br>4. $1 \times 10^{-6}$ mm Hg | 20 mm rolling contact bearing | (34) |
| Modified 4-ball wear machine | 1. 1000°F<br>2. 200–700 ft/min<br>3. 2–8 Kg | ½ in. diam balls | (35) |
| High-temperature, high speed rubbing wear apparatus | 1. 1000–1800°F<br>2. 100–200 ft/sec<br>3. 5–50 psi | Rotating washer vs stationary pad stators | (36) |

| Device | Conditions | Specimen | Ref. |
|---|---|---|---|
| Pellet friction machine | 1. 80–1000°F<br>2. 600 ft/min<br>3. 128–326 | Pellet vs Rex AAA steel track | (37) |
| Press fit test | 1. 77°F<br>2. 0.6–2 in./min<br>3. Variable load | Pin and bushing | (53) |
| Alpha lubricant tester model LFW-1 | 1. 77°F<br>2. 12–197 rpm<br>3. 30–630 lb | Test block and $1\frac{3}{8}$ in. timken bearing outer race | (47) |
| Falex lubricant tester | 1. 77°F<br>2. 290 rpm<br>3. 200–2500 lb (gauge) | Cylindrical pin and V-blocks | (54) |
| Timken tester | 1. 77°F<br>2. 200–1300 rpm<br>3. 6300–50,400 psi | Cylindrical cup rotating against a stationary rectangular block | (55) |
| Oscillating tester | 1. 400°F<br>2. 230 cycles/min<br>3. 62 deg. arc<br>4. 700 lb | Rotating ring vs stationary blocks | (56) |
| W.S.U. dry film lubricant tester | 1. 100–1700°F<br>2. 3.5 ft/min<br>3. 300 lb | Cylindrical pin and V-blocks | (57) |
| Sliding friction test apparatus | 1. 77°F to 300°F<br>2. 47.0 slides/hr<br>3. Oscillated $\pm 48°$<br>4. $10^{-6}$–$10^{-9}$ torr | Cylindrical sleeve slider sliding on a cylindrical rod | (58) |
| Bearing test apparatus | 1. 77°F<br>2. 1800 rpm<br>3. $\frac{3}{4}$ lb axial and $\frac{1}{2}$ lb radial<br>4. $10^{-7}$–$10^{-8}$ torr | 20 mm rolling contact bearing | (58) |

*(Continued)*

TABLE 12-20 (*continued*)

| Test apparatus | Conditions | Specimen | Reference |
|---|---|---|---|
| Fretting corrosion apparatus | 1. 77°F | Steel flat vibrating against steel flat | (59) |
| High temperature bearing radial and thrust rig | 1. 1200°F<br>2. 20,000–35,000 rpm<br>3. 50 lb thrust and/or 50 lb radial | 20 mm rolling contact bearing | (45) |
| MacMillan lubricant tester (modified) | 1. 77°F<br>2. 72 rpm<br>3. 630 lb | Rotating ring vs rectangular block | (46) |
| Modified Falex tester | 1. −196°C (liquid $N_2$)<br>2. 290 rpm<br>3. 1000 lb (gauge) | Rotating pin vs stationary V-blocks | (47) |
| Crossed cylinders friction apparatus | 1. 77°F<br>2. 8–367 sfm<br>3. 1–5 lb | Vertical cylinder—carbon tool steel, horizontal cylinder—solid section | (48) |
| Model A-3 friction and wear tester | 1. 77°F<br>2. 72 rpm<br>3. 630 lb | Timken test cup T-54148 and AISI-4130 steel blocks | (49) |
| Stick-slip slow-speed friction apparatus | 1. 80–1000°F<br>2. 0.17 mm/sec<br>3. 64,000–100,000 psi | $\frac{1}{2}$ in. diam. ball vs flat block | (50) |
| Rolling and sliding contact specimen test machine | 1. − 100 to + 2000°F<br>2. 22 cpm<br>3. Duration–30 min | Ball and plate | (51) |
| Hohman A-6 friction and wear tester | 1. 150–400°C<br>2. 1.00 m/sec<br>3. 32–170 kg | Rotating ring vs rectangular blocks | (27) |
| Boeing galling machine | 1. 900°F<br>2. 3.5–300 fpm<br>3. 20–2500 psi | Flat plate vs test cup | (52) |

density, melting point, thermal stability, corrosion properties, and oxidation characteristics. Detailed standards (74,75) including test methods have been defined for lubricating grades of graphite and molybdenum disulfide powders. Solid films deposited on surfaces from mixtures of lubricating solids and binder solids are studied for adhesion, thermal stability, corrosion properties, fluid compatability, film thickness, and storage characteristics. Standards and details for test procedures (76,77) have been described for two different types of resin bonded solid lubricants. Solid sections and composites are subjected to a variety of additional tests. These are:

| | |
|---|---|
| Tensile strength | Deformation |
| Yield strength | Heat distortion |
| Elongation | Thermal conductivity |
| Impact strength | Linear expansion |
| Compressive strength | Hardness |

A number of tests covering mechanical properties are included since the self-lubricating solid section is required to possess sufficient strength to function as a bearing component along with the capacity to reduce friction and wear independent of an external lubricant.

## A. Mechanism Factors

In general, the mechanism of failure for solid lubricants is considered to be a mechanical removal of micro layers of the lubricating material. This wear process eventually results in either a lack of dynamic stability for the bearing system due to the loss of required clearances or galling and seizing of metal surfaces. It is apparent that such a failure process imposes serious limitations on the possibilities for a lubricant. Laboratory research aimed at defining the variables directly related to maintaining the lubricating film has not only provided means for eliminating the limitations, but has expanded the technical scope, versatility, and potential for solid lubricants. A number of approaches to the problem of extending solid lubricant performance life have been explored. The following factors were studied by the Naval Air Systems Command to determine the degree of influence exerted on the war properties for solid lubricated surfaces:

*1.* Bearing design
*2.* Lubricant-bearing interaction
*3.* Surface characteristics

## B. Bearing Design

The importance of bearing design considerations was suggested by the fact that conventional bearings are designed for fluid or grease lubrication. Since the viscosity property associated with the film continuity of such lubricants is not exhibited by solids, it becomes apparent that different design concepts may be required to emphasize the properties of solid lubricants significant to long term operation. Some of the findings for rolling contact bearings, pertaining to two different categories of solid lubricants; i.e., solid sections and thin films, are provided to show the level of performance life increases that can be attained on the basis of bearing design.

In general, chemical or mechanical pretreatment of bearing surfaces prior to solid-film deposition increases the effectiveness of the lubricant and thereby promotes longer wear life. The improved performance has previously been attributed to adhesion since the surface area of the substrate is increased by pretreatment. It is postulated herein that better bonding is only a partial contribution, the predominant effect is produced by lubricant contained in a series of micro reservoirs. Further, the size, shape, number and location of the reservoirs determine the degree of wear-life increase.

During an initial investigation, it was found that the retainer component of the ball-bearing assembly is most frequently associated with bearing failure using solid films as lubricants. Accordingly, experiments to determine the validity of the aforementioned reservoir theory involved retainer modification. It appeared that the most suitable approach would be to produce a number of depressions in each of the retainer-ball pockets. The total number would be limited by the dimensions of the ribbon-type AISI-C1010 steel retainer (0.150 in. width, 0.035 in. thickness). This was accomplished using an automatic punch which produced a cone-shaped recess having a depth of 0.015 in. and a maximum diameter of 0.025 in. After this modification a phosphate pretreatment (15) was applied to the retainer surfaces. Subsequently, the solid film was deposited in the reservoirs and on the surfaces of the retainers and races (AISI-C52100). After assembly, performance life was determined using a standard test spindle (12). Careful examination of the retainer specimen indicated that the reservoirs located in the areas shown in Fig. 12-20 were the most effective. Additional specimens modified with cylindrically shaped recesses in the critical areas were prepared and optimum dimensions investigated. Table 12-21 contains a comparison of performance-life data for lubricant-bearing systems

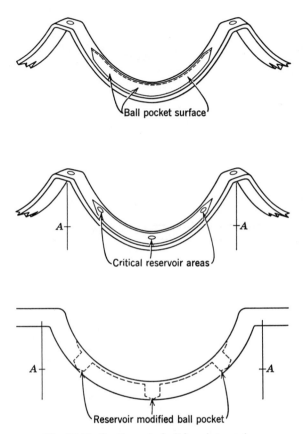

Fig. 12-20. Section of a ball bearing retainer.

showing the effect of reservoir modification. A graphical presentation of wear life (performance) versus cylindrical reservoir diameter is shown in Fig. 12-21. These results show that solid-film reservoirs extend performance life in ball-bearing applications and the degree of increase is determined by reservoir dimensions. It is further observed that the experimental results are in agreement with the proposed reservoir theory for the foregoing runs conducted at 350 F, 10,000 rpm for Cr-alloy steel, AISI-C52100 ball bearings having carbon steel, AISI-C1010 retainers.

## C. High-Temperature Lubrication

The significant reduction in hardness and dimensional stability at bearing temperatures above 350°F causes the Cr alloy steel, AISI-

TABLE 12-21. Reservoir Effect on Bearing Performance Life [a]

Apparatus: High temperature high speed bearing performance apparatus
Specimen: 204 size ball bearings, Cr alloy (AISI-C52100) races-balls, steel (AISI-1010) retainers, internal clearance = .0003–.0008 in.
Load: 5 lb thrust, 3 lb radial
Speed: 10,000 rpm
Temperature: 350°F

| Solid film composition (wt %) | Reservoir diam. (in.) | Reservoir depth (in.) | No. of reservoirs per ball pocket | Total no. of reservoirs | pretreatment | Performance life (hr) |
|---|---|---|---|---|---|---|
| 71% MoS$_2$, 7% graphite 22% sodium silicate | — | — | — | — | Phosphate | 21, 29 |
| 71% MoS$_2$, 7% graphite 22% sodium silicate | .025 (max) | .015 | 70 | 560 | Phosphate | 32, 33 |
| 71% MoS$_2$, 7% graphite 22% sodium silicate | .041 | .034 | 6 | 48 | Phosphate | 46, 58 |
| 71% MoS$_2$, 7% graphite 22% sodium silicate | .055 | .034 | 6 | 48 | Phosphate | 55 |
| 71% MoS$_2$, 7% graphite 22% sodium silicate | .063 | .034 | 6 | 48 | Phosphate | 65, 73 |
| 71% MoS$_2$, 7% graphite 22% sodium silicate | .067 | .034 | 6 | 48 | Phosphate | 89 |
| 71% MoS$_2$, 7% graphite 22% sodium silicate | .070 | .034 | 6 | 48 | Phosphate | 100, 96 |
| 71% MoS$_2$, 7% graphite 22% sodium silicate | .078 | 0.34 | 6 | 48 | Phosphate | 113, 107 |

[a] Tests were run on a continuous basis (no cycling).

Apparatus: High temperature high speed bearing performance apparatus
Specimen: 204 size ball bearing, internal clearance .0008 in.
Temp: 750°F continuous test
Load: 5 lb thrust, 3 lb radial
Solid film composition: 71% $MoS_2$, 7% graphite, 22% sodium silicate

| Ball-race material | Retainer material | Retainer pocket | | | | Retainer inner periphery | | | | Speed rpm | Performance life (hr) |
|---|---|---|---|---|---|---|---|---|---|---|---|
| | | Res. diam. (in.) | Res. depth (in.) | Site [a] | No. of reservoirs | Res. diam. (in.) | Res. depth (in.) | Site [a] | No. of reservoirs | | |
| 18-4-1 | | | | | | | | | | | |
| Tool steel | Cast iron | .093 | .025 | A | 48 | .113 | .075 | C | 16 | 10,000 | 20 |
| Tool steel | Cast iron | .093 | .075 | B | 48 | .113 | .075 | C | 16 | 10,000 | 23 |
| Tool steel | Cast iron | .093 | .037 | A | 48 | .113 | .075 | C | 16 | 10,000 | 27 |
| | | | .075 | B | | | | | | | |
| Tool steel | Cast iron | .093 | .050 | A | 48 | .113 | .075 | C | 16 | 10,000 | 29 |
| | | | .075 | B | | | | | | | |
| 18-4-1 | AISI-430 | .093 | .073 | A | 48 | .113 | .075 | C | 16 | 10,000 | 20 |
| | | | .075 | B | | | | | | | |
| 18-4-1 | AISI-430 | .093 | .037 | A | 48 | .113 | .075 | C | 16 | 10,000 | 24 |
| | | | .075 | B | | | | | | | |
| 18-4-1 | AISI-1010 | .093 | .050 | A | 48 | | | | | 10,000 | 24 |
| | | | .075 | B | 48 | | | | | | |
| 18-4-1 | AISI-430 | .093 | .037 | A | 48 | .113 | .075 | C | 16 | 3,500 | 96 |
| | | | .075 | B | | | | | | | |
| 18-4-1 | Cast iron | .093 | .050 | A | 48 | .113 | .075 | C | 16 | 3,500 | 455 |
| | | | .075 | B | | | | | | | |
| 18-4-1 | Cast iron | .093 | .037 | A | 48 | .113 | .075 | C | 16 | 3,500 | 333 |
| | | | .075 | B | | | | | | | |

[a] Location of sites is shown in Fig. 12-22.

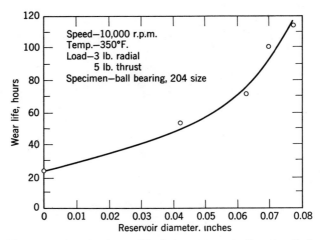

Fig. 12-21. Graph of wear life (hr) vs reservoir diameter (in.).

C52100, to be unsuitable as a bearing material for 750°F experiments. Two readily available bearing materials for elevated temperatures are W–Cr–V alloy (18-4-1 high speed tool steel) and Cr–Mo–V alloy (M-10 tool steel); however, technical information required to determine the most satisfactory retainer material is limited. Accordingly, a range of alloys must be investigated. In the preliminary runs, 204 size bearings with races and ball fabricated from 18-4-1 tool steel were utilized. The retainer materials included cast iron, stainless steel and low-carbon steel. In the 750°F studies, the retainer design was a machined two-piece assembly. Two areas of sliding motion encountered in this bearing design were ball retainer pocket and retainer inner race. Exact areas were determined by rotating an assembled bearing at 10,000 rpm for several hours, removing and disassembling the bearing and examining the surfaces. Based on this approach, the location of reservoirs for subsequent runs can be selected most effectively. A section of bearing retainer, including sliding-contact areas and reservoir sites, is shown in Fig. 12-22. In order to determine optimum reservoir diameter for the ball-pocket sites, the ratio of reservoir diameter to retainer width was equated to the ratio which produced the longest running time for the 350°F runs. This approach was utilized because of the difference in retainer widths existing in the retainers used for the 350 and 750°F runs, respectively. The diameter of the reservoirs for the inner periphery of the retainer was selected on the basis of the wear-track diameter measured after the pilot run. For these experiments, the depth of the reservoir located at the thinnest cross section of the ball pocket was the

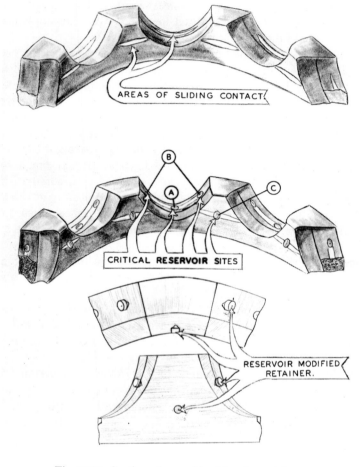

AREAS OF SLIDING CONTACT

CRITICAL **RESERVOIR** SITES

RESERVOIR MODIFIED
RETAINER.

Fig. 12-22. Section of a machined bearing retainer.

single variable studied for the purpose of determining the most suitable modification.

After modification, a vapor-blast pretreatment was applied to the retainer surfaces. The solid film was then deposited in the reservoirs and on the surfaces of the retainers and races. For purposes of reference, the formulation and preparation for the lubricant is shown in Appendix 1. Performance life at 750°F was determined using a high-temperature test spindle (6). In order to achieve a more uniform temperature for the bearing, drive shaft, and housing, metal clips were employed to replace the bearing cover plate and a bladed disk (diameter

1¼ in.) was attached to the test shaft. Bearing housings fabricated from M-2 tool steel were substituted for the V-alloy housings to minimize the effects of differential thermal expansion.

Instrumentation provided means for continuously measuring bearing outer-race temperature, oven temperature and power required to rotate the drive shaft. Lubricant-bearing failure can be initially detected by increases in outer-race temperature and power. Prior to catastrophic failure, usually within 2 hr, a gradual increase in temperature and power was observed. Since the recorded plot is essentially a straight line, the failure point can be detected by placing a straight edge on the plot and noting the point of departure from a straight line for both temperature and power. The mode of failure is considered to be an important attribute to the $MoS_2$, graphite, sodium–silicate solid film based on practical applications where such a failure mechanism for the lubricant could be used as a bearing-replacement criterion, thus avoiding possible damage or destruction of expensive instruments or other equipment. Performance-life data comparing the four retainer materials, reservoir depth for site A, Fig. 12-22, and speed are contained in Table 12-21. These results show that:

*1.* A significant performance life of several hundred hours can be obtained at 750°F, 3500 rpm for a bearing fabricated from 18-4-1 tool steel for the races and balls and a reservoir modified cast-iron retainer lubricated with $MoS_2$–graphite–sodium silicate solid film.

*2.* Major differences in running time at 750°F, 10,000 rpm are not produced by increasing the depth of the site A reservoir.

An analysis of the surfaces of the machined retainer after completion of the aforementioned 750°F performance tests indicated that a substantial increase in reservoir diameter or a different reservoir geometry would be required to extend running time further. Since the area of sliding contact was observed to be substantially increased, it was considered that a series of rectangular shaped reservoirs produced perpendicular to the forward motion of the ball and extending to the periphery of the retainer would be the more advantageous solution to the problem. A section of bearing retainer having this modification is shown in Fig. 12-23. Six retainer materials, i.e., cast iron, stainless steel, low-carbon steel, S-monel, iron–silicon–bronze and 18-4-1 tool steel, were utilized with 204-size ball bearings having 18-4-1 tool-steel races and balls. Hardness measurements using a Rockwell hardness tester were made on the retainer specimens prior to modification. After the rectangular shaped reservoirs were produced in the retainers, a vapor-blast pretreatment was applied to the retainer surfaces. The solid-film lubricant (Ap-

TABLE 12-23. Effect of Retainer Modification on Performance Life

Apparatus: High temperature high speed bearing performance apparatus
Specimen: 204 size ball bearing, internal clearance = .0008 in.
Temperature: 750°F
Speed: 10,000 rpm
Load: 5 lb thrust, 3 lb radial
Solid film composition: 71% $MoS_2$, 7% graphite, 22% sodium silicate

| Ball-race material | Retainer material | Retainer hardness | Performance life (hr) |
|---|---|---|---|
| 18–4–1 Tool steel | AISI–430 | $R_B76$ | 24 |
| 18–4–1 Tool steel | S-Monel | $R_C36$ | 31 |
| 18–4–1 Tool steel | AISI–1010 | $R_B75$ | 36 |
| 18–4–1 | Cast iron | $R_B72$ | 37 |
| Tool steel 18–4–1 Tool steel | Iron silicon bronze | $R_B58$ | 51 |
| 18–4–1 Tool steel | 18–4–1 tool steel | $R_B98$ | 53 |
| 18–4–1 | | | |

*Notes:* 1. Reservoir dimensions: Site A—.032×.032×.18 in.
                                    Site B—.032×.050×.18 in.
                                    Site C—.032×.050×.24 in.
2. Locations of sites are shown on Fig. 12-23.
3. Tests were run on a continuous basis (no cycling).
4. Running time for modified cast iron retainer under same test conditions without lubricant = 5 min.

pendix 1) was deposited in the reservoirs and on the surfaces of the retainers and races. Performance-life tests using the high-temperature spindle (6) were conducted at 750°F, 10,000 rpm. The data contained in Table 12-23 show the effect of the rectangular shaped reservoirs and provides a comparison for the effect of retainer alloy and hardness. These results show that:

*1.* The rectangular shaped reservoir is an effective modification for machined retainers lubricated with $MoS_2$–graphite–sodium silicate solid film.

*2.* Retainer alloy is an important variable in ball-bearing performance life at 750°F and 10,000 rpm.

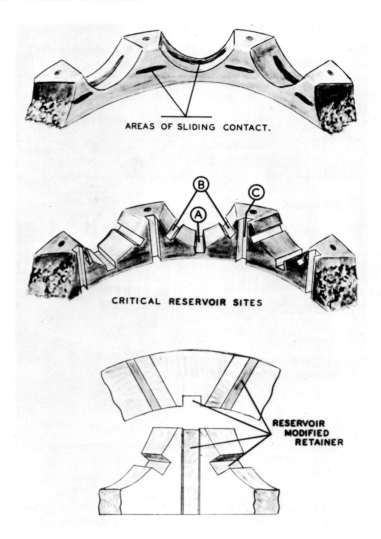

AREAS OF SLIDING CONTACT.

CRITICAL RESERVOIR SITES

RESERVOIR
MODIFIED
RETAINER

Fig. 12-23. Section of a machined bearing retainer.

## D. Temperature Effects

An important characteristic of the $MoS_2$-graphite-sodium silicate solid film is the capacity to provide lubrication over a wide temperature range. This capability has been demonstrated in recent applications involving ball-screw jacks operating from $-65$ to $+840°F$, liquid-oxygen pump bearings at a temperature of $-296°F$ and a plain bearing subjected to a temperature of +1200°F. Since no similarity existed between these applications for bearing design, metallurgy, load, type of motion, and so on, the performance life was varied. It was noted, however, that the running time in each case was of sufficient length to establish that the lubricant was effective.

Further, one series of laboratory runs at 77, 350 and 750°F was completed using 204-size ball bearings fabricated from 18-4-1 tool steel for the races and balls and cast iron for the retainers. The retainer design was a machined two-piece assembly. A cylindrical reservoir modification was utilized in the gall pocket and inner periphery of the retainers. After modification, a vapor-blast pretreatment was applied to the retainers and the solid film described in the foregoing was deposited in the reservoirs and on the surfaces of the retainers and races. The results of performance-life tests conducted at 3500 rpm are as follows: 1039 hr at 77°F, 531 hr at 350°F, and 455 hr at 750°F. Although substantial performance life was obtained at each temperature, the data show a decrease in running time with an increase in temperature. Factors that may partially account for the reduction are possible shrinkage of lubricant contained in the reservoirs and an increasing coefficient of friction for graphite with an increase in temperature. These factors as well as effect of higher temperatures on solid-film, ball-bearing lubrication is the subject of current study.

Data obtained from several experiments for the lubrication of ball bearings with solid films show that reservoir modifications for the retainer component can be an important performance factor. Essentially, reservoirs provide for an additional source of lubricant, reduce metal-to-metal contact area and allow for increased film thickness. Runs were conducted with cylindrical and rectangular-type reservoirs using several retainer alloys. A comparison of performance life at 750°F, 10,000 rpm for these two reservoir systems produced on four different retainer alloys indicates that the rectangular modification provided increases over those of the cylindrical modification. Studies are currently being conducted to determine optimum reservoir diameter and depth as well as determinations for the most suitable ratio of reservoir area to bearing–surface area. The failure mechanism for solid film-lubricated ball bearings appears to be film depletion. Examination of the sliding surfaces after film removal shows areas of high wear on the surfaces of the ball pocket and inner periphery of the unmodified retainer. Modifications to retainer at the sites mentioned produced performance life in the range of 400% over those obtained using unmodified retainers. Most failures in the runs using modified retainers are retainer breakage at one or more reservoir sites.

Significant information has been obtained from the examination of the surfaces of bearing components after completion of test runs on assembled specimens. Solid-film depletion from the retainer component allowing metal-to-metal contact in areas of ball-ball pocket and retainer periphery-inner land is indicated to be the mechanism of failure. The more pronounced contribution in limiting bearing performance based on observations of the substrate is produced by the effects of sliding contact between the retainer and land for bearings having inner-land guided machined retainers. The apparatus used in conducting tests on solid film-lubricated bearings is Pope Machinery Corporation Model No. P7605B high-temperature, high-speed bearing performance test unit. The design shown in Fig. 12-24 employs inner-race rotation with a stationary outer race for the test specimen.

In order to provide a basis for a solid film-lubricated ball bearing having long-term operating capability, means for reducing friction for the retainer-land contact area is a basic requirement. It was considered that such an effect could be provided by replacing the steel composition for that portion of the land in contact with the retainer periphery with a metal more susceptible to solid lubrication or a self-lubricating substance. In order to determine the feasibility and range of application of such an approach, three widely different materials selected on the basis of results from other phases of the program were utilized for the preliminary test runs. The materials included molybdenum, polyimide plastic and inorganic solid composed of $MoS_2$, graphite and sodium silicate. The bearing design proposed for the experiment is shown in Fig. 12-25 for molybdenum metal. High-speed bearing performance was determined at 10,000 rpm using a high-temperature test spindle (6). The results obtained for ball-bearing specimens having Cr–Mo–V alloy steel (AISI M-10) for the ball-race composition are shown in Table 21-24. These data further substantiated the thesis that lubricant research aimed at critical conditions requires simultaneous study of the contribution of the bearing to determine the mechanism of lubrication.

It was also considered that reservoirs located on the inner-land surfaces would decrease the metal-to-metal contact area and provide an additional source of lubricant thereby reducing the frictional effects associated with bearing failure. Further, the degree of reduction would be dependent on the size, shape, number, and location of such reservoirs. Numerous designs were projected for utilizing such an approach on bearing assemblies.

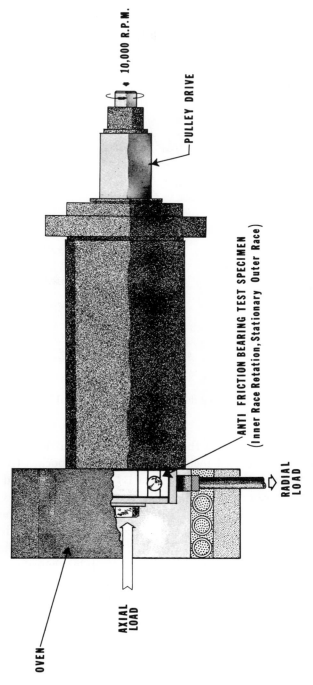

10,000 R.P.M.

PULLEY DRIVE

ANTI FRICTION BEARING TEST SPECIMEN
(Inner Race Rotation, Stationary Outer Race)

RADIAL LOAD

AXIAL LOAD

OVEN

Fig. 12-24. High temperature-high speed test spindle.

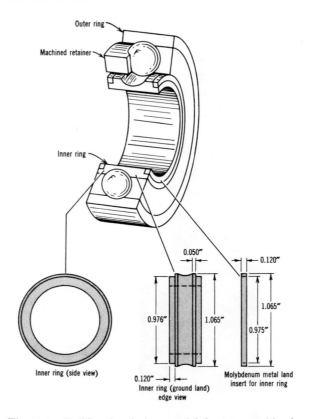

Fig. 12-25. Ball bearing design: molybdenum–metal lands.

Figure 12-26 shows some of the possibilities for antifriction bearings
The areas of sliding contact include the retainer-ball pocket (Area A),
the inner periphery of the retainer (Area B) and the inner land (Area
C). Some of the reservoir configurations and locations (Sites A, B,
C, D, and E) for initial runs are detailed for the aforementioned surfaces. The design selected on the basis of preliminary screening in high-
speed bearing tests is detailed in Fig. 12-27. It consists of cylindrical
reservoirs located in ball-pocket areas and rectangular shaped reservoirs
for the inner periphery of the retainer and inner lands. The formulation of the lubricant based on solids content for each constituent contained in the reservoirs and deposited on the surfaces of the bearing
assembly is $MoS_2$ (71 wt %), graphite (7 wt %), and sodium silicate
(22 wt %). Methods for preparation of spray and paste consistency of

TABLE 12-24. Effect of Bearing Land Composition on Bearing Performance Life

Apparatus: High speed bearing performance apparatus
Specimens: 204 size ball bearing, AISI M-10 balls, races, and retainers
Load: 5 lb thrust, 3 lb radial
Speed: 10,000 rpm
Solid film lubricant: $MoS_2$ (71 wt %), Graphite (7 wt %), Sodium Silicate (22 wt %)

| Inner land material | Lubricant | Temperature | Performance life (hr) |
|---|---|---|---|
| Cr–Mo–V alloy (AISI M–10) | Solid film | 750°F | 61 |
| Molybdenum metal | Solid film | 750°F | 208 |
| Inorganic solid section | Solid film | 750°F | 100 |
| Cr–Mo–V alloy (AISI M–10) | None | 350°F | 1 |
| Polyimide | None | 350°F | 22 |

*Notes:* 1. Inorganic solid section composed of $MoS_2$, graphite, and sodium silicate.
2. Tests were run on a continuous basis (no cycling).

the lubricant are provided by Appendixes 1 and 2, respectively. The technique for lubricant-bearing processing consists of:

*1.* Application of lubricant (paste consistency) to reservoirs.

*2.* Application of lubricant (spray consistency) to the surfaces of the retainer, races, and lands.

*3.* Curing lubricant composition.

*4.* Assembly of bearing components.

*5.* Rotating assembled bearing for approximately 1 min in each direction at several hundred rpm.

*6.* Removing loose adhering particles by subjecting the internal areas of the bearing to a dry stream of air or nitrogen.

The solid-lubricated bearings were then subjected to endurance life tests at 10,000 rpm and 750°F. A comparison of the effect of reservoir modification extending to the areas of the ball pocket, inner periphery and inner land versus reservoir modification for ball pocket and inner periphery only is shown in Table 12-25. Failure criteria included a 50% increase in power or a 20°F temperature rise of the test bearing. A considerable increase in performance was obtained for each run wherein reservoirs were extended to include the inner lands of the bearing. The extensive operating time observed for the bearing having arc cast molybdenum (0.5% Ti, 0.08% Zr) retainers is proposed to be a dual effect of inner-land reservoirs and

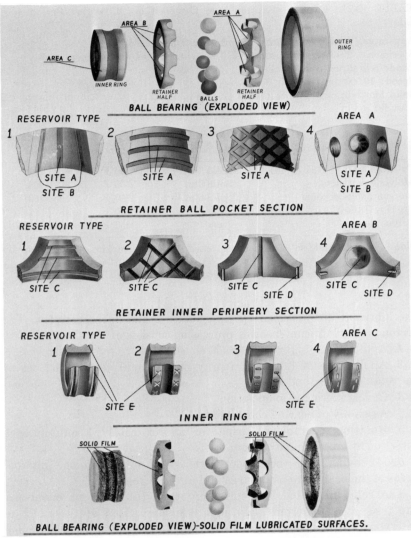

Fig. 12-26. Designs for solid film-lubricated ball bearings.

preferential lubrication displayed by sulfide compounds in contact with molybdenum metal. The relationship of alloy constituents of the bearing and chemical composition of lubricating solids represents a different phase of the program being conducted at the Naval Air Development Center.

An examination of the data covering the two experimental ap-

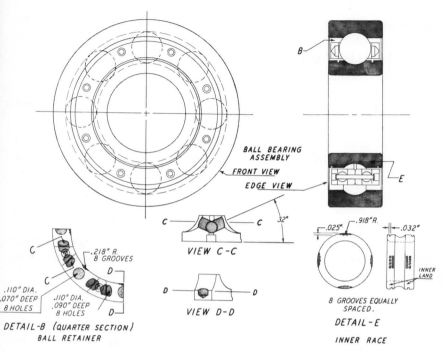

Fig. 12-27. Ball bearing assembly for solid-film lubrication.

TABLE 12-25.  Effect of Reservoir Location on Bearing Performance Life

Apparatus: High speed bearing performance apparatus
Specimen: 204 size ball bearing, AISI M-10 balls and races, retainers (as shown)
Load: 5 lb thrust, 3 lb radial
Speed: 10,000 rpm
Temperature: 750°F
Solid Film Lubricant: MoS₂ (71 wt %), graphite (7 wt %), sodium silicate (22 wt %)

| | Performance life (hr) | |
|---|---|---|
| Retainer material | Retainer reservoirs | Retainer-land reservoirs |
| Iron–silicon–bronze | 25 | 150 |
| W–Cr–V alloy (AISI T1) | 32 | 139 |
| Cr–Mo–V alloy (AISI M-10) | 61 | 300 |
| Molybdenum (0.5% Ti, 0.08% Zr) | 107 | 1148 |

*Notes:*  *1.* Tests were run on a continuous basis (no cycling).
  *2.* Lubricant deposited on surfaces of retainer, races, and lands.

proaches suggests several additional possibilities for extending the wear life of the antifriction bearings lubricated with solids. For example, the bearing design could include:

*1.* Molybdenum retainers and molybdenum lands.

*2.* Molybdenum balls.

*3.* $MoS_2$, graphite, sodium–silicate solid sections for retainer and land components.

It has been found that a substitution of molybdenum balls for the Cr–Mo–V balls in the reservoir modified bearing showing 300 hr at 750°F and 10,000 rpm produced an endurance life of 429 hr for identical conditions of speed, load, and temperature and the same solid-film lubricant. Test runs are in progress for bearings having molybdenum retainers guided by molybdenum lands.

The reservoir concept in application requires the selective removal of metal from sliding surfaces and replacement with solid lubricant. A reservoir-modified ball retainer is essentially a metal lattice capable of maintaining sufficient structural strength and flexibility for long periods and enabling the inclusion of sufficient lubricant for contacting surfaces to permit bearing operation. It can be extrapolated that the optimum design providing maximum lubricant would be achieved by forming bearing components from the constituents of the lubricating composition. Preliminary work was directed toward the development of a molding technique for the combination of inorganic solids stable under extreme conditions of temperature, reduced pressure, and nuclear radiation; i.e., $MoS_2$, graphite, and sodium silicate. It was found that by reducing the quantity of sodium silicate, a mixture was produced suitable for yielding a solid section when subjected to pressure. A cylindrical section having the dimension 1 in. × ¼ in. was prepared as follows:

*1.* Mix 10 g of $MoS_2$ and 1 g of graphite powders.

*2.* Wet the mixture with 3 g of sodium-silicate solution ($Na_2O$: $SiO_2 = 1:2.90$, 42.9% solids).

*3.* Mix thoroughly by dividing and subdividing the clumps.

*4.* Place mixture in mold.

*5.* Apply pressure in the range of 1000 psi at room temperature.

*6.* Remove solid section from mold.

*7.* Cure the solid section as follows: 0.5 hr, 77°F; 2 hr, 180°F; 2 hr, 300°F.

Figure 12-28 shows the sequences of the molding procedure. Tensile

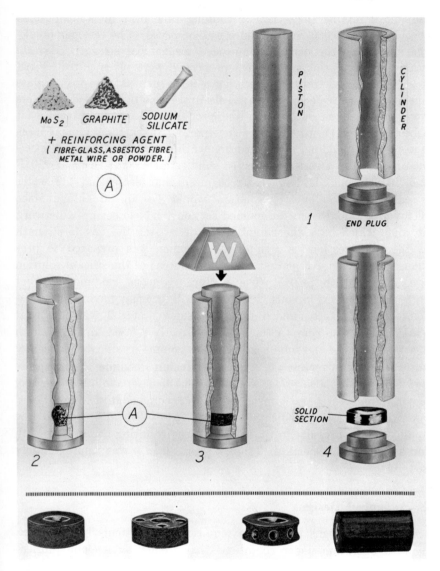

Fig. 12-28. Technique for preparation of solid section of lubricating composition.

tests conducted using an Instron apparatus showed a rupture strength of 280 psi for a specimen having a 1-in. od, $\frac{1}{2}$-in. id, and a thickness of $\frac{1}{4}$ in. A mold was prepared for fabricating solid sections of lubricant having dimensions equivalent to the metal retainers used in previous experiments. The composition described in the foregoing was selected for the initial retainer material. A running time of 7 hr was obtained at 750°F and 10,000 rpm. Failure was observed to be retainer breakage, indicating the need for improved mechanical strength. Several means for increasing mechanical properties were investigated. First, it was considered that incorporating a filler such as asbestos or glass fibers would provide for improved flexural strength. Molded retainers were produced as outlined in the preceding discussion except that asbestos fibers (1 wt %) were incorporated during sample preparation prior to molding. The performance life for a ball-bearing specimen having the asbestos-reinforced solid retainers was 16 hr at 750°F and 10,000 rpm. It was also recognized that decreasing the water contained in the silicate solution would be an advantage since removal of liquid from the molded section tends to set up a network of voids which have the potential for decreasing the tensile strength of the solid section. A cylindrical specimen was prepared as previously described except that the solids content of the silicate solution was increased to 54.0%. The rupture strength was measured at 440 psi. The performance life for a ball bearing having asbestos-reinforced retainers molded from the same material was 26 hr at 750°F and 10,000 rpm. A third factor directly related to the strength characteristics of the solid section is the volume of silicate physically adsorbed in the recesses of the molybdenum disulfide and graphite powders. Such adsorption would result in less available bonding agent. Sample preparation was varied to accommodate two additional rewettings with the silicate solution (54% solids) prior to the application of pressure to the mixture. The resulting rupture strength for a cylindrical specimen (1 in. $\times \frac{1}{2}$ in. $\times \frac{1}{4}$ in.) was approximately 800 psi.

## E. Advanced Designs

Advanced designs and future requirements particularly for space, demand operation under conditions that frequently exclude lubrication by oils and grease. Solids may be the only satisfactory lubricant for many of the applications to be encountered. Accordingly, research to determine the factors associated with the mechanism of solid lubrication can accelerate the design of the optimum lubricant-bearing system. The three interdependent components of the system are the lubricant, bearing design, and bearing composition. Phases of the laboratory program described herein have been concerned with antifriction-bearing design for solid lubrication. It is shown that the surfaces in sliding contact, i.e., the retainer ball-pocket, retainer periphery, and land areas, require a design to accommodate solid lubricant or a substance susceptible to solid lubrication. Further, possibilities for producing bearing components from solid lubricant have been achieved on the basis of a simplified molding technique thereby providing the potential for lightweight, low cost, self-lubricating solid sections.

Since the retainer component represents a means for providing lubrication when using solid lubricants, several self-lubricating solid sections have been employed as retainer materials. The primary aim of the work was to determine whether or not the bearing could be designed for a longer operating interval. Four different solid materials: e.g., TFE-glass, acetal, modified polyimide, and epoxy-$MoS_2$ were selected as the retainer components for 20 mm radial ball bearings. In view of the sliding friction generated at the retainer-land contact zone, additional bearings were prepared using the four aforementioned self-lubricating solids as land materials. The latter design is shown in Fig. 12-29. Bearing performance life was determined at 10,000 rpm using a high temperature test spindle. The test temperature was within the thermal stability range of the self lubricating solid. A comparison of test results is presented in Table 12-26. It can be observed that performance life increases realized by extending the design ranged from 40–400%.

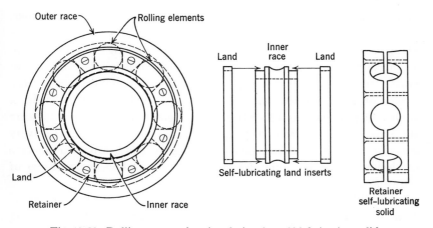

Fig. 12-29. Rolling contact bearing design for self-lubricating solids.

TABLE 12-26.   Effect of Bearing Design on Performance Life

Apparatus: High temperature—High speed bearing performance apparatus
Specimen: 20 mm radial ball bearing
Load: 5 lb thrust, 3 lb radial
Speed: 10,000 rpm
Lubricant: Self lubricating solid retainer and land (as shown)

| Bearing | Retainer | Land | Temp., °F | Performance life (hr) |
|---|---|---|---|---|
| AISI-C52100 | Acetal | AISI-C52100 | 77 | 71 |
| AISI-C52100 | Acetal | Acetal | 77 | 134 |
| AISI-C52100 | Epoxy–MoS₂ | AISI-C52100 | 250 | 156 |
| AISI-C52100 | Epoxy–MoS₂ | Epoxy—MoS₂ | 250 | 217 |
| AISI-M10 | Polyimide-graphite | AISI-M10 | 350 | 294 |
| AISI-M10 | Polyimide-graphite | Polyimide-graphite | 350 | 814 |
| AISI-M10 | TFE-Glass | AISI-M10 | 450 | 41 |
| AISI-M10 | TFE-Glass | TFE-Glass | 450 | 163 |

## F. Chemical Composition

Basic knowledge providing an understanding for the mechanism of solid lubrication is a recognized goal to enable the solution of diverse lubrication problems encountered in extreme environments. Certain properties of solids including hardness, film-forming characteristics, crystal structure, and thermodynamic considerations have been proposed or discussed (78,79) to describe solid lubricant behavior or project lubricating potential. The hypothesis proposed herein is that solids of different chemical type will display dissimilar friction and wear patterns for different metals and alloys. Further, synergistic lubricating effects may be produced as a result of establishing relationships between wear properties and metal composition. Accordingly, the interaction of lubricant constituents and metal bearing surfaces is considered to be of primary importance in the process of solid lubrication. Chemical reactivity is discussed in a number of publications (80–82) for fluids containing extreme pressure additives; however, such a parameter has not been quantitatively defined for solids. Further, such a finding for solids would accelerate the design of the optimum lubricant-bearing system for a range of operating media.

A suitable experimental approach consists of rotating an unlubricated surface in contact with a solid lubricant bonded to a mating substrate. The Falex wear configuration shown in Fig. 12-30 was

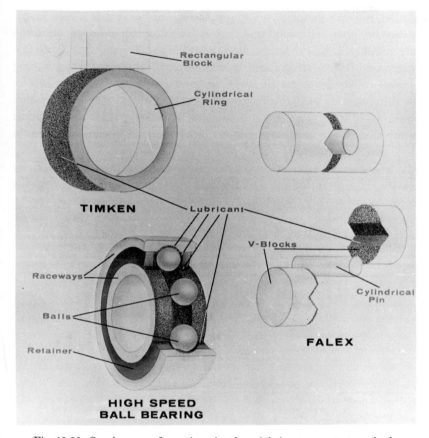

Fig. 12-30. Specimen configurations for three lubricant wear test methods.

selected for the initial exploratory work. The test specimens were comprised of two V-blocks and a cylindrical pin. Test pins were fabricated from a variety of materials including alloys of titanium, nickel, tantalum and nickel, tool steel, stainless steel, tungsten and molybdenum. The V-block material (AISI-C1137 steel) was maintained as the solid film lubricated component. Prior to deposition of the solid film, a phosphating pretreatment (15) was applied to the surfaces of the V-blocks. The test pins were subjected to degreasing and solvent cleaning only. No lubricant was applied to the surfaces of the pin material. Comparative wear tests were conducted at a gauge load of 1000 lb. Failure was determined by a torque rise of five inch pounds above the steady state value, seizure or breakage of the test pin, or breakage of the shear pin. The results of duplicate determinations for 18 test pin materials are shown in Table 12-27. It can be observed that the longest running times were obtained with unalloyed molybdenum and molybdenum containing 0.5% titanium and 0.08% zirconium. In comparison, alloys examined having a nickel constituent and titanium compositions show a low wear life. The difference in wear life for the AISI 302 stainless steel and tenelon should be noted since these materials have a similar composition except that the manganese content is higher and the nickel content much lower in tenelon.

It was also found that a molybdenum coating (83) deposited by metal spraying technique on a steel substrate in contact with the predominantly $MoS_2$ solid film exhibited the same effect as shown

TABLE 12-27.   Results of Wear Life Tests for Various Alloys

Apparatus: Falex lubricant tester
Specimens: V-blocks—steel (AISI-C1137), pin—as shown
Speed: 290 rpm
Temperature: 77°F
Load: 1000 lb
Solid film composition: 71% $MoS_2$, 7% graphite, 22% sodium silicate

| Pin designation | Pin hardness | Major metal | Alloy constituents | Running time (min) | |
|---|---|---|---|---|---|
| | | | | Run 1 | Run 2 |
| Titanium alloy | $R_C31$ | Ti | Al, V | 1 | 1 |
| Titanium alloy | $R_C29$ | Ti | Mn | 1 | 1 |
| AISI 302 | $R_C32$ | Fe | Cr, Ni | 6 | 5 |
| Inconel X | $R_C27$ | Ni | Cr, Fe, Ti | 18 | 10 |
| Hastelloy C | $R_B52$ | Ni | Mo, Cr, Fe, W | 19 | 16 |
| AISI 3135 | $R_B78$ | Fe | Ni | 21 | 18 |
| AISI 440C | $R_C57$ | Fe | Cr | 20 | 36 |
| Tungsten | $R_C36$ | W | — | 31 | — |
| AISI 1095 | $R_B90$ | Fe | — | 29 | 32 |
| TISI M2 | $R_B92$ | Fe | W, Mo, Cr, V | 28 | 36 |
| Tenelon | $R_C42$ | Fe | Cr, Mn | 37 | 32 |
| AISI 52100 | $R_C61$ | Fe | Cr | 38 | 44 |
| AISI 4130 | $R_B88$ | Fe | Cr | 47 | 39 |
| AISI T1 | $R_C60$ | Fe | W, Cr, V | 47 | 39 |
| Ta–782 | $R_B97$ | Ta | W | 53 | — |
| AISI M10 | $R_C60$ | Fe | Mo, Cr, V | 73 | 50 |
| Molybdenum | $R_B93$ | Mo | — | 160 | 123 |
| Molybdenum, 0.5 Ti, .08 Zr | $R_B97$ | Mo | — | 130 | 114 |

Solid film applied only to V-blocks, V-block surfaces phosphated prior to solid film deposition.

by the solid molybdenum. In view of these results and data for a graphite solid film showing no response in contact with molybdenum, it appeared that the molybdenum entered into the lubrication process in the presence of $MoS_2$. A reaction between the sulfur and the molybdenum at the surface represents a possible explanation of the phenomena. Increasing the concentration of $MoS_2$ by reducing binder concentration resulted in pronounced increases in the wear life for the molybdenum metal test pin. The effect of $MoS_2$ concentration on the wear life of the molybdenum pin and comparison with steel (AISI-C3135) are shown in Fig. 12-31.

The contribution of the chemical constituents of the metal bearing surface in the wear process under sliding conditions in contact

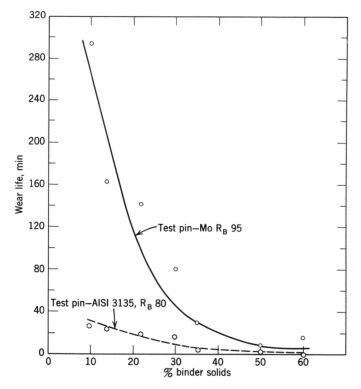

Fig. 12-31. Comparison of wear life curves for molybdenum and steel. Wear life vs % binder solids ($Na_2O:SiO_2$). Speed: 290 rpm; temp.: 77°F; gauge load: 1000 lb; V-blocks: A1S1-1137, $R_c$ 20. (*Note:* Solid film applied only to V-blocks; V-blocks phosphated prior to solid film deposition; solid film: $MoS_2$, graphite, sodium silicate. Ratio of $MoS_2$: graphite = 10:1.)

with a solid lubricant was established by these findings. The necessity for exploring solid lubricant formulation and bearing metallurgy jointly in research aimed at providing lubrication for extended periods is apparent. Wear test results for other S-compounds in contact with various metals and Mo would indicate the feasibility of the proposed mechanism for $MoS_2$ and Mo. A series of solid film lubricant formulations were prepared on the basis of volume substitution using different metallic sulfides in place of $MoS_2$ in the formulation described for the initial experiment. Wear tests were conducted under the same conditions of load, termperature, etc., employing nickel alloy, titanium alloy, tool steel, carbon steel, molybdenum and molybdenum containing 0.5% titanium and 0.8% zirconium. The results of the runs are shown in Table 12-28. The same preferential lubricating effect was observed with the additional metallic sulfides in contact with Mo as was found with $MoS_2$. In general, several metallic sulfides, i.e., $CaS$, $FeS_2$, $FeS$, have not been considered as lubricating substances. The data substantiates such a conclusion for the traditional steel on steel criteria. Also, the metallic sulfides with the exception of $MoS_2$ in the described solid film formulation displayed a lubricating effect only in contact with molybdenum. The common denominator for solid compounds effective as lubricants has been softness; however, a reevaluation of this parameter is proposed as warranted on the basis of chemical affinity factors as shown by the results for $FeS_2$ and $ZnS$. These compounds have reported (84) hardness values of 6–6.5 and 3.5–4, respectively. A hardness value of 1–1.5 is shown for $MoS_2$.

The binder fraction of solid film lubricants varies widely in composition. Previous studies described the development of sodium and potassium silicate, sodium borate and sodium phosphate as binders for inorganic solid film lubricants. Recent extensions of that work have shown the possibilities for the use of $BeF_2$ as a binder material. In many applications, the typical bonding agent for the lubricating solid is an organic resin; i.e., phenolic, silicone, epoxy, etc. Binder selection is usually based on anticipated operating conditions. In view of the wide differences in binder type and to determine the extent of the preferential lubricating effect of the metallic sulfide and molybdenum combination, a series of formulations were prepared wherein $MoS_2$ was dispersed in a variety of bonding substances. Wear studies were then conducted to compare endurance time in contact with molybdenum and steel (AISI-C3135) test pins for each of the solid film lubricants. A graphical presentation of the test

TABLE 12-28. Results of Wear Life Tests for Metallic Sulfides [a]

Apparatus: Falex lubricant tester
Specimen: V-blocks—steel (AISI-C1137), pin—as shown
Speed: 290 rpm
Load: 1000 lb
Solid film composition: Metallic sulfide (as shown), graphite, sodium silicate

| Metallic sulfide | Endurance life (min) for six pin compositions | | | | | |
|---|---|---|---|---|---|---|
| | Molybdenum | Molybdenum (0.5 Ti, 0.08 Zr) | SAE M-10 | AISI-C3135 | Inconel X | Ti-6Zr-4V |
| $MoS_2$ | 160,123 | 130,114 | 73 | 21 | 18 | 1 |
| $WS_2$ | 146 | — | <1 | 2 | 10 | 1 |
| $Ti_2S_3$ | 94 | 92 | <1 | <1 | <1 | <1 |
| $Cr_2S_3$ | 51 | 31 | <1 | <1 | <1 | <1 |
| $HgS$ | 72 | 103 | <1 | <1 | <1 | <1 |
| $ZnS$ | 84,86 | — | <1 | <1 | <1 | <1 |
| $FeS_2$ | 50 | 128 | <1 | <1 | <1 | <1 |
| $CaS$ | 130 | 120 | — | <1 | — | — |
| $FeS$ | 70 | 64 | — | <1 | — | — |
| $CdS$ | 6 | 8 | — | <1 | — | — |
| $TiS_2$ | 135,120 | — | — | <1 | — | — |
| $Ag_2S$ | 7,8 | — | <1 | <1 | <1 | <1 |
| $Bi_2S_3$ | 27 | — | <1 | <1 | <1 | <1 |
| $Sb_2S_3$ | 30 | — | <1 | <1 | <1 | <1 |

[a] Solid film applied only to V-blocks, V-blocks phosphated prior to solid film deposition. Solid film formulations equivalent on basis of volume substitution.

results is shown in Fig. 12-32. These data further substantiate the chemical constituent theory and establish the independence of the effect for a specific binder. A comparison of the molybdenum effect for seven different metallic sulfides in phenolic binders is shown in Fig. 12-33.

The Timken wear configuration shown in Fig. 12-30 was employed to investigate the effect of test design on the aforementioned findings. Comparison runs were conducted for test blocks fabricated from molybdenum and steel. The solid film lubricant was deposited on the test ring. Tests were conducted at 72 rpm, 77°F under a contact load of 630 lb. Duplicate runs for the steel (AISI-4130) have an

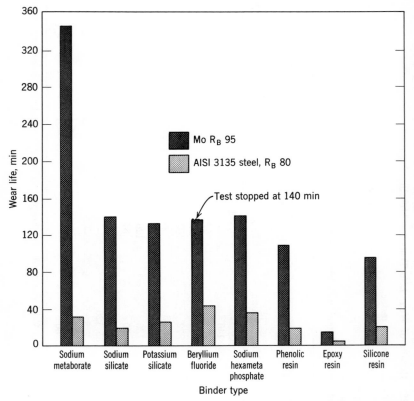

Fig. 12-32. Wear life comparison for molybdenum ND steel for various MoS₂–binder combinations. Apparatus: Falex lubricant tester; speed: 290 rpm; temp.: 77°F; guage load: 1000 lb; V-blocks: AlSl-1137 Rᶜ 20. (*Note:* Solid film applied only to V-blocks; V-blocks phosphated prior to solid film deposition; solid film: MoS₂, graphite plus binder; test pin: shown on graph.)

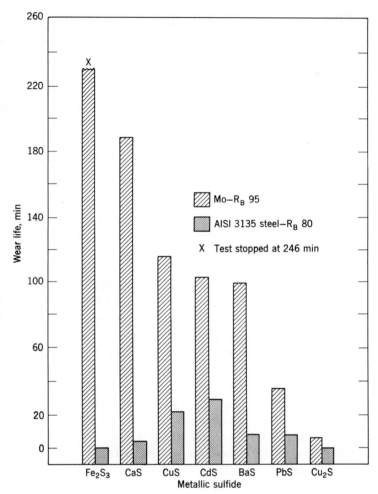

Fig. 12-33. Wear life comparison for molybdenum and steel for various metallic sulfide-phenolic resin lubricants. Apparatus: Falex lubricant tester; speed: 290 rpm; temp.: 77°F; gauge load: 1000 lb; V-blocks: AISI-1137 $R_c$ 20. (*Note:* Solid film applied only to V-blocks; V-blocks phosphated prior to solid film deposition; solid film: metallic sulfide as shown; test pin: shown on graph.)

average of 36,880 cycles to failure. The average number of cycles for molybdenum was 59,549.

The next phase in the study of the effect of solid lubricant-metal surface interaction was to explore a more complex wear configuration represented by a ball bearing assembly to determine the limitations or extensions of the principle established by the Timken machine for the low sliding velocity and line contact arrangements. The ball bearing assembly is shown in Fig. 12-30. The retainer or separator has been shown to be the critical wear component for ball bearings lubricated with solid films. There have been no guidelines established for the selection of materials for the retainer on the basis of lubrication. Properties for tensile strength, temperature stability, oxidation resistance, etc., are the general basis for determining candidate retainer alloys.

Essentially, sliding contact occurs on the surfaces of the retainer ball pockets and periphery. Since the lubricant must function to reduce friction and wear and research effort is aimed at extending endurance time, it is necessary to investigate the susceptibility of these surfaces for the chemical action of the lubricant. In order to provide comparative data, retainers were fabricated from alloys of nickel, titanium, and vanadium, stainless steel, cast iron, and arc cast molybdenum containing 0.5% Ti and 0.08% Zr. Reservoirs were incorporated into the areas of sliding contact and comparable weights for each metal and alloy was attained by removal of metal from noncritical surfaces. The solid film lubricant was deposited in the rservoirs and on the sliding surfaces of the bearing. Cr–Mo–V alloy (SAE M-10) was selected for the ball and race material. The solid film lubricant was also deposited on the races. Prior to test runs, the lubricated bearings were rotated several hundred revolutions in each direction and subjected to an air stream to remove loose particles. The technique and apparatus (12) for the test runs provided a speed of 10,000 rpm and a 750°F test temperature in air. The temperature at the outer race of the bearing and in the oven as well as the power required to rotate the bearing is recorded continuously during the run. Failure criteria included at 50% increase in power or a 20°F temperature rise of the test bearing. The data for the high speed, high temperature experiments for self contained lubricated bearings is presented in Table 12-29. The average performance life for duplicate determinations covering the $MoS_2$ lubricated molybdenum (0.5 Ti, 0.08 Zr) was 1108 hr. A Cr–Mo–V alloy (SAE M-10) showed the next longest running time having an average life of 300 hr. The remaining alloys ranged from 60 to 171 hr.

These findings indicate the possibilities for a system of classification for solids on a chemical basis and selection of a compound within a class would be dependent on the specified metal and operating conditions for the machine or bearing. Further, many substances

TABLE 12-29.  Effect of Metal Composition (Retainer Component) on Bearing Performance Life [a]

Apparatus: high speed bearing performance apparatus
Specimen: 204 size ball bearing, AISI M-10 balls and races, retainers (as shown)
Load: 5 lb thrust, 3 lb radial
Speed: 10,000 rpm
Temperature: 750°F
Solid film lubricant: $MoS_2$ (71 wt %), graphite (7 wt %), sodium silicate (22 wt %)

| Retainer designation | Major metal | Alloy constituents | Retainer hardness | Performance life (hr) |
|---|---|---|---|---|
| Inconel X | Ni | Fe, Cr, Ti | $R_B81$ | 60 |
| Ti–140A | Ti | Fe, Cr, Mo | $R_C37$ | 98 |
| AISI TI | Fe | W, Cr, V | $R_P98$ | 139 |
| AISI TI | Fe | W, Cr, V | $R_B98$ | 132 |
| AISI 430 | Fe | Cr | $R_B76$ | 143 |
| S–Monel | Ni | Cu, Fe, Si | $R_C36$ | 171 |
| AISI M–10 | Fe | Mo, Cr, V | $R_B98$ | 280 |
| AISI M–10 | Fe | Mo, Cr, V | $R_B98$ | 310 |
| Climelt TZM | Mo | Ti, Zr | $R_B94$ | 1069 |
| Climelt TZM | Mo | Ti, Zr | $R_B94$ | 1148 |

[a] Reservoirs located on retainer ball pockets and inner periphery and inner land. Solid film deposited on surfaces of retainer, races and lands.

not considered as lubricants by the steel vs steel criterion may be effective lubricants for metals of different composition. Recent laboratory studies conducted at the Naval Air Development Center have been aimed at exploring lubricant-bearing interaction for other combinations. Halogen containing solids were selected for the next series of test runs. Essentially, the test arrangement was the same as outlined previously for the $MoS_2$–Mo investigation. The results of initial determinations indicate that halogen compounds may be preferential lubricants for metal compositions having a nickel component. The following metal compositions were examined during an investigation of the lubricating properties of $PbI_2$: Ti alloy, AISI-3135, AISI-52100, AISI-302, AISI-316, Inconel X, Hastelloy C, and Rene 41. The latter five alloys have a nickel content ranging from 8 to 70%. It was observed that increased endurance life results for test specimens having a nickel alloy content greater than 8%. These findings are projected graphically in Fig. 12-34. In addition similar data has been obtained for the halogen compound $PbCl_2$. A phenolic resin binder was employed for the tests involving $PbI_2$ and $PbCl_2$.

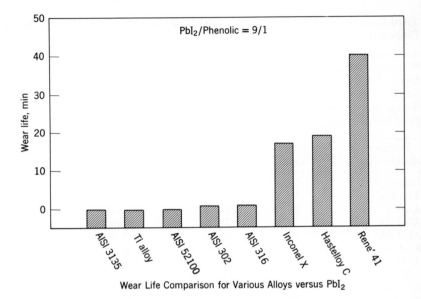

Fig. 12-34. Wear life comparison for various alloys vs PbI₂.

## G. Surface Characteristics

In general, pretreatment of metal surfaces prior to solid film lubricant deposition has been found to increase wear life characteristics. Reported findings (85) for an investigation aimed at reducing extrusion pressure for the cold extrusion of titanium also show the advantages of surface pretreatment. Examples of metal pretreatment include sandblast, acid etch, chemical conversion coating, and machining. These pretreatment designations are qualitative and do not define the range of variables encompassed by each process. An adequate description of sandblast or vapor blast should define type of grit and carrier, spray pressure, distance from spray discharge nozzle to surface of specimen, nozzle opening, spray duration, and spray angle. Composition, processing time, temperature, and rinsing procedure represent several significant factors in forming chemical conversion coatings such as zinc phosphate, iron manganese phosphate, etc. In examining comparative data covering wear or endurance life for various solid lubricants, it is important to recognize that valid technical conclusions pertinent to lubricant performance may be limited by the type of pretreatment selected for the lubricant. For example, the following Falex wear test results demonstrate the dif-

ferences in running time for a stainless steel pin rotated under load
against two steel V blocks:

| Test pin pretreatment | Running time (min.) |
|---|---|
| None | 28 |
| HF etch | 33 |
| Sand blast | 31 |
| Vapor blast | 188 |
| $H_3PO_4$ etch | 126 |

The solid film lubricant applied to the test pin after pretreatment
consisted of molybdenum disulfide, graphite, and sodium silicate. No
pretreatment or lubricant was applied to the V-block specimens.
It can be observed that by varying the type of pretreatment for a
solid lubricant, wear life can be increased by 500%.

Increased surface roughness usually results from pretreatment processing. The major effect has been proposed to be attributable to
micro reservoirs produced by the pretreatment. It was postulated
that the effectiveness of the lubricant is related to the size, shape,
number, and location of the reservoirs. Laboratory studies have been
aimed at establishing quantitative relationships for the type of pretreatment, solid lubricant composition, and wear properties. Several
variables associated with altering surface characteristics by mechanical means were studied during initial phases of the laboratory
program. Sandblasting represents one method commonly used for
mechanically producing surface asperities. This technique can promote removal of material from the surface of the specimen or a
series of surface compressions. Experiments were conducted to determine the significance of grit composition and mesh size on the wear
life of solid film lubricants. Specimen preparation consisted of manually rotating the wear test specimen while impinging an air (90 psi)
carried grit. The spray distance was 2 in. from a nozzle having
a $\frac{1}{4}$ in. opening. The spraying time was approximately 60 sec.
Silicon carbide, aluminum oxide, quartz, glass spheres, and iron shot
were selected for the grit materials. A comparison of wear test results
showing the effect produced by grit composition and particle size for
the sandblasting pretreatment and a solid lubricant composed of
molybdenum disulfide, graphite, and alkyd resin is presented on
Table 12-30. The importance of defining processing factors for surface
pretreatment is adequately demonstrated by these data. It should
be noted that optimum processing requirements may be dependent

TABLE 12-30.  Effect of Surface Pretreatment on Wear Life [a]

Apparatus: Falex lubricant tester
Specimens: V-blocks (AISI-C1137, $R_c20$), pin (AISI-C3135, $R_b80$)
Speed: 290 rpm
Load: 1000 lb
Solid film lubricant: $MoS_2$, graphite, alkyd resin

| Grit material | Mesh | Wear life (min) |
| --- | --- | --- |
| Silicon carbide | 60 | 217 |
| Silicon carbide | 240 | 3 |
| Aluminum oxide | 60 | 134 |
| Aluminum oxide | 240 | 8 |
| Quartz | 80 | 95 |
| Glass | −140+270 | 3 |
| Iron | 120 | 315 |

[a] Solid film applied to surfaces of V-blocks and pin.

on bearing material, physical properties, and bearing configuration, as well as solid lubricant composition.

## APPENDIX 1

**Formulation, Preparation and Application of $MoS_2$–Graphite–Sodium Silicate Solid-Film Lubricant (Spray Consistency)**
*1. Formula* (U.S. Pat. 3,079,204)

*grams*

$MoS_2$ powder
(Military Specification MIL-L-7866(ASG)) ........... 70
Graphite powder
(Military Specification MIL-G-6711) * .............. 7
Sodium–silicate solution
(% ratio $Na_2O:SiO_2 = 1:2.9$, 43% solids,
viscosity = 960 centipoises) ......................... 50
Water .......................................... 60

* Sieve—Utilize only that which passes through 325-mesh screen.

### 2. Preparation

(a)  $MoS_2$ powder (70 g) and graphite powder (7 g) are mixed in a beaker. Water is added slowly while stirring the mixture thoroughly. Continue addition of water, stirring to insure complete wetting of the powder mixture, until a pourable slurry is obtained. The total quantity of water is approximately 60 g. *Note:* An excess amount of water will result in separation. If separation is observed, the mixture should be discarded and a second preparation using fresh constituents initiated.)

(b) The pourable slurry is added to sodium-silicate solution (50 g) with stirring to obtain a uniform sprayable mixture. (*Note:* Sodium-silicate solution should be used within date specified on the container.)

### 3. Application

(a) The mixture is placed in a spray bottle (8 oz capacity) and the spray bottle attached to a spray gun.

(b) Mixture should be agitated immediately before spraying.

(c) Spray pressure is approximately 40 psi.

(d) Allow film to air dry prior to applying successive coats.

### 4. Curing

The coated specimens are then subjected to the following cure cycle:

(a) Air dry, $\frac{1}{2}$ hr.

(b) 180°F, 2 hr.

(c) 300°F, 2 hr.

## APPENDIX 2

### Preparation of Lubricant for Reservoir Application Materials

$MoS_2$ powder (Military Specification MIL-L-7866 (ASG)).

Graphite powder (Military Specification MIL-G-6711).

Sodium silicate solution (% ratio $Na_2O:SiO_2=1:2.9$, 43% solids, viscosity $=960$ cps).

### Procedure

1. Mix 70 g $MoS_2$ and 7 g graphite. Wet mixture with 3 cc water. Add 50 g sodium silicate solution.

2. Place the mixture in a blender and homogenize for 30 min at low speed. Care should be taken to refeed material to the rotor blades.

3. The unworked penetration after homogenizing is approximately 250 (converted from $\frac{1}{4}$ scale).

4. The paste consistency of $MoS_2$, graphite and sodium–silicate solution is placed in the reservoirs of the ball pocket, retainer periphery and inner land using a spatula. Place reservoir-filled specimens in an oven at 180°F for 1 hr. (Shrinkage will occur as a result of the loss of water.) After removal from oven, allow specimens to cool and refill reservoir voids with paste consistency. Replace specimens in oven at 180°F for 1 hr.

5. Remove from oven, allow to cool and apply solid-film solution (Appendix 1) on the surfaces of the ball pocket, inner ring, retainer inner periphery and races. Cure time and temperature are shown in Appendix 2.

## REFERENCES

1. W. M. Edwards and I. M. Robinson, U.S. Pat. 2,710,853 (June 14, 1955).
2. W. F. Gresham and M. A. Naylor, U.S. Pat. 731,447 (Jan. 17, 1956).
3. W. M. Edwards, I. M. Robinson, and E. N. Squire, U.S. Pat. 2,867,609 (Jan. 6, 1959).
4. W. M. Edwards, Austral. Pat. 52837 (Sep. 16, 1959).
5. W. M. Edwards, Austral. Pat. 58424 (March 16, 1960).
6. Federal Test Method Standard 791, "Lubricants, Liquid Fuels and Related Products; Methods of Testing" (Method 333).
7. W. E. Campbell, *Lubrication Eng.*, **9**, 195 (1953).
8. D. Godfrey and E. E. Bisson, Natl. Advisory Comm. Aeronaut., Tech. Note 2628 (Feb. 1952); *Ibid.*, 2802 (Oct. 1952).
9. M. T. Lavik, Wright Air Develop. Center, Tech. Rept. 57-455 Part II (Oct. 1958), Part III (June 1959).
10. H. E. Sliney, Natl. Aeronaut. Space Admin. Memo. 3-2-59E (Feb. 1959).
11. Philadelphia Quartz Co., Philadelphia, Pa., Bull. 17-1 (Oct. 1958).
12. Federal Test Method Standard No. 791 Lubricants, Liquid Fuels, and Related Products; Methods of Testing (Method 331.1).
13. Radio Corp. of America, "Instruction Book EMV-1 Vacuum Unit," (1946).
14. Am. Soc. Testing Materials, Standards on Petroleum Products and Lubricants, Method D 1478-57T, December 1958.
15. American Chemical Paint Co., Ambler, Pa., Technical Service Data Sheet TG-O-D (July 1957).
16. C. D. Thayer and H. G. Rudolph, Jr., SAE National Meeting (Sept. 12-15, 1960), "Molybdenum Disulfide as an Additive to Improve the Performance of an Automotive Multipurpose Grease."
17. K. B. Wood, Jr., ASME Design Engineering Conference (May 22-25, 1961), "Molybdenum Disulfide as a Lubricant."
18. Military Specification MIL-G-7866A (Dec. 22, 1955), "Molybdenum Disulfide Powder, Lubricant."
19. Federal Test Method Standard No. 791 "Lubricants, Liquid Fuels and Related Products; Methods of Testinng" (Method 6503).
20. Federal Test Method Standard No. 791 "Lubricants, Liquid Fuels and Related Products; Methods of Testing" (Method 335).

21. Federal Test Method Standard No. 791 "Lubricants, Liquid Fuels and Related Products; Methods of Testing" (Method 3453.1).
22. R. D. Brown, R. A. Burton, and P. M. Ku, "Long-Duration Lubrication Studies in Simulated Space Vacuum," presented USAF-SwRI Aerospace Bearing Conference, San Antonio, Texas, March 25-27, 1964.
23. M. T. Lavik, "Development and Evaluation of High Temperature Solid Film Lubricant," Quarterly Progress Rpt. No. 5 (April 1-June 30, 1960).
24. M. B. Peterson and R. L. Johnson, "PbO and Other Metal Oxides as Solid Lubricants for Temperatures to 1000°F," ASLE Paper 56LC-10 Oct. 1956. (Presented at ASME-ASLE Joint Lubrication Conference Atlantic City, Oct. 1956).
25. H. E. Evans and T. W. Flatley, "Bearings for Vacuum Operation Retainer Material and Design," NASA TND-1339 (May 1962).
26. D. S. Wilson and S. Gray, "The Development of Lubricants for High Speed Rolling Contact Bearings Operating Over the Temperature Range of Room Temperature to 1200°F," August 1960. (Prepared under Contract AF 3B(616)-6589 by Stratos Div. of Fairchild Engine and Airplane Corporation.)
27. F. A. Haley and R. H. McDaniel, "Effects of Reactor Radiation on Ceramic-Bonded Solid-Film Lubricants," Aug. 30, 1963. (Prepared under contract AF (657)-7201 by General Dynamics, Fort Worth.)
28. D. J. Boes, "Long Term Operation and Practical Limitations of Dry, Self-Lubricated Bearings from $1 \times 10^{-5}$ Torr to Atmospheric," *Lubrication Eng.*, **19**, No. 4 (April 1963).
29. "Research on High Temperature Bearings"—ASD-TR-61-605, Aug. 1962. (Prepared under Contract No. AF 33(616)-7209 by Southwest Research Institute).
30. T. J. Williams, "High Temperature Airframe Bearings and Lubricants." *Lubrication Eng.*, **18**, No. 1 (Jan. 1962).
31. A. J. Haltner and C. S. Oliver, "Frictional Properties of Some Solid Lubricant Films Under High Load," American Chemical Society, Division of Petroleum Chemistry, Vol. 5, No. 2-B (April 1960).
32. M. J. Devine, E. R. Lamson, and J. H. Bowen, Jr., "Anti-friction Bearing Design Considerations For Solid Lubrication," ASME Paper 63-MD-43 (May 1963).
33. D. H. Buckley, M. Swikert, and R. L. Johnson, "Friction, Wear, and Evaporation Rates of Various Materials in Vacuum to $10^{-7}$ mm Hg," ASLE Paper 61 LC-2 (Oct. 1961).
34. M. J. Devine, E. R. Lamson, and J. H. Bowen, Jr., "The Effect of the Chemical Composition of Metals In Solid Lubrication," American Chemical Society, Division of Petroleum Chemistry (April 1963).
35. S. L. Cosgrove, L. B. Sibley, and C. M. Allen, "Evaluation of Dry Powdered Lubricants at 1000°F In a Modified Four-ball Wear Machine," *ASLE Tran.* No. 2.
36. L. B. Sibley and C. M. Allen, "Friction and Wear Behavior of Refractory Materials at High Sliding Velocities and Temperatures," *Wear*, **5**, No. 4, (July/August. 1962).
37. M. T. Lavik, "Development and Evaluation of High Temperature Solid Film Lubricants," USAF Contract No. AF33(616)-6115, Progress Report No. 5 (April-June 1960).

38. M. T. Lavik, Gordon E. Gross, and George W. Vaughan, "Investigation of the Mechanism of Tungsten Disulfide Lubrication in Vacuum," ASLE, (April 1957).

39. M. B. Peterson, J. J. Florek, and S. F. Murray, "Considerations of Lubricants for Temperatures Above 1000°F," ASLE Paper 59AMIA2.

40. Glenn F. Hyde and John H. Fuchsluger, "Materials for Elevated Temperature Piston Ring and Seal Ring Applications (600F-1200F)," *Lubrication Eng.,* 17, No. 10, (Oct. 1961).

41. S. B. Twiss, P. J. Wilson, and E. J. Snyder, "Friction of Teflon as a Dry Lubricant Bearing," ASLE Paper 57AM5C-4 (April 1957).

42. J. W. Kissel, W. A. Glaeser, and C. M. Allen, "Frictional Behaviour of Sodium-Lubricated Materials in a Controlled High-Temperature Environment," ASME Paper 61-LUBS- (May 1961).

43. M. J. Devine, E. R. Lamson, and J. H. Bowen, Jr., "Inorganic Solid Film Lubricants," *J. Chem. Eng. Data,* 6, No. 1 (Jan. 1961).

44. F. K. Orcutt, H. H. Krause, and C. M. Allen, "The Use of Free-Energy Relationships in the Selection of Lubricants for High Temperature Applications," ASME Paper 61-LUBS-14 (May 1961).

45. D. S. Wilson and S. Gray, "The Development of Lubricants for High Speed Rolling Contact Bearings Operating at 1200°F," WADC TR-59-790 December 13, 1959, prepared under Contract No. AF 33(616)-6589 by Stratos, Division of Fairchild Engine and Airplane Corporation.

46. R. E. Crump, "Solid Film Lubricants—Factors Influencing Their Mechanism of Friction and Wear," ASLE Paper No. 56LC-8 (Oct. 1956).

47. C. F. Merrill and R. J. Benzing, "Solid Films—Lubricants for Extreme Environments," WADD Technical Note 60-59 (Feb. 1960).

48. W. C. Milz and L. B. Sargent, "Frictional Characteristics of Plastics," *Lubrication Eng.,* 11, No. 5 (Sept.-Oct. 1955).

49. Bernard C. Stupp, "Molybdenum Disulfide and Related Solid Lubricants," ASLE Preprint No. 57AM-5C-2, April 17, 1957.

50. H. H. Krause, S. L. Cosgrove, and C. M. Allen, "Phthalocyanines as High-Temperature Lubricants," *J. Chem. Eng. Data,* 6, No. 1, (Jan. 1961).

51. R. J. Matt, J. B. Muratore, R. E. Murteza, and C. J. Zupkus, "Research and Development of Airframe Bearings for Aerospace Vehicles," Progress Report No. 2 November 8, 1962, prepared under Contract AF33(567)-8431 by New Departure Division of General Motors Corporation.

52. M. E. Campbell and J. W. Van Wyk, "Development of Design Criteria For a Dry Film Lubricated Bearing System," Contract No. AF33(616)-7395 ASD-TDR-62-1057 (January 1963).

53. A. Sonntag, "Solid Lubricants for Extreme Pressures," *Product Eng.,* 30, No. 25 (1959).

54. W. C. Hart and B. Rubin, "Evaluation of Dry-Film Lubricant Coatings," WADC Technical Report 53-466 Part I (Sep. 1954).

55. Bernard Rubin, "Evaluation of Dry Film Lubricants," WADC Technical Report 53-466, Part II, ASTIA Document No. AD 97318 (Sep. 1956).

56. M. T. Lavik, "High Temperature Solid Dry Film Lubricants," WADC Technical Report 57-455 Part II, ASTIA Document No. 203121 (Oct. 1958).

57. John R. Jones and C. S. Armstrong, "Boeing Summary Report of W.S.U.

Contract on High Temperature Dry Lubricants," Document No. D2-5984 March 23, 1960.

58. R. D. Brown, R. A. Burton, and P. M. Ku, "Investigation of Lubricants for Satellite and Space Vehicle Instrumentation," Final Report April 30, 1963, prepared under contract No. DA 36-039 SC-89207 by Southwest Research Institute.

59. Douglas Godfrey and E. E. Bisson, "Effectiveness of Molybdenum Disulfide as a Fretting Corrosion Inhibitor," Natl. Advisory Comm. Aeronaut., Tech. Note 2180 (Sept. 1950).

60. G. Spengler and H. Hohm, U.S. Pat. 3,051,535 (August 28, 1962).

61. R. V. Klint and R. S. Owens, U.S. Patent 3,051,535 (August 28, 1962).

62. V. G. FitzSimmons and W. A. Zisman, "Microfilm Reinforcement of Polytetrafluoroethylene," NRL Report 5724 (Jan. 9, 1962).

63. F. Macks, "Lubrication Reference Manual for Missile and Space Vehicle Propulsion at Temperatures above 700°F," WADC Technical Report 58-638, Vol. 1, Part 1, ASTIA Document No. AD 213474 (Jan. 1959).

64. Federal Test Method Standard No. 791, "Lubricants, Liquid Fuels and Related Products; Methods of Testing," (Method 333).

65. M. J. Devine, E. R. Lamson, and J. H. Bowen, Jr., Journal of Chemical and Engineering Data, Vol. 6, No. 1, (Jan. 1961).

66. M. J. Devine, E. R. Lamson, and J. H. Bowen, Jr., "The Lubrication of Ball Bearings with Solid Films," ASME Paper No. 61-LUBS-11.

67. S. F. Murray and P. Lewis, GEL Report No. 60GL159 (1 Aug. 1960) and GEL Report No. 61GL48 (17 Feb. 1961).

68. F. J. Clauss, "Lubricants and Self-Lubricating Materials for Spacecraft Mechanisms," Lockheed Missiles and Space Division Report LMSD-894812 (18 April 1961).

69. M. P. Hnilicha, "High Vacuum Lubrication Research," Presented at 13th Meeting, Lubricants Group, Washington, D. C. (23 Oct. 1962).

70. V. Hopkins and D. Gaddis, Midwest Research Reports No. 9 (1 Sept.-30 Nov. 1961) and No. 15 (23 March-22 June 1962).

71. C. N. Coenraads and J. E. Lavelle, *Rev. Scientific Instruments,* **33**, No. 8 (Aug. 1962).

72. M. B. Peterson, "High Temperature Lubrication," Paper presented at Symposium on Lubrication and Wear, University of Houston (June 1963).

73. P. Lewis, S. F. Murray, and M. B. Peterson, "Investigation of Complex Bearing and/or Lubrication Systems," First Quarterly Progress Report prepared under Contract AF33(657)-8666 (Aug. 5, 1962).

74. Military Specification MIL-M-7866A, Molybdenum Disulfide Powder, Lubricant (Dec. 22, 1955).

75. Federal Specification SS-G-659A, Proposed, Graphite, Lubricating (Feb. 27, 1963).

76. Military Specification MIL-L-8937(ASG), Lubricant, Solid Film, Heat Cured (Feb. 12, 1963).

77. Military Specification MIL-L-23398(WEP), Lubricant, Solid Film, Air Drying (July 31, 1962).

78. M. B. Peterson, J. J. Florek, and S. F. Murray, ASLE Preprint 59 AMIA2.

79. F. K. Orcutt, H. H. Krause, and C. M. Allen, ASME Paper No. 61-LUBS-14.

80. The Texas Co., New York, N. Y., *Lubrication Eng.* **9**, (Aug. 1953).
81. A. C. West, *Lubrication Eng.*, **9**, No. 4 (Aug. 1953).
82. C. V. Smalheer and T. W. Mastin, *J. Inst. Petrol.*, **42**, No. 395 (Nov. 1956).
83. H. W. Schultze, R. R. Freeman, and J. Z. Briggs, "Molybdenum Coatings," *Mater. Design Eng.* (Jan. 1959).
84. N. A. Lange, *Handbook of Chemistry*, 7th ed. (1949).
85. A. M. Sabroff and P. D. Frost, "A Comparison of Lubricants and Coatings for Cold Extruding Titanium," ASLE Paper 59LC-4 (Oct. 1959).

## ADDITIONAL READING

J. K. Lancaster and P. A. Grattan, "Abrasion By Lamellar Solid Lubricants," Royal Aircraft Establishment Tech. Rep. No. 66012, Jan. 1966.

S. B. Seeley, "Natural Graphite," *Encyclopedia of Chemical Technology*, Vol. 4, 2nd ed., pp. 304–335.

S. F. Murray and P. Lewis, "Lubricant Life Tests on Ball Bearings For Space Applications," Final Report 28, Oct. 1965, prepared under Contract No. NAS5-9028 by Mechanical Technology Inc.

D. G. Flom, A. J. Haltner, and C. A. Gaulin, "Friction and Cleavage of Lamellar Solids in Ultra-High Vacuum," *Trans. ASLE*, **8**, No. 2 (April 1965).

J. E. Brophy and R. W. Ingranham, U.S. Pat. 2,902,417 (Sept. 1, 1959).

E. A. Smith, "Bearing Alloys Containing Solid Lubricants," *Metallurgia*, **72**, No. 431 (Sept. 1965).

E. W. Turns and R. D. Krienke, "Alloy Electrodeposition of Silver Matrix Solid Film Lubricants," *Plating*, **52**, No. 11 (Nov. 1965).

L. G. Kellogg and W. G. Dewart, "Snap 8 Reactor Bearing Development," ASLE Paper No. 66 AM 7A1 (May 1966).

"Bibliography on Solid Lubricants," NASA SP-5037, Clearinghouse for Federal Scientific and Technical Information, Feb. 1966.

W. O. Winer, "Molybdenum Disulfide as a Lubricant: A Review of the Fundamental Knowledge," University of Michigan, Feb. 1966.

M. Eitel and W. Sibert, Ger. Pat. 1,038,687 (11 Sept. 1958).

D. J. Boes, "Lubrication With Solids," *Intern. Sci. Technol.*, No. 54 (June 1966).

J. Economy and R. Anderson, "A New Route to Boron Nitride," *Inorg. Chem.*, **5**, No. 6 (June 1966).

M., Feir, "Properties of Powder-Metal Parts," *Machine Design*, **38**, No. 13, (9 June 1966).

E. R. Braithwaite, *Solid Lubricants and Surfaces*, Pergamon Press, New York, 1964.

E. Rabinowicz, *Friction and Wear of Materials*, Wiley, New York, 1965.

M. J. Devine and E. R. Lamson, Can. Pat. 735,896 (7 June 1966).

F. P. Bowden and D. Tabor, *The Friction and Lubrication of Solids*, Clarendon Press, Oxford, 1950.

W. D. Craig, Jr., "Friction Variation of PTFE and $MoS_2$," *Lubrication Eng.*, **20**, No. 7 (July 1964).

V. G. FitzSimmons, U.S. Pat. 3,245,906 (April 12, 1966).

Surveys of Foreign Scientific and Technical Literature, "Molybdenum Disulfide-Base Solid Lubricants," Aerospace Technology Division, Library of Congress, Report 66-52 (11 May 1966).

R. B. Lewis, "Wear of Plastics—Evaluation for Engineering Application," ASME Paper No. 63-WA-325 (Nov. 1963).

M. Moses, "Applying Solid Film Lubricants to Small Precision Timing Mechanisms with a Semi-Automated Process," *Lubrication Eng.*, **22**, No. 7 (July 1966).

J. K. Lancaster, "Anisotropy in the Mechanical Properties of Lamellar Solids and Its Effect on Wear and Transfer," *Wear,* **9**, No. 3 (May/June 1966).

W. J. Physioc, III, U.S. Pat. 3,259,519 (July 5, 1966).

N. P. Chironis, "Powder Lubrication," *Product Eng.*, **37**, No. 1 (Jan. 3, 1966).

R. P. Staijn, "The Effect of Time, Temperature and Environment on the Sliding Behavior of Polytetrafluoroethylene," ASLE Paper 65LC-22 (Presented at ASLE/ASME Lubrication Conference, San Francisco, Calif. Oct. 1965).

T. Sakurai and K. Sato, "Study of Corrosivity and Correlation Between Chemical Reactivity and Load Carrying Capacity of Oils Containing Extreme Pressure Agents," ASLE Paper 65-LC-11 (Presented at ASLE/ASME Lubrication Conference, San Francisco, Calif., October 1965).

G. M. Bartenev and A. I. El'kin, "Friction Properties of High Elastic Materials," *Wear,* **8**, No. 1 (Jan./Feb. 1965).

E. E. Bisson and W. J. Anderson, "Advanced Bearing Technology," NASA SP-38, U.S. Govt. Printing Office (1964).

H. J. Carper and R. A. Burton, "Design and Development of a Solid Film Lubricant Bearing Tester," Special Report March 15, 1965, prepared under Contract No. AF 33(657)-11088 by Southwest Research Institute.

R. Benzing, V. Hopkins, M. Petronio, and F. Villforth, Jr., "Friction and Wear Devices—A Survey," Report of Subcommittee on Wear, Lubrication Fundamentals Committee, American Society of Lubrication Engineers (1966).

R. B. Seymour, "Plastics—Annual Review," *Ind. Eng. Chem.*, **58**, No. 8 (Aug. 1966).

"Research in Materials Science and Engineering," Massachusetts Institute of Technology, Annual Report 1964-65 (April 1965).

A. J. Stock, "Solid Lubricants for Processing Plants," *Chem. Eng.*, **73**, No. 15 (July 18, 1966).

A. J. Lomax and J. T. O'Rourke, "TFE-Lubricated Thermoplastics," *Machine Design,* **38**, No. 15 (June 23, 1966).

Radiation-Effects State of the Art 1964-1965, Radiation Effects Information Center, Battelle Memorial Institute, REIC Report No. 38, June 30, 1965.

W. A. Glaeser, M. F. Amateau, and C. M. Allen, "A Study of Sleeve Bearings in Aircraft Support Structures," Summary Report, February 11, 1966, Prepared under Bureau of Naval Weapons Contract NOw-62-0432-C by Battelle Memorial Institute.

B. D. McConnell and T. Liu, "Research for Dry Lubricating Materials," Technical Papers for Air Force Materials Symposium/1965, AFML-TR-65-29 (May 1965).

C. M. Allen, U.S. Pat. 3,265,617 (August 9, 1966).

# 13

# Coatings

## Philip A. Di Mattia
*Supervisor in Education,*
*Research, and Development,*
*Massachusetts State Department*
*of Education, Boston, Mass.*

## CONTENTS

# I. INTRODUCTION

Plastics continue to be the backbone in the coating industry since almost all coatings are composed of polymeric materials. The most widely used are based on alkyds, vinyls, acrylics, urea-melamine, styrenes, epoxies and phenolics. Growth has been steady and reliable so that rashional and economic paint production can no longer be regarded, as was the case until comparatively recent, as an art or craft based solely on empirical expanse.

It is estimated that total shipment for coatings in 1965 was $2.1 billion or 760 millions of gallons, in 1966 sales should be at least $2.2 billion or 795 million gallons, and by 1970 sales will be $2.6 billion or 870 million gallons.

The products of the coating industry are essential for the protection and decoration of the majority of manufactured goods and architectural or industrial structures which characterize our complex material civilization. The protective function includes resistance to air, water, organic liquids and aggressive chemicals such as acids and alkalis, together with improved superficial mechanical properties such as greater hardness and abrasion resistance. The decorative effect may be obtained through color, gloss or texture or combinations of these properties.

In the case of many surfaces such as walls or floors, or objects such as interior fittings, furniture and other articles, the surface coating should also fulfill hygienic requirements. The surface should not be prone to collect dirt, bacteria and other impurities. It should be easy to clean with common cleaning agents.

In certain cases special qualities are required of the surface coating, for example, in road-marking paints, in safety-marking paints, in factories and in paints which make the surface either a good or poor

Fig. 13-1. Texas Gulf Coast has been expanding the use of elastomer liners in wire reinforced rubber hose for bulk transfer of chemicals. Pioneer for the DuPont Viton (fluoroelostomer) liner was the docking hose installation in Beaumont of Mobil Chemical Company. The hose is made by B. F. Goodrich Industrial Products Co.

electrical conductor. Metals may be surface coated to improve their workability in mechanical processing.

Substrates protected from different environmental conditions basically include the metals (steel, zinc, aluminum and copper), inorganic materials (plaster, concrete and asbestos) and organic materials (wood, wallboard, wallpaper and plastics). Different technical developments have occurred in the coating industry which permit the use of a variety of raw materials. It is possible to formulate surface coatings which are suitable for each and every kind of material. In many cases a number of different coating systems may come into consideration for painting a particular substrate. In almost all cases a painting problem may be solved in a variety of ways.

Fig. 13-2. Hose of solvent-resistent coating of Vitron (flouoroelastomer) has been in service at this dock since early 1962.

Plastic resins are employed in the manufacture of most of the coating compounds. Approximately one fourth of all the resins produced are consumed as coating materials in the various forms of paints, varnishes, enamels, etc.

There are many varied methods of coating including spraying, dipping, brushing and roller coating. Coating materials are composed of both thermosetting and thermoplastic resin. The spray, dip and brush methods allow a protective plastic covering to be placed on all surfaces of large and/or complex shapes, and lowers the overall cost of coating an article.

Based on the relatively low capital investments in coating producing plants, the return on investment can be considered excellent when compared to other industries. Net profit margins continue to be in the 6% of sales bracket. This is better than the national average for all manufacturers. At present profit for the major type products has been principally due to improved plant manufacturing efficiency. Most of today's production is by batch process. Automation and mass production techniques are still for the future after more standardization develops.

No positive tabulation exists on the number of companies involved in manufacturing coatings. Estimates for 1966 range from 1500 to 2000 in U.S. Sherwin-Williams Company has about 9% of the total market, followed with du Pont at 8%, Pittsburgh Plate Glass Company at 7% and Glidden at 5%. These four companies with the next 16 largest producers, represents 50% of total coating sales.

One of the fastest growing companies is DeSoto Chemical Coatings, Inc. producing over $60 million sales in coatings. Sears-Robuck Company owns 53% of the DeSoto stock.

## A. Definitions

Coatings are generally identified as paints, varnishes and lacquers. Other nomenclature includes enamels, hot melts, plastisol, organosol, aerospace coatings, masonry water repellents, polishes, magnetic tape coatings and overlays. There are 100% plastic coatings such as vinyl coated fabrics or polyurethane floor coverings. The more popular, and the largest user of plastics, are the paints. Almost all the binders in paints, varnishes and lacquers are made up principally of synthetic resins.

## 1. Paints

A paint consists of three main components; namely, the binder, the pigment and the solvent. The function of the binder is to provide the

TABLE 13-1. U.S. Consumption of Synthetic Resins in Paints annd Related Surface Coatings [a]

|  | Millions of pounds | | | |
|---|---|---|---|---|
|  | 1960 | 1961 | 1962 | 1963 |
| Alkyd | 521 | 513 | 533 | 540 |
| Epoxy | 18 | 20 | 33 | 39 |
| Phenolic | 27 | 27 | 35 | 32 |
| Polyurethane [b] | 6 | 8 | 12 | 20 |
| Poly(vinyl acetate) | 29 | 40 | 51 | 74 |
| Poly(vinyl chloride) | 38 | 36 | — | — |
| Styrene | 76[c] | 80[c] | 55 | 44 |
| Urea-melamine | 41 | 41 | 42 | 49 |

[a] Source: U.S. Tariff Commission, Synthetic Organic Coatings—data on such important coating resins as acrylics, nitrocellulose, polybutenes, and polyurethanes are not reported.

[b] Trade source estimates are included in this table. PU estimates are 30 million lb in 1965, 35 in 1966 and 52 in 1970.

[c] Includes styrenated alkyd polyesters.

TABLE 13-2. U.S. Estimated Consumption of Latex Paints [a]

|  | Millions of gallons | | | |
|---|---|---|---|---|
|  | 1962 | 1963 | 1964 | 1965 |
| Acrylics | 18 | 20 | 24 | 29 |
| Polyvinyl acetate and copolymers | 40 | 50 | 64 | 84 |
| Styrene butadiene | 38 | 30 | 29 | 32 |

[a] Estimates are that the total latex sales will go from the 150 million gallons in 1965 to 350 million gallons in 1975 using principally polyvinyl acetate and acrylic.

forces which hold the film together (cohesive forces) and which hold film and substrate together (adhesive forces) (1).

The pigment is a fine powder whose function is to give the coating its desired color and hiding properties. The pigment has a considerable influence on the consistency of the paint and in turn on its application properties. Pigments are also of importance for the resistance of the coating to external attack, in that they are partially responsible for such properties as hardeners and resistance to abrasion and weathering.

The solvent is a volatile liquid whose function is to dissolve such

Fig. 13-3. DeSoto Chemical Coatings, Inc. uses Hydrocide Colorcoat, a durable, long-life decorative waterproofing compound. After the storm (right photo), the building has shrugged off the snow and moisture and its Colorcoat exterior with its ultraviolet ray absorber now protects it against direct ultraviolet rays and those reflected by the surrounding snow and the lake. Colorcoat is an oil-based coating containing silicones, epoxies fiberglass filaments, low chalk pigmentation, and an ultraviolet ray absorber—particularly important here because of the reflection from the lake.

binders as would be solid or semisolid at normal temperature. In addition to these three basic components, modern coatings may contain additives of various kinds. Examples are plasticizers, dryers, wetting agents, flattenings agents and emulsifiers or other stabilizers.

The binder is the most important of the three main components and is always present in a manufactured paint. It usually represents 40–50 wt % of the paint. Many of the properties of paints are related products are determined directly by the nature of the binder. For this reason paints are often classified, and may even be named, according to the type of binder.

Some binders are identified or arranged according to type of drying. A differentiation is made between physical and chemical drying in accordance with the way a coating forms, such as:

*a.* Physical Film Formation (Evaporation of solvent—or of dispersion medium in the case of latices)

    Cellulosic:

        Nitrocellulose and other esters of cellulose

        Ethylcellulose

    Vinyl resins:

        Polyvinyl chloride

        Polyvinyl acetate

        Polyvinyl acetal

    Acrylic ester resins

    Chlorinated rubber

    Natural resins:

        Shellac

        Rosin and rosin ester (ester gum)

        Bitumen (asphalts)

        Glue

*b.* Chemical Film Formation (Convertible) Oxidative Drying

    Drying oils:

        Linseed oil

        Tung oil

    Varnishes, oleoresinous

    Alkyd resins, modified with drying oils

    Cold Curing

        Urea-formaldehyde resins

        Polyester resins, unsaturated

        Epoxide resins, amine cured

        Polyurethane resins

Thermosetting
> Alkyd resins, short or medium oil length, modified with non-dying oils
> Alkyd, water soluble
> Epoxide resins
> Addition polymers, water soluble
> Acrylic resins

Crosslinked with amino or phenolic resins

Curing may be defined as a process in which drying occurs by a chemical reaction between the molecules of the binder not involving gaseous oxygen. If the reaction occurs at room temperature the products are described inaccurately as "cold curing lacquers." If temperatures of 70°C or higher are necessary to cause rapid reaction, the materials are known as stoving or baking coatings. In view of the many different kinds of chemical reactions which are now used to produce insoluble coatings, the term convertible coating has been introduced.

A convertible coating may be defined as one in which the binder in its final form in the film differs chemically from the binder in the form in which it is applied. The conversion of the one form to the other may be achieved by the action of some component of the atmosphere, such as oxygen or water; by heat; by radiation; by the use of catalysts; or by reaction between two or more binder components which are mixed just prior to application.

These reaction-type coatings give films with greater hardness and chemical resistance than those obtained by oxidative drying.

## 2. *Water-Base Paints*

Water-base, water-thinned, aqueous and other terms are used to refer to paints containing water. Technically three types exist: (*1*) latex or emulsion paints made with synthetic resins such as acrylic, polyvinyl acetate or butadiene-styrene; (*2*) water-soluble oils or alkyds; and (*3*) emulsified oils or alkyds.

Original water-base paints using casein and the emulsion oil paints containing alkyd resin and water were introduced just prior to World War II. Latex paints using butadiene-styrene followed World War II. They were referred to as rubber base paints which lacked ruggedness. In 1953 the acrylic emulsion type paint was introduced for indoor surfaces and outside masonry surfaces. By 1957 acrylic emulsion types for exterior wood surfaces were on the market.

Water-based coatings continue to be the gleam in industries eye.

Elimination of the solvent fumes systems reduces fire and explosion hazards, improves working conditions and reduces insurance rates. These new systems are more expensive insofar as the coating is concerned, and also the "paint booth apparatus." Water is more costly to evaporate and its rate of evaporation is more difficult to control.

### 3. Varnishes

The word varnish was derived during the sixteenth century. It denoted a fluid mixture of amber and oil or more generally, of resin and oil. This latter meaning has survived to the present day.

### 4. Lacquers

This term is frequently applied to almost any coating composition which dries solely, and rapidly, by evaporation of the solvent. It originally was almost exclusively associated with nitrocellulose-based coatings. At the present time it generally refers to coatings having nitrocellulose or possibly another cellulose derivative.

## II. PROPERTIES OF POLYMERS

Almost all the binders in the paint, varnish, and lacquer coatings are composed of polymeric materials. The plastics are applied in one operation or built up during drying processes. The physical and chemical properties of the vinyl coating have a direct relationship to the basic polymeric material. The use of synthetic resins dates back to the turn of the century. Up until World War I they were principally used as low-cost substitutes for natural resins. Since 1915 many different synthetic resins have been used which offer many advantages compared with the natural resins.

The synthetic resins are less subject to variations in availability and consequently present a more stable cost. They may be produced to fairly close technical tolerances, while the natural resins show wide variations in quality. More important, however, is the fact that the synthetic resins can be varied in relation to the end use for which they are required.

The major long-range trend in paints and related surface coatings is towards greater efficiency. The target continues to be products with better environmental protection or decoration for longer periods of time at lower total cost per square foot. Paints compete with a variety of other surfacing materials, such as; wallpaper (vinyl, polyethylene and polyvinylfluoride films), porcelain enamels and electroplated, phosphated or oxidized metal films. In addition coatings and their substrates compete against structural materials requiring no special surface coatings; such as, stainless steel, aluminum, glass, stone and brick, reinforced plastics, extruded plastics or molded plastics. However, there are many new applications where the materials such as steel, aluminum, wood, concrete and brick are using plastic coatings to provide more durable and attractive products.

To meet competition, the paint industry continues to develop new formulations and new methods of applications. Since highest performance per unit cost is desired, there is continual effort to lower the cost per square foot per surface coated, either by lowering material costs per pound, using thinner films or devising more economical means of application. Application techniques have involved extensive laboratory tests with different composite resins.

## III. FUNDAMENTALS OF POLYMER FORMATION

Since 1929 when W. N. Carothers proposed a classification of polymers into two groups, resins continue to be identified as condensation or addition types. Condensation polymerization is the process by which a polymer is built up by successive reactions between monomer molecules and the growing polymer. In each reaction step, in addition to increasing the polymer size, it produces a small molecule such as water, hydrogen chloride or sodium chloride.

Addition polymerization is the process by which a polymer is built up by a repeated addition reaction between monomer molecules and the growing polymer. This action occurs within any other reaction product than the polymer being formed. The monomer, in the majority of cases of practical importance, is an unsaturated compound, usually a vinyl derivative. While an addition polymer has the same elementary composition as the monomer, this is not true for condensation polymers.

### A. Condensation Types

#### 1. Alkyd Resins

Alkyds are polyesters formed by repeated esterification reactions (polycondensation) between polyhydric alcohols and di- or poly-basic carboxylic acids (or their anhydrides). The name alkyd was coined to express the fact that these resins are products of an al-cohol and an a-cid, the "cid" being altered to "kyd" indicates the pronunciation and avoids too closely similarity to the word "acid" in print.

Many variations in the constituents and portions of the alkyd coating material is available. Also many different binders can be used, such as, drying oils, phenolic resins, amino resins, nitrocellulose, maleic resins, chlorinated rubber and cyclized rubber. As a group the alkyds are distinguished by rapid drying, good adhesion, elasticity, marproofness, and durability. Their principal weakness resides in the facility with which the ester groups, which form a large part of the molecules, are hydrolysed (particularly under alkaline conditions). Even in this respect it is possible to produce alkyds with greatly improved resistance to hydrolysis, by the use of polyols.

They were very instrumental in the coatings used in industry for producing automobiles, refrigerators, washing machines and many other consumer goods.

Styrenated alkyds (in contrast to the styrenated oils) have been used with a fair amount of success as binders in very rapid air-drying and rapid, low-temperature stoving finishes. Alkyds are also modified with vinyl derivatives such as esters of acrylic and methacrylic acids, or with mixtures of these compounds and styrene or vinyltoluene. It appears that none of these combinations have had practical commercial success.

### 2.   Unsaturated Polyester Resins

The term unsaturated polyester resins is now restricted to products consisting of straight-chain polyesters having reactive double bonds at intervals along the chain. They are supplied as solutions in a vinyl monomer, generally styrene. Before application an initiator and a promoter are added, usually together with extra vinyl monomer. A copolymerization is thereby initiated. The polyester chains become linked together in a crosslink network by means of bridges formed by polymerized vinyl monomers.

The major use for these resins are in reinforced laminates or moldings. The polyesters can be cured under low pressure and at low temperature.

The unsaturated polyesters are of particular interest in the coatings field. The monomer may be used to adjust the viscosity of the coating to the required value. In most cases this action occurs in conjunction with minor amounts of solvents. It has had limited successful use in the coating industry principally due to the fact that the curing is strongly inhibited by atmospheric oxygen. The result is that the surface of the polyester coating remains soft and sticky.

## 3. Phenolic Resins

The first phenolic resin appeared on the market in 1902. It was a spirit soluble, non-hardening novolac type. It was intended as a substitute for shellac and spirit varnishes. In 1907, Baekelind's historic patent for the preparation of phenolic resin molding compound was published. This type phenolic resin was not suitable for coatings.

The first patented for oil-soluble phenolic resin was issued in 1913. Then followed different patents for different phenolic resin coating formulations. Many different types are now available with extensive service life.

## 4. Amino Resins

A number of resins contained nitrogen are classed together as amino resins. This terminology tends to be confusing but continues to be used. Amino resins are obtained by condensation of amino or amido compounds with aldehydes. The most important are the urea and melamine resins (thermosetting) and the aniline resins (thermoplastics). The thermosetting coatings are of interest in the coatings field.

TABLE 13-3. Introduction Dates for Some of the Important Synthetic Coating Binders

| Year | Binder |
|------|--------|
| 1913 | Rosin-modified phenolic resin |
| 1920 | Nitrocellulose as binder in lacquers |
| 1928 | 100% phenolic resin |
| 1928 | Alkyd resin |
| 1930 | Chlorinated rubber |
| 1930 | Vinyl polymers |
| 1936 | Butanol-modified urea resin |
| 1940 | Melamine resin |
| 1940 | Polyurethane |
| 1944 | Silicone products |
| 1947 | Epoxide resin |
| 1948 | Emulsion polymer as binder in latex paints |
| 1950 | Unsaturated polyester resin |
| 1954 | Thixotropic alkyd |
| 1955 | Water soluble convertible binders |

Fig. 13-4. A 50-in. paper web unroll (right) through a phenolic resin bath, into the drying tower, and is rolled dry (left background). At the top of the tower are two new rollers protected with DuPont coatings of FEP-fluorocarbon resin.

Urea resins are not used alone as binders and coatings. When they cure the films are brittle and lack adhesion. The usual modifiers are alkyd resins, as well combinations with nitrocellulose. In the latter case the improved gloss tends to increase yellowing.

The melamine resins are replacing the ureas in many applications. The most important use for urea resin is in combination with alkyd resins. This combination improves water, alkali and chemical resistance. By suitable choice of alkyd virtually nonyellowing finishes may be obtained.

### 5. Melamine Resins

Melamine is a white, crystalline powder with a high melting point. It differs from urea being very sparingly soluble in water. They are prepared in the same way as urea resins by condensation with formaldehyde.

## 6. Epoxy Resins

Epoxies have provided the surface coatings industry with a wide variety of formulation possibilities. They are used alone or in combination with other plastics. Even though it is at a higher price than other types of binders, its outstanding properties and versatility continues to expand its applications.

It provides good chemical resistance, in particular, excellent resistance to alkalis, including caustic alkalis. A major asset is its excellent adhesion to many different substrates. Other important properties include exceptional hardness and flexibility.

On the disadvantage side, it is not soluble in the lower cost solvents. Compatibility with other film formers is limited. Finishes based on epoxy resins have a marked tendacy to chalk out of doors and their water resistance is not always the best.

They are used in combinations with phenolic, urea and melamine resins as crosslinking agents. Cold-curing coatings with polyamines or polyamides as curing agents are very popular. Air-drying coatings are also popular. They are produced after esterification with unsaturated fatty acids. The product is known as epoxide ester or epoxy ester.

The combination of epoxy with phenolic can give maximum resistance to chemicals and solvents combined, combined with adhesion, flexibility, hardness and abrasion resistance. The most suitable phenolic resins for cold blending are of the butylated resole type.

Polyamide resins which are formulated to contain free amine groups can serve as catalyst for epoxy resins. The polyamide resins are practically nontoxic or nonirritant to humans, whereas some of the amine catalyst (used with epoxies) must be handled with special precausions. The polyamide combinations produces tough films in combination with a lower resistance to solvents and chemicals.

## 7. Urethane Resins

There are many different types of urethane coatings on the market. For coating applications, a crosslinked film is preferred and thermoplastic urethanes are of little interest. The usual hazards associated with isocynates are applicable in preparing these coatings.

By a suitable choice of components it is possible to obtain almost any degree of flexibility and hardness, ranging from highly elastic films for coating rubber and leather articles to extremely hard, abrasion-resistant coatings for floors, boats and metals. These coatings are relatively new

Fig. 13-5. Fabric-backed urethane is used as a grain chute lining for highly abrasive corn and soybeans at the A. E. Staley Manufacturing Company's grain elevators at Decatur, Illinois. It makes especially rugged conveyor liners for handling ore slurries, coal, coke, rock, sand and gravel, glass and other abrasive materials that can wear through the toughest high carbon steel. The fabric backing provides ease of installation with conventional rubber-resin adhesives. Material produced by Armstrong Cork Company is based on a UNI Royal formulation developed by the chemical division.

Fig. 13-6. These two sections of grain loading chutes were used the same length of time. The unlined steel chute on the right was worn through while the section lined with Armstrong's new fabric-backed UNI Royal urethane shows only a slight amount of surface abrasion.

TABLE 13-4. How Coatings Compare in Cost and Performance

| Type of coating | Flexibility | Chemical resistance | Stain resistance | Exterior durability | Cost/gal |
|---|---|---|---|---|---|
| Vinyls (solution) | Excellent | Excellent except for solvents | Limited | Very good | $5.00–7.00 |
| Alkyds | Fair | Limited | Good | Good | 2.20–3.25 |
| Plastisols and organosols | Excellent | Excellent except for solvents | Good | Very good | 4.00–6.00 |
| Nitrocellulose | Poor | Fair | Very good | Good | 3.00–5.50 |
| Epoxies | Excellent | Excellent | Very good | Poor | 4.50–6.00 |
| Phenolics | Poor | Excellent | Excellent | Poor | 3.00–4.50 |
| Vinyl-alkyds | Very good | Good | Limited | Good | 4.00–6.00 |
| Acrylics | Limited | Good | Excellent | Very good | 3.90–5.00 |
| Fluorocarbon | Excellent | Excellent | Excellent | Excellent | 2.00–5.00 |
| Silicones | Excellent | Very good | Very good | Excellent | 8.00–12.00 |

products and therefore are not fully developed. However, their importance in the coating industry is recognized.

### 8. Silicone Resins

Silicone resins are heat-convertible and are used either alone, or in combination with other binders in coatings. Their most important and distinguished property is resistance to degradation when exposed to high temperatures. In addition, they have good electrical properties and outdoor durability. Suitably pigmented silicone coatings will stand temperatures of 260°F continuously, while most other coatings would not even survive long time exposures at 150°F.

Silicone resins pigmented with aluminum powder or zinc dust give films which good weather and corrosion resistance at temperatures as high as 500°F. Silicone finishes in the electrical industry provides a combination of heat-resistance installation and electrical installation.

## B. Addition Types

### 1. Polyethylene Resins

The important and significant properties available with polyethylene binders are flexibility and water and chemical resistant. However, since it is insoluble in all organic solvents at temperatures below about

50°F, it cannot find a place in normal surface coatings. It can be applied directly from the solid by flame spraying. Also in most applications the substrate has to be pretreated in order to provide suitable adhesion.

DuPont has produced a polyethylene compound which is soluble in urea resins and epoxy resins to provide different type of coatings. These stituted with chloro and chlorosulphonyl groups. This coating gives highly elastic films characterized by particularly good resistance to strong acids such as concentrated hydroschoric and sulphric acids, and to oxidizing agents such as ozone, hydrogen peroxide and chromic acid. It is not resistant to hot concentrated nitric acid.

Hypalon combines with other binders such as chlorinated rubber, urea resins and epoxy resins to provide different type coatings. These different coatings are used in various chemical bath containers.

## 2.  Vinyl Resins

The principle vinyl resins used in coatings are the copolymers of vinyl chloride and vinyl acetate. Polyvinylidene chloride and polyvinylbutyral are also important. Polyvinylacetate in emulsion form is widely used in architectural coatings.

The vinyl copolymers produce air-drying coatings which have excellent toughness and good resistance to water and chemicals. However, they are sensitive to heat, ultraviolet radiation and many solvents. They are high polymers and therefore require fairly strong solvents. Development of the dispersion type of vinyl resin permits their application as organisols and plastisols at high solid content which extend their usefulness considerably. They do not have high solids at spraying consistency.

Vinyl resins are widely used as fabric coatings because of their combination of toughness and flexibility, and their property of not supporting combustion. Because they are nonflammable they have replaced nitrocellulose lacquers for many applications on fabrics.

They produce excellent coatings on metals but care must be taken in their application because, like most high polymers, they have strong cohesives forces which may overcome the adhesive forces. The entire coating may flake off as a continuous sheet if the precise application conditions have not been complied with for the various modifications.

The absence of odor, taste and toxicity in vinyl coatings makes them suitable for the lining of beer cans. They have other applications in food containers but certain limitations exists. Namely, poor adhesion and sensitive to temperatures used in processing foods.

The vinyl copolymers can be used most efficiently in special applications such as hospital and dental equipment where durability is more important than initial cost. For laboratory equipment, epoxy resins may be preferred because the vinyls are sensitive to some solvents. The vinyl coating systems consisting of corrosion-inhibiting primer and chemical-resistant finish coats are used on new equipment for chemical plants. The metal conditioner based on zinc chromate and polyvinyl-butyral are widely used over sand-blasted steel as a use for vinyl systems on both industrial and marine equipment.

Polyvinyl acetate (PVA) in the pure and solid form is a colorless and transparent. It is somewhat brittle unless the degree of polymerization is low. Its softening temperature is between 40 and 90°F, depending on the molecular weight. It shows the phenomenon of cold flow.

Polyvinyl alcohol (PVAL) because of its water solubility has relatively a small part to play as a binder in surface coatings. It has been used as an impregnant in the production of grease proof paper, as a yarn sizing and for the production of water soluble packages. It is useful as a dispersing agent and protective colloid, for example in latex

Fig. 13-7. Bottled soft drinks are made in Finland from corrugated board coated with hot melt based on DuPont's ethylene vinyl acetate resin. The container is manufactured by Oy Tako of Tampere, Finland. It is made entirely of corrugated, except for reinforcing steel rod inside upper rim. The hot-melt coating protects the board from moisture and wear, providing as many as 10 return trips. The new case was awarded Finland's National Packaging Award at the recent International Trade Fair in Helsinki (1967).

paints. It has the advantage over glue and casein that it is much less susceptible to microbiological attack.

**a. Dispersion Coatings—PVC.** At this time, most dispersion coatings available on the market are based largely on the polyvinyl-chloride homopolymer type of resin. While other types of dispersion coatings, such as those based on polyvinyl fluoride and polyvinylidene fluoride are beginning to appear on the market place, major reference will be made to the polyvinyl chloride type of dispersion coatings which are finding important new applications in industrial finishes today (1966) because of their economy and excellent performance characteristics (3).

In 1944, a real breakthrough was made by Quarles and Powell of the Union Carbide Plastics Co., when they developed a new way of taking advantage of the good properties of high molecular weight vinyl chloride resins by discovering what is now known as the "dispersion technique." The dispersion coatings made by the "dispersion technique" and the improvements thereon will be the subject of our discussion in this paper.

Dispersion coatings, also known as organosols and plastisols, are much more recent than the conventional solution vinyl coatings which performed so well for the organic coatings industry over the past twenty-odd years, and which are still used today in good quantity. These solution vinyl resin coatings are based on copolymers of vinyl chloride and vinyl acetate and are of relatively low molecular weight. Polymers containing third components have also been introduced and are to provide the industry with vinyl polymers which are carboxyl (—COOH), hydroxyl (—OH) or otherwise terminated for the attainment of special properties.

It has long been known that the higher molecular weight vinyl resins produced films which gave the best toughness and resistance properties. The resultant coatings, however, had poor adhesion to metal substrates, gave very low solids when dissolved in even the strongest solvents and exhibited poor flow properties as well. By not dissolving this resin, but dispersing it suitably, the new family of coating materials which we shall discuss today was born—dispersion coatings.

A vinyl dispersion is a suspension of colloidal size particles in an organic medium which is not capable of dissolving the resin at room temperature, but which exerts some solvating or peptizing effect on the polymer particles. When the organic medium contains volatile solvent(s) the mixture is called an organosol. Mixtures which do not contain appreciable amounts of volatile thinner(s) are referred to as plastisols. Organosol dispersions normally contain 40–80% solids whereas plastisols contain 90–100% solids.

The resin particle diameter range varies from 0.1 to 1.0 $\mu$. Relative viscosity is in the range 2.50–3.0 for the higher molecular weight resins and 2.05–2.4 for the lower molecular weight materials. Relative viscosity ($\eta r$), also referred to as viscosity ratio, is defined as the ratio of the viscosity of a 1% resin solution in cyclohexanone at 25°C, to the viscosity of pure cyclohexanone at 25°C.

**(1) Composition.** In general, dispersion coatings are composed of the ingredients shown in Table 13-5. The liquid phase, i.e., solvents, diluents, and plasticizers of the dispersion system perform multiple functions such as wetting aids, dispersing media, viscosity depressants (thinner) and stabilizers, and fusion aids.

Because of this multiple role, these liquid components must be meticulously selected to achieve a dispersion system with proper application and coalescing properties. Not only must they be perfectly balanced for good flow properties to prevent flocculation or over-solvation and even gellation of the dispersion resin, but consideration must be also given to the requirements of and interactions with the other formula ingredients, such as the pigment, resin, and other modifying materials.

One of the defects noticeable in an organosol film with inadequate solvent balance is called "mud-cracking." The organosols are prone to this condition because they inherently tend to release solvents very rapidly. In a deposited film, a too rapid loss of solvent results in volume shrinkage and hence causes "mud-cracking." This condition can be avoided by combining a fast cure rate (to quickly coalesce or fuse the tiny resin particles) with a "slow" solvent system to keep the film "mobile" for as long as is necessary to obtain optimum film properties.

In some specially developed organosol coating systems, it has been practically impossible to design solvent systems which would produce good flow, aid in proper fuse-out of the film and still be viscosity-stable on storage. Such coating materials are sold as two-package systems. The organosol component contains a balanced solvent system for the ingredients contained therein, yielding a storage-stable liquid which may be clear or pigmented. The catalyst component, which may contain the modifying resins or crosslinking agents also utilizes solvents which are properly balanced for this component and it, too, forms a storage-stable liquid, clear or pigmented, as the case may be. The

TABLE 13-5.   General Composition of Dispersion Coatings

| | |
|---|---|
| Dispersion resin(s) | |
| Pigments | |
| Plasticizers | |
| Diluents and solvents | |
| Stabilizers and crosslinking agents | |
| Modifying resins | |
| Acrylic | Oleoresinous |
| Alkyd | Phenolic |
| Amino | Polyester |
| Epoxy | Silicone |
| Hydrocarbon | Vinyl copolymers |
| (incl. polybutadiene) | |
| Ketone | Other |

organosol and catalyst components are usually mixed equal parts by volume to form a coating with the desired end properties. In approximately six hours (depending on specific composition, ambient temperature and humidity), oversolvation may start and viscosity begin to rise. In such a case, fresh "equal parts" mixture is added, and the blend may normally be used with complete satisfaction. In commercial practice, the make-up or replenishing coating material effectively eliminates any practical concern regarding viscosity rise. Any catalyzed mixture held over a weekend, for example, is merely checked for fluidity and added to a fresh "equal parts" mixture.

When storing dispersion systems, one should recognize that the dispersants or polar solvents are more powerful in their action at higher temperatures and hence organosol materials should not be stored in the hot sun or next to radiators where the coating temperature will rise to higher than 120°F or oversolvation may occur. Also, since solvent power falls off with the reduction of ambient temperatures, undersolvation and possibly flocculation may occur if organosols are stored outside for long periods during the winter in cold areas. Never heat up dispersion coatings rapidly with devices such as immersion heaters or oversolvation and even gellation can occur.

**(2) *Methods of Applications.*** Dispersion resins can be applied by a variety of methods including spray, knife, roller, dip, and extrusion. While spraying techniques are mostly reserved for organosols and extrusion procedures for plastisols, the other methods are common to both type systems. The choice of method of application or dispersion systems (organosol or plastisol) is dictated by film thickness requirements, available application techniques (i.e., spray, extrusion) and/or processing equipment (i.e., shear mixers or roller mills) substrates, and of course, product performance.

It is interesting to note that, due to the puffy or thixotropic nature of dispersion coatings, these materials can be applied at much higher than normal viscosities. The shear forces exerted during recirculation and in the coating roller nip of a roller coater; or during spraying; or during extrusion are effective in reducing the actual coating viscosity of these materials. In addition, flow is assisted by the normal coalescence or fusion of the resin particles in the baking oven.

All dispersion coatings must be properly baked or fused in order to coalesce the tiny dispersed resin particles into a continuous, tough, and flexible film. Depending on formulation and dwell time, the required fusing temperatures (based on actual metal temperatures) varies from 300–525°F. The preferred cycle for sheet bakes is 10 min in the 350–525°F range. In moving web application, i.e., coil or strip coating, a cure cycle of 60 sec or less at about 525°F yields good results. These cited examples, of course, are for vinyl chloride dispersion systems. Fluorinated dispersion coatings require substantially higher temperatures, (approximately 550–600°F) for proper film formation.

Since fusion of the dispersed particles is the major objective in the curing procedure, the baking cycle for a given application depends upon how quickly the wet film reaches fusing temperature. When this critical temperature is reached, the tiny, partially solvated particles quickly coalesce into a homogeneous coating.

Problems of thermal degradation will occur if the coating is subjected to temperatures in excess of 500°F for vinyl chloride dispersion; in excess of 600°F for vinyl or vinylidene fluoride dispersions for prolonged periods.

In the instances of vinyl chloride dispersion, the rate of thermal decomposition is accelerated in the presence of iron; and such situations occur, for example, when microscopically exposed tin plate is subjected to extreme temperature for only a few seconds. The resultant film is discolored black. Discoloration of this type can also mean that the oven has been set too high or developed a hot spot or similar difficulty. To deter these thermal effects, 0.5–15 pph of a stabilizer is admixed in the dispersion composition. Effective stabilizers include, metallic soaps, organic tin and cadmium salts, and epoxide resins.

Vinyl and vinylidene fluoride systems, although more thermally stable than their vinyl chloride cousins, undergo thermal decomposition at relatively high temperatures (>600°F). The process is greatly accelerated in the presence of glass or silica and these materials are to be avoided in formulating these systems. Copper, aluminum, and iron show no catalytic degradation effects; although, surprisingly, rutile titanium dioxide shows a tendency to discolor the vinylidene fluoride systems and discoloration becomes more pronounced with increasing pigment concentrations. Effective stabilizer products for these dispersion resins are calcium–zinc complexes or pentaerythritol in combination with an antioxidant.

It has been found that film integrity, gloss, flexibility and process or hot water resistance are materially affected by the baking cycles used. In practice, the fusing cycle must be especially established for each application. In general, optimum results are obtained when the coated metal is exposed to relatively high temperatures in the first oven zone. By doing this, the solvents in the dispersion composition have an opportunity to help solvate the dispersion resin before they are evaporated. Of course, care must be taken to adjust the temperatures in the first oven zones so that no blistering or pin holes occur.

Based on practical and theoretical consideration with PVC dispersion coatings, we found that 335°F is the minimum metal temperature at which the polyvinyl chloride dispersion should be fused for good results. A recommended sheet coating schedule, for example, would be 340–365°F for 6–10 min. A representative coil bake would be 60 sec at 500°F for 0.6 mil film. Properly cured films, thus baked achieve tensile strengths of 8,000–10,000 lb/sq in. Elongation is approximately 300%.

Similar curing considerations apply to the fluoropolymers. However, these coatings require considerably more energy to properly coalesce the film. Metal temperatures of 475°, approximately 100°F above those used for the vinyl chloride systems, are demanded. A representative coil bake, for these resins, for example, would be 425–475°F for 30–45 sec.

Table 13–6 presents the results obtained when pigmented vinyl chloride dispersion films applied at 30 mg/4 in.$^2$ to 0.010 in. chromate-phosphate treated 5052 alloy are cured at different temperatures and then subjected to 60 min steam sterilization at 15 lb/in.$^2$ at 250°F. It is apparent from this example that optimum film properties are obtained only if adequate cure cycles are used.

**(3) *Environmental Advantages.*** Dispersion type coatings have the following advantages for the organic finishes industry (as shown in Table 13-7).

Dispersion films are generally less expensive, more durable, inert,

TABLE 13-6

| Cure cycle,<br>60 sec at °F | "Scotch Tape"<br>adhesion test | |
|---|---|---|
| 400 | Poor—30%<br>area remaining | Blistering<br>Moderate |
| 425 | Fair—85%<br>area remaining | Slight |
| 450 | O.K. | None |
| 475 | O.K. | None |
| 500 | O.K. | None |

chemically resistant and perform better than ordinary or solution vinyl films. The lower molecular weight of the solution resins and/or modifications with other monomers are major causes for these differences. The solution resins do, however, have important advantages such as high gloss, low temperature film formulation and good adhesion to metal substrates. They are often added to dispersion coatings to take advantage of these properties, in many instances, without diluting the outstanding properties of the dispersion resin.

Because of their excellent chemical resistance properties, dispersion resins have qualified for usage in such diverse areas as liquid detergents, and waxes, artist clay, water base paints and cleaners and shellac.

TABLE 13-7. Advantages of Dispersion Coatings for Organic Finishes

| | |
|---|---|
| Toughness .................. | Excellent |
| Impact resistance ............ | Very high |
| Tensile strength ............. | Very high |
| Chemical resistance .......... | Unaffected by dilute and concentrated acids and alkalis |
| | Resistant to organic solvents, alcohols, greases, and aliphatic hydrocarbons. Inert to water and aqueous salt solutions |
| Abrasion resistance .......... | Excellent |
| Water absorption ............. | Very low |
| Moisture vapor transmission... | Very low rate |
| Flammability .............. | Nonflammable |
| Toxicity .................. | Odorless, tasteless, and nontoxic |
| Heat sealing properties...... | Good |
| Weatherability ............. | Good–excellent |
| Stability .................. | Good–excellent |
| Adhesion (unmodified) ....... | Poor |
| Adhesion (modified) ......... | Poor–Excellent |

It is interesting, for example, that one of the first commercial utilizations of dispersion coatings in the metal-litho field was for the hard-to-hold liquid detergents which made their appearance on the American market about eight years ago. Prior to this time, the dispersion resins were used to contain strong liquid detergents, waxes and liquid cleaners; however, these earlier systems consisted of a size and a dispersion topcoat because at that time the dispersion coatings alone did not have adequate adhesion to tin plate and other metal substrates.

Shortly after vinyl chloride dispersion coatings were developed, it was apparent that these compositions were exceptionally suited for use as container and closure coatings for food and beverage products. They are effective in this application because of nontoxicity, lack of odor and taste, and the ability to take a deep draw in the making of aluminum cans. Since their introduction in this market, many proprietary coatings have been developed and these have met the extractability and other safety requirements of the Food and Drug Administration. A partial list of food products used in contact with vinyl dispersion linings are shown in Table 13-8.

During the past decade, coating research laboratories have been actively developing durable and weatherable coating compositions based upon vinyl dispersion resins and other newer synthetic resins. As a result of this work, a new "breed" of coatings materials have been created and many unique compositions are now used in the industrial and residential building products field.

TABLE 13-8.   Food Products Used in Contact with Dispersion Linings

| | |
|---|---|
| Applesauce | Liver pastes |
| Artichoke hearts | Mincemeat |
| Asparagus | Mushroom sauce |
| Baby foods | Olives |
| Beef stew | Pickled beets |
| Beer | Pickled fruits |
| Boiled onions | Pickles |
| Boned chicken | Pimento |
| Candied fruits | Potato salad |
| Carbonated beverages | Potted meats |
| Cheese spreads | Preserves |
| Chili | Red cabbage |
| Cocktail frankfurters | Salad dressing |
| Cooked fruits | Sauerkraut |
| Corned beef hash | Tomato juice |
| Cranberry relish | Tuna fish |
| Jellies | Vienna sausage |

Among those most suitable in this application, coatings containing silicone copolymers, fluorocarbon dispersion and vinyl chloride dispersion resins, have been found, in general, to possess good to excellent weatherability and inertness to atmospheric chemical polutants. The vinyl solution and acrylics have, in recent years, been found somewhat wanting in resistance to chalk and bodying on extensive weathering exposure.

As shown in Table 13-9, compositions prepared with silicone copolymers and fluorocarbon polymers perhaps perform the best on weathering, and although somewhat expensive, are in demand as "premium" coatings by high quality and/or institutional buyers. These expensive and durable coatings are primarily used in industrial, maintenance, residential siding, hospital, school and business building applications. Projections based upon extensive weatherometer aging, outside exposure and other performance data indicate that substrates coated with these materials have excellent protection against weathering and chemical decomposition for periods up to 20 years. As a result of these tests, buildings coated with these materials may carry a guarantee against chalking and discoloration. Vinyl organosol coatings represent a good value for these same end uses, being considerably less expensive but weathering reasonably well.

Weatherability refers to the physical condition of a coating after extensive exposure to a variety of natural climatic conditions; or exposure to equipment which is designed to simulate the effects of outside exposure.

In the instance of exterior exposure, coated panels are exposed at Arizona and Florida locations for extended periods, both at 45° so. and horizontal. At 6 month intervals (usually) the condition of each coating is evaluated with regard to chalking, checking, cracking, crazing, peeling, color stability and adhesion. Florida and Arizona

TABLE 13-9.  General Performance Comparison

| 1000 hours' exposure | Silicone polyester | Fluorocarbon resin | Vinyl chloride dispersion |
|---|---|---|---|
| Atlas weather-ometer | Excellent | Excellent | Good |
| Relative humidity resistance | | | |
| (100% R.H. at 100°F) | Excellent | Excellent | Very good |
| 5% Salt spray (ASTM D117-S7T) | Excellent | Excellent | Very good |
| Water soak | Excellent | Excellent | Very good |
| Cost/sq ft–1.0 mil film (range) | .95–1.75¢ | 5.0–8.0¢ | 0.75–0.9¢ |

locations are commonly used as test sites because they are widely accepted as being representative of severe exposure conditions within this country. The results obtained at these locations reflect a vigorous performance evaluation.

The basic problem with outside exposure techniques is the long periods required to obtain test results. To obtain data more rapidly, equipment has been developed which artificially produces a natural-type environment. Many investigators have reported on this equipment and the correlation obtained with outside exposure. The consensus is that this equipment offers a rapid and reproducible technique for rating the performance of materials. There is much controversy, at present, and as usual, regarding the interpretation of test data as it relates to natural exposure time.

For our purposes, it has been found that the Atlas Dew Point Weather-Ometer is an excellent unit for obtaining accelerated exposure information, for comparing and/or predicting the weathering performance, especially chalking of coatings.

In operation, the unit is programmed such that:

*1.* All exposures are run at 100% relative humidity.
*2.* The radiation sequence is composed of a 60-min light, 60-min dark cycle, and
*3.* A cold spray (40–42°F) is applied to the back of the panels during the dark cycle.

It is this combined sequence of events which gives controlled reproducible results. In comparing Dew Point Weather-Ometer exposure results of vinyl chloride organosol coatings with those of identical panels exposed in Florida, it has been found that 75–100 hr' exposure correlates quite well to "two summers" exposure in the natural climate.

Although not as unique as their other contemporary cousins, coatings containing vinyl chloride dispersion, vinyl chloride solution and acrylic resins offer adequate performance at moderate cost and hence are used in great abundance in about every facet of the organic finishes industry. Within the group, of course, performance differences do exist and Tables 13-10 and 13-11 reflect the degree that is to be expected.

From this comparison, it is interesting to note that the vinyl dispersion systems offer more than adequate performance at a low cost—a factor which has encouraged usage of this material in the residential building products field; particularly in roof-siding and related applications. Other applications include organic finishes for business machines, instrument panels, electronic devices and television cabinets.

TABLE 13-10.  General Performance Comparison

| 1000 hours' exposure | Vinyl chloride dispersion | Vinyl solution | Modified acrylic |
|---|---|---|---|
| Atlas weather-ometer | Good | Fair–good | Fair–good |
| Relative humidity resistance | | | |
| (100% R.H. at 100°F) | Very good | Good | Very good |
| 5% Salt spray (AST D4117-S7T) | Very good | Good | Fair–good |
| Water soak (77°F) | Good | Fair–good | Good |
| 12 months south Florida | | | |
| 45° south | | | |
| Resistance to dirt retention | Good | Good | Good–very good |
| Resistance to chalking | Excellent | Very good | Very good |

Through American-associated companies abroad, dispersion coatings, primarily the polyvinyl chloride type, are being used in Europe, Latin America, Australia and Japan in applications typical of those shown in Table 13-12. It is also noteworthy that these coatings are preferred for aerosol cans made with aluminum bodies and tinplate ends because the dispersion film, being excellent as an insulator, eliminates bimetallic couples and destructive electrolytic cell effects which might otherwise occur.

TABLE 13-11.  General Performance Comparison

| | | Vinyl chloride dispersion | Vinyl solution | Modified acrylic |
|---|---|---|---|---|
| Film corrosion (ASTM B-287-61) | | None | None | None |
| Film adhesion (Crosshatch) | | Excellent | Fair–good | Good |
| Flexibility | | | | |
| Conical mandrel | | Excellent | Excellent | Good |
| 28 mm screw cap | | Excellent | Excellent | Fair |
| Gardner impact (in. lb) | | | | |
| Unexposed | | Very good | Fair | Good |
| Water soaked | (High gloss) | Very good | Fair | Good |
| C | (Low gloss) | Good | | |
| Cass test | (High gloss) | Very good | Fair | Fair |
| | (Low gloss) | Fair | | |
| Tabor abrasion | (High gloss) | .0157 | .0112 | .0280 |
| (g loss/200 cycles- | (Low gloss) | .0061 | | |
| CS-10 Wheel—1000 | | | | |
| g wt) | | | | |
| Pencil hardness | (High gloss) | 2H | | |
| | (Low gloss) | 4H | 3H | 4H |
| Cost/ft²-1.0 mil film (range) | | 0.75–0.9¢ | 0.9–1.2¢ | 0.65–0.85¢ |

TABLE 13-12.  End Uses for Vinyl Dispersion Coatings Abroad—1965
Container Interiors

| |
| --- |
| Aerosol cans |
| Beer can ends |
| Beer crowns |
| Deep-drawn food cans |
| Detergent cans |
| Lay-seamed soldered cans (large size for gherkins and other acid products) |
| Spray coating for the interior of aluminum-drawn aerosol containers |

**b. Plasticizers—P.V.C.** This review on plasticizers is required since they play an important part in vinyl environmental performance. Total U.S. production of plasticizers in 1965 was approximately 1.05 billion pounds, worth $210 million. In 1959, 0.54 billion pounds were produced and sold for $142 million. In 1959, consumption represented 85% of production. Gradually this percentage has increased principally because of competitive pricing (see Fig. 13-8).

The future growth pattern will be on the increase, as over 90% of all plasticizers go into PVC and the PVC market is on the increase. The second largest market is in polyvinyl acetate, consuming 3–4%.

*(1) Functions of Plasticizers.* Plasticizers serve three basic functions: to lower the processing temperature of the polymer below the decomposition temperature, to modify the properties of the finished product, and to modify the processing properties.

Plastics can be made softer or flexible, their natural properties can be extended or modified, their viscosity can be reduced to make them easier to shape and from at high temperatures and pressures.

The mechanism by which inclusion of plasticizers in PVC results in increased flexibility is attributed to a reduction of the intermolecular forces, i.e. the plasticizer acts as a lubricating agent to allow the macromolecules to slide over one another freely, or by the solvation of the polymer. Unplasticized PVC can be regarded as a three-dimensional gel formed by the attachments between molecules at active centers. Plasticization can be looked upon as a reduction of polymer-polymer unions by creating polymer-plasticizer unions in their place.

Plasticizers for PVC are generally divided into two categories: true plasticizers (primary and secondary) and extenders. The primary types are materials which exhibit good compatibility with PVC. The secondary types usually exhibit from fair to good compatibility and are normally used in conjunction with the primary.

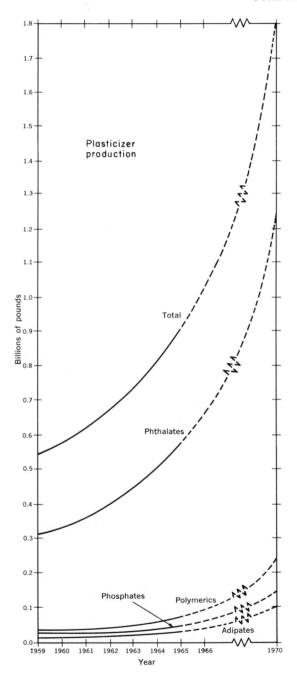

Fig. 13-8. Plasticizer production.

One main property which is highly desirable for a plasticizer is its capacity to impart to the polymer the characteristics of an elastomer over the widest possible temperature range, and to maintain them. Unfortunately, no single plasticizer embodies all the desired combinations of properties. Therefore, for any specific application it is necessary to choose the correct plasticizer combinations.

It is estimated that 20% of all plasticizers produced are used in the manufacture of wire and cable insulation, 30% in film and sheeting, 25% in flooring, 15% in coating and the remaining 10% in miscellaneous applications. Probably 5-6% of the total is already being used in the relatively new expandable PVC. More use will be made of these plasticized-expandable plastics in such products as outer garments, toys and upholstery.

Various companies are concentrating on the developing new plasticizers specifically to resist dry cleaning. Perchoroethylene and other solvents used in dry cleaning now extract practically all of the plasticizers in vinyl garments. Soapy water, though, does not affect plasticizers a great deal.

Even though PVC tile requires plasticizers in order to produce a

Fig. 13-9. Emery Industries Inc.'s high molecular weight polymeric plasticizer was developed for use in compounding dry-cleanable polyvinyl chloride constructions. It is highly resistant to perchlorethylene extraction, helping to eliminate vinyl shrinkage in dry cleaning: can be repeatedly used.

useful product, it remains the major ingredient which causes stains. The different types of vinyl tile, and the varied causes of staining have made it virtually impossible to formulate a tile impervious to all types of staining.

*(2) Phthalates.* These comprise the most important single group of plasticizers. Phthalates combine good properties with low price to become the most popular of all types. There are many esters of phthalic anhydride which range from fairly volatile, such as dimethl phthalate, to very high-boiling nonvolatile, such as ditridecyl phthalate. One of the best examples, di(2-ethylhexyl) phthalate (also called dioctyl phthalate, DOP), is a versatile and popular plasticizer often used as a standard of comparison for other plasticizers. DOP amounts to 30% of total plasticizer production. Octyl and decyl phthalates are quite permanent, and are used in applications where this property is most important: for example, automobile upholstery and wire.

Phthalates outperform commonly used low molecular weight polymerics. Among the key manufacturers of phthalates, Monsanto Company makes a specialty phthalates for industrial acrylic lacquers and vinyl plastisol adhesives, coatings, and molding compounds. Santicizer 262, an alkyl benzyl phthalate, is said to provide an unusual balance of properties which combine the compatibility and processability of a monomeric plasticizer with the permanence of many polymerics. It is reported that the lacquers plasticized with this material have improved adhesion to metal undercoats, weathering and solvent craze resistance. This material is also compatible with ethyl cellulose and nitrocellulose.

*(3) Monomers.* PVC is very sensitive to chemical composition with respect to plasticizer compatibility. At present it creates the largest single demand for ester-type plasticizers.

*(4) Secondary Plasticizers.* Special plasticizers, such as Mobil Chemical's new oil secondary plasticizer, Mobilsol 66, promise to improve epoxy road patches and surface overlays while making them more economical. California's Division of Highways is now testing oil-extended epoxy coatings on 22 bridges on Interstate 80 in the Sierra Mountain range. The bridges are coated with a $\frac{1}{8}$ in. layer of the oil-extended epoxy and aggregate using a conventional spray outfit equipped with an automatic mixer to dispense the epoxy resin mix.

The test coatings contain approximately 1 part of the Mobil plasticizer to 2 parts epoxy. In addition to the bridge surfaces, a 45 ft by 12 ft test patch has been laid on Interstate 80 at a point chosen for maximum severity. High in the Sierras, it will be exposed to frequent freeze-thaw conditions as well as rough treatment from snow plows and tire chains.

Petroleum-derived secondary plasticizer CD-101 of Boron Oil Company (SOHIO) is used primarily with PVC. It is used to replace 40% or more of primary types in order to reduce costs. The CD-101 bulk price is approximately 6¢ per pound.

*(5)* *Adipates.* The adipates and other dibasic acid esters, such as azelates and sebacates, contribute low-temperature flexibility to nearly all the common plastics, but are incompatible with both cellulose acetate and polyvinyl acetate. The extreme efficiency of di(2-ethylhexyl) adipate allows lower levels of the plasticizer to be used with vinyl, cellulosics, and others. They are also used in plastisols at low levels to give workable consistencies and semirigid end products.

Elastex 20-A plasticizer, the diisodecyl adipate of Allied Chemical Corp., is a clear liquid ester which combines good low-temperature performance with low volatility. It is only about half as volatile as dioctyle adipate, one of the former standard low-temperature plasticizers. A straightchain ester having minimum solvating action, it produces stable vinyl plastisols.

*(6)* *Phosphates.* Tricresyl phosphate (TCP) was one of the earliest commercial plasticizers for PVC. It has been replaced in various applications because of its restricted low-temperature characteristics. This disadvantage can be overcome to some extent by mixing it with certain other phosphate plasticizers—trioctyl phosphate, for instance.

TCP continues to be an important plasticizer. It has strong solvent power for many of the film forming plastics and is used with cellulosics, vinyls, alkyds, varnishes, rubbers, and phenolics in a wide range of coatings and other uses. Flameproofing of vinyl is achieved with as little as 5% TCP, based on total plasticizer.

PVC sheet is the biggest user of derivatives with phosphoric acid, because of their secondary functions of giving the plastic resistance to fungus and flames. They also provide reasonably good light stabilization.

Phosphates are particularly useful in formulating fire-retardant compositions. TCP performs this function better than the alkyl derivatives, one reason being that they are more permanent. Tri(2-ethylhexyl) phosphate gives excellent low-temperature flexibility characteristics, better than that offered by any phthalates and finds use in vinyl cable coatings and vinyl solution coatings.

When substituting as little as 10% TCP for phthalate plasticizers, increased processing speeds are achieved. Low levels of TCP significantly improved PVC processing rates without seriously affecting physical properties of the original plastic.

As reported by FMC, one of the major suppliers of phosphate esters, they are particularly useful in combinations of formulating fire-retardant compounds, providing good plasticizing action and permitting production of transparent products. The phosphate esters include KP-140 tributoxyethyl phosphate, Kroniflex TOF trioctyl phosphate, Kroniflex TBP tributyl phosphate, the triaryl phosphates, Kronitex TT, 1, K-3 and cresyl diphenyl phosphate, Kronitex MX.

These materials, particularly the tricresyl phosphates, carry a premium price, well above that of the conventional phthalates—hence, although they are excellent plasticizers in their own right, they are usually used in combination with lower priced phthalates to provide flame retardance and in some cases, processing advantages. The major market is film and sheeting and coated cloth, especially where dark colors are needed or clear films are required to have flame retardant properties. The most popular flame retardant additive is, of course,

Fig. 13-10. Phosphate ester plasticizers, such as FMC's Kronitex series, find wide use in clear film and sheeting which requires flame retardances. The girl and dog are wearing rainwear of vinyl film plasticized with Kronitex AA. This application highlights the use of esters in producing very flexible coated vinyls with outdoor endurance.

antimony oxide; but this being a white pigment, rules out its use for clear film or dark colors.

The most widely used phosphate esters in plasticizer applications are tricresyl phosphate and cresyl diphenyl phosphate. It is estimated that last year these three accounted for 32.5 million pounds of the total phosphate plasticizer market of about 38 million pounds. The total 1965 market was estimated to be 55 million pounds, including its use in gasoline additives and antifoam agents.

**(7)  Polyesters/Polymerics.**  The polyester group, together with epoxidized oils, are commonly referred to as polymeric plasticizers. This term is somewhat of a misnomer; high molecular weight plasticizer is technically preferred. They are used in compounds primarily to decrease the danger of migration and oil extraction even though they are more expensive and tend to be more difficult in process.

Polymeric plasticizers of medium to low molecular weight and comparatively low cost have been on the market for many years. The early products were introduced at prices close to those of DOP. They offered advantages in handling and processing over the very high molecular weight polyesters, but at some sacrifice in permanence. Even among these few early products, performance varied widely. In recent years there has been rapid growth in both number of products and sales volume. Rohm and Haas, with its Paraplex G-30, G-31 and G-32, reports that this growth has coincided with and undoubtedly has been partly caused by the precipitous drop in PVC resin and phthalate ester prices. Low-viscosity polyester Admex 517 provides rapid fusing, low initial viscosity with good viscosity aging properties and low temperature flexibility with good resistance to hexane and gasoline extraction. Their medium molecular weight polyester Admex 600 provides the capability of easing hard-to-process formulations without objectionable side effects, and good resistance to hexane and mineral oil. High molecular weight ester Admex 790 permits excellent resistance to soapy water, good hexane and mineral oil resistance, and light color.

**(8)  Negative Consumer Reaction.**  In the rapid postwar development of the vinyl industry, the few high molecular weight polyesters available were used only in a few specialty applications. The widespread use of monomerics then available resulted in compounds that were inadequate for some of the more demanding applications. The negative consumer reaction to shortlived garden hose, seat covers, shower curtains, toys, electrical and other products threatened to topple the vinyl industry. Polymerics came to the rescue.

Most applications do not require polymeric plasticizers. However, it has become important to insure that polymeric plasticizers be used in high performance vinyl applications. Upholstery can now be made to resist extraction under severe conditions, electrical insulation to resist embrittlement, and gaskets to resist deterioration.

Polymerics permit manufacture of dry cleanable PVC coated fabrics that will withstand repeated exposure to chlorinated solvents such as perchloroethylene and carbon tetrachloride. With the new developments in this type, more use is being made of PVC "washable" applications for both non-expanded and expanded materials. Good resistance to extraction by oils, solvents and soapy water makes these plasticizers suitable in garment, upholstery, wallpaper and other applications.

**(9) Hydrocarbons.** Permanence and durability are the basic requirements of plasticizers used in producing PVC wire and cable insulation. The appliance wire uses lower cost polymerics. In industrial machinery wire the higher cost polymerics are used since they have to resist extraction by contaminates such as oil.

Imperial Chemical Industries, Ltd. is one of the pioneers in chlorinated straight chain hydrocarbon plasticizers. This type is more compatible with PVC. Since the principal consideration in wire and cable insulation is to obtain better volume resistivity characteristics, its higher cost is not a problem. With the improved electrical properties, are retained when compared to PVC containing other plasticizers.

Various companies are working with smaller molecule formulations. These new chlorinated plasticizers can be substituted for DOP.

**(10) Epoxies.** Two main types of epoxy are produced: expoxidized triglycerides produced from soyabean and other oils, and epoxidized alkyl esters derived from fatty acids. In addition to providing plasticizing action, these epoxies also exhibit stabilizing action against heat and light. Their main applications are in floor tile and film and sheeting.

Baker Caster Oil Company is now introducing a new and superior grade epoxy soya plasticizer, Estynox 203. It is reported that this product is superior to the standard grades of epoxy soya in regard to effectiveness in vinyl heat stabilization, improved cold weather handling, absence of flock development, and lower solidification point. It has F.D.A. approval and is recommended for use in combination with nontoxic types of stabilizers. It is also suggested for stabilization and lubrication of rigid vinyls.

*(11) Chlorinated Paraffins.* Diamond Alkali Company has been producing chlorinated waxes for many years and is considered one of the pioneers in this area. In order to meet the demand for a better secondary plasticizer than the traditional hydrocarbon types, chlorowax 500 was developed. This is a secondary plasticizer for wire and cable compounds, profile extrusions and PVC plastisols. It is a low cost chlorinated normal paraffin with improved PVC compatibility compared with conventional secondary plasticizers. By replacing high levels of primary plasticizer, it maintains physical properties and reduces compound costs. It also offers good heat and light stability, low volatility, low temperature and good electrical properties when used in PVC.

*(12) Plasticizer-Extender Oil Cuts Costs.* Use of petroleum plasticizer-extender oil has reduced costs of PVC and urea molded products substantially at Synthetic Plastics Company. This company makes a wide variety of molded products: PVC footwear and urea buttons, ashtrays, poker chips and similar products. Mobil Oil Company's Mobilsol 44 has replaced more expensive chemical plasticizers. This oil is used as a substitute for 10–50 phr of the chemical plasticizers in urea products and for 10-80 phr in PVC. The amount of replacement in both materials depends upon color requirements. It is a highly aromatic oil compatible with a wide range of chemical and other petroleum plasticizers and synthetic resins.

*(13) Plasticizer-Adhesive.* A new dual-purpose additive gives vinyl dispersion coatings greater adhesion to metals and other surfaces without a primer, while plasticizing the formulation at the same time. Called Kodaflex AD-2, it is available from the Chemicals Division of Eastman Chemical Products, Inc.

The only effect on physical properties that the addition of AD-2 has on plastisol is a slight lowering of tensile strength and modulus. Elongation, hardness, extraction properties and torsion modulus values are equal or improved in comparison to the same formulation without the new additive. Adhesion with this system decreases significantly as the plastisol coating thickness increases, especially with coatings over 10 mils.

In simulated commercial applications, use of AD-2 is reported to have increased the adhesion or peel strength of a 10-mil PVC plastisol film on cold-rolled steel from $\frac{1}{8}$ lb/in. to 6–7 lb/in. The new additive shows excellent compatibility not only with other formulation in-

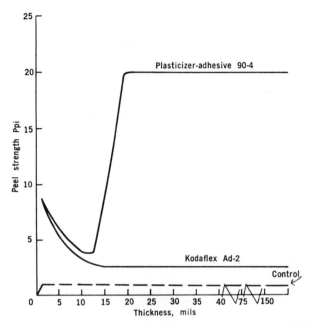

Fig. 13-11. Adhesion vs film thickness of plastisol containing plasticizer-adhesive 90-4 of Eastman.

gredients, but also with base resins other than vinyls. These include acrylics, vinyl acetate-ethylene copolymers, chlorinated rubbers, various cellulosics and polyamides.

Eastman reports that continued work on additives for PVC homopolymer dispersion coatings has produced another plasticizer-adhesive which is very effective in increasing the adhesion of thicker plastisol coatings. This new experimental adhesive numbered 90-4, is designed especially for coatings of over 20 mils in thickness. As a plasticizer it is 40–50% as efficient as DOP.

*(14) Summary.* Since the first plasticizer was used a century ago, thousands have been developed. At present there are approximately 200 produced commercially with probably less than 100 having real industrial value. Both poundage and dollar sales of plasticizers are climbing. Companies that are venturing into plasticizers which will meet the more rigorous environmental conditions are reporting comfortable profits.

### 3. *Fluorine-Containing Resins*

The high thermal stability of carbon-fluorine bond has lend to considerable interest in fluorine-containing polymers as heat resistant plastic and rubbers such as polytetrafluorethylene. PTFE is a material which also provides exceptional chemical-resistant properties. It is completely inert to halogens, fuming mineral acids, strong alkalis and oxidizing agents. It also has the advantage of being non-inflammable. However, it is attacked by molten alkali metals. Its insolubility in organic solvents makes its use in lacquers impossible. With its high crystalline melting point of 327°F, it cannot be used in organosols and plastisols. Other fluorine-containing plastics have been developed and in almost all cases they are not available for use in the coating industry.

Fig. 13-12. FEP resin shortly are used in ink train of new American Type Founders 38-in. web press. The large Wisconsin printing company of W. A. Kruger Company is obtaining reduction in "hickies," downtime, cleanup time, and maintenance costs with the roll covers. Rolls are used to cover distributor and ductor rollers in black and blue units of press. Operator holds roll cover before application by heat shrinking to roller.

## 4. Acrylic Resins

Acrylic resins are thermoplastic polymers ranging from very hard and tough to extremely flexible water-white materials. They are resistant to oxidation, ultraviolet degradation and many chemicals. However, they are softened by certain solvents (3).

They have been used for many years in speciality coatings. More recently acrylic resins have established a reputation for excellent durability in automotive lacquers. They can be used with plasticizers as the film-former or in combination with nitrocellulose. The combination is somewhat harder and has better resistance to solvents such as gasoline.

The very flexible types of acrylic resin have been used as coatings for elastic materials, such as rubber and for textile or leather coatings. Acrylic resins are compatible with many other film-formers and are often used in blends.

Since 1953 when Rohm & Haas Company introduced acrylic emulsions to be used as binders in latex paints, the latex paints have steadily increased in use as architectural coatings. Applications include interior plaster and exterior stucco, concrete and masonry surfaces.

The disadvantages which stem from the thermoplastic nature of the ordinary acrylic resins, solvent sensitivity and temperature sensitivity, have been overcome by the introduction within the past few years of thermosetting acrylic resins. They are crosslinked by stoving processes very similar to those used for the alkyd-melamine types. Available are water-soluble or emulsions, as well as those soluble in organic solvents.

## 5. Cellulosic Resins

Nitrocellulose was the first synthetic high polymer used in coatings. Its lacquers are still considered to be the fastest air-drying materials. This is due largely to its high softening point and good solvent release. It is compatible with many other resins and plasticizing materials.

It provides hard furniture finishes, flexible coatings for paper and fabrics and durable finishes for automobiles. The principal limitations of such lacquers are their relatively high-cost solvents and relatively low solids at spraying consistency, the sensitivity of the coatings to heat and ultraviolet radiations, and their high degree of flammability.

Ethyl cellulose is softer and more flexible than nitrocellulose. It is not as highly flammable and has a certain degree of resistance to degradation by heat. Chemical resistance is improved. They provide toughness in blends with hard resins and waxes for hot-melt coatings.

Cellulose acetate is used chiefly in plastics and sheeting. It finds only a few specialty applications in coatings. However, the acetate-butyrate is finding increasing uses. Its properties vary with the ratio of acetyl and butyryl groups. It is slightly softer than ethyl cellulose but has better resistance to moisture absorption.

### 6. Copolymer Resins

Many different copolymers are used as binders in surface coatings. A few of these types have been reviewed. The styrene-butadiene copolymers have been very popular since World War II.

Many different vinyl copolymers are used such as vinyl chloride, vinyl isobutyl ether, vinylidene chloride, vinyl acrylonitrile, etc.

### 7. Coumarone-Indene Resins

The coumarone resins are materials of low molecular weight. They are soluble in aliphatic, aromatic-hydrocarbons and in oils. They are thermoplastic and because of their hydrocarbon character are resistant to acid and alkalis.

They show a marked tendency to yellow in the light and their durability is poor. Because of these inherent restrictions, they have limited applications in coatings. Their main field of use is in binders for aluminum and bronze lacquers, where their low acid value leads to stability in the ready mixed finish. As they are protected from the atmosphere by the layers of bronze pigment, the durability of such finishes is surprisingly good. Improvements occur by adding tung oil. When added in asphalt lacquers, improved gloss and alkali resistance occurs.

## IV.  APPLICATIONS

This large industry produces two broad categories of coatings, namely, the "trade sales" and the "industrial finishes." Trade sales, or shelf goods, include products sold directly to consumers, contractors and professional painters for use on construction or painting, refinishing and general maintenance. These coatings are used chiefly on houses and buildings, although a sizeable portion are used for refinishing automobiles and machinery (4).

Industrial finishes, or chemical coatings, encompass a myriad of products for application by manufactures in the factory or for industrial maintenance and protection. They are custom made products sold to other manufacturers for such items as automobiles, appliances, furniture, ships and boats, metal containers, streets and highways, and government facilities.

In the past decade trade sales paints have accounted for 55–60% of the volume of all coatings produced, and 55–60% of dollar sales. In dollar value, shipments of industrial finishes have increased somewhat more rapidly than those of trade sales coatings.

Coatings have become so commonplace that few people realize what a remarkable commodity it is. Paint in the can remains liquid almost indefinitely, but when spread on a surface it is transformed in a few hours to a hard, durable coating which protects and beautifies for many years. With the new resins recently developed and used in coatings, some companies are now providing 20 to 30 year warranties on outside coatings. Coatings approximately a few mils, or less, in thickness are more durable than some metals of equal thickness. Paint protects billions of dollars in wood and steel structures, or metal goods, from decay and corrosion.

The chemical and physical nature of the substrate are of great importance in deciding the type of paint or painting system to be used. The preparation of surfaces for painting is important. As an example, not only should the surface be free from dirt and fatty materials, but the fine powdery "chalk" on an old paint film represents a serious danger if the subsequent painting is to be with a latex paint. The high molecular resin particles have no wetting power for such chalk so that adhesion failure at an early date is a certainty.

The majority of water-free paints require that the substrate be dry if satisfactory results are to be obtained. The presence of water, either at the time of painting or by subsequent migration to the surface will reduce adhesion almost to zero. If moisture cannot be avoided than it is necessary to use paint which will allow water to be readily transported through, such as a paint that will breathe.

Porous substrates tend to suck in the binder from paints which are applied to them. Proper precautions have to be taken to eliminate and rectify this problem.

Another important consideration to ensure that parts will be properly coated involves alkalinity. Fresh lime plaster, concrete and asbestos cement surfaces are sufficiently alkaline to drying oil paints in a very short time. Compatability of coating to these types substrates is possible and practical. Nonalkaline plaster or filler can be used as a primer. The alkalinity chemically can be neutralized by applying fluosilicate solutions or zinc phosphate solution. Hydrochloric acid has to be carefully applied since it forms highly hygroscopic calcium chloride which developes bond problems.

### A. Architectural

Different type paints or coatings are available for exterior and interior applications. In most cases premature failure of paint frequently is due to the condition of the substrate, structural characteristics and conditions of the building, weather conditions during application and proper application of the paint according to the instructions of the manufacture.

Structural characteristics which permit water to accumulate behind paint coatings may be the cause of blistering, cracking, and peeling. Problems such as this type can be eliminated.

### B. Automobile

The production of automobile coatings or finishes is an important branch of the service coatings industry, both technically and commercially. Until the quick-drying nitrocellulose lacquers were introduced in the early 1920's, the finishing of a car was a complex and time-consuming operation. It involved many coats and long drying times between coats. Nitrocellulose lacquers completely dominated the automobile finishing field for two decades.

Since World War II more car manufacturers have changed to finishing with synthetics; alkyd-amino resin systems. For a very short period of time urea resins were used. They were rapidly replaced by melamine resins.

With the changeover to synthetics, both advantages and disadvantages occurred. The process was speeded up since fewer coats could be use to give the same "body." Polishing operations were no longer needed. A major problem developed; namely stricter precautions against dust and overspray. Although the long term durability of synthetic and the nitrocellulose is of the same order, the synthetics retain their gloss better. They are less sensitive to mechanic damage caused by flying stones, etc.

While the alkyd-amino resin finishes are still used most widely, new finishes have been developed and are in use by certain manufacturers.

Fig. 13-13. Thio-Deck membrane system being applied between concrete courses on the parking deck of new Atlanta addition to Sears, Roebuck's catalog order plant. Small work crew can quickly cover large open area using notched, broom-like applicators and serrated trowels. Flowable material seals joints, curbs, and service openings and forms a continuous, seamless, moisture barrier. Two-component system is mixed, as needed, on the job, and can be applied over damp surfaces, thus simplifying work scheduling.

A membrane waterproofing system compounded of coal tar, pulysulfide liquid polymer, and reactive catalyst has been developed and field-tested by Toch Brothers, Inc. of Paterson, New Jersey, and is now being marketed nationally under the name of "Thio-Deck Membrane." The new system is designed to form a seamless, flexible, impervious barrier between concrete-slab courses of parking decks, bridges, roadways, and terrazzo and quarry tile floorings. Applied in a 30–50 mil thickness, the membrane system adheres to all customary roof and deck materials, including concrete, stone, brick, wood, metal, cement, asbestos, and most plastics. It cures at ambient temperatures into a rubber-based compound that resists bacterial and chemical attack as well as water and salts and remains flexible at temperatures from —40 to 175°F. It is able to expand, contract and move without losing bond to upper and lower slabs. Even if moisture reaches the membrane through cracks or pores in the top slab, the tough rubber keeps it from seeping to and through the lower slab.

The first of these were the thermoplastic acrylic finishes. The binder consisted of copolymers of acrylic esters. These finishes had excellent color retention, good durability and gloss retention. They could be formulated to give a high gloss straight from the gun, while at the same time minor defects could be removed by polishes. Their main weakness is a rather marked sensitivity to high octane gasolines.

In an attempt to overcome this disadvantage, the thermosetting acrylic binders were developed. They cured this problem but in turn provided a condition where it could not be polished. Attempts are now being made to carefully control the degree of crosslinking to reduce sensitivity but to allow polishing.

## C. Boat

All types of boat hulls require paint to provide anti-fouling properties, but in addition, particularly for steel hulls, anticorrosive paints are used. At the present time it is not possible to combine these two properties in a single paint. The present procedure is to first apply an anticorrosive primer with the top coating being the antifouling paint.

Anticorrosive primers previously used binders of oil and asphalt. Almost all of them now use synthetic binders, such as combinations of alkyd and tung oil/phenolic resin binders, vinyl resins and epoxy resins. The last two binders allow for the formation of primers having very fast drying times.

On acount of the long drying time it requires, red lead has been replaced as inhibitive pigment by zinc chromate, basic sulfate white lead and zinc dust.

The function of the antifouling paint is to prevent organisms such as barnacles, mussels, tubworms, and algal spores from getting a foot hold on the hull and growing. This may be achieved by using paints which contain a poison for the organisms. The poison slowly leaches out from the film into the water layer in contact with the surface.

The most important of the poisons, which has been used for a relatively long time, is cuprous oxide. It is sometimes used admixtures with mercuric oxide or with organic mercurials.

Their are two types of antifouling paint; the soluble matrix type and the insoluble matrix type (also referred to as the contact leaching type). The soluble matrix type is generally based on rosin or calcium rosinate as the binder. Alone these binders would become brittle and errode rapidly. They are plasticized and modified with other binders such as phenolic resins or chlorinated rubber.

The most commonly used matrix in the insoluble type is a copolymer of vinyl chloride and vinyl acetate. Chlorinated rubber may also be used. The cuprous oxide contained in the paint formulation has to be set in a definite pattern. The particles of the poison are to be in direct contact with each other.

Another hull coating uses metallic zinc as the antifouling filler. Tests have been conducted with polyvinyl acetate and a number of inorganic binders. It was found that sodium silicate gave the most promising results.

### D. Aircraft and Missile

Substantial advances in the areas of new materials availability from exploratory research and efforts to more widely use coatings to solve field applications problems have been realized. Concurrent with these materials advances, the advent of high performance, high speed aircraft and missiles has intensified the requirements for protective coatings which have improved erosive and oxidative stability at elevated temperature. Current design supersonic aircraft and missiles are expected to experience temperatures up to 650°F during flight. As the speeds of operational systems approach the hypersonic range, temperatures of 800–1000°F are anticipated (5).

### 1. Present Applications

**a. Available Coating Resins.** There are currently seven types of coatings which are used to any great extent for aircraft fininshing. These basic types are (*1*) nitrocellulose lacquers, (*2*) alkyd enamels, (*3*) vinyls (including the alkyd modified type), (*4*) epoxies, (*5*) poly-

Fig. 13-14. Plastics Coatings on aircrafts have to withstand extremes on different environments; i.e., temperatures, abrasions, pressure, rain, and others. This hypersonic experimental aircraft typifies the use of coatings subjected to aerodynamic heating.

urethanes, (*6*) acrylic lacquers, and (*7*) silicones. All of the systems based on these types possess some disadvantages as well as strong points and are available in a host of modifications. The strong and weak points of each type of system will be briefly discussed.

Nitrocellulose lacquers include the oldest aircraft finishes of the group. These materials have been used for many years. They are inexpensive, easy to apply, cure very rapidly, are easily touched up, and have fairly good color retention. However, they do not weather well, are not resistant to fuels and fluids, and do not possess good low or high temperature properties.

Alkyd enamels are still used quite extensively, especially on many commercial aircraft. They wear quite well, are resistant to most fuels and fluids, retain color and are weather resistant. However, they are not rapid drying, and cannot be touched up as readily as lacquers.

Vinyl materials are, of course, elastomeric to various degrees. As such they are very flexible and usually impact-resistant. However, they are generally not very resistant to fuels and lubricants, do not weather well, are very difficult to apply and touch up. Since they tend to decompose under conditions of temperature (160°F) and ultraviolent radiation, there is the problem of hydrochloric acid generation—an obvious corrosion problem.

Epoxies, generally, cover a whole host of coating materials. They are characterized by their good electrical properties, good adhesion to carefully prepared surfaces, fairly high temperature resistance (400°F) and good fuel and fluid resistance. They also possess fairly good abrasion resistance. On the other hand, they are two-package materials and thereby, sensitive to improper ratios, must be thoroughly mixed, and possess a short pot-life. They are quite sensitive to poorly cleaned and treated surfaces, often exhibiting complete adhesion failures (in sheet form, not flecks). Once cured on properly prepared surfaces, they are almost impossible to remove without acid activated strippers or sand blasting. Top coats do not weather well and the tendency to chalk is rapid. Hence, cleaning is often difficult and color retention is poor. They are not easy to touch up.

Polyurethanes which are in current use on aircraft are also two-component materials. In being two-component materials, they have the same disadvantages as epoxies in this regard. They are easy to clean and have good fluid resistance. They have good abrasion resistance and exhibit good flexibility generally. They are usually applied over epoxy primer and so exhibit the same type of problems with strippers although generally they are not so difficult to work with as epoxies. Since these coatings can be made more elastomeric and in one-package types, this is one of the most fruitful areas of possible improvement in the state of the art.

Acrylics cover a large group of lacquer and thermosetting types. These coatings, as a group, have the best weatherability of the coventional resin systems. They have the best color retention and ease of cleaning. The lacquers are easy to touch up and maintain. They dry and cure rapidly, and are generally quite easy to strip with conventional strippers. Properly primed and applied, they exhibit good adhesion, have good resistance to most common aircraft fluids (although not generally as good as epoxies or urethanes), and have fair flexibility at low temperature. But under exposure to synthetic fluids at elevated temperatures and after several years againg, they will tend to craze and crack. They have only fair abrasion resistance and hardness. Nitrocellulose is often added to improve hardness and to speed up the drying even more. In straight, unmodified form they possess fairly good high temperature resistance (approx. 400°F). After consideration of all factors and tradeoffs, coating systems based on these materials appear to be the best recommendation for general aircraft surface finishing under the current state of the art.

For high temperature capability, i.e., above approximately 400–500°F, silicones provide the only available solution in the organic or semiorganic aircraft coating field. With these materials we can obtain good heat resistance, color retention (depending on pigments used), and gloss retention above 500°F. These coatings exhibit fairly good flexibility and good hardness properties. They weather fairly well and have satisfactory adhesion to aircraft structural metals. However, they possess certain disadvantages which almost preclude their wide usage on aircraft components. To obtain maximum performance, a rather high curing temperature is necessary. In fact this usually exceeds the critical temperature of aluminum alloys. They do not possess good abrasion or mar resistance. They have only fair adhesion to steel surfaces without fluxing agents. Improvements are being made, especially in developing low temperature cure schemes so the innate temperature enduring capabilities of this type of coating make further work with them promising and necessary.

It should be emphasized, however, that even though the current systems are generally quite good for their specified environments and will usually provide several years of relatively maintenance-free performance, even if the optimum in surface preparation and application techniques are followed, all of these currently used coatings in time tend to become brittle (except perhaps for the vinyls) from exposure to ultraviolet radiation and other environmental conditions. In areas where the coating is highly stressed, such as at fast-wear locations, joints, and seams, cracking will occur. In high impingement areas such as landing gear and wheelwell areas, these embrittled coatings will chip and flake off. The breaks in the film allow corrosive environmental conditions to come into direct contact with the surface of the metal. These conditions include contact with highly corrosive salt-laden moisture, exhaust gases, acidic industrial deposits, etc. Therefore, the state of the art must be advanced to find a coating system which will still provide the desirable properties of the current systems, as well as good flexibility after weathering and low temperature cycling, and good impact resiliency without cracking, flaking, or peeling.

**b. Surface Preparation.** Let us now turn our attention to perhaps the most important step in the whole process of protection with organic coatings, that of surface preparation. No matter what strides are made in polymer chemistry and coating development, if we do not properly and conscientiously clean and prepare the surface we cannot obtain satisfactory life with any coating system. A conservative estimate would indicate that over 75% of our present problems in the protective coatings business stem from improper or careless cleaning.

In a broader sense, metal surface preparation includes the removal not only of grease, oil, and similar contaminants but also of oxide films or other coatings, i.e., rust, scale, patina, etc., as well as old paints and lacquers, grinding and polishing compounds, loose metal particles, sand, dust, grit, and so on. The first essential to obtain an adherent coating on a metal surface is adequate mechanical, physical, and chemical cleanness. The importance of absolute removal of even slight traces of contamination on the metal surface is attested to by the fact that if even a small finger print is not removed, corrosion can begin underneath the subsequently applied protective coating and can lead to the partial or complete adhesion failure of the system.

**c. Specific Applications and Problems.** Until the last few years there was no official Air Force recognition of the need for general aircraft exterior surface painting. However, as the problems with corrosion have become more rampant throughout the Air Force, largely because of the lack of protection provided, the philosophy has begun to change. It has now become rather common thinking among all echelons that to control corrosion best painting is essential. There is still some reticence because of costs and maintenance, but as this corrosion consciousness becomes more prevalent, even more extensive use of protective coatings will be accomplished.

The problems with corrosion on exterior aircraft surfaces range from bothersome general surface pitting and etching to serious exfoliation around fasteners and along joints. It has been proved that these problems can largely be solved by properly applied protective coatings. The general aircraft and missile finishing document MIL-P-7179, now requires a completely painted exterior.

During the years 1960 and 1961, when the Air Force began modification programs on the relatively new "wet wing" aircraft, the seriousness of integral fuel tank contamination and associated corrosion was recognized. Large amounts of sludge and mat-like deposits were discovered. When these deposits were removed, extensive corrosion was recognized. Large amounts of sludge and matlike deposits deposits. This problem was reported in scattered areas worldwide but generally was limited to tropical marine environments. The problem has been especially severe in aircraft experiencing wide service deployment. Some aircraft were observed with holes corroded completely through the lower skin, but most problems were of the severe pitting type, often as deep as $\frac{1}{4}$ in. of the skin thickness. Corrosion of the exfoliation type was also observed, as well as mild to severe general surface corrosion.

Attempts were made to provide test environments which would simulate actual service environments. The most difficult condition to simulate has been that of the microorganisms. It proved to be almost impossible to obtain a representative culture as a test medium. Finally a solution of organic acid was found to fairly well simulate the condition. Other tests such as resistance to fuel-salt water mixtures, chloride solution, low temperature flexibility, and intercoat compatibility were developed. From these tests, specification MIL-C-27725 was developed. At present one polyurethane-based coating has met the requirements of this specification. Several coatings are currently under evaluation. One rather serious handicap exists since all promising coatings to date are two-component systems. We are now engaged in a program to find a simple-packaged, rapidly curing, flexible, integral fuel tank coating.

One important problem, closely associated with surface coatings is sealing the fastener or joint areas. Even with a good surface coating, properly applied, trouble can appear in any area in which the end-grain of the metal is exposed. Exfoliation corrosion begins and proceeds in a direction parallel to the surface. It is therefore, necessary to seal the fastener and joint area. At present unthinned zinc chromate primer, MIL-P-8585, or uncured sealant, MIL-S-8802, is prescribed to seal these fasteners and joints. Because of the importance of this problem by itself, we are currently engaged in two programs to endeavor to improve the techniques for fastener sealing. One involves encapsulation of the sealant material, the other pure aluminum coatings, and specification is being prepared for an environmental joint sealing material. These programs, especially the one involving encapsulation, look very promising as a solution to the technical and practical problems involved in fastener sealing.

Let us turn our attention now to coatings for missile silos, which are not unlike basements of homes except they are larger and deeper. The silos are affected by the soil condition, the water table, the atmospheric conditions, the type of construction, and the degree of maintenance, and moisture to varying degrees is present in most of them. Moisture is often found seeping in around pipes and other structures and running down the silo walls. Water from condensation of humid air in contact with conditioning equipment is also prevalent. Current paints do not protect the metal structures in the silos against this high moisture environment. It is probable, though, that had even the less-than-optimum coatings now available been applied under optimum conditions and to adequately prepared surfaces initially, most problems of excessive maintenance which we now face could have been avoided. However, we all know the almost impossible task of eliminating all moisture from the basement of our own homes and this is even more difficult is silos. Therefore, we have been engaged in efforts to find coating systems which are more tolerant to high moisture conditions than conventional systems now available. Although we realize it is not a normally recommended coating practice, in view of the conditions discussed we have been evaluating these coating systems over glistening wet surfaces.

Because of the sacrificial protection provided to steel by metallic zinc, attention has almost exclusively been devoted to primers containing zinc dust for pigment. Most of these have been of the inorganic silicate type. These primers have been applied to dry and wet steel; to clean and rusty steel; under conditions of high, standard, and low humidity. We have exposed them to hard water, saltwater, and salt fog. One primer especially has performed very well. A specification, to cover the requirements for this primer, MIL-P-38336 has been written. The zinc pigment in these primers tends to oxidize if uncoated, therefore, topcoats are necessary to protect the primer as well as to provide the aesthetic effects desired. In the high moisture conditions prevalent, moisture-curing urethanes appear very promising. One topcoat, pigmented gray, and utilizing an intermediate tie coat has shown excellent performance even when applied over wet surfaces. A specification will be prepared to cover the requirements for this topcoat.

Associated with missile and missile equipment finishing is the need for resistance to fuel and oxidizer vapors and splashes. In areas of high incidence this can be a severe problem. We have not found a suitable coating system which will withstand the effects of nitrogen tetroxide for example. Just a few seconds' exposure to it will completely lift a good acid resistant coating. We have recently started a program to find a coating system which will give us more protection in this area.

In yet another problem area, rain erosion damage of exterior plastic surfaces was first reported in 1945 on an antenna housing of a B-29 aircraft. Consequently, a considerable amount of work has been conducted by many organizations in the aircraft industry ever since. The results of all of this work indicate that the rain erosion resistance of aircraft materials varies widely with the type of material. As aircraft attained ever increasing speeds the problems also increased. The erosive effects of rain at high speed are not now confined to paint coatings or glass-reinforced plastic parts. Tests on high speed subsonic aircraft flying through rain reveal that the rain droplets erode paint, plastic, and metals (such as aluminum and magnesium) on leading edges with such efficiency that they often appear as if they had been sand blasted.

The severity of his high velocity impingement is sufficient to cause complete structural failure of the radome, severe aerodynamic alteration to leading edges, and removal of protection against corrosion. The problem of obtaining structural materials which in themselves will resist erosion for extended periods of high speed flight through rain has not been solved. The problem has been further aggravated by the evolution of supersonic flight for both cruise and combat conditions. Fortunately, most pilots are aware of the damage that can be sustained in such an environment at these speeds and in emergencies they can usually throttle-back. Still improved protection must be provided for speed, and protection must be developed for operation at speeds exceeding Mach 1 in heavy rain environments.

Once again, the urethanes appear promising as a vastly improved subsonic rain erosion resistant coating.

Let us also consider for a moment the dilemma in which we find ourselves with regard to coating removal, necessitated by partial failure, inspection, or repair. As we improve coatings, making them more resistant to various chemicals and solvents, one-by-one we eliminate the very materials which may have been effective paint removers in the past. This throws us back into very strongly acidic or alkaline materials, which, in turn, tend to bery corrosive to common aircraft metals. Many organizations, both governmental and industrial, are working on this problem, but to date there is no satisfactory answer to the stripping of difficult-to-remove finishes, such as urethanes, epoxies, and heat-cured silicones.

**d.  Recent  Coating  Methods.** Polymeric coatings on metals are being used more and more as the advancing technology of polymers leads to the development of high-temperature high-stability polymeric coating materials. However, many of these new materials cannot be used because of inherent lack of such properties as solubility, fusibility, or adaptability by pigmentation.

*(1)  Fluidized Bed.* The most convenient process for applying coatings to objects which have to be completely enveloped is the method of fluidized dipping. The powder is contained in a tank fitted at the bottom with a porous screen. Below the screen is a chamber fed with compressed air. When the air passes through the screen and up through the powder, the apparent volume of the powder is increased by 30–50% and then it has the properties of free-flowing fluid. Coating procedure is to heat objects to a temperature above the fusing point of the polymer and to quickly dip them in the fluidized bed. Experience soon establishes the preheat temperature and the dipping time for each material. Some materials self-fuse after work has been withdrawn from the bed while others require subsequent fusing. The coating thickness depends upon the preheat temperature, dipping time, heat capacity of the substrate, the physical and chemical properties of the coating material employed.

Some of the current resin systems used today include vinyl, cellulosic, epoxy, nylon, chlorinated polyether, polyethylene, and FEP-fluocorcarbon coatings. Silicones have been known for a number of years, yet there is no data in the literature on the application of pure silicones by the fluidized bed method. Other coatings now under development are acetals, polybenzimidazoles, polyimides, low and high density polypropylenes and polycarbonates. Before these coatings become practical, they must be made amenable to preparation in particle shapes and sizes suitable for processing. At the present state of the art, silicone coatings tend to be brittle and high temperature aromatic polymers lack the proper fusion point molecular weight characteristics. These shortcomings may be overcome by combining the resins with other materials. The advantages of the method are that no powder is lost through overspray; complete coverage of complex metal objects is achieved in a few seconds and nonporous coatings of controlled thickness can be produced. The chief disadvantage with the fluidized bed method of coating is that the capital investment of a tankful of powder may be rather high unless there is a continuous production run. The method is also not adaptable to the coating of structural shapes in the field.

**(2) Electrostatic Spray Deposition.** Electrostatic spraying of dry powders permits coating of materials that would be difficult or sometimes impossible to coat with conventional equipment and techniques. Since its introduction about two years ago, electrostatic spraying of dry powders has gained increasing recognition. Most types of dry powders such as plastics, enamels, silicones, and ceramics can be applied by this process.

The theory of electrostatic coating is simple. An electrostatic charge that can be put on a material is a function of the surface area of the particle; forces to be overcome such as gravity and inertia are functions of the volume of the particle. Thus, electrostatic attraction is enhanced by small particles having the larger ratio of surface area to volume, and small charged particles will be attracted to any electrically grounded object near them. Because the particles are nonconducting, they do not easily lose their charge. Powder coatings adhere to the substrate from two hours to two days depending on the material and particle size. To apply a permament, continuous coating film, the particles must be fused and bonded to the base metal by curing the sprayed part in an oven.

The only restriction in choosing coating materials is that the powders must be relatively nonconducting. The important advantages are: (1) charged particles adhere evenly to objects without regard to corners, perforations, direction of spray, (2) uniformly pinhole-free coatings can be applied in thin coats on irregular and complex shapes, sizes and contours, and (3) powder utilization is almost 100 percent.

Electrostatic coatings are used for protection against corrosion,

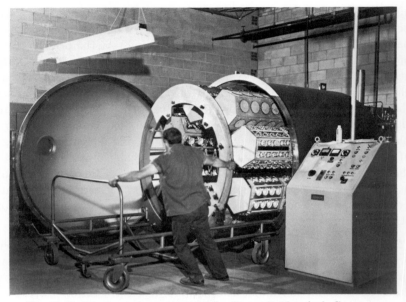

Fig. 13-15. Electrostatic coating tank by Pennsalt Chemicals Company,
Philadelphia, Penna.

weather, moisture, and contamination; electrical insulation for motors,
printed circuit boards, resistors and condensers; and industrial coating
operations of sheet metals, foils, machined parts, etc. Again, though,
adaptation of this method to field use on large structures is limited,
particularly if subsequent heat treatment is needed for a given
material.

**(3) Electrodeposition.** A new method of depositing paint from a
water dispersion by means of a potential of some 500 volts has been
recently announced. Instead of ions migrating to a cathode, this
process involves the migration of charged particles. Actually, the
particles are deposited on the anode, rather than on the cathode. The
phenomenon involves electrolysis, electrophoresis, and electro-osmosis.
The equipment for this process is very similar to that used in electroplating. An agitator is necessary to keep solution composition uniform
and a heat exchanger to control temperature.

The water-based coating solution contains resins, solubilizing agents
(such as amines), pigments, oil-phase solids, and other solid particles.
The resin portion of the paint film is deposited almost totally by
electrolysis. This means that when current is applied to the water

solution, the special resin ions are attracted to the anode. On the surface of the anode the resin ions are discharged, thereby being converted into water-insoluble resin, and are deposited on the anode surface, forming the coating. The pigment and other particles are incorporated into the film as inclusions. Such particles move with their associated resin through the influence of electrophoresis to the electrode surface, where they are deposited with the resin. After deposition, the resin is no longer chemically associated with the portion of the molecule which made it water soluble, that is, it is chemically changed as it is discharged in the process of deposition. There is some electro-osmosis, i.e., water migrating away from the deposited film under the influence of an electrical potential.

Electrocoating is an unusual painting process. It results in some unusual advantages. First, the film allows contours and complicated shapes. It produces no runs, tears, drips, sags, or paint-starved depressions. The most striking advantage is that any surface which will conduct electricity and can be wetted by these solutions, will be electrocoated. Coating uniformity is very good, usually varying no more than 0.2 mil between the thick and thinnest areas of coating. Corrosion resistance can be attained by proper formulation. Adhesion of topcoats to electrocoated primers is selective, just as with conventional primers. However, topcoats formulated for use over the electrocoated primer will have good adhesion.

There are some problems and some limitations, as with any new process. These process introduces a whole new set of variables into both paint application and paint manufacturing. A paint chemist formulating for this method now must be concerned with such things as ionization and conductivity of solutions and films; effect of additives and dragin upon the stability and coating properties of a very different kind of paint; and limitations as to kinds and combinations of resins which may be used. Also, the conditions which favor rapid deposition lead to instability of the coating and, therefore, formulators must compromise between production rate and the attainment of satisfactory long-term stability. There is no doubt that the electrodeposition process can efficiently paint some areas that cannot be coated satisfactorily by any other economically practical production painting method. This process is a major step forward. Certainly, it will be improved in the future to take advantage of potentialities as new polymeric systems are developed.

**(4) Flame and Plasma Spraying.** Organic and inorganic powders may be flame or plasma sprayed in the same manner and with the same equipment as metal powders. Good adhesion can be obtained on all common metals, such as brass, aluminum, steel, copper, etc. There are known processes for depositing nylon and Teflon coatings as well. The desired film thickness may be built up by several passes across the surface to be coated, in a manner similar to that practiced in ordinary paint spraying.

In most instances, most flame-sprayed organic coatings must be fused to produce adherent smooth uniform coatings. However, there is at least one process which makes it possible to spray Teflon directly on metallic surfaces without subsequent sintering. Such a process adapted for field use would be very useful when coating large, heavy pieces or components which are heat sensitive, such as foils or tempered steel parts. By controlling specific particle size and shape, other polymeric materials, including some new polymers to be mentioned later in this paper, with high fusion points and poor solubility, may be applicable to the flame or plasma spraying technique.

**(5) Organometallic Solution Decomposition.** A method of producing coatings which have promise for meeting some of the rigorous requirements encountered in space and reentry environments or in the operation of airborne vehicles is that of organometallic solution decomposition. The application of solutions of organometallic polymeric compounds in air to obtain thin film coatings upon subsequent thermal decomposition is a relatively unknown field.

To obtain thin films, organic compounds of precious and nonprecious metals are first made. The organic starting materials are chosen to obtain high solubility of the organometallic compounds in organic solvents, and to obtain solutions which are not reactive in air at ordinary temperatures. The organic starting materials are also chosen to provide compatibility when solutions of different metal compounds are mixed. Because of this compatibility, the method can be used to obtain very complex films of metals, alloys, oxides or mixtures of these from a single application of an appropriate solution. Application is performed in air and by a variety of methods such as brushing, spraying, dipping, roller coating, or printing. Subsequent heating decomposes and volatilizes all of the organics leaving thin films (of approximately 1000 Å).

The versatility of these solutions and the ease of application in air are advantages of the method. Scale-up of promising coatings from laboratory specimen to substrates of large size and complex shape is readily accomplished by conventional techniques such as spraying. A limitation of coatings obtained from organometallic solution is their extreme thinness which presently restricts their application to specific uses.

In work completed for the Air Force in 1962, this method was used to develop a solar absorbing film containing gold, rhodium, and oxides of bismuth, barium, chromium, and silicon. In 1963, this film was found to be reproducibly obtainable on a variety of diffusion barriers on Inconel. Despite the thinness of this film (about 1250 Å) it was found to undergo no change in optical properties after heating at 700°C for 50 hr. In current research attempts are being made to expand the organometallic solution decomposition method to new and improved coatings for temperature control and environmental protective functions. In the past, this method has been used to provide films of metals such as Au, Pt, Pd, Rh, and Ag; the present effort is directed toward films of B, Be, V, Ta, and Al. Similarly, alloys of precious metals have been developed in situ by this method; current emphasis is toward extending this versatility of intermetallics such as $TaAl_3$, $Ni_3Al$, $Cr_3Si$, and $TiB_2$. Also, the method is used to obtain thin films of $SiO_2$, $ThO_2$, $Al_2O_3$, $Y_2O_3$, $CeO_2$, $ZrO_2$, and $TiO_2$ on various substrates. In all cases, it is possible to use application by brush or spray in air at room temperature without having to resort to any special precauations. Depending on the nature of the film and the substrate, thermal decomposition is carried out in air, inert gas, hydrogen, or in vacuum.

A major finding in this investigation is that the intermetallic NiAl can be obtained from an organic solution of appropriate compounds of the two metals, applied in air, and decomposed under low pressure nitrogen at 550°C.

*(6) Electrophoresis.* When a dc potential is applied across two electrodes which are dipped into a dispersion of colloidal or near-colloidal size particles suspended in a nonaqueous medium, the particles are observed to migrate to one of the electrodes where their charge is neutralized and they are deposited. This phenomenon is termed electrophoresis. Electrodeposition of nonconducting materials such as rubber, synthetic polymers, inorganic oxides, and ceramic materials has been known and used in industry for many years. Any non-conductive material which exists in a finely divided state in an inert medium can be deposited on an electrode. Coagulation occurs because of the high potential existing in the vicinity of the electrode or because of coagulating ions which are formed at the electrode.

Recently Teflon has been deposited by electrophoresis from a water media. There are many problems encountered such as particle shape and size, media, and bonding of the coating. The commercial applications for Teflon were limited and other coating materials looked more promising for use by this process, but it has at least been demonstrated that polymers may be deposited and this opens up an entire new applied research area.

The most important characteristic of the electrophoretic process is that it makes possible the coating of any mixture of materials in controlled composition upon a conductive substrate. A second characteristic of electrophoretic deposition which differentiates it from other coating methods such as electroplating, vapor deposition, and pack cementation is that the coating rate is very rapid. Typical coating rates range from 0.2 to 2 mils/min. A disadvantage of the method is that coated parts usually have to be hydrostatically pressed and sintered to increase density and loading to the substrate. As new polymeric materials become available, this process may show promise as a new coating technique for depositing protective polymeric materials.

*(7)* *Vacuum-Deposited Polymers.* A unique method of organic coating of substrates by vacuum-deposition has been reported. Teflon powder can be vacuum-deposited on a variety of metals and plastics without the fluorocarbon losing any of its chemical or physical properties. In the past, organic compounds have not been considered suitable for deposition because of their susceptibility to chemical breakdown. However, it appears that Teflon as well as other organics can be deposited as thin films that retain properties of the source material.

*(8)* *Problems and Future Interest.* Several relatively new and unique coating methods have been described which may be applicable to some of the new polymeric systems being developed today. Some of these coating methods have been used very successfully with metals, alloys, and ceramic coating systems in the past. By taking the information learned from these systems and applying it to the polymeric systems, unique application methods and properties may be derived. Each of the processes described have their own particular problems. Research to optimize each method is needed if these methods are to be competitive with the normal methods of applying organic coatings and overcome their deficiencies.

## 2. Improved Coating Materials

**a. New Polymer Systems.** In discussing high-temperature polymer or macromolecular systems from the film-forming or coatings viewpoint, the present state of the art in polymeric coatings should first be noted very briefly. Most organic coating materials are not useful for lengthy periods of time at temperatures above 350°C (660°F). The best commercial coatings available for use in thermal environments up to 650°F are the semi-inorganic polymers, the silicones. However, above these temperatures, such polymers do not retain their protective properties due to thermal degradation; and at temperatures considerably lower than 650°F, conventional polymers suffer from lack of chemical and dielectric property stabilities. Thus, the high-temperature polymers which are of interest as precursors of future aerospace coatings must possess stabilities to temperature in excess of 400°C and preferably above 550°C and exhibit properties which make them coating candidates (film formation, solubility, etc.). For purposes of discussion such polymer systems may be divided into four main categories: (1) aromatic (or phenylene) polymers, (2) heteroaromatic or heterocyclic polymers, (3) semiorganic (or semi-inorganic) polymers and (4) inorganic polymers.

**b. Aromatic Polymers.** Polymers containing aromatic carbon or benzene rings in the polymer chain have received considerable attention for possible high-temperature applications in recent years. Such polymers generally possess good thermal stability, but those exhibiting a high degree of solubility or high molecular weights are difficult to obtain. The polyphenyls such as poly(p-phenylene) decomposes above 500°C but are infusible and insoluble in conventional solvents. Thus, although a polyphenylene is reported from thermogravimetric analysis (TGA) studies to be the most thermally stable of all phenylene-linked polymers evaluated this rigid macromolecule is unsuitable for the preparation of films or coatings.

However, if two methylene groups are inserted after every phenylene group in a polymer chain, the much more flexible poly(p-xylylene) is obtained. This material, Fig. 13-16, was prepared by the pyrolysis of p-xylene as an insoluble crystalline product which melts above 520°C and forms films. Other carbocyclic (or carbon-ringed) polymers of interest contain nitrogen or oxygen in their chains. Polyoxamides, derived from aromatic diamines and diphenyldithioloxalate, form clear, flexible films with melting points above 400°C.

Although polyesters generally possess lower melting points than

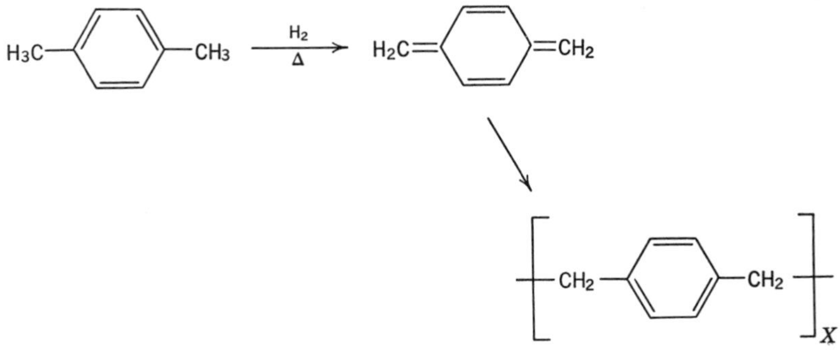

Fig. 13-16. Polyxylylenes.

do the corresponding polyamides, several high-melting polyester systems have recently been reported. Poly (*p*-hydroxybenzoic acid), from the autocondensation of *p*-acetoxybenzoic acid, Fig. 13-17, is reported to form tough, oxidation-resistant films which melt at 380 –450°C and are somewhat sensitive to hydrolysis. High molecular weight poly (*m*-hydroxybenzoic) acid as well as copolymers of *m*- and *p*-hydroxybenzoic acids were obtained by a two-stage, magnesium catalyzed, melt polymerization at 200°C, followed by solid phase polymerization at 300°C. Polyesters of hydroquinone and terephthalic or isophthalic acid have recently been obtained with melt temperatures of from 300 to 400°C. Such polymers are soluble and can be converted into clear, flexible films.

An interesting oxygen-containing carbocyclic system is that represented by the polyanhydrides. Although little is known about their film-forming properties, two high-melting polyanhydrides, poly (bis-*p*-carboxy-phenyl-methane anhydride) and poly (terephthalic anhydride), Fig. 13-18, have recently been reported with melting points of 325° and 400°C, respectively. The latter polymer may be of con-

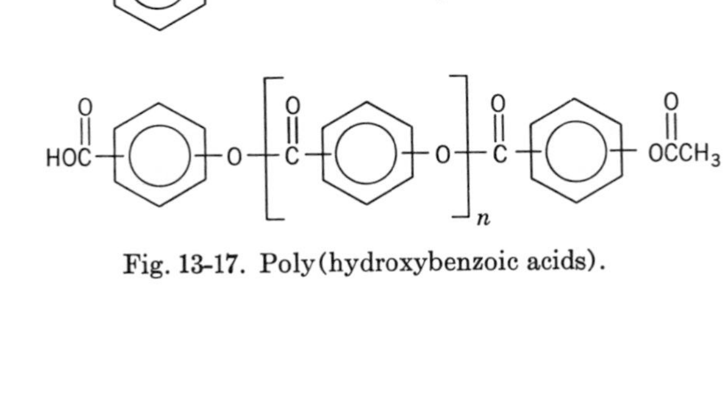

Fig. 13-17. Poly(hydroxybenzoic acids).

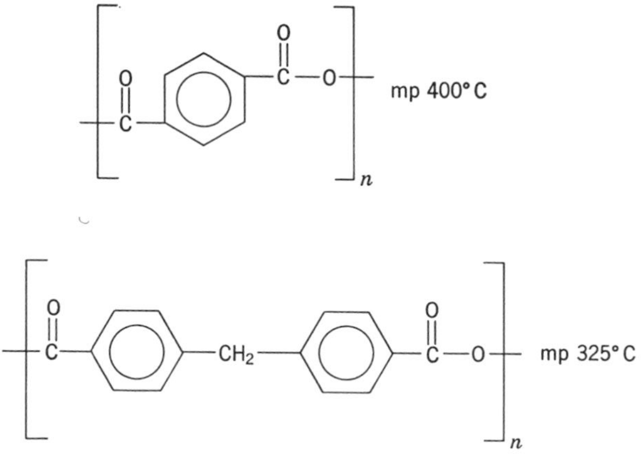

mp 400° C

mp 325° C

Fig. 13-18. Polyanhydrides.

siderable interest in the film and coating area, as it is resistant to attack by hydrochloric acid, nitric acid, and aqua regia.

**c. Heterocyclic Polymers.** All promising high temperature organic polymers appear to have the common feature of rings in the polymer chain. Although, in some cases such rings are strictly carbocyclic, the most interesting types of polymers under present investigation are the heterocyclics, in which nitrogen, oxygen, or sulfur is contained within the rings.

One class of heteroaromatic polymers which has received a great deal of attention in regard to coating and film applications in recent years in the polyimides. Of this class the poly(pyromellitimides) are perhaps the best known. These polymers are prepared from pyromellitic dianhydride and aromatic diamines in dimethylformamide or dimethylacetamide which react to first form poly(pyromellitamic acids). On heating, films cast from these solutions underwent cyclodehydration to yield the insoluble, infusible polyimides, Fig. 13-19. The tough, oxidation-resistant poly(pyromellitimide) films are reported to be stable up to 800°C and to exhibit high flame and radiation resistance. The polymer derived from the dianhydride and 4.4'-diaminodiphenylether (poly(4,4'-oxydiphenylene pyromellitimide) gives films with the best combination of thermal, mechanical, and electrical properties.

Other polyimides of interest include resins derived from benzophenone tetracarboxylic dianhydride or trimellitic anhydride, Fig. 13-20, and aromatic diamines. The resin obtained from the condensation

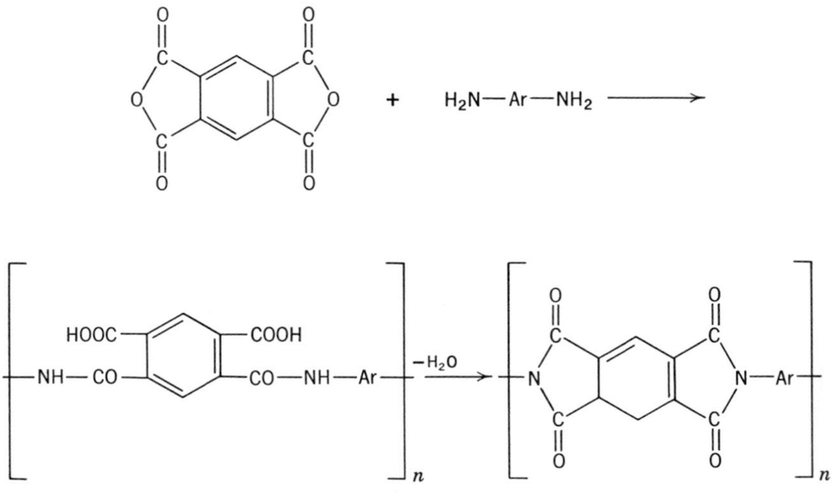

Fig. 13-19. Aromatic polypyromellitimides.

of benzophenone tetracarboxylic dianhydride and *m*-phenylenediamine softens enough at 350°C to provide some formability, is soluble in the uncured stage, and is reported to be stable for 1,000 hr at 315°C. The trimellitic anhydride-derived polymer, after curing, contains both imide and amide linkages, has a flow temperature range of 420–440°C and has found use as an insulating varnish.

A second class of heterocyclic polymers which has excited considerable interest is the poly(benzimidazoles). These materials, first

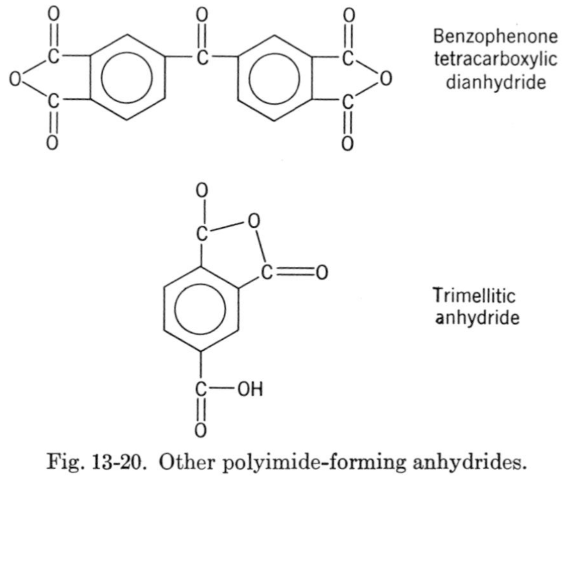

Benzophenone
tetracarboxylic
dianhydride

Trimellitic
anhydride

Fig. 13-20. Other polyimide-forming anhydrides.

reported by Marvel and du Pont researchers, are obtained from the condensation of the diphenyl esters of aromatic carboxylic acids and aromatic tetramines in a melt polymerization (Fig. 13-21), carried out over two temperatures, 220–260°C, and then 350–400°C, and presumably through the formation of a poly-(aminoamide) intermediate. The solubility, reactivity, and crystallinity of such polymers are a function of the polymerization temperature. Poly(benzimidazoles) derived from phthalic acids and 1,2,4,5-tetraaminobenzene or 3,3′-diaminobenzidine (Fig. 13-21 )are thermally stable to 600°C and exhibit a weight loss up to 30% at 900°C. Films have been cast from certain of the soluble (in DMSO and HCOOH) poly(benzimidazoles), the best being that from poly[2,2′-(m-phenylene)-5,5′-dibenzimidazole.]

Two other classes of attractive high temperature nitrogen-heterocyclic polymers are derived from the same prepolymers, the polyhydrazides, Fig. 13-22. The latter are quite stable thermally and exhibit melting points up to 400°C and above. However, through intramolecular condensation reactions similar to those involved in the formation of the poly(benzimidazoles), they form still more promising polymers. Upon heating or treatment with acids, the polyhydrazides are converted to poly (1,3,4-oxadiazoles), Fig. 13-23, which are quite high melting and cannot, with the exception of those derived from aliphatic acids, be pressed into films. When the prepolymers (the polyhydrazides) are treated with aniline and phosphoric acid in solution at 250–265°C poly(phenylenetriazoles) are obtained, Fig. 13-23. Films cast from formic acid solutions of poly (m-, p-phenylene-4-phenyltriazole) were tough, and exhibited high strength as well as dimensional stability at elevated temperatures. This triazole polymer, similar to poly [2,2′-(m-phenylene)-5,5′-bibenzimidazole], appears to offer promise for utility as a coating material at 1000°F in an inert atmosphere for limited periods of time.

A new class of nitrogen heteroaromatic polymers, the polyquinoxalines, were reported for the first time during the past year. These macromolecules are synthesized from polycondensation reactions of aromatic tetraamines and aromatic tetracarbonyl derivatives in dioxane or dimethyl formamide, followed by heat treatment in the solid phase, Fig. 13-24. The polyquinoxalines exhibit excellent thermal stabilities comparable to the poly(benzimidazoles), i.e., up to 600°C in nitrogen and 500°C in air, as may be noted from the thermograms of a typical representative of that class shown in Fig. 13-25. These somewhat flexible but infusible polymers are reported to form films.

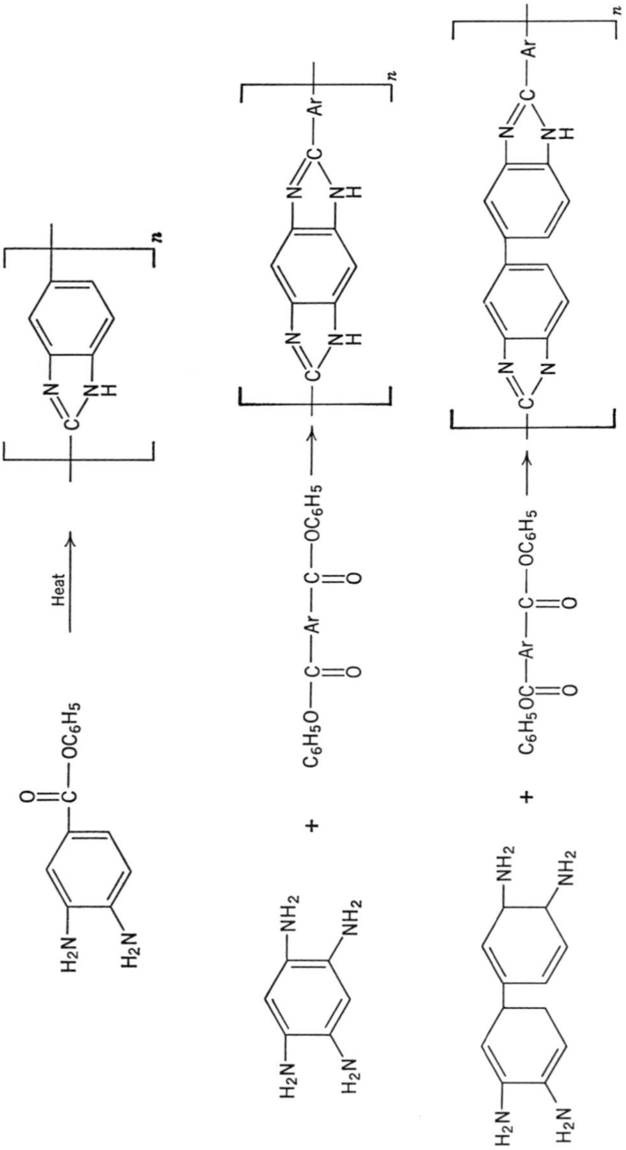

Fig. 13-21. Polybenzimidazoles.

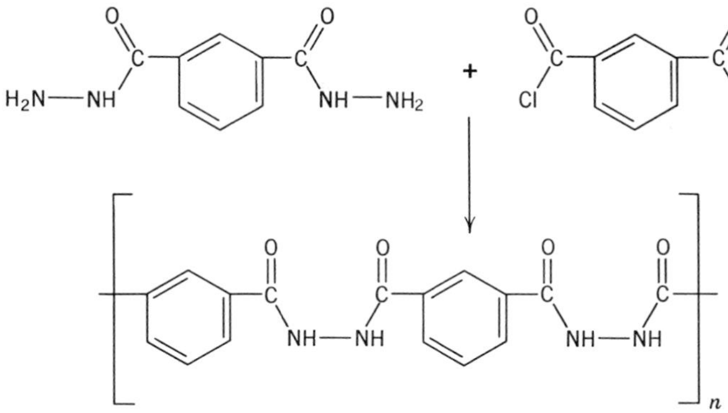

Fig. 13-22. Aromatic polyhydrazides.

**d. Semiorganic Polymers.** In view of the successes achieved with conventional techniques for moderate temperature applications, a good deal of effort in the semi-organic or semi-inorganic polymer area has been devoted to attempts to modify and improve upon the polysiloxane system. Although a number of elements such as aluminum,

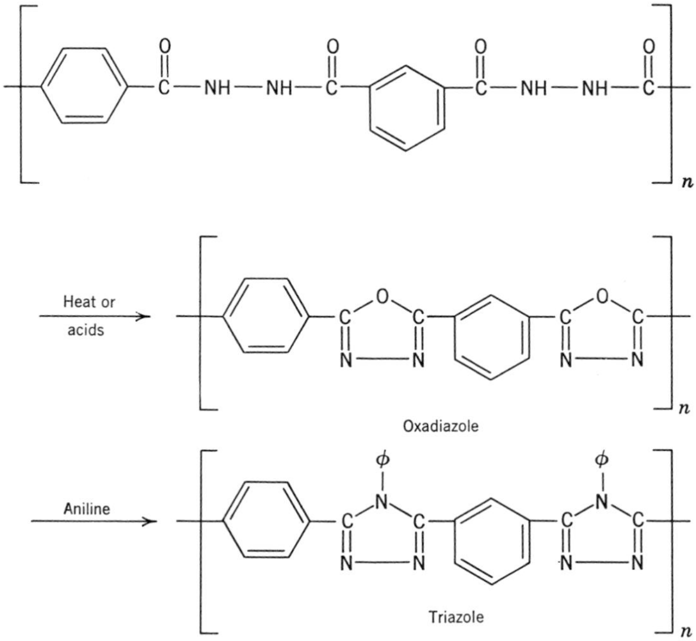
Heat or
acids
Oxadiazole
Aniline
Triazole

Fig. 13-23. Conversion of polyhydrazides.

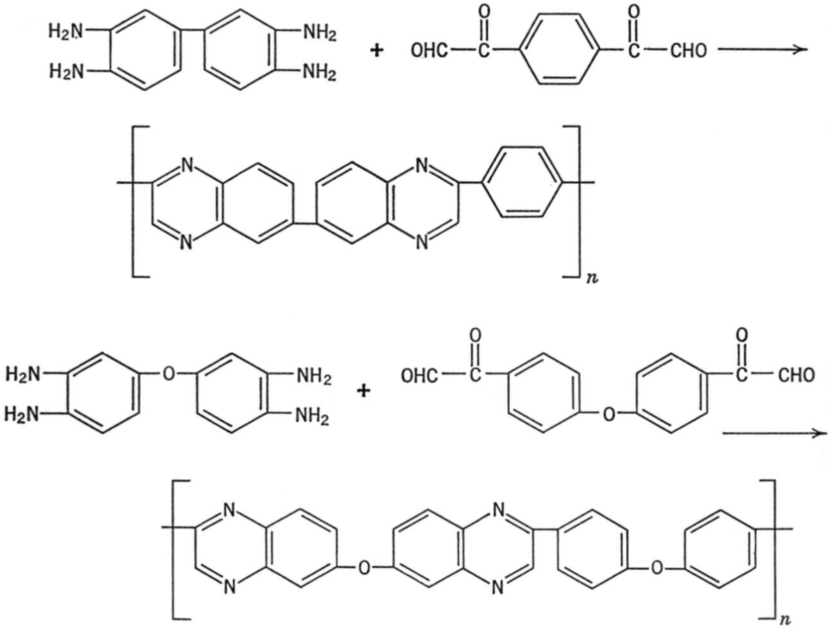

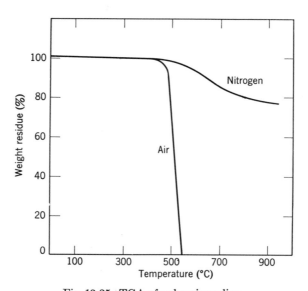

Fig. 13-24. Polyquinoxalines.

Fig. 13-25. TGA of polyquinoxaline.

titanium, tin, and boron have been utilized to wholly or partly replace silicon in silicone-like structures, the resulting polymers have shown no advantages and are generally inferior property-wise to conventional silicones. There are several exceptions, however, to such efforts and the silicon-containing systems involved not only are attractive as high-temperature materials, but appear to offer specific promise for utility in coating applications.

One family of polymeric analogs of the silicones is the poly (aryloxysilanes) which may be likened to polysiloxanes in which alternating silicon atoms are replaced by arylene spacer groups. These polymers, primarily investigated by the Marshall Space Flight Center, are dedived from reactions of diaryldichlorosilanes or bis(anilino)diphenylsilanes and aromatic diols, Fig. 13-26. They demonstrated high thermal stabilities, as evidenced by TGA studies in nitrogen, and have been used for the preparation of a number of coatings. Several of the better poly(aryloxysilanes), when cast as films on stainless steel, exhibited good integrity and adhesion after being heated at 1000°F for 8 hr in argon.

A second category of attractive silicon-containing polymers are the polysilazanes. Of this family, two types have been the subjects of considerable interest during the past several years. One type, the poly(phenylsilazanes), derived from pyrolysis of trimeric cyclosilazanes or the reaction of diphenyldichlorosilanes and ammonia, Fig. 13-27, are reported to possess high thermal resistance. A related system, poly("ethylenediaminesilazane"), from dimethyldichlorosilane and ethylenediamine is reported to yield a polymer containing five-

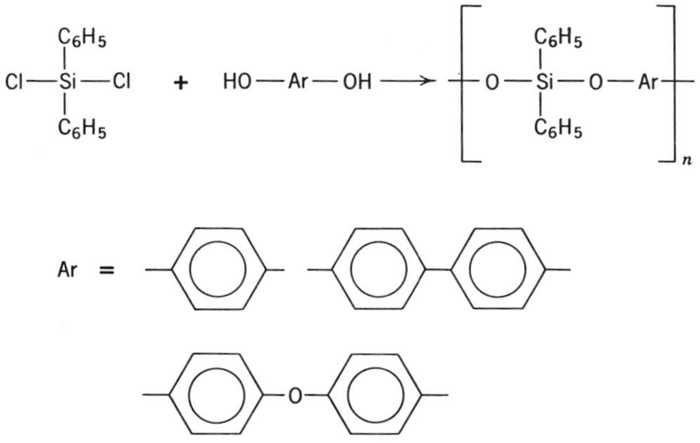

Fig. 13-26. Poly(aryloxysilanes).

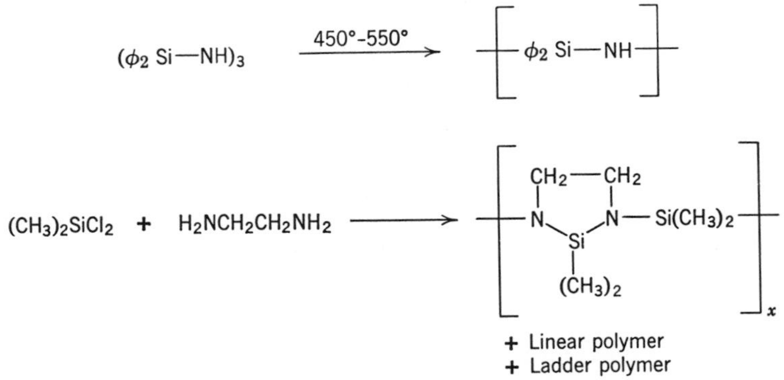

$$(\phi_2 \, Si-NH)_3 \xrightarrow{\;450°-550°\;} \left[ \phi_2 \, Si-NH \right]$$

$$(CH_3)_2SiCl_2 \;+\; H_2NCH_2CH_2NH_2 \longrightarrow \left[ \begin{array}{c} CH_2-CH_2 \\ N \quad\quad N-Si(CH_3)_2 \\ Si \\ (CH_3)_2 \end{array} \right]_x$$

+ Linear polymer
+ Ladder polymer

Fig. 13-27. Semiorganic polymers (Si—N).

membered silicon-nitrogen rings, in addition to linear and double—stranded types. A second type of interesting polymers containing silicon–nitrogen bonds are the poly(cyclodisilazanes) derived from the amine exchange reactions of aromatic diamines and bis(alkylamino) diphenylsilanes, Fig. 13-28. The linear polysilazanes, Fig. 13-27, of the first type, on thermal curing to infusible coatings, exhibited an 80-percent weight loss, although good integrity and adhesion were shown by the thin residual film after exposure to 1000°F in an inert

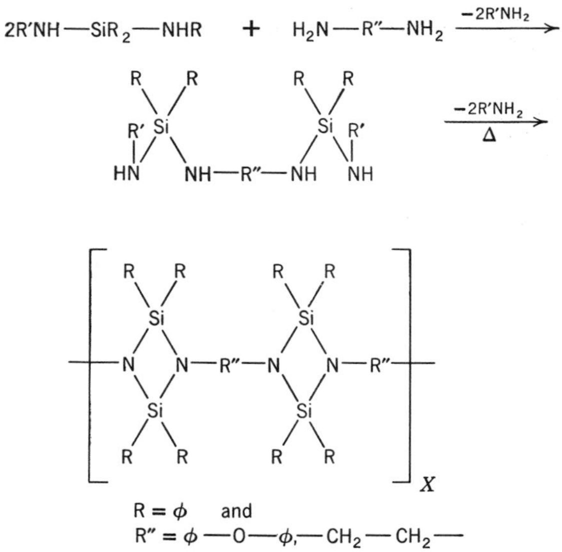

$$2R'NH-SiR_2-NHR \;+\; H_2N-R''-NH_2 \xrightarrow{\;-2R'NH_2\;}$$

$$\xrightarrow[\Delta]{\;-2R'NH_2\;}$$

$$\left[ \begin{array}{c} R \;\; R \\ Si \\ N \quad N-R''-N \quad N-R'' \\ Si \\ R \;\; R \end{array} \right]_X$$

R = φ    and
R″ = φ—O—φ,— CH₂—CH₂—

Fig. 13-28. Semiorganic polymers (Si—N).

atmosphere. The poly (cyclodisilazanes) had less weight loss but exhibited poor coating properties under similar conditions.

A third family of promising silicon-containing macromolecules and the one most closely related to the silicones is that represented by poly (phenylsilsesquioxane) or "Phenyl-T" polymer. This so-called "ladder polymer" is a double-strand structure, Fig. 13-29, in which the two strands or chains are bound together periodically by chemical bonds (such as, in this case, the Si—O linkage). In principle, such macromolecules should exhibit superiority to the linear types because their polymer chains cannot be severed by the breaking of a single bond. The poly (silsesquioxane), formed by the hydrolysis of phenyltrichlorosilane, is unfusible but soluble in organic solvents.

One other class of semiorganic polymers which appears to offer potential for high-temperature coatings is the aromatic phosphates. One example of this type, poly [ (m-phenylene)phenyl phosphate], Fig. 13-30, was evaluated as a high-temperature coating material and found to offer promise for utility at temperatures up to 1000°F in inert atmospheres where color is not an important consideration.

**e. Inorganic Polymers.** Since there has been a general belief on the part of many that polymers based on carbon chains are limited to a high-temperature-use ceiling of about 400–450°C, intensive efforts were made in recent years to develop inorganic polymer systems which might possess the thermal and oxidative stabilities of naturally occurring minerals. Although some stable inorganic polymers have been developed, they have, in general, been disappointing since

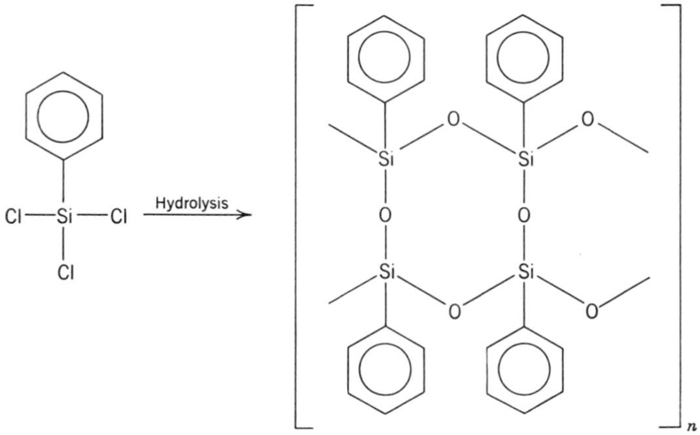

Fig. 13-29. Poly (phenylsilsesquioxane) ("phenyl-T" polymer).

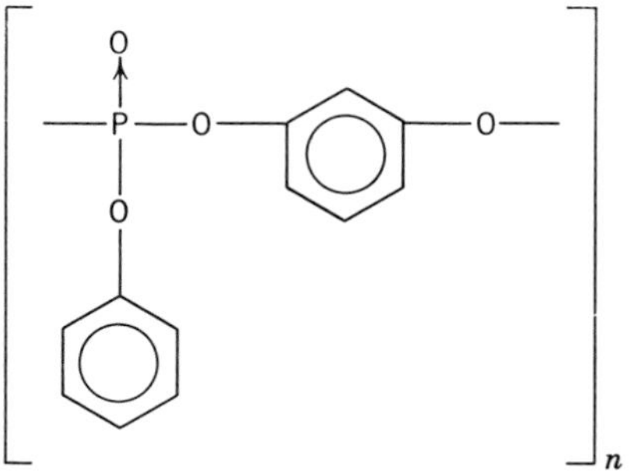

Fig. 13-30. Poly(*m*-phenylene) phenyl phosphate.

they are not suitable as technologically useful materials. Attempts to prepare stable, wholly inorganic macromolecules having linear chains of reasonably high molecular weight have been relatively unsuccessful.

However, work by Butler and Hathaway during the past year indicates the promise that still lies ahead for inorganic polymers. Their studies of inorganic siliceous polymers indicate that inorganic or organic-inorganic polymers which degrade or oxidize to stable inorganic residues may offer the greatest potential as coating materials for extended exposure to 1000°F in air. Pigmented polysiloxanes, polysilazanes, and polysilic acid copolymerized with hydrolyzed phenyltrichlorosilane, Fig. 13-31, were each heated at 1000°F in air.

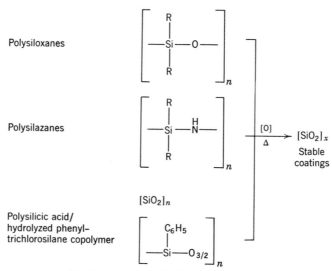

Fig. 13-31. Inorganic siliceous polymers.

In each of these cases it is believed that the film-forming or pigment-binding materials formed is essentially silica or $(SiO_2)_x$. However, before coatings with optimum properties can be developed a good deal of additional information is needed on the relationships between initial polymer structure and characteristics of the resulting siliceous materials.

**f. Some Trends in High-Temperature Polymers.** Although some workers in the high-temperature field have concluded that completely organic polymers cannot provide coatings which will stand exposure temperatures of 1000°F in air, one recent Soviet report indicates that there may still be hope in "carbon backbone" polymers for such high-temperature applications. Topchiev and coworkers have described the formation of white, translucent coatings, with exceptionally high thermal stability through the heating of poly(o-fluoro-$\beta$-nitrostyrene), Fig. 13-32, at temperatures as high as 1200°C for several hours.

Another approach to the possibility of extending the range of organic polymers may lie in the modification of some of the more promising types of high-temperature macromolecules discussed in this paper. Very recently studies by Thiokol chemists show that significant improvements may be achieved in the thermal and especially oxidative stability of polymers of the poly(benzimidazole) type by the incorporation of semiorganic moieties, such as those derived from carborane. By reaction of the sodium salt of poly(benzimidazole) with 1-bromomethylcarborane, a polymer, Fig. 13-33, is obtained which, in TGA studies, exhibited losses of only 18% in nitrogen and 25% in air when heated up to 900°C.

The poly(benzimidazoles) and other related heterocyclics provide difficult formation of coatings from solution due to poor solubility characteristics in conventional solvents. However, through the development of new coating techniques, such as flame or plasma spraying, described earlier, it would appear that such deficiencies as

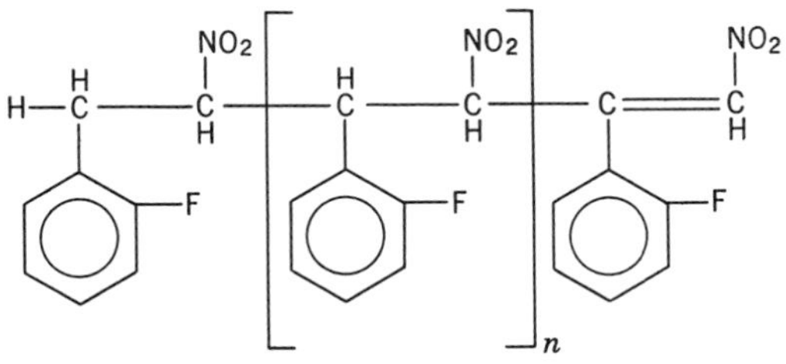

Fig. 13-32. Poly(o-fluoro-$\beta$-nitrostyrene).

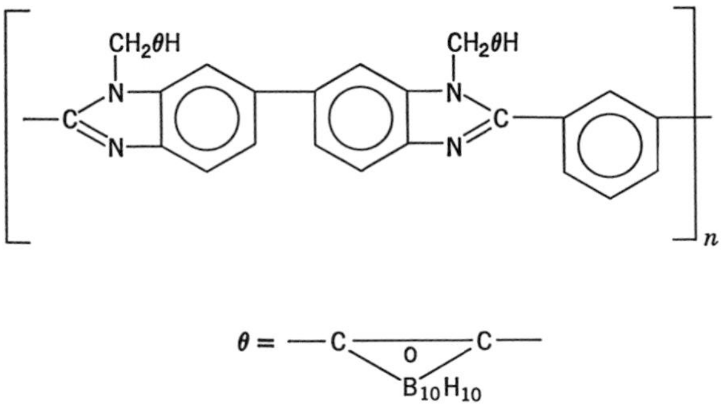

$$\theta = \ \underset{\displaystyle B_{10}H_{10}}{\text{—C}\diagdown\underset{O}{\phantom{x}}\diagup\text{C—}}$$

Fig. 13-33. A poly(carboranylmethylbenzimidazole).

insolubility in high-melting polymers may be circumvented in the future.

One area which should demand attention in future years is that of the "ladder polymers." As mentioned earlier in this report in connection with the "Phenyl-T" polymer, double-strand polymers offer hope for a significant breakthrough in the development of high-temperature materials. A number of investigators in this field feel that the next major step upward in the development of thermally-stable polymers will come from the area of ladder systems and that materials stable up to 1000°F may be achieved. In addition, to the previously described "Phenyl-T" polymer and the well-known cyclized polyacrylonitrile or black Orlon, recent examples of this type, such as the cyclized poly(vinylisocyanate) and cyclized 1,2-polyisoprene, Fig. 13-34, indicate that double-stranded organic and semiorganic

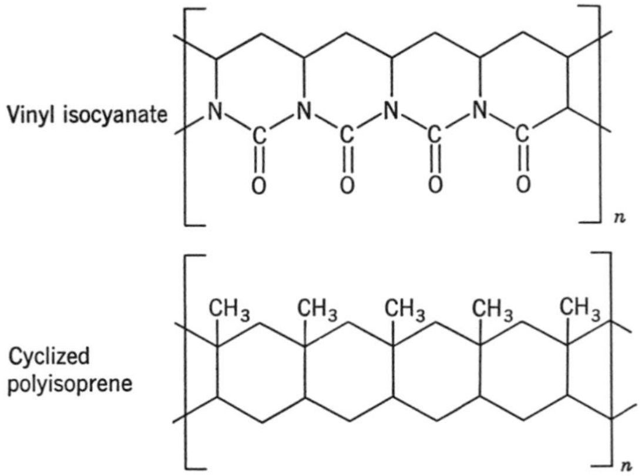

Fig. 13-34. Ladder polymers.

polymers may be obtained with high-melting points and may be cast into films.

While mention has been made of the need for high-temperature polymers stable in air, there also exist requirements for polymeric coating materials which must offer resistance to other oxidizing environments such as resistance to attack by novel oxidizers used in aerospace propellants. Efforts in the development of polymeric coatings to provide protection from the effects of such chemicals as nitrogen tetroxide have heretofore centered around the highly-fluorinated polymers of the poly(tetrafluoroethylene) variety. It may be that future possibilities in this field may lie in the investigation of systems analogous to the poly(anhydrides). But, polymers such as poly(terephthalic anhydride) exhibit little promise for use as films at elevated temperatures in air, their great resistance to oxidizing media, such as nitric acid, offers hope for their development as oxidizer-resistant coating materials.

**g. Polybenzimidazole (PBI).** Examination of two molecular weights of PBI (Fig. 13-31) revealed that it has poor film-forming properties, discolors all pigments, and exhibits limited thermal stability above 800°F.

This material at a higher molecular weight yielded much improved film properties but failed after short periods of exposure to elevated temperatures (800°F). The use of diffusion barrier coatings and phenolic antioxidants was attempted with no improvement in oxidative stability. The principal disadvantages of the PBI resin are its lack of oxidative stability and the lengthy heat cure (1 hr at 280°F, and 1 hr at 570°F) needed to develop optimum properties.

**h. Polypyromellitimide (PMI).** A polymer system (Fig. 13-19) which exhibits good oxidative stability and limited thermal stability at elevated temperatures is that of poly-4,4″-oxydephenylpyromellitimide (PMI). This polyimide is soluble in dimethylacetamide and will cure to a continuous film with the same cure schedule as the PBI resin. Pigmentation studies indicated discoloration by the resin but not as severe as with the PBI. Films of the coatings exhibited good adhesion and integrity upon cure but their thermal stability was limited even at 800°F. The advantage of this polymer is its relative stability in an oxidative atmosphere and its retention of dielectric properties up to its thermal degradation temperature.

**i. Polyphenylsilsesquioxane (Phenyl-T).** The phenyl-T (Fig. 13-14) is a colorless, lacquer-type resin which dries rapidly in air at room temperature. It accepts titanium dioxide and aluminum pigments well to yield formulations without discoloration. However, its adhesion to metal substrates is practically nonexistent. The use of additives was found necessary in both clear and $TiO_2$-pigmented films to promote even fair adhesion to stainless steel or titanium. Aluminum-pigmented films of the phenyl-T exhibited fair adhesion to the metal substrates and were subsequently employed as primers for the white phenyl-T topcoats. The intercoat adhesion was satisfactory. Another disadvantage of the phenyl-T is its tendency to degrade at elevated temperatures, similar to conventional silicones, leaving only $SiO_2$ pigment residue on the substrate.

**j.   Poly(4′-bisoxybiphenylene-diphenylsilane).** Films of this silanediol pigmented with titanium dioxide are light brown in color and exhibited poor stability at elevated temperatures (Fig. 13-26). Cured films did have low weight loss after 100 hr at 800° and 1000°F losing only 10.21 and 13.15%, respectively. Aluminum-pigmented films of the polymer lasted 25 hr at 800, 900, and 1000°F losing only 10.21 and 13.15%, respectively. Aluminum-limited by it extensive heat cure (3 hr at 570°F) and the discoloration of conventional white pigments.

**k. Siliazane Polymers.** Four silicon-nitrogen polymers (Figs. 13-27 and 13-28) developed by Southern Research Institute have been evaluated. These polymers included a resinous by-product hexaphenylcyclotrisilazane (PBHS), polymeric diphenylsilazane (PDS), ethylenediamine silazane (EDS), and boiled methylphenylsilazane made with triethylamine BMPS-TEA). These polymers are soluble in benzene and vary from colorless to dark yellow. Each requires an extremely high temperature cure (1 hr at 700°F) to develop properties.

Clear films of these polymers retained protective properties as follows:

800°F—25 hr on stainless, 25 hr on titanium, 10 hr on mild steel.
900°F—25 hr on stainless, 10 hr on titanium, 2 hr on mild steel.
1000°F—25 hr on stainless, 5 hr on titanium, 1 hr on mild steel.
Films pigmented with $TiO_2$ lasted 25 hr at 800, 900, and 1000°F on stainless steel and titanium and 10 hr at 1000°F on mild steel. After this exposure, only powder remained in most cases with fair integrity and poor adhesion. Aluminized silazanes exhibited excellent protective properties on all three substrates for periods up to 25 hr even at 1000°F. All silazanes evaluated will exhibit low

weight loss after cure because most of the volatiles will be removed when the curing schedule is complete.

**l. Carborane-Silicone Polymer.** The need for increased thermal stability in resins has led to the development of several systems which attempt to combine the desirable properties of each polymer. One of these polymers is a carborane-silicone which has the structure as shown in Fig. 13-35.

This polymer is colorless, soluble in toluene, and will cure to a continuous film after 6 hr at 212°F. Clear films of this polymer remain for 25 hr at 800 to 1000°F with a glassy residue protecting the substrate at that time. Aluminized films of the carborane-silicone will last 25 hr at 1200°F with some discoloration on titanium; on stainless steel, they peel in 1 hr above 900°F. However, the polymer pigmented with $TiO_2$ fails in 1 hr even at 800°F on titanium but will last 25 hr at 800 and 900°F on stainless steel. The clear film exhibits excellent adhesion to aluminum panels but the adhesion to stainless steel or titanium substrates is only marginal.

**m. PBI-Carborane Polymer.** Clear films of PBI-carborane polymer (Fig. 13-33) have been examined on stainless steel and titanium substrates at elevated temperatures in air and exhibit no change after 10 hr at 800°F, and are still intact but porous after 25 hr exposure. This represents a substantial improvement in oxidative stability for a PBI-based resin. The TGA curve for this copolymer indicates a weight loss of only 15% at 1850°F in air.

At present, the principal disadvantages of this copolymer are its low solubility in conventional solvents (1% in dimethylacetamide) ; once again, a heat cure is necessary. This time a temperature of 650°F was utilized to take advantage of the crosslinking reaction which was indicated by the first exotherm in a determination by differential thermal analysis on the copolymer. Film properties were

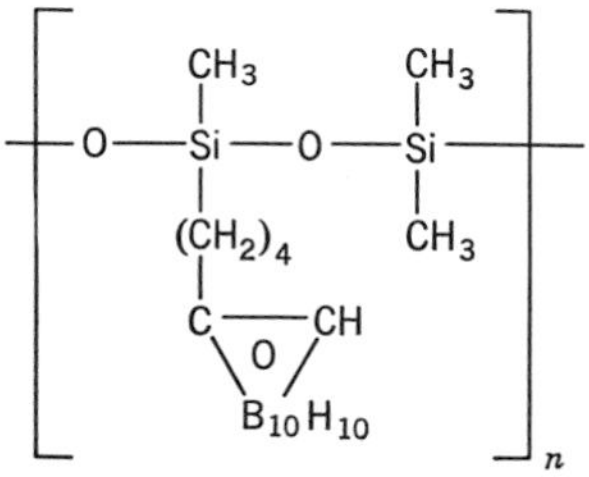

Fig. 13-35. Carborane-silicone polymer.

noticeably superior for a film cured at this temperature over one cured at a lower temperature.

**n. High Temperature Pigments.** Four types of conventional pigments have been evaluated for use with experimental resins in high temperature protective coatings. Titanium dioxide, strontium chromate, carbon black, and leafing aluminum powder were milled into the PBI, PMI, and Phenyl-T resins previously mentioned. All of these pigments have limited applications at high temperature. The titanium dioxide and strontium chromate appear to become highly oxidizing at temperatures of 800°F and above and promote volatilization of the resins. Films of PBI and PMI pigmented with $TiO_2$ (white and $SrCrO_4$ (bright yellow) had good color but oxidized rapidly even when applied over a primer.

Carbon black also promoted oxidation and failure of the films at elevated temperature. Incompatibility of this pigment with these resins was also noted: the films had a rough, textured surface and poor integrity. Extra grinding time was also necessary in order to obtain usable formulations. The aluminum powder shows the most promise as a high temperature pigment for novel polymer systems. It is compatible with all resins thus far evaluated and can be mixed mechanically in a short while. At elevated temperatures the aluminum partially oxidizes to $Al_2O_3$ which remains even when the resin volatilizes. A residue of alumina has been noted even with films exposed to 1200°F. In general, the aluminum gives sufficient hiding at lower pigment to binder ratios than the other pigments. It is the only pigment which combines with Phenyl-T resin to yield a film with adhesion to metal substrate. Aluminum is, of course, inapplicable for coatings where a high diffuse reflectance and high infrared emittance is desired. Unfortunately, many high performance aircraft applications require this combination of properties.

Previous work by Uhlig indicated molybdates might show promise for improved high temperature pigments. Also obtained were the stannates, titanates, and zirconates of barium, calcium, magnesium, and strontium as well as calcium tungstate. Formulations of these compounds in a modified silicone were prepared and evaluated. A thermally stable, nondegrading pigmented coating was desired. Cured films of these formulations varied in color from glossy-white to tan.

Upon exposure to 800°F or above, all compounds acted as oxidizing agents or catalysts and only powder remained after 10 hr at these temperatures. Some problems with adhesion of these films were noted in 900 and 1000°F exposures on titanium. The calcium tungstate, which remained white even at 1000°F (exhibiting none of the yellowing characteristic of $TiO_2$), oxidized the binder so that only powder was left in 5 hr at 800°F, 2 hr at 900°F, and 1 hr at 1000°F.

## 3. Evaluation Methods

Severe near-future requirements for polymeric protective coatings demand the use of all available methods of characterizing candidate materials. Only recently have several useful thermal, optical and electrical methods been so employed for coating research.

The two main thermal methods to consider are TGA (thermogravimetric analysis) and DTA (differential thermal analysis). Both may be used to characterize potential coating materials under conditions that would provide information for the best selection, formulation, and application of these materials, by investigating their thermal degradation patterns and mechanisms.

The optical methods of interest are spectrophotometric and photomicrographic. Spectrophotometry is used to investigate the changes in optical properties of coatings which have been subjected to various environmental conditions. Photomicrography can be used to either examine or determine the metal-coating interface. It can also be used to determine if a coating is crystalline, amorphous, continuous, or lacking in integrity.

An electrical method of importance is the measurement of the dielectric breakdown point of a coating. The instruments that are used for this purpose can also be used to determine the porosity and uniformity of a coating.

**a. Thermogravimetric Analysis.** Thermogravimetric analysis consists of a system that is capable of continuously measuring weight loss or gain versus time or temperature. It provides a rapid means for following the degradation of potential coating materials leading to mass changes over a wide temperature range. It has the following potential uses in the field of polymer coating technology:

*1.* TGA may be used to determine the best curing temperature of coatings, since it is possible to ascertain the minimum temperature where all the solvent is removed.

*2.* The effects of pigment, filler, and other additives, upon the thermal stability of the coating or polymer may be evaluated.

*3.* TGA can be used to compare coatings and to predict the overall stability at any temperature.

*4.* Interaction of polymers or coatings with different substrates may be examined with respect to thermal stability.

*5.* The effects of various solvents used in preparing coatings can be seen such as surface tension when the solvent evaporates, incomplete evaporation, and interaction with the polymer upon heating.

*6.* TGA may also be used to calculate the kinetics of degradation. The energy of activation, the order of decomposition, the frequency factor, and the specific rate constant may all be evaluated using this method. From these, some understanding of the processes occurring may be obtained and used as a guide for further synthetic or formulation research.

As with any investigative device TGA has certain limitations. For example, TGA can be used to follow the degradation of potential coating materials leading to *mass changes* over a wide temperature range. TGA cannot detect changes which are not accompanied by mass changes. A large weight loss need not be associated with loss of desirable properties, therefore, the residue must be examined. By the same token, a small weight loss cannot always be associated with a suitable material as the residue may be useless. In the evaluation of materials TGA should be used in conjunction with other tools such as DTA.

**b.  Differential Thermal Analysis.**  Differential thermal analysis consists of a system that is capable of detecting the *transitions* and *reactions* that a material undergoes on heating, not necessarily resulting in mass changes as in TGA. Like TGA, DTA experiments may be conducted under various atmospheric conditions. The end use of the material will determine the most suitable conditions for conducting the analysis. The method has several potential uses in polymeric coatings research, for example, it may be employed in determining:

*1.* The change in crystal form of pigments, fillers, and binders.

*2.* The melting, freezing, and secondary transition temperatures.

*3.* Sublimation or vaporization temperatures.

*4.* Thermal and oxidative degradation of materials and the kinetics of these processes.

Generally any reaction or transition that releases or absorbs energy (as heat) is detectable through the use of DTA. The main limitation is that the extent of oxidation, decomposition, and other reactions cannot be precisely determined, because DTA does not indicate where a reaction begins but where it takes place at the most rapid rate.

**c. Thermoparticle Analysis.** Another thermal technique which does not enjoy as widespread use as TGA and DTA is TPA (thermoparticle analysis). In TPA the decomposition particles of a degradation are carried in a stream of gas from the pyrolysis chamber to the particle measuring arrangement. Water droplets are condensed on the decomposition particles of the material. The particles of approximately $10^{-7}$ and $10^{-5}$ cm radii, after water condensation, are capable of scattering light. The scattered light is measured by a phototube in a dark-field optical system and is related to the original number of particles in the gas stream. The measuring system has the capability of measuring one part of material in $10^{15}$ parts of air. Application of this technique to coatings research remains to be accomplished.

**d. Reflectance Spectrophotometry.** In the high temperature protective coatings field, reflectance is the main characteristic measured with the spectrophotometer. The reflectance of the coating is measured in the spectral range 400–700 m$\mu$ (visible region). The standard of white reflectance is magnesium carbonate. Reflectance measurements are important since in some cases the loss of reflectance in a certain wavelength range may make the protective coating unsuitable, such as a coating for thermonuclear radiation protection.

After a coating is formulated, a sample is prepared and reflectance measurements are taken; the sample is then subjected to various tests and the reflectance is again recorded. The sample may be subjected to heat 800 or 1000°F) for varying lengths of time to see how the reflectance changes. The sample may also be tested in a salt spray cabinet, or under various atmospheric conditions that it may experience in actual use. In some cases there is a change in the coating that can be detected by the human eye; however, in other cases the changes are not this drastic, and must be measured electronically with a spectrophotometer. By using the spectrophotometer it is often possible to predict how a coating will stand up to various conditions after long exposure.

**e. Photomicrography.** Since coatings on metal substrates are opaque, they can be examined microscopically by light reflected from their surface. In order to accomplish this an instrumental method that was first used by Henry C. Sorby in England in 1861 is used. Generally known as metallography, this method has become an in indispensable tool of control and research in the field of metallurgy and ceramics. In the field of polymeric coating technology, this method has found relatively little use. Some of the information that can be acquired about coatings by this method are:

*1.* The uniformity of the coating with respect to coverage and porosity. The size of the pores can be measured since the field diameter of the microscope is known. There are also hairline devices that can be attached to the microscope for such measurements. The uniformity of the coating can be determined by using relatively high magnification and relating the focus point to the surface irregularity.

*2.* A cross section of the coating substrate can be examined to investigate adhesion, metal bonding, thickness, corrosion, and entrapment phenomena.

**f.  Dielectric Breakdown.** In the field of coating development the main use of dielectric breakdown instruments is to determine the porosity of a coating. The dielectric apparatus is a quick way of ascertaining the inherent and thermal degradation porosity, since there is a visible spark between the substrate and probe. The apparatus consists of a voltage amplification system capable of amplification to about 20,000 volts, variable over this range.

If the coating is not porous, the voltage where the coating will suffer electrical breakdown or puncture can be determined by raising the voltage gradually. An increase in the applied potential across a given sample of a coating increases the current through the material. This increase generally results in a removal of electrons leaving a positive space charge that concentrates the electric field to the vicinity of the cathode. Final breakdown is a result in part of the distortion of the electric field within the coating. This is known as polarization, and is best explained by examination of Fig. 13-36.

The atom in the absence of an electric field has a positive nucleus which is surrounded symmetrically by a negative charge cloud. In the presence of an electric field the positive nucleus is attracted toward the anode. The atom is thus elastically deformed in the presence of the field, and is said to possess an electric dipole moment equal to $z$. It is evident that if a coating is placed in an electric field, all atoms in the coating will be distorted in a fashion similar to the single atom. It is said that the coating is polarized by the electric field. Polarization of a material is measured in terms of the total electric dipole moment per unit volume of material. Polarization of a material is closely related to the measurable quantity, the dielectric constant $(n)$. Materials with a high $n$ deform easier than those with a lower $n$. Thus, it can be seen that measurement of

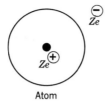

Atom

$Z$ is the atomic number of the atom
$e$ is the charge on one electron

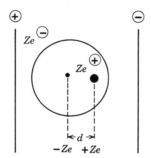

Atom in the charge field
Electric dipole moment $= Zed$

Fig. 13-36. Dielectric breakdown by polarization.

dielectric breakdown voltage is a valuable, simple but little used method of measuring changes resulting from environmental exposure.

## 4. Summary

Of the several available polymeric coating materials, some have historically been used to combat operational problems of corrosion, erosion, and thermal protection. Intensified requirements introduced by present design and production aircraft are taxing the state of the art, although increased emphasis on protective coating in production and in the field, employing proper procedures, is now beginning to solve some critical problems.

Further development using available materials, surface preparation, and control of maintenance methods will be needed.

For future requirements introduced by higher performance velocities and temperatures, the problems will be similar but materials requirements much more stringent.

Coatings from silicone resins currently available can afford protection at temperatures to 650°F but above this temperature new resins are needed which exhibit thermal and oxidative stability on a variety of substrates. The new polymers mentioned in this paper show promise in the area, but many refinements and improvements are necessary before they can be applicable for long periods of time above 800°F.

Conventional methods previously used to evaluate coatings can no longer supply all the information that is necessary. Therefore new methods must be employed which can better utilize and characterize coatings for the specialized end uses. As new and more stringent requirements are placed on coating materials, additional techniques will have to be employed to characterize the properties of interest.

A coordinated effort involving applications-oriented engineers, coating development engineers, instrumentation specialists and polymer chemists will be needed to overcome many short-range and long-term problems. Finally, the time of transition from initial synthesis through production availability will have to be reduced from that experienced in the past.

### E. Paper

Many different plastics are used successfully in coating application. This review will only concern itself only with one of the major plastics used—polyethylene.

The rise of polyethylene has been spectacular. Unknown 25 years ago, polyethylene went into wide production only 10 years ago and sales are now near three billion pounds a year (6).

A big contributing factor to this growth is the development of extrusion coating techniques for producing such items as polyethylene coated milk cartons. Extrusion coating is excellent for applying polyethylene at high rates, on continuous runs on the same type of substrate. However, because the extrusion coating operation is essentially oriented to high volume long run coating applications, it has suffered from a lack of flexibility and applicability in a number of coating areas.

The coating, packaging material, and paper industries have a strong interest in developing polyethylene coating techniques that will allow them to:

1. Applying coatings with a relatively low capital investment cost for equipment.

2. Operate without the material loss incurred in an extrusion coating operation during paper web breakage, from edge trim and from startup and shutdown purge requirements.

3. Operate in line with color printing presses which are subject to intermittent shut down from web breaks.

4. Realize excellent paper adhesion properties without oxidation of the polyethylene or priming of the substrate.

5. Apply patterns and embossed coatings or coatings on irregular surfaces.

6. Coat sheet stock.

7. Perform multiple coating and lamination operations of various substrates on one line.

8. Open up the possibility of applying polyethylene laminates and/or coatings on Fourdernier and cylinder type paper manufacturing lines.

Solution coating which applies polyethylene coatings from hot solvent solutions satisfies a number of these areas. However, its growth as a coatings application method has been limited by the need for specialized equipment, and the difficulties involved with handling and recovering, hot inflamable solvents.

## 1. Dispersion Coating

This paper-coating process has a definite place in the industry. While it will not supplant extrusion coating, it will certainly supplement it and put polyethylene coatings in areas not previously possible.

a. Advantages. These are some of the main advantages of the dispersion coating process:

1. Low capital investment.

2. Water dispersions of polyethylene may be applied to paper or cloth with equipment currently used for applying latices, clay-starch, or clay-casien coatings.

3. The dispersion coating process has the same flexibility as solution coating, that is, little or no edge trimming is required and coatings may be applied in stripes or transvers patterns.

4. There is little or no oxidation of the coatings because drying and fusion temperatures are lower than the melt temperatures for

the extrusion coater. This minimizes flavor and odor transfer from the coating.

5. Water can be used as the vehicle and there is no need for explosion-proof equipment.

**b. Disadvantages.** There are also a number of limitations to the dispersion coating process including:

1. Most of the older coating equipment does not have drying capacity sufficient to fuse Microthene F at commercial speeds.

2. While striped patterns are applied in thicknesses up to mils or more, patterns with transverse interruptions have only been applied up to 5–6 lb per ream or $\frac{1}{3}$ mil.

3. Water is indeed explosion-proof. However, it takes more heat to vaporize water than organic vehicles. This entails higher fuel costs and larger capital investment in drying and fusing equipment. For example, you will need more BTU input to the heaters, or a longer oven to increase exposure time for any given speed.

Under some circumstances paper manufacturers or converters reach a compromise between the solution process and the dispersion process by making a dispersion in an organic vehicle. These dispersions require much less heat to drive off the solvent, but this lower heat requirement must be balanced against the loss of solvent unless a solvent recovery system is available.

The first step in a coating process is making a dispersion of the resins in a suitable vehicle. In a water dispersion you need a surfactant which can be anionic, cationic or nonionic. Non–ionic surfactant is usually desired. The preferred solids level is 50–65%. The higher solids require less heat for drying and fusing. Hight solids dispersions (more than 50%) require 0.2% surfactant. The dispersions are made by either making a stiff paste of powder and surfactant, and diluting to the desired level, or by adding powder to an agitated mixture of water and surfactant.

For refinement of particle size and breaking up agglomerates use any high shear mixer such as a Cowles Dissolver, colloid mill, or similar device. If a thicker dispersion is needed, adding small amounts (as low as 0.02%) of water soluble gums increases viscosity several fold.

Organic dispersions are somewhat easier to make. When making these follow the same procedure except that generally no surfactant is required. In either case, strain the slurry or dispersion to remove any lumps or foreign material that might be present.

The coating machine applies a uniformly controlled amount of a film forming, sizing, or other desirable material to a web or a sheet of substrate.

The choice of coater—spread, spray, roll, dip, and air knife—depends on the coating and the substrate. Other factors such as solvent removal, drying, and production rate must be considered.

Spread coaters include the knife or bar coaters which scrape off a heavy layer of coating liquid to the desired thickness. The floating blade coater (Fig. 13-37) depends on web tension and blade contour to control thickness, whereas the knife-over-roll (Fig. 13-38) allows you to set the knife at a fixed distance from the roll. Modifications of knife contour control coatings of various viscosities and rheologies.

A unique form of spread coater operates by applying an excess of coating, and then metering with a transverse rod helically wrapped with a wire (Mayer rod). The gauge of the wire governs the thickness of the remaining coating (at constant solids content). A course wire gives heavier coatings, while a fine one leaves the thinner films. The Mayer Rod is most often used for thixotropic solutions and dispersions; dilatant liquids do not perform well with this method.

Apply fluid coatings to web by spraying, usually with multiple spray heads mounted on an oscillating carrier. Mount the spray heads so the

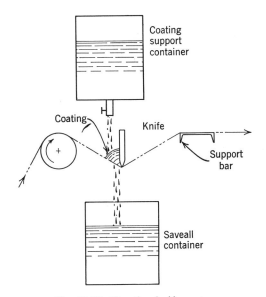

Fig. 13-37. Floating knife coater.

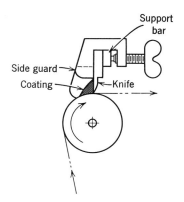

Fig. 13-38. Knife over roll.

patterns overlap, and move them to and fro across the web to lay down a uniform coating.

There are many types of roll coaters available, perhaps the most successful is some version of the reverse roll arrangement. The reverse roll is so called because the roll rotates counter to the substrate travel. This allows you to control coating thickness by adjusting the gap between either the metering roll or applicator roll or both. The reverse roll coater works best at applying coatings that are thixotropic, or at least Newtonian. Coatings of a dilatant nature generally run at lower speeds, because of the high shear between the applicator roll and substrate.

In some instances where both sides of a substrate must be coated, dip the paper directly into the coating, and remove the excess to leave the desired thickness. This is done by passing the coated substrate between two rolls, or two wire-wound Mayer rods. Fusing two-side coatings of sticky substances is generally difficult, and production speeds are usually very low.

Air knife coating machines are used for applying water dispersions or emulsions where solvent loss and resultant surface skinning is not a problem. By using an arrangement similar to Fig. 13-39 you can apply a smooth uniform coating. Fig. 13-40 illustrates the gravure or engraved roll coater, an excellent method of applying light (2–5 lb per ream) coatings.

## 2. Data

Table 13-13 list water vapor transmission rates (WVTR) of coatings made from water dispersisons of Microthene F (ASTM E96-53T Pro-

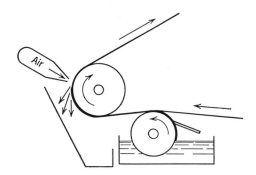

Fig. 13-39. Air knife coating.

cedure A). The dispersion coated paper compares favorably with extrusion coated material. The same table indicates the effect of latex particle binders on WVTR. As expected, the acrylic latex particle has some deleterious effect. Styrene-butadiene and polyvinylidene chloride latices however improve the resistance to water vapor.

Table 13-14 compares physical characteristics and water vapor transmission rates at 100 F and 90% relative humidity (ASTM E-96-53T Procedure E). Here the dispersion coated sample is slightly poorer than the extrusion coating in WVTR and gloss, but superior in adhesion.

As stated previously in this paper, coatings made from dispersions adhere to paper extremely well. Table 13-14 shows that paper coated with polyolefin dispersions must burst before the coating delaminates.

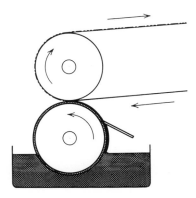

Fig. 13-40. Engraved roll coating.

TABLE 13-13.   WVTR[a] of Microthene F Dispersion Coated Papers
with Latex Modifiers

| Sample | WVTR |
|---|---|
| | (g/100 in.$^2$/24 hr)[b] |
| Extrusion Coated (1 mil thickness) | 0.14 |
| Microthene FN 500 | 0.13 |
| Microthene FN 500, 5% styrene–butadiene | 0.11 |
| Microthene FN 500, 5% acrylic | 0.15 |
| Microthene FN 500, 10% acrylic | 0.16 |
| Microthene FN 500, 5% Daran 210 | 0.12 |
| | Temperature 73°F. |
| | Relative humidity 50% |

[a] 1 Mil films.
[b] ASTME 96-53T Procedure A.

## F.  Fabric

Since tires represent the largest concentrated market for synthetic
fibers, producers of rayon, nylon and polyester set their sights on this
market and basically supply yarns developed for tire cord for use in
mechanical rubber goods and, to some extent, for coating and laminating.  However, coating and laminating applications also often call for
lower denier yarn than are used in tires, so yarns developed for apparel
and other uses are also employed here.  Coating and laminating alone
use large quantities of yarn and some yarn descriptions, 210 denier
nylon and 220 denier polyester for example, have been developed and
produced with coating and/or laminating being at least among the
most important end uses in mind.  Fiber producers are giving more

TABLE 13-14.   Comparison of Properties
Suspension Coated vs Extrusion Coated Paper

| | Suspension | Extrusion |
|---|---|---|
| Coating weight | 14.7 | 14.7 |
| lb/3000 ft$^2$ | | |
| Gloss %, 60° | 27.9 | 36.2 |
| Adhesion % | 100 | 29 |
| Perkins–Southwick | | |
| Adhesion | Good | Fair |
| Scotch Tape test | | |
| WVTR | 1.8 | 1.5 |

attention to developing fibers which have properties of particular interest to coaters and laminators as this market increases and as the producers become established in the field and begin to look for new areas to conquer (7).

## 1. Tire Cord

Tire cord plays such a predominant part in fibers and fabrics for the rubber industry. Rayon is largely used in new car tires and nylon is used in replacement tires. While nylon has excellent tirecord properties, it has a tendency to "flat spot" and cause a slight thump for a short distance after standing, and Detroit finds this objectionable in new cars. It is not so objectionable in replacement tires as they are generally bought after the car is a couple of years old and, hence the situation in which new car tires are largely rayon, and replacement tires are largely nylon.

Polyester is looked upon as having strong potentials in the tire cord field in both the new tire and replacement market. Radial-ply tires, widely used in Europe, seem to favor the use of polyester and rayon, and, possibly, glass fiber and steel wire, while nylon has yet to be fully evaluated. Nylon performs excellently in carcass plies, but a higher modulus yarn must be used in the under-tread belt. Rayon multifilament, nylon monofilament and nylon multifilament are used in that order of importance in tire chafers, the fabric nearest the bead in tubeless tires. Some weaving mills and the major tire producers weave and dip the multifilament chafer fabrics for elimination of airwicking.

## 2. Coating and Laminating

The major fibers used in both coating and laminating are nylon and polyester. Some acrylics are used in both processes. There is increased activity in evaluating polypropylene in vinyl laminates while cellulosics and polypropylene are used to a minor extent in coating.

The recent price reduction in 840 denier nylon will accelerate the replacement of cotton canvas and duck by neoprene, vinyl and Hypalon-coated fabrics; in fact, this acceleration is already taking place. The increased usage of standard 840 denier nylon fabric ($22 \times 22$ or 21) is now apparent as well as the increased use of standard 840 denier scrim ($14 \times 14$ and $12 \times 12$) for vinyl lamination, because of this price reduction. Eight hundred forty denier nylon for coating and laminating fabrics is momentarily in extremely short supply.

It is hoped that this situation will be corrected shortly so the rate of replacement of cotton by nylon will not be slowed.

**a. Coated Fabrics.** In the coated fabrics field, new fibers, fabrics and manufacturing processes have enlarged the capabilities of coated fabrics to the point where their uses in industrial and consumer applications are growing at a significant and steady rate.

Substrate fabrics are available for coating in widths from 36 in. to more than 80 in., and in weights of from one ounce per square yard and less, to 18 oz/sq yd. They are available in all weaves, including plain, twill or basket, and are woven of multifilament, monofilament and spun yarns.

These substrate fabrics may be ordered in the greige, heat set in the greige, scoured and heat set, dyed, and with a wide range of finishes for various purposes including polyvinyl chloride, polyvinyl butyral, polyvinyl acetate, resorcinol formaldehyde, butadient acrylonitrile, melamine formaldehyde, urea formaldehyde, neoprene, isocyanate and modifications of this finishes.

Fabrics may be engineered for special propreties such as high tear strength, dimensional stability, sunlight degradation resistance, etc.

These substrate fabrics can be converted, by means of knife coating or calandering with the proper elastomers, into coated fabrics having high strength to weight ratio—particularly high tear strength—water-proofness, resistance to weathering, abrasion, common chemicals, rot and mildew; ease of repair, and flexibility at high and low temperature extremes.

The most common elastomers used for coating are polyvinyl chloride and coplymers thereof, and neoprene. However, Hypalon is also gaining in importance. Other synthetic rubbers used for coating include butadiene styrene, butadiene acrylonitrile, butyl rubber, polyvinyl butyreal, and urethane, depending upon the properties desired.

**b. Laminating.** Among the available types of coated fabrics, vinyl laminates have shown outstanding promise because of their ability to combine great strength, lightness and economy, while retaining other advantages inherent in coated fabrics.

Vinyl laminates have higher tear strength and cost less than other coated fabrics. This is made possible through the use of open weave "scrim" fabrics. Since tear strength is related to yarn size rather than thread count, a vinyl laminated scrim embodying a low count, high denier fabric will achieve a high tear strength at a lower cost than knife coated fabrics of higher thread count.

In general, nylon and polypropylene are recommended when low cost per unit of strength is desired. Polyesters are desirable for somewhat better sunlight degradation and chemical resistance, as well as better dimensional stability. Acrylics are recommended for exceptional sunlight degradation and chemical resistance, which polypropylene also has.

The scrim laminating process would not be possible without resin treated scrims. The finishing resin bonds the scrim yearns at the intersections, so that the scrim does not shift at any stage prior to lamination. Available finishes include polyvinyl acetate, polyvinyl chloride, the predominant resin, melamine formaldehyde, butadiene styrene, butadiene acrylonitrile, resorcinol formaldehyde, neoprene, thioureas, and blends of the above. These can be and are, modified with plasticizers for softness and other properties. Choice of resin can be dictated by need for increased adhesion or for adhesion inhibition for improved tear strength.

**c. Technology Grows.** Because of the ever increasing number of synthetic fiber producers, basic generic fiber types and variations (in total denier, denier/filament, fiber cross section, staple length, tenacity, dimensional stability, polymer, mixed polymers, etc.) and because of the research, development and technical service of the fiber producers, a competitive situation is being established. The tire, mechanical rubber, and coating and vinyl laminating industry are being offered new fibers and fabrics at an accelerated rate. (See Chapter 10.)

## G. Factory Surfaced

For the future the big impact on traditional paint markets is the wider use being made in factory surfacing the conventional substrate materials such as wood, metal (coil-coating), fabrics, papers and masonry products. The building, construction and agricultural industries are primed for these products. New manufacturing techniques are being applied to provide faster and improved quality control procedures. Electron curing by High Voltage Engineering Corporation (Massachusetts) is one example. Another example is a fast high-frequency resistance welder of AMF-Thermatool, Inc. (Connecticut). This welder is used with coated metals so that very little or no loss of coating occurs.

These substrates compete with each other. An example is outside siding for homes made of wood, brick, aluminum, asbestos and steel. Factory plastic coatings, and even films, are providing all these materials with the modern age-old target for extending maintenance-free surfaces. Siding guarantees now range from 15 to 30 years without repainting.

In competition with factory surfaced substrates, there are the easier to use and longer lasting house paints than the oil-based alkyd paints. Water-based paints represent at least 70% sales for interior walls. Water-thinned latex paints on outside surfaces is now growing. In a few years they may be well on their way to providing more than one-half of the sales. At present these latex represents approximately 18% of sales.

## 1. Plywood

The American Plywood Association, Tacoma, Wash. has developed a program for evaluating promising new coatings and overlays for softwood plywood. The coatings considered are intended to provide long-term, maintenance-free surfaces for softwood plywood which may be promoted as "American Plywood Association Qualified Coatings." At present, exterior weatherable materials are covered in the program, although an interior class of finishes as well as special industrial finishes will be included as separate test methods for their evaluation are developed (8).

The program consists primarily of finding new coatings, which includes encouraging and assisting potential suppliers in developing new plywood surfacing materials, evaluating those coatings and reporting the resultant information to American Plywood Association members. Materials which pass the published test requirements of the program are designated "Qualified Coatings" when applied to plywood, and may be promoted by the Association.

The tests used in evaluating coatings are designed to determine the adequacy of materials on plywood as long-term, maintenance-free surfaces. It is recognized that such accelerated tests cannot gurantee performance, particularly since variables such as application conditions are beyond the control of the Association. Qualification and promotion of a coating by the Association, therefore, is limited to the fact that the Qualified Coating is one which, when applied in accordance with stated conditions, will satisfactorily pass the designated tests.

The program itself consists of several phases. Before actual evaluatio is undertaken by the American Plywood Association's Product Research Department laboratory, an agreement is obtained from the coatings supplier which permits the Association to inform its members of tests with the supplier's coating. In addition, the supplier presents to the Association evidence of performance of the material in tests conducted by himself. It is recommended that tests similar to those specified by the Association be used, although evaluation under all Association tests or under all cycles of a given test is not required at this stage.

On acceptance of a coating material in the program, the specimens prepared by the supplier are subjected to the three preliminary tests described in the attachment, and an announcement is sent to Association members advising them that evaluation of the given product has commenced. The three preliminary tests require at least eight weeks for completion, and at the end of that time a preliminary test report is mailed to Association members factually reporting the results of those tests. A material successfully passing the preliminary test requirements is then subjected to the four final tests which require an additional six months for completion.

If a material fails the preliminary tests, it may be reformulated and resubmitted if the manufacturer so desires, or work on the material may be discontinued if the mutual judgment of the supplier and the Association so indiciate. Supplementary test reports providing additional performance information may be issued at any time before or after the final test report. All test reports are confidential within the Association and the individual materials supplier.

A material which successfully passes all tests becomes a Qualified Coating and is awarded a Certificate of Qualification. The Certificate may be used for promotional purposes and is available to all interested parties. Qualification may be withdrawn on any material found to be unsatisfactory in use.

The Association Qualified Coatings Seal may not be applied to coated panels or used in any way which might imply more than the fact that the Qualified Coating has performed satisfactorily in the specified accelerated tests. Coatings Qualification is in no way associated with the Commercial Standards for plywood or with the American Plywood Association's DFPA Quality Control and Grade Trademarking functions. Qualified Coatings will not be subject to quality control by the Association.

Qualified Coatings may include both factory applied and field applied finishes. Qualification of a material includes specific identification of a material by the manufacturer's tradename or code number as well as application specifications. Promotion of a Qualified Coating generally will be restricted to those materials that are readily available.

**a. Description of Test Methods for Evaluating Exterior Coatings on Plywood.** *(1) Preliminary Tests.* New coatings are submitted to the American Plywood Association applied to ⅜ in. Exterior type plywood. A minimum of four 12 in.×12 in. samples are required for initial tests. Specimens are cut from these samples and exposed to test conditions with no edge or back sealing.

*Soak*

Two specimens, approximately 3 in.×6 in. Soak in ambient temperature water 8 hr, followed by drying with forced air circulation 16 hr at 145°F, continued for 25 cycles.

*Boil*

Two specimens approximately 3 in.×6 in. Immerse in boiling water 4 hr, followed by drying with forced air circulation 20 hr at 145°F, continued for 25 cycles.

*Hot Water*

If materials fail the boil test, two similar specimens are exposed to a constant 180°F hot water soak in place of the boil, followed by the same drying conditions noted under the boil test, and continued for 25 cycles.

*Freeze*

Two specimens approximately 4 in.×6 in. Soak in ambient temperature water 8 hr, followed by freezing at 0°F or lower 16 hr, followed by drying with forced air circulation 24 hr at 145°F, continued for 10 cycles.

After each cycle of each test, the coating is examined with particular respect to adhesion, surface ruptures, blisters, chalking, discoloration and other evidence of unacceptable performance. Failure is determined by one or all of the following criteria:

*1.* extensive loss of adhesion
*2.* coating checks or ruptures totaling 6 in. in length, accumulative measurement
*3.* extensive chalking
*4.* objectionable overall appearance degradation

Coatings which successfully pass the Preliminary Tests are subjected to a series of additional tests, as described under "Final Tests."

***(2) Final Tests.*** A coating which successfully passes the Preliminary
Tests is subjected to the following additional tests. Specimens are
exposed in all cases with edges and backs unsealed.

*Exterior weathering*

Specimen size, 12 in. A minimum of 6 months outdoor weather-
with a South facing exposure is required and performance after
longer exposure times noted and reported by supplementary test
report.

*Weather-Ometer*

Specimen size, $2\frac{5}{8}$ in.× 6 in. Specimens exposed for an equivalent of 10 years outdoor exposure. Testing conducted in either
Atlas Electric Devices Model BWM-C Single Arc Weather-Ometer,
with manufacturer's estimated exposure rating of 1500 KWH per
one year equivalent outdoors; or Atlas Model DMC Twin Arc
Weather-Ometer with exposure rating of 350 machine hours per
one year equivalent outdoors. Both machines operate under continuous light exposure and intermittent tap water spray, in a two-
period cycle of 102 min dry followed by 18 min wet. Drum revolution rate is 1 rpm.

*Weather-Ometer: Soak*

Specimen size $2\frac{5}{8}$ in.×6 in. Specimen removed from Weather-
Ometer every 6 months (equivalent exposure), soaked 8 hr in
ambient temperature water, dried with forced air circulation at
145°F for 16 hr and then replaced in Weather-Ometer. Cycles
continued for a total Weather-Ometer exposure of 5 years equivalent
outdoor exposure.

*Infrared*

Specimen size, approximately 12 in.× 12 in. Exposure under infrared heating elements to produce a surface temperature of 180°F
for 8 hr, followed by 16 hr ambient temperature cooling, continued
for 5 cycles.

Samples will be checked periodically for adhesion, surface ruptures,
blisters, chalking, discoloration and other evidence of unacceptable
performance. Failure is determined by one or all of the following
criteria:

*1.* extensive loss of adhesion
*2.* coating ruptures totaling 6 in. in length, accumulative measurement
*3.* extensive chalking
*4.* extensive discoloration
*5.* objectionable overall appearance degradation

TABLE 13-15.  Coatings Approved on Plywood per American Plywood Association Specification

| Manufacturer | Coating | Date of Approval | File |
|---|---|---|---|
| Armstrong Cork Company | Travelon Weather Deck System | Jan. 19, 1966 | B-1-5 |
| Archer-Daniels-Midland Company | Aroflint 505, Formulation #L-472-1 | June 14, 1965 | A-1-3-b |
| The Baker Castor Oil Company | Vinyl-Urethane, formulation EC-167 (over sanded plywood) | Aug. 12, 1965 | A-5-9 |
| The Baker Castor Oil Company | Vinyl-Urethane, formulation EC-167 (over Medium Density overlaid plywood) | Aug. 12, 1965 | A-5-11 |
| The Borden Chemical Company | Colordur (Synthetic Elastomers) | Apr. 8, 1964 | A-4-8 |
| Chemical Coatings & Engineering Co. | Corrocote (Synthetic Elastomers) | Jan. 24, 1964 | A-4-6 |
| Chemical Rubber Products, Inc. | Chemwall (Chlorosulfonated Polyethylene) | Sept. 17, 1963 | B-3-2-a |
| Chevron Chemical Company | Polyester formulation AC 2243, based on Chevron Polyester 6020 | Nov. 4, 1965 | A-3-5 |
| Chevron Chemical Company | Polyurethane formulation AC 2212, based on Chevron Alkyd 1114 cross linked with an isocyanate | Nov. 8, 1965 | A-7-4 |
| Desco Chemical Co., Inc. | Desco Neolon (Synthetic Elastomers) | Apr. 29, 1965 | A-4-9 |
| E. I. duPont de Nemours & Co., Inc. | Tedlar (Polyvinyl fluoride) | Dec. 28, 1962 | B-1-3 |
| Gaco Western, Inc. | Liquid Neoprene and Hypalon | June 1, 1961 | A-4-1 |
| Gates Engineering Co. | Liquid Neoprene and Hypalon | May 3, 1963 | A-4-4 |
| Gibson-Homans Company | Eternaflex (Synthetic Elastomers) | Oct. 21, 1965 | A-4-11 |
| Hodges Chemicals Company | Hycon 75 Sanspray (Solventless Epoxy) | Feb. 4, 1963 | A-2-1-b |
| R. M. Hollingshead Corporation | Cocoon #501 (vinyl) | Dec. 14, 1965 | A-5-7-a |
| R. M. Hollingshead Corporation | Cocoon #560 (vinyl) | Dec. 14, 1965 | A-5-10 |
| Interchemical Corporation | Polymerin | Nov. 18, 1965 | A-1-12 |
| National Lead Company | PLYRENE (Acrylic Emulsion) | Sept. 28, 1964 | A-1-8 |
| Union Carbide Corporation | Vinyl-Urethane | Oct. 21, 1964 | A-5-6-a |
| United States Plywood Corp. | Weldwood Pf'-L | Dec. 3, 1965 | |
| West Chester Chemical Company | Maintz (Liquid Neoprene Hypalon) | Feb. 12, 1963 | A-4-2-a |
| R. M. Hollingshead Corporation | Whiz Hypalon | Jan. 23, 1963 | A-4-7 |
| R. M. Hollingshead Corporation | Cocoon 560 | Sept. 14, 1964 | A-5-10 |
| A. C. Horn Products | Deck Tread System | June 4, 1963 | A-2-11 |

| Manufacturer | Product | Date | No. |
|---|---|---|---|
| Kish Industries, Inc. | Vinylflex | Dec. 10, 1962 | A-5-5 |
| Kish Industries, Inc. | PM-5-1027 | May 14, 1964 | A-5-5-a |
| Midland Industrial Finishes Co., Inc. | Modified Silicone 700-14 | May 7, 1965 | A-1-11 |
| Midland Industrial Finishes Co., Inc. | Silicone Alkyd 700-30 | May 3, 1965 | A-1-10 |
| Mosaica | Mosaica | Apr. 16, 1960 | B-1-1 |
| National Lead Company | PLYRENE | Nov. 5, 1963 | A-1-8 |
| National Starch & Chemical Corp. | Vinyl Polymer Cementitious Primer Topcoat | June 4, 1959 | A-5-2 |
| Permagile Corporation of America | Red Slip Proof PG 1013F | Apr. 23, 1962 | A-2-8 |
| Permagile Corporation of America | Clear Polyurethane PG-1065 | Apr. 23, 1962 | A-7-3 |
| Pittsburg Chemical Company | Tarset Standard | June 5, 1959 | A-6-1 |
| Plaxicrete, Inc. | DECORIT | Dec. 12, 1964 | A-2-13 |
| Ply-On Coatings, Inc. | PLY-ON "Mono-Ply" | Nov. 24, 1961 | A-5-3 |
| Ply-On Coatings, Inc. | Ply-On A–B–C | Sept. 18, 1962 | A-5-4 |
| | | Sept. 5, 1963 | A-5-4-a |
| Poly Form Manufacturing Corporation of California | #706 White Gloss Marine Poly Form | July 3, 1961 | A-7-2 |
| Reichhold Chemicals, Inc. | #8173 Polylite | May 1, 1960 | A-3-1 |
| Reichhold Chemicals, Inc. | Epotuf ED-1025 and 2602 | May 15, 1961 | A-2-4 |
| Reichhold Chemicals, Inc. | Epotuf ED-1025 and Versamid 140 | May 15, 1961 | A-2-5 |
| Reynolds Metals Company | Aluminum Foil | Sept. 1, 1959 | B-2-1 |
| Reynolds Metals Company | Aluminum Foil | July 1, 1960 | B-2-2 |
| The Robson Corporation | Horsey Set | Oct. 4, 1962 | A-2-10 |
| Shell Chemical Company | Epon Resin Formulation No. 1109-82B | June 21, 1963 | A-2-12 |
| Structure Coatings, Inc. | Gun Tex P-400 | Oct. 17, 1962 | A-1-7 |
| Terrawall Corporation | Terrawall | Nov. 24, 1961 | A-1-4 |
| Tuff-Kote Company | Tuff-Kote | Mar. 1, 1962 | A-1-5 |
| Union Carbide Corporation | Vinyl-Urethane | Dec. 14, 1962 | A-5-6 |
| | | May 7, 1964 | A-5-6-a |
| Varni-Lite Corporation of America | Varni-Lite "Marine" | Sept. 18, 1961 | A-2-6 |
| Varni-Lite Corporation of America | Industrial Special & Industrial Coating | Aug. 31, 1964 | A-2-6-a |
| West Chester Chemical Company | Neoprene Hypalon | Mar. 1, 1962 | A-4-2 |
| | | Aug. 22, 1962 | A-4-2-a |

## 2. Metals

**Coil-Coating (Metal-Coating).** Processes involve high speed and continuous mechanized procedures for paint coating one or both sides of a coil of sheet metal at speeds of 50–400 ft/min. Coating equipment, metal cleaning and new paint formulations provide ease of formability with environmental durability. The basic operations in the process involve unwinding steel coil, chemically pretreating steel, reverse roll-coating paint, baking paint, applying additional coatings in certain processes, cooling coated metal, inspection and rewind coil.

The National Coil Coaters Association, Chicago, Ill., organized in 1962, has already been very active in such operations as developing industry standards, exchange of technical information, preparing technical manuals and keeping records of sales growth. From 1962 to 1964 a 72% increase occurred and by 1965 another 40% jump occurred. Total value in 1965 for the coil coated rolls was $400 million. This included one million tons of steel.

The first extensive market for this product was for venetian blinds, followed with metal awnings, metal sidings, automobile trims, light reflectors, luggage, metal doors, etc.

## 3. Reinforced Plastics

New style interchangeable 8 ft by 8 ft by 20 ft shipping container for marine, truck, rail and/or rail uses woven glass fiber-polyester resin surfaced plywood construction—plastic provides protective coating and strength. Lunn Laminates, Inc. produced the 8 ft by 160 ft or 13 ft by 40 ft sandwich panels used in delivering 1,000 containers to U.S. Lines for service from New York to Antwerp (12).

The American Plywood Associating reports (1966) that up to 200,000 of these type double door containers are expected to be used in the next three to five years. The reinforced plastic sheathed plywood permits a container to be durable, rigid, weather-tight, easy to maintain, economical and resistant to impact or corrosion. Fabrication of container involves fitting panels into extruded aluminum corner posts and side rails, embedded in a neoprene caulking compound assuring a permanent water-tight seal. The structural fastening is achieved with stainless steel bolts on 6 in. centers. The flooring is $1\frac{1}{8}$ in. laminated, shiplapped oak over aluminum floor beams on 15 in. centers.

For shipping lines, the container concept means faster turnaround time (as little as 12 hr vs 72). Better cubetare ratio. More pay-

TABLE 13-16. Metal Coatings (Coil-Coating) (9)

| Coatings | Characteristics | Applications |
| --- | --- | --- |
| Vinyls | Excellent flexibility and exterior durability; can withstand rigorous fabrication | Aluminum screen doors, TV cabinets, dashboard panels, exterior siding |
| Alkyds | Good exterior durability and color retention; economical; not suitable for severe forming operations | Exterior finishes for metal containers, drapery hardware, shelving, any decorative purposes not involving severe forming |
| Plastisols, organosols | Excellent scuff and mar resistance, color durability; good formability; both belong to vinyl dispersion family, but plastisols (100% solids) yield thicker finishes; both require primer for adhesion | TV cabinets, metal furniture, gasketing, interior wall paneling |
| Epoxies | Excellent hardness, toughness, flexibility, abrasion resistance; not recommended for exterior use | Sanitary coating, ash trays, cap coating |
| Phenolics | Good stain, acid, solvent resistance; poor flexibility and adhesion; require modified vinyl size coat to withstand normal bends | Beer can interior lining, closures |
| One-coat organosols | Excellent forming, durability properties; high solids content; similar to conventional vinyl solution coatings | Roof decking, exterior siding, cabinets |
| Vinyl-alkyds | Compromise in price and properties between vinyl and alkyds; good exterior durability | Exterior siding, applications where straight alkyd would be used but where more than normal fabrication is involved |
| Acrylics | Excellent stain, abrasion, mar resistance; good durability; limited formability, full-gloss appearance, acceptable for decorative uses | Appliance housing, cabinets, lighting fixtures, exterior siding, refrigerators, plastisol overfinishes |

TABLE 13-17.   Properties of Metal Coatings (19,11)

| | Thin films, 0.1-1.2 mils | | | | | | | | | | Thick films | | Laminates | |
| --- | --- | --- | --- | --- | --- | --- | --- | --- | --- | --- | --- | --- | --- | --- |
| Performance rating<br>1—Excellent<br>2—Good<br>3—Fair<br>4—Poor | Amine-alkyd | Vinyl-alkyd | Thermoset acrylic | Solution-vinyl | Oil-free polyester | Epoxy-ester | Straight epoxy | Silicone alkyd | Polyvinyl fluoride | Polyvinylidene fluoride | Organosol | Plastisol | Polyvinyl fluoride | Polyvinyl chloride |
| **Appearance considerations** | | | | | | | | | | | | | | |
| Ability to achieve high gloss (above 85 units 60°) | 1 | 2 | 1 | 1 | 1 | 2 | 1 | 1 | 3 | 4 | 4 | 4 | 4 | 4 |
| Resistance to color fading | 3 | 3 | 2 | 2 | 2 | 4 | 4 | 1 | 1 | 1 | 2 | 2 | 1 | 2 |
| Long-time retention of color and gloss | 3 | 3 | 1 | 3 | 1 | 3 | 3 | 1 | 2 | 2 | 3 | 3 | 2 | 3 |
| **Fabricating properties** | | | | | | | | | | | | | | |
| Film adhesion | 2 | 2 | 1 | 1 | 2 | 1 | 1 | 2 | 2 | 2 | 1 | 1 | 2 | 1 |
| Film flexibility | 3 | 2 | 2 | 1 | 2 | 3 | 3 | 3 | 1 | 1 | 1 | 1 | 1 | 1 |
| Adaptability to embossing of substrate | 4 | 3 | 3 | 2 | 3 | 3 | 4 | 4 | 1 | 1 | 1 | 1 | 1 | 1 |
| Resistance to metal marking | 2 | 2 | 2 | 2 | 2 | 2 | 1 | 2 | 3 | 3 | 3 | 3 | 2 | 3 |
| Ability to fabricate after aging in storage | 4 | 2 | 2 | 1 | 2 | 3 | 3 | 3 | 1 | 1 | 1 | 1 | 1 | 1 |
| **Performance in service** | | | | | | | | | | | | | | |
| Film hardness | 2 | 2 | 2 | 2 | 1 | 2 | 1 | 2 | 2 | 2 | 2 | 3 | 2 | 3 |
| Abrasion resistance | 3 | 2 | 2 | 2 | 2 | 2 | 2 | 2 | 1 | 1 | 1 | 1 | 1 | 1 |
| Mar resistance (fingernail test) | 2 | 2 | 1 | 2 | 1 | 2 | 1 | 2 | 3 | 3 | 3 | 3 | 2 | 3 |
| Stain resistance (food and household agents) | 3 | 3 | 2 | 2 | 2 | 2 | 1 | 2 | 1 | 1 | 2 | 2 | 1 | 2 |
| Resistance to grease and oil | 2 | 2 | 1 | 1 | 2 | 2 | 1 | 2 | 1 | 1 | 1 | 1 | 1 | 1 |

| | | | | | | | | | | | | | |
|---|---|---|---|---|---|---|---|---|---|---|---|---|---|
| **Outdoor exposure** | | | | | | | | | | | | | |
| General corrosion resistance, industrial atmospheres | 2 | 2 | 2 | 2 | 2 | 1 | 2 | 1 | 1 | 1 | 1 | 1 | 1 |
| Salt-spray resistance | 3 | 2 | 1 | 1 | 2 | 1 | 1 | 1 | 1 | 1 | 1 | 1 | 1 |
| Weather durability, pigmented | 2 | 3 | 2 | 2 | 2 | 4 | 4 | 1 | 1 | 1 | 1 | 1 | 1 |
| Weather durability, clear films | 3 | 3 | 4 | 3 | 3 | 4 | 4 | 2 | 1 | 4 | 4 | 3 | 4 |
| **Resistance to solvents and chemicals** | | | | | | | | | | | | | |
| General chemical resistance—acids and alkalis | 3 | 3 | 2 | 2 | 3 | 1 | 2 | 1 | 1 | 1 | 1 | 1 | 1 |
| Resistance to aliphatic hydrocarbon solvents | 2 | 2 | 1 | 2 | 2 | 1 | 1 | 1 | 1 | 1 | 1 | 1 | 1 |
| Resistance to aromatic hydrocarbon solvents | 2 | 3 | 2 | 4 | 2 | 1 | 1 | 1 | 3 | 3 | 1 | 1 | 3 |
| Resistance to ketones or oxygenated solvents | 3 | 3 | 2 | 4 | 3 | 2 | 2 | 1 | 4 | 4 | 1 | 1 | 4 |

Relative cost:  L—0.65 or less, M—0.65 to 0.85, MH—0.85 to 1.10, H—1.10 to 2.5, VH—2.5 and over

| | | | | | | | | | | | | | |
|---|---|---|---|---|---|---|---|---|---|---|---|---|---|
| Finishing cost, cents per sq ft for 1-mil dry film | L | M | M | MH | M | MH | H | H | VH | VH | L | L | VH | VH |

# PLYWOOD/FIBERGLASS CARGO CONTAINER

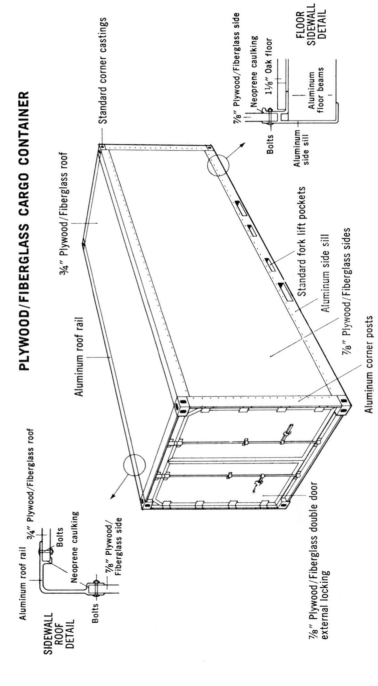

Fig. 13–41. Plywood/fiberglass cargo container.

load. Less handling. Less pilferage. Far less damage. (Plywood-and-fiberglass containers are strong and rugged, almost impossible to break or puncture). And the prospect of lower insurance rates.

Manufacturers will get real door-to-door transoceanic service. Simpler packaging. Faster, safer delivery. And a cut of 25% in overseas shipping costs.

Now, the same big box can go all the way from an inland factory to the ultimate consumer on the other side of the ocean, by any or all means of transport: truck, trailer, rail, ship, and perhaps before long by air.

Fig. 13-42. The air scrubber fabricated by Beetle Plastics, Division of Crompton & Knowles Corporation, Fall River, Mass., removes sulfur dioxide, hydrogen bromide, bromine, and hydrogen chloride from air as the contaminated air passes through water saturated packing. The air cleaned as it passes through the scrubber returns to the atmosphere in a purified state.

Three factors made the breakthrough possible: agreement on an international standard for container and hardware; a new, revolutionary plywood container; and ships with special handling equipment and cellular holds.

## H. *Corrosion and Chemical Resistant*

Corrosion and chemical resistant paints are used to protect industrial products and structures from attack by the weather and corrosive materials. A wide range of protective coatings have been developed to meet the various different service conditions, method of application, drying schedules, and other performance and economic requirements.

Some of these coatings are used without pigment and are based on synethetic resins and rubbers. Others contain special corrosion-inhibiting pigments; their binders are materials such as drying oils, varnishes, alkyds, and epoxies.

Another important group of these coatings is based on bituminous materials. Although they are designed to provide a protective barrier between the surface to be protected and the corroding elements or materials, they utilize two different methods of protection. For example, clear coatings and those based on bituminous materials protect essentially by providing a barrier which is of sufficient thickness and/or resistance to service conditions to prevent the corroding environment from reaching the surface to be protected.

However, corrosion resistant coatings based on drying oils, varnishes, etc., are quite permeable to water and oxygen. These coatings depend almost entirely on their inhibiting pigment to control corrosion. In addition the electrolytic resistant of coatings is an important factor in their ability to inhibit corrosion.

Many different factors must be considered in the development of a suitable coating system. In many cases the best results are obtained by combinations of corrosion-inhibiting primers and highly resistant finished coats. However, in all cases it has been demonstrated quite clearly that the paint system must have sufficient thickness if adequate protection is to be obtained. It is generally believed that the minimum thickness of the paint system should be 5 mils.

## I. **Fire-retardant**

The majority of paint binders are organic in nature and hence are inflammable. The inflammability of organic material can be reduced by incorporating additives such as chlorine, bromine, nitrogen-bound in particular ways, phosphorus or silica. Coatings based on noninflammable binders include lime washers, cement paints, and silica paints.

Inorganic pigments are generally non-inflammable. Antimony trioxide and zinc borate are particularly effective. Combinations of organic and these inorganic pigments provide fire-retardant characteristics.

Very few clear fire retardant coatings are available. They are generally two-part systems using epoxy or urethane resin. Industry has put on the market a transparent polyurethane type for use on wood and metal parts such as walls, ceilings, building fixtures and furniture. When subjected to fire, it swells, creating an insulating surface of charred foam which prevents further burning. This is fundamentally a practical application for what was developed during the Korean War as fire walls for use in different military vehicles.

These coating are not moisture sensitive, as were the previous types. A dry coating can expand 166 times, or go from 6 mils thickness to

Fig. 13-43. Technicians of Sprayfoam Associates, Youngstown, New York, are shown applying first coating of rigid, closed cell Hetrofoam urethane to maze of huge gas lines at Iroquois Gas Corporation's Porterville Compressor Station. A 1 in. layer of flexible urethane was then wrapped around lines, fastened securely, and sprayed with another 1 in. layer of the nonburning urethane.

1 in. This new system provides a major forward step in saving lives and property when fire develops.

In the mean time all industry is targeted to develop a fire-retardant coating which does not cause the usual loss in other properties with the real big problem of not significantly increasing cost. Of course the real push for these coatings will occur if state and local governments adopt more stringent building codes.

### J. Heat-resistant

Different type coatings are available to meet the different heat-resistant environments. There are coatings which can be exposed to high temperature intermittantly. The film is subjected to mechanical forces by differential expansion and contraction. Limiting factors involve breaking the bond to the substrate and the effective oxygen attack at elevated temperatures on the coatings (when in an oxygen atmosphere).

Inorganic polymers and semiorganic polymers are the binders which show the best heat resistance. Extensive research and development is presently being undertaken to study such polymers containing boron, nitrogen, phosphorus, silicon, etc.

The esters of silicon and titanium, and the silicones, are the only binders at present available which are suitable for continuous use at temperatures above 150°F. For the best practical results, they are pigmented with leafing alumium. This composite protects the organic part of the binder from oxygen attack and also forms a metal–ceramic complex.

For temperatures up to 150°F many binders may be used to obtain a useful life. Short oil phenolic varnishes, oxidized rubber and melamine/alkyd resin stoving finishes (where the alkyd is a saturated fatty acid/isophthalic acid type) have been used in various coating system.

### K. Thermal Control

Since 1960, the area of passive thermal control of space vehicles and their components has emerged into a role of increasing importance among the space sciences. This role is destined to achieve greater stature as man's ventures into space become longer in duration and complexity. Indicative of this importance is the research now being devoted to this area of space exploration (13).

In contrast to the active thermal control, passive thermal control offered the advantages of no moving parts and hence the absence of mechanical failure, plus a considerable weight savings. The fundamental parameters in controlling the space vehicle temperature by passive means are the optical characteristics of the surface of the spacecraft, that is, the solar absorptance ($a_s$) and the emittance ($\epsilon$). However, in order to function as a thermal control surface, a coating must be stable, with respect to its optical properties, to the effects of the space environment, primarily ultraviolet radiation, particulate radiation, high vacuum and temperature. In addition, the properties of the coating, such as flexibility, adhesion, ease of application and ability to air cure could not be overlooked.

The major effort over the past several years has thus been directed towards the preparation of organic and inorganic coatings with desirable temperature control properties. At the same time, a critical evaluation of the factors of the space environment and laboratory research involving their effects on the optical and physical properties on coatings and coating materials, was being pursued.

In his attempt to simulate the environment of outer space, the research worker was faced with many unknown factors. The definition of the space environment has been and is presently a major area of scientific research in itself. This lack of overall knowledge, plus the economics involved in simulating the space environment in its entirety, meant compromises in the exposure chambers.

Research in thermal control surfaces resolved somewhat into individuality governed by particular systems requirements and needs. Due to this tendency towards isolation and lack of coordination, each individual formulated his own testing procedures, methods of measurement of the changes in the optical properties and the manner in which the generated data was presented.

Major emphasis in the area of thermal control coatings has been directed towards the low $a_s$, high $\epsilon$ or low $a_s/\epsilon$ ratio) type coatings. To enumerate all the research in this area is beyond the scope and intent of this paper. In addition, the field of measurement of the optical properties of the coatings is not being covered by this particular paper.

Although white organic coatings have been shown to be subject to degradation, primarily by ultraviolet radiation, their properties of flexibility, adhesion, ease of application, air drying characteristics and high emittance have induced considerable research time and effort in their behalf. Inorganic coatings, however, offered the promise of stability to ultraviolet radiation and high vacuum, but presented problems in adhesion, flexibility and involved heat cures. The effects of particulate radiation, although not forgotten, remained somewhat in the background.

The initial goal of a coating with an $a_s<.1$ and $\epsilon_{th}>0.9$ with a $\Delta a_s$ less than 0.05 over an exposure of 2000+ space hours still remains a challenge. However, several significant accomplishments will serve to point out the success achieved to date in both organic and inorganic coatings in the role of thermal control.

## 1. Organic Coatings

Organic formulations have now been developed with air cure properties and optical properties of $a_s=.14$ to .20, $\epsilon_{th}=.85$ to .90 with a $\Delta a_s$ of only .02 to .08 after 2000+ solar hours exposure. Typical coatings are shown in Fig. 13-44. Pigment research, with regards to stability, compatibility, index of refraction, particle size, purity, etc., has shown ZnO, $TiO_2$, and ZnS to offer the most promise. The most stable vehicles in combination with these pigments involved the silicones and variations thereof, acrylics, silicone alkyds and certain fluorocarbon polymers. With the synthesis of colorless ultraviolet radiation absorbers, such as the derivatives of osmocene and ruthenocene, it has been possible to enhance the stability of otherwise border-

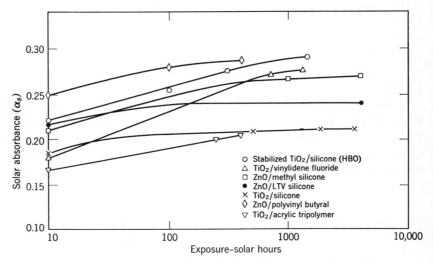

Fig. 13-44. Vacuum-ultraviolet radiation effects on organic coatings.

line acceptable thermal control coatings to the point where these coatings become candidate materials (Fig. 13-45). The derivatives of ferrocene, although enhancing the stability of certain white coatings, gave a high initial $a_s$ due to its inherent red coloration. The derivatives of osmocene and ruthenocene, however, were white to light yellow.

Controlled pigment addition to both basic white and black formulations has provided design engineers with a series of coatings with a wide range of $a_s/\epsilon$ ratios for specific applications. These formulations involve either a variation in $a_s$ or $\epsilon_{th}$ or both. These variations are shown in Figs. 13-46 and 13-47.

## 2. Inorganic Coatings

Foremost among the pigmented inorganic coatings have been the silicates with zinc oxide, zirconium silicate and lithium aluminum silicate the most effective pigments. These coatings have been formulated with optical properties of $a_s = .12$ to .20, $\epsilon_{th} = .85$ to .90 and a $\Delta a_s$ of less than .04 after 2000+ solar hours exposure (Fig. 13-48). In several instances, air cure properties have been obtained. However, the problems of adhesion and flexibility have not as yet been completely resolved.

Research in anodized coatings has produced the low $a_s/\epsilon$ type coatings both from the sulfuric acid and Ematal baths. Initial $a_s$ values have been low (.16 to .22). Although the coatings experience a $\Delta a_s$ of .15 to .20 after only 500 solar hours, further $\Delta a_s$ has been negligible. The variables of the processes are now receiving intensive investigation in an attempt to overcome this deficiency.

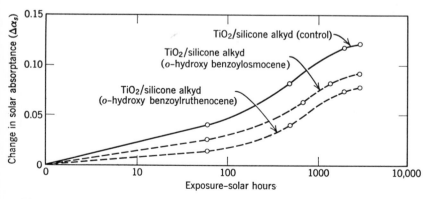

Fig. 13-45. Vacuum-ultraviolet radiation effects on stabilized organic coatings.

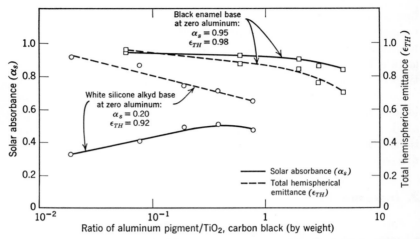

Fig. 13-46. Relationship between solar absorbance, total hemispherical emittance and pigment ratios.

As with the case of the organic coatings, a large selection of tailored inorganic coatings are available with a wide range of $a_s/\epsilon$ ratios.

Conversion type coatings have been centered in the chromate-phosphate type systems with control of the $a_s/\epsilon$ ratio being dependent upon

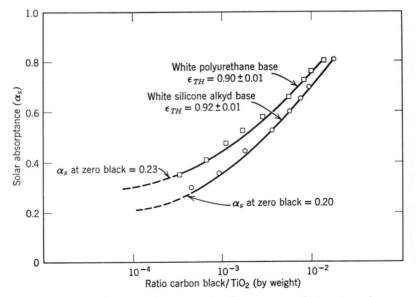

Fig. 13-47. Relationship between solar absorptance and pigment ratios.

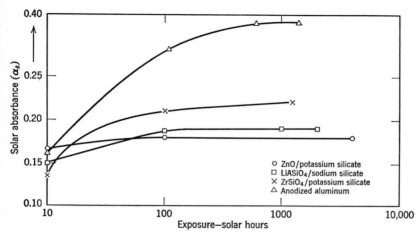

Fig. 13-48. Vacuum-ultraviolet radiation effects on inorganic coatings.

control of the coating thickness. This type of coating has been used successfully on the Echo II and also on a recent micrometeoroid satellite.

## 3. Pigments and Vehicles

Initial research in the area of rare earth oxides, such as $Dy_2O_3$, $Yb_2O_3$ and $Eu_2O_3$, as pigments has shown that these materials have good stability to the effects of the space environment and are also stable to temperatures of 1000–1200°F (Fig. 13-49). Preliminary

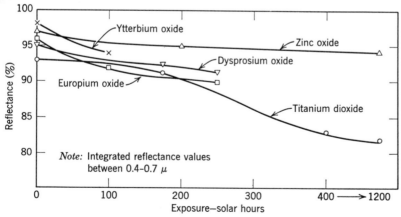

Fig. 13-49. Effects of vacuum-ultraviolet radiation on pigments.

results, when incorporated into silicones and silicates, have been encouraging but more research is required to prove their eventual worth in the space environment. Cost may also be a limiting factor.

Independent polymer research has recently provided such polymers as Phenyl-T, silicone-carboranes, and silazanes whose value is yet to be fully explored as candidate material. Several of these polymers are shown in Fig. 13-50.

## 4. The Space Environment

Since the usefulness of the thermal control coating depended primarily upon its stability in the space environment, one of the first hurdles to be overcome was the simulation of the space environment itself in which the coatings would be exposed. Overall lack of precise space data on pressure, particulate and electromagnetic radiation, micrometeoroids, and so forth, lead to a variety of equipment for space simulation. Within the past two years, two significant events have

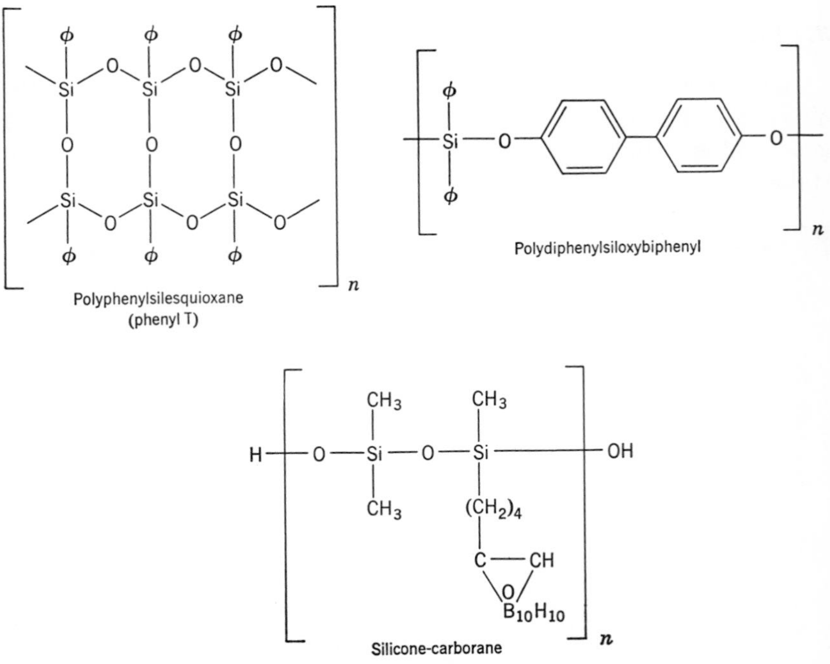

Fig. 13-50. Promising polymers for thermal control coatings.

occurred which have attempted to coordinate the simulation effects of the various laboratories.

Under the auspices of NASA, Ames and JPL, and the AFML, and with the cooperation of 16 laboratories throughout the country, a round-robin was conducted on four specially selected thermal control coatings. The coatings were exposed in each individual's space simulation facilities and then an attempt made to correlate results. The wide scatter of data (Fig. 13-51) served to indicate the need for some "standardization" in space simulation techniques. Although some correlations in temperature and intensity could be made, several variables such as pressure, solar spectrum simulation and method of measurement still need further clarification.

A further stride towards this "standardization" was taken with the formation of Committee E-21 (Space Simulation) within ASTM. This Committee is charged with the development of definition of terms, nomenclature, methods of test and specifications for simulated space environmental testing of vehicles, components and materials intended for space applications. In the short period of its existence, many tentative specifications in several areas have been prepared for approval by the members.

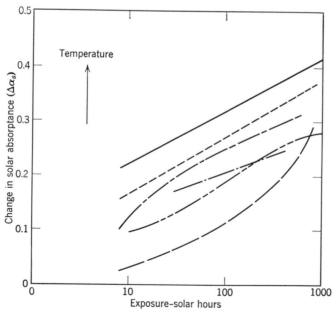

Fig. 13-51. Round robin results on $TiO_2$/epoxy coating.

## 5. Space Experiments

Although we may attempt to simulate outer space in our earthbound laboratories, it is the environment of space itself that is the final test of all the thermal control coating research. Several active programs in this area are now bearing fruit.

Under the direction of NASA Ames, a thermal control coatings experiment is aboard OSO-1. Two of the coatings were included in the referenced round robin program to give the first basic correlation between space data and "simulated" data.

## 6. Problem Areas and Future Interest

In the many areas discussed, work still remains in improving the $a_s/\epsilon$ ratio of the white pigmented coatings with reference to lower $a_s$ and improved stability to the vacuum-ultraviolet radiation environment. This would involve new polymers, binders and/or new or improved pigments. Anodized aluminum still offers promise as a thermal control coating but more research is needed to increase the stability of the coating. Incorporation of pigment particles into the pores of the anodize offers one possibility.

Liquid propellants, such as liquid oxygen, hydrogen, etc., now being used in space vehicles, has added a need for minimizing the heating and eventual vaporization of these propellants. Heat loss can be minimized by means of insulating materials. However, heat absorption from solar radiation can be reduced by the proper use of stable coatings having a low $a_s$ and a high $\epsilon_{th}$. A considerable weight saving may be realized by use of the coating technique.

In simulating the environment of space in which candidate thermal control coatings would be exposed, researchers have combined vacuum and ultraviolet radiation or vacuum and particulate radiation but very rarely a combination of all three. Since future vehicles, containing thermal control coatings, will be traveling more in, or in the vicinity of the space radiation belts, it is imperative that the effect of particulate radiation in combination with solar radiation and high vacuum upon the optical properties of these coatings, be assessed. Preliminary research has indicated a qualitative similiarity between the optical degradation of organic coatings caused by particulate and ultraviolet radiation. The status of inorganic coatings, which are relatively stable to the ultraviolet radiation, needs to be assessed for exposure to the added element of particulate radiation.

Thermal control coatings developed to the present time for satellite systems had one goal in common—constant or very little change in optical properties regardless of temperature or solar flux impinging on the vehicle. The feasibility of developing a single coating with the capability of temperature and/or solar intensity dependent reversibility with respect to optical properties would have far reaching effects in the area of thermal control. Several apparent advantages would be derived from such a coating system, such as reduction of the number of coatings on a single vehicle, weight savings and a more constant thermal control with particular reference to a solar probe where temperature would be of prime importance.

## L. Electrical Insulating

A new and revolutionary idea is being explored for the application of enamels to copper magnet wire. It is electrodeposition, a process of coating copper wire in an aqueous solution by an electric current. In this method, an organic resin particle is dispersed in water in such a manner that it has an electrical charge. Then, under the influence of an electrical field, it is attracted to a positive electrode, the anode, and deposited onto it. Copper wire is used as the anode (14).

This method of application has been used for years in electroplating of metals. It was not until the resin chemist was able to formulate superior water soluble, or water dispersible resins, that these basic principles could be applied to the coating industry.

The process of electrodeposition produces an unusual phenomenon. The resin plays a dual role in the process. The material is a conductor at one point and a few minutes later it is an insulator. The objective of the program covered in this article was to solve these two paradoxical processes.

By this time, many engineers must be thinking that they do not want any part of an insulator that is water soluble during its processing. If the resin is "at home" one time in water, the question is "would the coating still have an affinity for water?" The answer is that the coated enamel has lost its water solubility through the baking cycle during which it becomes an insoluble, thermoset resin. Correct formulating principles permit the resin to perform this dual role.

Although this report discusses electrodeposition as applied to copper magnet wire, as a part of the program numerous experiments were conducted on utilizing the process for aluminum magnet wire and for foil

Fig. 13-52. Cablework for world's tallest buildings are being installed which use plastics underground environmental protective coatings. The excavation scene is one of many at the site where 70 existing underground cables are being relocated. Almost 28 miles of new cable will be needed from Western Electric, the Bell System's manufacturing unit. A team of 40 New York Telephone splicers will tackle the big job involving 150,000 circuits.

and strip coatings of either aluminum or copper. The same type of formulations will coat all of these products.

## 1. *Advantages*

The principal advantages of electrodeposition over conventional methods are:

(*a*). Faster production rates. Production of coated wire can be increased four to six times per hour. Only one passage of the wire through the dip tank is required. For example, a processing wire mill will have to run #18 AWG copper magnet wire through the dip tank only one time to obtain heavy build rather than the present four to six passages.

(*b*). Superior properties through formulation of higher molecular weight materials. The resin chemist will be able to develop unusually long chain polymers because water is used in the system.

(*c*). Elimination of offensive odors—especially cresylic acid fumes in a city. With air pollution becoming a national problem, everyone will welcome methods that will reduce air pollution.

(*d*). Complete and uniform coverage. In electrodeposition, the charged negative particles are attracted to positive metal surfaces. This attraction will continue until all the metal surface is covered.

## 2. *Electrodeposition Theories*

The phenomena of electrodeposition as applied to a protective coating application method are complex. Although the method uses theories established years ago, the practical application of these principles has introduced variables that complicate the deposition.

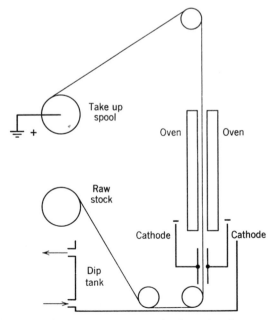

Fig. 13-53. Electrodeposition sketch for application of resins to magnet wire or strip.

To accomplish deposition by this method, it is necessary to have the following:

A water soluble resin (or water dispersible resin or emulsion).
A dip tank with two electrodes.
When the current is turned on, the following reactions occur:
(a) Electroysis.
(b) Electrophoresis.
(c) Electrocoagulation.
(d) Electroosmosis.

All four of these reactions usually occur simultaneously during the deposition of a resin. They play an important role in the correct application of the resin to the wire.

### 3. Solubilizing the Resin

The term solubilizing is frequently used in electrodeposition. It means that the resin should be dissolved in water or at least dispersed in water. (Actually water is not the only medium that can be used, but it is the most desirable.)

Polyesters and alkyds can be solubilized by polymerizing the resin to a relatively low molecular weight and then reacting the carboxyl groups with an amine, which is basic. For example, ammonium hydroxide could be used. Often, more complexed amines are used. These amines attach themselves to the resin particle and become soluble in water. They also dissociate into ions and produce the charged particle which will move under the influence of a potential gradient. For example, one species is listed below:

$$RCOOH + R'_3N \rightleftharpoons [RCOO]^- R'_3 NH^+$$
$$[RCOO]^- R'_3 NH^+ \rightleftharpoons [RCOO]^- + R'_3 NH^+$$

The same principle can be applied to resins of other compositions. For example, acrylics, epoxies, plain enamels (oleoresinous types), and polyamide-polyimide behave somewhat in the same manner. Naturally, every composition has its own peculiarities which determine the success or failure of that particular formulation.

### 4. Properties of the Coated Wire

The properties of the coated wire depend upon the type of composition. At the beginning of the program, the polyesters and plain enamel types were investigated. As expected, the plain enamel types gave very early indications that they would accomplish the objective faster than the tougher and more thermally resistant polyesters and polyimides. However, the experiments were concentrated on these latter two types because they generally are the wire enamels desired by the trade.

The properties of a polyester wire enamel applied by electrodeposition are approximately similar to those of a polyester enamel applied by conventional methods. However, it is well recognized that the coating by electrodeposition should give higher values for some electrical properties before commercialization of the product. This objective

Fig. 13-54. A new family of plastics—produced as films only a few millionths of an inch—has been created in the General Electric R&D Center, Schenectady, N. Y. The polymer coatings are applied in gaseous form inside a vacuum chamber, such as the one shown above. When the system is irradiated with ultraviolet light, a polymer film is deposited upon the surface of the object to be coated. These new polymers have potential application ranging from superior electrical insulation for microelectronic devices to corrosion-resistant protective coatings for metals and other materials.

will be accomplished through formulation techniques and application methods. Other types of polymers have been studied and their properties on coated wire approached the properties obtained by conventional methods. The epoxies are very interesting, but the most promising areas have been with the acrylics and the polyamide-polyimide types. These latter two polymers should some day offer extremely desirable properties for coatings applied by electrodeposition.

Preliminary estimations of the cost of coating resins by electrodeposition show that the technique is competitive with conventional methods. The amount of current to be drawn is small. Cost of the resins should be in the same area as the present conventional enamels.

## M. Others

In this section applications for important uses of coatings are described by pictures in Figs. 13-55 through 13-64. In Fig. 13-65 information is provided on the consumption rate for coatings.

Fig. 13-55. This modern factory building of the Pennsalt Equipment Division plant in Warminster, Pa., uses all metal sliding. The aluminum and galvanized steel panels are coated with long-life finishes based on Pennsalt's polyvinyldene fluoride resin, expecting no change until at least the year 2000.

Fig. 13-56. A joint development by Bethlehem and du Pont, a new plastic system, protective covering made from Lucite acrylic sirup approx. ⅛ in. thick, heavily reinforced with glass fibers, has been installed on Bidwell Bar Bridge (Calif.).

## V. SIMULATED SERVICE TESTS

Many different service tests have been used throughout the centuries —and more tests will be developed in the future. This way of life is directly related to progress. Of course the real test is when parts are in use. Many of the laboratory tests described throughout this book will provide useful ideas for conducting simulated service tests.

In this section a review will be presented on how to evaluate coated fabrics. Different tests can be used to evaluate elastomer coated fabrics. The typical tests are described (15).

### A. Abrasion Resistance

Of primary importance with materials that are exposed to much abrasion, e.g., truck covers. Where fabric may be tenderized by liquids,

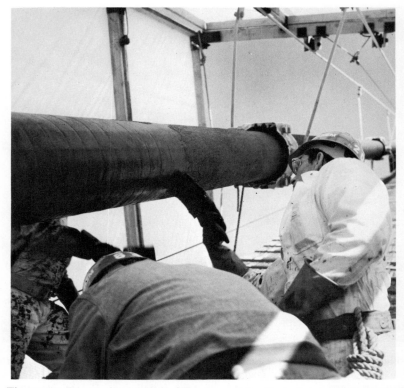

Fig. 13-57. The most important advantage of Lucite is the assured watertight protection it provides to bridge cables. Other advantages include speedy installation, handsome appearance, gritty nonslip walking surface, and minimum maintenance.

tests should be conducted after exposure to the liquid in which it will operate. Test values have only relative merit. Projection of results to service is difficult, since many factors affect performance.

*1.* Taber abrasion test. Abrasion wheels and weights are used in various combinations to abrade one or both sides of a fabric. Values are reported in number of cycles needed to achieve either first exposure of the base fabric or to cause initial tearing. In another method, abrader is run for a number of given cycles and then weight loss of coating is measured. A less accurate method is judging of appearance of fabric after a given number of cycles.

Reference: Fed Spec CCC-T-191b, Method 5306.

*2.* Du Pont scrub test. Sample, inserted between two moving jaws, is vigorously scrubbed against itself. Number of cycles needed to first

Fig. 13-58. A ton of General Electric Company's high temperature silicone coating is used on North American's XB-70A giant aircraft. At Mach 3 speeds its fuselage and wings are expected to develop temperatures from 500 to 600°F.

expose base fabric is reported. Values usually determined for each side and for warp and filling direction. Visual inspection after a given number of cycles is not as accurate.

Reference: Vanderbilt Rubber Handbook, p. 433, 1948 edition.

*3.* Wysenback test. In this test, also called the oscillatory cylinder test, the fabric is subjected to unidirectional rubbing action under known conditions of pressure, tension and abrasive action. Specimens are tested by placing them in contact with an oscillating cylinder covered with an abrasive material. Values are reported for loss of breaking strength after 250 cycles of continuous abrasion under a 2-lb load.

Reference: ASTM D1175 and CCC-T-191b, Method 5304.

## B. Adhesion

Particularly important in applications where fabric is exposed to a great amount of flexing, pressure and stretching. For fabrics with several plies, adhesion between plies should be tested.

*1.* Scott test method. Adhesion tested with Scott tester by peeling coating from base fabric, or by peeling two plies apart. A 2-in. wide sample is inserted in jaws which separate at a given speed, most frequently 2 ipm or 12 ipm. Results are expressed in lb/2 in. width, or per in. of width, required to peel coating and fabric or two plies apart.

Fig. 13-59. Large Penton-clad reducing elbow for heat exchanger. Elbows of this type require much less maintenance than previous lead-lined pipe, and are lighter and easier to install.

Reference: Fed Sepc CCC-T-191b, Method 5950, Method 5970, Method 5972; Fed Std No. 601, Method 8211; ASTM D751 60T.

## C. Accelerated Aging in Hot Air

Useful measure of service life at atmospheric temperatures; particularly important for fabrics that must perform at elevated temperatures, e.g., automotive and heating equipment.

*1.* Hot air aging. Samples placed in a thermostatically controlled air circulating oven and aged for specified temperatures and times. Fabrics not expected to perform in elevated temperatures are usually aged for 72 hr at 158 F. Fabrics used in automotive applications are aged 72 hr at 200–300 F. If fabrics will be exposed to oils or other fluids during actual service, samples are immersed in suitable test fluids.

*2.* To test aging in stop-and-go applications, aging tests are inter-

Fig. 13-60. Cast iron diaphragm box (left) corroded after 2 weeks immersion in sulfuric acid system. Box coated with Microthene powdered polyethylene withstood over 4 mo immersion (right).

Fig. 13-61. Koppers new zinc-rich coating system dries to form an impact- and abrasion-resistant finish which has enabled it to be used as a single protective system on 1½ miles of exposed pipe lines which carry gaseous nitrogen and helium for Saturn rocket complexes 34 and 37 at Cape Kennedy.

Fig. 13-62. A urethane latex developed by Wyandotte Chemicals Corp. adds longer flexural life to materials as shown in this laboratory text. More than 500,000 flex cycles were obtained on these latex-treated materials with no sign of wearing.

rupted and fabrics are allowed to dry between tests. After aging, properties are compared with those taken before aging.

Reference: Fed Spec CCC-T-191b, Method 5850; Fed Std 601, Method 7221; ASTM D573-53.

Fig. 13-63. A heat and moisture resistant Lexan polycarbonate coating is responsible for a 25–800% increase in transmission of colored light in General Electric's line of transparent color sign lamps.

## D. Accelerated Aging in Oxygen

Establishes behavior of fabrics that are exposed to air and sunshine in critical applications, such as life rafts, tarpaulins and radome covers.

*1.* Oxygen bomb test. Samples are placed in bomb for specified period of time at a temperature of 158 F and 300 psi of oxygen pres-

Fig. 13-64. Plastic coated steeds for the airmobile cavalry. Helicopters awaiting shipment to Viet Nam for use by the Army's First Calvalry Division (Airmobile) are protected against the hazards of a long sea voyage by a two-layer strippable plastic coating. The base coat is Spraylat SC 1071, B, made by Spraylat Corporation, a tough black waterbased resin film which resists sunlight, oil, grease, and scratches. A white pigmented topcoat adds water resistance.

sure. After aging, most important physical properties are tested and checked against values obtained before aging.

Reference: Fed Spec CCC-T-191b, Method 5852; Fed Std 601, Method 7111; ASTM D52-61.

### E. Blocking

Shows tendency of certain elastomers, including natural rubber, to adhere to themselves.

*1.* Blocking test. Sample is folded and put under a 4-lb weight in an oven at 180°F for 30 min. After cooling, sample is unfolded and examined for adhering or peeling of coating.

Reference: Fed Spec CCC-T-191b, Method 5872; ASTM D1893-61T.

### F. Burst Strength

Important guide in applications where fabric is exposed to high and sudden pressures, such as in gas regulators and controls.

*1*. Mullen test. Sample is clamped across orifice of Mullen tester with rubber diaphragm. Power is applied, and pressure at which rupture occurs is recorded in gross and net psi values.

Reference: Fed Spec CCC-T-191b, Method 5122; ASTM D751-60T.

## G. Cementability

Particularly critical property in such products as life rafts, life vests and other bonded inflatables.

*1*. Test method. Samples, $2 \times 12$ in., are cleaned with solvents and cemented together. After drying and curing, pieces are pulled apart in a Scott tester at a speed of 12 ipm. Results are expressed in lb/in. of width. Minimum values frequently specified are 6 or 10 lb-in., depending on end use. To reproduce test, solvent and cement preparation techniques should be standardized.

Reference: No industry or government standards issued.

## H. Compression Set

This measure of permanent deformation of fabric exposed to constant pressure or deflection can be important, particularly with coated fabric diaphragm assemblies in units with bolts or crimps.

*1*. Test methods. Sample is held under either constant load (method A) or constant deflection (method B) for specified length of time in specified constant temperature. Residual decrease in thickness, either a percentage of original thickness (method A) or a percentage of deflection under load (method B) is reported as compression set. An interval of at least one week between removing load and measuring residual decrease in thickness or deflection is necessary to evaluate permanent set.

Reference: ASTM D-395-5A and B: ASTM D-395-61 5A and B.

## I. Curl

A measure of this characteristic is unimportant with very thin diaphragms which may show a tendency to curl. Curl is an inconvenience in assembly, especially when using automatic assembly equipment. Fabrics having same coating on both sides normally should not curl; however, materials coated on one side almost always curl.

*1*. Test method. A disc, $2\frac{1}{4}$-in. in diameter is allowed to rest 24 hr at 70 F with the side up that shows the tendency to curl. The distance from

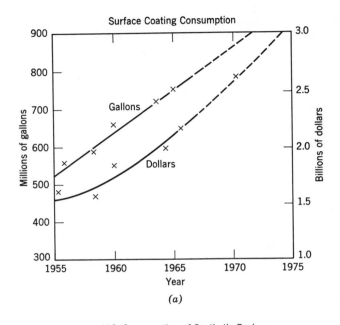

(a)

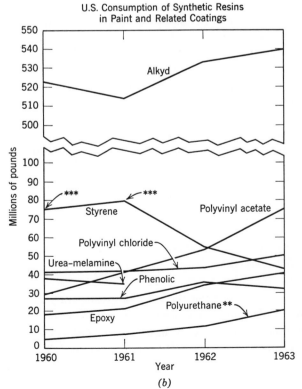

(b)

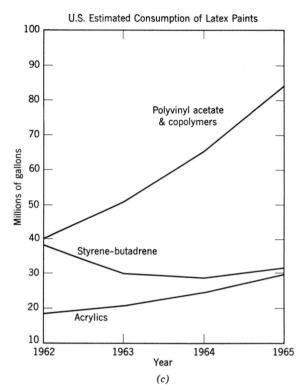

U.S. Estimated Consumption of Latex Paints

Fig. 13-65. Consumption of coatings in the U. S. is increasing rapidly. It is estimated that approximately 30% of all plastics produced is used to provide some type of protective coating.

table top to highest point of curl is reported as curl value. A curl of ¼ in. or more is usually considered excessive for a diaphragm assembly.

Reference: No standard industry or government test.

## J. Elongation

Elongation without rupture is desirable in diaphragms that pulse with a long stroke. In other applications (such as metering devices) where dimensional stability is of utmost importance, elongation of a fabric is undesirable.

*1.* Test method. Sample is stretched in a Scott tester until it ruptures. Amount of stretch that occurs between bench marks at time of rupture is the ultimate elongation of fabric. Values are expressed as a percentage of original distance between marks.

Reference: ASTM D751-60T.

## K. Flame Resistance, Vertical

A guide to flame resistance is important with any coated fabric used where a fire hazard exists. Several flame tests are available of which the severest and most widely used is vertical flame test.

*1.* Vertical flame test. Sample 2¾-in.×12 in., is clamped between metal flanges and suspended in metal cabinet to shield it from drafts. A flame of standard size and standard intensity is placed under sample for 12 sec. The burner is then removed without opening cabinet. Three values are usually measured: (*a*) length of time the flame continues to burn after removal of burner, (*b*) length of time glow continues, and (*c*) char length, expressed as distance to which charred sample will tear when subjected to a specified load.

Reference: Fed Spec CCC-T-191b, Method 5902; Method 5910 (a les severe, 30° flame resistance test) of same Fed Spec.


## L. Flexibility

This property is important in many lightweight fabric diaphragms used in delicate sensing devices.

*1.* Tinius-Olsen test. One end of 1×3-in. sample is placed in a clamp that will rotate the sample up to 90°. The other end of the sample actuates a balanced arm which gives readings up to 100 units. Stiffest samples give highest readings; weights can be added to balance very stiff samples. Values (expressed in weights plus units) can be read at various degrees of rotation of sample. Most commonly, value at 30° rotation is read.

Reference: Fed Spec CCC-T-191b, Method 5202.

*2.* Clark test. A 1¼-in. wide strip is placed between two 1-in. dia rollers held together by spring pressure. One of the rollers is slowly rotated. The overhanging sample is adjusted until it falls over in both directions of rotation when the frame work is rotated clockwise and counter clockwise. Length of overhanging portion, in mm, is the flexibility value.

Reference: Fed Spec CCC-T-191b, Method 5204.


## M. Hardness

A measure of hardness is important in such products as rubber offset blankets. Hardness of coating is usually measured before the coating material is applied to the base fabric.

*1*. Shore durometer. Usually gives valid readings only with unsupported elastomers of at least ¼ in. thickness. On coated fabrics does not produce reliable, absolute values because instrument registers some of hardness of base fabric. Shore durometer measures resistance sample to penetration of indenter of point of instrument, which extends 0.1-in. beyond surface of presser foot. Durometer reads 0 when indenter is fully extended and 100 when it is pressed to a flat piece of plate glass; thus, high value indicates hard sample. Coated fabric, to be hard, should give reading of about 70.

Reference: Fed Std 601, Method 3021.

## N. Hydrostatic Resistance

A measure of this characteristic is useful for coated fabrics intended for rainproof applications.

*1*. Mullen test. For high water pressure resistance. A sample is clamped between jaws with circular openings and water pressure is raised until first drop of water passes through sample. Pressure at this point is expressed in psi.

Reference: Fed Spec CCC-T-191b, Method 5512; Fed Std 601, Method 10511; ASTM D751-60T.

*2*. Suter test. For medium or low water pressure resistance (up to 2 psi); employs a rising water column placed over a test sample. Resistance is reported as the height of column in cm at which pressure causes the first drop of water to penetrate the sample.

Reference: Fed Spec CCC-T-191b, Method 5514.

*3*. Impact spray test. For low water pressure resistance. Fabric sample is bombarded with spray of water from specified height, usually a 3-ft column. The water that passes through a sample of standard area within a specified time is accumulated in a 6-in. × 6-in. blotter mounted behind fabric. The increase of weight in mg of blotter is the spray penetration value.

Reference: Fed Spec CCC-T-191b, Method 5524.

## O. Low Temperature Cracking

This guide is important with fabrics that must perform outdoors in cold climates, e.g., gas meter and regulator diaphragms. Test temperatures of −40 F and −67 F are commonly used.

*1*. Bent loop and hammer test. A weight is dropped on a bent sample until it cracks. Test measure is given as the number of cycles to failure.

1610  PHILIP A. DI MATTIA

*2.* Bar test. Two 1-in. wide samples are threaded under a $\frac{1}{8}$-in. dia bar which forms the hinge between a center plate and a longer plate on each end. The end plates are lifted and then allowed to drop on the center plate, flexing the fabric samples around the bar until they crack. The measure of resistance is the number of cycles to failure.

*3.* Fold and roll tests. A 10-lb roller is rolled over a sample, first folded in one direction and then folded in the opposite direction. The test is continued until the sample cracks and the number of cycles to failure is used as the measure of resistance.

*4.* A number of other tests also exist and are included in the following list:

Reference: Fed Spec CCC-T-191b, Method 5874; Fed Std 601, Methods 5211, 5311, 5321, 5611; MIL Spec C-20696 (para 4.4.1.3); ASTM D736-54T; ASTM D746-57T; ASTM D797-58; ASTM D1053-61.

## P. Modulus

A low modulus coating is desirable in highly flexible coated fabric applications such as rapidly pulsating diaphragms. Modulus can be measured satisfactorily only with the elastomer before it is applied to the base fabric. It is usually measured by the stress in psi at any given elongation; most commonly used values are obtained at 300% elongation.

*1.* Test method. In this method a Scott tester is used to measure elongation of an unsupported sample in shape of a dumbbell.

Reference: No industry or government specifications.

## Q. Gas Permeability

Permeability measurement of gases is important for coated fabrics used in life vests and other inflatable products. It is also vital for gas meter and regulator diaphragms.

*1.* Cambridge permeameter test. Samples are tested in an apparatus using hydrogen gas. Tests are usually conducted for 2 min, and the instrument converts readings into values expressed in 1/sq m/24 hr. For life vests and rafts, a reading of 5 1/sq m/24 hr is acceptable. Results can be converted into equivalent values for helium, carbon dioxide or other gases by using factors recommended by the Bureau of Standards.

Reference: Fed Spec CCC-T-191b, Method 5460; ASTM D815-47.

## R. Liquid Permeability

Liquid permeability measurement is significant for fabrics used as fuel containers or vapor traps, such as breather balloons.

*1.* Test method. A specified amount of test liquid is placed in a cup or jar of specified dimensions over which the fabric sample is placed and sealed. After allowing the sample to reach equilibrium, the cup or jar is weighed accurately, then the cup is inverted and allowed to stand for a specified period, after which it is weighed again. Weight loss is calculated generally in fl oz/sq ft/24 hr.

Reference: No standard government or industry specifications.

## S. pH Value

The pH value of a coating is useful to know in applications where the coating comes in contact with metal parts. Normally, the coating should have a neutral pH.

*1.* Test method. The fabric or coating is cut into small pieces and placed in distilled water for 3 hr. The pH is then measured with a standard meter. A reading of 7 represents neutrality; $<7$ shows acidity; $>7$ shows alkalinity.

Reference: Fed Spec CCC-T-191b, Method 2811.

## T. Resiliency

Resiliency can be an important index in many applications, such as rubber coated offset printing blankets.

*1.* Bashore resiliometer test. In this test a bob is dropped vertically onto a fabric sample at the base of instrument. The distance that the bob bounces back after impact is reported as a percentage of the original height from which it was dropped. It should be remembered that the resiliometer records the combined resiliency of the coating and base fabric. If a reading of the elastomer coating alone is wanted, then a fairly thick sample of elastomer coating material before coating must be tested.

Reference: No standard government or industry specifications.

## U. Stretch

Temporary stretch and permanent residual stretch are undesirable in a coated fabric that is used where great accuracy is required, such as a metering diaphragm or an offset printing blanket.

*1.* Test method. A 10-in length (accurate to the nearest 0.01 in.) is marked off on a 1×12-in. sample. A clamp is applied to each end, and a 50-lb weight is suspended from one end for 10 min. The amount that the fabric stretches during testing is reported as temporary stretch, and is expressed in % of the original 10-in. length. If a stretch remains after removing the weight this is reported as permanent residual stress.

Reference: No standard government or industry specifications.

## V. Swelling

A test for swelling is required for any coated fabric that may come in contact with oils, solvents or other liquids during use.

*1.* Test method. Oblong samples are immersed in a graduated cylinder containing alcohol to measure their volume. The samples are then dried and immersed in the test medium for a specified period and temperature. Following exposure they are removed and their volume is measured again. The increase in volume from swelling is recorded as % of original volume.

*2.* Alcohol is used to measure the fabric volume because it is clear, does not cause swelling, and it permits the sample to sink.

*3.* Toluol is the most frequently used swelling medium because its swelling properties match those of many media. However, several other fluids are available for determining swelling characteristics.

*4.* Many brands of gasolines, oils and other fluids have proprietary formula ingredients. Also, the composition of fluids used may be affected by dust, fumes, temperature, etc. Therefore, in critical applications such as fuel and brake systems, extensive life tests should be conducted with fabrics under the expected operating conditions.

If the coated fabric has to perform at elevated temperatures then swelling tests are run at the expected temperatures. In some cases, the percent increase in gauge or weight, rather than the change in volume is measured.

## W. Tear Strength

Fabric that will be stressed should be tested for tear strength.

*1.* Pendulum method (Elmendorf). In this test a 2.5×4-in. fabric sample is held between two clamps at the base of an Elmendorf instrument. After nicking the sample with a knife attachment, a pendulum is released which falls through the sample. The pendulum carries a circumferential scale which indicates the force required to tear the specimen. Scale readings can be multiplied by appropriate factors to give results in lb or gm. Values are determined for both the warp and filling direction of the fabric.

Reference: ASTM 751-57T; Fed Spec CCC-T-191b, Method 5132.

*2.* Tongue method (strip). In this method a cut is made at the center of the 3 in. edge of a 3 x 8-in. sample. The two 1½-in. ends are then placed in two jaws of a Scott tester. The jaws are separated at a speed of 12 ipm. An autographic recorder records tear as a high point on a chart. The average of five tests is reported as tear strength in lb. Values are determined for both warp and filling direction.

Reference: Fed Spec CCC-T-191b, Method 5134.

*3.* Trapezoid method. Here a trapezoidal sample, 6-in. long on one side and 3-in. long on the opposite parallel edge is given a small cut at the center of the 3-in. edge. The non-parallel edges are clamped into the jaws of a Scott tester and the sample is torn apart at a speed of 12 ipm. Using an autographic recorder, average of five high points is reported as tear strength in lb.

Reference: Fed Spec CCC-T-191b, Method 5136.

## X. Tensile Strength

A standard tensile strength value is normally supplied by the coated fabric manufacturer by the grab method in both warp and filling directions.

*1.* Grab method. In this standard test 4×6-in. fabric samples are inserted in 1 x 1-in. jaws of a Scott tester. The jaws, 3 in. apart at the start, are separated at 12 ipm. Values are reported in lb-in. To obtain accurate results, extreme care must be used to obtain proper alignment of the yarns in jaws.

Reference: ASTM D751-60, Fed Spec CCC-T-191b, Method 5100.

*2.* Cut strip method. Strips, 1×6 in. are cut in both the warp and filling directions, and the yarns are carefully aligned in the dies. Samples are ruptured in a Scott tester; values are recorded in lb-in.

Reference: Fed Spec CCC-T-191b. Method 5102; ASTM D751-60T.

*3.* Ravel strip method. Strips, 6 in. long, are raveled, in both the warp and filling directions to a width of exactly 1 in. Samples are ruptured in a Scott tester and values reported in lb-in.

Reference: Fed Spec CCC-T-191b. Method 5104; ASTM D1682-59T.

## Y. Thickness

It is essential to have uniform thickness over the entire surface of a coated fabric in many applications.

*1.* Test methods. A Federal Gauge with 0.001-in. graduations can be employed for thickness measurements. Since the gauge uses a dead weight, rather than a spring gauge, great care must be taken to apply an absolutely straight load to obtain accurate readings. A spring-loaded Randall Stickney Gauge that is suitably tipped can also provide accurate readings.

*2.* A DWL micrometer, used in lithography for rubber offset printing blankets, has a dial surface and can be used to measure thickness over a wide surface. Micrometers used in metal working do not give accurate readings on the resilient surface of a coated fabric.

Reference: Fed Spec CCC-T-191b, Method 5030; Fed Std 601, Method 2011; ASTM D751-60T.

## Z. Wicking

In some critical applications it is essential to measure the air or gas leakage through pin holes, or through internally exposed edges of vent holes into the fabric from where it bleeds to fabric edges. Coated fabric diaphragms performing in critical applications, such as air brake controls, must be proofed against wicking.

*1.* Test methods. In this test a coated fabric sample is clamped into a test jig immersed in water. Flange clamping pressure must be sufficient to prevent loss of gas between the sample and flanges, but not so high as to impede the flow of gas through the edges. After immersing the jig in water, gas pressure is applied to the jig and pressure is gradually raised until bubbles are visible at the outer edge of sample. Pressures are usually raised at increments of 10 psi up to a maximum of 100 psi. The pressure at which initial leakage occurs is recorded and the next lowest pressure is defined as antiwicking value or the pressure up to which the fabric will perform without wicking.

Reference: No standard industry or government specifications. Test and tester are developments of Vulcan Plant, Reeves Brothers, Inc.

## AA. Weathering

With any coated fabric that is to be used outdoors it is very useful to have a guide to weathering properties before the fabric is placed in service.

*1.* Test methods. To obtain accelerated results, Weatherometer equipment can be used to simulate rain and sunshine by use of water spray and carbon arc. Both physical tests and visual examination can be used to indicate the deterioration that occurs after a specified period of time. Military specifications frequently stipulate the minimum physical test values that must be met after a specified time of exposure. Comparative evaluations can provide an indication of the weather resistance of different fabrics.

Reference: Fed Spec CCC-T-191b, Method 5804; ASTM D750-55T.

## REFERENCES

1. H. F. Payne, *Organic Coating Technology*, Vol. II, Wiley, New York, 1961.
2. M. A. Glaser and P. Rosenberg, "Vinyl Dispersion Coatings in the Organic Finishes Industry," SPEC-RETEC, April 29, 1966.
3. P. Nylen and E. Sunderland, *Modern Surface Coatings*, Interscience, New York, 1965.
4. D. V. Rosato, "Coatings," *Plastics World,* **24** (July 7, 1966).
5. G. F. Schmitt, Jr., H. Rosenberg, J. J. Stepnowski, J. H. Weaver, A. S. Dalton, and J. J. Mattice, "Polymeric Protective Coatings," AFML-TR-65-29, pp. 173-202, June, 1965.
6. S. Garry Howell, L. J. Memering, and L. R. Ridgewood, "Coating Paper with Microfine Polyolefin Powders," SPE-ANTEC, pp. X111-2, Mar. 1, 1966.
7. G. W. Ewald, *Review,* J. P. Stevens & Co., Inc., New York, 1966.
8. American Plywood Association, Tacoma, Washington, Coated Plywood Program, 1966.
9. "Metal Pre-Coating: New Resin Boom," *Chemical Week,* pp. 51-52 (Dec. 7, 1963).
10. National Coil Coaters Association, Chicago, Ill., Status Report, 1966.
11. Prepaint or Post-Paint, *Product Eng.,* pp. 84-87 (Feb. 28, 1966).
12. American Plywood Association, Tacoma, Wash., Plywood/Fiberglass Cargo Container, 1966.
13. H. H. Hormann, "Thermal Control Coatings," AFML-TR-65-29, pp. 205-219, June, 1965.
14. J. P. Haughney, "Electrodeposition of Insulation Coatings—for the Magnetic Wire and Strip and Electrical Industries," *Insulation,* pp. 55-59 (May, 1966).
15. E. C. Hemes, "How to Evaluate Coated Fabrics, Materials in Design Engineering," pp. 92-96, July 1964.

# 14

# Elastomers

**J. K. Sieron**
and
**R. G. Spain**

*Air Force Materials Laboratory,*
*Wright-Patterson Air Force Base, Ohio*

## CONTENTS

A short dissertation upon almost any extensive subject is usually blessed by the reader's understanding that generalizations were not only justifiable but mandatory in order to cover the scope of the subject. On the other hand, a learned treatise of ponderous bulk can be readily exempted from criticism for tedious passages devoted to details in that the author or authors are attempting to present a full and uncompromised assay of the subject. Somewhere in between lies the chapter on a specific subject in a technical volume of wide scope.

Often the authors of such a chapter set their own ground rules in a probably futile attempt to satisfy the inquisitiveness of those from another technical discipline in an expeditious manner, and yet not to incur the criticism of those highly knowledgeable in the subject area. The writers have followed this perilous course.

Hence this chapter is not a review of elastomer technology, since collections dealing with major facets of this field could approach the dimensions of a library, but rather is an attempt to present aspects of this technology particularly pertinent to the overall use of elastomers in the field of aerospace endeavor. Some deviations from this intent, primarily of historical or economic impact, seemed unavoidable.

## I. INTRODUCTION

Elastomers are unique engineering materials. In a host of applications, the decision is not one as to the use of elastomers or other materials, but only as to which elastomer may be best utilized for the particular application. In contrast, the use of plastics and plastic composites or metallics often shifts from one to the other in the light of required performance and/or economics.

## A. Definition

Until about 1910, the term "rubber" was sufficiently descriptive for most purposes. It typified natural products derived from various trees and plants which could be formed into solids of various shapes which could be bent, flexed rapidly, or stretched with the amazing ability to return to essentially the initial form. As synthetic materials emerged, particularly synthetics which were directed toward capabilities different from those of natural rubber, considerable confusion resulted as to descriptive terminology. Hence the literature was rife with such terms as "rubber," "rubbery," "rubberlike," and similar inept descriptions. While this terminology persists today, H. L. Fisher struck a major blow to this confusion and coined the term "elastomer" to embrace natural as well as synthetic products with those mechanical properties generally associated with natural rubber. Subsequently, innumerable efforts, both formal and informal, have been directed to the further improvement of a more technical definition. Part of the difficulty encountered lies in the manner in which elastomers find their way to use as end items. While additives, such as stabilizers, coloring agents, and reinforcing agents, are utilized in various combinations with polymeric materials formed into fibers and various plastics, many of these polymer forms have significant value in essentially unmodified form. Polystyrene and poly(methyl methacrylate) are examples of thermoplastics of this type, and nylons (polyamides) and rayons (cellulosics) are examples of fibers. In contrast, rubber (or better, elastomeric) polymers rarely find use as end items without substantial modification.

Of the many, many modifications utilized to transform elastomeric polymers to useful end items, vulcanization, or crosslinking, is the most important. While exceptions exist, base elastomeric polymers generally consist of essentially linear polymers with molecular weight ranges of a few tens of thousands to several million. (A molecular weight of a single polymer molecule can be thought of as the total of the atomic weights of all the atoms comprising the molecule. Thus a polymer of 10,000 repeating —$CH_2$— units has a molecular weight of 140,000 as carbon has an atomic weight of 12 and hydrogen of 1.) Vulcanization, briefly, is a process which induces bonding between neighboring polymer chains at comparatively infrequent intervals.

An idealized two-dimensional schematic drawing of the effect of vulcanization on an elastomer is illustrated in Fig. 14-1. Here the unvulcanized elastomer resists the application of tensile stress by the viscous flow or slippage of the molecules by one another. This phenomenon is always present in the vulcanized elastomer although as distortion becomes more pronounced, the crosslinks between polymer chains tend to restrict the viscous flow and the elastic component comes into play. For a given vulcanized elastomer, the relative contributions of the viscous and elastic components are primarily dependent upon temperature and strain rate.

A second difficulty in adequately defining an elastomer lies in the established habit of the general characterization of the state of a material in relation to "normal" temperatures. An unwritten but very widespread agreement indicates that this "normal" is "room temperature" and is about 75°F. An examination of the effect of temperature on the modulus or viscosity of a typical thermoplastic polymer is shown in Fig. 14-2. Here we see that as temperature is increased the polymer changes from a rigid solid to an elastomeric phase and finally to a liquid. Thus, if the temperature of our planet were a modest amount higher, familiar rigid plastics, such as polystyrene, would be elastomers.

Thus elastomers are difficult to define. Generally, at the temperature at which their vulcanizates are used, they are (*1*) low moduli

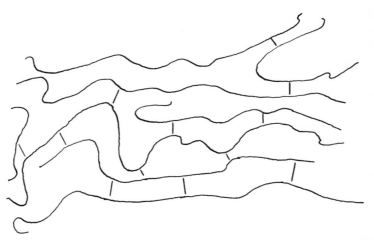

Fig. 14-1. Schematic representation of a vulcanized elastomer. Actual vulcanizates are composed of a three-dimensional network resulting from the crosslinking of the elastomer chains.

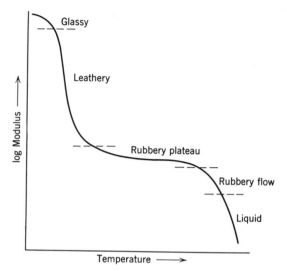

Fig. 14-2. Generalized temperature-modulus curve for the thermoplastic polymers. While vulcanized elastomers will not become liquids on heating without degradation, all other general features of the curve are observed.

polymeric solids, (*2*) capable of substantial distortion resulting from applied stresses, and (*3*) returned quickly to their approximate original shape on release of the stress.

Some small consolation in the inadequency of elastomer definition can be found in turning to other phases of polymer technology. While elastomer technology is one of respectable age, fiber technology predates it by several thousands of years. And the controversy as to what constitutes a fiber is still current.

## B. Unique Engineering Properties

Perhaps the primary points of the unique potential of elastomers as engineering materials can best be described diagrammatically. Figure 14-3 illustrates the stress–strain behavior to rupture of vulcanized natural rubber as contrasted to another familiar material, glass. It's radically different performance is evident. Figure 14-4 also represents stress–strain behavior of vulcanized natural rubber, but to an extension short of rupture after which the retraction curve is shown. While this curve utilizes tensile stress, similar curves result if compressive stresses are employed. This type of evaluation is particularly important in predicting the performance of an elasto-

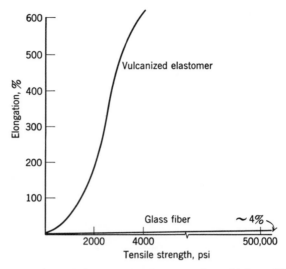

Fig. 14-3. A comparison of the stress-strain curves for a high quality elastomeric vulcanizate and glass fiber.

Fig. 14-4. Hysteresis curve for a natural rubber vulcanizate on extension short of rupture and decrease in stress.

meric vulcanizate in a dynamic application as the area between the curves represents the energy which is not returned and is manifested as heat. Thus in dynamic applications, if the area between the curves is large and/or the frequency at which the vulcanizate is deformed is high, the vulcanizate can continually rise in temperature to a point of catastrophic thermal degradation.

Essentially all efforts expended in the preparation of synthetic elastomers have been directed toward maintaining the salient features of either or both of properties of natural rubber illustrated in Figs. 14-3 and 14-4. Other objectives of syntheses have been directed toward increased resistance to oxygen and ozone, increased thermal stability, increased chemical resistance, and resistance to swelling by contact with various fluids.

## C. History

### 1. Natural Rubber

Columbus reportedly returned from his second voyage of 1493–1496 with rubber balls used in play by the natives of Haiti. Cortez is reported to have attended a game played between teams of ten or more with the objective of knocking a solid rubber ball through the stone rings at either end of the game court of the Aztec king, Montezuma II. The indefatigable historian F. J. de Torquemada recorded that the Spaniards in the New World, observing the native's use of a white liquid from a tree to coat their cloaks to render them impervious to rain, coated hemp or linen bags in a similar manner for the transportation of mercury. The Spaniards are also credited with fabricating personal articles from the liquid (now known as latex) such as cloaks, boots, and shoes as well as other objects for protection from the weather. However, de Torquemada said that in the sun such objects became sticky and smelled bad.

The scientific community of Europe remained essentially in ignorance of this material until in 1736 the French Academy of Science sent a survey party to Peru, under the leadership of Charles de la Condamine, on a mission concerned with his talents as a noted astronomer. La Condamine was also a naturalist and he observed the natives collecting a white syrup from trees and drying it over fires. He sent samples of this rubber back to France. He must also have been something of an athlete, for he engaged in a journey of over 2000 miles before making the acquaintance of Francois Fresneau, an engineer employed by Louis XV of France. Inevitably, Fresneau was also a naturalist who had previously seen samples of rubber but not the parent trees. While Louis VI's rule of France was something of a historical disaster, his choice of dedicated engineers was excellent. Fresneau spent 14 years in searching for the tree responsible for rubber. He subsequently found the trees and reported that turpentine could be used as a solvent for natural rubber, allowing the formation of rubber coatings and objects by solvent evaporation and eliminating the difficulties encountered in the fermentation on exposure to air of the natural latex.

Joseph Priestley, of fame as the discoverer of oxygen, noted in 1770 that gum elastic (as the natural product was then known) would rub out pencil marks from paper; hence the birth of the term "rubber."

The tempo of developments began to pick up quickly in 1819 as Charles Mackintosh, in a business venture involving coal tar by-products, found that coal tar naphtha was an excellent rubber solvent. For this he patented a waterproof fabric in 1823 which consisted of two layers of woolen cloth with an interlayer of rubber deposited from solution. Mackintosh's efforts in time interested the industrious Thomas Hancock who fabricated, among other things, elastic tops for pockets to thwart pickpockets.

Noting that in cutting the tops for his pockets, a considerable portion of scrap resulted, Hancock set out to find a way to utilize this waste. Reasoning that if he could tear the scraps to small pieces, he could possibly reform them into a sheet, he designed an apparatus consisting of concentric cylinders lined with teeth with the inner cylinder rotated to achieve the desired shredding action. Instead of attaining shreds, Hancock found the rubber in a dough-like mass to which other materials could be readily added. This process, now known as mastication, and the type of apparatus, now known as internal mixers are vital to the modern elastomer processing industry. Minor progress continued until about 1839 when Charles Goodyear found that sulfur mixed with rubber followed by heating produced remarkable increases in properties and virtually eliminated the previous deleterious effects of hot weather and sunlight. No question exists as to who made this notable discovery, but Hancock, not Goodyear, obtained the vital *English* patent in 1843 while Goodyear's American patent was issued in 1844. Thus Thomas Hancock died in comparative wealth in 1865, having outlived Charles Goodyear indebted at death, by five years.

While other advances, and setbacks, were to occur, it was Good-year's discovery that marked the beginning of the great natural rubber industry and the certain challenge of synthetics some decades later.

## 2. Synthetics

Borchardat in 1879 conceived the "bold idea" that a comparatively simple molecule, isoprene, $C_5H_8$, was the foundation of natural rubber. Efforts leading to this postulation, which was correct, were based upon results of several researchers throughout the previous 50 years. Subsequent efforts were substantially devoted to the attempt to duplicate natural rubber by the polymerization of isoprene. In essence, these efforts were frustrating.

Popular belief holds the birth of synthetic elastomers to have been in about 1940 in response to the demands for strategic materials imposed by World War II. Facts, however, contradict this. In 1912, at the Eighth International Congress of Applied Chemistry in New York, C. Duisberg, the managing director of Bayer and Company, exhibited synthetic rubber tires that had been used on the Kaiser's car. The magnitude, efficiency, and duration of the Allied blockade, posed serious problems for Germany. With Teutonic determination, Germany produced 2350 tons of synthetic rubber from 2,3-dimethyl-butadiene during the holocaust of World War I. This monomer differed from isoprene, the basic unit of natural rubber, by the addition of one methyl ($CH_3$) group. The German technicians responsible for this remarkable achievement were (like Louis XV's engineer, Fresneau) dedicated and patient men. For while methyl rubber B was polymerized with metallic sodium in an atmosphere of carbon dioxide, methyl rubber H (hard) was polymerized by a process in which the monomer was stored in drums for 2 to 3 months at room temperature, and methyl rubber W was prepared from the monomer by polymerization at 70°C (158°F) for 3 to 6 months!

While progress was erratic until about the 1930's, synthetic elastomers were not only born, but yelling. It is perhaps notable that the first few products of the synthetic elastomer industry's resurgence then brought forth elastomers which offered environmental resistances vastly superior to natural products. Most notable of these were Thiokol (polysulfides) in 1929, neoprene (polychloroprene) in 1931, buna N (copolymers of butadiene and acrylonitrile) in 1937, and butyl (copolymer of isobutylene and isoprene) in 1940. Many more were to follow, and will be described in subsequent sections of this chapter.

## II. PREPARATION OF ELASTOMER VULCANIZATES

This section is devoted to the general synthesis techniques, the compounding, and the fabrication of elastomeric vulcanizates. It is hoped that the discussion will adequately inform the reader as to the tremendous complexity involved in the preparation of some elastomeric end items. While great strides are being made at an increasing rate in understanding the relation of molecular composition and structure to physical, chemical, and mechanical behavior, elastomer technology has largely proceeded as an art rather than a science.

### A. Syntheses of Elastomers

Elastomer preparation, as for polymers generally, can be grouped into two areas. As with most advancing technologies, however, the precise and lucid early divisions and definitions often become less descriptive as more cases and more complexities evolve. Elastomers are no exception. Many cases now exist, and many more are sure to follow, which belabor the following preparative divisions.

### 1. Addition Polymerization

Addition polymerization can be described as a chain reaction in which an ion or a free radical (a substance with an unpaired electron) is capable of reacting with a vinyl monomer to produce a larger free radical which now incorporates the monomer unit.

Repetition of the process leads to a successively larger and larger molecule until reaction with another free radical causes termination and hence further growth of the molecule. The whole process of growth of a single molecule usually occurs within a few seconds or less. However, the typical substantial scale addition polymerization of an elastomer usually requires several hours, although small laboratory polymerizations can be conducted in minutes and even seconds. These longer polymerization times permit control and modifications of the polymerization processes if necessary. Further, many polymerizations are not carried to 100% completion (conversion of all monomer to polymer), and the reaction is terminated at some intermediate point. Figure 14-5 illustrates the polymerization of butadiene

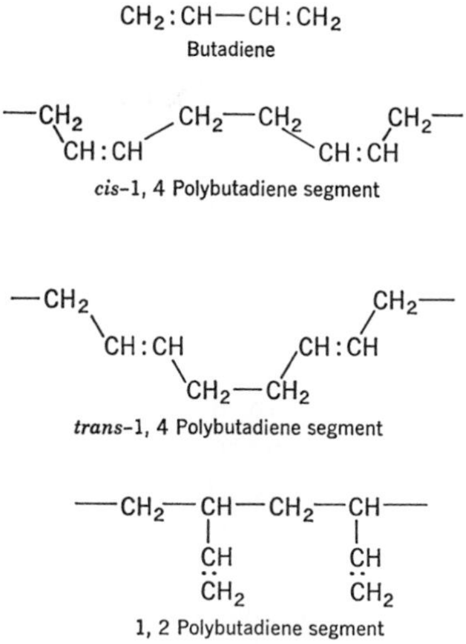

$$CH_2:CH—CH:CH_2$$
Butadiene

cis-1, 4 Polybutadiene segment

trans-1, 4 Polybutadiene segment

1, 2 Polybutadiene segment

Fig. 14-5. Modes of butadiene polymerization. In free radical induced polymerization or copolymerization all polymer forms are usually present in the final polymer.

and is also typical of copolymers containing large amounts of butadiene and hence significant polymer segments of butadiene. It should be noted that no by-products are formed in addition polymerization. Butadiene is the single largest volume monomer used in the polymerization of elastomers. While it can be copolymerized with a great many other olefinic monomers to form elastomers it is principally copolymerized with styrene and acrylonitrile. Significant amounts of butadiene are also utilized in the syntheses of resins.

Emulsion polymerization is by far the most widely used technique for the preparation of synthetic elastomers from the standpoint of the volume of elastomers produced. Basically, emulsion polymerization is almost always a form of addition polymerization in which the monomers are emulsified in water and then polymerized in the emulsified state. The resultant latices, if stable, are often modified and used per se in the forming of coatings and dipped goods. The great bulk of latices are reduced to solid elastomers by coagulation of the latices and drying of the solid product. Styrene-butadiene elastomers (SBR) are the prominent member of this class, although highly specialized elastomers such as the hydrofluorocarbon elastomers are also prepared by this technique.

## 2. Condensation Polymerization

In contrast to addition polymerization, condensation polymerization is not a typically fast reaction (although it can be in some instances). Generally condensation polymerization involves two polyfunctional molecules and is often accompanied by the formation of a by-product such as water. Unlike addition polymerization, where molecules of very high molecular weight can exist with large amounts of as yet unreacted monomer, condensation polymerization is generally a process wherein no such great diversity of molecular weight exist. Usually, restrictions as to attainable molecular weights are imposed by the nature of impurities present as well as inabilities to predict and control proper reactant ratios. While condensation polymerization is utilized in the preparation of only a very small fraction of the total volume of elastomeric polymers in use today, this type of polymerization seems likely to become of increasing importance in the syntheses of elastomers destined for use in severe environmental applications. To a large degree this is due to the versatility of polymer structures which can be formed by condensation reactions for which no parallel exists by addition reactions.

A typical condensation polymerization of an elastomeric polymer is presented in Fig. 14-6. The example, a polysulfide elastomer, has a commerical history of about 35 years.

## B. Types of Elastomers

The definitive titling of a class of elastomers is a hazardous affair. Names which would at least mollify a precise chemist are often so unwieldy that their acceptance is precluded. In contrast, accepted

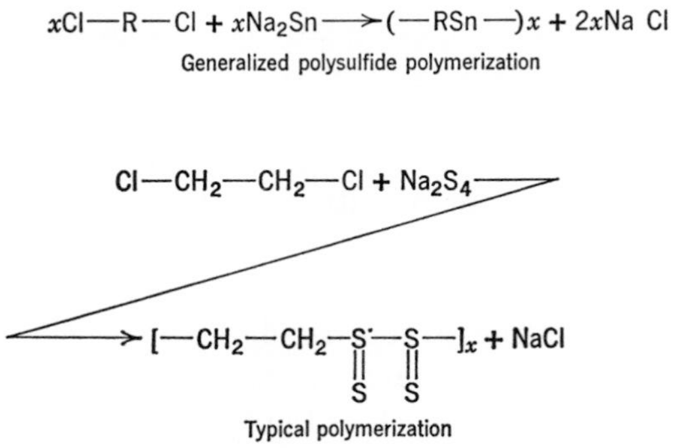

$$x\text{Cl}\!-\!\text{R}\!-\!\text{Cl} + x\text{Na}_2\text{Sn} \longrightarrow (-\text{RSn}-)x + 2x\text{Na Cl}$$

Generalized polysulfide polymerization

$$\text{Cl}\!-\!\text{CH}_2\!-\!\text{CH}_2\!-\!\text{Cl} + \text{Na}_2\text{S}_4$$

$$[-\text{CH}_2\!-\!\text{CH}_2\!-\!\underset{\underset{\text{S}}{\|}}{\text{S}}\!-\!\underset{\underset{\text{S}}{\|}}{\text{S}}-]_x + \text{NaCl}$$

Typical polymerization

Fig. 14-6. Condensation polymerization of polysulfide elastomers.

names are often very nondescriptive. Polyurethane, for example, is currently in common use to describe a host of actual and potential elastomers which have only one thing in common—the urethane linkages present are a very small constituent! Also, a surprisingly large number of specialty elastomers have appeared but briefly on the commercial market. The elastomers presented in Table 14-1 are therefore far from complete, but are believed to include most elastomers now available.

## C. Compounding of Elastomers

As mentioned previously, elastomers per se are of little utility. The first operation toward modifying elastomers to end items involves the addition of other materials, both solid and liquid, which eventually enhance the performance or the economics of the final product.

### 1. Solid Systems

The bulk of the compounding of elastomers is concerned with the addition of other materials to solid elastomers. Some consideration of the difficulties involved can perhaps be gained by inspection of Table 14-2 which represents the typical ingredients in a compound (the ratio by weight of ingredients with the elastomer represented by 100) destined to yield a relatively common article, a resilient floor tile. While this represents something of an extreme case regarding compounding, it is apparent that the elastomer represents a modest fraction of the total ingredients. In order to achieve an efficient compound, two objectives must be attained: (*1*) the solid additives must be reduced to a comparatively small particle size (usually this entails the reduction of agglomerates of the solid fillers), and (*2*) the resultant compound must be homogeneous. Additionally, the compounding procedures must avoid conditions which lead to premature vulcanization, or "scorching."

Virtually all compounding of solid elastomers is conducted on a batch basis using a two roll mill or an internal mixer, although production of some items may involve several such devices. As can be seen in the schematic drawings of Fig. 14-7, both devices continuously squeeze and tear a portion of the elastomer. In the case of the mill, desired additives are added at the excess of the elastomer above and between the two rolls. Solids are thus subjected to a considerable shearing force which aids (but does not insure) dis-

TABLE 14-1. Types of Elastomers

| Elastomer | Typical structure | Comments |
| --- | --- | --- |
| cis-Polyisoprene | $\left[\begin{array}{c}\text{H} \quad \text{H} \\ -\text{C}-\text{C}=\text{C}-\text{C}- \\ \text{H} \quad | \quad \text{H H} \\ \text{CH}_3\end{array}\right]_n$ | Historically natural rubber (Hevea) now also prepared synthetically; configurations other than cis of minor importance |
| Styrene-butadiene copolymers | $\left[\begin{array}{c}\text{H} \\ -\text{C}-\text{C}=\text{C}-\text{C}- \\ \text{H} \quad \text{H H H}\end{array}\right]_x\left[\begin{array}{c}\text{H H} \\ -\text{C}-\text{C}- \\ \text{H}\end{array}\bigcirc\right]_y$ | Largest volume elastomer in the U.S.; $x:y$ usually 3:1, but varied from about 10:1 to 1:1 |
| Polysulfides | $\left[\begin{array}{c}\text{H H} \\ -\text{C}-\text{C}-\text{S}-\text{S}- \\ \text{H H}\end{array}\right]_n$ | Numerous structural variations obtainable available as solids, liquids, and water dispersions; first commercial oil-resistant elastomer |
| Polychloroprene | $\left[\begin{array}{c}\text{H} \\ -\text{C}-\text{C}=\text{C}-\text{C}- \\ \text{H} \quad | \quad \text{H H} \\ \text{Cl}\end{array}\right]_n$ | First general purpose elastomers, combining high mechanical properties with good resistance to weathering, heat, and oils. |
| Acrylonitrile-butadiene copolymers | $\left[\begin{array}{c}\text{H} \\ -\text{C}-\text{C}=\text{C}-\text{C}- \\ \text{H} \quad \text{H H H}\end{array}\right]_x\left[\begin{array}{c}\text{H H} \\ -\text{C}-\text{C}- \\ \text{H} \quad | \\ \text{C}\equiv\text{N}\end{array}\right]_y$ | Largest volume highly oil-resistant elastomer; $x:y$ varied from about 8.5:1.5 to 5.5:4.5 |
| Isobutylene-isoprene copolymers | $\left[\begin{array}{c}\text{CH}_3 \\ -\text{C}-\text{C}- \\ \text{H} \quad | \quad \\ \text{CH}_3\end{array}\right]_x\left[\begin{array}{c}\text{H} \\ -\text{C}-\text{C}=\text{C}-\text{C}- \\ \text{H H} \quad | \quad \text{H} \\ \text{CH}_3\end{array}\right]_y$ | Highly resistant to oxygen and ozone; low air permeability; $x:y$ high, typically 98:2 |
| Ethyl acrylate copolymers | $\left[\begin{array}{c}\text{H H} \\ -\text{C}-\text{C}- \\ \text{H} \quad | \\ \text{C}=\text{O}\end{array}\right]$ | Highly resistant to oils, oxygen, and ozone; $x:y$ typically 95:5; several polyacrylates and copolymers have been available |

| Name | Structure | Description |
|---|---|---|
| Chlorosulfonated polyethylene | $\left[\begin{array}{c}H\ H\\-C-C-\\H\ H\end{array}\right]_x\left[\begin{array}{c}H\ H\\-C-C-\\H\ Cl\end{array}\right]_y\left[\begin{array}{c}H\ H\\-C-C-\\H\ SO_2Cl\end{array}\right]_z$ | Very high oxygen and ozone resistance; widely used as coatings; $y:y:z$ about $72:26:2$ |
| Polysiloxanes | $\left[\begin{array}{c}CH_3\\-Si-O-\\CH_3\end{array}\right]_n$ | Excellent thermal stability and low temperature flexibility; available as solids and liquids |
| Polyfluorosiloxanes | $\left[\begin{array}{c}CH_3\\-Si-O-\\HCH\\HCH\\CF_3\end{array}\right]_n$ | Similar to the polysiloxanes, but with substantially better oil resistance |
| Ethylene-propylene copolymers or terpolymers | $\left[\begin{array}{c}H\ H\\-C-C-\\H\ H\end{array}\right]_x\left[\begin{array}{c}H\ H\\-C-C-\\H\ CH_3\end{array}\right]_y\left[\begin{array}{c}H\ H\\-C-C-\\H\ HCH\\HCH\\HC=C\\H\end{array}\right]_z$ | $x:y$ typically $45:55$, $z$ minor component for vulcanization of terpolymers; excellent ozone and oxygen resistance |
| Fluoroelastomers | $\left[\begin{array}{c}H\ F\\-C-C-\\H\ F\end{array}\right]_x\left[\begin{array}{c}F\ F\\-C-C-\\F\ CF_3\end{array}\right]_y$ | $x:y$ about $82:18$; variations include chlorinated segments and perfluoroter-monomers; excellent oil and thermal stability |
| cis-Polybutadiene | $\left[\begin{array}{c}H\ H\ H\ H\\-C-C=C-C-\\H\ \ \ \ \ \ \ H\end{array}\right]_n$ | Primarily used in blends with other elastomers for tires |

TABLE 14-2.   Resilient Floor Tile Compound

|  | Parts by weight |
|---|---|
| Styrene-butadiene elastomer | 100.0 |
| High styrene-butadiene resin | 7.5 |
| Petroleum base plasticizer | 3.0 |
| Zinc oxide | 10.0 |
| Polyalkyl polyphenol antioxidant | 2.0 |
| Coumarone-indene resin | 12.0 |
| Light process oil plasticizer | 20.0 |
| Magnesium oxide | 10.0 |
| Dixie clay | 175.0 |
| Talc | 100.0 |
| Calcium carbonate | 75.0 |
| Titanium dioxide | 25.0 |
| Cellulosic fiber | 7.0 |
| Pigment | 1.0 |
| Salicylic acid | 1.0 |
| Sulfur | 10.0 |
| Benzothiazyl disulfide | 1.5 |
| Tetramethylthiuram disulfide | 0.65 |

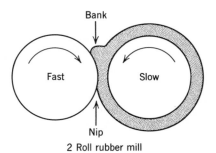

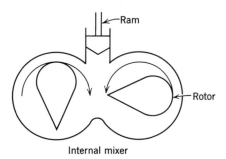

Fig. 14-7.   The 2 roll rubber mill and the internal mixer are the most widely
used items for solid elastomer compounding.

persion in the elastomer matrix. Some solids, such as resins, anti-oxidants, accelerators, and vulcanizing agents, also achieve dispersion due to their solubility in the elastomer. In mill mixing, uniformity of the compound is attained by cutting the compound across a portion of the band and then peeling the following portion of the compound from the roll and folding it back upon itself. Considerable skill is involved in the efficient operation of a mill, particularly if the operator is responsible for a variety of compounds. Processes utilizing only a mill for compounding are usually limited to small volumes of materials. Large volume processes, such as tire manu-

Fig. 14-8. No. 11 size Banbury two stories high. The modern Banbury will mix 1000–1100 lb raw materials into rubber compounds ready for fabrication using 2500 hp motors.

Fig. 14-9. Rubber mill onto which the Banbury mixed compound is dropped for further blending prior to being used as tread compound or tire carcass compound.

facture, almost always utilize internal mixers for the predominant portion of the mixing. In addition to operation on a much shorter time cycle, internal mixers afford a much cleaner method for incorporating large amounts of fine fillers which on mill mixing inevitably find their way into the surrounding atmosphere as well as into the compound. Both mixers often result in the formation of large quantities of heat. While this is not always undesirable, both types of mixers are typically equipped to permit heating or cooling of the rolls of the mill and the rotors and mixing chamber jacket of the internal mixer.

## 2. Liquid Systems

Liquid systems for the fabrication of elastomeric items fall into three general categories: latices, solvent cements, and liquid polymers. While the first two categories were well established when nature was the only source for elastomers, the third category of liquid polymers is essentially a product of synthetic elastomer technology.

**a. Latices.** Latices constitute an intermediate stage of the bulk of synthetic elastomers, both from a volume and a value standpoint, which are produced today. While varying obviously in composition, the various systems are analogous to natural rubber latices in that they are an aqueous dispersion of small particles of the particular elastomer. One of the principal advantages of latex technology resides in the fact that it is the oldest method for the fabrication of elastomer or elastomeric coated goods. Thus much of the considerable technology developed for natural rubber latices was adaptable to synthetic elastomers as they appeared. As latices are subject to coagulation on shearing, compounding techniques used for solid elastomer compounding are generally inapplicable. Usually, additives required for the compounding are reduced to aqueous dispersions separately and then added to the elastomer latex. Compounded latices have been prepared with solids content in excess of 80% and, of course, all solids levels below that figure. Items resulting from latex compounding include devices for containment of the human female form, medical and hygienic devices, and innumerable foamed objects used in transportation and as furniture.

**b. Cements.** While cements also encompass the use of compounded elastomers as adhesives, this usage is not included in this discourse. Rather, cements are to be discussed solely as solvent dispersions of elastomer compounds. Such cements are generally prepared as needed in the fabrication of a more complicated end item. Typically, conventional elastomer compounding techniques are employed for the solid elastomer and the necessary additives, with the resulting mix blended with appropriate solvents by slow agitation. A good example is the preparation of elastomer cements for the coating of fabrics. Desired thicknesses of cement can be continuously applied by various techniques to the fabrics followed by passage through ovens to remove the solvent and to vulcanize the elastomeric coating. For end items requiring a minimum of porosity, such as fuel diaphragm and protective clothing, multiple coatings of the cements on fabrics are often employed.

**c. Liquid Polymers.** While virtually all elastomers can be prepared in sufficiently low molecular weights to exhibit fluid behavior, only those liquid polymers which can be converted to an elastomeric solid will be discussed. It might appear that this could be accomplished by crosslinking, but this is not the case. While some crosslinking is desirable, the primary reaction required is one of chain extension which is the end-to-end attachment of the low molecular weight chains via reactive terminal groups. In some cases this extension reaction is initiated by the use of a second reactant, and this is termed a two-component system. After mixing, the life of such systems can often be extended for considerable periods of time by low temperature refrigeration. A second type, the one-component system, utilizes an extension mechanism initiated by exposure to the atmosphere.

While a number of applications for such liquid polymers exist, aerospace applications consist primarily in the areas of sealants and encapsulations.

Examples of various sealants are presented elsewhere in this chapter.

### 3. Additives

It is a well-known fact that both natural and synthetic elastomers are essentially useless as engineering materials in their raw state. To obtain strong resilient vulcanizates, raw gum must be compounded with several ingredients, each of which must do a specific job. Literally thousands of chemicals are used to accomplish this purpose, and it is our intent to acquaint the reader with the general types of materials used and the job they perform.

**a. Reinforcing Additives.** All amorphous elastomers, such as the commonly used general-purpose rubber, SBR (styrene-butadiene rubber), have very little mechanical strength even when they are adequately crosslinked. For example, a sulfur-cured SBR gum stock has a tensile strength in the neighborhood of 200 psi; however, progressive addition and proper dispersion of a fine particle size carbon black such as HAF (high abrasion furnace) raises this number to 3500–4000 psi when the black concentration is 50 phr. (The expression phr refers to "parts per hundred of rubber.") Typical reinforcing carbon blacks such as HAF have an average particle diameter of 50–100 m$\mu$. Other reinforcing pigments used include hard clays, precipitated calcium carbonate, and silica. To summarize, almost all elastomers require the presence of large amounts of reinforcing pigments. Without these pigments, vulcanizates are deficient in desired engineering properties such as stiffness, hardess, tensile strength, and resistance to abrasion or tear.

**b. Plasticizing Additives.** Raw elastomer gums vary considerably in toughness and normally must be broken down by mechanical mixing before other ingredients are added. To aid breakdown and to provide softer and hence easier processing compounds, liquids such as naphthenic oils or esters typified by dioctyl phthalate are often added early in the mixing cycle. Addition of plasticizers or softeners provides many benefits including rapid incorporation of fillers with minimum power consumption during the mixing cycle, and reduced friction in succeeding operations such as calendering or extruding. Reduction of friction or heat buildup is necessary to eliminate the danger of premature vulcanization, or "scorch," to the rubber compounder. Certain plasticizers such as dioctyl sebacate are added to improve the flexibility of vulcanizates at low temperatures, and other softeners such as wood rosin, or pine tar are used to impart tack to elastomers like SBR which are deficient in this property. Anyone who has been in or close to Akron, Ohio (U.S.) can detect the presence of pine tar in the atmosphere. In addition to the softeners mentioned above, a host of other materials are used. These include coal tar, vegetable oil, vulcanized vegetable oil, process oil, pitch, and synthetic or naturally occurring resins.

**c. Stabilizing Additives.** Stabilizing chemicals are added to elastomers to provide protection for vulcanizates primarily against deteriorating environmental conditions such as ultraviolet light, oxygen, ozone, and heat. Elastomers containing chemical unsaturation are especially susceptible to attack by the above environmental conditions. Thus, natural rubber, SBR, and nitrile rubber require additives known as antioxidants and antiozonants. Antioxidants fall into two general categories: (1) those which cause staining, generally substituted aromatic amines such as phenyl-$\beta$-naphthylamine (PBNA), and (2) those which are nonstaining, generally phenolic antioxidants, and typically an alkylated bisphenol. Antioxidants provide protection against the deteriorating effects of oxygen and, more particularly, the combined effects of oxygen and heat. Even saturated elastomers such as ethylene-propylene rubber and chlorosulfonated polyethylene benefit from antioxidants when high temperatures are encountered in service. While the need for antioxidants was recognized many years ago, it has only been in recent years that the need for antiozonants was recognized. It was known a long time ago that rubber, particularly when under stress or elongated, cracked more quickly in areas of high ozone concentration; but not until tires began to crack in storage in a large city in the western part of the U.S., known to have an overabundance of ozone in the atmosphere, did work on antiozonants accelerate. Generally, addition of 2 or 3 phr of an antiozonant such as *N*-alkyl-*N'*-phenyl-*p*-phenylene diamine to susceptible elastomer formulations (i.e., natural rubber, SBR) will prevent premature cracking of vulcanizates. Another commonly used class of stabilizers are metallic oxides such as magnesium or zinc oxides. These chemicals act as both vulcanization accelerators and heat stabilizers in halogenated elastomers such as neoprene, Hypalon, or hydrofluorocarbons.

**d. Vulcanizing Additives.** As mentioned earlier, elastomers must be vulcanized or crosslinked to obtain strong, dimensionally stable resilient materials. To accomplish this purpose, a formidable array of chemicals are employed. Classically, sulfur vulcanizes unsaturated elastomers such as SBR and natural rubber; however, because the rate of vulcanization is too slow for industrial applications, chemicals like benzothiazyl disulfide (MBTS) are added. The latter is typical of a class called accelerators.

Along with accelerators, yet another group of additives called activators are used. Using the above example, zinc oxide and stearic acid are activators used in conjunction with the accelerator MBTS in the sulfur vulcanization of SBR or natural rubber. The sulfur, thiazole, zinc oxide, stearic acid vulcanization system is probably the largest used combination. Other commonly used vulcanization systems for elastomers are given in Table 14-3. Generally the types and concentration of the various vulcanization systems are selected along with appropriate cure retarders so as to obtain a good cured vulcanizate in a period of 15–60 min at temperatures ranging from 280–350°F.

**e. Other Additives.** In addition to the categories mentioned above, many other additives are used. For example, mineral pigments and

TABLE 14-3. Some Vulcanization Systems for Elastomers

| Elastomer | Vulcanization system |
|---|---|
| Neoprene | Magnesium oxide, zinc oxide, ethylene thiourea |
| Nitrile, SBR, natural rubber, EPT (ethylene propylene terpolymer) | Sulfur, zinc oxide, stearic acid thiazole |
| Butyl | (*1*) Sulfur, thiazole, zinc oxide; (*2*) quinoid (quinone dioxime and lead oxide); (*3*) methylol phenol resin |
| Silicone, ethylene propylene | Peroxides |
| Fluoroelastomer | Blocked diamines, metal oxide |

organic dyes are added to obtain colored articles; reodorants or scented substances are added to neutralize characteristic odors or impart a pleasant odor to vulcanizates; blowing agents such as sodium bicarbonate or organic compounds which decompose to produce nitrogen or other gases at vulcanization temperatures are used to make sponge or foam products; and abrasives such as pumice or Carborundum are required in products like erasers or grinding wheels. Needless to say, the list of specialized additives is almost endless.

Lastly, very large amounts of fillers and oils are often employed to "extend," or increase the volume, to produce more economically articles which do not require high mechanical property levels.

## D. Fabrication Techniques

While exceptions exist, the great bulk of elastomeric end items which are produced today are formed by a variety of techniques involving heat and pressure. While some logical divisions as to

Fig. 14-10. Sheet of tire cord fabric, with rubber compound, being rolled up into liner just subsequent to having rubber compound applied to each side of the cords with adhesive applied.

forming techniques are possible, in many cases combinations of techniques are employed. As is usually the case, the best choice among fabrication techniques is the one which will result in the required number of finished articles of the desired quality of the desired point in time in the most economical fashion.

## 1. Compression Molding

As the name implies, this method consists of a mold of at least two pieces which is charged when open with the compounded elastomer. In its simplest form, the top piece or lid is placed over the loaded cavity of the bottom piece and the assembly closed in a heated press. Heat from the press causes the compounded elastomer to become more fluid and the pressure generated on closing the mold forces the stock to assume the shape of the cavity. After a suitable residence time in the mold the article is vulcanized and can be removed

Fig. 14-11. Typical tire in process of assembly. Tire plies are wrapped around a barrel-shaped drum and stitched or rolled together prior to applying the contoured tread strip.

from the mold. This technique usually necessitates the use of pre-forms of the uncured compounded elastomer and is best fitted for the fabrication of items of relatively simple shapes.

Some variations of this technique are positive and semipositive compression molding. In positive compression molding a plunger transfers the full force of the press directly to the charged stock. As the volume of the charged stock determines the size of the final item, its volume on loading must be carefully controlled.

Semipositive compression molding is a compromise of the above two techniques and results in an intermediate molding pressure and requires less accuracy in the control of the volume of compounded elastomer on loading the mold.

## 2. Transfer Molding

Transfer molding is so titled as it involves the transfer of the compounded elastomer from one place within the mold to another place. Unlike compression molding the mold is closed with the cavity, or cavities, empty. A charge of the compounded elastomer is then placed in a reservoir and force from the press is transmitted via a piston. The compounded elastomer, softened by heat, then flows through channels to the molding cavity. The process is particularly adaptable to the molding of complex shapes, and is often used in the preparation of items consisting of a vulcanized elastomer bonded to metallic components. In such cases the inserts may form a lining in the mold, or become a part of the mold during the process. After vulcanization, the item is broken from the vulcanized elastomer in the channels.

## 3. Injection Molding

Injection molding of compounded elastomers is similar to the injection molding of thermoplastics but is more complicated as a heated mold is used and a longer residence time in the mold is necessary to effect vulcanization. Stock is fed into a heated screw and barrel assembly which in turn forces the stock through channels into the mold cavities. In principle, the technique utilizes many features of transfer molding and is often highly automated. It is best adapted to high production of items of small volumes.

## 4. Extrusion

Extrusion also employs a screw and barrel assembly as does injection molding, but differs in that the nozzle forms the desired end item cross-sectional shape, but no mold per se is employed. Care must be taken in compound design to insure that the extruded item has sufficient integrity to maintain its shape during subsequent vulcanization in ovens, autoclaves, or hot fluids. The technique is highly adaptable to the fabrication of great lengths of door and hatch seals, hoses of all types, and elastomer-coated wires and cables. It is also commonly used to prepare preforms for subsequent use in other fabrication techniques.

Many other techniques have been employed. Blow molding is used to prepare hollow or sponged items where the incorporation of heat initiated gas releasing agents in a compact or dispersed form in the molding composition develops its own pressure and expands to the confining walls of the mold. Mandrel wrapping is often used in the preparation of elastomer coated rolls such as used in printing. Here the uncured compounded elastomer is spirally wrapped about the roll and is then again wrapped with a shrinkable fabric. Heat is typically furnished in a steam autoclave and the shrinking fabric develops the pressure required.

### E. Elastomeric End Items

An average of various estimates as to the types of elastomeric end items yields a number of about 10,000. Lest the reader panic at the thought of being exposed to a complete listing, the writers hasten to state that any such listing is wildly beyond the scope of this chapter. It should be emphasized, however, that the major single class item which absorbs the bulk of the total output of natural and synthetic elastomers is tires. Tires account for the use of elastomers in an amount greater than all other items combined.

Having disposed of well over half the total elastomer production, a few illustrative examples of relatively new applications specific to the aerospace environment will be mentioned here.

Ablative insulation, and its displacement of a host of other candidates as a solution to a serious problem of aerospace vehicles and weapons, has been discussed in detail elsewhere in this volume. Several instances exist, however, where such insulation must be a low modulus load bearing material capable of surviving both exten-

Fig. 14-12. Typical aircraft tire on dynamometer qualification test.

sion and compression; in other words, elastomeric. With regard to missiles, external insulation must survive extension due to the growth of solid rocket motor cases on pressurization. Similarly, dimensional changes within the motor case must be withstood without damage to the integrity of the insulation. Elastomeric materials are also used as protective coatings for numerous supporting equipment at missile sites for protection from the launch blast, with umbilical cords a particularly good example. Overall, surprisingly good performance has been realized from the specialized compounding and application of materials based on readily available elastomers. Silicones and copolymers of butadiene and acrylonitrile have been the most widely used base elastomers, although considerable promise has been indicated for other types.

Fig. 14-13. Qualified aircraft tire.

Elastomeric sealants have been, and will no doubt continue to be, an invaluable component in all types of aerospace vehicles. By function, sealants can be generally classed as pressurization sealants or as integral fuel tank sealants.

Pressurization sealants are, as the name implies, used to render the cabins or capsule of aerospace vehicles pressure tight by their sealing of seams, joints, fasteners, and the like of the overall structure. Silicone sealants in particular have found wide application as pressurization sealants in recent years as they are easily applied and are available as one-component systems, curing to an elastomeric solid from a prior state of a thixotropic fluid on exposure to atmospheric moisture. One-component sealants, in contrast to those requiring the mixing of two or more components immediately prior to use, greatly simplify the fabrication of structures. As the interior of manned vehicles must be maintained at the modest environments necessary to support life, the most serious environmental factors to be encountered are the thermal and oxidative degradation of sealants on the exterior of vehicles where aerodynamic heating and atmospheric oxygen combine to form a formidable problem. Current capabilities of silicone and the lesser known hydrofluorocarbon elastomer sealants are, at best, a few thousand hours in air at 500°F. Unfortunately, temperatures above 500°F cause an increasingly rapid rate of deterioration of all current sealants. One currently important use of silicone sealant is clearly illustrated in Fig. 14-14 which shows sealing of hot hair ducts for the modern jet aircraft, the DC-9.

Integral fuel tank sealants are used in a similar manner to render cavities within aerospace vehicles fluid tight at modest pressures. Thus modern aircraft design does not utilize fuel tanks as such, but converts cavities within the vehicles, with sealants, to integral fuel tanks. Figure 14-15 illustrates main sealants types, but additionally a fill-and-drain type sealant (actually a coating) is often applied over the entire interior of integral fuel tanks after all other fabrication steps including the application of other sealants has been com-

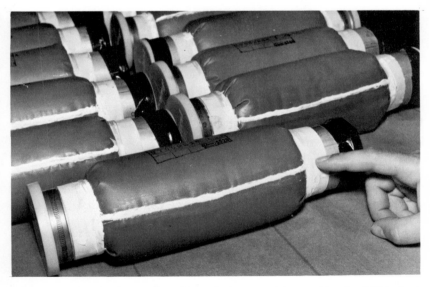

Fig. 14-14. Production sealing of hot air ducts used in new Douglas DC-9 short-to-medium range transport is achieved with a silicone rubber compound, applied in pastelike form from a cartridge. Material, identified as G.E.'s RTV-102 silicone rubber, cures in place to form a solid rubber that completely seals integral parts of the ducting as well as between sections and metal fixtures, where temperatures reach to 500°F and above. Excellent resistance of silicone to heat, permits material to provide permanently flexible sealing for the lifetime of the unit. (Courtesy of Douglas Aircraft Company.)

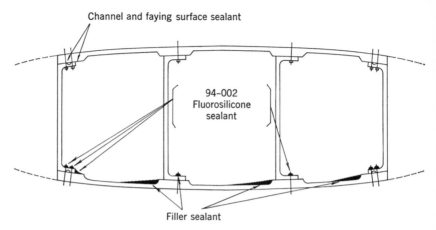

Fig. 14-15. Types of integral fuel tank sealants for the F-111 are illustrated. Faying surface sealants are applied to joining of mating surfaces. Channel sealants are injected into machined groves after assembly.

pleted. Unlike pressurization sealants, oxygen is not a formidable environmental problem as high speed aircraft will require pressurization of hydrocarbon fuels with an inert gas. Data for a fluorosilicone sealant on aging in jet fuel vapor is given in Fig. 14-16, and an equivalent capability has been indicated for hydrofluorocarbon elastomer sealants. In addition to substantial thermal resistance, integral fuel tank sealants must exhibit, at most, a modest volume increase on exposure to hot fuel and fuel vapor.

Expulsion bladders constitute another application which is comparatively new for elastomers. Basically, an expulsion bladder consists of a flexible inner liner for a tank containing liquids with a design such that the tank and liner have common exits. Thus, the comparatively simple pressurization of the volume between the tank and the liner insures positive exodus of the contained fluid. This "toothpaste tube" delivery of liquid insures a high efficiency in applications where "up" and "down" are meaningless and/or where terrestial landings are best made without copious amounts of energetic materials on board.

While as yet elastomeric materials seem woefully inadequate for the containment and hence expulsion of cryogenic liquids due to their low temperature embrittlement, elastomeric vulcanizates and elastomer-coated fabrics are preferred over plastic films or to multiple films as expulsion bladders in the temperature regions where the storable

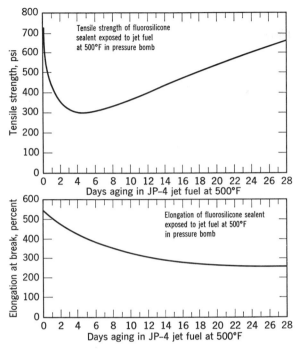

Fig. 14-16. Retention of room temperature mechanical properties of a fluoro-silicone sealant after aging in JP-4 jet fuel vapor at 500°F for periods up to 28 days.

propellant systems predominate. Primarily the potential advantage of elastomeric or elastomer coated fabrics lies in their compliance so that the possible catastrophic failure of films due to "three corner tear" on distortion of a compacted state is avoided.

Some guidance as to elastomer materials selection can obviously be gained from propellant–elastomer compatibility investigations although expulsion bladders generally further impose the requirement of low permeability.

## III. ENVIRONMENTAL EFFECTS ON ELASTOMERS

Due to their extreme versatility, elastomers are used in almost every imaginable type of media. Not only must they resist temperature extremes ranging from cryogenic to the 7000°F heat generated in rocket motors, but also irradiation, fluid degradation as typified by liquid rocket propellants, and mechanical energy such as abrasion.

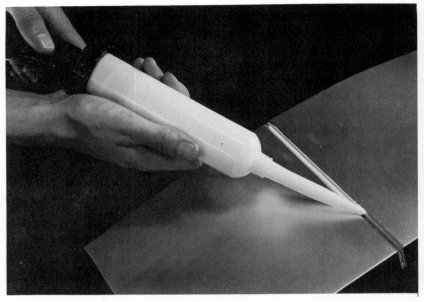

Fig. 14-17. Typical application of a filleting sealant to a seam from a pneumatic actuated cartridge. Filleting sealants are used at joints, seams, and over fasteners in pressurization and integral fuel tank applications of aircraft.

## A. Temperature

While most elastomer vulcanizates have reasonably good physical properties at room temperature, they suffer considerably when exposed to temperature extremes.

### 1. Low Temperature Embrittlement

The temperature at which vulcanizates lose their rubbery properties varies widely among elastomers. Basically, the rubbery state is maintained until the glass transition temperature $(T_g)$ of the base polymer is reached, although in practice, vulcanizates become "leathery" as $T_g$ is approached. Perhaps the most useful method of determining the lowest temperature at which a given vulcanizate retains elastomeric properties is a test called temperature retraction. The test is generally carried out by elongating a specimen to 75% of ultimate elongation, locking it in the elongated state, freezing it to essentially a nonelastic state, releasing the frozen specimen and allowing it to retract freely while raising the temperature at a uniform rate. Generally the temperature at which the vulcanizate retracts by 10% (called TR-10) is considered to be the practical limit for low temperature performance. This type of test is especially useful for predicting the ability of a vulcanizate to seal at low temperatures. Of the high performance elastomers, silicone rubber has excellent low temperature properties. The brittle point for a typical vulcanizate is near $-140°F$, and the TR-10 value is approximately $-100°F$. As a contrast, fluoroelastomer vulcanizates typically have a TR-10 ranging from 0 to $-10°F$. Brittle points for general purpose elastomers such as Buna N, neoprene, natural rubber, and SBR range from $-10$ to $-70°F$. Polybutadiene vulcanizates, with values in the range of $-160°F$, have perhaps the lowest brittle points of available elastomers. While brittle point $(T_g)$ and temperature retraction evaluations serve as guides below which elastomers are stiff and nonconformable, it does not mean that applications such as sealing cannot be maintained at lower temperatures. For example, O rings compressed to 90% in a tongue and groove flange have performed well at temperatures as low as $-330°F$.

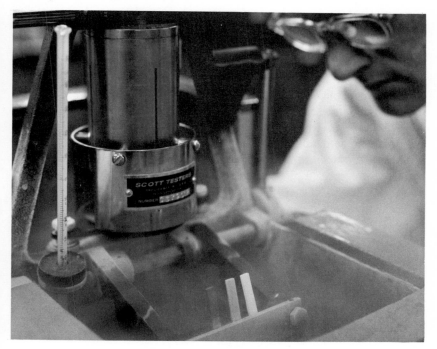

Fig. 14-18. A low temperature evaluation of molded silicone sealants is illustrated in which cold specimens are subjected to impact loading. Silicone sealants exhibit remarkable low temperature flexibility at temperatures lower than $-100F$.

## 2. High Temperature Degradation

Degradation of elastomers at high temperatures may occur in several fashions. However, in general, the two processes which predominate are thermal degradation and loss of mechanical properties at high temperatures. An important aspect of controlled thermal degradation lies in ablative elastomeric materials which are used as insulation for solid propellant rocket motors.

**a. Loss of Mechanical Properties.** For most applications, the utility of elastomers at high temperatures is adversely affected by two factors, aging or thermal degradation and loss of strength while at high temperatures. The latter is generally reversible; thus, strength lost at elevated temperatures is regained when vulcanizates are cooled.

Thermal degradation entails permanent damage and is evidenced by embrittlement, softening, weight loss, or stress relaxation of vulcanizates. Degradation of elastomeric vulcanizates is greatly accelerated at high temperatures when oxygen is present. Vulcanizates of general purpose elastomers containing unsaturation such as natural rubber, SBR, Buna N, and neoprene generally lose excessive strength and are not useful after aging for periods of as little as 8 hr at 350°F. Butyl rubber when vulcanized with a standard sulfur curing system tends to soften or revert when heated for short periods at 300°F. However, by curing the elastomer with a phenolic resin and using appropriate stabilizers, compounds capable of withstanding days at 400°F in air have been prepared. Aging in an inert atmosphere is much less severe. For example, vulcanizates of resin-cured butyl or ethylene propylene terpolmer are essentially unaffected even at 400°F when aged in the absence of oxygen. Fluorocarbon and silicone or fluorosilicone vulcanizates have the best thermal degradation resistance of presently available elastomers. When properly compounded, fluoroelastomers have good resistance to 600°F for extended periods. Silicone rubber vulcanizates age well at 500°F, but degrade rapidly if confined in the absence of air at temperatures over 350°F. Stabilizers such as magnesium or calcium oxide are beneficial to fluoroelastomers and red lead is a leading silicone stabilizer.

When stable elastomer vulcanizates are heated tensile strength also drops rapidly; however, upon cooling, the strength is recovered. Thus, loss of strength in this case is reversible, providing of course, that the vulcanizates are not held at temperatures sufficiently long enough for permanent heat degradation to occur. To illustrate the importance of reversible tensile strength, a high performance fluoroelastomer vulcanizate having a room temperature tensile strength of 3000 psi, retains only 400–600 psi at 400°F. Other elastomeric vulcanizates are no better. For example, a high quality natural rubber compound with a tensile strength exceeding 4000 psi, retains only 300 psi at 350°F. Improvements in high temperature tensile strength can be made by judicious selection of reinforcing fillers. In general, fine particle size, high structure carbon blacks are best for hydrocarbon elastomers, and carbon in fibrous form, a rather recent discovery, imparts maximum hot tensile strength to fluoroelastomers.

**b. Ablative Insulation.** One of the newer and more exciting applications for elastomers lies in their use as base materials for solid rocket motor insulation and rocket nozzle skirts. Without the use of elastomeric materials as ablative case insulation for solid propellants, catastrophic burnthrough and destruction of the rocket would occur. A typical nitrile rubber insulation compound filled with asbestos fiber and reinforced with a thermosetting phenolic resin has an erosion rate of approximately 3 mil/sec when exposed to a 5000°F flame. Silicone elastomers also show outstanding ablative performance when exposed to extremely high heat fluxes. Figures 14 and 15 illustrate the effect of heat fluxes varying from 300 to 1100 Btu/ft$^2$-in. on silicone elastomers. Flame temperatures were 5000 and 5500°F, respectively. While several

Fig. 14-19. A 5000°F flame is impinged on an elastomeric silicone ablative insulation material. Heat flux id 300 Btu/ft$^2$-sec.

Fig. 14-20. A 5500°F kerosene-oxygen flame is impinged on an elastomeric silicone ablative insulation material at Mach 3. Heat flux is 1100 Btu/ft$^2$-sec.

processes occur when elastomeric compounds are exposed to extreme heat fluxes, a truly effective ablative elastomer composition must degrade by a mechanism whereby a substantial char structure remains and low molecular weight gases are evolved to effect transpirational cooling. One method which has demonstrated promise is the addition of catalysts to the rubber compound to promote cracking of polymeric hydrocarbon chains to low molecular weight gases while leaving a residual char structure.

## B. Fluid Degradation

Fluid degradation of elastomeric vulcanizates can be divided into the effects of physical and chemical phenomena.

If a vulcanizate is completely nonreactive chemically to a particular fluid, the vulcanizate may change in volume due to various combinations of swelling due to the uptake by the vulcanizate of the fluid or of shrinkage of the vulcanizate due to extraction of vulcanizate components by the fluid. Swelling is by far the most common problem as excessive shrinkage can almost always be avoided by eliminating soluble components from the vulcanizates.

Chemical degradation is for the most part attributable to the chemical attack of the polymer network structure of the vulcanizate by the fluid resulting in crosslinking (hardening) or in scission (softening). In either case, the mechanical properties of the vulcanizate are changed. Fluids which chemically degrade vulcanizates often also induce physical degradation to the additional detriment of the vulcanizate.

### 1. Physical Degradation

By far, most attention has been devoted to investigations of the physical degradation of vulcanizates by liquid, rather than gaseous, fluids. The swelling of vulcanizates is both time and temperature dependent and will, after sufficient time, essentially equilibrate to a constant value. Common practice, however, is to report the change in vulcanizate volume after exposure of a small specimen of the vulcanizate to a particular fluid at a particular temperature for a particular time. More detailed investigations additionally include mechanical property evaluations. Volume change, however, is a convenient and informative indication of expected performance, and often data for chemically related fluids is valuable in estimating performance. If, for example, the performance of a vulcanizate is completely unacceptable in normal octane it will almost certainly also be unacceptable in normal heptane at similar conditions.

Table 14-4 is a comprehensive evaluation of 12 different vulcanizates in numerous fluids. Physical degradation (or the lack of it) predominates, but some chemical degradation data are also present.

It should not be inferred that the volume change of a vulcanizate on fluid exposure is detrimental. On the contrary, the effectiveness of seals in particular is often enhanced in low pressure seals if a modest (ca. 20%) swelling occurs.

TABLE 14-4.  Volume Change of Elastomeric Vulcanizates in Various Fluids [a]

| | Nitrile | EPR [b] | Butyl | EPT [c] |
|---|---|---|---|---|
| Fluid | | | | |
| 70 hr at room temp. | | | | |
| Acetone | +125 | +2 | +2 | +1 |
| Aniline | +225 | +1 | +1 | +10 |
| Benzene | +155 | +82 | +92 | +80 |
| Benzaldehyde | +195 | +5 | +3 | +5 |
| Butyl acetate | +115 | +18 | +27 | +12 |
| Butylamine | +102 | +30 | +58 | +23 |
| Butyl carbitol | +40 | +1 | NC | −1 |
| Butyl Cellosolve | +38 | +2 | +1 | NC |
| Carbon disulfide | +56 | +135 | +139 | +136 |
| Carbon tetrachloride | +81 | +152 | +173 | +167 |
| Chlorobromomethane (CBM) | +257 | +33 | +54 | +31 |
| Chloroform | +279 | +113 | +139 | +119 |
| Cyclohexane | +11 | +148 | +195 | +122 |
| Dichloroethylene | +159 | +108 | +153 | +112 |
| Diethyl sulfate | +110 | −1 | NC | +2 |
| Dioxane | +155 | +9 | +10 | +7 |
| Diphenyl (Dowtherm A) | +145 | +16 | +10 | +16 |
| Ethyl chloroformate | +140 | +14 | +16 | +8 |
| Ethylene dichloride (dichloroethane) | +230 | +16 | +19 | +11 |
| Ethyl ether | +44 | +58 | +51 | +64 |
| Formaldehyde | +2 | +1 | NC | +1 |
| Isooctane | +2 | +103 | +112 | +71 |
| 30% Aromatics | +31 | +128 | +145 | +93 |
| Methylene dichloride | +243 | +44 | +74 | +47 |
| Nitrobenzene | +246 | +4 | | +2 |
| Nitromethane | +75 | NC | NC | NC |
| Orthodichlorobenzene | +212 | +116 | +118 | +125 |
| Phenyl Cellosolve | +83 | NC | NC | −1 |
| Pyridine | +208 | +10 | +16 | +14 |
| Sodium hydroxide | +1 | NC | NC | −1 |
| Styrene | +180 | +87 | +78 | +88 |
| Tetrachloroethane | +305 | +61 | +88 | +59 |
| Tetrachloroethylene | +56 | +153 | +197 | +160 |
| Trichloroethane | +256 | +49 | +49 | +23 |
| Trichloroethylene | +178 | +163 | +178 | +191 |
| Turpentine | +9 | +163 | +182 | +146 |

| Neoprene | SBR | Thiokol | Poly-acrylate | Urethane | Silicone | Fluoro-silicone | Viton [d] |
|---|---|---|---|---|---|---|---|
| +31 | +18 | +7 | +201 | +87 | +18 | +205 S | +165 |
| +51 | +24 | +325 | +272 | +261 | +2 | −4 | +1 |
| +168 | +180 | +113 | +214 | +109 | +70 | +23 | +10 |
| +131 | +94 | +203 | +210 | +100 | +6 | +17 | +67 |
| +107 | +99 | +34 | +175 | +100 | +78 | +175 | +294 |
| +85 | +81 | S | +183 | D | +145 | D | D |
| +42 | +18 | +15 | +84 | +81 | +4 | +5 | +67 |
| +31 | +23 | +7 | +89 | +72 | +100 | +7 | +8 |
| +163 | +191 | +51 | +51 | +42 | +48 | +20 | +1 |
| +142 | +207 | +53 | +214 | +76 | +103 | +12 | +1 |
| +175 | +185 | +298 | +260 | +216 | +44 | +24 | +6 |
| +191 | +217 | +311 | +296 | +263 | +99 | +36 | +9 |
| +73 | +143 | +3 | +24 | +21 | +102 | +15 | NC |
| +137 | +174 | +78 | +234 | +137 | +104 | +58 | +27 |
| +5 | +4 | D | +208 | +127 S | +2 | +31 | +297 |
| +120 | +107 | +175 | +207 | +176 | +23 | +32 | +100 |
| +185 | +174 | +150 | +375 | +110 | NC | +4 | NC |
| +74 | +65 | D | +256 | +172 | D | +185 | +164 |
| +126 | +113 | +224 | +250 | +171 | +25 | +39 | +11 |
| +64 | +82 | +12 | +99 | +36 | +101 | +60 | +97 |
| +2 | +2 | +3 | +13 | +9 | +2 | +2 | +1 |
| +14 | +52 | NC | −2 | NC | +93 | +3 | NC |
| +65 | +112 | +10 | +39 | +12 | +109 | +24 | +1 |
| +169 | +165 | +249 | +255 | +257 | +72 | +68 | +22 |
| +143 | +66 | +195 | +197 | +162 | +3 | +68 | +22 |
| +6 | +3 | +39 | +173 | +63 | +2 | +25 | +127 |
| +190 | +192 | +155 | +226 | +143 | +40 | +15 | +8 |
| +5 | +84 | +80 | +192 | +85 | +2 | +2 | NC |
| +144 | +125 | +220 | +233 | +304 | +14 | +28 | +118 |
| +1 | −2 | NC | NC | +2 | NC | NC | NC |
| +178 | +181 | +132 | +212 | +131 | +52 | +16 | +4 |
| +193 | +205 | +335 | +302 | +301 | +42 | +4 | +1 |
| +150 | +187 | +29 | +108 | +151 | +82 | +11 | +1 |
| +156 | +165 | +293 | +277 | +244 | +36 | +23 | +4 |
| +187 | +212 | +150 | +248 | +152 | +98 | +26 | +4 |
| +60 | +153 | −4 | +22 | +21 | +98 | +13 | +1 |

TABLE 14-4 (continued)

| | Nitrile | EPR [b] | Butyl | EPT [c] |
|---|---|---|---|---|
| Acids | | | | |
| Acetic acid, conc. | +55 | +16 | +1 | +6 |
| Benzoic acid | +2 | +1 | NC | NC |
| Carbolic acid (phenol) | +250 | NC | NC | NC |
| Chromic acid (10%) | D | −3 | NC | NC |
| Cresylic acid | +200 | +1 | NC | +1 |
| Hydrochloric acid, conc. | +7 | +2 | NC | +10 |
| Nitric acid, conc. | D | +2 | +4 S | +4 |
| Phosphoric acid, conc. | +3 | NC | NC | NC |
| Sulfuric acid, conc. | D | +7 | S | +8 |
| Sulfuric acid, 50% | +1 | −1 | +1 | −6 |
| 70 hr at 158°F | | | | |
| Diacetone alcohol | +119 | −1 | +1 | −6 |
| Furfural alcohol | +163 | NC | +1 | −4 |
| Hexyl alcohol | +31 | +12 | +10 | +6 |
| Methyl alcohol | +18 | +1 | −2 | −5 |
| Soal sol. (conc. Castile) | +4 | +2 | NC | +4 |
| 70 hr at 212°F | | | | |
| ASTM Oil #1 | −2 | +83 | +104 | −89 |
| ASTM Oil #3 | +15 | +120 | +217 | +140 |
| Benzyl alcohol | +180 | +1 | −2 | −5 |
| Brake fluid (Wagner) | +47 | NC | +3 | −5 |
| Castor oil | +6 | −2 | NC | −8 |
| Chlorobenzene | +192 | +137 | +239 | +158 |
| Detergent sol (conc surf) | +3 | +22 | NC | +5 |
| Diethylene glycol | +3 | +2 | −2 | −1 |
| Ethylene glycol | +3 | +2 | −1 | −1 |
| Glycerol | +1 | −1 | NC | −1 |
| Linseed oil | +5 | +22 | +11 | +17 |
| Cyclohexanone | +164 | +54 | +62 | +52 |
| Neatsfoot oil | +11 | +126 | +216 | +132 |
| Salt sol (conc NaCl) | −1 | +1 | NC | −1 |
| Sperm oil | +2 | +69 | +106 | +66 |
| Tri normal butyl phosphate | +134 | +15 | +18 | +8 |
| Water | +11 | +6 | +1 | +1 |
| 70 hr at 300°F | | | | |
| Diphenyl (Dowtherm A) | D | +77 | D | +133 |
| EP Lube (Parapoid 10C) | +9 H | +124 | D | +211 |
| MIL-L-7808 | +27 | +81 | S | +112 |
| Silicate ester | +3 | +36 | D | +27 |
| Silicone oil (DC-200) | −4 | −5 | −5 | −10 |

[a] D—Indicates that material disintegrated.
H—Indicates that material hardened excessively.
S—Indicates that material has excessive softening and loss of physical properties.
NC—Indicates no change.

| Neoprene | SBR | Thiokol | Poly-acrylate | Urethane | Silicone | Fluoro-silicone | Viton [d] |
|---|---|---|---|---|---|---|---|
| +16 | +19 | +23 | +154 | +172 | +3 | +12 | +112 |
| +3 | +2 | +5 | +15 | +6 | +2 | +1 | NC |
| +13 | +15 | +466 S | +323 | +336 | +2 | +2 | NC |
| +3 | D | D | +6 | S | NC | −1 | NC |
| +11 | +32 | +260 | +266 | +404 | +4 | +2 | NC |
| +2 | +3 | D | +4 | +50 S | +12 S | +5 | +4 |
| D | D | D | +52 | D | +25 S | +2 | +5 |
| −1 | +1 | D | +30 | +50 | NC | −1 | NC |
| D | D | D | D | D | D | D | NC |
| NC | +3 | D | +3 | +36 | NC | NC | NC |
| +27 | +11 | +35 | +190 | +131 | +6 | +40 | +218 |
| +37 | +13 | D | +215 | +153 | +3 | +14 | +80 |
| +14 | +17 | +14 | +104 | +77 | +27 | +7 | +5 |
| +8 | +2 | +15 | +140 | +28 | NC | +8 | +68 |
| +6 | +5 | +5 | +33 | −1 | +4 | +1 | +1 |
| +8 | +44 | −2 | +2 | −8 | +7 | NC | NC |
| +68 | +105 | +5 | +16 | +5 | +23 | +3 | +1 |
| +52 | +30 | D | +255 | +428 | +2 | +4 | +8 |
| +13 | +10 | +23 | +116 | D | +8 | D | +50 S |
| +10 | +4 | −3 | +11 | +19 | +2 | NC | NC |
| +202 | +219 | +526 | +276 | +443 | +77 | +29 | +27 |
| +7 | +4 | +11 | +31 | +15 | +2 | +3 | +2 |
| +6 | −1 | +3 | +27 | +12 | +2 | +1 | NC |
| +7 | +4 | +10 | +37 | +8 | +3 | +1 | +1 |
| +4 | +1 | +4 | +16 | +2 | +1 | NC | NC |
| +40 | +56 | +1 | +4 | NC | +3 | NC | NC |
| +99 | +107 | D | D | +386 | +28 | +109 | +211 |
| +65 | +94 | +8 | +9 | +59 | +26 | +1 | NC |
| NC | NC | +1 | +2 | +1 | NC | +1 | +16 |
| +40 | +69 | −1 | +6 | −4 | +5 | +1 | NC |
| +138 | +72 | +78 | +158 | +234 | +36 | D | +430 S |
| +7 | +10 | +45 | +23 | +15 | +3 | NC | NC |
| D | D | D | D | D | +15 | +9 | +13 |
| S | +154 | S | +30 | D | +16 S | D | D |
| +87 | D | −8 | +36 | S | +16 | +8 | +10 |
| +34 | D | S | +8 | −6 | +35 | +5 | +4 |
| −2 | −3 | S | −3 | −9 | +17 | NC | NC |

[b] EPR—Ethylene-propylene rubber.
[c] EPT—Ethylene-propylene terpolymer.
[d] Viton—Copolymer of vinylidene fluoride and perfluoropropylene.

Physical degradation of vulcanizates by gases is difficult to describe in any detail as it is a much less frequent problem and is related to much more specific uses. High pressure gas seals can be cited, however, as a particular problem if the seals are subjected to high speed decompression. If, when subjected to high pressures, the seals assimilate substantial amounts of dissolved gas, sudden release of pressure on the exterior of the seal may generate force gradients across the seal sufficient for its mechanical disintegration.

## 2. Chemical Degradation

Problems arising from the chemical degradation of elastomers cover a time span equivalent to the general use of elastomers. By far the greatest amount of effort expended to date on the solution to the chemical degradation of vulcanizates has been directed toward elimination, or at least mitigation, of the reactions of vulcanizates with oxygen. This is readily understandable as natural rubber and the great bulk of synthetic elastomers which have been produced are highly unsaturated and hence highly susceptible to oxidative attack, particular at even moderately elevated temperatures. Even today, the bulk of all synthetic elastomers produced are unsaturated. To a great extent the problem of oxidative degradation for unsaturated vulcanizates in normal civilian use, where the only environmental component is air at moderate temperatures, has been resolved by the continuous development of a host of organic protective additives which are added during compounding. More recently, highly protective additives have been developed for unsaturated vulcanizates from ozone attack. This form of degradation, unlike oxidation, does not involve the vulcanizates surface overall, as does oxidation, but manifests itself by the appearance and progressive deepening of cracks on the exposed surface. These cracks grow normal to the direction in which the vulcanizate is stressed, and a moment's reflection will reveal that most common elastomeric items are utilized in a stressed condition. As degradation of unprotected vulcanizates can proceed quite rapidly at ozone concentrations of .025% the development of protective additives was a timely one as the smog, and hence ozone, contents of the atmospheres of most large cities has experienced a rapid rise in recent years.

The advent of the aerospace age, however, resulted in requirements which completely eclipsed the bulk of the then existing elastomer technology. Higher engine temperatures, aerodynamic heating due to high speed flight, and, in particular, the use of propellant systems of high chemical activity created a host of problems. This latter area will be subsequently discussed as illustrative of recent efforts and accomplishments.

Liquid rocket bipropellant systems consist, in essence, of a reducing agent (or fuel) and a strong oxidizing agent. Historically, the problem of elastomer compatibility with the oxidants has been much more severe than has compatibility with the fuel. Hence this problem has received the most attention. About ten years ago, red fuming nitric acid was considered as a potential liquid propellant oxidant. At the conclusion of a series of definitive, but often disastrous, experiments, the state-of-the-art at that time can be seen in Table 14-5.

In recent years, red fuming nitric acid has given way to nitrogen tetroxide ($N_2O_4$) as a storable liquid propellant oxidizer. Like red fuming nitric acid, it is a highly reactive chemical, and additionally is often a powerful solvent. The considerable advance of elastomer technology has resulted in formulations based on butyl rubber which evidence a substantial resistance to nitrogen tetroxide as illustrated in Table 14-6. It should be noted, however, that all vulcanizates employ a phenolic, rather than a sulfur, vulcanization system. Further, considerable benefit has been gained from a prolonged high temperature postcure. These few compounds illustrate that for chemically resistant applications, elastomeric vulcanizates should be held to a minimum number of components and that processing conditions alone may contribute significant advantages.

Even more recently, nitro elastomers (not vulcanizates) consisting

TABLE 14-5. Resistance of Vulcanizates to Red Fuming Nitric Acid at 70°F (CA 1956)

| Base elastomer | Kel F 5500 [a] | Kel F 3700 [a] | Kel F 3700/ Viton A 50/50 | Viton A |
|---|---|---|---|---|
| Type vulcanization | Peroxide | Peroxide | Amine | Peroxide |
| Original properties | | | | |
| Tensile strength, psi | 2820 | 1940 | 2860 | 1680 |
| Elongation | 400 | 300 | 350 | 300 |
| Properties after 7 days exposure | | | | |
| Tensile strength, psi | 335 | 360 | 315 | 95 |
| Elongation, % | 1100 | 300 | 675 | 600 |
| Volume increase, % | 41 | 47 | 58 | 49 |

[a] KEL-F-5500, KEL-F-3700: Copolymers of chlorotrifluoroethylene and vinylidene fluoride.

TABLE 14-6.  Resistance of Butyl Vulcanizates to Nitrogen Tetroxide

| | | | |
|---|---|---|---|
| Butyl 218 | 100 | 100 | 100 |
| HAF carbon black | 65 | 65 | 65 |
| Zinc oxide | 5 | 5 | 5 |
| Phenolic resin (Amberol ST–137) | 12 | 12 | 50 |
| Hypalon 20 | 5 | 5 | 5 |
| Cure (min/°F) | 45/320 | 45/320 | 45/320 |
| Postcure (hr/°F | | 16/300 | 16/300 |
| Original properties | | | |
| Tensile strength, psi | 1860 | 1740 | 1850 |
| Elongation, % | 325 | 175 | 200 |
| Aged: 7 days, $N_2O_4$, 70°F | | | |
| Tensile strength, psi | 900 | 1560 | 1490 |
| Elongation, % | 650 | 375 | 250 |
| Volume increase, % | 70 | 40 | 40 |
| Aged: 30 days, $N_2O_4$, 70°F | | | |
| Tensile strength, psi | 420 | 1250 | 1140 |
| Elongation, % | 650 | 300 | 350 |
| Volume increase, % | 75 | 40 | 35 |
| Aged: 5 days, $N_2O_4$, 100°F | | | |
| Tensile strength, psi | 290 | 970 | 640 |
| Elongation, % | 550 | 400 | 400 |

of copolymers of tetrafluoroethylene and trifluoronitrosomethane have evidenced no degradation after immersion in nitrogen tetroxide for 60 days at 150°F. Elastomers of related structure appear promising for use in contact with oxidants of greater reactivity than nitrogen tetroxide. For example, the nitrosoelastomer itself has shown remarkable stability on exposure to chlorine trifluoride, an oxidant of extremely high chemical reactivity. However, the elastomer stability has not been translated to vulcanizates of the elastomer, and efforts are now underway to obtain related terpolymers which will contain chemical groups capable of forming crosslinkages of similar stability to that of the elastomer chains.

While the single most important element in designing a vulcanizate for use in a severe chemical environment is the elastomer per se, unfortunate choices as to the vulcanization, reinforcement and stabilizing systems can easily lead to disastrous results.

## C. Irradiation

Like other organic materials, elastomers also are attacked by irradiation, notably ultraviolet light and nuclear radiation.

## 1. Light

The problems associated with photodegradation of organic materials have been with us for many years, and we have learned to combat them in elastomers largely through the use of protective fillers or organic chemicals which screen out the harmful energy. Photochemical degradation normally occurs when elastomeric materials are exposed to sunlight. Approximately 99% of solar radiation encompasses wavelengths exceeding 2000 Å (Angstroms), and most degradation is experienced over the range of 2000–4000Å. In general, the principal reaction occurring when elastomers are exposed to ultraviolet light is photodissociation of the polymer chain into free radicals. These free radicals then react readily with oxygen to form peroxy radicals which in turn decompose in various ways to oxygenated degradation products in a chain reaction. However, if oxygen is not present, a condition which exists in an extraterrestial environment, the radicals react in other ways such as: (1) hydrogen abstraction which is a chain transfer process; (2) recombination, which forms the same or a new crosslink; or (3) unzipping, which is essentially depolymerization. These reactions are largely competitive, and the preference of each depends upon the molecular structure of particular polymers. The effect of light on elastomeric materials in the presence of oxygen or ozone is similar to that of a catalyst; thus, light promotes the oxidation process at the surface of rubber and the usual result is hardening or stiffening of the rubber surface. The relative resistance of elastomers to ultraviolet degradation is somewhat similar to their resistance to oxidation; therefore, saturated elastomers such as silicone, ethylene-propylene, fluorocarbon, and chlorosulfonated polyethylene are more resistant to light degradation than natural rubber, styrene-butadiene, etc. Even the latter can be effectively protected rather easily by addition of absorbing pigments such as carbon black. Other ultraviolet absorbers, especially substituted benzophenones are effective in unpigmented stocks.

Degradation experienced by vulcanizates in a space environment is less severe than terrestial degradation largely because of the absence of oxygen or ozone. The general result occurring in vacuum when elastomers are exposed to light is abstraction of hydrogen from the polymer backbone followed by crosslinking of adjacent chains. An exception to the above rule is ethylene-propylene rubber which demonstrates chain scission. The noticeable effect of this process is softening of exposed areas of the vulcanizate as contrasted with embrittlement when crosslinking occurs. Carbon black also is very effective as a protectant of the bulk properties of vulcanizates exposed to ultraviolet light in vacuum. This simply means that since degradation occurs on the elastomer surface, thicker and/or more opaque articles will last longer in service than thin materials.

## 2. Nuclear Radiation

The effect of nuclear radiation on elastomeric materials is much more severe than ultraviolet radiation. In general, the effect on most elastomeric vulcanizates is one of progressive deterioration of properties as the amount of absorbed radiation increases. For the most part ultimate elongation and tensile strength decrease and modulus of elasticity and hardness increase. This condition arises by increased crosslinking similar to that caused by ultraviolet light. The apparent contradiction of increased modulus and hardness but decreased tensile strength is explained by the fact that chain scission occurs simultaneously with crosslinking. Thus the change in physical properties of irradiated vulcanizates largely depends upon the dynamic balance between the rates of crosslinking and chain scission. In most vulcanizates crosslinking predominates and the net result is hardening or stiffening of the rubbers. Two notable exceptions are polysulfide and butyl rubbers. As the radiation dose increases vulcanizates of these elastomers decrease in elastic modulus, hardness, and tensile strength. Elongation increases initially but numbers are meaningless as the vulcanizates approach the consistency of tar. Two practical applications for radiation are vulcanization of elastomers, and graft polymerization of monomers onto a base elastomer at free radical sites on the polymer backbone which have been induced by radiation. In general, a radiation exposure of 10–40 Mrads is necessary to achieve an optimum cure of elastomers. Examples of elastomers which crosslink when exposed to γ (gamma) radiation listed in order of decreasing resistance to molecular weight change are styrene-butadiene, polybutadiene, natural rubber, nitrile-butadiene, and dimethyl silicone. Those which primarily undergo chain scission are polysulfide, vinylidene fluoride-perfluoropropylene copolymer, and butyl rubber.

While approximately 20Mrads of γ radiation will vulcanize those elastomers in which crosslinking predominates over chain scission, the reaction proceeds to embrittlement after doses of 60–90 Mrads. Thus a natural rubber compound with an original tensile strength of 5000 psi and elongation of 300% is reduced to a material with 2000 psi tensile and 50% elongation after a dose of 90 Mrads of γ radiation. Of the existing elastomers poly(ester-urethanes) retain superior properties even after radiation doses in the range of 1000 Mrads. Efforts to improve the radiation resistance of existing elastomers have resulted in marginal success. Chemicals called "antirads" offer some improvement in resistance. These materials are similar to conventional antioxidants (i.e., substituted phenylene diamines, quinones, or naphthols) and act mainly by inhibiting chain scission by preferentially reacting with radiation-induced free radicals on the polymer chains. Synthesis of new elastomers for radiation resistance has demonstrated that aromatic constituents lead to improved stability. This is not too surprising since benzene type structures are known to be excellent energy sinks for radiation.

In Table 14-7 a summary of the relative damage imparted to typical vulcanizates of various elastomers is given. The radiation dose imparting "threshold damage" is not considered serious and vulcanizates subjected to this level generally remain serviceable. After subjection to the dose designated as "moderate damage," elastomeric articles retain questionable utility. However, upon receiving the level labeled as "severe damage," the materials are largely no longer useful. The upper limit beyond which all elastomeric vulcanizates lose their rubbery properties is generally considered to be 1000 Mrads.

### D. Pressure

Elastomeric materials must perform over a pressure range of $10^{-12}$ psi to $10^3$ psi or higher. Applications requiring resistance to the lower

TABLE 14-7.  Radiation Damage to Elastomer Vulcanizates

| | γ Radiation, Mrads | | |
| Elastomer | Threshold damage | Moderate damage | Severe damage |
| --- | --- | --- | --- |
| Polyurethane | 50 | 100 | 800 |
| Butadiene-styrene | 40 | 90 | 400 |
| Natural rubber | 40 | 90 | 400 |
| Acrylic | 10 | 60 | 100 |
| Hypalon | 10 | 60 | 100 |
| Neoprene | 10 | 60 | 100 |
| Butadiene acrylonitrile | 10 | 60 | 100 |
| Polysulfide | 30 | 80 | 100 |
| Silicone | 10 | 40 | 70 |
| Fluorocarbon | 10 | 30 | 50 |
| Butyl | 1 | 3 | 5 |

pressure are obviously found in space. Seals, gaskets, pressure suits, and propellant expulsion bladders comprise a few of the more important jobs performed successfully by elastomers in an extraterrestial environment. Properly compounded elastomers designed for space perform very well largely because loss of material by evaporation is essentially nil. Other flexible materials such as poly(vinyl chloride) require plasticizers and embrittle rapidly when exposed to space pressure.

On the high side, elastomeric O rings are required to seal hydraulic and pneumatic systems under conditions of high pressure. In many hydraulic systems pressures of 1000 psi and higher must be resisted by O rings. Unfortunately, even the best optimized O ring compounds extrude when subjected to such forces require the use of hard backup rings to perform effectively with minimum leakage. Backup rings made with Teflon and various filled varieties of it are necessarily used with high performance nitrile, neoprene, and fluoroelastomer O rings to seal high pressure hydraulic and pneumatic systems. While pressure alone is sufficient to cause failure of seals in many instances, additional factors such as temperature and degradation of seals by hydraulic fluid tend to make matters worse. Future systems will require seals to withstand pressures in the neighborhood of 3000 psi and temperatures in the range of 600°F. Obviously, much work remains to be done if such stringent requirements are to be met.

### E. Mechanical Energy

Not listed in the many environmental efforts previously discussed are those contributed by sources such as abrasion, hysteresis, and tension or compression. The importance of abrasion resistance is demonstrated to most people by such phenomena as bald tires and worn shoe soles. Engineers are more concerned with O ring wear or abraded V belts. The abrasion resistance of a product fabricated from a given elastomer depends to a large extent upon the reinforcing fillers used and the state of cure of the product. A proper concentration of carbon black, generally 50–60 phr for natural rubber or SBR, coupled with an optimum crosslink density and a minimum amount of plasticizer, results in excellent wear or abrasion resistance for tire tread stock. Abrasion is a very difficult mechanical property to define. In the case of elastomers a useful explanation is that deformations occur at points where a vulcanizate moves over a hard surface and contacts microprotrusions on the hard surface. These minute local deformations then may be large enough to tear or break the vulcanizate surface resulting in continuous removal of small pieces of vulcanizate from the damaged surface. In general elastomeric vulcanizates have excellent resistance to abrasion, especially when compounded for this requirement.

Elastomers are viscoelastic polymers and therefore exhibit characteristics of both elastic materials such as steel springs and viscous materials such as liquids. Thus, when elastomers are deformed or stretched, part of the deformation energy is stored as potential energy and part is dissipated as heat. The energy dissipated as heat manifests itself as mechanical damping, and vulcanizates which exhibit good damping are said to have high hysteresis. Butyl rubber vulcanizates have high hysteresis and are well known for their performance in isolating vibrations in heavy machinery, automobiles, bridges, aircraft, etc. Vulcanizates having high hystersis necessarily absorb considerable heat as they are deformed, and rubber parts subjected to continuous deformation may fail if they are not designed properly. Thus tires are usually constructed with low hysteresis elastomers such as natural rubber or polybutadiene for cooler running temperatures.

When vulcanizates are stressed in either tension or compression for long periods of time, they normally will not return to their original dimensions when the stress is released. Thus, depending upon the particular elastomer and compounding ingredients used, the force required to deform a vulcanizate in a given manner diminishes with time, and with the added influence of factors such as heat, ozone, or ultraviolet light can ultimately become zero. Obviously, one important group of products which cannot tolerate complete relaxation are seals. Unfortunately, seals made from high performance elastomers such as the fluorocarbons exhibit high compression set when exposed alternately to high temperatures. Closer to home, the same phenomenon is often exhibited by less than high quality rubber washers found on most faucets.

### F. Comparative Properties and Combined Environmental Effects

Table 14-8 presents a comparison of various properties of general interest for a number of types of elastomeric vulcanizates. It should be emphasized, however, that some generalizations must be present in tabulations of this type and that a well-designed and processed compound is implied. Table 14-9 presents a guide for the selection of elastomeric vulcanizates where combinations of environmental effects are to be solved. This represents the typical case for almost all selections of the type of elastomeric vulcanizates for particular end items.

TABLE 14-8. Comparative Properties of Elastomeric Vulcanizates [a]

| Property | Ethylene-propylenes | Poly-sulfides | Nitriles | Polyurethanes | Neoprenes | Chlorosulfonated polyethylenes | Propylene oxides | Silicones | Acrylates | Fluoro-elastomers |
|---|---|---|---|---|---|---|---|---|---|---|
| Hardness (Shore A) | 40–80 | 40–85 | 40–95 | 50–100 | 20–95 | 50–90 | 40–80 | 40–85 | 40–90 | 60–90 |
| Tensile strength, 1000 psi | | | | | | | | | | |
|   Pure gum | <1000 | <1000 | <1000 | >4000 | >3000 | >1000 | >1000 | <1000 | <1000 | >2000 |
|   Reinforced | >2000 | <1000 | >2000 | >4000 | >3000 | >2000 | >2000 | >1000 | >1000 | >2000 |
| Compression set resistance | G | P | VG | G | G | G | F | G | G | VG |
| Modulus of elasticity | | | | | | | | | | |
|   Dynamic | G | — | G | VG | G | G | VG | G | G | — |
|   Static | G | — | G | VG | G | G | VG | G | G | — |
| Resiliency | G | P–F | F–G | P–G | VG | F | VG | G | P | VG |
| Hysteresis resistance | G | — | G | G | — | — | VG | — | G | — |
| Flex cracking resistance | | | | | | | | | | |
|   Slow rate | G | F | G | VG | E | G | VG | F | G | G |
|   Fast rate | G | P | P | VG | E | F–G | VG | P–G | G | G |
| Tear strength | G | F | F | E | G | G | E | P | F | P–G |
| Abrasion resistance | G | P | VG | O | VG | E | G | — | F | G |
| Dielectric strength | E | — | — | E | G | E | — | E | — | — |
| Electrical insulation | VG | F | P | F | F–G | G | — | E | F | F–G |
| Service temperature, F | | | | | | | | | | |
|   Min. continuous use | −65 | −65 | −65 | −65 | −50 | −40 | −90 | −180 | −20 | −10 |
|   Max. continuous use | <350 | <200 | <250 | <250 | <200 | <300 | <250 | <500 | <350 | <500 |
| Aging | | | | | | | | | | |
|   Sunlight | E | VG | P | VG | VG | E | VG | G | E | E |
|   Oxidation | E | VG | G | VG | G | E | VG | E | E | E |
|   Ozone | VG | VG | F | E | VG | E | VG | VG | E | VG |
| Water resistance | VG | E | E | G(RT), P(212 F) | G | G | E | E | P | VG |
| Acid resistance | | | | | | | | | | |
|   Dilute (10%) | E | G | G | P | VG | E | G | G | P | E |
|   Concentrated | VG | F | F | P | G | VG | G | E | P | VG |
| Alkali resistance | | | | | | | | | | |
|   Dilute (10%) | VG | G | G | F–G | G | VG | VG | F | P | VG |
|   Concentrated | VG | F | VP | P | G | VG | E | P | P | F–G |
| Solvent resistance | | | | | | | | | | |
|   Aliphatic hydrocarbons | P | E | E | E | F | G | F | P | G | E |
|   Aromatic hydrocarbons | P | E | G | G | P | P | P | P | P | E |
|   Oxygenated (ketones, etc) | VG | VG | P | P | P | P | P | P | P | P |
|   Halogenated | P | F | VP | — | VP | F–G | P | VP | VP | F–G |
| Oil resistance | | | | | | | | | | |
|   Low aniline | P | O | F–E | F–G | F | G | F–G | P | G | VG |
|   High aniline | P | O | F–E | F–G | G | G | F–G | G | G | VG |
| Gasoline resistance | | | | | | | | | | |
|   Aromatic | P | E | F–G | F–G | F | G | P | P–G | P | VG |
|   Nonaromatic | P | E | G–E | F–G | G | G | F–P | G | G | VG |

[a] O = outstanding; E = excellent; VG = very good; G = good; F = fair; P = poor.

# IV. FUTURE ELASTOMERS

After absorbing the information presented in the previous pages, it should be clear that elastomers with greater capability are needed. In addition to the numerous problems which have been present for some time, the requirements placed on elastomeric materials by advanced weapons systems are ever increasing in scope.

## A. Requirements for Greater Capability

Obviously the starting point for greater capability of vulcanizates must be in new or improved polymers. However, some of the short-comings of existing elastomers can potentially be overcome by new developments in reinforcing materials, stabilizers, accelerators, vulcanizing chemicals, etc. In the final analysis, if one were to describe the requirements for tomorrow's ideal elastomer, they would include the conditions given in Table 14-10.

## B. Proposed Polymer Systems

While several types of organic and inorganic polymer systems are being investigated, the following systems appear to offer the most promise for greater capability.

## 1. Organic

One general class of promising organic systems consists of stable heterocyclic groups such as oxidiazole, benzimidazole, triazine, pyrazole, etc., separated by aliphatic fluorocarbon or fluoroalkylene oxide segments. The heterocyclic groups are extremely stable and the aliphatic fluorocarbon segments contribute necessary flexibility to the polymer. Inclusion of polar heterocyclic groups in the polymer chain also may offer sites for strong interaction with reinforcing fillers resulting in stronger vulcanizates with good retention of strength at high temperatures. One example of this class of polymer which is still in the developmental stage is the polyperfluoroalkyl triazine system. Hopefully, this system will result in vulcanizates with temperature resistance up to 800°F and have good fluid and chemical resistance.

Other classes of materials offering considerable promise are car-borane-siloxane elastomers; polymers or copolymers of carbonyl or

TABLE 14-9.  Selection of Elastomeric Vulcanizates for Combined Environmental Effects

| Secondary requirement | Material cost | Oil resistance | Primary requirement | | |
|---|---|---|---|---|---|
| | | | Heat resistance | Weather resistance | Wear resistance |
| Minimum material cost | | 1. NBR 2. PS 3. ACR | 1. EPR 2. IIR 3. HYP | 1. EPR 2. CR, IIR 3. HYP | 1. IR, SBR 2. BR, NR |
| Oil resistance | 1. CR 2. NBR 3. PS | | 1. ACR, FLU 2. HYP 3. NBR, PS, PU | 1. PS, PU, ACR, FLU 2. CR, HYP | 1. NBR, PU 2. CR 3. ACR |
| Heat resistance | 1. EPR 2. IR, SBR 3. NR, BR | 1. FLU, ACR 2. NBR 3. PU, PS | | 1. EPR, SIL, HYP, ACR, FLU, IIR | 1. PU 2. OR, NBR, NR, IR, SBR, OR |
| Weather resistance | 1. EPR 2. IR, SBR 3. NR, BR | 1. PS, PU, ACR, FLU 2. NBR, POR | 1. EPR, SIL, HYP, ACR, FLU, IIR | | 1. PU, OR 2. NBR, NR, IR, SBR, BR, POR |
| Wear resistance | 1. IR, SBR 2. EPR 3. NR, BR | 1. NBR, PU 2. CR 3. ACR | 1. EPR, HYP, FLU, IIR 2. ACR | 1. CR, PU 2. EPR, HYP, ACR, FLU, IIR | |
| Tear resistance | 1. IR, SBR 2. NR 3. BR | 1. PU 2. NBR, CR 3. ACR, HYP, POR | 1. HYP, ACR, IIR | 1. PU 2. HYP, ACR, CR, IIR | 1. PU, NR 2. IR, SBR, BR, CR, NBR |
| Cold flow resistance | 1. IR, SBR, EPR 2. NR, BR | 1. PU, FLU 2. NBR, ACR 3. CR, HYP | 1. SIL, FLU 2. EPR, HYP, ACR, IIR | 1. PU, SIL, HYP 2. CR, ACR, EPR, IIR | 1. PU 2. NR, IR, SBR |
| Resilience | 1. IR 2. EPR, SBR 3. NR, BR | 1. PU 2. NBR, PS, ACR, FLU | 1. EPR, SIL, HYP, ACR, FLU, IIR | 1. CR, PU 2. PS, SIL, IIR, HYP, ACR, FLU | 1. CR, PU, NR, IR, BR, POR |
| High tensile strength | 1. EPR, IR, SBR 2. NR 3. BR | 1. PU 2. NBR 3. FLU | 1. EPR, FLU 2. HYP, IIR | 1. PU 2. CR 3. EPR, FLU, IIR | 1. PU 2. NR, NBR 3. CR |
| High hardness | 1. SBR 2. EPR 3. IR | 1. PU 2. NBR, ACR, FLU | 1. IIR 2. EPR, ACR, FLU | 1. PU, IIR 2. CR, HYP | 1. PU 2. SBR, NR, NBR |
| Electrical resistance | 1. IR, SBR, EPR 2. NR, BR | 1. PS, PU, ACR, FLU 2. HYP, CR | 1. EPR, SIL, IIR 2. HYP, ACR | 1. EPR, SIL, IIR 2. CR, PS, HYP, PU, ACR, FLU | 1. NR, IR, BR, SPR 2. CR, PU |

|  | Primary requirement | | | | | |
|---|---|---|---|---|---|---|
|  | Tear resistance | Cold flow resistance | Resilience | High tensile strength | High hardness | Electrical resistance |
| Minimum material cost | 1. NR<br>2. PU<br>3. EPR, IR, SBR | 1. PU<br>2. SIL<br>3. FLU | 1. IR<br>2. NR, BR<br>3. CR | 1. NR<br>2. CR<br>3. PU | 1. SBR<br>2. NR<br>3. IIR | 1. EPR, IR, SBR<br>2. NR, BR |
| Oil resistance | 1. PU<br>2. NBR, ACR, POR<br>3. CR, HYP | 1. PU, FLU<br>2. ACR, NBR<br>3. CR, HYP | 1. PU<br>2. CR<br>3. NR, PS, ACR, FLU, POR | 1. PU<br>2. NBR, FLU<br>3. CR | 1. PU<br>2. HYP<br>3. NBR, ACR, FLU | 1. PS, PU, ACR, FLU<br>2. HYP, CR |
| Heat resistance | 1. PU<br>2. HYP, ACR, IIR, POR | 1. SIL, FLU<br>2. PU | 1. CR, PU, NR<br>2. IR, BR, POR | 1. PU<br>2. NR<br>3. EPR, FLU | 1. IIR<br>2. PU, NR, SBR | 1. EPR, SIL, IIR<br>2. NR, IR, SBR |
| Weather resistance | 1. PU<br>2. NR<br>3. CR, HYP, ACR | 1. PU, SIL, FLU<br>2. EPR, CR, HYP, ACR, IIR | 1. CR, PU, POR<br>2. NR, IR, BR | 1. PU<br>2. CR<br>3. NR | 1. IIR, PU<br>2. NR, SBR | 1. EPR, SIL, IIR<br>2. NR, IR, SBR |
| Wear resistance | 1. PU, NR<br>2. NBR, CR, IR, SPR, BR, POR | 1. PU<br>2. FLU<br>3. CR, NBR, NR, IR | 1. CR, PU, NR<br>2. BR, IR, POR | 1. PU<br>2. NR, NBR<br>3. CR | 1. PU, NR, SBR<br>2. IIR, NBR | 1. NR, IR, SBR, BR<br>2. EPR, IIR |
| Tear resistance | 1. PU<br>2. NR, IR, SBR | 1. PU<br>2. NR<br>3. NBR | 1. PU, NR<br>2. CR, IR, BR, PO | 1. PU<br>2. NR<br>3. CR | 1. PU, NR<br>2. SBR, IIR | 1. NR<br>2. IR, SBR, IIR, BR |
| Cold flow resistance |  |  | 1. PU<br>2. CR, NB, IR, BR | 1. PU<br>2. NR<br>3. CR | 1. PU<br>2. NR, SBR, IR | 1. SIL<br>2. EPR, NR, IR, SBR, IIR, BR |
| Resilience | 1. PU, NR<br>2. NR, IR, SBR | 1. PU, SIL, FLU<br>2. NR, IR, BR, CR |  | 1. PU<br>2. NR<br>3. CR | 1. PU, NR<br>2. CR | 1. NR, IR, BR<br>2. EPR, SIL, SBR |
| High tensile strength | 1. PU<br>2. NR<br>3. CR | 1. PU<br>2. FLU<br>3. SIL | 1. PU<br>2. NR<br>3. CR |  | 1. PU<br>2. NR<br>3. SBB, IIR | 1. NR<br>2. IR, SBR, IIR, BR, EPR |
| High hardness | 1. PU, NR<br>2. BR, IIR | 1. PU<br>2. FLU<br>3. SIL | 1. PU, NR<br>2. CR<br>3. IR, BR | 1. PU<br>2. NR<br>3. CR |  | 1. NR, SBR, IIR<br>2. EPR |
| Electrical resistance | 1. NR<br>2. PU<br>3. IIR, SBR, IR, BR | 1. SIL<br>2. PU, FLU<br>3. EPR, NR, IR, SBR, IR, IIR | 1. NR, IIR, BR<br>2. CR, PU | 1. NR<br>2. PU<br>3. CR | 1. NR, IIR, SBR<br>2. PU |  |

a Source: Republic Rubber Div., Aeroquip Corp., et al. Numbers indicate first, second, and third choices.

b Key: NR—natural rubber, IR—synthetic rubber, SBR—styrene butadiene rubber, IIR—butyl rubber, BR—polybutadiene rubber, EPR—ethylene propylene rubber, CR—neoprene, NBR—nitrile rubber, PS—polysulfide, PU—polyurethane, SIL—silicone, HYP—chlorosulfonated polyethylene, ACR—acrylate, FLU—fluoroelastomers, POR—propylene oxides.

TABLE 14-10.   The Ideal Elastomer

| Property | Requirement |
| --- | --- |
| Radiation resistance | >1000 Mrads |
| Vacuum | $10^{-12}$ mm Hg |
| Temperature resistance | — 425–6000°F |
| Pressure | Atmospheric to 8000 psi |
| Chemical resistance | Compatible with fluids ranging from hydraulics to rocket propellants |
| Aging resistance | Maintain original properties for at least 10 years of ambient or field storage conditions |

thiocarbonyl compounds; or copolymers of carbonyl compounds with fluorocarbon monomers.

## 2. Inorganic

Although much research has been and is currently being conducted in the area of inorganic polymers, very few systems offering elastomeric characteristics have emerged. Systems such as phosphorus–nitrogen or aluminum–oxygen polymers generally are either hard resins or lack hydrolytic stability. The most promising system for inorganic elastomers probably lies in polymers based on silicone and nitrogen.

## V. PRODUCTION AND CONSUMPTION OF ELASTOMERS

### A. Production

The United States annual production in 1967 of elastomers will just pass the 4-billion-pound mark, worth $1.1 billion. This 4 billion is not included in the expected 15.5 billion reported as the plastics annual production. Total world production of elastomers is now more than 12.7 billion pounds, while the rate of consumption is only slightly lower. Natural rubber production is now only three-fourths that of elastomers in the United States and four-fifths that of the world. All this has developed since the 1920's, at which time elastomers became available. At that time, when the foundations of polymer science were being set, natural rubber was supreme and its use was growing rapidly.

This world situation changed in 1963 when elastomer production exceeded rubber production for the first time. But in 1960, the United States' share of the world markets for elastomers started a declining pattern which continues today. This is due to rapidly expanding production abroad, primarily in styrene-butadiene rubber (SBR). Future export potential may well be restricted as foreign plants meet more of their internal market requirements.

## B. Rate of Growth

Elastomers have increased annually since the demand for production developed during World War II. The annual average rate of growth in the past 10 years has been $9\frac{1}{2}\%$. Based on industry indications, the next 10 years will average above 6%, while it is believed that the production of natural rubber cannot increase at a rate exceeding 3%.

Existing facilities for producing synthetic rubber in the United States are operated by at least two dozen companies, 8 of which account for over 80% of annual output. But only 75% of total available facilities is presently being used.

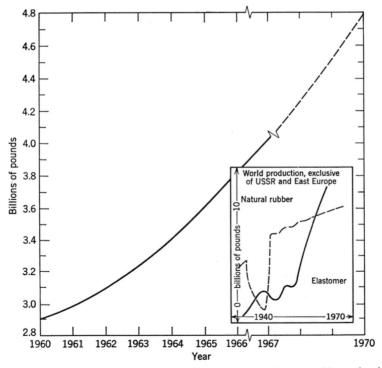

Fig. 14-21. United States production of elastomers. Total world production: 12.7 billion per year.

Wholesale prices have shown relatively little change since the early 1950's. The total average cost now ranges from 27¢ to 28¢ per pound. Average costs for specific materials are 22¢ to 24¢ for styrene-butadiene, 94¢ to $1.18 for urethane, 48¢ to 51¢ for butadiene-acrylonitrile, and $3.94 to $4.02 for silicone. Higher natural rubber prices are expected, stemming from the decision to reduce releases from the federal government stockpile to the 1965 level of 270 million pounds. The government released only 380 million pounds in 1966.

## C. Consumption

The history of elastomer development closely parallels that of automotive transporation. It started during 1923–1925, when Dr. Herman F. Mark first worked in the field of high polymers. The idea that long chain molecules existed or could be synthesized was not universally accepted. His theory suggested that the high molecular weights of certain natural polymers, including rubber, could result from aggregation of much smaller molecules. He was right. Since the study of polymers has become a science of macromolecules, thousands of elastomers have been developed, and more are on the horizon. However, only a few dozen are produced in commercial quantities.

The early growth of the rubber industry owned little to pure science in its development but reached a highly creditable technological level by patient empiricism. In contrast, the elastomer industry has, almost from the start, profited from fundamental scientific knowledge relating to the nature of the polymerization reactions and the structure of the polymers.

The automotive industry is the major end-product user. In the United States, about two-thirds goes into original equipment, replacement tires and tire products. The biggest gain in 1966 was in truck and bus tires. Most of the remainder is consumed in the production of a diverse range of mechanical rubber goods, waterproofing footwear and shoe soling materials, and various molded, extruded and coated products.

In 1967 estimated compilation by quantity shows that the proportions of different elastomers to be used by many of the approximately 2,000 United States manufacturers of rubber goods will follow the past trend with styrene-butadiene (SBR) at 66%, chloroprene at 10%, butyl at 7%, acrylic at 3%, silicone at $\frac{1}{4}$%, urethane at $\frac{1}{4}$%, and the remaining $13\frac{1}{2}$% made up of the other materials reviewed in this report. Since 1959 these percentages of total elastomer consumption have remained almost constant. The two exceptions are SBR, which went from 80 to 66%, and the miscellaneous category, which went from 1 to $13\frac{1}{2}\%$.

The generic classification of elastomers is given in Table 14-11 and a list of producers is given in Table 14-12 or as added reference.

TABLE 14-11.  Generic Classification of Elastomers

| ASTM designation | Common or trade name | Chemical designation |
|---|---|---|
| IR | Synthetic natural rubber | Synthetic polyisoprene |
| IIR | Butyl, Chloro-butyl | Isobutylene-isoprene |
| ABR | Acrylic | Polyacrylate |
| AU | Urethane (UR) | Polyurethane (polyester) |
| EU | Urethane (UR) | Polyurethane (polyether) |
| BR | CBR, PBd | Polybutadiene |
| CO | Hydrin (CO, ECO) | Polyepichlorohydrin |
| CR | Neoprene | Chloroprene |
| CSM | Hypalon (HYP) | Chlorosulfonyl polyethylene |
| EPM | EP elastomer | Ethylene propylene copolymer |
| EPDM | EP elastomer | Ethylene propylene terpolymer |
| ET | Thiokol A | Ethylene polysulfide |
| EOT | Thiokol B | Ethylene ether polysulfide |
| EPM | Viton, Fluorel, Kel-F | Fluorinated hydrocarbon |
| NBR | Buna N, Nitrile | Butadiene-acrylonitrile |
| SBR | GR-S, Buna S | Styrene-butadiene |
| Si | Silicone | Organopolysiloxane |
| FVSi | Silastic LS | Fluorosilicone |
| — | Plaskon CPE | Chlorinated polyethylene |
| NR | Natural rubber | Natural polyisoprene |

TABLE 14-12.   Elastomer Producers

| Company | Type | Trademark |
|---|---|---|
| Allied Chemical Co. | CPE | Plaskon CPE |
| American Cyanamid Co. | PU | Cyanaprene |
| | ABR | Cyanacryl |
| American Rubber & Chemical Co. | BR | Cisdene |
| American Synthetic Rubber Corp. | SBR | ASRC |
| | SBR | Flosbrene |
| Columbian Carbon Co. | IIR | Bucar |
| Copolymer Rubber & Chemical Corp. | SBR | Copo |
| Dow Corning Corp. | Si | Silastic |
| | FV Si | Silastic |
| E. I. du Pont de Nemours & Co., Inc. | CR | Neoprene |
| | EPDM | Nordel |
| | FPM | Viton |
| | CSM | Hypalon |
| | AU | Adiprene |
| | EU | Adiprene |
| Enjay Chemical Co. | IIR | Enjay Butyl |
| | EPM | Enjay EPR 404 |
| | EPDM | Enjay EPT 3509 |
| Firestone Tire & Rubber Co. | SBR | FR-S |
| | NBR | FR-N |
| | BR | Diene |
| | SBR sol | Duradene |
| General Electric | SIL | GE Silicone |
| General Tire & Rubber Co. | SBR | Gentro-SBR |
| | AU | Genthane |
| | EU | Genthane |
| | BR | Duragen |
| Goodrich, B. F., Chemical Co. | NBR | Hycar |
| | SBR | Good-rite |
| | ABR | Hycar |
| | AU | Estane |
| | EU | Estane |
| | CO | Hydrin 100 |
| | ECO | Hydrin 200 |
| Goodrich-Gulf Chemical Co. | SBR | Ameripol |
| | BR | Ameripol CB |
| Goodyear Tire & Rubber Co. | SBR | Plioflex |
| | NBR | Chemigum N |
| | IR | Natsyn |
| | BR | Budene |
| Minnesota Mining & Mfg. Co. | FBM | Kel-F, Fluorel |
| | AU | Scotchcast |
| Mobay Chemical Co. | AU | Texin |
| | EU | Texin |

TABLE 14-12 (*Continued*)

| Company | Type | Trademark |
|---|---|---|
| Phillips Petroleum Co. | SBR | Philprene |
| | BR | Cis-4 |
| | SBR sol. | Solprene |
| Polymer Corp. Ltd. | SBR | Polysar, Krylene, Krynol |
| | IIR | Polysar, Butyl |
| | NBR | Polysar, Krynac |
| | CBR | Polysar, Taktene |
| | ABR | Krynac |
| Shell Chemical | SBR | Shell |
| | SB copol. | Kraton, Themolastic |
| | IR | Shell Isoprene |
| Texas-U.S. Chemical Co. | SBR | Synpol |
| | BR | Synpol |
| Thiokol Corp. | ABR | Thiacril |
| | ET, EOT | Thiokol (FA, ST, etc.) |
| | AU, EU | Elastothane |
| | | Elastothane |
| UNIRoyal | SBR | Naugapol |
| | NBR | Paracril |
| | EPDM | Royalene |
| | ABR | Paracril |
| | AU | Vibrathane |
| | EU | Vibrathane |
| Union Carbide | Si | Union Carbide Silicone |

# REFERENCES

The following publications presented under various categories are admittedly far from complete. In most instances they represent references familiar and accessible to the authors. In defense, the authors point out that these references often contain extensive references themselves so that sources for additional or more detailed information can be readily found.

HISTORY

D. W. Huke, *Natural and Synthetic Rubbers*, Chemical Publishing Company, New York, 1961.

H. L. Fisher, *Chemistry of Natural and Synthetic Rubbers*, Reinhold, New York, 1957.

ELASTOMERS, GENERAL

H. L. Fisher, "Nomenclature of Synthetic Rubbers," *Ind. Eng. Chem.*, **31**, 941 (1939).

*Air Force Materials Symposium/1965 Technical Papers*, AFML-TR-65-29.

F. W. Billmeyer, Jr., *Textbook of Polymer Science*, Interscience, New York, 1962.

G. G. Winspear, Ed., *The Vanderbilt Rubber Handbook,* R. T. Vanderbilt Company, New York, 1958.

M. Morton, Ed., *Introduction to Rubber Technology,* Reinhold, New York, 1959.

B. Golding, *Polymers and Resins,* Van Nostrand, New York, 1959.

H. R. Clauser, Ed., *The Encyclopedia of Engineering Materials and Processes,* Reinhold, New York, 1963.

E. R. Bartholomew, G. Richard Eykamp, and W. E. Gibbs, "High Temperature Elastomeric Compounds and Polymers," *Rubber Chem. Technol.,* **32,** No. 5 (1959).

STRUCTURES AND THEORY

L. R. G. Treloar, *The Physics of Rubber Elasticity,* Clarendon Press, Oxford, 1958.

SYNTHESES

J. H. Saunders and K. C. Frisch, *Polyurethanes. Part I. Chemistry,* Interscience, New York, 1962.

G. S. Whitby, Ed., *Synthetic Rubber,* Wiley, New York, 1954.

MECHANICAL PROPERTIES

Lawrence E. Nielsen, *Mechanical Properties of Polymers,* Reinhold, New York, 1962.

Thor L. Smith, *Characterization of Ultimate Properties of Elastomers,* ML-TDR-64-264, 1964.

N. Luyendijk, *Research on Stress Relaxation and Curing Mechanism of Fluorinated Elastomers,* ACD-TDR-63-806, 1963.

COMPOUNDING

J. K. Sieron and K. Murray, *Compounding of Hydrocarbon Elastomers for Potential High Temperature Applications,* ASD Technical Report 61-604, 1961.

Eds. of Rubber World, *Compounding Ingredients For Rubber,* 3rd ed., Bill Brothers, Cambridge, Mass., 1961.

REINFORCEMENT

O. W. Burke, Jr. and B. P. Hunt, *Synthesis of Elastomer Reinforcing Polymeric Particles,* AFML-TR-65-7, 1965.

J. K. Sieron, *Pyrolyzed Fiber: A High Temperature Reinforcing Material For Fluoroelastomers,* ASD-TDR-63-419, 1963.

STABILIZATION

J. K. Sieron, *High Temperature Stabilization Systems For Hydrocarbon Elastomers,* ASD-TDR-62-1113, 1963.

VULCANIZATION

G. Alliger and L. J. Sjothun, Eds., *Vulcanization of Elastomers,* Reinhold, New York, 1964.

FABRICATION

D. C. Thompson, *Mechanical Molded Goods Neoprene and Hypalon,* E. I. du Pont de Nemours and Company, 1955.

ELASTOMERS 1677

EVALUATION
*1958 Book of ASTM Standards, Part 9,* American Society For Testing Materials, Philadelphia, Pa.
APPLICATIONS
*General*
R. E. Headrick, "Elastomers For Advance Design Flight Vehicles," *Rubber Plastics Age,* **42,** No. 6 (1961).
"Specialty Elastomers," *Mater. Design Eng.,* August 1965.
*Cryogenics*
D. H. Weitzel, R. F. Robbins, P. R. Ludtke, and Y. Ohoric, *Elastomeric Seals and Materials At Cryogenic Temperatures,* ML-TDR-64-50, 1964.
*Propellants*
N. B. Levine et. al., *Elastomeric and Compliant Materials For Contact With Liquid Rocket Fuels and Oxidizers,* ASD-TR-61-76, Part III, 1963.

John H. Baldridge, *Development of Rubberlike Materials For Applications Involving Contact With Liquid Rocket Propellants,* WADC Technical Report.
*Coatings*
"Elastomeric Coatings," *Materials and Process Manual, No. 222,* 99, August 1964.

Raymond G. Spain and Alexander V. Sanger, *Development Of A Fabric To Provide Personal Protection From Toxic Materials,* WADD Technical Report 60-198, 1960.
*High Temperature*
Marlyn V. Brock et al., *High Temperature Resistant Elastomer Compounds,* AFML-TR-65-178, 1965.
*Sealants*
Bartell, J. F., *High Temperature Fuel Resistant Silicone Sealants,* ML-TDR-64-190.

Anspach, W. F. and T. L. Graham, *New Hydrofluorocarbon High Temperature Integral Fuel Tank Filleting Sealants,* ML-TDR-64-265, 1964.
*Actinic Radiation*
C. D. Miller, *Ultraviolet Radiation Resistance of Elastomeric Vulcanizates Under High Vacuum,* ASD-TM-61-84, Part III, 1963.
*Nuclear Radiation*
Richard G. Bauman, *A Design Manual For Elastomers Used in Nuclear Environments,* WADC Technical Report 58-114, 1958.

Robert O. Bolt and James G. Carroll, *Radiation Effects on Organic Materials,* Academic, New York, 1963.
*Ablative Insulation*
L. Gilman, J. E. Wyman, and V. V. Byrne, *Research For High Temperature, Elastomeric Insulating Materials,* ML-TDR-64-31, 1964.

R. E. Headrick, *Elastomer Research For Extreme Temperature Insulation and Ablative Materials,* ML-TDR-64-287, 1964.

J. E. Wyman, V. V. Byrne, and A. F. Wilde, *Research For High Temperature, Elastomeric Insulating Materials,* ASD-TDR-63-535, 1963.
*Production and Consumption*
D. V. Rosato, "Report on Elastomers," *Plastics World,* **25,** No. 4 (April 1967).

# 15

# *Reinforced Plastics Composites*

### Albert G. H. Dietz
*Massachusetts Institute of Technology, Cambridge, Massachusetts*

### H. S. Schwartz
*Wright-Patterson Air Force Base, Ohio* and

### Donald V. Rosato
*Boston College, Boston, Massachusetts*

## CONTENTS

# I. INTRODUCTION

## by Donald V. Rosato

Industry is going through a major evolution in structural and semistructural materials. Reinforced plastics are being developed to produce the strongest material known to mankind. It is estimated that this country presently consumes 7 billion pounds of reinforced plastics every year exposed to many different environments. The RP products normally contain from 10 to 40%, by weight, of plastic resin, although in some cases, resin content may go as high as 60% or more.

Composites are tailor-made materials which provide the designer, fabricator, equipment manufacturer and consumer engineered flexibility to meet different environments and create different shapes. They can sweep away the designer's frequent crippling necessity to restrict performance requirements of designs to traditional monolithic materials. The objective of a composite is to combine similar or dissimilar materials in order to develop specific properties related to desired characteristics. Composites can be designed to provide practically any variety of characteristics. For this reason, practically all industries use them. Economical, efficient, and sophisticated parts are made, ranging from toys to reentry insulation shields or miniature printed circuits for the Apollo spacecraft.

Almost any thermoset or thermoplastic matrix property can be im-

Fig. 15-1. Made of reinforced isophthalic polyester, gas storage tanks are installed at American Oil Co. facility.

proved or changed to meet varying requirements by using reinforcements. Typical resins are polyester, phenolic, epoxy, silicone, diallyl phthalate, alkyd, melamine, polyamide, fluorocarbon, polycarbonate, acrylic, acetal, polypropylene, ABS copolymer, and polyethylene. Thermosets predominate, however. Recently, there has been successful concentrated effort to expand use of reinforced thermoplastics in the electronic, die-casting, automotive, appliance, and camera industries (see Table 15-1).

## A. Definitions

Many combinations of reinforcements and resins are used by industry to effect a diversity of performance and cost characteristics. These may be in layered form, as in typical melamine-phenolic impregnated paper sheets, and polyester impregnated glass fiber mat or fabric, or in molding compound form, as in asbestos or cotton-filled phenolic or urea molding compounds. The resulting composites have

Fig. 15-2. New power lawn mower is 25% lighter than comparable metal covered mowers. The reduced weight has been made possible through the use of reinforced plastics in the cover, housing and disc cover. (Courtesy of Structurlite Plastics Corp.)

TABLE 15-1. General Properties of Reinforced Plastics: ASTM Test Procedures

| Material | Specific gravity | Tensile Strength, $10^3$ psi | Tensile Modulus, $10^6$ psi | Compressive strength, $10^3$ psi | Flexural strength, $10^3$ psi | Izod impact strength, ft lb/in. notch | Heat resistance, continuous °F | Arc resistance, sec |
|---|---|---|---|---|---|---|---|---|
| Polyester | | | | | | | | |
| Glass cloth | 1.5–2.1 | 30–70 | 1–3 | 25–50 | 40–90 | 5–30 | 300–350 | 60–120 |
| Glass mat | 1.3–2.3 | 20–25 | ½–2 | 15–50 | 25–40 | 2–10 | 300–350 | 120–180 |
| Asbestos | 1.6–1.9 | 30–60 | 1–3 | 30–50 | 50–70 | 2–8 | 300–450 | 100–140 |
| Paper | 1.2–1.5 | 6–14 | ½–1½ | 20–25 | 13–28 | 1–2 | 220–250 | 28–75 |
| Cotton cloth | 1.2–1.4 | 7–9 | ½–1½ | 23–24 | 13–18 | 1–4 | 230–250 | 70–85 |
| Epoxy | | | | | | | | |
| Glass cloth | 1.9–2.0 | 20–60 | 2–4 | 50–70 | 70–100 | 11–26 | 330–500 | 100–110 |
| Glass mat | 1.8–2.0 | 14–30 | 1–3 | 30–38 | 20–26 | 8–15 | 330–500 | 110–125 |
| Paper | 1.4–1.5 | 10–19 | ½–1 | 20–28 | 19–24 | ½–1 | 260–300 | 30–100 |
| Phenolic | | | | | | | | |
| Glass cloth | 1.8–2.0 | 40–60 | 1–3 | 35–40 | 65–95 | 10–35 | 350–500 | 20–130 |
| Glass mat | 1.7–1.9 | 5–20 | | 17–26 | 10–60 | 8–16 | 350–500 | 40–150 |
| Asbestos | 1.7–1.9 | 40–65 | 2–5 | 45–55 | 50–90 | 1–6 | 350–600 | 120–200 |
| Paper | 1.3–1.4 | 8–20 | 1–2 | 20–40 | 10–30 | ⅓–1 | 225–250 | Tracks |
| Cotton cloth | 1.3–1.4 | 7–16 | ½–1½ | 30–44 | 14–30 | ½–3 | 225–250 | Tracks |
| Nylon cloth | 1.1–1.2 | 5–10 | ¼–½ | 28–36 | 9–22 | 2–4 | 150–165 | Tracks |
| Silicone | | | | | | | | |
| Glass cloth | 1.6–1.9 | 10–35 | 1–2 | 25–46 | 10–38 | 5–13 | 400–700 | 150–250 |
| Asbestos cloth | 1.7–1.8 | 10–25 | 1–2 | 40–50 | 12–20 | 6–9 | 450–730 | 150–300 |

many properties superior to the component materials. The most universally used terms are reinforced plastic (RP), composite, and filled plastic.

A composite is the assembly of two or more materials made to behave as a single product. Good examples are vinyl-coated fabric used in air mattresses, or laminated metal bonded together with a plastic adhesive used in helicopter blades. The reinforced plastic type of composite combines a plastic resins with a reinforcing agent which can be fibrous, powdered, spherical, crystalline or whiskered, made of organic, inorganic, metallic or ceramic material.

Filled plastic is generally associated with low-cost material where no changes in properties occur, although there are premium-priced molding compounds—melamine, for instance—that have fillers of glass or alpha cellulose. However, in the past decade it has also come to refer to reinforced plastics. Sometimes it is difficult to differentiate between the basic reinforcement and filler since their functions overlap.

A reinforcement is a strong inert material bound into a plastic to improve its strength, stiffness or impact resistance. Reinforcements are usually fibers of glass, asbestos, sisal, cotton and others in woven or nonwoven form. To be structurally effective, there must be a strong adhesive bond between the resin and reinforcement (see Table 15-2).

A filler is usually an inert substance (cellulose, cotton, asbestos, etc.) added to a plastic to make it less costly or to add body. A filler may also be added as a reinforcement to increase physical properties: strength, hardness, stiffness and impact strength. Fillers are most commonly inorganic particles, pellets, spheres, needles or powders, granular rather than fibrous, in contrast to reinforcements.

The development of reinforced polyester laminates during World War II, and the sophisticated achievements in reinforced plastics made since then have contributed probably more than anything else to today's open-minded attitude toward composite materials as materials. They helped provide the impetus to a fast-growing technology of structural composite materials (1).

Now, largely stemming from and serving Government aerospace and military needs, composite materials, including reinforced plastics, will be serving industrial requirements to a much greater degree in the next few years. As costs of some of the rarer raw materials are reduced, as new combinations of materials are tried and tested, as manufacturing skill goes up and costs come down, composites will come into an age of their own.

A precise definition of composites is difficult or impossible to formu-

Fig. 15-3. The New York State pavilion during the 1964-1965 World's Fair, held in New York, had a translucent and decorative RP roof. (Courtesy of Filon Corporation.)

late because of the scale factor. At the atomic level all elements are composites of nuclei and electrons. At the crystalline and molecular level materials are composites of different atoms. And at successively larger scales materials may become new types of composites, or they may appear to be homogeneous.

Wood is a complex composite of cellulose and lignin; most sedimentary rocks are composites of particles bonded together by a natural cement; and many metallic alloys are composites of several quite different constituents. On a macro scale these are all homogeneous materials.

In this discussion, composites are considered to be combinations of materials differing in composition or form on a macro scale. But all of the constituents in the composite retain their identities and do not dissolve or otherwise completely merge into each other. This definition is not entirely precise, and it includes some materials often not considered to be composites. Furthermore, some combinations may be thought of as composite structures rather than composite materials. The dividing line is not sharp, and differences of opinion do exist.

TABLE 15-2.   Comparison of Fibrous and Wire Reinforcements [a]

| Fiber/Wire | Density, lbs/cu in. | Specific gravity | Melting point, °F | Tensile | | | |
|---|---|---|---|---|---|---|---|
| | | | | Strength | | Mod. of elasticity | |
| | | | | Ultimate psi, $\times 10^{-3}$ | Ratio to density, $\times 10^{-2}$ | psi, $\times 10^{-6}$ | Ratio to density, $\times 10^{-7}$ |
| Aluminum | 0.097 | 2.70 | 1,220 | 90 | 9 | 10.6 | 11 |
| Aluminum oxide | 0.144 | 3.97 | 3,780 | 100 | 7 | 76 | 53 |
| Aluminum silica | 0.140 | 3.90 | 3,300 | 600 | 43 | 15 | 11 |
| Asbestos | 0.090 | 2.50 | 2,770 | 200 | 22 | 25 | 28 |
| Beryllium | 0.067 | 1.84 | 2,343 | 190 | 28 | 44 | 66 |
| Beryllium carbide | 0.088 | 2.44 | 3,800 | 150 | 17 | 45 | 51 |
| Beryllium oxide | 0.109 | 3.03 | 4,650 | 75 | 7 | 51 | 47 |
| Boron | 0.091 | 2.30 | 3,812 | 500 | 55 | 64 | 70 |
| Carbon | 0.051 | 2.50 | 6,700 | 500 | 99 | 29 | 57 |
| Glass | | | | | | | |
| E-Glass | 0.092 | 2.54 | 2,400 | 500 | 54 | 10.5 | 11 |
| S-Glass | 0.090 | 2.49 | 3,000 | 700 | 78 | 12.4 | 14 |
| R & D Target | 0.090 | 2.49 | 3,000 | 1,000 | 111 | 18.0 | 20 |
| Graphite | 0.054 | 1.50 | 6,600 | 400 | 74 | 50 | 93 |
| Molybdenum | 0.367 | 10.20 | 4,730 | 200 | 5 | 52 | 14 |

| | | | | | | |
|---|---|---|---|---|---|---|
| Polyamide | 0.041 | 1.14 | 480 | 120 | 29 | 0.4 | 1 |
| Polyester | 0.050 | 1.40 | 480 | 100 | 20 | 0.6 | 1 |
| Quartz (fused silica) | 0.079 | 2.20 | 3,500 | 1,000 | 127 | 10 | 13 |
| Steel | 0.282 | 7.87 | 2,920 | 600 | 21 | 29 | 10 |
| Tantalium | 0.598 | 16.60 | 5,425 | 90 | 2 | 28 | 5 |
| Titanium | 0.170 | 4.72 | 3,035 | 280 | 16 | 16.7 | 10 |
| Tungsten | 0.695 | 19.30 | 6,170 | 620 | 9 | 58 | 8 |
| Tungsten monocarbide | 0.565 | 15.70 | 5,200 | 106 | 2 | 104 | 20 |

[a] Boron fiber contains tungsten boride core.

Also of interest are whiskers with extreme high E and strength.

Examples:

Aluminum oxide: $1.8 \times 10^6$ psi tensile strength

Graphite: $3.0 \times 10^6$ psi tensile strength; $10 \times 10^{12}$ psi tensile modulus

Iron: $2.0 \times 10^6$ psi tensile strength

Union Carbide data of 165,000 psi tensile strength tested at 4,800°F.

Fig. 15-4. New $8 \times 8 \times 20$-ft glass fiber reinforced polyester laminated surface plywood cargo containers being used by American President Lines are designed for fast off-loading from a trailer into a ship's hold. The units are equipped with pockets for fork-lift handling, as well as hoist hooks at the top for handling by crane. They are strong enough to allow six-high stacking below deck in the ship's hold. They can also be placed on the top deck of a ship without stacking.

The constituents of a composite may assume various forms. In many, discrete units are embedded in and bonded together by a continuous matrix. In others, the bonding phase may be discontinuous, as the bonding layers of a laminate. A continuous matrix may be absent altogether if the discrete units can bend or interlock directly.

Composites can be classified in the three broad categories of fibrous, laminar, and particulate; each of these categories has several subdivisions.

Fig. 15-5. RP are used extensively by Grumman in their E-2A Hawkeye aircraft; rotodome, vertical stabilizers, bellow radome, electrical paneling, etc.

## 1. Fibrous Composites

Materials in the form of fibers are often vastly stronger than the same materials in bulk form. Glass fibers, for example, may develop tensile strengths of 1,000,000 psi or more under laboratory conditions, and commercial fibers attain strengths of 400,000–700,000 psi, whereas massive glass breaks at stresses of a few thousand pounds per square inch. The same is true of many other materials whether organic, metallic, or ceramic.

Still stronger and stiffer forms of fibrous materials are the unidirectional crystals called "whiskers." Under favorable conditions crystal-forming materials will crystallize as extremely fine filamentous single crystals a few microns in diameter and virtually free of the imperfections found in ordinary crystals. Whiskers are far stronger and stiffer than the same material in bulk form. Strengths of sapphire (aluminum oxide) and graphite whiskers are reported to be as high as 2,800,000 and 3,000,000 psi. Also, some of these materials have extremely high elastic moduli.

Fine filaments or fibers by themselves have limited engineering use.

They need support, something to hold them in place in a structure or device. This is accomplished by embedding the fibers in a continuous supporting matrix sufficiently rigid to hold its shape, to prevent buckling and collapse of the fibers, and to transmit stress from fiber to fiber. The matrix may be, and usually is, considerably weaker, of lower elastic modulus, and of lower density than the fibers. By itself it would not withstand high stresses. When fibers and matrix are combined into a composite, a combination of high strength, rigidity, and toughness frequently emerges that far exceeds these properties in the individual constituents.

## 2. Laminar Composites

Combining layers of materials into a laminated composite is an ancient art, as illustrated by Egyptian plywood, Damascus and samurai swords, and medieval armor. There are many reasons for laminating; among them are superior strength, often combined with minimum weight; toughness; resistance to wear or corrosion; decoration; safety and protection; thermal or acoustical isolation; color and light transmission; shapes and sizes not otherwise available; controlled distortion; and many others.

Many processes involving temperature fluctuations are made self-regulating by employing laminates of two metals having different coefficients of expansion. When a strip of such metal changes temperature, the different expansivities of the two metals cause the strip to bend, rotate, or elongate, depending upon its shape. In so doing it can make or break electrical contacts, control the position of a damper, or perform many other functions. These bimetals or thermostat metals are servomechanisms; they respond to stimuli from the environment to provide self-regulating behavior. They have this ability because they are composites; each metal by itself would not provide this behavior.

High-strength aluminum alloys are frequently deficient in resistance to corrosion. High-purity aluminum and certain aluminum alloys are considerably more resistant to corrosion but are deficient in strength. By applying surface layers of the corrosion-resistant metal to a core of the strong alloy a clad aluminum composite is achieved that has a corrosion unattainable by either constituent acting alone.

Window glass by itself is hard and durable but brittle, and upon impact may shatter into lethal shards. Polyvinyl butyral by itself is a tough but limp and easily scratched plastic material unsuitable for windows. When it is laminated between two sheets of glass a com-

Fig. 15-6. Filament wound, glass-epoxy, launcher-carrying case and launcher for the Army's M-72 bazooka rocket provides double duty. Taylor Corporation manufacturers these lightweight, extremely mobile, reliable weapon tubes.

posite results in which the tough plastic layer, firmly bonded to the glass, prevents the shards from flying when the sheet is struck. Safety glass is thus a composite laminate having properties unattainable by the constituents alone while offering the most valuable characteristics of each.

Some laminates have become so familiar as to be practically household words. Among them are the composites consisting of layers of heavy strong kraft paper impregnated with phenolic resins. The resulting sheet is serviceable for many mechanical and electrical purposes. When combined with a melamine-formaldehyde saturated decorative overlay sheet, a familiar decorative sheet is obtained that is widely used for counters, furniture, and wall covering.

For heavy-duty purposes such as bearings, tough strong fabrics like cotton duck are substituted for the paper. Fabric-based laminates may be further modified with graphite, fluorocarbons, or other low friction materials to provide low-friction composite bearings requiring no lubricant.

These are only a few of the great many laminates already in use and emerging from the developmental stage. Their use can be expected to continue at a rapidly accelerating pace.

### 3. Particulate Composites

Particulate composites are undoubtedly used in greater volume than any others because concrete is a particular composite. In many ways, concrete is the archetype of this class of composites. It consists of particles or aggregates of various sizes almost always of mineral materials, bonded together by a matrix of an inorganic cement originally mixed with and hardened by its chemical reaction to water. Many types of particles are employed, at least five different types of portland cements and several other types of inorganic cements act as binders.

Concrete is an example of a large class of particulate composites composed of nonmetallic particles in a nonmetallic matrix. A few of the other classes of particulate composites include: (1) metals in metal, (2) metals in plastic, (3) ceramics and metal, (4) dispersion-hardened alloys, and (5) organic–inorganic.

a. **Metals in Metal.** Many such combinations exist. Among the most common are copper alloys and steel containing insoluble particles of lead. Lead makes the metal free-machining, that is, it comes off in chips instead of long streamers. Lead in copper alloys also acts as a lubricant in bearings.

Tungsten, chromium, molybdenum, and other metals are brittle at room temperatures and normally must be worked when hot. By embedding particles of these metals in a more ductile matrix metal, a ductile composite is obtained which retains much of the elevated-temperature resistance of the refractory metal particles. The liquid sintering technique employed to infiltrate the matrix metal results in rounded particles of the embedded metal, a form most favorable to ductile behavior.

b. **Metals in Plastic.** Cold solders, possessing good strength and hardness, consist of metal powders dispersed in a thermosetting resin. The addition of metal improves thermal and electrical conductivity. Copper in epoxy may increase the conductivity by a factor of approximately $10^{12}$. High lead content in plastics acts as a sound deadener and a shield against gamma radiation. Plastics molds, used for short runs in forming sheet metal, have their thermal conductivity and hardness improved by incorporating metal particles such as iron and steel.

Among the new developments of plastics and metal are bearing materials, usually based on fluorocarbons. Metallic inclusions increase thermal conductivity, lower the coefficient of expansion, and may reduce the wear rate drastically.

**c. Ceramics and Metals.** Among the most important composites of ceramics and metals are the cermets, particles of ceramic materials dispersed in a metal matrix. Of the many combinations possible and in use, oxide-based and carbide-based composites are among the most important.

In oxide-based cermets either the oxide or the metal may be the particle or the matrix. Oxide-based cermets are extensively used as tool materials for high-speed cutting, thermocouple protection tubes, furnace mufflers, and a variety of high-temperature erosive applications.

Tungsten carbide and a cobalt matrix is used for cutting, wire-drawing dies, valve parts, precision gauges, and similar purposes. Chromium carbide's corrosion resistance, abrasion resistance, rigidity, and thermal expansion closely approximating that of steel make it useful for valve parts, nozzles, and high-load bearings, some operating without lubricant at temperatures as high as 1800°F.

Other cermets find their way into nuclear fuel elements and control rods. Uranium oxide particles are embedded in stainless steel ceramic, for example, and some control rods are boron-carbide stainless steel.

**d. Dispersion-Hardened Alloys.** In dispersion-hardened alloys, small hard particles often of submicron size, are mechanically dispersed in a softer matrix. In this they differ from precipitation-hardened alloys in which the particles are precipitated from the matrix. Because of the small size and the low concentration, usually less than about 3% by volume, they differ from cermets in which the sizes of the particles are much larger and the proportions much greater.

Although their sizes and their proportion of the total volume are

Fig. 15-7. Comfortable year-round swimming is possible under the removable pool cover made by Ray-O-Lite Southeast, Inc., of Atlanta, Georgia. Two-foot sections of 600 flat Alsynite translucent fiberglass is used in double layers with an air space between to provide both insulation and strength to the self-supporting structure. Easy assembling and disassembling is made possible by a simple latching device at top and ends of the cover.

both small, the dispersed particles largely control the properties of the alloy, especially the strength. Particle size and spacing are important, the finer the particle size and the smaller the spacing, generally the better the properties.

Hard refractory particles such as oxides and intermetallic compounds are best. A fine dispersion of such particles combined with cold work impedes the movement of dislocations and strengthens the metal.

**e. Organic–Inorganic.** Solid rocket propellants are organic-inorganic particulate composites in which a continuous matrix such as polysulfide rubber or polyurethane surrounds particles of materials such as aluminum powder and perchlorate oxidizers. The composition may be as much as 75% particles, with only 25% matrix.

Many inorganic structural materials are hard, durable and have high compressive strength but are brittle and low in tensile strength. Many organics are relatively soft but elastic or viscoelastic and tough and have good tensile strength. Concrete is an example of an inorganic particulate composite that is hard and has high compressive strength but is brittle and deficient in tensile strength. The possibility of combining organic materials with concrete to form a new type of inorganic-organic composite reflecting the properties of each has intrigued investigators. In one set of tests, for example, the addition of 10–20% by weight (of the portland cement only) of styrene-butadiene, polyvinylidene chloride, polyvinyl acetate, acrylic, and asphalt, with 2–10% entrained air, resulted in increases of compressive strength as high as 100% and tensile strength increases as high as 50%, with in some instances complete suppression of scaling after 30 or more cycles of freezing and thawing in calcium chloride solution.

### 4. The Future

Composite materials, old in principle, are experiencing intensive research and rapid development to meet the extreme demands of today's technology in space, the depths, and on the surface of the earth. Many problems remain to be solved, science and engineering will be taxed to the utmost to find the answers, but the performance already attained is a bright promise for the future.

### B. Reinforcing Materials

The large-production reinforcing agents used today are glass, cotton, cellulosic fiber, sisal, polyamide and other synthetic fibers, jute, and asbestos. Specialty agents are carbon, graphite, boron, whiskers, and steel, which are already technically important. They all offer wide variations in cost, composition, and properties.

Glass fibers are widely used in many forms for producing different commercial and industrial products, also for parts in space, aircraft, surface water and underwater vehicles. The older and still polular form is E-glass. Now S-glass produces higher strength properties. More advanced forms of glass fiber are ahead.

Paper of three types are in common use: kraft paper (high strength when compared to other papers), alpha paper (electrical use), and rag paper (low moisture pickup with good machinability).

Cotton fabrics provide combinations of different properties such as strength, weather resistance, machinability and toughness. Thickness and weight provide important controls on properties.

Polyamide (nylon) reinforcements most often is fabric and provides excellent electrical grade laminates for conventional industrial use. It has low water absorption, good abrasion resistance and resistance to many chemicals.

Asbestos offers strength, heat and flame resistance, heat ablation and chemical resistance.

Carbon and graphite fibers are made by the pyrolysis of certain naturally occurring and man-made fibers, such as regenerated cellulose (rayon) fibers. A wide range of physical, mechanical and chemical properties may be obtained dependent on amount of dehydration. In 1966, Union Carbide Corporation, produced a commercially available graphite filament known as Thornel. This product is one of the most structurally efficient reinforcements. Unlike any other reinforcement,

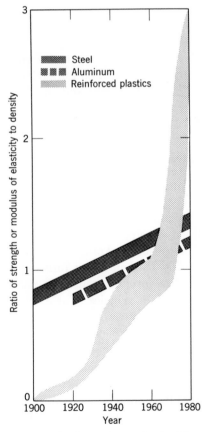

Fig. 15-8. Structural properties trends of reinforced plastics, steel, and aluminum.

it retains its 400,000 psi tensile strength when tested up to a temperature of 4800°F. The porous nature of graphite fibers can open up a new method to produce preimpregnated sheet materials.

Boron in high modulus and strength properties is available with this type of fiber. A vapor deposition process is the principal method to produce boron filaments, using $\frac{1}{2}$ mil tungsten wire as a plating substrate.

Steel, in the form of wire, is beginning to be a factor. Research on wire reinforcement is presently being conducted by Brunswick Corporation, U.S. Steel Company and National Standard Company. Metallic filaments with modulus of elasticity of $30 \times 10^6$ psi are being evaluated.

## C. Fillers

Fillers used in large quantities to reinforce plastics are alumina (aluminum oxide), asbestos, calcium carbonate, calcium silicate, cellulose flock, cotton (different forms), glass fiber, glass beads, glass spheres, graphite, iron oxide powder, mica, quartz, sisal, silicon carbide, titanium oxide, and tungsten carbide. Choice of filler varies and depends to a great extent upon the requirements of the end item and

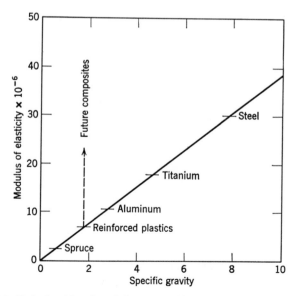

Fig. 15-9. Relationship of modulus to specific gravity of various materials.

method of fabrication. Fillers are also used with long fiber reinforcements.

Fillers offer a variety of benefits: increased strength and stiffness, reduced cost, shrinkage reduction, exothermic heat reduction, thermal expansion coefficient reduction, improved heat resistance, slightly improved heat conductivity, improved surface appearance, reduced porosity, improved wet strength, reduced crazing, improved fabrication mobility, increased viscosity, improved abrasion resistance and impact strength. Fillers also can have disadvantages. They may limit the method of fabrication, inhibit cure of certain resins, and shorten pot life of the resin.

## D. Progress with Glass

More than one billion pounds of glass fiber of all types are used annually (2). The major types used have the following composition: E-glass with 52% silicon dioxide, 18% calcium oxide, 14% aluminum oxide, 11% boron oxide, 4% magnesium oxide, and 1% sodium and potassium oxide and S-glass (previously called AF X-994 or AF S-994) with 65% silicon dioxide, 25% aluminum oxide, and 10% magnesium oxide.

The SPI has the only qualified and published statistics on glass fiber-reinforced plastics. The Society estimates 1965 production was at least 340 million pounds of glass-reinforced plastics. Another industry source shows glass reinforced plastic transparent panels production to be 80 million pounds or 130 million square feet, with Filon Corporation manufacturing approximately 25%. The International Filon Producers Association, made up of producers in 11 countries, estimates worldwide sales of 350 million square feet will approach $100 million. The panels are used in housing, industrial and commercial construction.

Consumption of glass composites by the boat industry is another source of limited consumption knowledge. In 1965, the small boat market of 12–24 ft, predominately glass RP, was expected to be 300,000 to 400,000 units, or $166 million. No one company dominates this market. In fact, the top eight manufacturers appear to have less than 30% of the market. One of these companies, using 2 million pounds of glass and 3 million pounds of polyester annually, does not report these figures to any association. Only two of the companies do any respectable reporting. The Navy, Army, and Coast Guard are interested in standardizing RP boats up to 50 ft. Designs are now being conceived for minesweepers 190 ft long and trawlers 110 ft long.

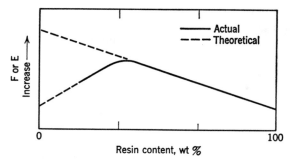

Fig. 15-10. Effect of matrix content on strength (F) or elastic moduli (E) of reinforced plastics.

Military use of RP—filament wound grommets for artillary shells, for example—is extensive, but in 95% of the applications, consumption is not reported to any organization.

## 1. Glass Fabric

As the reinforced plastics business continues its growth, its early methods and materials are often taken for granted. Glass fabric and reinforced plastics, for example, are nearly synonymous, having been used in combination for more than two decades. It provides high strength, dimensional stability, flame resistance, resistance to oils and acids, corrosion and rot resistance, high thermal conductivity, good electrical properties.

Once glass fabric has been chosen as the substrate, it is essential that the correct fabric be specified. Numbers and types of yarns, weight, thickness, porosity and weave pattern can be altered to achieve endless variations. For this reason, a thorough understanding of desirable end use properties and glass fabric parameters can save the engineer time and effort in designing his product.

**a. High Pressure Laminates.** These are composites molded at specific temperatures and presures in the range of 400 psi and 1000 psi. Resins normally used are epoxy, phenolic, silicone, and melamine.

Finish selection is critical and should assure optimum bonding of organic matrix to inorganic substrate at the interface; the finish is actually a combination of heat cleaning and coupling agents. Typical heat cleaning methods are numbers 111, 112, and 210; typical coupling agents are amino silanes, vinyl silanes, epoxy silanes, and methacrylic chronic chlorides.

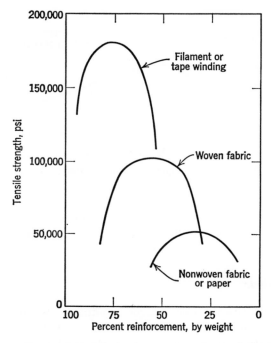

Fig. 15-11. Strength of reinforced plastics versus amount of glass reinforcement and type reinforcement.

**b. Low Pressure Laminates.** These are made at pressures ranging from atmospheric to 400 psi. Polyester and epoxy resins are most often used; phenolics find accasional use. In addition to wet layup, vacuum and pressure bag molding are frequently used; moreover, these methods are often combined. There are more than 300 numbers of fabrics, woven roving, and glass tape styles used to reinforce a variety of resins.

**c. Coated and Impregnated Fabrics.** The flexible coated laminated and impregnated products are an important market for glass fabric. Glass fabric may be used to reinforce themoplastics (vinyls) or the natural and synthetic elastomers. Calendering sheet stock onto glass fabric and application by a doctor blade are the most familiar methods used in the coating industry. Whether in high pressure laminates, low pressure laminates, or as a substrate for flexible coatings, glass fabrics increase the versatility of any matrix.

# E. Other Reinforcements in Vast Usage

Asbestos—2 billion pounds—goes into pipe, building panel, heat cal tiles, and automotive parts. Principal types used are chrysotile and rockets, brake linings, roofing compositions, gaskets, packings, acoustical tiles and automotive parts. Principal types used are chrysotile and crocidolite in fabric, felt, mat, or loose form.

Little data exist on consumption of cellulosic paper, cotton, and polyamide (nylon). The amount used could range from 3 to 4 billion bounds. NEMA is the only established group that develops reliable data but only pertaining to its 19 member companies. High pressure laminates, predominantly flat sheets, could total 40 million pounds or $120 million for industrial use (1964: 33 million pounds or $96 million). Of this, the decorative will account for approximately 100 million sq. ft (0.045 in.–0.100 ft thick) or $50 million. Most of the industrial high pressure laminates are used for metal clad printed circuit boards.

Another important growth material is sisal, both U.S. and foreign grown, used in combination with thermosets and thermoplastics in the automotive, appliance and luggage industries. Of particular importance is vinyl-sisal compound used in luggage. Many plants are enlarging to meet the growing industrial and decorative RP business.

# F. Applications

A few of the important applications which have caused more material to be used include television, business machines, wire ducts, electrical switch-gear, electrical control panels, and computers, with many complicated printed circuits, housings, insulators and other parts. More ball bearing retainers are being used in heavy- and lightweight machines, such as in steel rolling mills, dental drills, and sophisticated aerospace guidance systems.

Corrosion resistance has expanded its use for chemical fume ducts, tanks and pipes. Heat insulation parts are used in automobiles, appliances, missiles and even tin plating rollers outperform the steel or laminated rolls alone.

Automobiles, trucks and tank cars use reinforced thermosets and thermoplastics on interiors and exteriors. Transportation pods for aircraft, food trays, luggage, animal housing and cages represent growth industries. City transportation vehicles need reinforced plastics for laminated interior seats, partitions and doors to give better service and low maintenance. Boston and Philadelphia city transit authorities are doing what other cities are doing in replacing upholstered seats with RP. New York City, in 1958, started experimenting with reinforced polyester seats for its 6700 subway cars and 2200 buses. Now 1100 subway cars are being refitted with fiber glass reinforced polyester seats using Hooker's Hetron resin.

Underground tanks for storage of gasoline and diesel fuels may one day be one of the largest RP markets. Installation and replacement costs, compared to steel tanks, are making the tanks become very competitive. A major step forward was the recent contract by Pure Oil Company to Owens-Corning Fiberglas Corporation for 17 tanks, all with Underwriters' Laboratories approval.

To construct large capacity tanks on site, filament winding is an answer for the chemical and agricultural industries. To wit: the 30,000 gallon tank of Justin Enterprises and 36,000 gallon tank of Northwest Industries. Government requirements use up millions of pounds of glass-reinforced filament wound grommets for artillery shells. Aeroget-General Corporation, in conjunction with the Navy, investigated the feasibility study of producing RP submarine hulls. Submerged in the ocean for 3 years at a depth of 5,300 feet, the test cylinders retained burst strengths within 3% of original strength.

Future high-speed aircraft flying at low altitudes will require smooth aerodynamic surfaces, corrosion resistance, ease of maintenance or repair and high resistance to impact damage that can be produced from sand and gravel set in motion by down wash impingement on noncommercial landing areas. At present, RP stands out as the most suitable material to meeet these criteria. Another advantage of the plastic is weight saving; 27% occurs when similar designs are used for aluminum and plastic. Extra performance and 25% weight saving can occur just in the helicopter rotor blades.

Douglas Aircraft Company engineers, in a design feasibility study, showed that an all glass fiber RP airplane is superior in strength and performance to conventional metal types. Design was based on a lightweight, low-wing monoplane. RP structural components and skin panels have been in use by Douglas and other airplane manufacturers since 1943; even though this concept is not new, it could now have potential new merit, based on present structural, environment, cost, and industry requirements.

Development and marketing of preimpregnated B-stage RP mats are now on the increase. The dream of materials suppliers, fabricators, and users is to use mats in automated operations that mass-produce parts on a par with stamping sheet metal. Matched die molding extru-

TABLE 15-3.  Statistical Summary: 2,898 Recreational Stock Boat Models on United States Market for 1965 [a]

| Type | No. of builders | No. of models | % of total models | With berths | % with berths | Price range ($) | Size range |
|---|---|---|---|---|---|---|---|
| Inboard boats | 80 | 483 | 16.7 | 375 | 77.6 | 1,995 to 260,000 | 15–75 ft |
| Stern drive (I/O) boats | 95 | 392 | 13.5 | 151 | 38.5 | 525 to 33,000 | 13 ft 7 in. to 37 ft 4 in. |
| Outboard boats | 125 | 870 | 30.0 | 80 | 9.2 | 79 to 5,875 | 7 ft 6 in. to 24 ft |
| Cruising sailboats | 80 | 248 | 8.5 | 244 | 98.4 | 1,595 to 150,000[b] | 15 ft to 64 ft |
| Day and one-design sailboats | 107 | 342 | 11.8 | 32 | 9.4 | 99 to 9,800[b] | 7 ft 8 in. to 32 ft 5 in. |
| House and pontoon boats | 25 | 118 | 4.1 | 45 | 38.1 | 325 to 29,000 | 12 ft to 65 ft |
| Rowboats, dinghies, canoes, and specialty boats | 78 | 445 | 15.4 | — | — | 24 to 1,871 | 5 ft 8 in. to 34 ft |
| Totals | 590[c] | 2,898 | 100 | 927 | 100 | 24 to 260,000 | 5 ft 8 in. to 75 ft |

[a] As compiled by the editors of *Popular Boating*.
[b] Sailboats prices in most cases less sails.
[c] 381 unduplicated companies.

sion and molding operations could be used. Since the late 1940's, various prepreg mats have been produced, but due to high costs they were never successful. More recently, asbestos RP was successfully produced in limited degrees by Raybestos-Manhattan Inc. and Johns-Manville Corp. Newer glass fiber products in the past months have been produced: U.S. Rubber Company now has its Vibrin polyester in mat or rope form, and the Standard Oil Company (Ohio) has structoform polyester in sheet form, based on a resin system containing no styrene.

Industry and government specifications will provide more quality-controlled RP parts. The FHA Underwriters letter No. 1995, dated August 11, 1965, extends inspection of RP bathtubs. Specification MIL-T-253-63B for filament wound pressure vessels with 100 to 2,500 cu. in. volume developed an approved source for the first time

TABLE 15-4.   Summary of 2,898 U.S. Stock Boat Models for 1965 by Construction Material [a]

| Type | Total no. of models | Number of models and % by construction material | | | | | | |
|---|---|---|---|---|---|---|---|---|
| | | Reinforced plastics | Aluminum | Wood | Plywood | Wood and glass | Steel | Others |
| Inboard boats | 483 | 111 (23.0%) | 15 (3.1%) | 213 (44.1%) | 99 (20.5%) | 12 (2.5%) | 26 (5.4%) | 7 (1.4%) |
| Stern drive (I/O) boats | 392 | 263 (67.1%) | 39 (9.9%) | 17 (4.3%) | 67 (17.1%) | 3 (.8%) | — | 3 (.8%) |
| Outboard boats | 870 | 481 (55.3%) | 201 (23.1%) | 64 (7.4%) | 107 (12.3%) | 9 (1.0%) | 3 (0.3%) | 5 (0.6%) |
| Cruising sailboats | 248 | 145 (58.5%) | — | 48 (19.3%) | 24 (9.7%) | 24 (9.7%) | — | 7 (2.8%) |
| Day and one design sailboats | 342 | 225 (65.8%) | — | 24 (7.0%) | 68 (19.9%) | 10 (3.0%) | — | 15 (4.3%) |
| House and pontoon boats | 118 | 6 (5.1%) | 24 (20.4%) | — | — | 5 (4.2%) | 71 (60.2%) | 12 (10.1%) |
| Rowboats, dinghies, canoes, and specialty boats | 445 | 133 (29.9%) | 178 (40.0%) | 6 (1.3%) | 33 (7.4%) | 2 (.4%) | 11 (2.5%) | 82 (18.5%) |
| Totals | 2,898 | 1,364 (47.1%) | 457 (15.8%) | 372 (12.8%) | 398 (13.7%) | 65 (2.3%) | 111 (3.8%) | 131 (4.5%) |

[a] As compiled by the editors of *Popular Boating*.

(Whittaker Corporation). NEMA issued the first industry standard for filament wound tubes (LI 10-1965). Other NEMA standards are HSI-1965 on household electric dishwashers, LI 4-1965 on hot peel strength of laminates and TC 1-1965 on plastic ducts and duct fittings.

Reinforced plastics, or composites, utilizing stronger and higher modulus of elasticity fibers in a suitable matrix offer promise of a structural material with mechanical properties substantially better than those of metals. Military and space needs provide the impetus for research and development which in turn will accrue to commercial and industrial markets.

Government-sponsored research is producing more efficient structural materials for Air Force aerospace vehicles, Navy deep submersibles, Army gun barrels and NASA satellites. To increase heat-resistant properties, polyimide and polybenzamidazole resins, which can operate from 500 to 1,000°F, are now available.

Composites with exceptionally high strength and modulus are on the threshold of a spectacular future, but the cost is high. Estimates of development costs, in total, are in the billion dollars. Some fibers cost $200 to $2,000 per pound. But eventually these new materials are expected to be economically useful in commercial applications. This success will have to be accompanied by new concepts of design and manufacture. Design in metals can draw on a huge 100 year reservoir of knowledge and experience which, in many cases, has been compiled in engineering handbooks. The most structurally efficient materials, compared to any other material, are reinforced plastics.

## G. Size of Market

Total production of all types of reinforced plastics (or composites) is not well defined or understood by industry. The different statistics available from industry associations and the U.S. Department of Commerce are very limited in direct identification of reinforced materials. Many companies, including those who use the major portion of RP, are not members of these associations and do not report their consumption. Most of the identification in reports to the government is by the individual component, such as phenolic resin or cellulose paper, and by end product: electrical connector or luggage, for instance.

The major reasons for incomplete statistics are proprietary company positions and captive facilities with captive markets: automotive, farm equipment, building, transportation, furniture, electronics, aircraft, marine, missile, and chemical industries. Many companies are in the unique position of producing their own resin, weaving their own fabric or making their own papers.

Nevertheless, it is predicted that growth of this industry will climb from the 1966 total of 7 billion pounds in the United States. This prediction is based on various industry surveys and estimates of The Society of Plastics Industry, Inc. (SPI) (see Table 15–5), National Electrical Manufacturers Association (NEMA), Asebestos Textile Institute (ATI), and Institute of Electrical and Electronics Engineers (IEEE).

## H. Ceramoplastics Composites

Falling between organic plastics and ceramics in heat resistance, a relatively new class of composites gives a hint of the versatility to be expected from new types of composites which will advance the field of design beyond the capabilities of existing materials.

As explained by J. Harry DuBois (1) the upper thermal limit of organic plastics presently lies with the polyimides, TFE fluorocarbons, silicones, and G-10 epoxy-glass laminates. These materials may give satisfactory short time performance at temperatures in the 500–700°F (260–370°C) range, after which they deteriorate rapidly. Above this temperature range, some applications can be served by the cement-asbestos or phosphoasbestos cold mold compounds, provided dimensional control and stability are not too critical. These latter materials may have adequate arc resistance for many applications but may not be used in high radiation fields; they do have high moisture absorption. None of the organic plastics has absolute dimensional stability and most have high thermal expansion rates.

The silicones of Dow and GE and the glass resins of Owens-Illinois are leading the way into high temperature composites with inorganic fillers. In this process the resin is converted from an organic to an inorganic by a post molding firing operation. Such products have shown thermal endurance up to 2500°F.

At the high upper limit of thermal endurance, a variety of ceramics is available to provide extremely high temperature capability and arc and radiation resistance. Another desirable plus value is gained from berylium oxide ceramic which, in addition to having high thermal endurance (4000°F or 2205°C) offers heat conductivity as good as brass (120 Btu-ft/ft²-hr-°F) with an associated value of high thermal shock resistance. These ceramics, however, cannot be molded closely to size and are very expensive to machine.

Between the organic plastics and the ceramics are the ceramoplastics or glass-bonded mica products. Many of these unique combinations of inorganic materials have been serving industry since 1919. The develoment of synthetic mica in 1957 upgraded their temperature limit and improved machinability and moldability. Parts molded of glass-bonded mica will operate satisfactorily at 750°F (400°C) continuously. They also are arc and radiation resistant and have a thermal expansion that matches stainless steel for squibbs, hermetic seals, headers, and similar products.

Fig. 15-12. Industrial laminated plastic materials for virtually every mechanical application and a complete line of fabricated parts are made by Synthane Corporation, leading manufacturer and largest fabricator of laminates in the U.S.

A ceramic material with the moldability of plastics, the dimensional stability and thermal expansion of stainless steel, and the electrical properties of low loss organic plastics is a truly versatile product. Using beryllia fillers, the moldability, insert inclusion, and electricals are maintained and high thermal conductivity (as good as zinc) is attained. The molding of glass-bonded ferrites facilitates production of RF absorber products. Alternate glasses give various dielectric properties with $K$ values as high as 30.

Typical of the new applications for glass-bonded mica is the substrate in the carrier board for the Bell System solid state (ESS) switching program. The heat of this revolutionary new telephone switching system is a glass-bonded mica insulating carrier board. High dimensional stability—even under extremes of temperature and humidity—made the choice of glass-bonded mica for this job a natural.

Squibbs for the missile program are now molded complete and offer indefinite shelf life, perfect seals, zero moisture absorption, and the highest electrical breakdown stability.

Other applications of glass-bonded mica include instrument and computer components that must have absolute dimensional stability, high frequency induction coil forms, pyrometry insulation, internal vacuum tube components, arc chutes, fire detection and fire starting components, heater supports, radiation structural and functional components, high altitude and high voltage components, hermetic seals and headers, plus all ceramic products that must be fabricated by machining. Glass-bonded mica is a machinable and moldable-with-inserts composite which has ceramic properties and plastics moldability for a wide variety of applications.

## II. FIBER REINFORCED COMPOSITE MATERIALS ENGINEERING ANALYSIS

### by Albert G. H. Dietz

### A. Design Theory

Fibrous reinforced plastics differ from many other engineering materials because they combine two essentially different materials, fibers and synthetic resin, into a single composite. In this they are somewhat analogous to reinforced concrete which combines concrete and steel, but in reinforced plastics the fibers are generally much more evenly distributed throughout the mass and the ratio of fibers to resin is much higher than the ratio of steel to concrete. In the design of fibrous reinforced plastics, it is necessary to take into account the combined action of fiber and resin. Sometimes the combination can be considered to be homogeneous and, therefore, to be similar to engineering materials like metal but, in other cases, homogeneity cannot be assumed and it is necessary to take into account the fact that two widely dissimilar materials have been combined into a single unit (3).

In designing fibrous reinforced plastics, certain important assumptions are made. The first and most fundamental is that the two materials act together and that the stretching, compression, and twisting of fibers and of resin under load is the same, that is, the strains in fiber and resin are equal. This assumption implies that a good bond exists between resin and fiber to prevent slippage between them and to prevent wrinkling of the fiber.

The second major assumption is that the material is elastic, that is, strains are directly proportional to the stresses applied, and when a load is removed the deformation disappears. In engineering terms the material is assumed to obey Hooke's Law. This assumption is probably a close approximation of the actual behavior in direct stress below the proportional limit, particularly in tension, if the fibers are stiff and elastic in the Hookean sense and carry essentially all of the stress. The assumption is probably less valid in shear where the resin carries a substantial portion of the stress. The resin may undergo plastic flow leading to creep or to relaxation of stress, especially when stresses are high.

More or less implicit in the theory of materials of this type is the assumption that all of the fibers are straight and unstressed or that the initial stresses in the individual fibers are essentially equal. In practice it is quite unlikely that this is true. It is to be expected, therefore, that as the load is increased some fibers reach their breaking points first, and as they fail their loads are transferred to other as yet unbroken fibers, with the consequence that failure is caused by the successive breaking of fibers rather than by the simultaneous breaking of all of them. The effect is to reduce the overall strength and to reduce the allowable working stresses accordingly, but the design theory is otherwise largely unaffected as long as essentially elastic behavior occurs. The development of higher working stresses is, therefore, largely a question of devising fabrication techniques to make the fibers work together to obtain maximum strength.

The following discussion of design theory shows that the values of a number of elastic constants must be known in addition to the strength properties of the resin, fibers, and combination. In a field as new as this one, much of this information is still lacking and, until the necessary experimental information has been obtained, reasonable assumptions must be made in carrying out designs. *In the examples used, more or less arbitrary values of elastic constants and strength values have been chosen to illustrate the theory.* Any other values could be used just as well.

The following sections attempt only to set forth the elements of design theory of reinforced plastics. Space does not permit exhaustive treatment. As experience is gained in the design of these materials, and as more complete experimental data are forthcoming, the design procedures will no doubt be modified. This review can be related to the effects of environment.

## B. Theory of Combined Action

Any material, when stressed, stretches or is otherwise deformed. If the resin and the fiber in reinforced plastics are firmly bonded together, the deformation is the same in both. For efficient structural behavior high-strength fibers are employed, but these must be more unyielding than the resin, therefore for a given deformation, or strain, a higher stress is developed in the fiber than in the resin. If the stress to strain relationships of fiber and resin are known, e.g., from their stress-strain diagrams, the stresses developed in each for a given strain can be computed, and their combined action determined.

In Fig. 15-13 stress–strain diagrams for glass fiber and for two resins are shown. Curve *A*, typical of glass, shows that stress and strain are very nearly directly proportional to each other to the breaking point. Stiffness, or modulus of elasticity, as measured by the ratio of stress to strain, is high. Curve *B* represents a hard resin. Stress is directly proportional to strain when both are low, but stress gradually levels off as strain increases. Stiffness, or modulus of elasticity, is much lower than that of glass. It is measured by the tangent to the curve, usually at the origin. Curve *C* represents a softer resin intermediate between the hard resin and the very soft plastics. Stress and strain are again directly proportional at low levels, but not when the strains become large. Modulus of elasticity, as measured by the tangent to the curve, is lower than for the hard resin.

These stress–strain diagrams may be applied, for example, to the investigation of a rod in which half the total volume is glass fiber and half is resin. If the glass fibers are laid parallel to the axis of the rod,

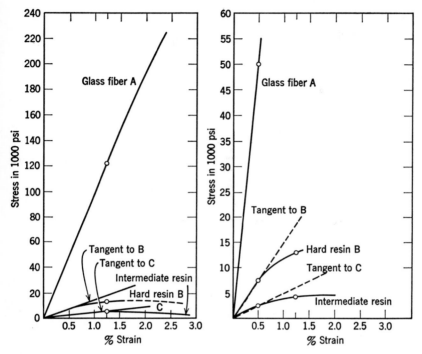

Fig. 15-13. Stress–strain diagrams of glass fiber A and two resins, B and C. Resin B is hard, high-strength material; resin C is intermediate strength and hardness.

at any cross section, half of the total cross-sectional area is glass and half is resin. If the rod is stretched 0.5%, reference to the stress–strain diagrams of Fig. 15-13 shows that the glass is stressed at an intensity of 50,000 psi and the resin, if resin B, at 7500 psi, or if resin C, at 2500 psi. If, for example, the rod has a total cross section of one-half square inch, the glass is one-quarter square inch, and the total stress in the glass is one-quarter times 50,000 or 12,500 lb. Similarly, the stress in the resin, if resin B, is 1875 lb, and in resin C is 625 lb. The load required to stretch the rod made with resin B is therefore the sum of the stresses in glass and resin, or 14,375 lb. Similarly, for a rod utilizing resin C, the load is 13,125 lb. The average stress on the one-half square inch cross section is therefore 28,750 psi or 26,250 psi, respectively.

An analogous line of reasoning shows that at a strain of 1.25% the stress intensity in the glass is 125,000 psi, and in resins B and C it is 12,600 and 4,500 psi, respectively. The corresponding loads on rods made with resins B and C are 34,400 and 32,375 lb, respectively.

The foregoing can be put into the form of an equation

$$\sigma A = \sigma_f A_f + \sigma_r A_r \tag{15-1}$$

where

$\sigma =$ mean stress intensity on entire cross section
$\sigma_f =$ stress intensity in fiber
$\sigma_r =$ stress intensity in resin
$A =$ total cross-sectional area
$A_f =$ cross-sectional area of fiber
$A_r =$ cross-sectional area of resin

If the moduli of elasticity, as measured by the tangents to the stress–strain diagrams, are known the following relationships hold:

$$\sigma_r/\sigma_f = E_r/E_f \quad \text{or} \quad \sigma_r = (E_r/E_f)\sigma_f \tag{15-2}$$

$E_r =$ modulus of elasticity of resin

$E_f =$ modulus of elasticity of fiber

Substituting (15-2) in (15-1)

$$\sigma A = \sigma_f \left( A_f + \frac{E_r}{E_f} A_r \right) \tag{15-3}$$

Referring to Fig. 15-13, the tangent to the stress–strain curve for glass gives a value of modulus of elasticity $E_f = 10 \times 10^6$ psi. The tangents to the two resin curves give values of $E_r$ equal to $1.5 \times 10^6$ psi and $0.5 \times 10^6$ psi, respectively. Substituting these values in Eq. 15-3 and solving for the stresses in the one-half square inch rod of the previous example, gives

$$\text{Resin B} \quad \sigma A = 50,000 \left( 0.25 + \frac{1.5}{10} 0.25 \right)$$
$$= 14,375 \ \text{lb}$$
$$\sigma = 28,750 \ \text{psi}$$

$$\text{Resin C} \quad \sigma A = 50,000 \left( 0.25 + \frac{0.5}{10} 0.25 \right)$$
$$= 13,125 \ \text{lb}$$
$$\sigma = 26,250 \ \text{psi}$$

Average values of modulus of elasticity of the entire cross section may be computed by dividing $\sigma$ by the strain. The strain is 0.5%, therefore the two average values of $E$ of the rod, incorporating resins B and C, are $5.75 \times 10^6$ psi and $5.35 \times 10^6$ psi, respectively.

For a cross section made up of a number of different materials, Eq. 15-1 may be generalized to

$$\sigma A = \sum_{i=1}^{i=n} \sigma_i A_i \tag{15-4}$$

in which $\sigma_i$ is the tensile strength and $A_i$ the cross-sectional area of any component of the cross section. This equation can be still further generalized to include tension, compression, and shear

$$SA = \sum_{i=1}^{i=n} S_i A_i \qquad (15\text{-}5)$$

in which $S_i$ is the strength property of the cross-sectional area $A_i$ of component $i$, and $S$ is the mean strength property over the entire cross section $A$.

Similarly, to find the overall modulus of elasticity of a cross section, the equation becomes

$$EA = \sum_{i=1}^{i=n} E_i A_i \qquad (15\text{-}6)$$

in which $E$ is the overall modulus of elasticity, $A$ the total cross section, and $E_i$ the modulus of elasticity corresponding to the partial cross-sectional area $A_i$. For shear modulus $G$ the equation becomes

$$GA = \sum_{i=1}^{i=n} G_i A_i \qquad (15\text{-}7)$$

## C. Plain Reinforced Plates

Fibrous reinforced plates, flat or curved, are commonly made with mat, fabrics, and parallel filaments, either alone or in combination. Mat is usually used for good strength at minimum cost, fabrics for high strength, and parallel filaments for maximum strength in some particular direction.

Because the fibers in mat are randomly oriented, mat-reinforced materials have essentially the same strength and elastic properties in all directions in the plane of the plate, that is, they are essentially isotropic in the plane. Consequently, the usual engineering theories and design methods employed for isotropic engineering materials may be applied. It is only necessary to know strength, modulus of elasticity, shearing modulus, and Poisson's ratio of the combined mat and resin. These can be obtained from standard stress–strain measurements made on specimens of the particular combination of fiber and resin under consideration.

In fabric and roving-reinforced materials the strength and elastic properties are different in different directions, that is, they are not isotropic, and the usual engineering equations must accordingly be modified. Because fabrics are woven with yarns at right angles (warp and fill directions), a single layer of fabric-reinforced material has two principal directions or natural axes, longitudinal (warp) and transverse (fill) at right angles to each other. This structure is called orthotropic (right-angled directions). Parallel strands of fiber, as in a single layer of roving-reinforced or unidirectional fabric-reinforced plates, also result in orthotropic materials, with one direction parallel, and one at right angles to the fibers. Multilayer plates, in which layers of fabric or of roving are laid up parallel or perpendicular to each other, are also orthotropic. If the same number of strands or yarns is found in each principal direction (balanced construction), the strength and elastic properties are the same in those directions but not at intermediate angles; if the number of strands or yarns is different in the two principal directions (unbalanced construction), the strength and elastic properties are different in those directions as well as at all intermediate angles.

In the foregoing discussion the direction perpendicular to the plane of the plate has been neglected because the plate is assumed to be thin and the stresses are assumed to be applied in the plane of the plate rather than perpendicular to it. This assumption, which considerably simplifies the theory, carries through all of the following discussion. It is true, of course, that properties perpendicular to the plane of the plate are undoubtedly different than in the plane of the plate, and in thick plates this difference has to be taken into account, particularly when stresses are not planar.

For isotropic materials, such as mat-reinforced construction, if $E$ is the modulus of elasticity in any reference direction, the modulus $E_1$ at any angle to this direction is the same, and the ratio $E_1/E$ is therefore unity. Poisson's ratio $v$ is similarly a constant in all directions, and the shearing modulus $G = E/2(1+v)$. If $v$, for example, is 0.3, $G/E = 0.385$ at all angles. These relationships are shown in Fig. 15-14.

The following familiar relationships between direct stress $\sigma$ and strain, $\epsilon$, and shearing stress $\tau$ and strain $\gamma$ hold:

$$\epsilon = \sigma/E \tag{15-8}$$

$$\gamma = \tau/G \tag{15-9}$$

A transverse strain (contraction or dilation) $\epsilon_T$ is caused by $\sigma$ equal to

$$\epsilon_T = -v\epsilon \tag{15-10}$$

For orthotropic materials, such as fabric and roving-reinforced con-

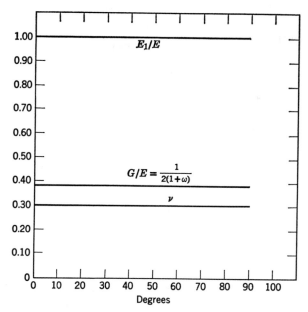

Fig. 15-14. Modulus of elasticity, shear modulus, and Poisson's ratio for iso-tropic material such as mat-reinforced plastics. Constants do not vary with angle of load, consequently ratio of modulus $E_1$, at any angle, to $E$ at any reference direction, is unity. Shear modulus is constant proportion of $E$, and Poisson's ratio is constant.

struction, $E_L$ and $E_T$ are the elastic moduli in the longitudinal $(L)$ and transverse $(T)$ directions, $G_{LT}$ is the shearing modulus associated with these directions, $\nu_{LT}$ is the Poisson's ratio giving the transverse strain caused by a stress in the longitudinal direction, and $\nu_{TL}$ is Poisson's ratio giving the longitudinal strain caused by a stress in the transverse direction. The modulus at any intermediate angle is $E_1$, and if $\sigma_1$ is a stress applied in the 1-direction at an angle $a$ with the longitudinal direction (see Fig. 15-15, top), the stress $\sigma_1$ causes a strain $\epsilon_1$

$$\epsilon_1 = \sigma_1/E_1 \qquad (15\text{-}11)$$

in which $E_1$ may be found from

$$\frac{E_L}{E_1} = \cos^4 a + \frac{E_L}{E_T}\sin^4 a + \frac{1}{4}\left(\frac{E_L}{G_{LT}} - 2\nu_{LT}\right)\sin^2 2a \qquad (15\text{-}12)$$

This relationship is plotted as $E_1/E_L$ in Fig. 15-15, in which 0° corresponds to the longitudinal direction and 90° to the transverse direction.

A transverse strain $\epsilon_2$ is caused by $\sigma_1$

$$\epsilon_2 = -\nu_{12}\epsilon_1 \qquad (15\text{-}13)$$

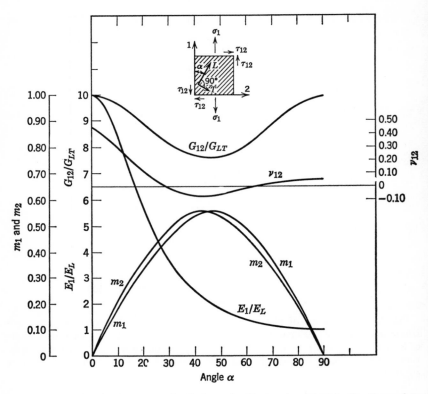

Fig. 15-15. Elastic constants of unbalanced orthotropic material. $E_1$, $G_{12}$, and $\nu_{12}$ are all functions of the angle between direction of stress and the longitudinal axis (warp direction) of the material. Factors $m_1$ and $m_2$ account for direct and shear strains caused by shear and direct stresses, respectively. Angle 0° is longitudinal direction, and angle 90° is transverse direction.

in which (see Fig. 15-15)

$$\nu_{12} = \frac{E_1}{E_L}\left\{ \nu_{LT} - \frac{1}{4}\left( 1 + 2\nu_{LT} + \frac{E_L}{E_T} - \frac{E_L}{G_{LT}} \right)\sin^2 2a \right\} \qquad (15\text{-}14)$$

Unlike isotropic materials, stress $\sigma_1$, when applied at any angle except 0° and 90°, causes shear distortion and the shear strain $\gamma_{12}$ is found from

$$\gamma_{12} = -m_1\sigma_1/E_L \qquad (15\text{-}15)$$

in which (see Fig. 15-15)

$$m_1 = \sin 2a\left\{ \nu_{LT} + \frac{E_L}{E_T} - \frac{1}{2}\frac{E_L}{G_{LT}} - \cos^2 a\left( 1 + 2\nu_{LT} + \frac{E_L}{E_T} - \frac{E_L}{G_{LT}} \right) \right\} \qquad (15\text{-}16)$$

A shearing stress $\tau_{12}$ applied in the 1–2 directions causes a shear strain $\gamma_{12}$

$$\gamma_{12} = \tau_{12}/G_{12} \tag{15-17}$$

in which (see Fig. 15-15)

$$\frac{G_{LT}}{G_{12}} = \frac{G_{LT}}{E_L}\left\{\left(1 + 2\nu_{LT} + \frac{E_L}{E_T}\right) - \left(1 + 2\nu_{LT} + \frac{E_L}{E_T} - \frac{E_L}{G_{LT}}\right)\cos^2 2a\right\} \tag{15-18}$$

This relationship is plotted as $G_{12}/G_{LT}$ in Fig. 15-15.

Unlike isotropic materials, stress $\tau_{12}$ causes a strain $\epsilon_1$ in the 1-direction

$$\epsilon_1 = -m_1\tau_{12}/E_L \tag{15-19}$$

and a strain $\epsilon_2$ in the 2-direction

$$\epsilon_2 = -m_2\tau_{12}/E_L \tag{15-20}$$

in which (see Fig. 15-15)

$$m_2 = \sin 2a\left\{\nu_{LT} + \frac{E_L}{E_T} - \frac{1}{2}\frac{E_L}{G_{LT}} - \sin^2 a\left(1 + 2\nu_{LT} + \frac{E_L}{E_T} - \frac{E_L}{G_{LT}}\right)\right\} \tag{15-21}$$

The two values of Poisson's ratio are related:

$$\nu_{LT}/\nu_{TL} = E_L/E_T \tag{15-22}$$

In plotting Fig. 15-15 the following values were used:

$E_L = 5{,}000{,}000$ psi
$E_T = 500{,}000$ psi
$G_{LT} = 550{,}000$ psi
$\nu_{LT} = \nu_{0°} = 0.450$
$\nu_{TL} = \nu_{90°} = 0.045$

These values, for example, might correspond to a parallel glass filament reinforced panel employing an intermediate polyester resin.

When the orthotropic material is balanced, the longitudinal and transverse properties are the same, that is, $E_L = E_T$ and $\nu_{LT} = \nu_{LT} = \nu_{TL}$. The properties are symmetrical about the 45° angle, as shown in Fig. 15-16, in which the following values were used:

$E_L = E_T = 3{,}000{,}000$ psi
$G_{LT} = 500{,}000$ psi
$\nu_{LT} = \nu_{TL} = 0.20$

These values might correspond, for example, to a square-weave or symmetrical satin-weave fabric-reinforced construction.

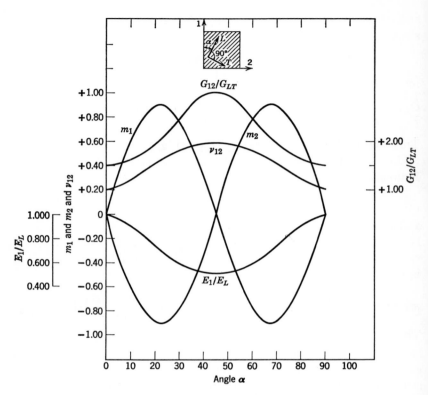

Fig. 15-16. Elastic constants of balanced orthotropic material. Constants and angles have same meanings as Fig. 15-4.

As an example of the application of the foregoing equations, the tensile stress $\sigma_1$ acting on the small plate at the top of Fig. 15-15 is 10,000 psi, the shear stress $\tau_{12}$ is 4000 psi, and the angle $a$ is 30°. Then from Fig. 15-15,

$$E_1/E_L = 0.367 \quad \text{or} \quad E_1 = 0.367 \times 5,000,000 = 1,830,000 \text{ psi}$$
$$G_{12}/G_{LT} = 0.81 \text{ or } G_{12} = 0.81 \times 550,000 = 445,000 \text{ psi}$$
$$\nu_{12} = -0.0286 \quad m_1 = 4.66 \quad m_2 = 4.98$$

Then, strains caused by $\sigma_1$ are

$$\epsilon_1 = 10,000/1,830,000 = 5.45 \times 10^{-3} \tag{15-23}$$
$$\epsilon_2 = -(-0.0286)5.45 \times 10^{-3} = 0.16 \times 10^{-3} \tag{15-24}$$
$$\gamma_{12} = -4.66 \times 10,000/5,000,000 = -9.32 \times 10^{-3} \tag{15-25}$$

and strains caused by $\tau_{12}$ are

$$\gamma_{12} = 4,000/550,000 = 7.28 \times 10^{-3} \tag{15-26}$$
$$\epsilon_1 = -4.66 \times 4,000/5,000,000 = -3.73 \times 10^{-3} \tag{15-27}$$
$$\epsilon_2 = -4.98 \times 4,000/5,000,000 = -3.98 \times 10^{-3} \tag{15-28}$$

Total strains, therefore, are

$$\gamma_{12} = -2.04 \times 10^{-3}$$
$$\epsilon_1 = 1.72 \times 10^{-3}$$
$$\epsilon_2 = -3.82 \times 10^{-3}$$

Problems involving Fig. 15-16 can be solved in an analogous manner. It must be kept in mind that Eqs. 15-12, 15-14, 15-16, 15-18, and 15-21 are valid and useful if the fibers and the resin behave together in accordance with the assumptions upon which their derivation is based. If only the values of $E_L$, $E_T$, $G_{LT}$, and $\nu_{LT}$ are available, the intermediate values of $E_1$, $G_{12}$, $\nu_{12}$, and the values of $m_1$ and $m_2$ can be estimated by means of these equations.

## D. Composite Plates

Fibrous reinforced plates in practice are often made up of several layers, and the individual layers may be of different construction, such as mat, fabric, or roving. Furthermore, the various layers may be oriented at different angles with respect to each other in order to provide the best combination to resist some particular loading condition. Outside loads or stresses applied to a composite plate of this type result in internal stresses which are different in the individual layers. External direct stresses may result not only in internal direct stresses but in internal shear stresses, and external shear stresses may result in internal direct stresses as well as internal shear stresses.

Fig. 15-17 depicts a small composite plate made up of materials $a$ and $b$ having principal longitudinal and transverse directions $L_a$ and $T_a$, and $L_b$ and $T_b$, respectively. Several layers of each are present but their total thicknesses are $t_a$ and $t_b$, respectively, and the overall thickness is $t$. Outside stresses $\sigma_1$, $\sigma_2$, and $\tau_{12}$ are applied in the 1 and 2 directions, as shown. The 1-direction makes an angle $a$ with $L_a$, and a reverse angle $\beta$ with $L_b$. The angle $a$ is considered to be positive and the angle $\beta$ negative.

The internal stresses $\sigma_{1a}$, $\sigma_{2a}$, $\tau_{12a}$, and $\sigma_{1b}$, $\sigma_{2b}$, $\tau_{12b}$ in the individual layers can be found by observing that the sums of the internal stresses in the 1 and 2 directions must equal the external stresses in these directions, and that the strains must be the same in all layers. These relationships may be written in the following forms:

$$\sigma_{1a}t_a + \sigma_{1b}t_b = \sigma_1 t; \quad \sigma_{1b} = \frac{\sigma_1 t - \sigma_{1a}t_a}{t_b} \tag{15-29}$$

$$\sigma_{2a}t_a + \sigma_{2b}t_b = \sigma_2 t; \quad \sigma_{2b} = \frac{\sigma_2 t - \sigma_{2a}t_a}{t_b} \tag{15-30}$$

$$\tau_{12a}t_a + \tau_{12b}t_b = \tau_{12} t; \quad \tau_{12b} = \frac{\tau_{12} t - \tau_{12a}t_a}{t_b} \tag{15-31}$$

$$\epsilon_{1a} = \epsilon_{1b} = \epsilon_1 \tag{15-32}$$

$$\epsilon_{2a} = \epsilon_{2b} = \epsilon_2 \tag{15-33}$$

$$\gamma_{12a} = \gamma_{12b} = \gamma_{12} \tag{15-34}$$

Strains and stresses are induced in each layer. Because the layers are firmly bonded together the strains are the same in the $a$ and $b$ layers, and are equal to the strains in the whole plate:

$$\epsilon_1 = \begin{cases} \epsilon_{1a} = \dfrac{\sigma_{1a}}{E_{1a}} - \nu_{21a}\dfrac{\sigma_{2a}}{E_{2a}} - m_{1a}\dfrac{\tau_{12a}}{E_{La}} \\[4mm] \epsilon_{1b} = \dfrac{\sigma_{1b}}{E_{1b}} - \nu_{21b}\dfrac{\sigma_{2b}}{E_{2b}} - m_{1b}\dfrac{\tau_{12b}}{E_{Lb}} \end{cases} \tag{15-35}$$

$$\epsilon_2 = \begin{cases} \epsilon_{2a} = -\nu_{12a}\dfrac{\sigma_{1a}}{E_{1a}} + \dfrac{\sigma_{2a}}{E_{2a}} - m_{2a}\dfrac{\tau_{12a}}{E_{La}} \\[4mm] \epsilon_{2b} = -\nu_{12b}\dfrac{\sigma_{1b}}{E_{1b}} + \dfrac{\sigma_{2b}}{E_{2b}} - m_{2b}\dfrac{\tau_{12b}}{E_{Lb}} \end{cases} \tag{15-36}$$

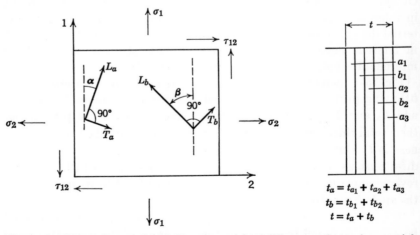

Fig. 15-17. Composite panel with layers $a$ and $b$ of different orthotropic materials oriented at arbitrary angles $\alpha$ and $\beta$ with respect to applied stresses $\sigma_1$, $\sigma_2$, and $\tau_{12}$.

$$\gamma_{12} = \begin{cases} \gamma_{12a} = -m_{1a}\dfrac{\sigma_{1a}}{E_{La}} - m_{2a}\dfrac{\sigma_{2a}}{E_{La}} + \dfrac{\tau_{12a}}{G_{12a}} \\[4mm] \gamma_{12a} = -m_{1b}\dfrac{\sigma_{1b}}{E_{Lb}} - m_{2b}\dfrac{\sigma_{2b}}{E_{Lb}} + \dfrac{\tau_{12b}}{G_{12b}} \end{cases} \qquad (15\text{-}37)$$

Solution of the foregoing Eqs. 15-29 to 15-37 leads to the following simultaneous equations:

$$A_{11}\sigma_{1a} + A_{12}\sigma_{2a} + A_{13}\tau_{12a} = \frac{t}{t_a t_b}\left(\frac{\sigma_1}{E_{1b}} - \nu_{21b}\frac{\sigma_2}{E_{2b}} - m_{1b}\frac{\tau_{12}}{E_{Lb}}\right) \qquad (15\text{-}38)$$

$$A_{21}\sigma_{1a} + A_{22}\sigma_{2a} + A_{23}\tau_{12a} = \frac{t}{t_a t_b}\left(-\nu_{12b}\frac{\sigma_1}{E_{1b}} + \frac{\sigma_2}{E_{2b}} - m_{2b}\frac{\tau_{12}}{E_{Lb}}\right) \qquad (15\text{-}39)$$

$$A_{31}\sigma_{1a} + A_{32}\sigma_{2a} + A_{33}\tau_{12a} = \frac{t}{t_a t_b}\left(-m_{1b}\frac{\sigma_1}{E_{Lb}} - m_{2b}\frac{\sigma_2}{E_{Lb}} + \frac{\tau_{12}}{G_{12b}}\right) \qquad (15\text{-}40)$$

in which:

$$A_{11} = \frac{1}{E_{1a}t_a} + \frac{1}{E_{1b}t_b} \qquad A_{12}^* = -\frac{\nu_{21a}}{E_{2a}t_a} - \frac{\nu_{21b}}{E_{2b}t_b} \qquad A_{13} = -\frac{m_{1a}}{E_{La}t_a} - \frac{m_{1b}}{E_{Lb}t_b}$$

$$A_{21}^* = -\frac{\nu_{12a}}{E_{1a}t_a} - \frac{\nu_{12b}}{E_{1b}t_b} \qquad A_{22} = \frac{1}{E_{2a}t_a} + \frac{1}{E_{2b}t_b} \qquad A_{23} = -\frac{m_{2a}}{E_{La}t_a} - \frac{m_{2b}}{E_{Lb}t_b}$$

$$A_{31} = A_{13} \qquad\qquad A_{32} = A_{23} \qquad\qquad A_{33} = \frac{1}{G_{12a}t_a} + \frac{1}{G_{12b}t_b}$$

*Example:*

The application of the foregoing expressions may be illustrated by a cylindrical pressure vessel as shown in Fig. 15-18a. The wall of this vessel, having an external radius of 5 in., and wall thickness of 0.20 in., may be considered to be a thin plate. It is subjected to an internal pressure of 800 psi. The circumferential stress $\sigma_1$ and the longitudinal stress $\sigma_2$ in the wall are calculated

$$\sigma_1 = \frac{pr_0}{t} = 19{,}200 \text{ psi}$$

$$\sigma_2 = \frac{pr_0}{2t} = 9{,}600 \text{ psi}$$

The stresses acting on a small part of the wall are therefore as shown in Fig. 15-18a.

Three types of construction will be investigated as shown in Fig. 15-18(1), (2), (3). All three employ the balanced fabric having the characteristics shown in Fig. 15-16. In (1) the fabric is simply wrapped

* $A_{21} = A_{12}$, numerically.

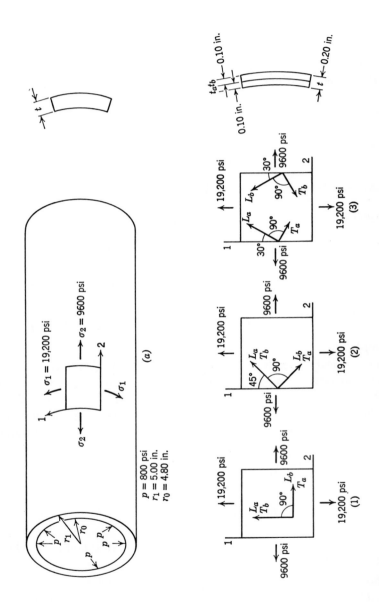

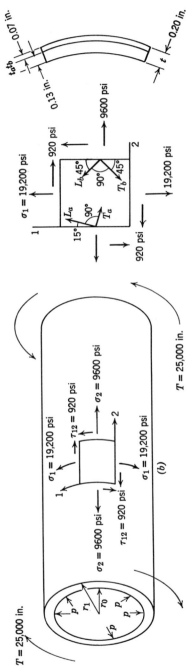

Fig. 15-18. Fibrous glass-reinforced plastic thin-walled cylinder. (*a*), internal pressure alone; (*b*), internal pressure plus twisting moment.

in layers $a$ and $b$ with the $L$ and $T$ directions laid in the circumferential and axial directions. In (2) the layers are laid at 45° to the axis of the cylinder, and in (3) they are laid at alternate 30° angles in left-hand and right-hand spirals as shown. In each instance $t_a = t_b = 0.10$ in.

Referring to Fig. 15-16, it is seen that for Case 1

$$E_{1a} = E_{1b} = E_{2a} = E_{2b} = 3 \times 10^6 \text{ psi}$$

$$\nu_{13a} = \nu_{21a} = \nu_{12b} = \nu_{21b} = 0.20$$

$$m_{1a} = m_{1b} = m_{2a} = m_{2b} = 0$$

$$A_{11} = A_{22}, \ A_{12} = A_{21}$$

$$A_{\cdot 3} = A_{31} = A_{32} = A_{23} = 0$$

Eqs. 15-38 to 15-40 therefore become

$$A_{11}\sigma_{1a} + A_{12}\sigma_{2a} + 0 = \frac{t}{t_a t_b}\left(\frac{\sigma_1}{E_{1b}} - \nu_{21b}\frac{\sigma_2}{E_{2b}} + 0\right)$$

$$A_{21}\sigma_{1a} + A_{22}\sigma_{2a} + 0 = \frac{t}{t_a t_b}\left(-\nu_{1:}\frac{\sigma_1}{E_{1b}} + \frac{\sigma_2}{E_{2b}} + 0\right)$$

$$A_{33}\tau_{12a} = 0$$

Solution of these equations and reference to Eqs. 15-29 to 15-31 show that

$$\sigma_{1a} = \sigma_{1b} = \sigma_1 = 19{,}200 \text{ psi}$$

$$\sigma_{2a} = \sigma_{2b} = \sigma_2 = 9{,}600 \text{ psi}$$

$$\tau_{12a} = \tau_{12b} = 0$$

This proves what might have been expected intuitively; because of symmetry with respect to the 1-2 directions chosen; the internal direct stresses $\sigma_{1a}$, $\sigma_{1b}$, $\sigma_{2a}$, and $\sigma_{2b}$ are equal to the imposed stresses $\sigma_1$ and $\sigma_2$, and there is no internal shear stress.

The same result is found for Case 2. In this balanced fabric $m_1 = m_2 = 0$ at 45°, there is no shear distortion caused by direct stress, and shear therefore is zero. In Case 3:

$$E_{1a} = E_{1b} = E_{30°} = E_{60°} = E_{2a} = E_{2b}$$

$$= 0.597 \times 3 \times 10^6 = 1.78 \times 10^6 \text{ psi}$$

$$G_{12a} = G_{12b} = 1.82 \times 0.5 \times 10^6 = 0.91 \times 10^6$$

$$\nu_{12a} = \nu_{12b} = \nu_{30°} = \nu_{60°} = \nu_{21a} = \nu_{21b} = 0.523$$

$$m_{1a} = m_{30°} = 0.775, \ m_{1b} = -m_{1a} = -0.775$$

$$m_{2a} = m_{60°} = 0.775, \quad m_{2b} = -m_{2a} = -0.775$$

The values of $m_{1b}$ and $m_{2b}$ are negative because the 30° angles of orientation of the longitudinal direction $L_b$ of layers $b$ is measured in the negative direction whereas it is positive for the $a$-layers.

Equations 22 become

$$A_{11}\sigma_{1a} + A_{12}\sigma_{2a} + 0 = \frac{t}{t_a t_b}\left(\frac{\sigma_1}{E_{1b}} - \nu_{21b}\frac{\sigma_2}{E_{2b}} + 0\right)$$

$$A_{21}\sigma_{1a} + A_{22}\sigma_{2a} + 0 = \frac{t}{t_a t_b}\left(-\nu_{12b}\frac{\sigma_1}{E_{1b}} + \frac{\sigma_2}{E_{2b}} + 0\right)$$

$$0 + 0 + A_{33}\tau_{12a} = \frac{t}{t_a t_b}\left(-m_{1b}\frac{\sigma_1}{E_{Lb}} - m_{2b}\frac{\sigma_2}{E_{Lb}} + 0\right)$$

The first two of these equations are exactly like the first two equations for Cases 1 and 2 and show that the internal direct stresses are equal to the imposed, that is

$$\sigma_{1a} = \sigma_{1b} = \sigma_1 = 19{,}200 \text{ psi}$$

$$\sigma_{2a} = \sigma_{2b} = \sigma_2 = 9{,}600 \text{ psi}$$

The third equation, however, is not equal to zero, and its solution, together with equation 19c, shows that

$$\tau_{12a} = 6750 \text{ psi}$$

$$\tau_{12b} = -6750 \text{ psi}$$

Appreciable shear stresses are set up within the body of the cylinder wall when layers are oriented as in Case 3, even though no shear forces are applied to the cylinder itself. The shear stresses in layers $b$ are oriented in the direction opposite to the shear stresses in layers $a$.

The difference in the shear stresses between the two layers must be taken up by shear in the adhesive bond between them, that is, in the layer of resin that holds the fiber-reinforced layers together. The difference is

$$6750 - (-6750) = 13{,}500 \text{ psi}$$

This shear stress in the resin bonding the layers together is therefore seen to be high.

In Cases 1 and 2 the orientation of the fibers with respect to the 1–2 directions chosen resulted in zero shear stresses associated with those directions, whereas in Case 3 the shear stresses were not zero. In all three cases, symmetry of the fiber orientations with respect to the stress directions resulted in internal stresses equal to the external stresses. These are special cases. In the more general case the internal direct stresses in the individual layers are not necessarily equal to the external direct stresses, nor are they the same in the various layers. Furthermore, even symmetrical Case 3 leads to internal shear stresses when external shear stresses are absent. In the more general case it is still more true that internal shear stresses may be appreciable, or they may be absent, depending upon the magnitude of the external stresses and the orientation of the 1–2 directions with respect to the external stresses.

A more general case in shown in Fig. 15-18b in which the same cylinder is chosen as in Fig. 18a except that torsional effect equal to a twisting couple of 25,000 in.-lb has been added. The construction of the wall has also been changed. Layers $a$ of unbalanced material having the properties of Fig. 15-15 are a total of 0.13 in. thick, and are oriented at 15° to the circumferential direction as shown. Layers $b$, of balanced material having the properties of Fig. 15-16, are a total of 0.07 in. thick and are oriented at 45° as shown. Referring to Figs. 15-7 and 15-16, the properties are found to be

|  $a$-layers | $b$-layers |
|---|---|
| $t_a = 0.13$ in. | $t_b = 0.07$ in. |
| $a = 15°$ | $a = 45°$ |
| $E_{1a} = 0.703 \times 5 \times 10^6$ | $E_{1b} = E_{2b} = 0.526 \times 3 \times 10^6$ |
| $\quad = 3.515 \times 10^6$ psi | $\quad = 1.578 \times 10^6$ psi |
| $E_{2a} = 0.109 \times 5 \times 10^6$ | $\nu_{12b} = \nu_{21b} = 0.579$ |
| $\quad = 0.545 \times 10^6$ psi | $m_{1b} = m_{2b} = 0$ |
| $\nu_{12a} = 0.193$ | $G_{12b} = 2.5 \times 0.5 \times 10^6$ |
| $m_{1a} = 2.63$ | $\quad = 1.250 \times 10^6$ psi |
| $m_{2a} = 2.94$ | |
| $G_{12a} = 0.93 \times 0.5 \times 10^6$ | |
| $\quad = 0.465 \times 10^6$ psi | |

Solving for the various constants and substituting in Eqs. 15-38 to 15-40

$$11.2412\sigma_{1a} - 5.6641\sigma_{2a} - 4.0461\tau_{12a} = +190,180$$

$$-5.6641\sigma_{1a} + 23.2030\sigma_{2a} - 4.5156\tau_{12a} = -21,150$$

$$-4.0461\sigma_{1b} - 4.5156\sigma_{2a} + 26.4668\tau_{12a} = +16,190$$

The solution of the foregoing simultaneous equations leads to the following results for stresses in the $a$-layers:

$$\sigma_{1a} = 21,100 \text{ psi}$$

$$\sigma_{2a} = 5,200 \text{ psi}$$
$$\tau_{12a} = 4,740 \text{ psi}$$

When these results are employed with Eqs. 15-29 to 15-31 it is found that stresses in the $b$-layers are:

$$\sigma_{1b} = 15,700 \text{ psi}$$
$$\sigma_{2b} = 17,800 \text{ psi}$$
$$\tau_{12b} = -6,150 \text{ psi}$$

## E. Bending of Beams and Plates

Plates and beams of fibrous glass reinforced plastics may be homogeneous and isotropic or composite and nonisotropic depending upon their structure. Mat-reinforced plates may be considered to be essentially isotropic and the usual engineering formulas may be applied. Composite structures require suitably modified formulas but otherwise the procedures for computing bending stresses, stiffness, and bending shear stresses are essentially the same as for isotropic materials. The differences and similarities may be brought out by considering two beams of identical overall dimensions, one isotropic and the other composite. Two such cross sections are shown in Fig. 15-19. For each cross section it is necessary to know the stiffness factor $EI$ to compute deflection, the section modulus to compute bending stresses, and the statical moments of portions of the cross section to compute shear stresses. For isotropic materials ($a$) the neutral axis of a rectangular cross section is at middepth, and the familiar formulas are

$$\text{Moment of inertia } I = \frac{bd^3}{12}, \text{ stiffness factor} = EI \qquad (15\text{-}41)$$

$$\text{Section modulus} = \frac{I}{y} = \frac{bd^2}{6} \text{ for outermost fiber} \qquad (15\text{-}42)$$

$$\text{Bending stress} = \sigma = M\frac{y}{I} = \frac{6M}{bd^2} \text{ for outermost fiber} \qquad (15\text{-}43)$$

$$\text{Shear stress} = \frac{VQ}{bI} = \frac{3}{2}\frac{V}{bd} \text{ for maximum shear at the neutral axis} \qquad (15\text{-}44)$$

For composite materials the neutral axis is not necessarily at middepth of a rectangular section, and it must first be found.

$$\text{Neutral axis } x = \Sigma E_i A_i x_i / \Sigma E_i A_i \qquad (15\text{-}45)$$

in which $E_i$, $A_i$, $x_i$ are the modulus of elasticity; cross-sectional area

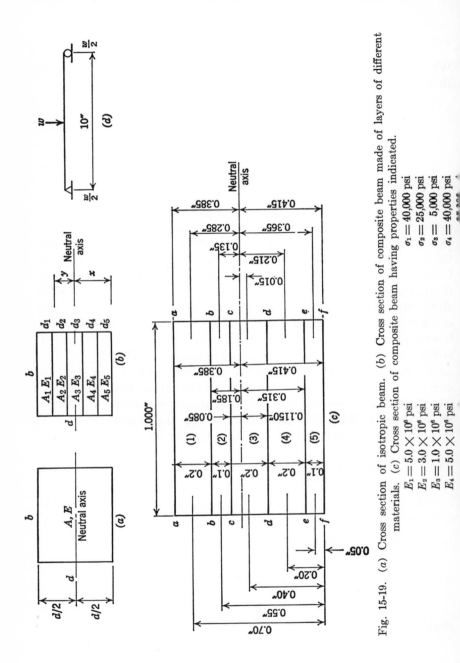

Fig. 15-19. (*a*) Cross section of isotropic beam. (*b*) Cross section of composite beam made of layers of different materials. (*c*) Cross section of composite beam having properties indicated.

$\sigma_1 = 40{,}000$ psi
$\sigma_2 = 25{,}000$ psi
$\sigma_3 = 5{,}000$ psi
$\sigma_4 = 40{,}000$ psi

$E_1 = 5.0 \times 10^6$ psi
$E_2 = 3.0 \times 10^6$ psi
$E_3 = 1.0 \times 10^6$ psi
$E_4 = 5.0 \times 10^6$ psi

$(bd_i)$ ; and distance from some reference line, such as the bottom of the cross section, to the center of gravity of any particular layer.

$$\text{Stiffness factor} = EI = \Sigma E_i I_i \qquad (15\text{-}46)$$

in which $E_i$ and $I_i$ are, for any particular layer, the modulus of elasticity and the moment of inertia about the neutral axis.

$$\text{Bending stress } \sigma = M E_y y / EI \qquad (15\text{-}47)$$

in which $y$ is the distance from the neutral axis to any point, and $E_y$ is the modulus of elasticity of the layer at that point. The maximum bending stress does not necessarily occur at the outermost (top or bottom) fiber, as it does in isotropic materials.

$$\text{Shear stress } \tau = V Q' / b EI \qquad (15\text{-}48)$$

in which $V$ is the total shear on the cross section, $\tau$ is the shear stress intensity along some horizontal plane, and $Q'$ is the weighted statical moment, $E_i A_i y$ about the beam's neutral axis, of the portion of the cross section between the horizontal plane in question and the outer edge (top or bottom) of the cross section.

An example of the foregoing is illustrated in Fig. 15-19$c$ in which a composite beam is made up of five layers having three different moduli of elasticity, and three different strengths, as shown.

The neutral axis, found by applying Eq. 15-45 is 0.415 in. from the bottom of the cross section. Distance from the neutral axis to the centers of the individual layers are computed, and the stiffness factor $EI$ calculated by means of Eq. 15-46. This is found to be

$$EI = \Sigma E_i I_i = 0.174 \times 10^6 \text{ lb in.}^2$$

Bending stresses are next computed for the top and bottom edges of the cross section and for the outer edge of each layer, that is, the edge of each layer farther from the neutral axis. From these, the bending moment the cross section is capable of carrying can be computed. This may be done for example by applying a bending moment $M$ of one in.-lb and computing the unit bending stresses. These unit bending stresses divided into the strengths of the individual layers give a series of calculated resisting moments, the smallest of which is the maximum bending moment the beam is capable of carrying without exceeding the strength of any portion of the cross section.

For a unit bending moment $M = 1$ in.-lb,

$$\sigma_y = \frac{E_y y}{EI} \text{ from Eq. 15-47}$$

| Plane | $y$ | $E_y$ | $\sigma_y/\text{in.lb}$ | $\dfrac{\sigma}{\sigma_y/\text{in.lb}} =$ | $M$ |
|---|---|---|---|---|---|
| $a$-$a$ | 0.385 in. | $5 \times 10^6$ | 11.1 psi | $40{,}000/11.1 = 3{,}600$ in.-lb | |
| $b$-$b$ | 0.185 in. | $3 \times 10^6$ | 3.19 psi | $25{,}000/3.19 = 7{,}800$ in.-lb | |
| $c$-$c$ | 0.085 in. | $1 \times 10^6$ | 0.49 psi | $5{,}000/0.49 = 10{,}200$ in.-lb | |
| $d$-$d$ | 0.115 in. | $1 \times 10^6$ | 0.66 psi | $5{,}000/0.66 = 7{,}600$ in.-lb | |
| $e$-$e$ | 0.315 in. | $5 \times 10^6$ | 9.07 psi | $40{,}000/9.07 = 4{,}400$ in.-lb | |
| $f$-$f$ | 0.415 in. | $3 \times 10^6$ | 7.16 psi | $25{,}000/7.16 = 3{,}500$ in.-lb | |

If, for example, the beam were a simple beam carrying a load W on a 10-in. span, as shown in Fig. 15-19, the bending moment at the center of the span would be $WL/4$. Setting this equal to 3,500 in.-lb. gives the load W as 1400 lb. Shear V is $W/2$ or 700 lb. Using this value, the shear stress intensity at various horizontal planes in the beam may be computed by means of Eq. 15-48.

For planes $b$-$b$, $c$-$c$, and $d$-$d$, for example:

| Plane | Layers | $E_i A_i$ | $y'$ | $Q'$ | $\tau$ |
|---|---|---|---|---|---|
| $b$-$b$ | 1 | $0.2 \times 5 \times 10^6$ | 0.285" | $0.285 \times 10^6$ | 1150 psi |
| $c$-$c$ | 1 | $0.2 \times 5 \times 10^6$ | 0.285 | $0.326 \times 10^6$ | 1315 psi |
| | 2 | $+0.1 \times 3 \times 10^6$ | 0.135 | | |
| $d$-$d$ | 4 | $0.2 \times 5 \times 10^6$ | 0.215 | $0.324 \times 10^6$ | 1310 psi |
| | 5 | $+0.1 \times 3 \times 10^6$ | 0.365 | | |

These would be the critical planes because they represent planes between layers of different materials, and consequently the resin alone would largely carry the stress. The shear stress at the neutral axis would be slightly higher and might or might not represent the critical plane, depending upon the structure of the material in layer 3.

## 1. Structural Sandwiches

In usual construction practice, a structural sandwich is a special case of a laminate in which two thin facings of relatively stiff, hard, dense, strong material are bonded to a thick core of relatively lightweight material considerably less dense, stiff, and strong than the facings.

With this geometry and relationship of mechanical properties, the facings are subjected to almost all of the stresses in transverse bending or in axial loading, and the geometry of the arrangement provides high stiffness combined with lightness because the stiff facings are at maximum distance from the neutral axis, similar to the flanges of an I-beam.

The continuous core takes the place of the web of an I-beam or box beam, it absorbs most of the shear, and it also stabilizes the thin facings against buckling or wrinkling under compressive stresses. The bond between core and facings must resist shear and any transverse tensile stresses set up as the facings tend to wrinkle or pull away from the core.

**a. Stiffness.** For an isotropic material with modulus of elasticity $E$, the bending stiffness factor $EI$ of a rectangular beam $b$ wide and $h$ deep is

$$EI = E(bh^3/12) \tag{15-49}$$

In a rectangular structural sandwich of the same dimensions as above whose facings and core have moduli of elasticity $E_f$ and $E_c$, respectively, and a core thickness $C$, the bending stiffness factor $EI$ is

$$EI = \frac{E_f b}{12}(h^3 - c^3) + \frac{E_c b}{12}c^3 \tag{15-50}$$

This equation is exact if the facings are of equal thickness, and approximate if they are not, but the approximation is close if facings are thin relative to the core.

If, as is usually the case, $E_c$ is much smaller than $E_f$, the last term in the equation can be ignored.

For unsymmetrical sandwiches with different materials or different thicknesses in the facings, or both, the more general equation for $\Sigma EI$ given in the previous section may be used.

In many isotropic materials the shear modulus $G$ is high compared to the elastic modulus $E$, and shear distortion of a transversely loaded beam is so small that it can be neglected in calculating deflection. In a structural sandwich the core shear modulus $G_c$ is usually so much smaller than $E_f$ of the facings that shear distortion of the core may be large and therefore contribute significantly to the deflection of a transversely loaded beam. The total deflection of a beam is therefore composed of two factors: the deflection caused by bending moment alone, and the deflection caused by shear, that is

$$\delta = \delta_m + \delta_s \tag{15-51}$$

where

$\delta = $ total deflection
$\delta_m = $ moment deflection
$\delta_s = $ shear deflection

Under transverse loading, bending moment deflection is proportional to the load and the cube of the span and inversely proportional to the stiffness factor $EI$. Shear deflection is proportional to the load and span and inversely proportional to a shear stiffness factor $N$ whose value for symmetrical sandwiches is

$$N = \frac{(h+c)b}{2} G_c \tag{15-52}$$

where

$$G_c = \text{core shear modulus}$$

The total deflection may therefore be written

$$\delta = \frac{K_m W L^3}{EI} + \frac{K_s W L}{N} \tag{15-53}$$

The values of $K_m$ and $K_s$ depend on the type of load. Values for several typical loading conditions are given as shown in Table 15-5.

**b. Stresses in Sandwich Beams.** The familiar equation for stresses in an isotropic beam subjected to bending

$$\sigma_y = \frac{M_y}{I} \tag{15-54}$$

must be modified for sandwiches to the form

$$\sigma_y = \frac{M E_y y}{EI} \tag{15-55}$$

TABLE 15-5

| Loading | Beam ends | Deflections at | $K_m$ | $K_s$ |
|---|---|---|---|---|
| Uniformly distributed | Both simply supported | Midspan | 5/384 | 1/8 |
| Uniformly distributed | Both clamped | Midspan | 1/384 | 1/8 |
| Concentrated at midspan | Both simply supported | Midspan | 1/48 | 1/4 |
| Concentrated at midspan | Both clamped | Midspan | 1/192 | 1/4 |
| Concentrated at outer quarter points | Both simply supported | Midspan | 11/768 | 1/8 |
| Concentrated at outer quarter points | Both simply supported | Load point | 1/96 | 1/8 |
| Uniformly distributed | Cantilever, 1 free, 1 clamped | Free end | 1/8 | 1/2 |
| Concentrated at free end | Cantilever, 1 free, 1 clamped | Free end | 1/3 | 1 |

where $y=$ distance from neutral axis to fiber at $y$

$\qquad E_y=$ elastic modulus of fiber at $y$

$\qquad EI=$ stiffness factor

For a symmetrical sandwich the stress in the outermost facing fiber is found by setting

$$y=h/2$$

$$E_y=E_f$$

and the stress in the outermost core fiber by setting

$$y=c/2$$

$$E_y=E_c$$

The mean stress in the facings of a symmetrical sandwich can be found from

$$\sigma=\frac{2M}{bt(h+c)} \qquad (15\text{-}56)$$

where $t=$ facing thickness

Similarly the general equation for the shear stresses in a laminate (see preceding section)

$$\tau=\frac{VQ^*}{bEI} \qquad (15\text{-}57)$$

can be used for any sandwich. For the symmetrical sandwich the value of $\tau$ can be closely approximated by

$$\tau=\frac{2V}{b(h+c)} \qquad (15\text{-}58)$$

**c. Axially-Loaded Sandwich.** Edge-loaded sandwiches such as columns and walls are subject to failure by overstressing the facings or core, or by buckling of the member as a whole. Direct stresses in facings and core can be calculated by assuming that their strains are equal, so that

$$P=\sigma_f A_f+\sigma_c A_c \qquad (15\text{-}59)$$

$$=\sigma_f\left(A_f+A_c\frac{E_c}{E_f}\right) \qquad (15\text{-}59\text{a})$$

where

$\quad P=$ total load

$\quad \sigma_f=$ facing stress

$\quad \sigma_c=$ core stress

$\quad A_f=$ cross-sectional area of facings

$\quad A_c=$ cross-sectional area of core

Usually the elastic modulus $E_c$ of the core is so small that the core carries little of the total load, and the equation can be simplified by ignoring the last term, so that for a sandwich $b$ wide with facings $t$ thick,

$$P = 2\sigma_f b t \tag{15-60}$$

The column buckling load of a sandwich $L$ long simply supported at the ends is given by

$$P = \frac{\pi^2 E I}{L^2 \left(1 + \frac{\pi^2 E I}{L^2 N}\right)^2} \tag{15-61}$$

This variation of the Euler equation takes into account the low shear stiffness of the core.

For wall panels held in line along their vertical edges an approximate buckling formula is

$$P = \frac{4\pi^2 E I}{b^2 \left(1 + \frac{\pi^2 E I}{b^2 N}\right)^2} \tag{15-62}$$

provided the length $L$ of the panel is at least as great as the width $b$ and provided the second term in the bracket of the denominator is not greater than unity.

## 2. Filament-Wound Shells, Internal Hydrosatic Pressure

This presentation is based upon the work reported by Pipkin and Rivlin (4).

**a. Basic Equations.** Cylindrically symmetric shells are considered which are of the form $r = r\ (z)$ in a system of cylindrical polar coordinates $(r,\ \theta,\ z)$. Inextensible fibers are wound on and bonded to this shell in such a way that at any point on it equal numbers of fibers are inclined at angles $a$ and $\pi - a$ to the line of latitude ($z =$ constant) passing through that point. At a point $(r,\ \theta,\ z)$ of the shell there are $n_1,\ n_{12}$ . . . $n_p$ fibers, per unit length measured perpendicular to the length of the fibers, with positive inclinations $a_1,\ a_2,\ \ldots\ a_p$; and an equal number of fibers with inclinations $\pi - a_1,\ \pi - a,\ \ldots\ \pi - a_p$, to the line of latitude passing through $(r,\ \theta,\ z)$. The number $n_1,\ n_2\ \ldots\ n_p$, and angles $a_1,\ a_2\ \ldots\ a_p$ are independent of $\theta$ and, since $r$ is a function of $z$, they may be regarded as functions of $z$ only.

The shell is subjected to internal hydrostatic pressure $P$ and all resulting forces are carried by the fibers, which are considered to constitute an undeformable membrane. $T_1$ and $T_2$ are the normal components of stress in the latitudinal and longitudinal directions at a point $(r, \theta, z)$. Because of cylindrical symmetry, $T_1$ and $T_2$ are independent of $\theta$; and because there are equal numbers of fibers inclined at $a_i$ and $\pi - a_i$, $(i=1,2, \ldots p)$, the shearing components of stress are zero.

Let $\tau_1, \tau_2, \ldots \tau_p$ be the tensions at $(r, \theta, z)$ in the fibers inclined at $a_1, a_2 \ldots a_p$. Then because of symmetry, $\tau_i$ $(i=1, 2, \ldots p)$ must also be the tensions in the fibers inclined at $\pi - a_i$. The number of fibers with inclination $a_i$ per unit length measured along a line of longitude $(\theta = \text{constant})$ is $n_i \cos a_i$. Resolving the tensions in the fibers in the latitudinal direction the latitudinal tension $T_1$ is obtained

$$T_1 = 2 \sum_{i=1}^{p} \tau_i n_i \cos^2 a_i \qquad (15\text{-}63)$$

Similarly, the number of fibers inclined at $a_i$ per unit length measured along a line of latitude $(z = \text{const})$ is $n_i \sin a_i$, and resolving the tensions in fibers parallel to the longitudinal direction, the longitudinal tension $T_2$ is obtained

$$T_2 = 2 \sum_{i=1}^{p} \tau_i \sin^2 a_i \qquad (15\text{-}64)$$

If $k_1$ and $k_2$ are the curvatures of the membrane in the latitudinal and longitudinal directions

$$k_1 = \frac{1}{r} \frac{dz}{d} \qquad \text{and} \qquad k_2 = \frac{d}{dr}\left(\frac{dz}{d\sigma}\right) \qquad (15\text{-}65)$$

where $\tau$ is the distance from the equator, measured along a line of longitude.

The equations of equilibrium for the membrane are

$$k_1 T_2 = \tfrac{1}{2}P \quad \text{equilibrium in direction normal to membrane}$$

$$k_1 T_1 + k_2 T_2 = P \quad \text{equilibrium along a line of longitude} \qquad (15\text{-}66)$$

Solving for $T_1$ and $T_2$ and combining

$$\sum_{i=1}^{p} \tau_i n_i \cos^2 a_i = \frac{P}{4k_1}\left(2 - \frac{k_2}{k_1}\right)$$

$$\sum_{i=1}^{p} \tau_i n_i \sin^2 a_i = P/4k_1 \qquad (15\text{-}67)$$

Since $\tau_i$ and $n_i$ must be positive, and $P$ and $k_i$ are inherently positive

$$2k, \geq k_2$$

**b. Weight of Fiber.** Consider a ring lying between $z$ and $z+dz$. A single fiber with inclination $a$ to the latitudinal direction has a length $d\sigma/\sin a$, where $d\sigma$ is the width of the ring measured along a line of longitude. The number of fibers at inclination $a_i$ per unit length of a line of latitude is $n_i \sin a_i$. The total length of fiber in the ring is therefore $4\pi_r$.

$$(n_1 + n_2 \ldots n_p)\,d\sigma$$

If the mass per unit length of fiber is $\rho$, the total mass of fiber covering the surface is

$$M = 4\pi\rho\!\int r(n_1 + n_2 + \ldots n_p)\frac{d\sigma}{dz}dz \tag{15-68}$$

**c. Minimum Weight.** If each fiber supports its maximum tensile force $\tau_1$ the minimum weight of fiber required to withstand the internal pressure $P$ is simply related to the volume of the vessel $V$ by the following relationship

$$M = (3\rho P/\tau)V \tag{15-69}$$

For example, for an ellipsoid of revolution in which $Z$ is the semi-axis of revolution, and $R$ is the semiaxis at right angles to $Z$, $V = (4/3)\pi R^2 Z$, and

$$M = 4\pi\rho P R^2 Z/\tau \tag{15-70}$$

**d. Isotensoid Design.** In isotensoid design every fiber is at the same tension $\tau$ and if $\tau$ is at the same time the maximum stress the fiber is permitted to carry, this also becomes the minimum weight design. For this to be true, the inequalities must become equalities in which $\tau_i = \tau$.

Rewriting:

$$\sum_{i=1}^{p} n_i \cos^2 a_i = \frac{P}{4\tau k_1}\left(2 - \frac{k_2}{k_1}\right)$$

$$\tag{15-71}$$

$$\sum_{i=1}^{P} n_i \sin^2 a_i = P/4\tau k_1$$

Adding these together

$$\sum_{i=1}^{P} n_i = \frac{P}{4\tau k_1}\left(3 - \frac{k_2}{k_1}\right) \qquad (15\text{-}72)$$

Any choice of $n_i \cos^2 a_i$ and $n_i \sin^2 a_i$, both functions of $z$ which satisfy the equation, provides an isotensoid design of minimum mass $M$.

**e. Geodesic-Isotensoid Design.** On a surface of revolution, a geodesic satisfies the following equation

$$r \cos a = R \cos \beta \qquad (15\text{-}73)$$

in which $a$ is the inclination of the geodesic to the line of latitude that has a radial distance $r$ from the axis, and $\beta$ is the inclination of the geodesic to the line of latitude of radius $R$. Attention here is restricted to shells of revolution in which $r$ decreases with increasing $z^2$. An equator occurs at $z = 0$, all geodesics cross the equator, and all geodesics have an equation with $R$ the radius at the equator.

If $r > R \cos \beta$, then $\cos a > 1$ and $a$ is imaginary. Therefore $r = R \cos \beta$ gives the extreme lines of latitude on the shell reached by the geodesic.

If $N(\beta) \sin \beta d\beta$ is the number of fibers per unit length of the equator with inclinations to it lying between $\beta$ and $\beta + d\beta$, it can be shown that for a sphere

$$N(\beta) = PR/\tau\pi \qquad (15\text{-}74)$$

The fiber distribution is independent of the angle $\beta$. For a cone with half-vertex angle $\gamma$

$$N(\beta) = \frac{3PR \cos \beta}{4\tau \cos \gamma} \qquad (15\text{-}75)$$

For an ellipsoid of revolution

$$N(\beta) = \frac{PR^2}{\tau\pi Z}\left[\frac{1 + (3/2)\nu \cos^2\beta}{1 + \nu \cos^2\beta}\right.$$
$$\left. + \frac{3}{4}(-\nu)^{\frac{1}{2}} \cos \beta \ln\frac{1 - (-\nu)^{\frac{1}{2}} \cos \beta}{1 + (-\nu)^{\frac{1}{2}} \cos \beta}\right] \qquad (15\text{-}76)$$

in which $\nu = (Z^2 - R^2)/R^2$ and provided that $\nu \geq 0$.

## III. PROGRESS IN HEAT-RESISTANT POLYMER DEVELOPMENT

### by Donald V. Rosato

This review will provide information on different resins which are applicable for use in reinforced and also unreinforced plastics. Recent years have seen intensive research efforts to develop more stable and oxidation-resistant polymer systems for continuous service at 300°C and above. The impetus for these efforts has been supplied largely by current and anticipated aerospace requirements. Scores of new polymer systems are currently being investigated, but only a relatively few significantly improved materials have achieved commercial status to date. However, the remarkable rapidity with which some of these latter polymers have moved from the laboratory to the market place provides some insight into the probable pace of future developments (4).

Polymers are highly valued engineering materials because they possess unique properties and combinations of properties. These properties include low density, high strength-to-weight ratios, ease of fabrication into end-use items, valuable electrical and thermal insulative properties, together with relatively good moisture and chemical resistance. Unfortunately, these valuable properties can be destroyed by heat at temperatures at which engineering materials are often required to perform.

If any polymer is heated to a sufficiently high temperature, both reversible and irreversible changes in its structure occur. These changes can be either useful or highly undesirable. Useful changes include: (*1*) the reversible softening of thermoplastics that permits them to be converted into useful shapes, and (*2*) irreversible chemical changes occurring during the curing of thermoset materials. The undesirable changes include chain scissions, the development of strength-destroying degrees of crosslinking, the formation of low molecular weight volatile products, or various combinations of these modes of degradation.

Realistic appraisals of the potentials of many of the new polymer systems still in their early stages of development are virtually impossible. The true thermal stability of a polymer is most meaningfully defined by the temperature range over which it retains useful properties. In general, these critical properties are not determined until a polymer reaches a fairly advanced state of development.

Experimentally, the primary method used for screening, evaluating, and comparing the stabilities of various heat-resistant polymers is thermogravimetric analysis (TGA). In this technique, a polymer sample is heated, either isothermally or at a constant rate on a thermobalance in air, an inert atmosphere, or a vacuum, and the sample's weight change versus temperature or time is recorded. This technique provides an excellent means for screening new materials, but the polymers' maximum practical service temperatures cannot be determined from a thermogram which shows weight changes, and not property data. Very significant property changes can occur in a material without a weight change being detected. In many cases these changes can be observed by supplementing the TGA analyses with differential thermal analyses (DTA), which reveal enthalpic changes associated with oxidation, glass transition and crystalline melting temperatures, crosslinking, etc., occurring as the temperature of the polymer is increased. Despite their limitations, thermograms illustrate some basic differences between conventional thermoplastic and thermoset materials, and the new generation of more heat-resistant polymers.

To possess useful properties at elevated temperatures, a polymer must retain some degree of chain integrity and rigidity. Most conventional thermoplastics soften or melt at temperatures below their decomposition points, so their service temperature ceilings are determined more by their softening than actual decomposition temperatures (Fig. 15-20). On the other hand, thermoset materials are essentially infusible after curing and tend to retain their useful properties at temperatures which more nearly correspond to their thermal breakdown temperatures (Fig. 15-21). In addition to somewhat higher service temperatures, the thermosets generally provide relatively stable residues at high temperatures, while most thermoplastics are reduced to volatile decomposition products.

Typical thermograms of the newer heat-resistant polymers (Fig. 15-22) show that the initial breakdowns of these polymers tend to occur at somewhat higher temperatures than for the conventional thermoplastics and thermosets. In addition, some of these polymers undergo small weight losses at high temperatures, indicating that relatively stable residues are formed.

For some years, modest increases in the maximum service temperatures of thermoplastic materials have been achieved by modifying the polymer chains to render them more rigid at elevated temperatures. This has been accomplished by building crystallinity into the polymers and by the use of polar groups in, or polar groups or bulky substituents as pendent groups on, the chains. However, the thermal decompositions of these, as well as thermoset materials, depends ultimately on the stabilities of the structural units and linkages that make up the polymer chains.

Polymer research has revealed certain structural requirements that the more heat-resistant polymeric materials must possess. These requirements include:

*1.* A high molecular weight to provide strength, flexibility, toughness, and general "plastic properties";

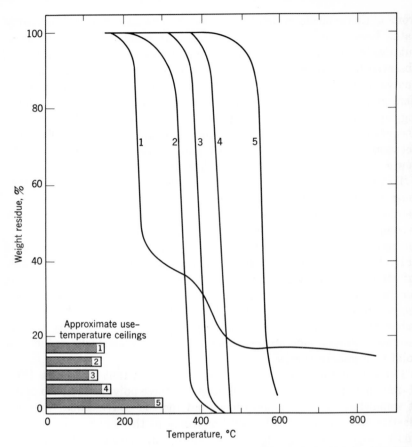

Fig. 15-20. TGA curves and use-temperature ceilings of thermoplastics. The TGA curves of typical thermoplastics (except PTFE) show that they decompose catastrophically at below 400°C. Their service temperature ceilings are considerably below their decomposition temperatures. *1*, polyvinyl chloride; *2*, polymethyl methacrylate; *3*, polystyrene; *4*, polyethylene; *5*, polytetrafluoroethylene.

*2.* A minimum of readily oxidizable hydrogen atoms, and a maximum of highly stable structural units (aromatic and/or heterocyclic rings) in the chains;

*3.* Connecting linkages for the stable chains units which provide flexibility, and which are also highly stable;

*4.* No mechanism by which the chains can readily undergo thermal depolymerizations;

*5.* The polymer must, at some time, exist as a soluble or formable intermediate to permit its fabrication into useful forms;

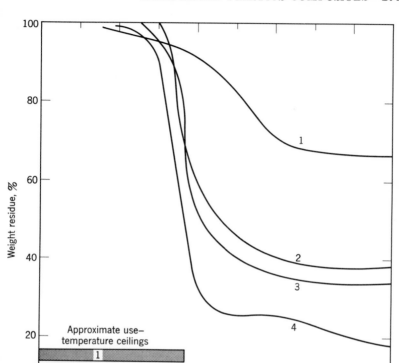

Fig. 15-21. TGA curves and use-temperature ceilings of thermosets. The thermo-sets decompose drastically at below 400°C. As indicated by the plateaus to the right, however, thermosets form heat-stable residues. Their use-temperatures tend to be higher than most thermoplastics with similar breakdown temperatures. *1*, silicone resin; *2*, phenolic; *3*, epoxy; *4*, polyester.

*6.* Technologically useful properties for a prolonged period of use at the intended service temperature.

Most of these requirements are common to polymers in general. The breakthrough providing a new generation of heat-resistant organic polymers has come from research on criteria 2 and 3. Clues to the identities of the required stable chain units and connecting linkages were provided largely by studies of the stabilities of model organic compounds and polymers. A brief consideration of some of the interesting new polymer systems will serve to illustrate the progress that

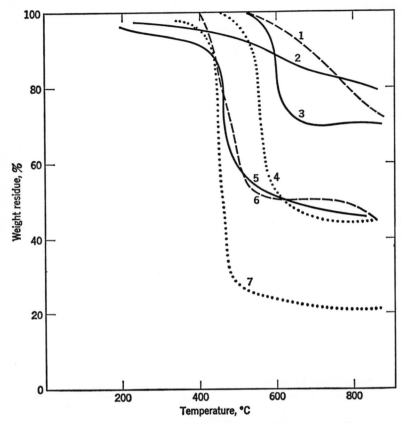

Fig. 15-22. TGA curves of polyaromatic polymers. The decomposition temperatures of these materials are in the 400–600°C range. At the same time, a number of the polyaromatics have extremely stable residues. *1,* polybenzimidazole; *2,* polyphenylene; *3,* polyimide; *4,* polyphenyl ether; *5,* polyoxadiazole; *6,* polyphenyl sulfide; *7,* polycarbonate.

has been made in the development of more heat-resistant materials. Several of these polymers are now being marketed, and property and processing data are available. Others are still in their early stages of development, and data are fragmentary or nonexistent. In some cases where a new polymer is intended primarily for use in composites, the ultimate properties are extremely dependent upon fabrication variables. In these cases, it is probably still too early to attempt a valid appraisal of their actual properties and potentials.

An infinite variety of polymers containing stable aromatic and heterocyclic rings in their chains can be synthesized, and numerous structural modifications of the polymer types discussed in this article can and do exist. Consequently, the chemical structures shown (Fig. 15-23) are simply intended to illustrate representative examples of the subject polymer types.

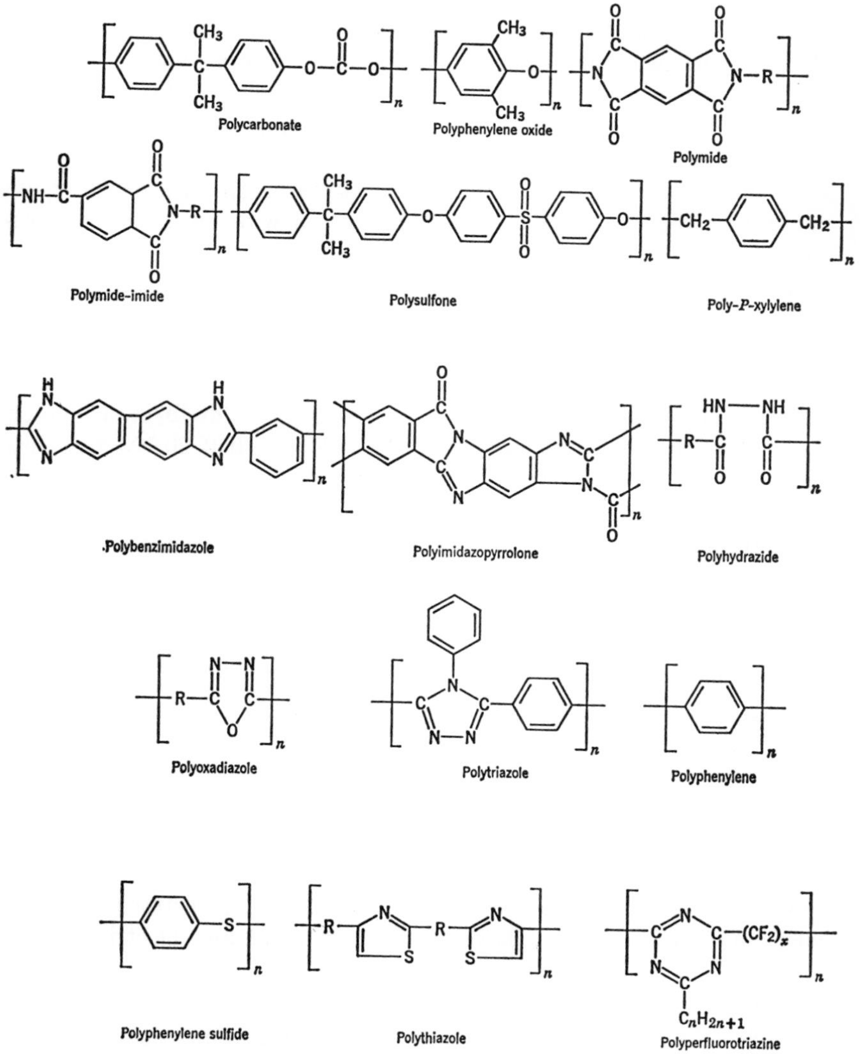

Fig. 15-23. Chemical structures of some of the heat resistant organic polymers discussed in this article. (From *Plastics Design and Processing*.)

## A. Polycarbonates

The polycarbonates, originally developed in Germany by Farbenfabriken Bayer AG, have been marketed in the United States under the tradenames Merlon (Mobay Chemical Co.) and Lexan (General Electric Co.) for about five years. These polymers, prepared by reacting bisphenol-A with either phosgene or a dialkyl carbonate, are available in either transparent or opaque forms, and are noted for their exceptional toughness over a wide temperature range. The polycarbonates are highly ductile (more than 100% in standard tests) are self-extinguishing, have heat deflection temperatures (264 psi) in the 130–138°C temperature range, and can withstand continuous service at temperatures up to 122°C. The electrical properties of the polycarbonates remain relatively constant over a wide range of temperatures and humidity. The polymers resist water, acids, and oxidizing and reducing agents, but can be dissolved in aromatic and chlorinated solvents.

Typical mechanical properties for the polycarbonates include tensile strength, 8000–9500 psi; tensile modulus, $3.5 \times 10^5$ psi; flexural strength, 13,000 psi; and impact strength, 12–16 ft-lb/in. of notch. The polycarbonates are moldable (249–330°C/1,000–20,000 psi) into parts having very close tolerances, and which are exceptionally dimensionally stable and machineable. Present applications for the polycarbonates capitalize on the toughness, heat-resistance, and insulative properties of the polymers, and include housings for hand tools and electrical appliances, lighting fixtures, glazing, blow molded bottles, etc.

## B. Polyphenylene Oxide

The polyphenylene oxides are commercially available (General Electric Company) aromatic polyethers prepared from 2,6-xylenol by a rapid oxidation process known as "oxidative coupling." Both transparent and opaque grades are available. The polyphenylene oxides have good hydrolytic resistance, are soluble in chlorinated and aromatic hydrocarbons, and have good mechanical and electrical properties over a wide temperature range (−170 to 190°C), but are not so thermally stable as polyimides or polybenzimidazoles. General Electric's Grade C-1001 PPO is a tough, rigid, dimensionally stable polymer exhibiting high modulus values at temperatures exceeding 120°C. The material is self-extinguishing, and has a brittle-point of

−170°C. Representative properties of the polyphenylene oxides include heat deflection temperature, 192–194°C at 264 psi; tensile strength at yield, 10,000–11,000 psi; tensile modulus, $3.6$–$3.8 \times 10^5$ psi; tensile elongation at break, 5–6%; and flexural strength at yield, 14,000–15,000 psi. The polyphenylene oxides can be injection molded (343°C/8,000–12,000 psi) or extruded (288°C) on standard equipment, and can be machined like brass.

## C. Polyimides

One of the most highly developed classes of new heat-resistant polymers are the polyimides, obtained by condensing aromatic tetrabasic acid anhydrides with aromatic diamines. At present, du Pont, Narmco Research and Development, General Electric, and Shawinigan Resins (Monsanto) have interests in these materials. Du Pont has been marketing polyimide-based wire enamel (Pyre-ML), insulating varnish, and coated glass fabrics since 1961. The insulating varnish possesses good electrical properties in the −190 to 340°C temperature range. Polyimide film (Kapton) having useful mechanical and electrical properties from −269 to 400°C was made commercial by du Pont in 1965. This film can be Teflon-coated to render it heat-sealable. Since polyimides are essentially nonfusible and difficult to fabricate by conventional polymer shaping processes, Du Pont is employing special processes, including a high temperature-pressure procedure similar to that used in powder metallurgy, to fabricate its polyimide (Polymer SP) into finished parts (called Vespel). This process is useful for producing parts for low friction, high temperature applications.

The polyimides show good radiation resistance, and retain useful properties after absorbing radiation doses as high as 6.000 megarads. The Air Force Materials Laboratory has evaluated polyimide laminates. Typical curing conditions are 200 psi at 370°C for 1 hr. Laminates have shown 25% strength retention after 1000 hr at 315°C. The resins do lose considerable strength in air at service temperatures above 315°C. Typical polyimide film properties include tensile strength, 24,000 psi; modulus, 415,000 psi; elongation, 65%. Present applications seen for polyimides include radomes, aircraft leading edge structures, turbine compressor blades, bearings, adhesives, laminates, wire and cable wrap, motor insulation, coatings, etc.

## D. Polyamide-Imide and Polyester

The polyamide-imides are structurally similar to the polyimides, but contain amide linkages to make them more readily processible. Amoco Chemicals Corporation has commercialized a polyamide-imide (AI Polymer) for use in wire coating, laminates, electrical insulation (to 220°C) and high temperature coating applications. Polymers of this type can be produced by reacting trimellitic dianhydride with an aromatic diamine. The Amoco polymer is supplied as a powder that is soluble in a number of organic solvents. The polymer is generally fabricated from its solutions using thermal cures at about 250°C. Monsanto provides a similar laminating resin (Skygard 700) for use in glass cloth laminate applications requiring extended exposure at temperatures up to 370°C. Westinghouse is also developing polyamide-imide wire insulation, laminate, and molding resin materials.

## E. Polyesterimide

General Electric's Insulating Materials Department is doing exploratory work on polyesterimide polymers which are expected to rival polyimide and polyamide-imide materials. These polymers show good physical and electrical properties at high temperatures and a 20,000 hr service life at 230°C. The thermal-oxidative stabilities of the polyesterimides are described as being less than the best polyimides, but better than the aromatic polyesters.

A new type of thermally stable, fast curing thermosetting polyester resin system is being introduced (1967) to the reinforced plastics industry. This review deals with the general properties of the new B78-156 resins and the utilization of the unique properties of these materials with various reinforcements to give general purpose and specific type composites. Frank Fekete and John S. McNally from the Research Department, Koppers Company, Inc., Monroeville, Penna, have provided the information to be reviewed in this section which pertains to the Koppers B78-156 polyester resins.

A review of the various resins used in the moderate and high temperature areas of application in the electrical insulation and reinforced plastics industry is covered. The chemical structure of the various systems is shown. The advantages and disadvantages of each system in terms of electrical, thermal and handling properties are compared. The properties of the "new" B78-156 resins, as compared to the currently available systems, are highlighted.

The high degree of reactivity of the B78-156 resins resulting in very fast curing systems is supported by SPI Gel data determined at 180 and 240°F. The influence of the types of monomer, concentration of monomer, fillers, types of filler, catalysts and catalyst concentrations on the SPI Gel times of the B78-156 resins is fully covered.

The thermal resistance of the B78-156 resins in cast and reinforced composite form is reported in terms of weight loss and retention of physical properties through the temperature range of 150–260°C.

The unique electrical properties of these B78-156 resins in cast form are described. The retention of electrical properties after subjection to various temperatures, is shown for the cast and reinforced composite forms. These electrical properties include dielectric strength, arc resistance, track resistance, power factor, dielectric constant, volume resistivity, surface resistivity and insulation resistance.

Special emphasis is placed on the properties of B78-156 resins in composite uses. These composite uses include filament winding, laminating (glass mat and glass fiber laminates), premixes, pultrusion, prepreging and prethickened reinforced systems.

The composite properties of other resin systems in glass mat systems are compared with that of the B78-156 resins. A description of some special features of these new resins in terms of gloss, fast release, excellent wetout, craze and crack free surface properties and surface smoothness is reported.

## 1. Introduction

In the past two years, a great deal of interest has been generated in the reinforced plastics industry for very fast curing resin systems. Much of this interest centers around producing matched metal molded parts for the automotive, transportation and appliance fields at a production rate which would be more competitive with a metals industry stamping procedure.

A series of resins have been introduced for use in prethickened glass mat and in premix molding applications. These resins are reported to respond to being cured rapidly when USP-245 is used as the catalyst system. These materials are described as general purpose type materials without any degree of thermal stability. These systems also lack chemical resistance, good electricals at higher than room temperatures and lack of higher temperature physical properties, specifically modulus retention at 300°F and higher.

The B78-156 resins are being introduced to the reinforced plastics industry as highly reactive fast curing thermosetting polyester resins. The B78-156 resin can be diluted with the most commonly used monomers, such as styrene and vinyltoluene in concentrations up to 55–60%. The use of 55% vinyltoluene produces a very fast curing and thermally stable resin system, utilizable through 225°C range of operation. This resin and its styrene counterpart exhibit the very fast cures needed for automation, along with a very necessary companion property of excellent release and surface smoothness and gloss.

The B78-156 resin systems exhibit low specific gravity and can be utilized to produce molded parts with ~25% less resin per square foot area. The B78-156 resin system is the only resin system available to the various facets of the cast, filled and reinforced plastics industry with a very high degree of versatility. This versatility permits the use of various styrene or vinyltoluene diluted versions of this resin in a wide range of general purpose and specific plastics applications. The areas of use include materials requiring heat resistance, high heat distortion properties, excellent electrical properties, good chemical resistance, retention of physical properties in cast and laminate form at room, moderate and elevated temperatures (specifically high modulus), high compatibility and coreactivity, and alloying and blending properties.

## 2. Review of Resins Used in Composites

Over the years, a variety of different resins have been and are presently being used for moderate and high temperature structural and electrical composites. Some of the disadvantages have included high cost, low reactivity (slow cures), handling problems, dermatitis, toxicity, high cure temperatures, need of exotic difunctional monomers as dilutents, poor filler wet-out, poor glass wet-out, poor electricals, crazing at temperature, long-time stepwise postcure for optimum properties, high weight loss, degradation—oxidation at temperature, poor monomer coreactivity, poor mold release characteristics, poor surface gloss, poor track resistance, poor ultraviolet stability, poor chemical resistance and lack of weatherability. One or more of these disadvantages apply to the resins to be chemically depicted in the following paragraphs.

The epoxy resins have been the workhorses of the industry for many years. Different structural types have been synthesized for use

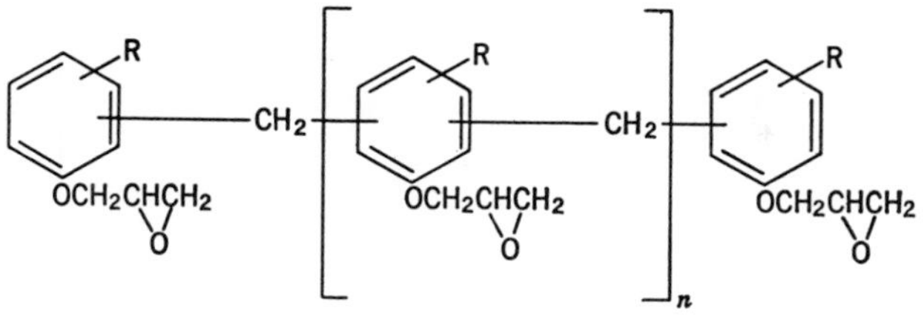

Fig. 15-24. Epoxidized phenol-formaldehyde Novolac resins.

at various temperature ranges. Figure 15-24 shows the chemical structure of epoxidized phenolformaldehyde novolak resins. These systems gave good electricals and good heat resistance. They require specific hardeners, have handling problems and are expensive.

Recent patents by British (989,201 April 14, 1965 and 1,006,587 October 6, 1965), Canadian (725,249 January 4, 1966) and United States (3,221,043 November 30, 1965 and 3,256,226 June 14, 1966) are issued in the authors name in which the epoxidized phenolformaldehyde novolak resins depicted in Fig. 15-24 have been chemically modified for greater reactivity. Figure 15-25 shows the formation of thermosetting acrylic phenol-formaldehyde novolak resins by reacting the novolak resins in Fig. 15-24 with n moles of acrylic or methacrylic acid. The resulting resins are more reactive and can be cured by free radical catalysts. These resins have good electricals, better monomer compatibility, and good physicals at temperature. Some of the drawbacks are high cost, need of expensive difunctional monomers for heat resistance, poor mold release and fairly high weight loss at temperatures of 225°C and above.

A series of other epoxies have been synthesized and used for inter-

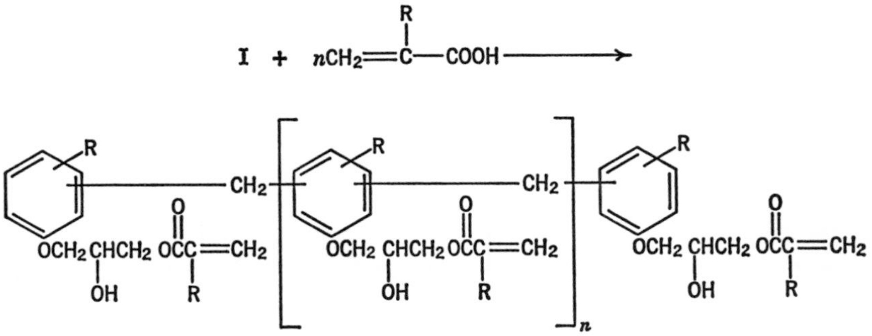

Fig. 15-25. Phenol-formaldehyde Novolac thermosetting acrylic resin.

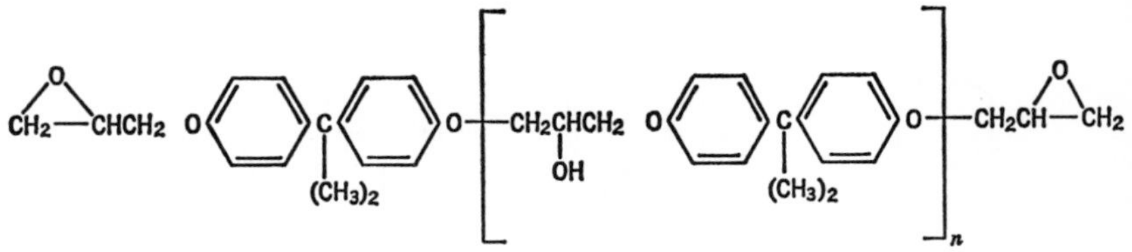

Fig. 15-26. Polybisphenol epoxy resins.

mediate temperature performance. Figure 15-26 shows the structure of a series of polybisphenol epoxy resins. British, Canadian and United States patents shows that these polybisphenol epoxy resins have been modified by reaction with acrylic or methacrylic acid to give thermosetting acrylic polybisphenol resins as depicted in Fig. 15-27. Another aromatic type epoxy being used today is the bisphenol epoxy resins as shown by Fig. 15-28. Again, recent patents have been issued showing the modification of the bisphenol epoxy resins with acrylic or methacrylic acids to give thermosetting acrylic bisphenol resins as depicted in Fig. 15-29. The same advantages and disadvantages apply to these systems as was described for the novolak epoxy and thermosetting acrylic novolak resins.

Several years ago some comprehensive work work was carried out by one United States company with the triglyceride epoxy compound (aliphatic type) shown in Fig. 15-30. This aliphatic epoxy derivative was modified to an unsaturated thermosetting acrylic triglyceride resin by reacting with acrylic or methacrylic acid as shown in Fig. 15-31. These resins were free radical initiated, more reactive with a range of monomers with fairly good room temperature physicals and electricals. Drawbacks were lack of heat resistance, no retention of higher temperature physicals and electricals, toxicity (dermatitis) and fairly high cost systems.

A new variation of thermosetting resins is depicted in Fig. 15-32

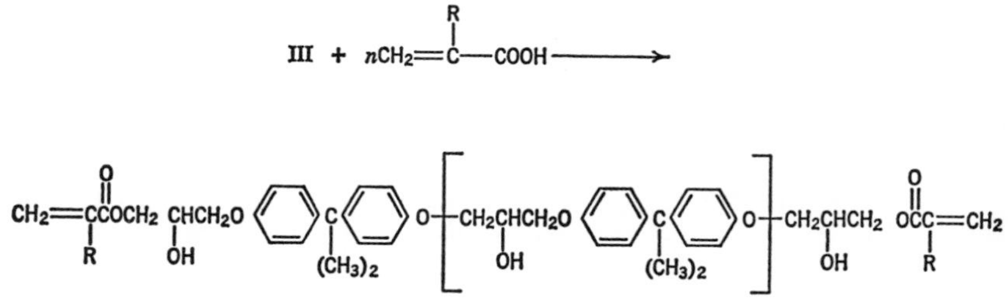

Fig. 15-27. Polybisphenol thermosetting acrylic resin.

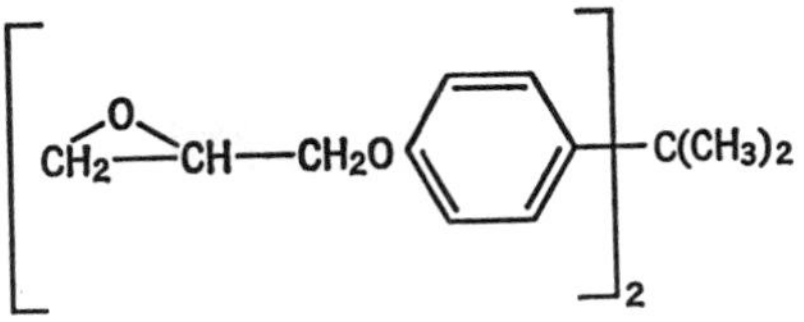

Fig. 15-28. Bisphenol epoxy resin.

as a vinyl thermosetting resins and appears to be a modification of bisphenol epoxy resins with a maleic or fumaric form of unsaturation. The claimed advantages are rapid cures, high filler acceptance and good molding properties. The disadvantages are dermatitis, lack of high heat resistance, lack of high temperature electricals and physical properties.

Table 15-6 describes the properties of another series of distinctly different materials used for higher temperature areas of applications. These are polybutadiene or modified copolymer versions of these butadiene resins. Advantages are good heat resistance, good electricals and good physicals. Disadvantages include slow cures, higher cure temperatures, poorer filler and glass wet-out, the need of specific high temperature monomers, and high pressure molding conditions.

The B78-156 resin systems were synthesized with the expressed objective of introducing a moderate cost resin system to the industry and capable of a multiplicity of uses. The B78-156 resin system can be used in almost all areas of use depicted by the previously described resins. The specific properties of B78-156 resins are shown in Table 15-7. The present and potential areas of use for the B78-156 resins are described in Table 15-8. The composite uses and potential composite applications are summarized in Table 15-9.

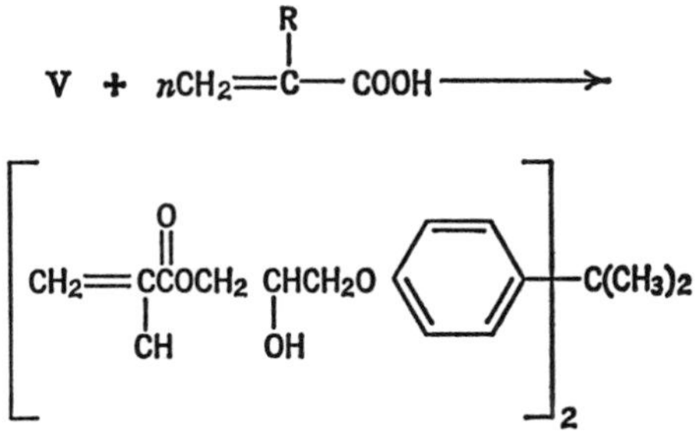

Fig. 15-29. Bisphenol thermosetting acrylic resin.

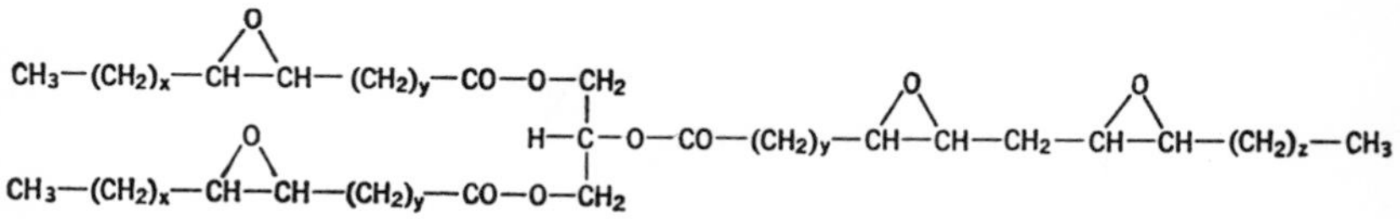

Fig. 15-30.  Triglyceride epoxy compound.

## 3. Typical Properties of B78-156 Resins

The B78-156 resin in basic monomer-free form ranges from semi-solid to solid in appearance. The resins are almost water white in appearance. Table 15-10 shows the typical properties of the B78-156 resin cut with 40 and 55% styrene and vinyltoluene. The acid number ranges from 10–20 and the color by the Gardner scale ranges from 1–2. The specific gravity of these systems range from 0.922 to 1.050. The styrene systems range in viscosity from 1100 to 120 and in vinyltoluene systems from 1750 to 150 cps. These values are representative as absolute specifications, have not been established.

## 4. Curing Characteristics of B78-156 Resins

The B78-156 resins exhibit very fast cures. To determine the degree of reactivity and fast curing characteristics of different monomers and monomer concentrations, SPI Gel data was run at 180 and 240°F. The SPI Gel data was determined for 40 and 55 percent styrene and vinyltoluene utilizing 0.5% USP-245 and 1.0% BPO. The data is recorded in Table 15-11. The table shows gel time, cure

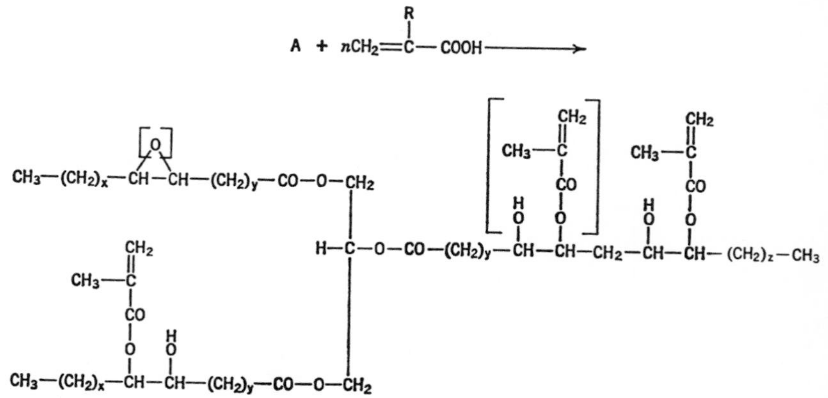

Fig. 15-31.  Aliphatic acrylic thermosetting resin.

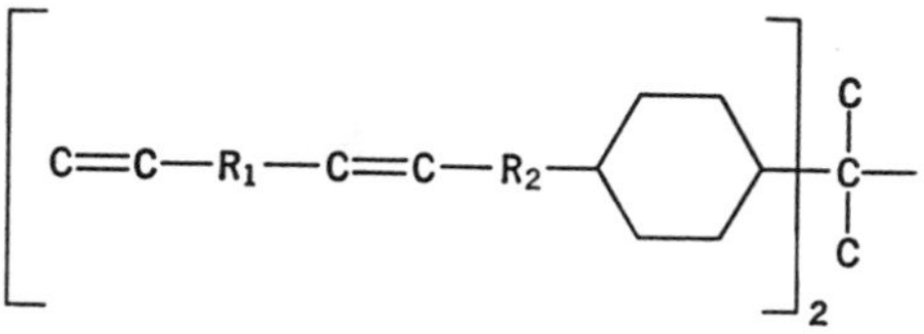

$$\left[\ C{=}C{-}R_1{-}C{=}C{-}R_2{-}\bigcirc{-}\overset{\displaystyle C}{\underset{\displaystyle C}{|}}\overset{|}{C}{-}\ \right]_2$$

Fig. 15-32. Vinyl thermosetting resin.

time, kickoff and peak exotherm data. Table 15-11 shows that the USP-245 system is faster at 180 and 240°F than the BPO system. The data also shows that the 40 and 55% vinyltoluene systems are faster curing than the 40 and 50% styrene systems. The 55% styrene and vinyltoluene systems exhibit faster gel times than the 40% dilutions at 180°F but are reversed at the 240°F temperature.

The data shows that gel times as low as 10 sec and cure times of 35 sec are possible at 240°F with the vinyltoluene system and USP-245 as the catalyst.

Table 15-12 shows the reactivity of four different monomer systems at 180 and 240°F with 0.5% USP-245 and 1.0% BPO. Chlorostyrene has the fastest gel times at 180°F. with both USP-245 and BPO. At 240°F the 40% vinyltoluene system is as reactive as the 40% chlorostyrene and possibly more reactive.

TABLE 15-6.  Polybutadiene Resins

Composition and Physical Properties of Buton Resins

| Resin | Buton 100 | Buton 150 | Buton A500 | Buton impreg. varnish |
|---|---|---|---|---|
| Chemical composition | Butadiene-styrene copolymer | Polybuta-diene | Butadiene-styrene 20 wt % styrene | Butadiene-styrene graft polymer |
| Microstructure | 1,2-Adduct 65% | 1,2-Adduct 65% | 1,2-Adduct 65% | — |
| Iodins No. (approx.) | 330 | 410 | 320 | — |
| Specific gravity 73°F (23°C) | 0.92 | 0.89 | 0.92 | 0.95 |
| Physical state | Viscous liquid | Viscous liquid | Viscous liquid | Toluene solution |
| Viscosity Brookfield at 73°F (23°C), poise | 2000–3500 | 250–1000 | 3500 5000 | 7–14 |

TABLE 15-7.  Specific Properties of B78-156 Resins

| |
|---|
| 1. Excellent thermal resistance |
| 2. Outstanding electrical properties |
| 3. Good chemical resistance |
| 4. High surface gloss |
| 5. Craze and crack resistance |
| 6. Trouble-free mold release |
| 7. Fast, efficient cures |
| 8. High monomer and filler acceptance |
| 9. Low weight loss |
| 10. High heat distortion values |
| 11. Mechanical strength at high temperatures |
| 12. Retention of strength at intermediate and high temperatures |
| 13. Room temperature curability |
| 14. Excellent response to being prethickened |
| 15. Available with excellent fire resistance |
| 16. Excellent track resistance |
| 17. UV Stability and weather resistance |

## 5. Stability of B78-156 Resins

Table 15-13 covers the catalyzed and uncatalyzed stability of 40%S and VT diluted resin systems. The results show once more the greater reactivity of VT systems over S systems. The S system has a 13 day stability at 55°C as compared to 6 days for VT. With 1% BPO at room temperature the S stability is 8 days, while the VT stability is 5 days. When 0.5% USP-245 is the catalyst, the room temperature stability for the S system is 4 days while the VT sta-

TABLE 15-8.  Koplac B78-156 Potential Areas of Use

| |
|---|
| 1. Laminating |
| 2. Casting |
| 3. Premixing |
| 4. Prepreging |
| 5. Prethickening |
| 6. Filament winding |
| 7. Impregnating |
| 8. Potting and encapsulating |
| 9. Varnishes |
| 10. Track resistant applications |
| 11. Hand layup uses |
| 12. Coatings |
| 13. Pultrusion applications |

TABLE 15-9.   Composite Uses and Potential Use of B78-156 Resins

---

1. Banding tapes
2. Slotsticks and channel
3. Rod and wedges
4. Electrical mat laminates
5. Electrical premix molding compounds
6. Cast and molded insulators
7. Fast curing laminating uses
8. Special molding uses
9. Filament wound pipe & thermal tubes
10. Use in aircraft, transportation &
    automotive applications

---

bility is 3 days. The stability of the systems can be increased to 7 days with a proprietary additive.

## 6.  Room Temperature Gel Data of B78-156 Resins

The B78-156 resins can be readily room temperature cured. This applies to both the styrene and vinyltoluene systems. Table 15-14 shows that the 45% styrene systems can be catalyzed with 0.25–0.50% MEKP and 0.025–0.050% CoN, to give gel times ranging from 3.6 to 1.1 hours. These gel times make it possible to carry out filament winding operations with reasonable pot life properties. Table 15-14 shows, also, that fast gel times to 7–25 min are possible with 1% MEKP and 0.1–0.2% CoN or 0.05–0.10% DEA with the 40% S systems.

## 7.  B78-156 Resin-Monomer and Resin-Monomer-Filler Viscosity Relationships

Figure 15-33 shows that the B78-156 resin can be diluted to 60% S and VT giving dilution viscosities ranging from 30,000 at 25% S

TABLE 15-10.   Typical Properties [a] of B78-156 Resins

| Monomer | Styrene | Styrene | VT | VT |
|---|---|---|---|---|
| Monomer content, % | 40 | 55 | 40 | 55 |
| Acid value | 15–20 | 10–15 | 15–20 | 10–15 |
| Color gardner | 1 | 1 | 1 | 2 |
| Sp. gravity, 77/77°F | 1.050 | 0.922 | 1.050 | 0.993 |
| Wt per gal, lbs | 8.74 | 7.70 | 8.74 | 8.28 |
| Visc., Brookfield No. 4 spindle, 60 rpm, cps | 1100 | 120 | 1750 | 150 |

[a] Values given are representative. Specifications have not been established.

TABLE 15-11.   Curing Characteristics of B78-156 Resin
Monomer Influence in Vinyl Toluene and Styrene Systems

| % Monomer | USP-245 (0.5%) 180°F | | | | 240°F | | | |
|---|---|---|---|---|---|---|---|---|
|  | G.T. (min) | C.T. (min) | K.O. °F | P.E. °F | G.T. (min) | C.T. (min) | K.O. °F | P.E. °F |
| 40S | 5'17" | 6'37" | 197 | 482 | 37" | 1'12" | 171 | 510 |
| 55S | 4'35" | 6'37" | 206 | 507 | 1'15" | 2'07" | 204 | 555 |
| 40VT | 5'02" | 6'07" | 191 | 466 | 10" | 35" | 148 | 484 |
| 55VT | 4'00" | 5'45" | 204 | 485 | 56" | 1'35" | 200 | 507 |
|  | | | | 1% BPO | | | | |
| 40S | 8'50" | 11'20" | 219 | 463 | 1'00" | 1'40" | 191 | 516 |
| 55S | 8'11" | 10'45" | 209 | 509 | 1'26" | 2'22" | 222 | 544 |
| 40VT | 7'35" | 9'30" | 207 | 446 | 30" | 1'00" | 165 | 484 |
| 55VT | 5'34" | 7'48" | 209 | 475 | 1'15" | 2'07" | 205 | 510 |

to 70 cps at 60% S and 50,000 to 80 cps for the 25% VT and the 60% VT. The viscosity relationships of these systems allows for high filler acceptance with several filler types.

Figure 15-34 shows the effect of ASP-400, McNamee Clay and silica flour on 40 and 55% styrene diluted B78-156 resins. Figure 15-35 shows the effect of the same fillers on 40 and 55% VT diluted B78-156 resins. The curves show that silica flour has the least effect on the viscosity of the resins, followed by ASP-400 and then McNamee Clay.

TABLE 15-12.   Curing Characteristics of B78-156 Resin
Monomer Influence at 180 and 240°F

|  | USP-245 (0.5%) 180°F | | | | 240°F | | | |
|---|---|---|---|---|---|---|---|---|
|  | G.T. (min) | C.T. (min) | K.O. °F | P.E. °F | G.T. (min) | C.T. (min) | K.O. °F | P.E. °F |
| 40S | 5'17" | 6'37" | 197 | 482 | 37" | 1'12" | 171 | 510 |
| 40VT | 5'02" | 6'07" | 191 | 466 | 10" | 35" | 148 | 484 |
| 20S/20VT | 5'12" | 6'10" | 191 | 470 | 25" | 1'03" | 166 | 495 |
| 40CS | 2'24" | 3'23" | 185 | 429 | 07" | 46" | 110 | 385 |
|  | | | | 1% BPO | | | | |
| 40S | 8'50" | 11'20" | 219 | 463 | 1'00" | 1'40" | 191 | 516 |
| 40VT | 7'35" | 9'30" | 207 | 446 | 30" | 1'00" | 165 | 484 |
| 20S/20VT | 7'25" | 9'22" | 205 | 455 | 40" | 1'10" | 182 | 499 |
| 40CS | 3'08" | 3'56" | 181 | 438 | 07" | 36" | 109 | 415 |

TABLE 15-13.  Catalyzed and Uncatalyzed Stability of B78-156 Resins

| % Monomer | System | Cat., % | Temp., °C | Stability, days |
|---|---|---|---|---|
| 40%S | B78–156 | 0 | 55 | 13 |
| 40%VT | B78–156 | 0 | 55 | 6 |
| 40%S | B78–156 | 1% BPO | R.T. | 8 |
| 40%VT | B78–156 | 1% BPO | R.T. | 5 (7) |
| 40%S | B78–156 | 0.5% USP–245 | R.T. | 4 (7) |
| 40%VT | B78–156 | 0.5% USP–245 | R.T. | 3 (7) |

Further studies with the calcium carbonate, hydrated alumina, and other fillers are underway.

## 8. B78-156 Resin-Monomer Copolymer Casting Properties

The physical properties of castings prepared from the 40 and 55% styrene and vinyltoluene systems are recorded in Table 15-15. The styrene systems were cured with 0.75% BPO, followed by 2 hr at 75°C and 2 hr at 135°C. The vinyltoluene systems were catalyzed with 0.75% USP-245, followed by 2 hr at 60°C, 1 hr at 75°C and 2 hr at 135°C. The data shows that very good tensile, flexural, impact, Barcol and heat distortion points are obtained, even at 55% styrene and vinyltoluene. The thermal resistance of the 55% styrene and vinyltoluene castings are as good as the 40% monomer systems. The weight loss being ~3.2% for the styrene systems and 1.0% for the VT systems. This information indicates that favorable economics is possible through the use of very high monomer dilutions without sacrificing the necessary physical and thermal properties.

The incorporation of a relatively small percent of a difunctional monomer, divinylbenzene, was studied in styrene, vinyltoluene and S/VT systems. The cures for each of the three systems are described

TABLE 15-14.  Room Temperature Gel Time Data for B78-156 Resin System

| System | % Styrene | % MEKP | % CoN | Gel time Min | Hours |
|---|---|---|---|---|---|
| B78–156 | 45 | 0.25 | 0.050 | 219 | 3.6 |
| B78–156 | 45 | 0.25 | 0.025 | 211 | 3.5 |
| B78–156 | 45 | 0.50 | 0.025 | 131 | 2.2 |
| B78–156 | 45 | 0.50 | 0.050 | 66 | 1.1 |

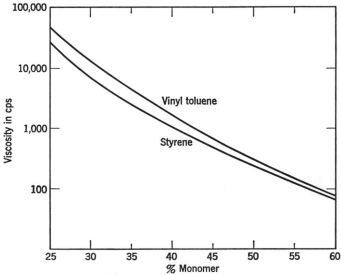

Fig. 15-33. Effect of monomer on the viscosity of B78-156 resins.

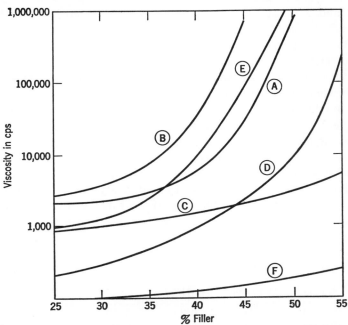

Fig. 15-34. Effect of fillers on the viscosity of B78-156 resins (styrene). *A,* 40% S-ASP-400; *B,* 40% S-McNamee clay; *C,* 40% S-silica flour; *D,* 55% S-ASP-400; *E,* 55% S-McNamee clay; *F,* 55% S-silica flour.

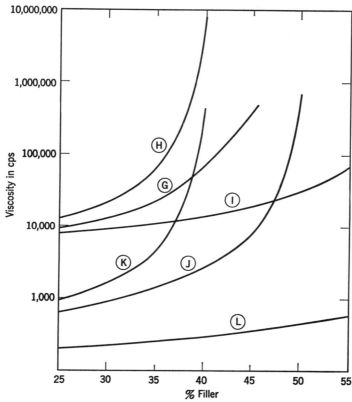

Fig. 15-35. Effect of fillers on the viscosity of B78-156, resins (vinyl toluene). *G*, 40% VT-ASP-400; *H*, 40% VT-McNamee clay; *I*, 40% VT-silica flour; *J*, 55% VT-ASP-400; *K*, 55% VT-McNamee clay; *L*, 55% VT-silica flour.

at the foot of Table 15-16, which records the physical properties of these systems. Very acceptable physicals, including very high heat distortions are obtained by incorporating DVB in the system. The weight loss data is low for all systems with the VT/DVB casting exhibiting the lowest value. The use of DVB in this manner has been shown to increase and retain the modulus properties of composite materials at higher temperatures.

## 9. Thermal Resistance of B78-156 Resins in Cast and Composite Form

Table 15-17 lists the range of weight losses for B78-156 resin castings and composite in laminate form. After 240 hr at 180, 200 and 220°C

TABLE 15-15.   B78-156 Casting Properties

|  | 40% C [a] | 55% S [a] | 40% VH [b] | 55% VT [b] |
|---|---|---|---|---|
| Izod | 0.75 | 0.85 | 0.67 | 0.80 |
| Tensile str. | 6–8,000 | 5–7,000 | 6–8,000 | 5–7,000 |
| Modulus $\times 10^{-6}$ | 0.47 | 0.50 | 0.51 | 0.48 |
| % Elongation | 0.84 | 0.89 | 0.76 | 0.75 |
| Flex. str. | 15–17,000 | 13–15,000 | 15–17,000 | 13–15,000 |
| Modulus $\times 10^{-6}$ | 0.49 | 0.48 | 0.50 | 0.45 |
| Distortion temp, °F | 275 | 281 | 275 | 260 |
| Barcol hardness | 47 | 45 | 47 | 47 |
| % $H_2O$ absorption, 24 hrs, R.T. | 0.23 | 0.20 | 0.19 | 0.15 |
| % Wt loss, 8 days, 220°C | 3.3 | 3.2 | 1.0 | 1.0 |

[a] $\frac{3}{4}$% BPO; 2 hr 75°C; 2 hr 135°C.
[b] $\frac{3}{4}$% USP-245; 2 hr 60°C; 1 hr 75°C; 2 hr 135°C.

the weight loss for castings range from 0.2–0.6, 0.3–0.9 and 0.7–3.2%, and from 0.3–0.8, 0.45–1.5, and 0.9–4.0% for the laminates at the respective temperatures.

A more specific study of long range thermal resistance was carried out with the objective of determining the influence of monomer type and concentration on the weight loss data of B78-156 resins. Table 15-18 tabulates weight loss data for 40 and 55% styrene and vinyltolu-

TABLE 15-16.   B78-156 Casting Properties

|  | 35% S [a] 5% DVB | 35% VT [b] 5% DVB | 17.5% S [b] 17.5%VT 5% DVB |
|---|---|---|---|
| Izod | 0.67 | 0.41 | 0.60 |
| Tensile str. | 5–7,000 | 5–7,000 | 5–7,000 |
| Modulus $\times 10^{-6}$ | 0.52 | 0.53 | 0.49 |
| % Elongation | 0.93 | 0.59 | 0.74 |
| Flex. Str. | 12–14,000 | 12–14,000 | 12–14,000 |
| Modulus $\times 10^{-6}$ | 0.45 | 0.45 | 0.42 |
| Distortion temp, °F | >260 | >260 | >260 |
| Barcol hardness | 43 | 47 | 46 |
| % $H_2O$ absorption 24 hr, R.T. |  |  |  |
| % Wt loss, 8 days, 220°C | 2.7 | 1.5 | 1.9 |

[a] $\frac{3}{4}$% BPO; 2 hr 75°C; 2 hr 135°C.
[b] $\frac{3}{4}$% USP-245; 2 hr 60°C; 1 hr 75°C; 2 hr 135°C.

TABLE 15-17. B78-156 Resins

| Thermal resistance | |
| --- | --- |
| Castings | Range of % wt loss |
| 240 hr at 180°C | 0.2–0.6 |
| 240 hr at 200°C | 0.3–0.9 |
| 240 hr at 220°C | 0.7–3.2 |
| Glass mat laminates | |
| 240 hr at 180°C | 0.3–0.8 |
| 240 hr at 200°C | 0.45–1.5 |
| 240 hr at 220°C | 0.9–4.0 |

ene castings over a 1250 hr subjection period at 220°C. The data shows that the vinyltoluene systems are more stable than the styrene system and that the 55% VT castings show lower weight loss than the 40% VT castings. The 55% VT casting weight loss was only 1.5% compared to 3.0% for the 40% VT casting after 1250 hr at 220°C. Figure 15-36 shows the plot of weight loss after 800 hr at 220°C. The dotted lines were projected curves for 1000 hr. The actual weight loss curves were run through 1250 hr and are depicted in Fig. 15-37. The styrene systems are showing a lightly increased weight loss pattern after this period of time. The VT systems continue to hold to a low loss curve pattern and projections through 1600 hr look very good.

## 10. Physical Properties of Composite Glass Mat Laminates

The range of physical properties in terms of tensile, flexural, compression and impact strengths for approximately 33% glass mat reinforced laminates prepared from various monomer-B78-156 resin systems has been summarized and tabulated. Table 15-19 shows the range of tensile strength, modulus and elongation as molded, postcured, postcured and aged 240 hr at 220°C and run at room temperature

TABLE 15-18. Weight Loss of B78-156 Resins (Long Time Aging at 220°C)

| System casting | 168 hr | 504 hr | 744 hr | 1008 hr | 1250 hr |
| --- | --- | --- | --- | --- | --- |
| B78–156–40S | 2.8 | 6.3 | 6.2 | 6.2 | 7.2 |
| B78–156–55S | 2.0 | 5.1 | 6.4 | 6.8 | 8.2 |
| B78–156–40VT | 0.74 | 2.1 | 2.2 | 2.6 | 3.0 |
| B78–156–55VT | 0.64 | 0.61 | 1.1 | 1.1 | 1.5 |

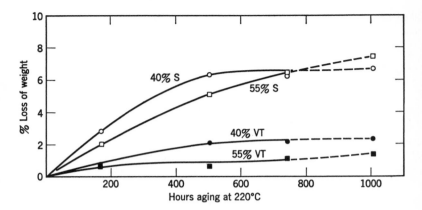

Fig. 15-36. Weight loss of B78-156 resins (long time aging at 220°C).

and aged 240 hr at 220°C and run at 220°C. The data shows very good retention of tensile properties over this range of conditioning.

Table 15-20 covers the range of flexural strength and modulus properties of glass mat composites. The table covers as molded, postcured, aged 240 hr at 220°C run at room temperature, aged 240 hr at 220°C run at 180°C, aged 240 hr at 220°C run at 220°C, and aged 240 hr at 220°C run at 260°C properties. The retention properties through the range of subjection cycles are considered to be very good.

Table 15-21 covers the unaged and aged compression strength and modulus properties, unaged and aged izod impact strength and Barcol hardness properties of the B78-156 composite glass mat laminates.

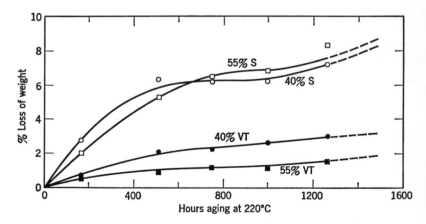

Fig. 15-37. Weight loss of B78-156 resins (long time aging at 220°C).

TABLE 15-19.  B78-156 Physical Properties:  Tensile Properties  (Glass Mat Laminates)

| | Range |
|---|---|
| Tensile st., psi | 16,000–18,000 |
| Tensile mod., psi×10⁶ | 1.6 –1.9 |
| Tensile elong., % | 1.55–1.88 |
| Tensile st., psi | 13,000–14,000 |
| Tensile mod., psi×10⁶ | 1.45–1.75 |
| Tensile elong., % | 1.40–1.6 |
| Tensile st., psi | 13,300–14,500 |
| Tensile mod., psi×10⁶ | 1.54–1.67 |
| Tensile elong., % | 1.60–1.80 |
| Tensile st., psi | 12,500–13,500 |

These values substantiate B78-156 composite thermal resistance performance.

## 11. Electrical Properties of B78-156 Composites

The versatility of these B78-156 resins is demonstrated by the un-aged and aged electrical properties of composites in the form of glass mat reinforced laminates. Table 15-22 shows that the range of arc resistance for as molded, postcured and aged composites range from 167–182, 175–185 and 182–192 sec, respectively.

The dielectric strengths, perpendicular and parallel, short-time are recorded in Table 15-23. The unaged, postcured, aged and aged—

TABLE 15-20.  B78-156 Physical Properties:  Flexural Properties (Glass Mat Laminates)

| | Range |
|---|---|
| Flex. st., psi [1] | 27,000–33,000 |
| Flex. mod., psi×10⁶ | 1.46–1,57 |
| Flex. st., psi [2] | 25,000–29,000 |
| Flex. mod., psi×10⁶ | 1.40–1.60 |
| Flex. st., psi [3] | 23,000–26,000 |
| Flex. mod., psi×10⁶ | 1.65–1.80 |
| Flex. st., psi [4] | 22,000–26,000 |
| Flex. mod., psi×10⁶ | 1.40–1.50 |
| Flex. et., psi [5] | 18,000–20,000 |
| Flex. mod., psi×10⁶ | 1.20–1.50 |
| Flex. st., psi [6] | 14,000–17,000 |
| Flex. mod., psi×10⁶ | 0.90–1.30 |

TABLE 15-21.   B78-156 Physical Properties:   Compression, Impact and Hardness Properties (Glass Mat Laminates)

| | |
|---|---|
| Compression st, psi, unaged | 25,000–28,500 |
| Compression mod., psi×10, unaged | 1.10–1.21 |
| Izod impact st. ft lb/in, unaged (notched) | 13.0–14.5 |
| Izod impact st. ft lb/in., aged 240 hr at 220°C. Run at R.T. | 11.0–14.2 |
| Barcol hardness, unaged | 52–58 |
| Barcol hardness, aged 240 hr at 220°C | 60–65 |

23°C-$H_2O$ dielectric strengths, perpendicular, range from 435 to 480, 486–496, 473–502, and 480–490 V/mil, respectively. The dielectric strengths, parallel, short-time under the same aging conditions range 62.5–65.5, 60.5–62.5, 55.5–58.5, and 52.5–55.5 kV, respectively.

The volume resistivity, surface resistivity, insulation resistance, power factor and dielectric constants for as molded, postcured and aged glass mat composites were determined and recorded in Table 15-24. The volume resistivity over the conditioning sequence ranged from $1.45 \times 10^{15}$ to $4.14 \times 10^{14}$ ohm-cm. The surface resistivity ranged from $1.54 \times 10^{14}$ to $4.95 \times 10^{13}$ ohms and the insulation resistance ranged from $1.27 \times 10^{14}$ to $1.02 \times 10^{13}$ ohms over the as molded to aged conditioning range. The dissipation factor went from 0.0120 to 0.0086 to 0.0155 for as molded, postcured and aged laminates and the dielectric constant varied from 4.35 to 4.37 to 4.38 for the conditioning range.

The track resistance of B78-156 resins appears to be one of its outstanding electrical properties. The track resistance of castings, filled castings and glass mat laminates has been determined by the inclined plane test procedure. Table 15-25 shows that track resistance values >1000 min have been obtained with 40% styrene and vinyltoluene castings.

The incorporation of 50% silica flour in a 40% VT system resulted

TABLE 15-22.   B78-156 Resins: Electrical Properties (Glass Mat Laminates)

| | |
|---|---|
| Arc resistance, sec unaged | 167–182 |
| Arc resistance, sec postcured | 175–185 |
| Arc resistance, sec aged 240 hr at 220°C | 182–192 |

TABLE 15-23. B78-156 Resins: Electrical Properties (Glass Mat Laminates)

| | |
|---|---|
| Dielectric st. perpendicular | |
| Unaged, V/mil | 435–480 |
| Postcured, V/mil | 486–494 |
| Aged, 240 hr at 220°C, V/mil | 473–502 |
| Aged, 240 hr at 220°C, then 24 hr/23°C/$H_2O$ | 480–490 |
| Dielectric st. parallel | |
| Unaged, KV | 62.5–65.5 |
| Postcured, KV | 60.5–62.5 |
| Aged 240 hr at 220°C, KV | 55.5–58.5 |
| Aged 240 hr at 220°C, then 24 hr/23°C/$H_2O$, KV | 52.5–55.5 |

TABLE 15-24. Electrical Properties of B78-156 Resin Systems

| | As molded | Postcured | Aged |
|---|---|---|---|
| Volume resistivity, Ω/cm | $1.45 \times 10^{15}$ | $1.40 \times 10^{15}$ | $4.14 \times 10^{14}$ |
| Surface resistivity, Ω | $1.54 \times 10^{14}$ | $1.65 \times 10^{14}$ | $4.95 \times 10^{13}$ |
| Insulation resistance, Ω ASTM D257-61 | $1.27 \times 10^{14}$ | $2.1 \times 10^{13}$ | $1.02 \times 10^{13}$ |
| Dissipation factor | .0120 | .0086 | .0155 |
| Power factor, % | 1.20 | 0.89 | 1.55 |
| Dielectric constant | 4.35 | 4.37 | 4.38 |

TABLE 15-25. Track Resistance of B78-156 Resin Systems
Inclined Plane Test Method

| Resin | % Monomer | % Filler | % Glass mat | (In min.) Track resistance |
|---|---|---|---|---|
| B78–156 | 40VT | — | — | >1000 |
| B78–156 | 40VT | 50 Silica flour | — | >850 |
| B78–156 | 40VT | 33 MacNamee clay | 33 Glass mat | >450 |
| B78–156 | 40S | — | — | >1000 |

in >850 min and the use of 40% VT system with 33% McNamee Clay and 33% glass mat produced a composite with >450 minutes track resistance.

Figure 15-38 shows the influence of temperature on the percent power factor of clear unfilled B78-156 resins and shows a fairly low power factor loss through 120°C. The incorporation of 125 parts of silica flour in our B78-156 resins causes the power factor to increase to 6% at 120°C, but at a lower rate than a cycloaliphatic epoxy system with the same concentration of silica flour. This kind of data with different fillers can establish the best system for retention of low power factor over a range of temperatures through 200°C.

Table 15-26 shows the power factor and dielectric constant properties of glass mat composites based on S/VT modified B78-156 resin systems. As molded power factor and dielectric constant properties at 100 cycles and 1 kc frequency range from 3.87 to 2.80% and 5.86 to 5.66%. Postcuring the composites and running the properties under the same conditions reduces the power factor from 1.12 to 1.03% and the dielectric constants from 5.90 to 5.06.

Figure 15-39 shows the influence of temperature on the percent

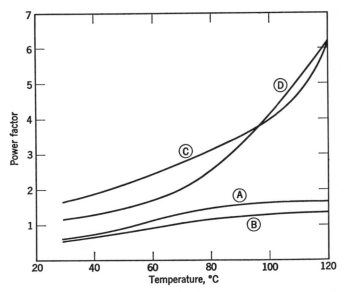

Fig. 15-38. Power factor properties of B78-156 resins (40% VT). *A*, clear castings cured with 0.2% USP-245; *B*, clear casting cured with 0.5% DNF and 0.10% Co; *C*, casting filled with 125 parts of silica flour per 100 parts resin and cured with 0.5% USP-245; *D*, cycloaliphatic epoxy resin.

TABLE 15-26. Power Factor and Dielectric Constant Properties of B78-156 Resin Systems. Glass Mat Laminates

| System | Cure | Freq. | D.F. | P.F. % | D.C. (K) |
|---|---|---|---|---|---|
| B78-156-40VT/S | A.M. | 100 C | .0387 | 3.87 | 5.86 |
|  |  | 1 KC | .0280 | 2.80 | 5.66 |
| B78-156-40VT/S | P.C. | 100 C | .0112 | 1.12 | 5.90 |
|  |  | 1 KC | .0103 | 1.03 | 5.06 |

power factor of a composite glass mat laminate prepared from a VT modified B78-16 resin system. The gradual loss up to 16% at 180°C, and 100 cycles and 10% at 1 kc for the as molded laminate are good. Postcuring the laminate will improve these properties, as was shown in Table 15-26 for the S/VT system. Figure 15-40 shows the same curves for the S/VT system and shows percent power factors of ~20, 9, and 1% at 180°C and 100 cycles, 1 kc and 10 kc frequencies. This was an as molded laminate. Postcuring will serve to improve this property. The power factor does not appear to "run away" at a specific temperature, as is the case with some phenolic and epoxies. The B78-156 resin composites appear to follow a gradual increasing power factor with increasing temperatures. The "run away" points are yet to be determined.

## 12. Composite Properties: Glass Cloth Laminates

The B78-156 resins diluted with styrene or vinyltoluene have been used in preparing glass cloth reinforced composites. These reinforced

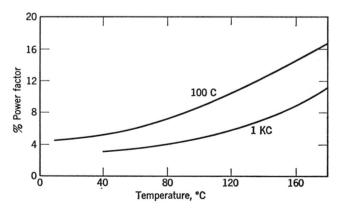

Fig. 15-39. B78-156 VT system (AM) (glass mat laminate).

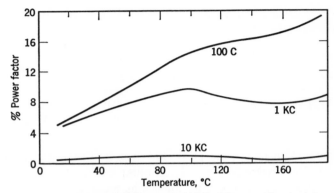

Fig. 15-40. B78-156 S/VT system (AM) (glass mat laminate).

composites have exhibited the unique property of improving in physical properties with further aging at specified temperatures. Table 15-27 describes the as molded, postcured, and aged properties of a 12 ply glass cloth laminate prepared with a 37% styrene modified B78-156 resin. The tensile strengths and modulus, izod impact strength, flex strength and modulus, compression strength and modulus remain al-

TABLE 15-27.   B78-156 12 Ply Glass Cloth Laminates—$\frac{1}{8}$ in.

| | 37% Styrene | | |
| | As molded [a] | Post cured [b] | Aged [c] |
| --- | --- | --- | --- |
| Izod | 13,33 | 13.29 | 12.11 |
| Tensile str. | 42,000 | 42,000 | 38,000 |
| mod.$\times 10^{-6}$ | 3.43 | 2.83 | 2.71 |
| % Elongation | 1.43 | 1.55 | 1.53 |
| Flex. str., R.T. | 40,000 | 47,000 | 42,000 |
| mod.$\times 10^{-6}$ | 2.43 | 2.57 | 2.29 |
| Flex. str., 150°C | 20,000 | 25,000 | 32,000 |
| mod.$\times 10^{-6}$ | 1.89 | 2.12 | 2.22 |
| Compr. str. | 23,000 | 23,000 | 20,000 |
| mod.$\times 10^{-6}$ | 1.70 | 1.79 | 1.95 |
| % Ash | 64.5 | 66.0 | 65.0 |
| Barcol hardness | 65 | 65 | 65 |
| % $H_2O$ absorption 24 hrs, R.T. | 0.77 | 0.66 | 0.92 |
| % Wt loss, 8 days at 180°C | — | — | 0.74 |

[a] $\frac{3}{4}$% USP-245; 5 min 250°F, 250–300 psi.
[b] 16 hr 135°C; 2 hr 150°C; 2 hr 180°C.
[c] Postcured as (2) then aged 8 days at 180°C.

most unaffected after the conditioning sequence and run at room temperature. One important observation is that the flexural strength and modulus is lowered when run at 150°C, compared to the room temperature properties. Postcuring and aging continue to improve the flex strength and modulus when run at 150°C. The as molded, postcured and aged flex strengths at 150°C. increases from 20,000 to 25,000 to 32,000 psi, and the modulus from 1.89 to 2.12 to $2.22 \times 10^6$ psi. The weight loss after 8 days at 180°C. was 0.74%. This product could find use in G-10 and 11 type laminates where a criterion of performance is 50% retention of room temperature properties at 150°C. (NEMA Grades)

Table 15-28 covers the composite properties of a glass cloth laminate prepared from B78-156 resin modified with 32% styrene and 5% DVB. Again, we see very good retention of properties going from as molded to postcured to aged type of conditioning. As was noted in Table 15-27 the flexural strength at 150°C is again improved with aging. The values go from 20,000 to 24,000 to 30,000 psi. The weight loss after 8 days at 180°C, is 0.74%. This system could also find use in applications where a certain retention of properties is required at a specific temperature.

TABLE 15-28. B78-156 12 Ply Glass Cloth Laminates—$\frac{1}{8}$ in.

| | 32% Styrene-5% DVB | | |
| | As molded [a] | Post cured [b] | Aged [c] |
| --- | --- | --- | --- |
| Izod | 14.85 | 13,65 | 12.09 |
| Tensile str. | 44,000 | 41,000 | 34,000 |
| mod.$\times 10^{-6}$ | 2.63 | 2.53 | 2.51 |
| % Elongation | 1.73 | 1.63 | 1.32 |
| Flex. str., R.T. | 38,000 | 42,000 | 36,000 |
| mod.$\times 10^{-6}$ | 2.32 | 2.46 | 2.47 |
| Flex. str., 150°C | 20,000 | 24,000 | 30,000 |
| mod.$\times 10^{-6}$ | 1.98 | 1.34 | 1.55 |
| Compr. str. | 20,000 | 27,000 | 22,000 |
| mod.$\times 10^{-6}$ | 1.86 | 1.58 | 1.69 |
| % Ash | 65.0 | 64.6 | 64.9 |
| Barcol hardness | 65 | 67 | 67 |
| % H$_2$O absorption 24 hrs, R.T. | 0.72 | 0.81 | 0.98 |
| % Wt loss, 8 days at 180°C | — | — | 0.74 |

[a] $\frac{3}{4}$% USP-245; 5 min 250°F, 250–300 psi.
[b] 16 hr 135°C; 2 hr 150°C; 2 hr 180°C.
[c] Postcured as (2) then aged 8 days at 180°C.

### 13.  Composite Properties:   Glass Mat Reinforced Laminates

Composite systems have been prepared from a B78-156 resin modified with vinyltoluene using 40% resin, 30% filler, and 30% glass mat reinforcement.  Table 15-29 records the as molded, postcured and aged properties of the laminate.  Again, the aging improves the flex strength and modulus values run at 150, 180, 200, 220 and 260°C. Aging also improves the tensile and compression strengths and modulus properties.

The same influence is noted for styrene/vinyltoluene modified B78-156 resins when evaluated in a glass mat composite form.  Table 15-30 covers the as molded, postcured and aged properties.  Once more, aging improves the retention of physical properties at 150, 180, 200, 220, and 260°C. The same influence carries over to the improvement in tensile and compression properties.  These systems are recommended for structural and electrical application where temperature resistance is required.

Table 15-31 summarizes the properties of a glass mat composite

TABLE 15-29.  Properties of B78-156-VT Glass Mat Laminate (40% Resin-30% Filler-30% Glass Mat)

|  | As molded | Postcured | Aged 10 days at 220°C |
|---|---|---|---|
| Flex. st. (R.T.) | 28,900 | 31,900 | 28,900 |
| Flex. mod. (R.T.) | $1.499 \times 10^6$ | $1.618 \times 10^6$ | $1.715 \times 10^6$ |
| Flex. st. (150) | 12,800 | 18,000 | 21,900 |
| Flex. mod. (150) | $0.837 \times 10^6$ | $0.953 \times 10^6$ | $0.991 \times 10^6$ |
| Flex. st. (180) | 11,100 | 14,200 | 20,500 |
| Flex. mod. (180) | $0.754 \times 10^6$ | $0.831 \times 10^6$ | $1.001 \times 10^6$ |
| Flex. st. (200) | 9,700 | 11,950 | 19,700 |
| Flex. mod. (200) | $0.699 \times 10^6$ | $0.797 \times 10^6$ | $0.935 \times 10^6$ |
| Flex. St. (220) | 9,200 | 10,700 | 14,800 |
| Flex. mod. (220) | $0.727 \times 10^6$ | $0.860 \times 10^6$ | $0.816 \times 10^6$ |
| Flex. st. (260) | 9,350 | 9,600 | 9,550 |
| Flex. mod. (260) | $0.681 \times 10^6$ | $0.790 \times 10^6$ | $0.694 \times 10^6$ |
| Tensile st. | 18,100 | 14,500 | 15,200 |
| Tensile mod. | $2,003 \times 10^6$ | $1,689 \times 10^6$ | $2,094 \times 10^6$ |
| Tensile elong. % | 1.72 | 1.71 | 1.21 |
| Comp. st. | 28,270 | 15,500 | 27,225 |
| Comp. mod. | $1.196 \times 10^6$ | $0.701 \times 10^6$ | $1.038 \times 10^6$ |
| Izod impact, ft #/in. | 15.2 | 13.9 | 9.20 |

TABLE 15-30. Properties of B78-156-S/VT Glass Mat Laminate (40% Resin-30% Filler-30% Glass Mat)

|  | As molded | Postcured | Aged 10 days at 220°C |
|---|---|---|---|
| Flex. st. (R.T.) | 26,650 | 28,500 | 29,250 |
| Flex. mod. (R.T.) | $1.357\times10^6$ | $1.661\times10^6$ | $1.735\times10^6$ |
| Flex. st. (150) | 11,300 | 18,800 | 21,200 |
| Flex. mod. (150) | $0.659\times10^6$ | $0.963\times10^6$ | $1.049\times10^6$ |
| Flex. st. (180) | 9,700 | 13,300 | 21,000 |
| Flex. mod. (180) | $0.621\times10^6$ | $0.828\times10^6$ | $1.023\times10^6$ |
| Flex. st. (200) | 9,300 | 11,650 | 17,300 |
| Flex. mod. (200) | $0.658\times10^6$ | $0.828\times10^6$ | $0.840\times10^6$ |
| Flex. St. (220) | 8,500 | 9,700 | 15,400 |
| Flex. mod. (220) | $0.617\times10^6$ | $0.736\times10^6$ | $0.799\times10^6$ |
| Flex. st. (260) | 8,800 | 11,300 | 9,500 |
| Flex. mod. (260) | $0.577\times10^6$ | $0.805\times10^6$ | $0.600\times10^6$ |
| Tensile st. | 17,400 | 18,325 | 17,100 |
| Tensile mod. | $1.674\times10^6$ | $1.991\times10^6$ | $2.137\times10^6$ |
| Tensile elong. % | 1.74 | 1.57 | 1.33 |
| Comp. st. | 25,125 | 15,400 | 33,100 |
| Comp. mod. | $1.199\times10^6$ | $0.683\times10^6$ | $1.233\times10^6$ |
| Izod impact, ft #/in. | 13.0 | 13.5 | 8.8 |

based on a vinyltoluene-divinylbenzene modified B-78-156 resin. The laminate was prepared using 0.5% USP-245 as the catalyst and molding at 250 psi at a temperature of 240°F for 2½ min. This is referred to as the as molded laminate. The as molded laminate was postcured for 16 hours at 135°C followed by 2 hr at 180°C and then aged 9 days at 220°C. This is referred to as the aged laminate. This system retains a high percentage of the as molded properties when run immediately at 280, 200, and 220°C. The aging procedure helps retain the high retention of properties after aging and run at room temperature at 180, 200 and 220°C. The tensile, compression and Izod impact properties remain the same as at molding and in many cases are improved with aging. The heat distortion properties remain high even through extensive aging which indicates a resistance of B78-156 resins to degradation at temperature. The aged water absorption is very low and the Barcol hardness increases from 61 to 66. The weight loss after postcure is 0.40% and increases to only 0.90% after 9 days at 220°C. This type of composite is recommended for Class H type heat resistance applications and high strength retention structural uses.

TABLE 15-31. B78-156 Glass Mat Laminates—⅛ in.

| | 35% VT-5% DVB | |
| | As molded [a] | Aged [b] |
| --- | --- | --- |
| Izod impact | 13.5 | 10.1 |
| Tensile str. | 15,000 | 15,000 |
| Mod.$\times10^{-6}$ | 1.53 | 0.71 |
| % Elongation | 1.70 | 1.45 |
| Flex. str., R.T. | 29,000 | 22,000 |
| Mod.$\times10^{-6}$ | 1.45 | 1.40 |
| Flex. str., 180°C | 21,000 | 20,000 |
| Mod$\times10^{-6}$ | 0.94 | 0.93 |
| Flex. str., 200°C | 21,000 | 16,000 |
| Mod.$\times10^{-6}$ | 0.96 | 0.80 |
| Flex. str., 220°C | 17,000 | 16,000 |
| Mod.$\times10^{-6}$ | 0.81 | 0.88 |
| Compr. str. | 20,000 | 31,000 |
| Mod.$\times10^{-6}$ | 1.07 | 1.24 |
| % Ash | — | 56.3 |
| Barcol hardness | 61 | 66 |
| Distortion temp, °F | 500+ | 500+ |
| % $H_2O$ absorption | 0.51 | 0.30 |
| % Wt. loss, postcure | — | 0.40 |
| % Wt. loss, aging 9 days at 220°C | — | 0.90 |

[a] ½% USP-245; 2½ min at 240°F; 250 psi
[b] Molded as (1), postcured 16 hr at 135°C; 2 hr at 180°C, then aged 9 days at 220°C

## 14. Comparative Properties of B78-156 Glass Mat Composite Versus other Composite Systems

Tables 15-32 through 15-35 summarize the properties of B78-156 glass mat laminates as compared to other regular polyesters, epoxies, silicones and diallylphthalate type composite glass mat laminates. From this comparative data the fast molding high heat resistance, good electricals, excellent track resistance and good physical properties at room temperature and specifically at temperature, characterize the B78-156 resins.

## 15. Suggested Composite Uses and Applications

The B78-156 resins are being evaluated for use in a variety of composite type applications. The system lends itself to filament winding applications. Average and fairly thick sections have been wound.

TABLE 15-32. Comparative Properties of B78-156 Resins Vs. Other Polyester Resins

| Property | Test meth. | B78-156 glass mat. lam. | Polyester preformed chopped roving |
|---|---|---|---|
| Molding qualities | — | Excellent | Excellent |
| Avg. molding temp. °F | — | 230–280 | 170–320 |
| Av. molding press., psi | — | 200–2000 | 250–2000 |
| Compression ratio | — | | — |
| Mold shrinkage in./in. | — | 0–0.002 | 0–0.002 |
| Specific gravity | D792 | | 1.35–2.3 |
| Specific vol in.$^3$/lb | D792 | | 20.5–13.9 |
| Refractive index | D542 | | |
| Tensile strength, psi | D638, 651 | 15,000–30,000 | 25,000–30,000 |
| % Elongation | D638 | 1.0–3.0 | 0.5–5.0 |
| Avg. ten. mod., $10^5$ psi | D638 | 10.0–22.0 | 8.0–20.0 |
| Comp. strength, psi | D695 | 20,000–35,000 | 15,000–30,000 |
| Flex. strength, psi | D790 | 20,000–45,000 | 10,000–40,000 |
| Impact strength | D256 | 9–15.0 | 2–10 |
| Hardness, Rockwell | D785 | 55–65 (Barcol) | M70–M120 |
| Thermal cond. | D177 | | — |
| Spec. ht. cal/°C/g | — | | — |
| Thermal exp., $10^{-5}$/°C | D696 | | 2–5 |
| Resist. to ht., °F (cont.) | — | >400–500 | 300–350 |
| Deflection temp., °F | D648 | >500$^+$ | — |
| Vol. resistivity | D257 | >$10^{16}$ | $10^{14}$ |
| Dielectric str. S.T. | D149 | 450–525 | 350–500 |
| Dielectric str. S.S. | D149 | 450–500 | — |
| Dielec. const. 60 cycles | D150 | 3.5–5.0 | 3.8–6.0 |
| Dielec. const. $10^3$ cycles | D150 | 3.5–5.0 | 4.0–6.0 |
| Dielec. const. $10^6$ cycles | D150 | 3.0–4.5 | 3.5–5.5 |
| Dissip. factor 60 cycles | D150 | 0.005–0.05 | 0.01–0.04 |
| Dissip. factor $10^3$ cycles | D150 | 0.005–0.06 | 0.01–0.05 |
| Dissip. factor $10^6$ cycles | D150 | 0.005–0.05 | 0.01–0.03 |
| Arc resistance, sec | D495 | 150–190 | 120–180 |
| % $H_2O$ absorp. 24 hr R.T. | D570 | 0.01–1.0 | 0.01–1.0 |
| Surface resist. ohm | | >$10^{15}$ | |
| Insul. resist. ohms | | >$10^{13}$ | |
| Track resist. min | | 400–600 | |

Filament wound tubes from the vinyltoluene system exhibit very low power factors in the range of 0.9%. The use of these resins in filament winding reinforced pipe, for use in the petroleum and chemical resistance fields is under study.

The inherent good ultraviolet and weather resistance and the excellent track resistance of B78-156 resins makes them excellent candidates

TABLE 15-33.   Comparative Properties of B78-156 Resins vs. Epoxy Resins

| Property | Test meth. | B78-156 glass mat. lam. | Epoxy glass fiber filler |
|---|---|---|---|
| Molding qualities | — | Excellent | Excellent |
| Avg. molding temp. °F | — | 230–280 | 300–350 |
| Av. molding press., psi | — | 200–2000 | 300–5,000 |
| Compression ratio | — | | 2–7 |
| Mold shrinkage in./in. | — | 0–0.002 | 0.001–0.002 |
| Specific gravity | D792 | | 1.8–2.0 |
| Specific vol in.$^3$/lb | D792 | | 14.2–15.4 |
| Refractive index | D542 | | — |
| Tensile strength, psi | D638, 651 | 15,000–30,000 | 14,000–30,000 |
| % Elongation | D638 | 1.0–3.0 | 4 |
| Avg. ten. mod. $10^5$ psi | D638 | 10.0–22.0 | 30.4 |
| Comp. strength, psi | D695 | 20,000–35,000 | 30,000–38,000 |
| Flex. strength, psi | D790 | 20,000–45,000 | 20,000–60,000 |
| Impact strength | D256 | 9–15.0 | 8–25 |
| Hardness, Rockwell | D785 | 55–65 (Barcol) | M100–M108 |
| Thermal cond. | D177 | | 7–10 |
| Spec. ht. cal/°C/g | — | | 0.19 |
| Thermal exp. $10^{-5}$/°C | D696 | | 1.1–3 |
| Resist. to ht. °F (cont.) | — | >400–500 | 330–500 |
| Deflection temp. °F | D648 | >500+ | 400–500 |
| Vol. resistivity | D257 | >$10^{16}$ | $3.8 \times 10^{15}$ |
| Dielectric str. S.T. | D149 | 450–525 | 350 |
| Dielectric str. S.S. | D149 | 450–500 | 340 |
| Dielec. const. 60 cycles | D150 | 3.5–5.0 | 5.5 |
| Dielec. const. $10^3$ cycles | D150 | 3.5–5.0 | — |
| Dielec. const. $10^6$ cycles | D150 | 3.0–4.5 | — |
| Dissip. factor 60 cycles | D150 | 0.005–0.05 | 0.087 |
| Dissip. factor $10^3$ cycles | D150 | 0.005–0.06 | — |
| Dissip. factor $10^6$ cycles | D150 | 0.005–0.05 | — |
| Arc resistance, sec | D495 | 150–190 | 125–140 |
| % $H_2O$ absorp. 24 hr R.T. | D570 | 0.01–1.0 | 0.05–0.095 |
| Surface resist. ohm | | >$10^{15}$ | |
| Insul. resist. ohms | | >$10^{13}$ | |
| Track resist. min | | 400–600 | |

to replace epoxy or ceramic materials in preparing insulators and other pole line equipment and underground distribution molded secondary and primary terminations.

Special highly filled glass reinforced premixes are being investigated for specific use in molding and premix laminates for the electrical insulation industry.

The fast cure, uniform low shrinkage and excellent release character-

TABLE 15-34. Comparative Properties of B78-156 Resins vs. Silicone Resins

| Property | Test meth. | B78-156 glass mat lam. | Silicone glass fiber filler |
|---|---|---|---|
| Molding qualities | — | Excellent | Good |
| Avg. molding temp. °F | — | 230–280 | 310–360 |
| Av. molding press., psi | — | 200–2000 | 1000–5000 |
| Compression ratio | — | | 6–9 |
| Mold shrinkage in./in. | — | 0–0.002 | 0–0.005 |
| Specific gravity | D792 | | 1.68–2.0 |
| Specific vol in.$^3$/lb | D792 | | 16.5–13.8 |
| Refractive index | D542 | | — |
| Tensile strength, psi | D638, 651 | 15,000–30,000 | 4,000–5,000 |
| % Elongation | D638 | 1.0–3.0 | — |
| Avg. ten. mod. 10$^6$ psi | D638 | 10.0–22.0 | — |
| Comp. strength, psi | D695 | 20,000–35,000 | 10,000–15,000 |
| Flex. strength, psi | D790 | 20,000–45,000 | 10,000–14,000 |
| Impact strength | D256 | 9–15.0 | 3–15 |
| Hardness, Rockwell | D785 | 55–65 (Barcol) | M84 |
| Thermal cond. | D177 | | 7.51–7.54 |
| Spec. ht. cal/°C/g | — | | 0.24–0.30 |
| Thermal exp. 10$^{-5}$/°C | D696 | | 0.8 |
| Resist. to ht. °F (cont.) | — | >400–500 | >600 |
| Deflection temp. °F | D648 | >500$^+$ | >900 |
| Vol. resistivity | D257 | >10$^{16}$ | 10$^{10}$–10$^{14}$ |
| Dielectric str. S.T. | D149 | 450–525 | 200–400 |
| Dielectric str. S.S. | D149 | 450–500 | 125–300 |
| Dielec. const. 60 cycles | D150 | 3.5–5.0 | 3.3–5.2 |
| Dielec. const. 10$^3$ cycles | D150 | 3.5–5.0 | 3.2–5.0 |
| Dielec. const. 10$^6$ cycles | D150 | 3.0–4.5 | 3.2–4.7 |
| Dissip. factor 60 cycles | D150 | 0.005–0.05 | 0.004–0.03 |
| Dissip. factor 10$^3$ cycles | D150 | 0.005–0.06 | 0.0035–0.02 |
| Dissip. factor 10$^6$ cycles | D150 | 0.005–0.05 | 0.002–0.02 |
| Arc resistance, sec | D495 | 150–190 | 150–250 |
| % H$_2$O absorp. 24 hr R.T. | D570 | 0.01–1.0 | 0.1–0.2 |
| Surface resist. ohm | | >10$^{15}$ | |
| Insul. resist. ohms | | >10$^{13}$ | |
| Track resist. min | | 400–600 | |

istics of B78-156 resin are being utilized in pultrusion operations. This area of use includes wedges, rods, spacers, channels and sheet for specific uses in the electromotive fields.

B-staging of the B78-156 resins can be utilized to produce prepreg mat or prepreg roving for specific uses. These resins can find utility in banding tape processes which utilize unidirectional roving for high strength properties.

TABLE 15-35.   Comparative Properties of B78-156 Resins vs. DAP Resins

| Property | Test meth. | B78-156 glass mat lam. | DAP glass filled |
|---|---|---|---|
| Molding qualities | — | Excellent | Excellent |
| Avg. molding temp. °F | — | 230–280 | 270–330 |
| Av. molding press., psi | — | 200–2000 | 500–4000 |
| Compression ratio | — | | 1.9–10 |
| Mold shrinkage in./in. | — | 0–0.002 | 0.001–0.005 |
| Specific gravity | D792 | | 1.55–1.90 |
| Specific vol. in.$^3$/lb | D792 | | 17.8–14.5 |
| Refractive index | D542 | | Not applicable |
| Tensile strength, psi | D638, 651 | 15,000–30,000 | 5,000–12,000 |
| % Elongation | D638 | 1.0–3.0 | — |
| Avg. ten. mod. $10^5$ psi | D638 | 10.0–22.0 | 15–22 |
| Comp. strength, psi | D695 | 20,000–35,000 | 25,000–29,000 |
| Flex. strength, psi | D790 | 20,000–45,000 | 9,500–18,000 |
| Impact strength | D256 | 9–15.0 | 0.5–15.0 |
| Hardness, Rockwell | D785 | 55–65 (Barcol) | M108–M110 |
| Thermal cond. | D177 | | $1.7 \times 10^{-15}$ |
| Spec. ht. cal/°C/g | — | | — |
| Thermal exp. $10^{-5}$/°C | D696 | | 1–3.6 |
| Resist. to ht. °F (cont.) | — | >400–500 | 350–450 |
| Deflection temp. °F | D648 | >500$^+$ | 325–500 |
| Vol. resistivity | D257 | >$10^{16}$ | $10^5$–$10^{16}$ |
| Dielectric str. S.T. | D149 | 450–525 | 350–450 |
| Dielectric str. S.S. | D149 | 450–500 | 350–400 |
| Dielec. const. 60 cycles | D150 | 3.5–5.0 | 4.3 |
| Dielec. const. $10^3$ cycles | D150 | 3.5–5.0 | 4.1–4.5 |
| Dielec. const. $10^6$ cycles | D150 | 3.0–4.5 | 3.8–4.5 |
| Dissip. factor 60 cycles | D150 | 0.005–0.05 | 0.01–0.05 |
| Dissip. factor $10^3$ cycles | D150 | 0.005–0.06 | 0.004–0.010 |
| Dissip. factor $10^6$ cycles | D150 | 0.005–0.05 | 0.009–0.018 |
| Arc resistance, sec | D495 | 150–190 | 115–150 |
| % $H_2O$ absorp. 24 hr R.T. | D570 | 0.01–1.0 | 0.12–0.35 |
| Surface resist. ohm | | >$10^{15}$ | |
| Insul. resist. ohms | | >$10^{13}$ | |
| Track resist. min | | 400–600 | |

The B78-156 can be blended with other polyester resins to impart improved modulus, higher heat resistance, improved electrical properties, faster cures and improved gloss and release characteristics in the resultant composite materials.

The unique properties of B78-156 resins are being investigated alone or in blends for the preparation of uniform thickness, glossy, smooth surfaced parts for use in the automotive, transportation and appliance fields.

Fig. 15-41. Giant Sikorsky CH-53A military transport helicopter with canopy is constructed entirely of RP. (Courtesy of Cordo Division, Ferro Corporation.)

The B78-156 resins respond to various thickening agents much more effectively than general purpose resins. The use of these resins in pre-thickened glass mat and premix systems is under study.

## 16. Conclusions

The B78-156 thermosetting special purpose polyesters represent the first series of a very fast curing thermally stable family of new and versatile materials. The compatibility and coreactivity of these systems with various monomers in high concentrations allows the resins to be used in a range of applications.

The resins in dilutions as high as 55% styrene and vinyltoluene exhibit high heat resistance, low weight loss, high heat distortion points, mechanical strength at temperature, retention of strength at moderate and elevated temperatures, good electrical properties, good chemical resistance, good molding properties in terms of filler acceptance, wet-out and flow.

The B78-156 resins lend themselves to many composite uses. These composite properties are of interest to almost all facets of the reinforced plastics and electrical insulation industry.

## F. Polysulfone

The polysulfones are a new family of aromatic, moderately heat-resistant thermoplastics recently introduced by Union Carbide Corporation. These polymers, prepared from the sodium salt of bisphenol-A and p,p'-dichlorodiphenylsulfone, have good electrical properties and resistance to acids, bases, detergents, oils, etc. The polysulfones have useful properties in the $-100$ to 150°C temperature range. Representative properties include tensile strength, 10,000 psi; tensile modulus, $3.6 \times 10^5$ psi; tensile elongation at break, 5–6%; flexural strength, 15,400 psi; and heat deflection temperature, 174°C at 264 psi. The polysulfones are currently available in transparent and opaque forms which can be injected, extruded, or blow molded at 344–400°C using standard equipment.

## G. Parlyene

The poly-$p$-xylylenes combine the stability of aromatic phenylene units with the flexibility of aliphatic connecting linkages. Union Carbide produces these polymers, tradenamed Parylenes, by pyrolyzing $p$-xylene at 950°C in the presence of steam. The cyclic dimer di-$p$-xylylene forms initially and is further pyrolyzed to $p$-xylylene vapor. This vapor, upon being cooled below 50°C, spontaneously polymerized to form linear polymers which are usually deposited as thin films on a suitable substrate. Solid chemicals can be encapsulated by this process, and free films can be prepared by coating surfaces from which the films can conveniently be stripped.

The thermal stabilities of the poly-$p$-xylylene are good, but not exceptional. In an inert atmosphere, the materials can provide long-term service up to 222°C and short-term service to 350°C. However, service temperatures below about 80°C are more realistic in air. Under cryogenic conditions, the polymers show excellent flexibilities at $-201$°C, and good electrical insulation properties near absolute zero. The electrical properties also remain good at elevated temperatures, even after the mechanical properties begin to degrade.

The poly-$p$-xylylenes are insoluble in all organic solvents below 150°C, and resist permeation by all except aromatic hydrocarbons. Thus, the polymer films exhibit excellent barrier properties against gases and moisture. Tough, homogeneous moldings of poly-$p$-xylylenes have been prepared at 400°C/2000 psi.

## H. Polybenzimidazoles

The polybenzimidazoles are being explored by several groups, including the Narmco Materials Division of Whittaker Corporation, the Air

Force Materials Laboratory, and Celanese. The better polybenzimidazoles show TGA-indicated thermal breakdown temperatures as high as 600°C in nitrogen, but their thermal resistance is reduced to about 300°C in air. Polybenzimidazoles are prepared by condensing aromatic tetraamines with aromatic diacids or diacid derivatives. They are generally infusible after curing, and must be converted as prepolymers into useful forms prior to the final cures. Several B-stage forms (known as "Imidites") of polybenzimidazoles are provided in development quantities by Narmco. Cure and post-cure temperatures are generally higher (up to 420°C) than can be obtained with conventional equipment. Fabrication of the polybenzimidazoles is further complicated by the phenol and water side-products emitted during cures. Most polybenzimidazoles are insoluble in all but exotic solvents, and show excellent resistance to oils, acids, and alkalies. They are reported to show useful stress and modulus properties in −253 to +650°C temperature range (for at least short periods of time). Some polybenzimidazole resins have been made recently that are more soluble and fusible. Reported mechanical properties of structural laminates made from such resins and 181-style AF-994-HTS glass cloth reinforcement were:

| Temp., C | Flexural strength, psi | Compression strength, psi |
|---|---|---|
| Ambient | 130,000 | 68,000 |
| 316 for 200 hr | 37,000 | 10,000 |
| 427 for 1 hr | 47,000 | 21,000 |

Among the possible applications for PBI resins are laminates, adhesives, structural dielectrics, rocket motor cases, and structural parts for solid-propellant rockets.

## I. Polyimidazopyrrolones

The polyimidazopyrrolones, also known as pyrrones, are experimental materials prepared from aromatic dianhydrides and aromatic tetraamines being explored by the Langley Research Center of NASA, and the University of Arizona. The polymer syntheses provide soluble prepolymers which are converted to the pyrrone structures by thermal or chemical dehydration. The precursors can be used to cast films or coatings, or can be molded under very high pressures into filled or unfilled forms. The pyrrones combine some of the best properties of the polybenzimidazoles and polyimides. Reported properties for pyrrone films include: tensile strength, 15-22 × 10³ psi; elongation, 3–7%, and Young's modulus, 6–10 × 10⁴ psi.

The pyrrone films are exceptionally radiation resistant and retain their strength properties after 10,000 megarads of 1-MeV electrons. Possible applications for the pyrrones include high temperature films, coatings, adhesives, binders, and use in a variety of advanced spacecraft components.

## J. Polyhydrazides

The polyhdrazides are experimental polymers prepared from diacid chlorides and hydrazine or dihydrazides being developed by du Pont. The aromatic polyhydrazides are soluble in solvents such as dimethylsulfoxide, and can be converted into tough films and fibers. Polyhydrazide fibers having tenacities of 5–6 gr den and 8–14% elongations at break have been prepared. Some of the aromatic polymers have melt temperatures as high as 350–400°C.

## K. Polyoxadiazoles

The polyhydrazides can readily be converted by cyclodehydration to the corresponding polyoxadizoles. In general, the polyoxadiazoles are insoluble in organic solvents, but can be converted into fibers or films from their polyhydrazide precursors. The aromatic polyoxadiazoles have good oxidation resistance, do not degrade below 450°C (by TGA), and may retain 60% of their room temperature properties at 300°C. Several polyoxadiazoles that can be melt spun to highly crystalline fibers have been prepared, but these materials show low melting points (about 100°C) and have little high temperature potential.

## L. Polytriazoles

The reaction of polyhydrazides with aniline produces a class of polymers known as polytriazoles. These experimental polymers are being investigated by Chemstrand. While little has been reported with respect to properties, films and fiber having good stabilities in the 450–500°C (by TGA) temperature range have been prepared from the polytriazoles.

## M. Polyphenylene

The polyphenylene resins are research materials being studied in several laboratories, including those of the Hughes Aircraft Company, and the Case Institute of Technology. These polyaromatics show high resistance to oxidative and reductive environments, excellent thermal stability, and are particularly attractive candidates for ablative applications. Moldable polyphenylenes have been achieved by cationic-oxidative polymerizations of biphenyl and terphenyl. Low molecular weight poly-m-phenylenes have been cured with xylene glycol to provide hard, crosslinked resins. Such resins have shown improved ablation properties as compared to some widely used phenolics.

## N. Polyphenylene Sulfide

Polyphenylene sulfide polymers, prepared by heating cuprous p-bromothiophenoxide, are being investigated by the Dow Chemical Company. These polymers can be molded to partially transparent, tough, flexible films, melt spun into fairly strong and flexible fibers, and used to make laminates. Typical melting points for the polymers are reported in the 270 to 290°C temperature range. Thermogravimetric analyses indicate stability to about 450°C in either air or nitrogen, but better stability in nitrogen. The polymers can be crosslinked by heating at 400°C in nitrogen to provide increased toughness and adhesive strength properties. Adhesive bond strengths up to 2700 psi (at room temperature) have been obtained. The polyphenylene sulfides could find future applications in the high temperature laminate and adhesive areas.

## O. Polythiazoles

Polythiazoles are produced by solution polymerizing dibromoketones with dithioamides. These experimental materials, being investigated by the Southern Research Institute, can be converted to tough fibers or films, but have relatively low softening points (164–250°C). Other modifications of these polymers fail to melt at 500°C and show excellent thermal stabilities, but have poor fiber and film-forming properties. Representative properties reported for polythiazole films are: tensile strength, $6.3$–$6.8 \times 10^3$ psi; elongation at break, 4.2–24%; modulus, $1.6 \times 10^5$ psi.

## P.  Polyperfluorotriazines

Polyperfluorotriazines which contain alternating heterocyclic rings and totally fluorinated carbon chains are being explored by the Air Force Materials Laboratory, and the University of Florida. The perfluoralkyl chain segments are employed as oxidation- and heat-resistant flexibilizing units. Alternation of these units with highly stable triazine rings has resulted in the formation of some processable and moldable experimental elastomers reportedly stable to above 400°C, and resistant to attack by strong oxidizing agents. However, the tensile and elongation properties of these materials are poor, and will need to be improved if the polymers are to find application as engineering materials.

## Q.  Other  Promising  Polymers

It is not possible, within the scope of this book, to even touch on many of the new and promising polymer systems, such as the polybenzoxazoles, polyphenylpyrazoles, polytetrazopyrenes, polyquinoxalines, etc., that are being explored today. Many of the polymer systems presently being investigated contain several different types of heat-stable chain units, and show promise of providing unique combinations of properties and processibility not possessed by polymers containing only a single type of unit.

Specialized types of aromatic ring-containing polymers known as ladder polymers have received a good deal of attention in recent years. These materials are double-strand structures with the polymer chains bound together periodically by chemical bonds. In principle, these materials should show superior thermal stabilities because their chains cannot be severed by breaking a single bond. Du Pont has produced pyrolzed polyacrylonitrile fibers that are stable to 900°C, and which may have ladder structures, but have very low abrasion resistance and tenacity. Brooklyn Polytechnic Institute has produced a ladder polymer stable to 385°C (by TGA) from vinyl isocyanate. Many polymer chemists feel that the next breakthrough in the development of heat-resistant organic polymers will be in the area of ladder structures. However, no polymers of this type combining high heat-resistance, processibility, and useful mechanical properties have been reported to date.

It is doubtful if any of today's polymers can truly meet the test of continuous service at 300°C in air. However, many present materials perform admirably at this and much higher temperatures for limited, and quite useful, periods of time. This represents quite an advance over resistance to boiling water which was, not too long ago, the mark of a thermally stable polymer. There is every reason to believe that continued research will result in the development of still more heat-resistant polymers within the near future.

It seems unavoidable that most of the heat-resistant polymers discussed will be relatively costly. Even so, their extensive application will be assured since heat resistance combined with the desirable properties of plastics is not likely to be obtained with any other type of material.

## Reference Information

G. F. L. Ehlers, *Technical Documentary Report No. ASD TR 61-622*, Feb., 1962.
*Materials in Design Engineering, Materials Selector Issue*, p. 24, Oct., 1963.
J. M. Lancaster, B. A. Wright, and W. W. Wright, *J. Appl. Polymer Sci.*, *9*, 1955–1971 (1963).
R. L. McCombie, *Modern Plastics Encyclopedia*, **43**, No. 1A, 239-243 (1966).
Lieng-Huang Lee, *J. Polymer Sci.*, **2**, 2859-2873 (1964).
R. A. Ekvall and J. R. Low, Jr., *J. Appl. Polymer Sci.*, **8**, 1677 (1964).
*Chem. Eng. News*, p. 57, Dec. 7, 1964.
*Chem. Eng. News*, pp. 48–49, Apr. 26, 1965.
*Plastics Design and Processing*, pp. 13-15, Dec., 1964.
A. S. Hay and G. F. Endres, *J. Polymer Sci. B*, **3**, 887-889 (1965).
H. E. Hyd et al., *J. Appl. Polymer Sci.*, **8**, 1633-1644 (1964).
J. F. Heacock and C. E. Berr, *SPE Trans.*, **5** (2), pp. 105-110, April, 1965.
*Chem. Eng. News*, p. 39, May 17, 1965.
*Plastics Technol.*, pp. 26-28, Dec., 1962.
*Chemical Week*, p. 37, Oct. 9, 1965.
*Materials in Design Engineering*, p. 145, Jan., 1963.
*The Iron Age*, pp. 88–89, May, 1963.
Amoco Chemicals Corporation, Bulletin HT-1a.
T. Unishi, *J. Polymer Sci. B*, **3**, 679-683 (1955).
*Chem. Eng. News*, p. 28, Apr. 12, 1965.
*Plastics Design and Processing*, pp. 16-19, May, 1965.
*Chemical Week*, p. 59, Feb. 27, 1965.
L. A. Errede and N. Knoll, *J. Polymer Sci.*, **60**, 33-42 (1962).
*Chem. Eng. News*, p. 41, Mar. 1, 1964.
*Chem. Eng. News*, p. 39, May 3, 1965.
*Chemical Engineering*, p. 100, July 19, 1965.
AFML-TR-65-114, April, 1965.
*Plastics Design and Processing*, pp. 25-27, Mar., 1964.
R. T. Foster and C. S. Marvel, *J. Polymer Sci. A*, **3**, 417-421 (1965).
*Materials in Design Engineering*, p. 92, May, 1963.
V. L. Bell and G. F. Pezdirtz, *Polymer Letters*, **3**, 977-984 (1965).

F. Dawans and C. S. Marvel, *J. Polymer Sci. A*, **3**, 3549-3571 (1965).

A. H. Frazier and F. T. Wallenberger, *J. Polymer Sci. A*, **2**, 1147-1156 (1964).

C. J. Abshire and C. S. Marvel, *Makromolekular Chemie*, **44-64**, 388 (1961).

*Chem. Eng. News*, p. 40, Mar. 11, 1963.

M. Hasegawa and T. Unishi, *J. Polymer Sci. B*, **2**, 237-239 (1964).

A. W. Frazier and F. T. Wallenberger, *J. Polymer Sci. A*, **2**, 1171-1179 (1964).

M. R. Lilyquist and J. R. Holsten, *Polymer Preprints*, Division of Polymer Chemistry, New York Meeting of the American Chemical Society, p. 6 (1963).

C. S. Marvel, ASD-TDR-62-372, May, 1962.

W. W. Wright, S.C.I. Monograph No. 13, London, p. 259 (1961).

H. A. Smith and C. E. Handlovits, ASD-TDR-62-322, Part 1, Mar., 1962.

S. Tsunawaki and C. C. Prince, *J. Polymer Sci. A*, **2**, 1511-1522 (1954).

R. W. Lentz, C. E. Handlovits and H. A. Smith, *J. Polymer Sci. A*, **58**, 351-367 (1962).

W. C. Sheehan, *Polymer Engineering and Science*, pp. 263-269, October, 1965.

W. C. Sheehan, T. B. Cole and L. G. Picklesimer, *J. Appl. Polymer Sci.*, **9**, 1455-1471 (1965); *J. Polymer Sci. A*, **3**, 1443-1462 (1965).

J. M. Craven and T. M. Fischer, Jr., *J. Polymer Sci. B*, **3**, 35-37 (1965).

H. C. Brown, *J. Polymer Sci. A*, **44**, 9 (1960).

W. R. Griffin, ASD-TDR-62-1114, June, 1963.

T. Kubota and R. Nakanishi, *J. Polymer Sci. B*, **2**, 655-659 (1964).

W. W. Moyer, Jr., C. Cole and T. Anyos, *J. Polymer Sci. A*, **3**, 2107-2121 (1965).

J. P. Shaefer and J. L. Bertram, *J. Polymer Sci. B*, **3**, 95-98 (1965).

C. S. Marvel, *SPE Transactions*, pp. 29-33, Jan., 1965.

G. P. de Gaudemaris and B. J. Sillion, *J. Polymer Sci. B*, **2**, 203-207 (1964).

J. K. Stille and J. R. Williamson, *J. Polymer Sci. B*, **2**, 209-211 (1964).

J. K. Stille, J. R. Williamson and F. E. Arnold, *J. Polymer Sci. A*, **3**, 1013-1030 (1965).

J. Preston and W. B. Black, *J. Polymer Sci. B*, **3**, 845-849 (1965).

R. C. Houtz, *Textile Research J.*, **80**, 786 (1950).

W. J. Burlant and J. L. Parsons, *J. Polymer Sci.*, **22**, 249 (1956).

C. G. Overberger, S. Ozaki and H. Mukamal, *J. Polymer Sci. B*, **2**, 627-629 (1964).

# IV. MOLECULAR STRUCTURE CRITERIA FOR HEAT RESISTANT LAMINATING RESINS

by Herbert S. Schwartz

In aerospace, various laboratories have been developing high performance fiber-reinforced plastics for almost two decades. Its principal areas of research and development in reinforced plastics have been in high performance structural composites as well as ablative composites materials. This effort has been greatly expanded in the past two years from the standpoint of advancing the technology of fiber-reinforced composites in materials fabrication, design methods and prototype demonstrations in order to prove the value of composites (1). In structural plastics research the objectives are to develop materials having higher stiffness/density and higher strength/density ratios than previously used metals and other plastics. These new plastics are for use as "primary structures" in applications such as: fuselage, wings, rudder, and horizontal stabilizer of aircraft; rotor blades and fuselage of helicopters; rocket motor cases; reentry vehicle structures of missiles; compressor blades and stator vanes of jet engines; and other similarly critical parts.

The use of structural reinforced plastics having lighter weight than alternate materials improves the performance of the flight vehicle in terms of increased payload, range, and other factors.

The development of high strength boron fibers was the initial basis for many analyses which showed that use of the fiber composites could theoretically result in weight reduction of 20–50%, depending on the application. Experimental programs are in effect to prove these predictions in hardware. For example, property levels for boron fiber are now 450,000 psi tensile strength and $60+10^6$ psi modulus of elasticity. The density varies slightly with the diameter but is approximately 2.5. The use of fibers other than boron is developing rapidly.

For supersonic and hypersonic aircraft there is emphasis on extended high temperature resistance, in addition to the usual requirements for improved stiffness, strength and weight reduction. This runs into the limitation of existing laminating resins used in the matrix.

Therefore, the main objectives of the Air Force Material Laboratory are new materials for structural plastics, experimental developments in composites, and assessment of the results. Follow-up efforts on new materials consist of determination of engineering and design data on the composites, fabrication and test of prototype structures, and development of manufacturing processes for the composites.

Research on new reinforcements is aimed toward fibers having higher modulus/density ratio than boron fibers, plus having strength/density ratios at least as good or better than the previous fibers. The current "front-runner" among the new reinforcements is graphite fibers.

Laboratory production has shown a modulus of elasticity as high as 100 million psi; the current commercial form has a modulus of 25 million psi. Density of the high modulus graphite fibers is low, only $\frac{2}{3}$ that of glass or boron, but the current strength levels need improve-

Fig. 15-42. Filament wound room size structure on footings now undergoing service test at University of Michigan, was built in cooperation with Hercules Powder Co.

ment. The method of achieving the elasticity and strength is also in need of further development.

For some applications, reinforcements with special properties in addition to high modulus and strength are needed. For high temperature structural use, the Air Force Materials Laboratory is developing silicon carbide and boron carbide filaments. For high temperature structural dielectric use, such as radomes, development of aluminum oxide fibers is underway. For structural uses, particularly for attachment areas, isotropic high strength, high modulus reinforcements such as thin films of boron are being investigated on an exploratory basis.

Most of the reinforcements which are being developed are in continuous filament form, because they are advantageous for fabrication and structural efficiency in composites. For some fibers, such as oxide ceramics, significant reductions in fiber formation costs may be possible for non-continuous fibers. This possibility is also being investigated. To complement this activity, research is being done on collimating and resin impregnating these fibers into intermediate "prepreg" material for subsequent fabrication into structurally efficient composites.

In the plastic matrix area, the Air Force Materials Laboratory objectives are to develop resins having higher modulus, strength and toughness; improved retention of strength and modulus after long time exposure to elevated temperature; and greater ease of fabrication. Attaining all these attributes in a single resin system is, of course, extremely difficult; however, progress is being made in developing resins having certain combinations of these advantages. For example, cycloaliphatic epoxies have been recently developed which have a modulus of elasticity and strength almost twice that of conventional epoxies. New polyimide resins are being developed which have a hundred degrees Fahrenheit higher operating temperature capability than current commercially available polyimides. Work still needs to be done to simplify the fabrication procedures for polyimide laminates and to reduce their void content. For temperature capabilities beyond polyimides, certain aromatic heterocyclic ladder polymers are being investigated.

The development of chemical coupling agents for good bonding between reinforcement and matrix under a range of humidity and temperature conditions is being carried out by the Air Force Materials Laboratory as the need is indicated. For example, the conventional aliphatic silane coupling agents for use with glass fibers and epoxies or phenolics do not have as high heat resistance as the newly developed resins, polyimides and PBI. New heat resistant aromatic silane coupling agents are being developed which have higher temperature capability. These should result in better composite mechanical properties.

In addition to composites development, the lab also performs fundamental research on the micromechanics of composites, the chemistry and physics of the fiber-matrix interface, and mechanism of thermal degradation of polymers. This research aids in selecting promising technical approaches for developing new improved composite materials.

At the more applied end of technology, the Air Force Materials Laboratory is developing and evaluating prototype structural components made from boron fibers and other high modulus, high strength reinforced plastics. One example is the horizontal stabilizer of the F-111 aircraft. This activity is expected to demonstrate to designers the practical payoffs in using high performance structural plastics in primary aerospace structures. So far, this "hardware" effort continues to show the high potential. Sucess is anticipated in several types of system application prototypes.

In the ablative plastics area, the objectives are to develop improved heat shield materials for advanced ballistic missiles, shields for reentry vehicles, and improved materials for rocket nozzles and thrust chambers. Here the requirements include resistance to detection and to nuclear weapon interception by hostile forces.

The Air Force Materials Laboratory is advancing the technology of fiber-reinforced composites at a gratifying rate. The need for high performance composites in the aerospace field has necessitated these developments.

## A. Thermal Degradation

Investigations of thermal degradation and high temperature oxidative degradation of polymers and laminating resins have revealed certain features of their molecular structure which explains the performance of existing resins and serve to guide the development of new and better ones (6). Some of these features which tend to enhance or promote good thermal-oxidative stability are as follows:

*1.* The resin molecules should have a high percentage of stable structural units, such as benzene rings or the other thermally stable ring units in the molecule.

*2.* The molecules should have a minimum of readily available hydrogen atoms. It is preferable in some cases that sites normally occupied by hydrogen atoms be replaced by halogen atoms or by methyl or phenyl groups.

*3.* The linkage between the thermally stable structural units should have thermal-oxidative stability approaching that of the structural units themselves. In this regard, it is important to differentiate between strictly thermal stability and thermal-oxidative stability. Some resins, such as phenolics, are thermally stable in vacuum or inert gas environments up to temperatures approaching 1000°F, but the upper limit on their service temperature in air for long times is only about 450-500°F, in the case of phenolics, the weak link in the thermal-oxidative degradation process is the methyl bridge between the benzene rings.

In general, aliphatic linkages tend to degrade thermal-oxidative stability and the longer the link between the stable unit the more susceptible the resin is to degradation.

Fig. 15-43. This 13-ft diameter reinforced plastics rocket motor case has been built by B. F. Goodrich Aerospace and Defense Products, Akron, Ohio, for Thiokol Chemical Corp., which is developing RP cases for solid fuel Air Force rockets.

## B. New Polymers

A new structure is the "polyaromatic heterocycle" resin linkage typified by polybenzimidazole (PBI), (PI), and polybenzothiazole resins. One way of increasing thermal stability for some types of resins such as phenolics, epoxies and polyesters is to increase the amount of crosslinking. However, this is not a prerequisite if the molecule is inherently rigid. The current polyaromatic heterocyclies (PBI and PI) are not crossliked but derive their good thermal stability and good strength due to their "stiff-backbone" chain structure.

## C. Preparation of Laminates from High Temperature Resistant Laminating Resins

### 1. Processing Steps

There are four principal processing steps in preparing high temperature resistant reinforced plastic laminates, using either woven or non-woven fibers as reinforcements. These are:

*1.* Impregnation of the reinforcement with the laminating resin.

*2.* Laying up the impregnated reinforcement on a mold or mandrel.

*3.* Curing the resin impregnated layup in the mold with heat and pressure.

*4.* Postcure of the part at elevated temperature, usually after removal from the mold.

The methods used for impregnating the reinforcement with resin are primarily wet layup, solution prepreg, and hot melt prepreg. The wet layup technique is used primarily for low viscosity resins such as polyesters and some epoxies. These wet layup resins cure by addition polymerization without release of volatiles. They are therefore ideally suited to low pressure fabrication techniques such as vacuum bag or vacuum bag plus autoclave.

The majority of the heat resistant resins are either highly viscous, semi-solid or solid at room temperature. In order to obtain thorough impregnation of (7) the reinforcement with them, a solution prepregging technique is generally used. In this technique the resin is dissolved in an organic solvent, the fabric is passed through the resin solution, picking up a controlled amount of resin and then the resin impregnated reinforcement is passed through an oven or drying tower.

A solution prepreging, the oven drying is an important and sometimes critical step. In this step, the solvent is removed, and the polymerization of the resin is advanced. This serves to reduce the flow of the resin during fabrication, and for condensation polymerization resins such as phenolics, silicones, and polyimides, removes some of the volatile byproducts of polymerization.

The degree of advancement of the resin in the prepreg has a strong influence on the optimum cure cycle for that particular type prepreg. Therefore, a single resin system may be used to make different grades for prepreg for different types of molding or fabrication.

Although, the hot melt impregnation technique is used infrequently for high temperature resistant laminating resins, it is used commercially for polybenzimidazole (PBI) resin. One of the reasons for using the hot melt technique with this resin is that the solvents for PBI have high boiling temperatures and would not be completely removed during the oven drying cycle. The residual solvent would reduce the elevated temperature mechanical properties of the PBI laminates.

## 2. Fabrication Procedures and Cure Cycles for Typical Specific High Temperature Resistant Resin

**a. Vibrin 136-A Polyester.** Vibrin 136-A of U.S. Rubber Company is a triallyl cyanurate modified polyester resin. It may be handled in much the same manner as the general pupose, low-pressure, styrene-based resins. An elevated temperature postcure is recommended to obtain optimum properties.

Vibrin 136-A is a clear, amber liquid resin at room temperature. If stored at low temperatures, the container of resin should be allowed to reach room temperatures before opening. If the resin has crystallized (as may happen below room temperature), it should be warmed at 120°F and stirred until homogeneous.

For its preparation glass fabric laminates having the maximum mechanical and electrical properties and free of crazing, it is necessary to impregnate the glass fabric as completely as possible. The production of void-free laminates is materially aided by:

*1.* Reducing the resin viscosity by warming to 120–140°F.

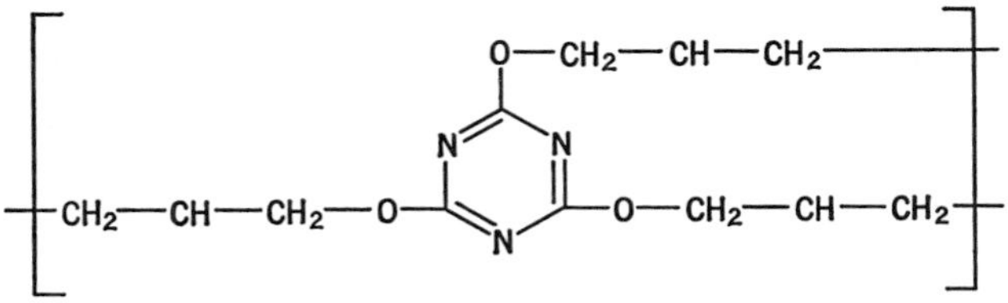

Fig. 15-44. Triallyl cyanurate polyester.

*2.* Complete removal of dissolved gases in the resin by vacuum treatment.

*3.* Predrying the glass fabric in an oven at 230°F for at least one hour just before using.

*4.* Periodic warming of the ungelled saturated layup to maintain reduced resin viscosity (care must be taken to avoid premature gelation of layup because of too much heat or too long a time at the warm temperature).

*5.* Sufficient mechanical work during squeegeeing to wet individual filaments of glass fabric yarns.

**b. CTL-91LD Phenolic Resin.** CTL-91LD is a resole resin produced by the reaction of phenol and formaldehyde under the influence of heat and an alkaline catalyst. The chemical structure of the A-stage uncured resin is in all probability comprised mainly of phenolic alcohol intermediates and complexes of the alkaline catalyst plus water of condensation, free formaldehyde and free phenol.

Parts fabricated from CTL-91LD are many and varied, ranging in size from an ounce to as much as 350 lb each. Typical of the parts fabricated by the major aircraft and missile manufacturers are the following:

Hot air ducts and baffles
Radomes
Honeycomb structures
Air frame structural components and surfaces
Rotor blades, spacers, and rings
Telemetering windows
Antenna housing
Missile Nose, bodies, and fins
Structural sections

Flame barriers
Missile rocket motor guidance vanes
Plastic pipe and couplings
Base sheet for printed circuits
Fuel tanks
Terminal strips
Rocket nozzles, insulators, fins, diffusers, and chambers
Flare cases
Structural rings
Marine and commercial installations

CTL-91LD resin is available in form of preimpregnated glass fabric and molding material. The molding material is available in the forms of preimpregnated chopped glass fabric, macerated glass fabric and chopped parallel glass fiber strand.

Most CTL-91LD parts are made either by vacuum bag plus autoclave molding or matched die molding to provide the higher pressures necessary to achieve a dense, low porosity part.

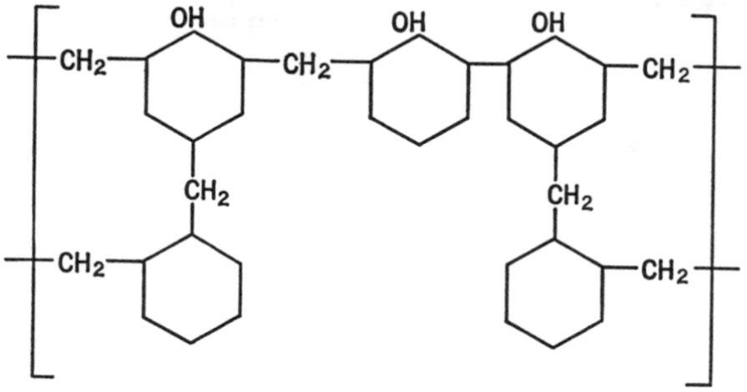

Fig. 15-45. Phenolic.

**c. DC-2106 Silicone Resin.** Dow Corning 2106 resin is a silicone laminating resin especially designed for fabricating parts by low pressure forming methods. Included in such methods are filament winding, vacuum bag molding, matched metal bolds or mandrel wrapping combined with cellophane lagging techniques.

The resin is usually used in combination with an inorganic reinforcing material such as glass roving or fabric, asbestos, and quartz fibers. Laminated parts made from these resin-reinforcement combinations have outstanding thermal stability. They remain serviceable almost indefinitely at temperatures up to 500°F, and withstand many hours of exposure at temperatures to 700°F and shorter periods at temperatures to 1000°F.

They have low dielectric losses, good electrical properties under wet conditions and very stable electrical properties over a wide range of frequencies and temperatures.

Dow Corning 2106 resin is used to make such parts as laminated radomes, filament wound nose cones and pressure bottles, aircraft ductwork, thermal and arc barriers., covers and cases for high frequency equipment.

**d. Epon 1031 Epoxy Resin.** This resin of Shell Chemical Company

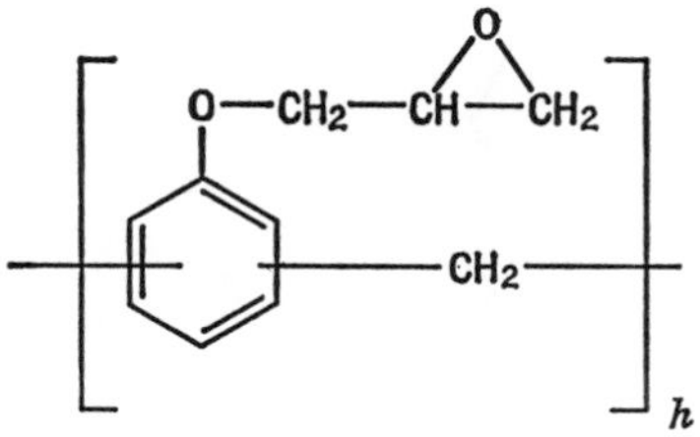

Fig. 15-46. Epoxy-Novolac.

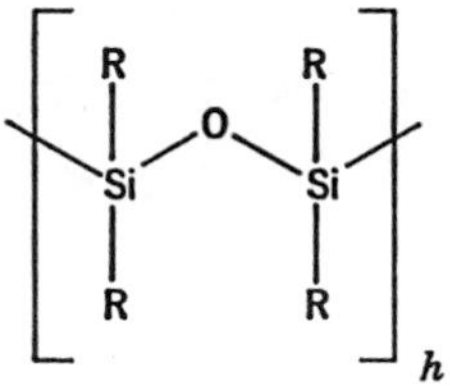

Fig. 15-47. Silicone.

is an epoxy resin which provides good strength characteristics at elevated temperatures (500°F range) as well as retention of these strength characteristics after prolonged exposure to these elevated temperatures. It is a solid epoxy resin with high functionality and reactivity. It consists of a mixture of isomers and homologues.

This resin reacts more readily with all classes of curing agents than does a conventional bisphenol-A based resin such as Epon 828. The tetra functionality of Epon 1031 results in a cured product of higher crosslink density. Consequently, it is not surprising to find that with a given curing agent Epon 1031 gives higher heat distortion points than Epon 828.

It is available as a solid resin or as a solution of this resin in methyl ethyl ketone at 80% solids (±1%). The resin as sold conforms to the following specifications:

In the absence of a catalyst or curing agent, Epon 1031 is unchanged after storage for one year at normal ambient temperatures. If Epon 1031 is maintained at 300°F for 24 hr, some additional polymerization will occur. Heating at higher temperatures or for longer times may result in an insoluble crosslinked product.

The solid nature of the resin imposes some limitations on the fabricating methods that may be employed. Dry layup laminates and molded articles present no unusual fabricating problems, but vacuum

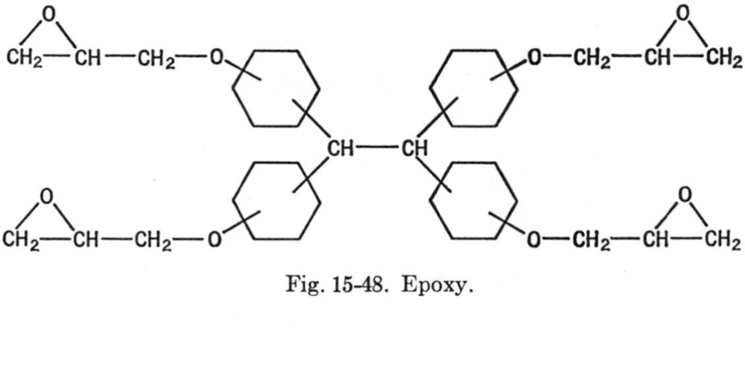

Fig. 15-48. Epoxy.

bag laminates and castings require special techniques and are limited to certain curing systems having low viscosity and reasonable pot life at elevated temperatures.

**e. Skygard 700 Polyimide Resin.** Physical properties of the Monsanto Company Skygard 700 is a heat reactive aromatic system containing active amino and carboxyl groups. It is specifically designed for structural, electrical and specialty applications where extended exposure at temperatures up to 700°F, is required. Application of this product in a glass-cloth laminate structure to obtain optimum physical characteristics, heat resistance and electrical properties is described.

There are many factors in processing laminates for optimum high temperature resistance that must be taken into consideration. "B" staging of the impregnated material, pressing and postcuring conditions are recommended. Deviation can be expected to result in a lowering of some properties.

Since oxidation degradation is the principal factor in long-term loss of laminate strength in the 700°F range, a dense, nonporous laminate will withstand such exposure conditions much better than a porous one. Adequate resin flow during pressing helps to achieve this structure. Flow values recommended are measured at the pressing conditions to be used. A four-inch square, twelve-ply laminate is pressed. Weight loss due to resin squeeze-out is calculated as percentage flow.

**f. Imidite 1850 Polybenzimidazole Resin (on Glass Fabric).** Imidite 1850 supplied by Namco Materials Division, Whittaker Corp., is a hetrocyclic, polyaromatic linear polymer based laminating material coated on a water-resistant balanced weave glass fabric. It can be considered for use where long-term exposure at temperatures ranging from −423 to 600°F are required, and for short-term applications as high as 1200°F.

Some possible applications are high-temperature deicer ducts, radomes, deflectors, nose fairings, radiation covers, missile and air-

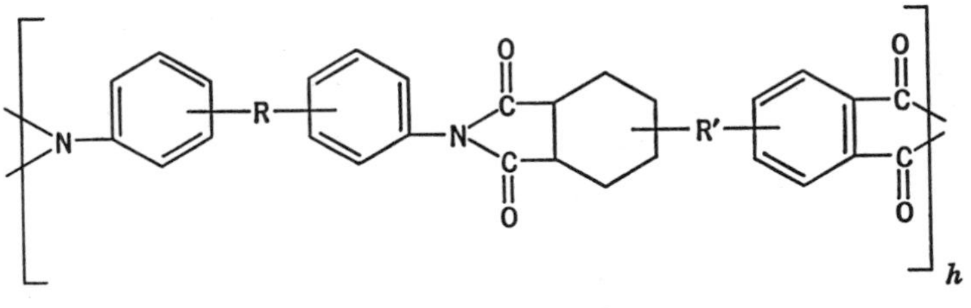

Fig. 15-49. Polyimide.

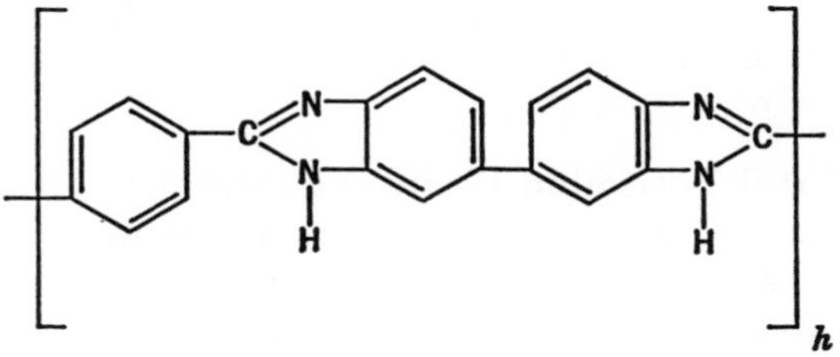

Fig. 15-50. Polybenzimidazole.

craft wings, turbine blades, reentry nose cones, leading edges, and various control surfaces of missiles and aircraft.

As is the case with most preimpregnated laminating materials, if optimum properties to be obtained, the curing cycle must be adapted to compensate for variation between individual applications. A cure cycle which yielded good mechanical properties on 18 in. × 18 in. 15-ply laminates was:

1. The layup was placed in a preheated press at 700°F.
2. The press was closed and a pressure of 35 psi was applied for 30 sec.
3. Pressure was increased to 200 psi.
4. The laminate was held at 200 psi at a temperature of 700°F for 3 hr.
5. The temperature was reduced to 500°F or below, and the laminate was removed from the press.

Subsequent studies have indicated that pressures as low as 85 psi can be used and that the material can be cured by autoclave techniques as well as in presses. Postcures can involve putting parts placed in a container (such as stainless steel bag) and purged of air using nitrogen, (or a vacuum oven). The part is then postcured in the nitrogen atmosphere or vacuum using the following recommended postcure:

24 hr at 600°F
24 hr at 650°F
24 hr at 700°F
24 hr at 750°F
8 hr at 800°F

Argon or helium may be substituted for the nitrogen.

## D. Characterization of High Temperature Resistant Laminating Resins

The characterization of high temperature resistant laminating resins starts with relatively simple procedures and techniques for screening purposes, and progresses to more sophisticated techniques to yield engineering data and design data if the resin proves its worth in the preliminary screening.

For candidate high temperature resistant resins which are competing with each other for selection for further development, the principal screening is weight loss resins temperature and exposure time. Resins which pass this screening are then made into glass fabric base plastic laminate flexural test specimens for determination of flexural strength and flexural modulus of elasticity at room temperature and elevated temperatures. At this stage interlaminar shear strength determinations may also be performed. Next tensile and compressive strengths and moduli are determined to round out static mechanical property determinations. Panel shear strength and panel shear modulus may also be performed depending on the specific material being investigated.

The next stage of mechanical property characterization consists primarily of determining time-dependent properties such as creep, stress–rupture, and fatigue properties. Other mechanical properties which are sometimes determined are bearing, impact, notch sensitivity, and Poisson's ratio.

In this chapter, comprehensive physical and mechanical property data on laminates will be presented for four resin systems. These are CTL-91-LD phenolic, CTL-37-9X phenylsilane, DC-2106 silicone, and Epon 1031 epoxy. Descriptions of the mechanical property test procedures used for these laminates is given in Appendix 2(8). In addition some physical and mechanical property data will be presented on Vibrin 136A polyester, Skyard 700 polyimide, and Imidite 1850 polybenzimidazole.

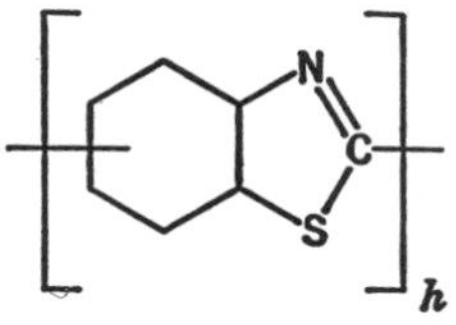

Fig. 15-51. Polybenzothiazole.

## 1. Comparative Screening

**a. Weight Loss.** **(1)** **TGA.** Thermogravimetric analysis of laminating resins consists of heating a small quantity of the material at a predetermined rate of temperature rise and plotting the residual weight fraction versus temperature. The amount of material required is a few tenths of a gram, the rate of temperature rise is in the order of 150°C/hr, and the ambient environment is usually nitrogen or vacuum. A typical TGA curve (in nitrogen) for a phenolic resin compared to one for a polymide resin is shown in Fig. 15-52(9) TGA curves for polymeric materials typically show the threshold temperature of decomposition and the residual weight fraction (char yield) at the maximum temperature of exposure. For the curves shown, the phenolic resin has an apparent threshold decomposition temperature of about 230°C. However, the initial weight loss is likely due to loss of some water of condensation. The true decomposition temperature is about 310°C and the find weight fraction at 900°C is about 0.40. For the polyimide, the threshold decomposition temperature is about 460°C and the find residual weight fraction is about 0.58.

### 2. Isothermal Air Aging at High Temperatures

Thermogravimetric analysis is a useful tool to candidate high temperature resistant in the early stages of their development. However, it does not adequately discriminate between the long time high temperature aging characteristics of resins due to its inherent dynamic

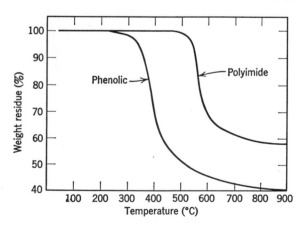

Fig. 15-52. TGA curves (in dry nitrogen) for phenolic and polyimide.

nature meaning the rapidly rising temperature. Weight loss during isothermal air aging of either pure resin or fiber reinforced resin laminates is usually more indicative of the performance of the resin during actual use, especially for long time use situations. The temperatures of exposure currently are between 400 and 1000°F for the resins now available for exposure periods of from less than an hour to over a thousand hours.

Comprehensive isothermal aging weight loss data on CTL-91-LD phenolic, CTL-37-9X phenylsilane, DC-2106 silicone and Epon 1031 epoxy glass fabric reinforced plastic laminates are presented graphically in Figs. 15-53 through 15-56 (10). In reviewing the weight loss data, it should be remembered that the resin is the constituent which is lost by heating, and therefore the final weight will consist of reinforced (glass fiber) plus resin residue or undegraded resin.

For the CTL-91-LD phenolic laminates, deterioration due to continued exposure to elevated temperatures was measured through the weight lost by the specimens during the exposure period. Weights retained are shown as percent of initial weight. For various temperatures and periods of exposure at those elevated temperatures. The data show that at 300 and 400°F for exposures of from 0.5 to 1000 hr, the specimens retained 98% or more of their weight. The effect of increases in temperature at all periods of exposure caused less weight retention and, of course, there was less weight retention with increases in duration of exposure. The most rapid loss in weight appears

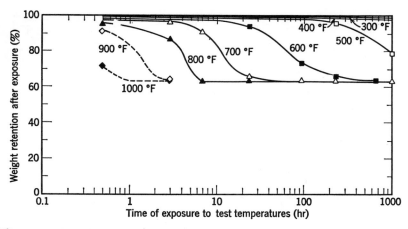

Fig. 15-53. Deterioration (as weight loss) at elevated temperatures of phenolic laminates made of CTL-91LD resin and 189-A1100 glass fabric.

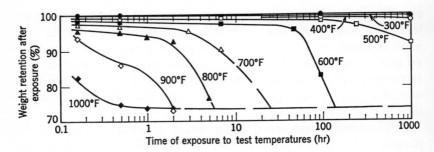

Fig. 15-54. Deterioration (as weight loss) at elevated temperatures of phenyl-silane laminates made of CTL 37-9X resin and 181-A1100 glass fabric.

to be at about 500 hr for 500°F, at 70 hr at 600°F, at 12 hr for 700°F, 5 hr at 800°F, and 1.5 hr for 900°F.

As seen from Fig. 15-54, for the CTL-37-9X laminates, the most rapid loss in weight appears to be at about 1000 hr for 500°F, at 70 hr for 600°F, at 10 hr for 700°F, at 4 hr for 800°F, at 1.5 hr for 900°F, and 1/6 hr for 1000°F.

As shown in Fig. 15-55, for the DC-2106 silicone laminates, exposure at 300, 400, and 500°F for 1000 hr show less than 1% weight loss. At temperatures of 900°F and higher, the rate of weight loss is much higher than that for the lower temperatures.

Data on the Epon 1031 epoxy laminates, shown in Fig. 15-56 indicate that temperatures above 400°F and below 600°F may be called critical

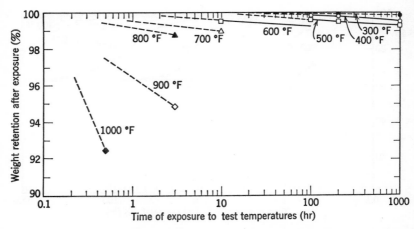

Fig. 15-55. Deterioration (as weight loss) at elevated temperatures of silicone laminates made of DC 2106 resin and 181 heat-cleaned glass fabric.

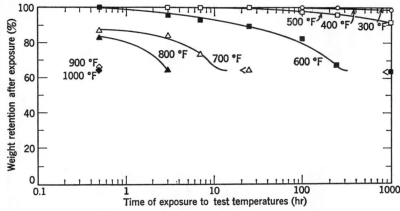

Fig. 15-56. Deterioration (as weight loss) at elevated temperatures of laminates made of Epon 1031 resin and 181-Volan A glass fabric.

temperatures at which there is a noticeable loss in weight and change in color of the laminate. The first color change from a light brown to a dark brown was observed after 1000 hr at 300°F, 24 hr at 400°F, and 3 hr at 500°F.

Higher temperatures and longer durations caused the color to change to a very dark brown, followed by the change to the white resinless fabric. All 500°F specimens, except after ½-hr exposure, were dark brown or very dark brown even though there was less than 9% weight loss. This indicated that 500°F is a critical temperature and that serious deterioration of resin and of strength could be expected at this and higher temperatures. The laminate lost all of its resin after one-half hour of exposure at 900°F.

**a. Flexural Strength and Flexural Modulus of Elasticity.** The flexural properties of glass fiber reinforced plastic laminates give a good comparative indication of the strength, stiffness, and resin-to-fiber adhesion for the resins. This, together with the ease of preparing and testing flexural specimens, both at room and elevated temperatures, has made the flexural test a popular and widely accepted characterization test by materials development people, even though it is not recognized as a valid design property by structural design engineers.

Laminate flexural test specimens are generally rectangular strips having a span-to-depth-ratio of 15–1, and are tested as simply supported beams using 3 point loading. A typical test fixture setup for elevated temperature flexural testing is shown in Fig. 15-57.

Flexural strength and flexural modulus of elasticity data are given

Fig. 15-57. Tensile test at elevated temperature showing 12 × 12 × 14 in. oven, grips, specimen, extensometer, and deflectometer.

for CTL-91LD phenolic, CTL-37-9X phenylsilane, DC-2106 silicone, and Epon 1031 epoxy in Figs. 15-58 through 15-65 (8,11,12). The exposure conditions for the laminates ranges from room temperature through 1000°F, and the exposure times range from 10 min through 100 hr. Specimens exposed during aging to a given temperature were tested at the exposure temperature. Flexural strength data are presented as percentages of room temperature strength, whereas flexural moduli are presented in absolute terms.

For the CTL-91-LD material, at 900 and 400°F there is a slight initial drop in the flexural strength and modulus from the room temperature values, then a gradual increase to about 100 hr, followed by a slight decrease to 1000 hr exposure. At 500°F, a sharp rate of

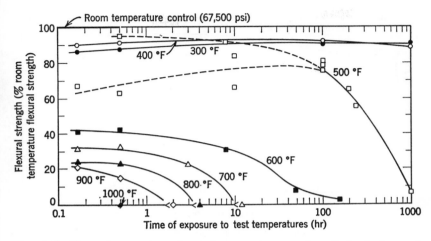

Fig. 15-58. Flexural strength at elevated temperatures of phenolic laminates made of CTL-91LD resin and 181-A1100 glass fabric.

decrease of both flexural strength and modulus starts at about 100 hr by a slight decrease to 1000 hr exposure. After 1000 hr at 500°F exposure there is practically no mechanical integrity left in the material.

The principal difference between the flexural properties of CTL-37-9X and CTL-91-LD is that at 500°F the rate of degradation of CTL-37-9X is much slower than that of CTL-91-LD. The CTL-37-9X material, after 1000 hr of exposure to 500°F has a respectable flexural strength and modulus of 16,500 psi and 2.4×10⁶ psi, respectively.

The DC-2106 material shows a sharp initial drop in flexural strength

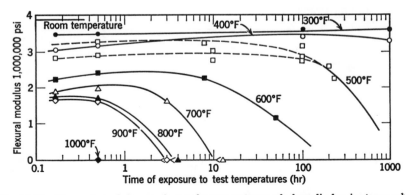

Fig. 15-59. Flexural modulus at elevated temperatures of phenolic laminates made of CTL-91LD resin and 181-A1100 glass fabric.

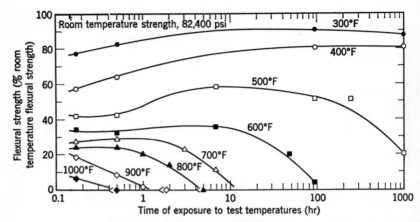

Fig. 15-60. Flexural strength at elevated temperatures of phenyl-silane laminates made of CTL 37-9X resin and 181-A1100 glass fabric.

from the room temperature value, dropping to 40% of the room temperature strength at 500°F initially. However, after continued exposure at 500–600°F for as long as 1000 hr there is no appreciable further reduction in strength. The modulus of elasticity values for DC-2106 remain fairly close to the room temperature value for prolonged exposure at temperatures as high as 800°F.

The Epon 1031 material shows useful serviceability at temperatures as high as 500°F. However, at 600°F, the material has extremely low flexural strength and modulus. Based on these data, the apparent

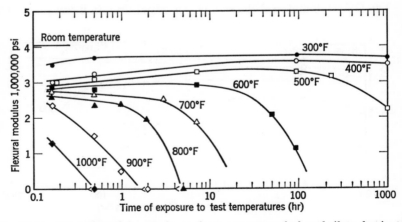

Fig. 15-61. Flexural modulus at elevated temperatures of phenyl-silane laminates made of CTL 37-9X resin and 181-A1100 glass fabric.

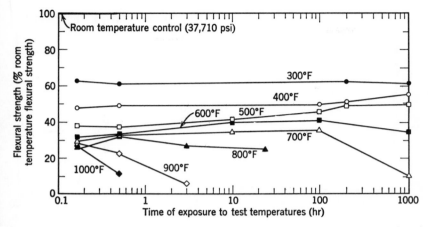

Fig. 15-62. Flexural strength at elevated temperatures of a laminate made of DC 2106 resin and 181 heat-cleaned glass fabric.

critical or maximum serviceability temperature for this material is between 500 and 600°F.

**b. Interlaminar Shear Strength.** Interlaminar shear strength determinations on fiber reinforced plastics have been used to obtain a comparative indication of the cohesive and adhesive strengths of laminating resins. Two different methods are principally used. In method (ARTC-11, Test Method VI) a rectangular strip having grooves cut on opposite faces is pulled in tension with the direction of force perpendicular to the grooves. The other method employs a short beam, with a span-to-depth ratio of 6:1 to 8:1 loaded in 3 point loading. The short

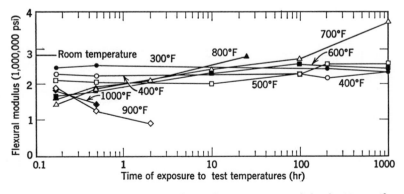

Fig. 15-63. Flexural modulus at elevated temperature of laminates made of DC 2106 resin and 181 heat-cleaned glass fabric.

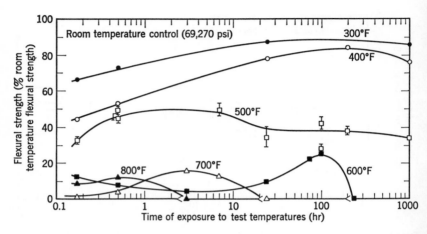

Fig. 15-64. Flexural strength at elevated temperatures of laminates made of Epon 1031 resin and 181-Volan A glass fabric.

beam method gives values which are about three times as high as the rectangular strip ARTC-11 method.

Interlaminar shear strength values for CTL-91-LD, CTL-37-9X, DC-2106 and Epon 1031 glass fabric reinforced laminates, determined by the ARTC 11 method, are shown in Figs. 15-66 through 15-69. Based on these results, it appears that interlaminar shear strength determined by this procedure does not indicate resin degradation, especially from a rate versus exposure time standpoint, as well as flexural strength.

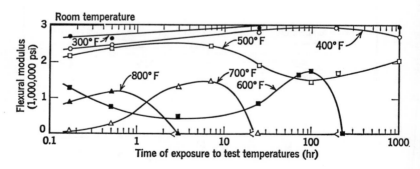

Fig. 15-65. Flexural modulus at elevated temperatures of laminates made of Epon 1031 resin and 181-Volan A glass fabric.

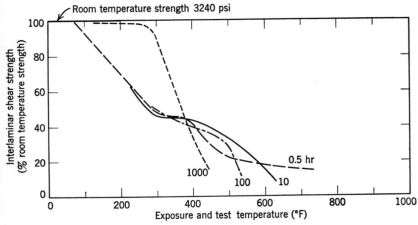

Fig. 15-66. Interlaminar shear strength at elevated temperatures and various soak periods for CTL-91LD phenolic resin and 181-A1100 glass fabric.

## 3. Engineering Properties and Design Data

**a. Static Mechanical Properties.** **(1)** *Edgewise compression and tension-conventional heat aging.* For preliminary structural design purposes, or for comparative assessment of the structural efficiency of materials, information on their compressive and tensile strengths and moduli of elasticity are needed. For glass fiber reinforced plastic laminates the laminating resin is a dominant factor in establishing the compressive strength of the laminate, whereas the glass fiber is

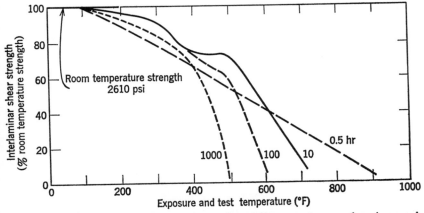

Fig. 15-67. Interlaminar shear strength at elevated temperatures and various soak periods for CTL-37-9X phenyl-silane resin and 181-A1130 glass fabric.

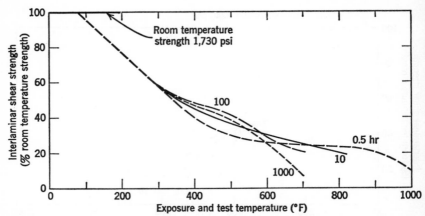

Fig. 15-68. Interlaminar shear strength at elevated temperatures and various soak periods for DC 2106 silicone resin and 181 heat-cleaned glass fabric.

dominant in establishing the tensile strength. The tensile and compressive moduli are usually fairly close to the flexural moduli and are influenced by both the reinforcement and resin.

Tensile and compressive strength data for CTL-91-LD, CTL-37-9X, DC-2106 and Epon 1031 glass fabric reinforced laminates, over the same range of temperature and time as shown previously, are presented in Figs. 15-70 through 15-73. As can be seen from the graphs, the percent reduction in tensile strength for a given temperature-time condition is generally less than the percent reduction in edgewise compressive strength at the same condition.

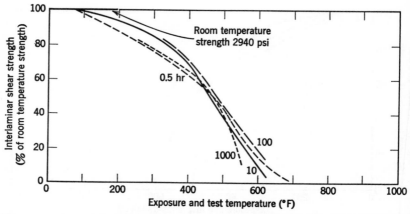

Fig. 15-69. Interlaminar shear strength at elevated temperatures and various soak periods for Epon 1031 epoxy resin and 181-Volcan A glass fabric.

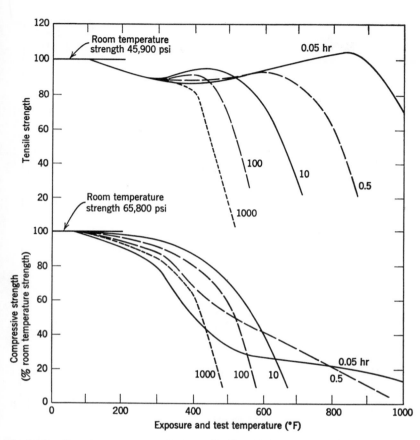

Fig. 15-70. Tensile and compressive strength at elevated temperatures and various soak periods for CTL-91LD phenolic resin and 181-A1100 glass fabric.

**(2) Edgewise Compression and Tension after Rapid Heating.**
Edgewise compressive and tensile strengths for CTL-91-LD, DC-2106 and Epon 1031 determined after heating specimens to an elevated temperature and holding the specimens at that temperature for 2 minutes prior to testing, are shown in Figs. 15-74 and 15-75, respectively (13). It was essential that the heating rate be increased rapidly, so instead of using the conventional air-circulating ovens that heat specimens relatively slowly, heating equipment was used that would heat specimens to the desired temperature in less than 60 sec.

The specimens were heated in the unstressed condition and tested at constant temperatures ranging from 300 to 1000°F. The data indicate that of the three laminates evaluated, the CTL-91-LD performs best

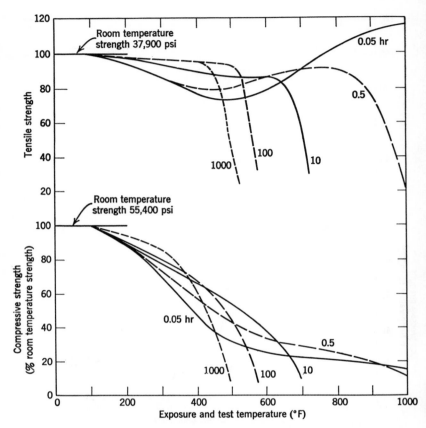

Fig. 15-71. Tensile and compressive strength at elevated temperatures and various soak periods for CTL-37-9X phenyl-silane resin and 181-A1100 glass fabric.

on an overall basis, even though there is a sharp reduction in edgewise compressive strength between 300 and 600°F.

**(3) *Edgewise Compressive and Tensile Strengths of Laminates Having Temperature Gradients through the Thickness.*** For glass fabric base plastic laminates having a temperature gradient through the thickness, the load bearing capability is not the summation of strengths of the individual laminate at their respective temperatures. An analysis has been made for predicting the effective strength of laminates having a temperature gradient through the thickness (14). The principal assumptions were: (*1*) a linear temperature gradient through the thickness, and (*2*) that the strength of the laminate was a straight line function of temperature.

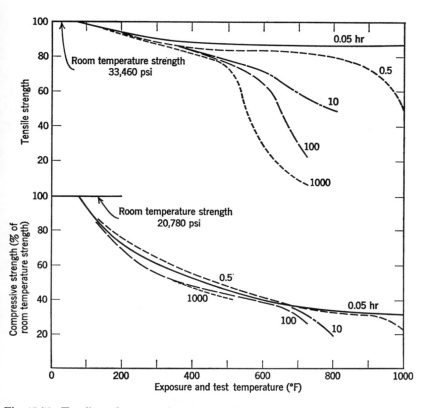

Fig. 15-72. Tensile and compressive strength at elevated temperatures and various soak periods for DC 2106 silicone resin and 181 heat-cleaned glass fabric.

The conclusions were as follows:

Experimental tests on CTL-91-LD and DC-2106 glass fabric base plastic laminates were in general agreement with these results:

If one-half the strength of the material on the cold face is less than the strength on the hot face, a rapid progressive failure would result. The strength of the laminate would thus be expected to equal the strength of the material on the hot face; for example, complete failure occurs when the hot face ruptures.

If one-half the strength of the material on the cold face is greater than the strength on the hot face, the strength of the laminate would be the result of a slower progressive failure and would be expected to equal one-fourth of the strength available on the cold face squared, divided by strength on the cold face minus strength on the hot side.

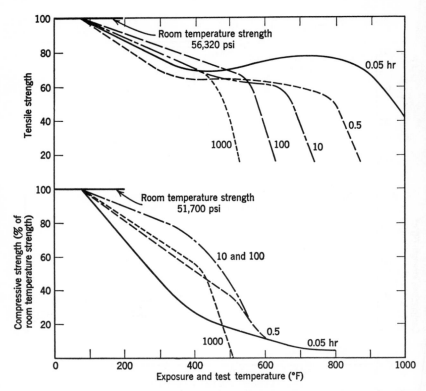

Fig. 15-73. Tensile and compressive strength at elevated temperatures and various soak periods for Epon 1031 epoxy resin and 181-Volan A glass fabric.

**b. Time Dependent Mechanical Properties.** *(1) Stress Rupture-Edgewise Compression and Tension.* Tensile and compressive stress rupture curves for CTL-91-LD, DC-2106 and Epon 1031 glass fabric laminates, exposed and tested at room temperature, 300°F, and 500°F for periods up to 1000 hr, are presented in Figs. 15-76 through 15-81. The results are, in most cases, straight lines on semilog plots of "applied stress" versus "duration of applied stress," where the log axis is duration.

*(2) Fatigue Properties.* The fatigue properties of a ¼ in. thick CTL-91-LD laminate were subjected to relatively high stress levels (15). The room temperature tensile and compressive strengths of this laminate were approximately 59,000 and 79,000 psi, respectively. Fatigue tests were made at a zero mean stress at the rate of about 5 cpm. The load was applied parallel to the warp direction of the

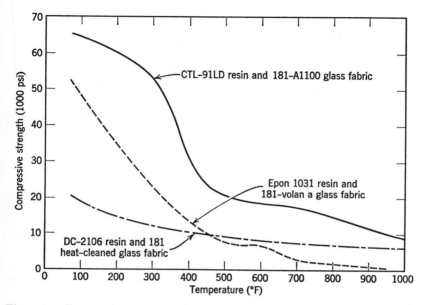

Fig. 15-74. Compressive strength of laminates at elevated temperatures after rapid heating and a soak of 0.03 hr.

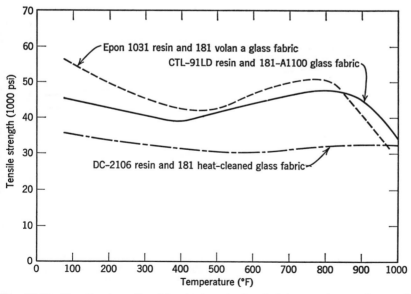

Fig. 15-75. Tensile strength of laminates at elevated temperatures after rapid heating and a soak of 0.03 hr.

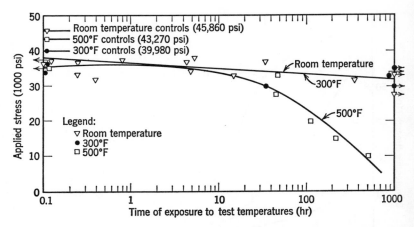

Fig. 15-76. Tensile stress-rupture curves for phenolic laminates made of CTL-91LD resin and 181-A1100 glass fabric.

laminate. Based on the test results, the following observations were made:

(*1*) Failure under repeated loading at high stress levels occurred on that portion of the load cycle, tension or compression that had the least strength in the static control test.

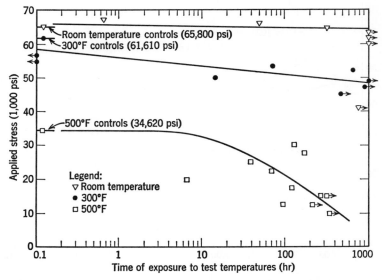

Fig. 15-77. Compressive stress–rupture curves for phenolic laminates made of CTL-91LD resin and 181-A1100 glass fabric.

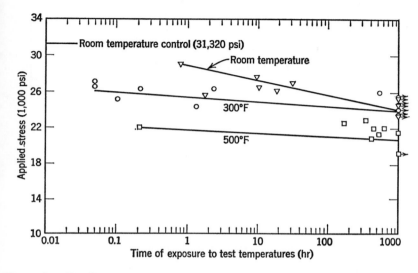

Fig. 15-78. Tensile stress–rupture curves for laminates made of DC 2106 resin and 181 heat-cleaned glass fabric.

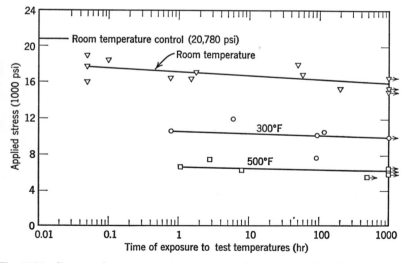

Fig. 15-79. Compressive stress–rupture curves for laminates made of DC 2106 resin and 181 heat-cleaned glass fabric.

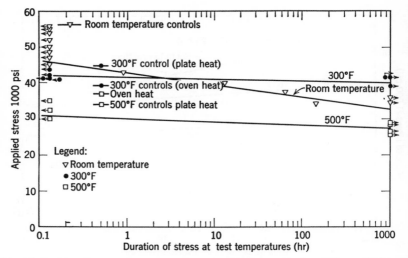

Fig. 15-80. Tensile stress–rupture curves for laminates made of Epon 1031 resin and 181-Volan A glass fabric.

(*2*) At 73°F, the fatigue strength at 200 cycles was about 80% of the control strength.

(*3*) At elevated temperatures, the fatigue strength up to about 150 cycles was essentially constant. This effect reflects the complex strength–time–temperature relationships. Permanent degradation ef-

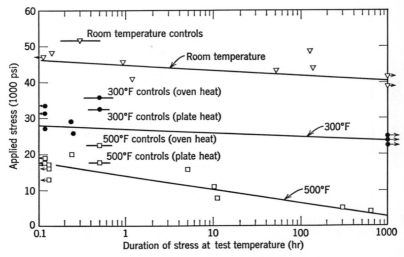

Fig. 15-81. Compressive stress–rupture curves for laminates made of Epon 1031 resin and 181-Volan A glass fabric.

fects due to time of heating were noted at 800°F after 150 cycles of loading.

(3) *Fatigue characteristics under Cyclic Axial or Shear Loading* (16). This report presents the fatigue characteristics of plastic laminates made of two new resin systems reinforced with unwoven S glass fibers. This knowledge adds to the data that have already been generated to evaluate the fatigue properties of typical laminates. Previous work included such laminates reinforced with glass fabrics, glass-asbestos mats, and unwoven E and S glass fibers in combination with various resin systems. The resins in this investigation were in combination with S glass fibers which were oriented (1) with alternate plies at 0° and 90° to the principal axis and, (2) with alternate plies at +5° and −5° to the principal axis. S–N curves were obtained by axially loading specimens at constant stress amplitudes superimposed on a constant mean load of zero stress, i.e., a stress ratio of −1.0. All experiments were conducted on unnotched specimens at 900 cpm at 73°F. Fatigue life of these laminates is compared with that from other laminates.

Even though considerable data are available on fatigue of axially loaded laminates, very little is known about the fatigue characteristics of laminates loaded in shear. Loads within a laminate are transferred from one fiber to another through the resin matrix usually by means of shear stress. This review presents the interlaminar shear strength of plastic laminates reinforced with unwoven glass fibers as obtained by five test methods. The magnitude of the values is, of course, a function of the test method and specimen. One of the static test methods was adapted to apply repeated shear loads so that S–N curves of the shear stress versus number of cycles were generated at 900 cpm and at a stress ratio of 0. The static and dynamic test methods are described.

The results show that by incorporating stronger resins to bind the fiber bundles the axial fatigue life of a laminate is increased. For example: the number of median life cycles at 54,000 psi for crossply constructions was increased from 3,000 to 53,400, and at 40,00 psi it was increased from 17,850 to 659,250 when shear strengths of the resin systems were changed small amounts from 8,800 to 9,320 or 4,740 to 4,880 lb/in.,[2] depending on method of test. Another example: the number of median life cycles at 75,000 lb/in.[2] for a ±5° construction was increased from 7,500 to 18,500 cycles when shear strength only changed from 10,620 to 11,120 psi.

(a) **Materials.** All of the laminates used for this fatigue study were

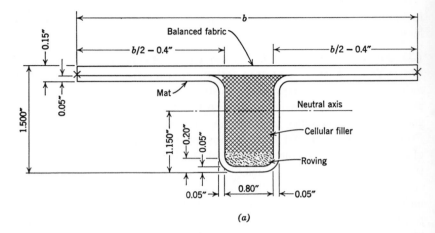

(a)

supplied by the Minnesota Mining and Manufacturing Company, St. Paul, Minn. Details of the materials and fabrication were provided by the supplier and are summarized in Table 15-36.

The glass roving was 20 end, S 994 glass made into a web with Scotchply type XP234S (Project 207006, Lot 1) or XP251S (Project 206706, Lot 26) resin system, coated on a laboratory coater. The glass was stored at a temperature less than 40°F before and after coating.

This web or tape of unidirectional glass fibers was laminated into the panels 10 by 12 in., finished size, and about ⅛ in. thick. Each panel consisted of 19 plies, with alternate plies at 0° and 90° or ±5° to the principal axis. Fabrication details are presented in Table 15-36.

The physical properties of these panels, namely, specific gravity, Barcol hardness, and resin content, are presented in Table 15-37. Each hardness and gravity value is the average of the 18 or 22 panels of each type. The range in hardness for XP234S material crossplied was 76 to 81 and for ±5° was 77 to 80; for XP251S crossplied was 78 to 80 and for ±5° was 77 to 80. The range in specific gravity for XP234S crossplied was 1.960 to 2.124 and for ±5° was 1.978 to 2.060; for XP251S crossplied was 1.876 to 1.955 and for ±5° was 1.919 to 2.020. The difference in specific gravity values was as high as 8 percent. Additional data are shown in Tables 15-38 through 15-44.

**c. Thermal Properties.** Thermal properties which have been measured for high temperature resistant 181 weave glass fabric reinforced plastic laminates include: thermal conductivity; specific heat; coefficient of thermal expansion; total normal emittance; and solar, absorbance (17). Thermal conductivity values for glass fabric reinforced

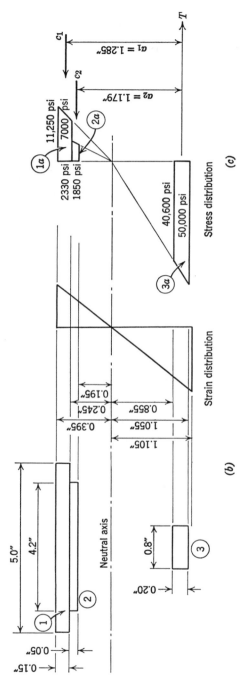

Fig. 15-82. (*a*), Cross section of ribbed plate. (*b*), Flange and rib sections used in design, showing position of neutral axis. (*c*) Stress distribution in ribbed beam, resultant compression and tension, and internal moment arms.

$A_1 = 5 \times 0.15 = 0.75$ in.²
$E_1 = 3 \times 10^6$ psi
$A_2 = 4.2 \times 0.05 = 0.21$ in.²
$E_2 = 1 \times 10^6$ psi
$A_3 = 0.2 \times 0.8 = 0.16$ in.²
$E_3 = 5 \times 10^6$ psi

$\sigma_1 = 20{,}000$ psi
$\sigma_2 = 5{,}000$ psi
$\sigma_3 = 50{,}000$ psi

TABLE 15-36.  Fabrication Description of Plastic Laminates Made of Scotchply Resins and Unwoven S Glass Fibers

| Resin | Ply orientation [a] | Number of panels | Pressure and cure procedure for all panels |
|---|---|---|---|
| XP234S | Alternate plies at 0° and 90° | 22 | 300°F press, 2 min. slow close to 300 lb per square in., 30 min. at 300°F and |
|  | Alternate plies at ±5° | 22 | 300 lb/sq in., postcured 4 hr at 350°F in an oven. |
| XP251S | Alternate plies at 0° and 90° | 18 | 300°F press, 2 min gel at contact pressure, 2 min close to 100 lb/sq in., 30 |
|  | Alternate plies at ±5° | 22 | min at 300°F and 100 lb/sq in., postcured 4 hr at 350°F in an oven. |

[a] Orientation relative to principal axis.

phenolic, polyester, silicone, and epoxy laminates from 100 to 400°F are shown in Fig. 15-83. Specific heat values for glass fabric reinforced polyester, phenolic, and silicon laminates from 100 to 500°F are shown in Fig. 15-84. Coefficients of thermal expansion for a variety of high temperature resistant plastic laminates are shown in Table 15-45. Total normal emittance of phenolic, silicone, epoxy, and TAC polyester laminates is shown in Table 15-46 and solar absorbances for the same laminates is shown in Table 15-47. See Table 15-48 for thermal conductivity determinations combining asbestos or glass fibers with epoxy, phenolic, silicone, phenyl silane and epoxy-novalac resins (18).

*(1) Effect of Thermal Cycling.* Tables 15-49 and 15-50, also Figs. 15-85 through 15-88, presents the modulus of elasticity and strength values of four reinforced plastic laminates in tension and compression at room temperature and at 500°F.  Prior to evaluation at these temperatures, the test specimens were exposed to thermal-shock cycling.  Three of the laminates evaluated in this study were reinforced with 181-A1100 glass fabric and represented three resin systems: a phenolic resin (CTL 37-9X), an epoxy resin (ERSB-0111), and a phenyl-silane (Narmco 534).  The fourth was a phenolic-asbestos laminate made of R/M Pyrotex felt style 41-RPD (19).

The effects of thermal-shock cycling on properties vary with the type of resin and reinforcement.  In general, thermal-shock cycling had less effect on modulus of elasticity than on strength.  Properties at room temperature tended to decrease after exposure to cycling, while the properties of most laminates evaluated at 500°F were not seriously affected.

TABLE 15-37.  Strength [a] and Related Properties [b] of Plastic Laminates Made of Scotchply Resins and Unwoven S Glass Fibers

| Resin type | Orientation of fibers to principal axis | Specific gravity | Barcol hardness | Resin content, % | Modulus of elasticity | | Stress at proportional limit | | Maximum stress | | Maximum strain, in./in. |
|---|---|---|---|---|---|---|---|---|---|---|---|
| | | | | | Value, mill psi | Coefficient of variation, % | Value, 1000 psi | Coefficient of variation, % | Value, 1000 psi | Coefficient of variation, % | |
| | | | | | Compression [c] | | | | | | |
| XP234S | Cross | 2.02 | 79 | 19.9 | 5.72 | 4.1 | 29.7 | 1.1 | 97.1 | 7.8 | 0.020 |
| | ±5° | 2.02 | 78 | 21.1 | 7.99 | 4.7 | 60.9 | 13.9 | 115.1 | 7.0 | 0.015 |
| XP251S | Cross | 1.91 | 79 | 25.0 | 4.83 | 5.1 | 42.2 | 1.9 | 97.5 | 6.8 | 0.020 |
| | ±5° | 1.96 | 79 | 25.1 | 7.46 | 9.0 | 70.6 | 6.9 | 119.3 | 1.3 | 0.017 |
| | | | | | Tension [d] | | | | | | |
| XP234S | Cross | 2.02 | 79 | 19.9 | 4.31 | 5.8 | — | — | 141.4 | 5.1 | 0.030 |
| | ±5° | 2.02 | 78 | 21.1 | 8.30 | 4.9 | — | — | 155.3 | 4.2 | — |
| XP251S | Cross | 1.91 | 79 | 25.0 | 4.02 | 6.0 | — | — | 136.7 | 5.6 | — |
| | ±5° | 1.96 | 79 | 25.1 | 7.60 | 1.9 | — | — | 143.9 | 3.9 | — |

[a] Average of 10 specimens.
[b] Average of all panels delivered.
[c] Speed of test = 0.009 inch per minute head speed.
[d] Speed of test = 0.08 inch per minute head speed.

TABLE 15-38.  Interlaminar Shear Strength [a] of Plastic Laminates Made of Scotchply Resins and Unwoven S Glass Fibers as Measured by Five Test Methods (1,000 psi)

| Material and orientation of fibers | Short beam ($\frac{1}{d}$ ratio = 8:1) | Short clamped cantilever ($\frac{1}{d}$ ratio = 2:1) | Cantilever ($\frac{1}{d}$ ratio = 4:1) | Notched compression | Notched tension |
|---|---|---|---|---|---|
| XP234S | | | | | |
| 1:1 | 8.80 | 7.11 | 7.54 | 7.95 | 4.74 |
| Standard deviation | ±.85 | ±.90 | ±.77 | ±.36 | — |
| ±5° | 10.62 | 8.32 | 10.60 | 10.05 | 5.32 |
| Standard deviation | ±.22 | ±.35 | ±.73 | ±.39 | — |
| XP251S | | | | | |
| 1:1 | 9.32 | 6.64 | 8.09 | 8.67 | 4.88 |
| Standard deviation | ±.47 | ±.72 | ±.39 | ±.26 | — |
| ±5° | 11.12 | 8.75 | 11.30 | 10.13 | 5.51 |
| Standard deviation | ±.78 | ±.61 | ±.56 | ±.55 | — |
| 1002S | | | | | |
| 1:1 | — | — | — | — | 4.7 [b] |
| ±5° | — | — | — | — | 4.3 [b] |

[a] Values are the average of eight specimens.
[b] Specimen had ¼-in. notch distance.

TABLE 15-39.  Fatigue Strengths in Axial Loading of Plastic Laminates Made of Scotchply Resin Type XP234S and Unwoven S Glass Fibers. Tested at 0 Mean Stress, 73°F, and 900 cpm

| Orientation of fibers to principal axis | | | |
|---|---|---|---|
| Alternate plies 0 and 90°C | | Alternate plies ±5°C | |
| Alternating stress amplitude, 1000 psi | Cycles to failure | Alternating stress amplitude, 1000 psi | failure Cycles to |
| 100 | 700 | 100 | 770 |
| 95 | 540 | 90 | 7,700 |
| 90 | 1,000 | 80 | 58,700 |
| 85 | 600 | 75 | 7,500 [a] |
| 80 | 200 | | 13,400 |
| 70 | 3,600 | | 7,700 |
| 60 | 1,800 | | 6,500 |
| 54 | 3,100 | | 6,700 |
| | 3,000 [a] | 70 | 118,200 |
| | 2,900 | | 11,700 |
| | 7,500 | 60 | 113,800 |
| | 2,400 | | 143,000 |
| 50 | 18,000 | 56 | 296,700 [a] |
| 40 | 34,600 | | 240,900 |
| | 28,100 | | 24,800 |
| | 10,000 | | 338,700 |
| | 16,000 | | 3,165,900 |
| | (17,850) [b] | 50 | 3,440,400 |
| | 7,300 | | 367,500 |
| | 19,700 | | 1,879,400 |
| 30 | 393,300 | 37.5 | 4,046,900 |
| 26 | >10,000,000 | | 2,245,200 |
| | 6,186,300 | | 9,313,000 |
| | 883,400 | | 8,127,100 |
| | 1,769,100 [a] | | 4,110,800 [a] |
| | 746,800 | | 4,491,000 |
| 25 | 609,400 | | 2,854,600 |
| 20 | 1,553,900 | 30 | >10,000,000 |
| 15 | >10,000,000 | | |
| | 8,942,300 | | |

[a] Median life cycles (a test value).
[b] Median life cycles (an average value).

TABLE 15-40. Fatigue Strengths in Axial Loading of Plastic Laminates Made of Scotchply Resin Type XP251S and Unwoven S Glass Fibers. Tested at 0 Mean Stress, 73°F, and 900 cpm

| Orientation of fibers to principal axis | | | |
|---|---|---|---|
| Alternate plies 0 and 90°C | | Alternate plies ±5°C | |
| Alternating stress amplitude, 1000 psi | Cycles to failure | Alternating stress amplitude, 1000 psi | Cycles to failure |
| 100 | 300 | 90 | 16,000 |
| 90 | 900 | 80 | 28,300 |
| 80 | 370 | 75 | 3,500 |
| 70 | 3,000 | | 18,500 [a] |
| 60 | 1,800 | | 22,300 |
| 54 | 70,700 | | 12,200 |
| | 53,400 [a] | | 32,300 |
| | 61,500 | 70 | 36,600 |
| | 30,400 | 60 | 309,700 |
| | 4,300 | | 396,600 |
| 50 | 43,600 | 56 | 579,000 [a] |
| | 173,100 | | 557,600 |
| 45 | 424,400 | | 865,600 |
| | 127,900 | | 1,053,900 |
| | 172,500 | | 463,200 |
| 40 | 1,172,900 | 55 | 967,700 |
| | 917,600 | 40 | >10,000,000 |
| | 109,000 | 37.5 | >10,000,000 |
| | 73,100 | | >10,000,000 |
| | (659,250) [b] | | >10,000,000 |
| | 400,900 | | >10,000,000 |
| | 1,678,400 | | 14,109,500 |
| 30 | 1,869,900 | | |
| | 566,400 | | |
| 26 | >10,000,000 | | |
| | >10,000,000 | | |
| | >10,000,000 | | |
| | >10,000,000 | | |
| | >10,000,000 | | |
| 20 | >10,000,000 | | |

[a] Median value (a test value).
[b] Median value (an average value).

TABLE 15-41.  Fatigue Strengths in Shear of Plastic Laminates Made of Scotch-ply Resin Type XP234S and Unwoven S Glass Fibers.  Tested at Stress Ratio of 0, 73°F, and 900 cpm as a Short Cantilever Beam

| Orientation of fibers to principal axis | | | |
|---|---|---|---|
| Alternate plies 0 and 90°C | | Alternate plies ±5°C | |
| Maximum stress, 1000 psi | Cycles to failure | Maximum stress, 1000 psi | Cycles to failure |
| 7.0 | 1,400 | 8.0 | 100 |
| 6.5 | 400 | 7.5 | 7,700 [a] |
| 6.0 | 2,300 | | 3,200 |
| | 3,400 | | 27,700 |
| 5.5 | 2,500 | | 2,400 |
| | 3,900 | | 2,700 |
| | 1,000 | | 19,500 |
| | 5,800 | | 12,400 |
| | 12,200 | 7.0 | 115,900 |
| | 5,100 | 6.5 | 227,100 |
| | (4,500) [b] | | 221,900 |
| 5.0 | 33,400 | | 249,400 |
| | 31,700 | 6.0 | 372,900 |
| | 20,200 | | 1,243,100 |
| 4.0 | 1,838,000 | | 885,100 |
| | 546,000 [a] | | 352,000 |
| | 366,800 | | 68,600 |
| | 958,200 | | 638,500 |
| | 292,100 | | (495,250) [b] |
| | 177,900 | 5.75 | 1,281,100 |
| | 1,556,900 | 5.5 | 560,500 |
| 3.0 | 10,784,700 | | 3,391,400 |
| | | 4.5 | 6,011,400 |
| | | | 1,842,300 |

[a] Median value (a test value).
[b] Median value (not a test value).

**d. Electrical Properties.**  Glass fiber plastic laminates are widely used in fabricating aircraft antenna housings for communication, navigation, and radar equipment because of their desirable combination of mechanical and electrical properties.  Electrical properties affecting antenna housing design are dielectric constant and loss tangent.  In VHF and UHF integral antennas, the loss tangent alone is critical; for separate antenna housings, or radomes, both the dielectric constant and the loss tangent influence electrical design.

TABLE 15-42. Fatigue Strengths in Shear of Plastic Laminates Made of Scotchply Resin Type XP251S and Unwoven S Glass Fibers. Tested at Stress Ratio of 0, 73°F, and 900 cpm as a Short Cantilever Beam

| Orientation of fibers to principal axis | | | |
|---|---|---|---|
| Alternate plies 0 and 90°C | | Alternate plies ±5°C | |
| Maximum stress, 1000 psi | Cycles to failure | Maximum stress, 1000 psi | Cycles to failure |
| 7.5 | 250 | 10.0 | 80 |
| 7.0 | 500 | 9.0 | 2,500 |
| 6.0 | 1,100 | | 6,600 |
| 5.75 | 4,600 | 8.5 | 2,600 |
| 5.5 | 500 | | 14,800 |
| | 1,000 | 8.25 | 12,000 |
| | 9,500 | 8.0 | 4,100 |
| | 2,600 | 7.75 | 14,700 |
| | 1,900 | 7.5 | 40,800 [a] |
| | 11,100 | | 34,600 |
| | (3,000) [b] | | 131,100 |
| 5.25 | 1,450 | | 5,600 |
| 5.0 | 17,800 | | 19,400 |
| | 8,000 | | 18,700 |
| 4.75 | 50,300 | | 24,100 |
| 4.5 | 148,800 | 7.25 | 107,800 |
| 4.25 | 1,875,300 | 7.0 | 158,600 |
| 4.0 | 59,300 | 6.5 | 243,600 |
| | 26,700 | 6.25 | 105,000 |
| | 20,000 | | 297,300 |
| | 48,300 | 6.15 | 320,000 |
| | 650,100 | 6.0 | 1,246,000 [a] |
| | 58,200 | | 129,200 |
| | 1,263,600 | | 1,195,400 |
| | (400,000) [b] | | >10,000,000 |
| | 190,400 | | 2,191,200 |
| | 167,500 | | >10,000,000 |
| | 80,300 | | 6,049,500 |
| | 176,000 | 5.5 | 10,720,100 |
| | 114,400 | | |
| 3.5 | 4,369,900 | | |
| 3.0 | >10,000,000 | | |

[a] Median value (a test value).
[b] Median value from S-N curves.

TABLE 15-43. Comparison of Static Strengths of Plastic Laminates Made of Scotchply Resins and Unwoven Glass Reinforcement [a]

| Mechanical test | Laminate | | | |
|---|---|---|---|---|
| | 1002E,[a] 1000 psi | 1002S,[a] 1000 psi | XP234S, 1000 psi | XP251S, 1000 psi |
| 1:1 Crossply construction | | | | |
| Tensile | | | | |
| Modulus of elasticity | 2,470 | 3,810 | 4,310 | 4,020 |
| Maximum stress | 67.3 | 105.8 | 141.4 | 136.7 |
| Compressive | | | | |
| Modulus of elasticity | 2,810 | 3,610 | 5,720 | 4,830 |
| Maximum stress | 76.4 | 73.2 | 97.1 | 97.5 |
| Interlaminar shear | | | | |
| Maximum stress | — | 4.7[b] | 4.74[c] | 4.48[c] |
| ±5° Construction | | | | |
| Tensile | | | | |
| Modulus of elasticity | 5,400 | 6,620 | 8,300 | 7,600 |
| Maximum stress | 118.3 | 147.8 | 155.3 | 143.9 |
| Compressive | | | | |
| Modulus of elasticity | 4,530 | 5,470 | 7,990 | 7,460 |
| Maximum stress | 99.3 | 88.6 | 115.1 | 119.3 |
| Maximum stress | — | 4.3[b] | 5.32[c] | 5.51[c] |

[a] From previous tests.
[b] Notched tensile distance $= \frac{1}{2}$ in.
[c] Notched tensile distance $= \frac{1}{4}$ in.

Factors influencing electrical properties are frequency, composition, moisture absorption, weathering, and temperature. In general, the dielectric constant and loss tangent of glass-fiber plastic laminates decrease with increasing frequency above VHF frequencies. At all frequencies, the dielectric constant and loss tangent generally rise with rising temperature.

**e. Outdoor Weathering.** Both conventional and heat resistant glass fabric base plastic laminates have been exposed to outdoor weathering at sites throughout the world for periods up to one year.

Exposure sites and conditions of exposure were (*1*) Alaska (arctic), (*2*) Panama (jungle), (*3*) Florida (salt air), (*4*) New Mexico (arid), and (*5*) Wisconsin (temperate).

The method for mounting the exposure panels is illustrated in Fig. 15-89 for the Florida salt air site.

The effect of weathering on the mechanical and electrical properties was investigated.

TABLE 15-44.  Comparison of Median Fatigue Life of Plastic Laminates Made of Scotchply Resins and Unwoven Glass Reinforcement

| Type of fatigue test | Stress level, 1000 psi | Laminate | | | |
|---|---|---|---|---|---|
| | | 1002E, No. of cycles | 1002S, No. of cycles | XP234S, No. of cycles | XP251S, No. of cycles |
| 1:1 Crossply construction | | | | | |
| Axial load—stress | 54.0 | 403 | 1,190 | 3,000 | 53,400 |
| ratio of —1.0 | 40.0 | 1,700 | 7,200 | 17,850 | 659,750 |
| | 26.0 | 95,200 | >10,000,000 | 1,769,100 | >10,000,000 |
| Shear test —stress | 5.5 | — | — | 4,500 | 3,000 |
| ratio of 0 | 4.0 | — | — | 546,000 | 400,000 |
| ±5° Construction | | | | | |
| Axial load—stress | 75.0 | 704 | 1,826 | 7,500 | 18,500 |
| ratio of —1.0 | 56.0 | 3,200 | 37,900 | 296,700 | 579,000 |
| | 37.5 | 585,000 | 7,122,000 | 4,110,800 | >10,000,000 |
| Shear test—stress | 7.5 | — | — | 7,700 | 40,800 |
| ratio of 0 | 6.0 | — | — | 495,250 | 1,246,000 |

Laminates were about $\frac{1}{8}$ in. thick and reinforced with 181 glass fabric. Resins used were of the polyester, heat resistant polyester, epoxy, silicone, and phenolic types. The most severe weathering effects appeared to be on the heat-resistant polyester laminates, while the least effect appeared to be on the silicone laminate. In practically all cases, the laminates exposed to salt air at Florida showed the greatest amount of erosion of resin on the exposed face, while the least erosion occurred on those specimens exposed to conditions of the jungle in Panama. Considering all strength values as a group, the most detrimental weathering effects also occurred at the Florida site and the least detrimental effects at the Panama site.

The effect of weathering on the edgewise compressive strength of a heat resistant glass fabric base phenolic laminate compared to that of a conventional polyester and epoxy laminate is shown in Fig. 15-90. On the basis of one year exposure at the south Florida site, the percent reduction in compressive strength of the phenolic laminate was slightly greater than that of the polyester and epoxy laminates.

**f. Effects of Exposure to Nuclear (Gamma) Radiation.** CTL-91-LD phenolic, Epon 1031 epoxy, and DC-2106 silicone glass fabric base laminates were exposed simultaneously to elevated temperature and gamma radiation, and their mechanical and electrical properties

TABLE 15-45. Coefficients of Thermal Expansion for Parallel-Laminated Glass Laminates (per °F)

| Resin type | Temperature, °F | Coefficient of thermal expansion | | | |
|---|---|---|---|---|---|
| | | Parallel to warp, $10^6$ in. per in. | Perpendicular to warp, $10^6$ in. per in. | 45° to warp, $10^6$ in. per in. | Through thickness, $10^6$ in. per in. |
| Epoxy-phenolic | −100 to 200 | 4.8 | 5.0 | 5.0 | 10.0 |
| | 300 to 600 | 2.8 | 2.5 | 4.5 | 6.3 |
| Silicone (MIL-R-25506) | −100 to 100 | 4.0 | 5.0 | 5.0 | 38.0 |
| | 100 to 600 | 3.0 | 3.0 | 3.0 | 80.0 |
| Phenolic [a] (MIL-R-9299) | −100 to 200 | 6.0 | 5.8 | 6.4 | 11.1 |
| | 300 to 600 | 3.2 | 2.9 | 3.0 | 6.2 |
| Polyester [b] (MIL-R-7575) | −100 to 100 | 7.8 | 9.3 | 8.5 | 19.1 |
| | 200 to 400 | 1.4 | 2.3 | 1.3 | 237.6 |
| Triallyl cyanurate polyester (Mil-R-25402) | −100 to 200 | 5.5 | 5.2 | 5.2 | 11.0 |
| | 350 to 600 | 3.6 | 3.9 | 3.6 | 12.0 |
| Epoxy (MIL-R-9300) | −100 to 200 | 5.5 | 6.7 | 6.7 | — |
| | 300 to 600 | 3.3 | 1.5 | 2.3 | — |

[a] Average of data from laminates made with 181 fabric and two mats.
[b] Average of data from laminates made with several styles of fabric (116, 112, 181, and 143).

TABLE 15-46.  Total  Normal  Emittance  of  Heat-Resistant  Glass-Fabric-Base
Plastic Laminates

| Resin type | Surface temperature °F | Emissivity |
|---|---|---|
| Phenolic (MIL-R-9299) | 254 | 0.80 |
| Silicone (MIL-R-25506) | 248 | 0.83 |
| Epoxy (visually opaque) | 230 | 0.79 |
| Triallyl cyanurate polyester (MIL-R-25042) | 230 | 0.82 |

were determined after various time increments of exposure for comparison with room temperature control values, elevated temperature
exposure alone, and gamma radiation exposure alone (20). The materials were exposed at a temperature of 500°F for up to 200 hr, while
being irradiated at a flux of about $4.15 \times 10^7$ ergs (gram $e$ from a 19,000
cure cobalt-60 source).

It was found that the silicone material was not affected by the above
exposure. However, the epoxy and the phenolic showed increased
strengths with irradiation at elevated temperature compared to exposure at elevated temperature above (21).

**g. Manufacturer's Data on High Temperature Resistant Plastic
Laminates.** There are several heat resistant laminating resins, in
addition to those for which data have already been presented, which
have good physical, mechanical and electrical properties at elevated
temperature, but which have not yet been evaluated over as broad a
spectrum of properties, temperature or time of exposure at elevated
temperature. Three such resins are Vibrin 136-A polyester, Skygard
700 polyimide and Imidite 1850 polybenzimidazole.

TABLE 15-47.  Solar Absorbances of Heat-Resistant Glass-Fabric-Base Plastic
Laminates

| Resin type | Solar absorptivity Above atmosphere | Solar absorptivity At sea level |
|---|---|---|
| Phenolic (MIL-R-9299) | 0.819 | 0.808 |
| Silicone (MIL-R-25506) | 0.492 | 0.445 |
| Epoxy (visually opaque) | 0.850 | 0.830 |
| Triallyl cyanurate polyester (MIL-R-25042) | 0.577 | 0.532 |

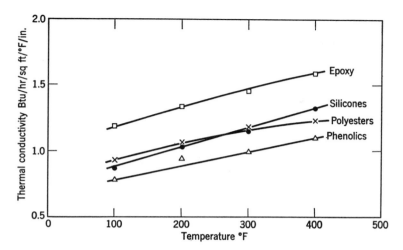

Fig. 15-83. Thermal conductivity of various glass fabric reinforced plastic laminates.

Although Vibrin 136-A does not have as high a temperature capability as Skygard 700 and Imidite 1850, it does have greater ease of fabrication by virtue of its liquid form. This permits simple fabrication processes such as vacuum bag molding to be used.

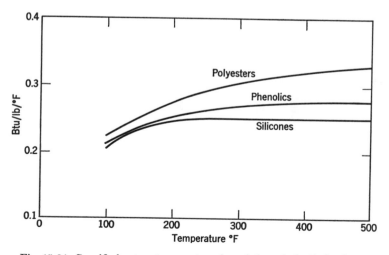

Fig. 15-84. Specific heat vs temperature for reinforced plastic laminates.

TABLE 15-48.   Results of Thermal Conductivity Determinations for Various Reinforced Plastics at Different Mean Temperatures [a]

| Specimen | Resin | | Reinforcement | | Thickness, in. | Specific gravity [2] | Mean temperature, °F | Thermal conductivity, $k$, Btu in./hr, sq ft, °F |
|---|---|---|---|---|---|---|---|---|
| | Kind | Content, % | Kind | Orientation | | | | |
| SC-E | Scotch-ply 1002 | 32.4 | Unwoven E-glass | ±5° | 0.267 | 1.82 | −267 | 1.20 |
| | | | | | | | − 95 | 2.03 |
| | | | | | | | +102 | 2.66 |
| | | | | | | | +304 | 3.12 |
| | | | | | | | +401 | 2.62 |
| | | | | | | | +498 | 1.98 |
| SC-S | Scotch-ply 1002 | 34.1 | Unwoven S-glass | ±5° | .253 | 1.81 | −250 | 1.68 |
| | | | | | | | −127 | 2.18 |
| | | | | | | | +102 | 3.14 |
| | | | | | | | +306 | 3.50 |
| | | | | | | | +398 | 3.18 |
| | | | | | | | +508 | 2.45 |
| EP-E | Epoxy ERSB-0111 | 36.0 | E-glass 181 fabric | Parallel | .201 | 1.92 | −284 | 1.90 |
| | | | | | | | −100 | 2.59 |
| | | | | | | | +100 | 3.00 |
| | | | | | | | +304 | 3.28 |
| | | | | | | | +399 | 3.24 |
| | | | | | | | +490 | 2.86 |

| Code | Resin | | Reinforcement | Orientation | | | Temp | Ratio |
|---|---|---|---|---|---|---|---|---|
| EP-S | Epoxy ERSB-0111 | 35.0 | S-glass 181 fabric | Parallel | .231 | 1.82 | −279 | 1.61 |
| | | | | | | | −118 | 2.14 |
| | | | | | | | +112 | 2.98 |
| | | | | | | | +305 | 3.24 |
| | | | | | | | +407 | 3.25 |
| | | | | | | | +491 | 2.78 |
| PH-A | Phenolic | 34.0$^e$ | Asbestos | Parallel | .248 | 1.86 | −250 | 2.23 |
| | | | Asbestos | Parallel | | | −116 | 3.18 |
| | | | | | | | +102 | 3.71 |
| | | | | | | | +302 | 4.06 |
| | | | | | | | +399 | 4.02 |
| | | | | | | | +500 | 3.18 |
| SI-A | Silicone | 20.0$^b$ | S-glass 181 fabric | Parallel | .271 | 1.52 | −268 | 1.00 |
| | | | | | | | −128 | 1.42 |
| | | | | | | | +101 | 1.90 |
| | | | | | | | +303 | 2.16 |
| | | | | | | | +400 | 2.09 |
| | | | | | | | +498 | 2.03 |
| NA-S | Narmco 534 phenyl-silane | 29.6 | S-glass 181 fabric | Parallel | .252 | 1.81 | −229 | 1.97 |
| | | | | | | | −99 | 2.45 |
| | | | | | | | +105 | 3.10 |
| | | | | | | | +300 | 3.42 |
| | | | | | | | +402 | 3.43 |
| | | | | | | | +500 | 3.22 |
| DEN-S-R | DEN 438 Epoxy Novalac | 19.3 | S-glass 181 fabric | Parallel | .245 | 1.99 | −245 | 2.33 |
| | | | | | | | −99 | 3.16 |
| | | | | | | | +99 | 4.01 |
| | | | | | | | +300 | 4.86 |
| | | | | | | | +400 | 4.85 |
| | | | | | | | +500 | 4.46 |

(continued)

TABLE 15-48 (*continued*)

| Specimen | Resin | | Reinforcement | | Thickness, in. | Specific gravity [2] | Mean temperature, °F | Thermal conductivity, $k$ Btu in./hr, sq ft, °F |
|---|---|---|---|---|---|---|---|---|
| | Kind | Content, % | Kind | Orientation | | | | |
| DEN-S-L | DEN 438 Epoxy Nova-lac | 32.0 | | | .277 | 1.65 | −251 | 1.26 |
| | | | | | | | −108 | 1.98 |
| | | | | | | | + 95 | 2.50 |
| | | | | | | | +299 | 2.52 |
| | | | | | | | +398 | 2.47 |
| | | | | | | | +495 | 2.21 |

[a] The coefficients of termal conductivity for mean temperatures ranging from about −300 to +500°F were determined for nine combinations of asbestos fiber or glass fiber and cloth reinforcement, with epoxy, phenolic, silicone, phenyl silane, and epoxy-novalac resins. Values of conductivity are only valid to maximum mean temperatures between +300 and 350°F (depending on resin) because of thermal degradation of the plastic due to "hot-side" temperatures in excess of mean temperature.

Values of thermal conductivity were obtained using a "heat meter" wherein samples were placed in a stack consisting of heated plate, calibrated heat meter of fused silica, specimen, a second calibrated meter of fused silica, and a heat sink. Values of thermal conductivity ($k$) for a mean temperature of 0°F ranged from 1.73 Btu, inch of thickness per hour, square foot, degree Fahrenheit difference in temperature for a silicone-asbestos plastic with a specific gravity of 1.52 to a conductivity of 3.60 for the DEN epoxy-novalac, glass-fabric-reinforced plastic with a specific gravity of 1.99. Approximate conductivity-specific gravity relationships are presented for mean temperatures of −200°, 0°, and +200°F. Values of thermal conductivity for each plastic are presented for mean temperatures of −250, −200, −100, 0, +100, +200, and +300°F for more accurate estimates of heat flow.

[b] Based on weight and volume at prevailing laboratory conditions.

[c] Volatile component only.

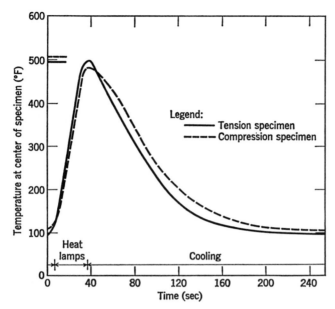

Fig. 15-85. Average temperature variation curves for specimens of CTL 37-9X phenolic resin laminates reinforced with 181-A1100 glass fabric during one cycle of heating and cooling.

## E. High Temperature Resistant Glass Fabric Reinforced Plastic Honeycomb

One of the principal uses of reinforced plastics in aircraft and missiles is in radar antenna housings (radomes), and one of the principal forms of construction of the radomes is sandwich construction (22). Structural sandwich is a layered construction formed by bonding two thin facings to a thick core. It is a type of stressed-skin construction in which the facings resist all, or nearly all, of the applied edgewise loads and flatwise bending moments. The thin spaced facings provide all, or nearly all, of the bending rigidity to the construction. The core spaces the facings and transmit shear between them so that they are effective about a common neutral axis. The core also provides most of the shear rigidity of the sandwich construction.

By proper choice of materials for facings and core, constructions with high ratios of stiffness to weight can be achieved. A basic design concept is to space strong, thin facings far enough apart to achieve a high ratio of stiffness to weight; the lightweight core that does this must provide the required resistance to shear and be strong enough to

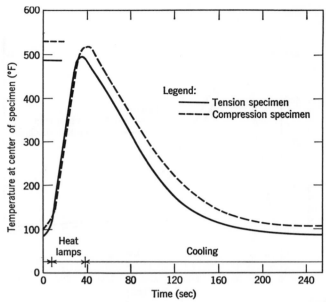

Fig. 15-86. Average temperature variation curves for specimens of ERSB-0111 epoxy resin laminates reinforced with 181-A1100 glass fabric during one cycle of heating and cooling.

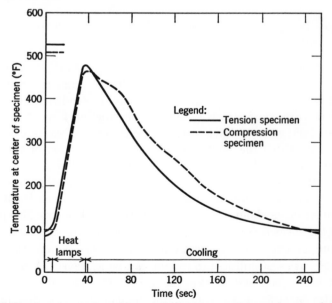

Fig. 15-87. Average temperature variation curves for specimens of phenolic asbestos laminates (R/M Pyrotex felt style 41-RPD) during one cycle of heating and cooling.

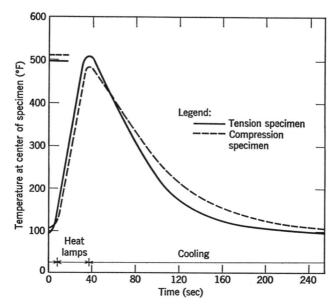

Fig. 15-88. Average temperature variation curves for specimens of NARMCO 534 phenyl-silane resin laminates reinforced with 181-A1100 glass fabric during one cycle of heating and cooling.

stabilize the facings to their desired configuration through a bonding medium such as an adhesive layer. The sandwich is analogous to an I-beam in which the flanges carry direct compression and tension loads, as do the sandwich facings, and the web carries shear loads, as does the sandwich core.

The core materials used in radome sandwich structures are usually glass fabric reinforced plastic in a hexagonal honeycomb cell configuration, although other additional cell configurations may be used.

For service at moderate temperatures, such as up to about 160°F, conventional polyester resins are suitable for honeycomb cores. However, for higher temperatures, especially above 300°F, heat resistant resins must be used. During the period 1953-1955 heat resistant phenolic, trially cyanurate polyester, and silicone resins were undergoing development as laminating resins.

These resins were also evaluated as resins for glass fabric base honeycomb core materials. A comparison of the flatwise compressive strength of honeycomb cores made with these three types of resins, at temperatures up to 700°F, is shown in Fig. 15-91. The honeycomb materials were $\frac{3}{16}$ in. cell size having a nominal density of 9 lb/ft³.

TABLE 15-49.  Average [a] Compressive Properties of Controls and Specimens Exposed to Thermal-shock Cycling

| Number of cycles | Phenolic resin CTL 37-9X and 181-A1100 glass fabric [b] | | | | Epoxy resin ERSB-0111 and 181-A1100 glass fabric | | | | Phenyl-silane resin (Narmco 534) and 181-A1100 glass fabric | | | | Phenolic resin and asbestos felt R/M Pyrotex felt style 41-RPD [b] | | | |
|---|---|---|---|---|---|---|---|---|---|---|---|---|---|---|---|---|
| | Modulus of elasticity, mill. psi | Strength, 1000 psi | Strength as percentage of control, % | Loss in weight, % | Modulus of elasticity, mill. psi | Strength, 1000 psi | Strength as percentage of control, % | Loss in weight, % | Modulus of elasticity, mill. psi | Strength, 1000 psi | Strength as percentage of control, % | Loss in weight, % | Modulus of elasticity, mill. psi | Strength, 1000 psi | Strength as percentage of control, % | Loss in weight, % |
| **Properties at room temperature** | | | | | | | | | | | | | | | | |
| 0 | 3.85 | 63.6 | 100 | 0.00 | 3.44 | 44.1 | 100 | 0.00 | 3.90 | 51.4 | 100 | 0.00 | 5.31 | 25.0 | 100 | 0.00 |
| 2 | 3.71 | 40.1 | 63 | .82 | — | — | — | — | — | — | — | — | — | — | — | — |
| 5 | 3.59 | 41.3 | 65 | .79 | — | — | — | — | — | — | — | — | — | — | — | — |
| 10 | 3.58 | 44.3 | 70 | .76 | 3.85 | 38.0 | 75 | .46 | 3.93 | 56.1 | 109 | .27 | 5.34 | 26.0 | 104 | 1.58 |
| 50 | 3.57 | 38.0 | 60 | 1.18 | 2.84 | 25.5 | 58 | .50 | 3.86 | 58.3 | 118 | .62 | 5.55 | 28.9 | 116 | 2.00 |
| 300 | 3.54 | 32.2 | 51 | 1.20 | — | — | — | — | — | — | — | — | 5.19 | 25.3 | 101 | 1.89 |
| 600 | — | — | — | — | — | — | — | — | — | — | — | — | — | — | — | — |
| 1,200 | — | — | — | — | 2.65 | 15.3 | 35 | 3.44 | 3.81 | 59.4 | 116 | .88 | 5.26 | 24.3 | 97 | 1.80 |
| 2,000 | — | — | — | — | 2.83 | 12.3 | 28 | 4.57 | 3.87 | 57.1 | 111 | .84 | 5.28 | 22.9 | 92 | 1.93 |
| **Properties at 500°F [c]** | | | | | | | | | | | | | | | | |
| 0 | 2.73 | 19.7 | 31 | — | 2.44 | 10.7 | 24 | .35 | 3.08 | 22.8 | 44 | .18 | 4.04 | 14.2 | 57 | — |
| 2 | 2.82 | 20.0 | 31 | .77 | — | — | — | — | — | — | — | — | — | — | — | — |
| 5 | 2.74 | 20.2 | 32 | .85 | — | — | — | — | — | — | — | — | — | — | — | — |
| 10 | 3.00 | 20.8 | 33 | .77 | 2.47 | 12.6 | 29 | .46 | 3.23 | 32.4 | 63 | .27 | 4.49 | 18.1 | 72 | 1.55 |
| 50 | 3.06 | 22.3 | 35 | 1.14 | 2.43 | 14.0 | 32 | .52 | 3.26 | 37.4 | 73 | .65 | 4.60 | 20.2 | 81 | 2.02 |
| 300 | 2.90 | 24.2 | 38 | 1.16 | — | — | — | — | — | — | — | — | 4.58 | 21.4 | 86 | 1.90 |
| 600 | — | — | — | — | — | — | — | — | — | — | — | — | — | — | — | — |
| 1,200 | — | — | — | — | 2.61 | 12.5 | 28 | 3.85 | 3.50 | 39.5 | 77 | .86 | 4.85 | 20.7 | 83 | 1.78 |
| 2,000 | — | — | — | — | 2.45 | 10.7 | 24 | 4.46 | 3.44 | 36.7 | 72 | .85 | 4.79 | 18.7 | 75 | 1.85 |

[a] Each value is an average for 5 specimens.
[b] Data obtained from Technical Report AFML-TR-64-404.
[c] Specimens were heated for 1 minute prior to loading.

TABLE 15-50. Average[a] Tensile Properties of Controls and Specimens Exposed to Thermal-shock Cycling

| Number of cycles | Phenolic resin CTL 37-9X and 181-A1100 glass fabric | | | | Epoxy resin ERSB-0111 and 181-A1100 glass fabric | | | | Phenyl-silane resin (Narmco 534) and 181-A1100 glass fabric | | | | Phenolic resin and asbestos felt R/M Pyrotex felt style 41-RPD | | | |
|---|---|---|---|---|---|---|---|---|---|---|---|---|---|---|---|---|
| | Modulus of elasticity | | Strength, 1000 psi | Strength as percentage of control, % | Modulus of elasticity | | Strength, 1000 psi | Strength as percentage of control, % | Modulus of elasticity | | Strength, 1000 psi | Strength as percentage of control, % | Modulus of elasticity | | Strength, 1000 psi | Strength as percentage of control, % |
| | Initial, mill. psi | Secondary, mill. psi | | | Initial, mill. psi | Secondary, mill. psi | | | Initial, mill. psi | Secondary, mill. psi | | | Initial, mill. psi | Secondary, mill. psi | | |
| | | | | | Properties at room temperature | | | | | | | | | | | |
| 0 | 4.33 | 3.01 | 40.3 | 100 | 2.75 | — | 55.5 | 100 | 4.10 | 2.83 | 39.1 | 100 | 5.48 | — | 52.6 | 100 |
| 50 | 3.81 | 3.02 | 39.8 | 99 | 2.78 | — | 52.5 | 95 | [a]4.12 | [a]2.80 | [a]40.2 | 103 | — | — | — | — |
| 300 | 3.70 | 2.95 | 36.9 | 92 | 2.73 | — | 52.1 | 94 | 3.89 | 2.67 | 37.6 | 96 | — | — | — | — |
| 600 | — | — | — | — | — | — | — | — | — | — | — | — | 5.43 | — | 48.4 | 83 |
| 1,200 | 3.68 | 2.88 | 37.5 | 93 | 2.72 | — | 48.1 | 87 | 3.99 | 2.76 | 38.2 | 98 | 4.55 | — | 33.3 | 63 |
| 2,000 | [a]3.13 | — | [a]33.4 | 83 | 2.71 | — | 25.9 | 47 | [a]4.02 | [a]2.86 | [a]38.5 | 98 | 4.47 | — | 32.1 | 61 |
| | | | | | Properties at 500°F[d] | | | | | | | | | | | |
| 0 | 3.22 | 2.94 | 31.7 | 79 | 2.43 | — | 52.2 | 94 | 3.31 | 2.96 | 29.4 | 75 | — | — | — | — |
| 50 | 3.20 | 2.89 | 33.6 | 83 | 2.42 | — | 52.0 | 94 | 3.37 | 2.90 | 31.4 | 80 | — | — | — | — |
| 300 | 3.29 | 2.84 | 35.3 | 88 | 2.46 | — | 51.8 | 93 | 3.50 | 2.85 | 31.3 | 80 | — | — | — | — |
| 1,200 | 3.04 | 2.74 | 36.4 | 90 | 2.41 | — | 45.4 | 82 | 2.82 | 2.82 | 31.2 | 80 | — | — | — | — |
| 2,000 | [a]2.84 | — | [a]35.2 | 87 | 2.43 | — | 18.8 | 34 | 2.86 | 2.88 | 31.3 | 80 | — | — | — | — |

[a] Average value for 5 specimens except as noted.
[b] Average value for 4 specimens except as noted.
[c] Average value for 3 specimens except as noted.
[d] Specimens were heated for 1 minute prior to loading.

Fig. 15-89. Method of mounting subpanels on boards and exposure racks at salt air exposure site in Florida.

For the specific exposure conditions, which were only 15 min at temperature, the phenolic honeycomb had the highest strength.

Under long time elevated temperature exposure conditions at temperatures of 500°F and higher, it is known that phenolic resins undergo extensive degradation. This has prompted the investigation of new high temperature resistant resins, such as polybenzimidazole, for use in glass fabric base honeycomb cores. In one investigation, the flatwise compressive strength and modulus of honeycomb made with AFR-100 polybenzimidazole resin was compared with that of a commercial glass fabric phenolic honeycomb (Hexcel's HRP-GF 13).

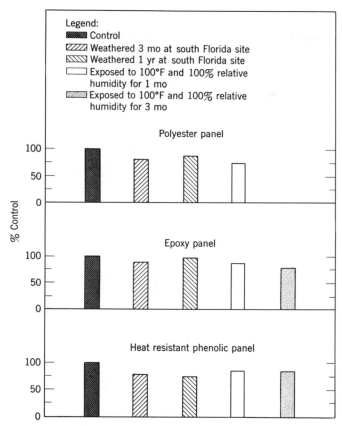

Fig. 15-90. Compressive strength of ⅛ in. thick solid glass fabric base plastic laminate panels at 73°F.

# V. REINFORCED PLASTICS—WHAT THEY CAN DO IN THE NEXT 10 YEARS

**by Donald V. Rosato**

In this complex age of the specialist, when man's research and development capabilities have exceeded his ability to grasp and control all of the knowledge available to him, it is not strange that present management needs and directions influence results more than in the past, particularly profits (23–25). The dramatic and significant progress in composite materials technology, specifically reinforced plastics,

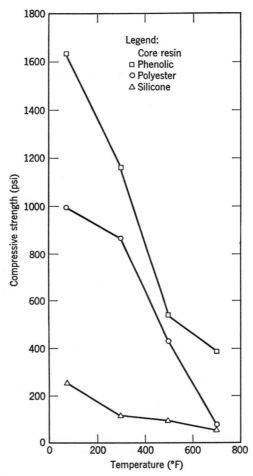

Fig. 15-91. Flatwise compressive strength of glass fabric plastic honeycomb curves at elevated temperature after 15 min exposure at the test temperature.

has proved this fact since the time high structural strength types were developed in the early 1940's (30).

Obviously, the basic elements of reinforced plastics as composite materials were understood, if little appreciated, by science and technology sometime before World War II. But it took the war to boost ultimate development of RP as competitive materials because of their inherent advantages. As early as 1941, government contracts were issued to fabricate semistructural parts using base materials, such as combed and carded cotton fibers impregnated with phenolic resin cured at

2000 psi. In 1942, low pressure curing polyester resin systems were developed. By the end of the war, glass fiber reinforced plastics had been used successfully in structural applications.

With demobilization, RP made of different reinforcements and resins gradually entered civilian life as material for boats, cars, appliance housing, trays, storage containers, and other items. The properties of fiber and resin matrix, in homogeneous composition, have proved to be superior to traditional materials in many ways.

Hindered initially by relatively high raw materials costs (which have continued on a downtrend) and slow, expensive processing methods for the more sophisticated parts, RP has nonetheless shown strong, steady progress as an industry—to the point that growth is measured in the billions of dollars each year. Very significant advancements are occurring at the present time with programs which will require faster and more mass production techniques for future commercial and industrial RP parts (Fig. 15-92).

The RP industry has been in the midst of an amazing evolution, but industry is convinced that it faces a dramatic challenge in the decade ahead. Barring a major recession, which seems unlikely, the use of RP will grow. The real breakthroughs will be associated principally with "management direction." Although some may disagree with the economic or technical theories behind this growth or the manner in

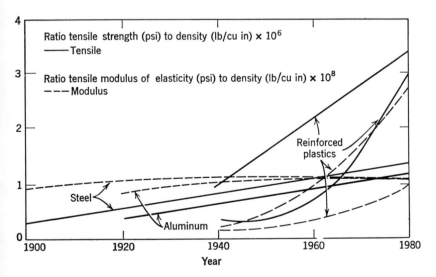

Fig. 15-92. Growth and forecast in structural properties of reinforced plastics and conventional materials.

which it is developing, there should be little disagreement about what is emerging (26–29).

## A. Consumption and Review of Basic Materials

Though it is difficult to obtain total production figures, as previously reviewed, a survey uncovered the surprising but believable estimate that this country presently consumes approximately 7 billion lb of RP per year (Fig. 15-93). This is the broad but literal view and includes laminates of various types, molding compounds with diverse fillers, and so on. The RP products normally contain 10–60% by weight of plastic resin, although is some cases resin content may go higher than 60% (3).

Total production of these composites is not well defined or understood by industry. The different statistics available from industry associations and the U. S. Department of Commerce are very limited in direct identification of reinforced materials. Many companies, including those who use the major portion of RP, are not members of these associations and do not report their consumption. Most of the identification in reports to the government is by the individual components, such as phenolic resin or cellulose paper, and by the end product (electrical connector or luggage, for instance). Military use

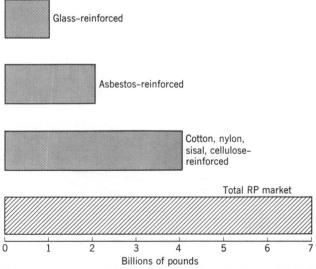

Fig. 15-93. Estimated United States annual production of reinforced plastics.

of RP is extensive, but in most cases consumption is not reported to any organization.

## B. Market Outlook

Prospects of all types of RP in the immediate future and for the next decade are excellent because more use is being made of them, new developments are moving at a faster rate and, most important, companies are more directly concerned with their profit and growth potential. Like all products, they are bound by their own market characteristics and basic economics (29,32–37).

It can be estimated that this year a volume of nearly $4 billion worth of RP products could develop. Just glass fiber-polyester resin composites could approach 0.4 billion lb. These materials have had a 17% growth rate in the years 1957–1964. The rate was 13% in 1962–1964. In comparison, world population at its rate of 1.9% compounded per year will exactly double from 3.2 billion to 6.4 billion people by the year 2000. By 1976 polyester composites alone could double in capacity (35). See Tables 15-51 through 15-53).

Success in the competitive marketplace for all RP's depends either on equal quality and performance at lower cost of manufacture, or on a more functional product at moderately higher cost. Many new RP markets are waiting for developments and some of those already

TABLE 15-51. Seven Leading Synthetic Resins (millions of pounds)

| Group | 1957 | 1960 | 1964 | Growth rate, % 1957-1964 | 1970[a] |
|---|---|---|---|---|---|
| Polyethylene | 708 | 1,337 | 2,600 | 19.6 | 4,500 |
| Polystyrene | 680 | 1,062 | 1,725 | 14.0 | 2,600 |
| Polyvinyl Chloride | 887 | 1,203 | 1,625 | 9.0[a] | 2,400 |
| Phenolics | 532 | 650 | 800 | 6.0 | 950 |
| Polypropylene | not avail. | 41 | 270 | 45.0 | 900 |
| Alkyds | 529 | 557 | 600 | 2.0 | 640 |
| Reinforced polyesters | 120 | 225 | 350 | 17.0 | 570 |

[a]Computed at one-half of the growth of the 1957-1964 period, except for vinyls which were extended at 6.5%. Because of broad technological changes in the industry and drastically lower resin prices, we draw attention to the growth percentage of 13% as demonstrated for the 1962-1964 period.

Note: Polyesters data include the estimated weight of major reinforcements as do phenolics which include fillers, pigments, etc. Urea and melamine are regarded as two groups—are not included herein.

TABLE 15-52.  Polyester RP:  Estimated Industry Output (in pounds)

| Year | Industry production, (mmlb) | Index 1959-61 = 100 |
|---|---|---|
| 1955 | 85 | 38 |
| 1956 | 105 | 47 |
| 1957 | 120 | 53 |
| 1958 | 135 | 60 |
| 1959 | 225 | |
| 1960 | 225 | 100 |
| 1961 | 225 | |
| 1962 | 265 | 118 |
| 1963 | 290 | 129 |
| 1964 | 350 | 155 |
| 1969 | 410 | 182 |
| 1974 | 550 | 244 |
| 2000 | 1950 | 870 |

Note:  Data include resin and reinforcements but exclude fillers, etc.

in existence are going to expand rapidly, such as fuel and storage tanks, appliances, outdoor signs, and automotive. With the vast opportunities, the risks can be high, in fact, one can be a loser before even starting if proper management philosophy is not used.

RP have a bigger future because they provide industry with multifunctional/useful properties, they are adaptable to different processes (from rotational molding to highly sophisticated filament wound structures), and they permit combining materials to withstand severe environments (38). Past and present history shows that the consumption of reinforced plastics can be considered comparable to the other successful new material developments; a steadily increasing market

TABLE 15-53.  Reinforced Polyester Application Methods, 1964

| Terminology | Major products | Pounds (mm) | % Distribution |
|---|---|---|---|
| Hand or wet lay up | Boats | 100 | 28 |
| Matched metal molds, preformed | Housings | 100 | 28 |
| Premix with chopped fiber | Ducts | 100 | 28 |
| Spray up (guns) | Pools | 40 | 12 |
| Filament winding | Pressure vessels | 5 | 2 |
| Miscellaneous | | 5 | 2 |
| | Totals | 350 | 100 |

expansion has been created. Of course, it has not been as spectacular as polyethylene, polyvinyl chloride, polystyrene, and some others. (See Table 15-54.)

The RP steady growth can be related to two conditions. One concerns property advantages, such as high strength-weight ratios, corrosion resistance, moldability, electrical insulation, thermal insulation, and asthetic appeal. The other concerns military and government requirements requiring RP in such areas as aerospace, ordnance, electronics, and hydrospace. Many of the modern missiles, aircraft, space vehicles, hydrospace vehicles, and others depend on RP. From the technological aspects RP can compete with steel and titanium on strength-weight ratios (up to 50 times higher than current steel), with a stiffness factor up to 4 times higher than current aluminum and also in temperature resistant and weldability characteristics.

The markets for RP are universal. Their corrosion resistance has built a market for chemical tanks, ducts, and pipe. Underground tanks for storage of gasoline and diesel fuels may one day be one of the largest RP markets. Installation and replacement costs, compared to steel tanks, are making the tanks very competitive. To construct large capacity tanks on site, filament winding is an answer for the chemical and agricultural industries (for example, the 30,000 and 36,000 gal tanks that have been built).

RP strength and damage resistance have built a market in building

TABLE 15-54.   Total U.S. Plastics Consumption, up to 1970
(millions of pounds)

|  | 1964 | 1965 Estimate | 1970 Estimate |
|---|---|---|---|
| Polyethylene | 2,600 | 3,000 | 5,800 |
| Vinyls | 1,970 | 2,300 | 4,500 |
| Styrenes | 1,728 | 2,000 | 3,200 |
| Phenolics | 830 | 875 | 1,400 |
| Urea and melamine | 570 | 590 | 750 |
| Alkyds | 594 | 575 | 650 |
| Polyester | 320 | 400 | 750 |
| Polypropylene | 270 | 370 | 800 |
| Cellulosics | 161 | 170 | 190 |
| Epoxy | 96 | 110 | 200 |
| Polyamides | 76 | 80 | 110 |
| Polyurethane | 200 | 255 | 650 |
| Others | 685 | 775 | 1,000 |
| All resins | 10,100 | 11,500 | 20,000 |

panels of opaque or translucent type. The largest market for RP and, in fact, all types of plastics is building construction. This market now uses approximately 25% of all types of plastics or the total United States plastic consumption. It is predicted that this year alone, close to 3 billion lb of all plastics ($½ billion worth of material) will be consumed in buildings, with vinyl being the most widely used. It is estimated that over 300 million lb of the 7 billion lb of RP are used: glass-polyesters, paper-phenolics, asbestos-phenolics, and so on. Plastics are found in the established markets of wall covering, electrical and heat insulation, flooring, paint, pipe and fitting, vapor barrier, and window trim. An additional total of 3 billion lb of all plastics are estimated to have been used in building by the rest of the world. By 1970, consumption in United States is expected to rise to at least 4½ or even 7 billion lb for all types of plastics, including RP (32,37, 38). See Table 15-55.

Plastics can be made to combine different desired characteristics or blend with other materials to produce useful composites. The major and most important growth of plastics is expected to be in the composite building shell of walls, roof, partitions, and floors, now representing one-third of all plastics used. They will serve three basic functions: structural, semistructural, and nonstructural components. The least use of plastics is in structural members, even though many people superficially assume that building construction materials encompass only structural members. Major use is in nonstructural components, where plastics can complement or be joined with structures.

Percentage consumption by application for all types of plastics this year appears to be similar to last year: 23% of the total in surface coatings, 20% in flooring, 20% in wire insulation, 10% in heat insulation and vapor barriers, 9% in plywood, and 8% in pipe. By type of plastic, consumption has been 27% vinyl, 16% polyethylene (PE), 12% in phenolic, 10% in alkyd, and 10% styrene. Other reports show 210 million lb of phenolic and melamine went into plywood construction; 205 million lb of phenolic, polystyrene (PS), and PE into heat insulation and vapor barriers; 200 million lb of polyvinyl chloride (PVC), acrylonitrile butadiene styrene (ABS), and the like into pipe and fittings; 90 million lb of acrylic, polyester, and PVC into glazing and skylights; and 70 million lb of melamine and phenolic into decorative laminates (32).

Data assembled provide interesting correlation of all types of plastics with competitive materials used for residential walls. Plastics were used in 1½% of the 2½ billion sq ft erected in 1964, and estimates

TABLE 15-55.   Construction Market (Billions of Dollars) [a]

| Type of construction | 1950 | 1955 | 1960 | 1964 | 1965 [b] |
|---|---|---|---|---|---|
| Private | 26.7 | 34.8 | 38.1 | 45.9 | 47.2 |
| Residential Buildings (nonfarm) | 18.1 | 21.9 | 21.7 | 26.5 | 27.3 |
| New housing units | 15.6 | 18.2 | 16.4 | 20.6 | — |
| Additions and alterations | 2.4 | 3.3 | — | — | — |
| Nonhousekeeping | 0.2 | 0.3 | 0.9 | 1.5 | — |
| Nonresidential buildings | 3.9 | 7.6 | 10.1 | 13.0 | 13.4 |
| Industrial | 1.1 | 2.4 | 2.9 | 3.3 | — |
| Office buildings and warehouses | 0.5 | 1.3 | 2.1 | 3.2 | — |
| Stores, restaurants and garages | 0.9 | 1.9 | 2.1 | 2.4 | — |
| Religious | 0.4 | 0.7 | 1.0 | 1.0 | — |
| Educational | 0.3 | 0.5 | 0.6 | 0.7 | — |
| Hospital and institutional | 0.3 | 0.4 | 0.6 | 1.4 | — |
| Social and recreational | 0.2 | 0.2 | 0.7 | 0.5 | — |
| Others | 0.1 | 0.2 | 0.2 | 0.4 | — |
| Farm dwellings and construction | 1.5 | 1.4 | 1.3 | 1.2 | 1.2 |
| Public utilities (telephone, RR, electric, etc.) | 3.0 | 3.8 | 4.6 | 4.9 | 5.0 |
| Others | 0.1 | 0.2 | 0.3 | 0.3 | 0.3 |
| Public | 6.9 | 11.7 | 15.9 | 20.0 | 20.6 |
| Residential buildings | 0.3 | 0.3 | 0.7 | 0.8 | — |
| Nonresidential buildings | 2.4 | 4.2 | 4.8 | 6.2 | — |
| Industrial | 0.2 | 0.7 | 0.4 | 0.4 | — |
| Educational | 1.1 | 2.4 | 2.8 | 3.3 | — |
| Others | 1.0 | 1.0 | 1.6 | 2.4 | — |
| Military facilities | 0.2 | 1.3 | 1.4 | 1.0 | — |
| Highways | 2.1 | 3.9 | 5.4 | 7.2 | — |
| Sewer and water systems | 0.7 | 1.1 | 1.5 | 2.3 | — |
| Others | 1.1 | 1.0 | 2.0 | 1.5 | — |
| Grand Total | 33.6 | 46.5 | 53.9 | 65.8 | 67.8 |

[a] Additional cost for maintenance and repair: 1950, 12.1; 1955, 16.0; 1960, 19.2; 1964, 21.0 estimate; and 1965, 22.0 estimate.
[b] Estimates.

are that 3–5% of 3 billion sq ft in 1970 will be plastic. Steel follows the same percentages. Brick and masonry will remain 29%. Wood will go from 33 to 30%, aluminum from 23 to 25%, asbestos from 9 to 8%, and other materials will sink from 3 to 2%. With success in marketing strategy and costs, the plastic wall prediction for 1970 could be over 10%, with part of this in RP.

By a slight stretch of the imagination, a potential of 1 billion lb of new business in curtain walls exists for all plastics, without including the futuristic and popular shapes viewed at the New York World's Fair or in the Apollo spacecraft assembly building.

Over 50% of all pleasure boats today have hulls or other major

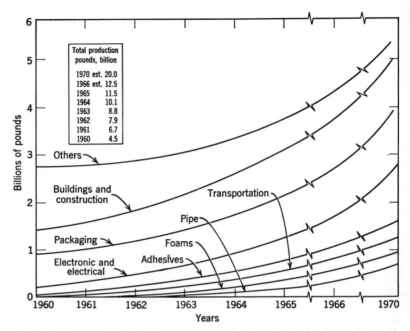

Fig. 15-94. Estimated United States consumption for all plastics, by major markets.

components of RP (Table 15-56). This market can be considered the second largest outlet for RP. Also in second place is transportation. Automobiles, trucks, and tank cars use reinforced thermosets and thermoplastics on interiors and exteriors. Transportation pods for aircraft, food trays, luggage, animal housing, and cages represent growth industries. City transportation vehicles need RP for laminated interior seats, partitions, and door to give better service and low maintenance. Boston and Philadelphia city transit authorities are following what other cities are doing in replacing upholstered seats with RP. New York City, in 1958, started experimenting with reinforced polyester seats for its 6700 subway cars and 2200 buses. Now 1100 subway cars are being refitted wih fiberglass reinforced polyester seats.

Glass reinforced epoxy pipe which is used by gas utilities (for main replacement by the insertion technique) and which meets or exceeds requirements established by ASTM specification D 2517-66T for reinforced thermosetting plastic pipe are being used in gas distribution and the like. Flame resistant laminates for printed circuits and other RPs in computers will require much more RP and as we know, the computer business continues to mushroom. In fact, office machines

TABLE 15-56. 1965 U.S. Stock Boat Models of Glass Fiber-Polyester Structure

| Type of boat | Inboard | Stern drive | Out-board | Cruising sailboat | Day and one-design sailboat | House and pontoon | Rowboat, dinghy, canoe | Total |
|---|---|---|---|---|---|---|---|---|
| Number of models | 111 | 263 | 481 | 145 | 225 | 6 | 133 | 1,364 |
| Percent of models using RP | 23.0 | 67.1 | 55.3 | 58.5 | 65.8 | 5.1 | 29.9 | 47.1 |

such as adding machines is important to RP. These "small computers" had domestic sales of $55 million in 1963 and is expected to reach $1 billion by 1970. When looking at the total computer business by IBM, all types of plastics including RP have continued to take a considerable share of the dollar market from metals. They increased from 20% in 1958 to a projected 60% this year (39).

Largest projected volume increase of RP is foreseen in the category of aircraft and missiles (and other government procured RP). Present industry statistics show approximately 40 million lb of RP is to be used this year, making it the fourth major market. Personally, the amount is exceptionally low and could easily be well over hundreds of millions of pounds. As an example, this year the government will use many millions of pounds of glass-polyester filament wound grommets for artillery shells, millions of pounds of glass-polystyrene in just the M18A1 antipersonnel mine (40,41).

Other important applications which have caused more material to be used include television, business machines, wire ducts, electrical switchgear, electrical control panels with many complicated printed circuits, housing insulators, and other parts. More ball bearing retainers are being used in heavy and lightweight machines such as in steel rolling mills, dental drills, and sophisticated aerospace guidance systems. Heat insulation parts are used in automobiles, appliances, missiles, and even in tin plating rollers. Laminates bonded with plastic adhesives to steel rollers outperform the steel or laminated rolls alone.

It is estimated that the total 1966 market for filament wound RP products is over 100 million lb, of which 35 million lb goes into pipe. This total market is over a half billion dollar value. In addition, many millions of dollars go for research and development. The average annual growth is expected to range 25–50%. Projected growth rate per year for commercial tanks is expected to be at least 100%, commercial pipe at 35%, small military parts at 70%, and large military parts at 50%. Cost of commercial products will continue to be reduced (29,36,38,39,42–44).

Cost per pound of these filament wound parts from the plastic fabricator average $1 for commercial, $12 for small military parts, and $100 for large military parts. It is now estimated that two dozen facilities exist in the United States to design and wind large parts; twice as many other facilities are involved in what can be referred to as small part producing facilities. In order to consider setting up competitive production facilities, a newcomer in the business may require from $\frac{1}{2}$ million to $2 million investment.

Filament winding represents part of the overall large RP market, with FW providing the most structurally efficient fabricating method. Industry is going through a major evolution in structural and semi-structural materials. RP are being developed to produce the strongest material known to mankind (45).

## C. Research and Development

Since 1941 scientific research in the United States has been developed principally by the government. Funds amounted to $700 million in 1947, but present yearly expenditure is approximately $23 billion. The government will spend $15.1 billion, industry $7.3 billion, and universities and other nonprofit institutes $0.6 billion.

It is sometimes unofficially reported that advances in technology

Figure 15-95. In the filament winding operations, glass rovings from separate spools are fed through guides into the resin bath and formed into a flat band prior to being wound on the mandrel in a predetermined pattern. Parts produced include corrosion resistant tanks, high pressure operating pipes and rocket motors. (Photograph is courtesy of Black, Sivalls and Bryson, Inc.)

through RP is more beneficial to publications for use as editorial reviews than the contribution made to company profits. It can be officially stated that probably better than 90% of government R&D sponsored program are successful in meeting requirements or targets. It can also be stated that most of these developments are not production oriented. This means that companies actively participating in these developments very rarely make profits based on the Wall Street Board approach, but then what happened to companies such as Boeing, Douglas, Aerojet, Avco, Grumman, McDonnell, Whittaker, and many others? Industrial and commercial product fallout from defense and space research has been far less than anticipated. High product costs have been the significant factor. Products built for defense or space use must be rugged and reliable because the operating environment is severe. This costs money, making these products expensive.

However, let us not forget that the government R&D programs have been, and will continue to be, most profitable for these companies who manage the programs properly. It is important for management of government oriented products to expand into commercial products. But of equal importance is to operate most efficiently with what is in-house.

Regardless, R&D from all sources is important to RP growth. Keep in mind that the overall plastics industry puts a greater proportion of its sales dollar on R&D than any other industrial group. In turn, it has had the highest rate of growth.

Major R&D efforts continue to be expended in RP and related composites for one basic reason. In composites, the potential exists for producing significant advances, as opposed to relatively minor improvements in wrought sheet-type metals such as steel, aluminum, and titanium. Composites can be at least twice as efficient as any other type material. With continued R&D in both the materials and production techniques, they will become more commercially available and competitive with other materials in the more profitable big markets.

### 1. Commercial

Examples of progressive thinking and action where R&D is becoming profitable are numerous. The comparatively limited research on plastics in building construction has been conducted largely by materials and end product manufacturers. Now, universities and colleges are taking on some of the research.

At the University of Michigan, programs sponsored by various plastic producers and the U. S. Department of State, Agency for International Development, are exploring the feasibility of using plastics for the resolution of housing problems in underdeveloped areas of the world. The approach has been to use plastics as primary structural materials. The feasibility of using a paper and urethane foam sandwich, glass fiber reinforced polyester with urethane foam in umbrella shaped domes, and glass fiber filament wound box shaped structures has been shown (32).

Development and marketing of preimpregnated B-stage RP mats are now on the increase. The dream of materials suppliers, fabricators, and users is to use mats in automated operations that mass produce parts on a par with stamping sheet metal. Matched die molding extrusion and molding operations could be used. Since the late 1940's various preimpregnated mats have been produced, but due to high costs they have not been successful. More recently, asbestos RP

Fig. 15-96. To provide a decorative effect and the maximum resistance to wear, the new International Bank, at 27th Avenue and Sixth Street, Miami, has plastic laminate panels surrounding tellers' booths. R. C. Nehm, executive vice president, who designed the arrangement personally, said the panels cover most areas which are subject to contact by the public as it stands in line at the booths.

The material, Westinghouse Micarta, never needs repainting or refinishing and can be wiped clean with a damp cloth. The velvet finish woodgrained material is bonded to a chipboard core. The woodgrain pattern gives it the appearance and texture of fine wood.

Fig. 15-97. Reichhold fiberglass-polyester RP trailers made by the Strick Trailer Company were put into service in 1956. After 2½ million miles of hauling heavy steel drums of chemicals, they are still in use and have required much less maintenance than would normally be expected with metal trailers. (Courtesy of Owens-Corning Fiberglas Corporation.)

was successfully produced in limited degrees. Newer glass fiber products in the past months have been produced: U. S. Rubber Co. now has its Vibrin polyester in mat or rope form, and the Standard Oil Co. (Ohio) has Structoform polyester in sheet form, based on a resin system containing no styrene (30).

### 2. Aerospace

Plastics in aircraft continues to expand profitably. At the same time more R&D programs are developing. These multimillion dollar programs of the past, present, and future continue to be major assets. However, from a military aspect, R&D efforts have been lagging since the Korean War. As an example, if more work had been conducted on the new very high strength and modulus reinforced plastics, the present F-111 fighter-bomber-reconnaissance aircraft could be 3000 lb lighter in weight, which in turn would give it more "striking power."

Future high speed aircraft flying at low altitudes will require smooth aerodynamic surfaces, corrosion resistance, ease of maintenance or repair, and high resistance to impact damage that can be produced from sand and gravel set in motion by down wash impingement on noncommercial landing areas. At present, RP stands out as the most suitable material to meet these criteria. Another advantage of the plastic is weight saving: 27% occurs in RP when similar designs are used for aluminum and plastic. Extra performance and 25% weight saving can occur just in the helicopter rotor blades (28).

In one of the most recent design feasibility studies, Douglas Aircraft Co. showed that an all-glass fiber RP airplane is superior in strength and performance to conventional metal types. Design was based on a lightweight, low wing monoplane. RP structural components and skin panels have been in use by Douglas and other airplane manufacturers since 1943; even through this concept is not new, it could now have potential new merit, based on present structural, environment, cost, and industry requirements (46,47).

One of several of the recent Air Force Materials Laboratory R&D contracts is a $1 million 2 year program awarded to the Columbus Div. North American Aviation, Inc. Techniques for applying filament winding to the design and construction of aircraft lifting surfaces will be investigated and aid to reduce the whole family of advanced composite materials and processed to production practices. Aerojet General Corp.'s Von Karman Center will be major subcontractor. The North American/Aerojet program is oriented toward the eventual automated production of aircraft wing and tail load carrying surfaces. There may be applications of filament winding to other structural portions of aircraft. Based on initial data, Aerojet will construct a subsonic wing which will be subjected to load tests (43).

More work continues principally under government sponsorship in the areas of reinforcements (glass, carbon, boron, and the like), matrix (polybenzimidazole, polyimide), and new data. These programs permit organic RP systems to operate from 500 to 1000°F and above, where 10 years ago we generally quoted 200–350°F and above. Work also continues with fiber reinforced ceramics having good strengths up to 1200°F using molding cycles similar to conventional RP (48).

### 3. Underwater

The composite requirements for development of operational vehicles—underwater, on the surface of the water, in the air and in space—are numerous and challenging in order to meet the many complex environments. Unusual requirements for deep ocean operation which make composites candidate materials include the capability

Fig. 15-98. The Grumman A-6A Intruder high-speed jet airplane now in mass production requires the use of a filament wound-epoxy resin nose radome fabricated by Brunswick Corp.

to resist external pressurized load, low weight to displacement, superior buoyancy, protective coatings and corrosion resistance. As an example, the glass structural contender could operate at extremely low depths; however, it is very sensitive to impact and bending shock loads. Protection is provided by using coatings of polycarbonate, butyl rubber, or urethane. The shallow water designs will continue to use more reinforced plastics in ships, hydrofoils, sonar domes and other applications. Plastics cavitation erosion coatings are finding more use with high modulus steel construction.

Although overshadowed by the advance and interest in aerospace technology, increasing attention is being focused on exploration and exploitation of the ocean depths. Today, man has only a limited capability with which to accomplish these desires, not only for scientific purposes, but also for commercial and military reasons. With the nuclear-powered submarines of today, he can move at will in a horizontal plane, but he is restricted to limited depth. With the presently available bathyscaphs Trieste and Archimede, he can probe to deep depth, but his horizontal movement is extremely limited. A prime requisite for achieving the capability of "going deep" is the development of long-endurance, highly-maneuverable, deep-diving hydrospace vehicles.

To obtain such vehicles, there is a continuing need to develop lightweight, highly reliable pressure hulls from structural materials possessing a high strength-to-density ratio (49). This is not to imply that high strength and low density are the only considerations, but they are one of the basic factors in the selection and evaluation of materials for pressure hull studies. Those materials that are currently

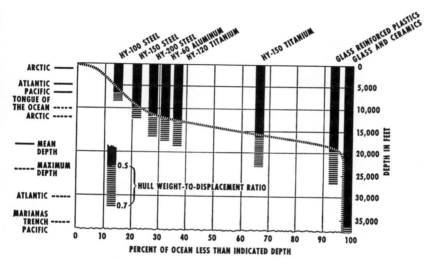

Fig. 15-99. Shown is the depth potential of near-perfect spheres superimposed on the familiar distribution curve of the ocean depths. The portion of the bars above the depth-distribution curve corresponds to hulls having a 0.5 W/D ratio, and the portion beneath the curve shows the deeper depth attainable by heavier hulls with 0.7 W/D ratio. To place materials in their proper perspective, the common factor relating the strength-to-weight characteristics for hulls of various materials to a geometric configuration for a specified design depth is the ratio of the weight of the pressure hull to the weight of seawater displaced by the submerged hull. This factor is referred to as the weight displacement ratio (W/D).

The ratio of 0.5 and 0.7 may appear to be arbitrary, but small sized vehicles can normally be designed with W/D ratios of 0.5 or less, whereas vehicle displacements become quite large as W/D ratios approach 0.7. The use of these values permits a meaningful comparison of the depth potential of various hull materials. An examination of the data reveals that for all the metallic pressure hull materials taken into consideration, the very best results would permit operations to about a depth of 20,000 ft only at the expense of increased displacement. It is significant that the nonmetallic materials of reinforced plastics and glass shown would permit operations to 20,000 ft and more with minimum displacement vehicles.

*Note:* HY denotes yield strength assumed in calculations.

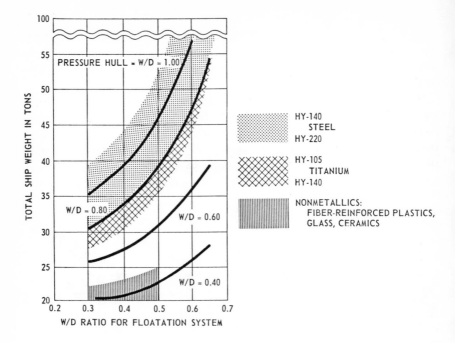

Fig. 15-100. Development of suitable lightweight floats for deep operations would permit considerable increase in the W/D ratio of the main pressure hull. Such a combination would permit the depth potential to be greater than that shown in Fig. 15-99. To provide a frame of reference showing the need for lightweight floats to be used with metallic pressure hulls, information was taken by the David Taylor Model Basin from a study conducted by the Naval Ship Engineering Center to develop the above curves showing the effect of the pressure hull and the flotation system on total weight of a vehicle designed for an operating depth of 20,000 ft. These curves are cited for a pressure hull with a volume of 382 cu ft, which corresponds to a 9 ft diameter sphere, and a maximum vehicle speed of 5 knots with an endurance of 30 hr at 3 knots. These curves represent a potential search vehicle to be developed under the Deep Submergence System Project. A family of curves is given which represents W/D ratios of pressure hulls fabricated from various hull materials under consideration. Crosshatched zones on the figure indicate applicable regions of pressure hull materials for HY-140 to HY-220 steel, HY-105 to HY-140 titanium, and the nonmetallics—reinforced plastics, glass, and ceramics. Present state of the art would dictate an HY-140 steel pressure hull and from 42 to 44 lb/cu ft of syntactic foam as a flotation system. This would result in vehicle weight of approximately 100 tons. Use of HY-110 titanium with improved foam of 37 lb/cu ft would result in vehicle weights of about 45 tons. If consideration is given to nonmetallic spheres as floats, vehicle weight can be reduced further. Floats made of materials such as reinforced plastics offer potential W/D ratios from 0.3 to 0.4. An HY-120 titanium pressure hull with a 0.4 W/D float would have a vehicle weight of approximately 33 tons. Further substantial reduction in vehicle weight would require using nonmetallic pressure hulls. For example, a vehicle with the aforementioned performance and a nonmetallic pressure hull of 0.5 W/D would weigh 27 tons, while a 0.4 ratio would result in a weight of approximately 22 tons.

being given most consideration include the family of high-strength metallics such as steel, aluminum, and titanium alloys and the high-strength nonmetallics such as glass, ceramics, and reinforced plastics.

It is apparent from Figs. 15-99 and 15-100 that to achieve depths of 20,000 ft and deeper, the designer is confronted with the need to use nonmetallic materials whether they be for the floatation systems or the main pressure hull.

It is for these reasons that the United States Navy is interested in developing nonmetallic materials for deep submergence application having properties of high strength and low density. Unfortunately, these materials also offer formidable problems in applications to pressure hull structures in particular foolproof nondestructive testing methods.

**a. Structural Behavior of Filament-Wound GRP Cylinders.** Test specimens of thick-walled, unstiffened cylinders with the ends restrained by metallic end-closure plates to prevent premature instability failure have developed compressive strengths from 150,000 to 170,000 psi and an effective modulus of $5 \times 10^6$ psi when subjected to hydrostatic pressure loading. These cylinders were filament wound from S-HTS glass roving preimpregnated with an epoxy resin. Similar strength levels have also been realized with flat-specimen tests of 2:1 orthogonal laminates under unidirectional compressive loading.

In realistic pressure hull structures, a stiffening system has to be incorporated into a cylindrically shaped hull to prevent premature instability failure and thereby to assist in utilizing the high-strength properties available in the material. When GRP (glass-reinforced plastics) cylinders were stiffened by ring frames, lower strength levels were observed as a result of localized bending and shearing stresses induced by the ring frames. Shear failure occurred in the cylindrical shell at the toe of the frame. The importance of considering the shear sensitivity of GRP material can be illustrated by the test results of two identical models in which one of the models incorporated generous fillets at the toe of the frame. Figure 15-101 shows the configuration of these two models. By including the fillets in the structure, the weight-displacement ratio was increased from 0.524 to 0.544. The model without fillets failed at a pressure of 12,200 psi, whereas the model with fillets failed at a pressure of 16,100 psi. The higher collapse pressure of the latter model more than offset the increase in weight of 4% that resulted from incorporating fillets into the hull structure. However, affective strength levels of only 115,000–120,000 were developed. Failures

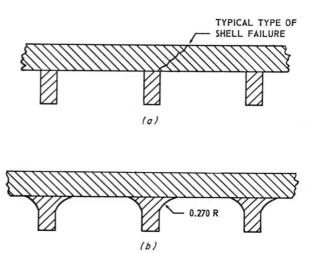

Fig. 15-101. Strength performance to two ring-stiffened cylinders. (*a*), cylindrical model without fillets: collapse pressure = 12,200 psi; weight-displacement ratio = 0.524; (*b*), cylindrical model with fillets: collapse pressure = 16,100 psi; weight-displacement ratio = 0.544. Basic dimensions of both models were identical: shell thickness = 0.388 in.; internal diameter = 6.0 in.; frame spacing = 1.544 in.; frame depth = 0.542 in.; frame width = 0.271 in.; number of internal frames = 19.

were directly related to the interlaminar shear strength of the material.

The best strength-weight performances obtained to date for ring-stiffened cylinders are shown in Fig. 15-102 along with the results of sandwich cylinders and hollow-glass, unstiffened cylinders.

A concept offering high instability resistance and reducing shear and bonding is the sandwich cylinder with a uniform core of syntactic foam. Tests have demonstrated that shells of this type can develop stress levels of 160,000 psi in the GRP facings. However, only a marginal increase in static-strength performance over the ring-stiffened cylinders has been achieved because of the relatively low strength-to-weight characteristics of present foams. The results of these tests are shown also on Fig. 15-102.

The simplest method of reducing shearing and bending stresses is to use an unstiffened cylinder. Development of lower density, hollow fiber, glass-reinforced plastics has made this concept practical for hulls having a collapse depth of or exceeding 35,000 ft, provided that the overall length of the cylinder is four diameters or less. The increase in thickness of the cylinder afforded by the lighter weight, hollow fibers more than offsets the loss of stability due to lower elastic modulus of the composite material. Also, because of the lower

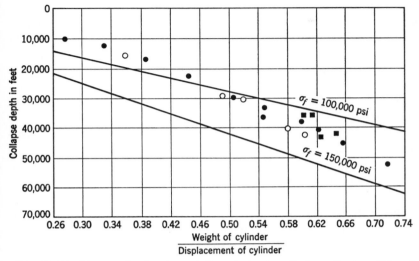

Fig. 15-102. Test results for glass-reinforced plastic cylinders. ●, ring-stiffened; ○, sandwich with syntactic foam core; ■, hollow glass fiber. Curves based on material; density of 128 lb/cu ft; $\sigma_t$ = maximum stress in an equivalent unstiffened cylinder.

rigidity of the hollow fibers, better compatibility exists between the glass reinforcement and the resin binder. To date, little or no static strength-weight advantage has been found for the hollow glass cylinder over the ringstiffened cylinder. However, improved cylic performance and simpler fabrication procedures are anticipated.

Still another potential method for alleviating the stiffener problem in cylindrical hulls is to use fibers with a higher modulus than glass fibers. Higher modulus composites would inherently give rise to hull structures with higher resistance against the instability modes of failure. Lighter frames would be required. Thus, shear and bending stresses would be reduced, and higher structural strength could be obtained. Higher-modulus fibers would also lead to more efficient utilization of composite materials for sandwich hull structures. The structures would be more stable and thus less core material would be required. Also, due to the substantial difference between moduli of the facing and core materials, less load would be transmitted to the low-strength core.

Calculations indicate that a cylinder with a W/D ratio of 0.44 and made of carbon-filament-reinforced plastics with an effective composite modulus of $15 \times 10^5$ psi would not require a stiffening system. With this W/D ratio an unstiffened cylinder of semi-infinite length would have an elastic buckling depth exceeding 70,000 ft. At a depth of 40,000 ft a composite stress of 100,000 psi would be developed. Present problems with high-modulus, carbon-fiber composites have been the inability of laminates to take high-compressive stresses. It is recognized that these fibers have only been recently available in the commercial market, and development of improved matrix-reinforcement, bonding efficiency, and fabrication techniques may be expected.

It is projected that in the period from 1970 to 1980 glass-fiber reinforcement will probably be replaced by superior materials offering large and sudden improvements over the upper limit of properties in GRP composites. The $25 \times 10^6$ psi modulus fibers, which are available, are expected to be the forerunner of carbone reinforcements having even higher properties. Modulus of $50 \times 10^6$ psi and tensile strengths of 400,000 psi for future carbon fibers have been forecasted. Densities of composites made from these fibers would only be 85–95 lb/cu ft less than 75% of the weight of GRP. These materials cannot be overlooked as future potential materials for deep-submergence application.

**b. Structural Details.** Studies with filament-wound cylinders have been extended to investigation of design details that arise in realistic pressure hulls such as closures, openings, and joints. Much of this work was conducted by H. I. Thompson Fiber Glass Company under the sponsorship of Naval Ship Engineering Center. Figure 15-103 is a drawing representing the type of structure that was investigated. The entire pressure hull was designed to obtain a collapse depth of 30,000 ft and to sustain 10,000 excursions to a depth of 15,000 ft without loss in overall strength. The basic ring-stiffened cylinder shown in Fig. 15-103 had a W/D ratio of 52%. It represented the lightest weight hull obtained that satisfied the strength requirements. The stiffening rings were relatively lightweight and in conjunction with the shell provided adequate resistance to premature failure due to overall instability.

The ring frame utilized only 19% of the material in the region representing efficient hull design. In the region of the cylindrical hull opening, a thicker shell, larger frames, and greater frame spacing were used. The latter geometry, representing a W/D ratio of 62% and less efficiency, was selected to provide sufficient space for an opening in the shell without interfering with the adjacent frames. The shell was of S-glass filaments wound to a 4C:2L fiber distribution; the frames were

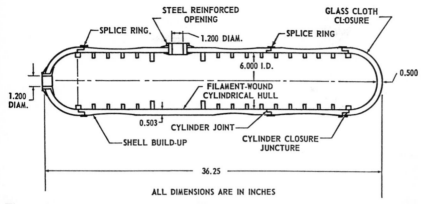

Fig. 15-103. Pressure hull of glass reinforced plastic showing structural details investigated. All dimensions are in inches.

of the same type of material but utilized a 9C:L fiber distribution. The end closures consisted of S-HTS glass cloth layups with a composite strength of 60,000 psi and were fabricated by a vacuum-bag molding process. Closures were attached to the cylindrical hull by adhesive-bonded lap joints.

A disconnectable transverse joint was incorporated in the cylindrical hull to provide a means of access for equipment and machinery. The openings into the pressure hull, both in the cylindrical section and the closure, were reinforced by 17-4 PH stainless steel fittings designed to carry inplane shell loads about the opening in both compression and bending. Light flanges were provided to locally support the cut-fiber ends of the shell and thereby to assist in the transfer of high-compressive bearing loads into the fitting.

One model such as that shown on Fig. 15-103 was tested to failure under static loading. The static model collapsed at a pressure of 12,000 psi. Two other models were subjected to 10,000 cycles to a pressure of 6,700 psi and then were tested to failure under static loading, resulting in collapse pressures of 10,700 and 11,800 psi. In addition to these models, there are other similar models that are presently being subjected to 2 cycles per day for an intended period of two years to determine the response of the structure under long-term, low-cycle fatigue.

It appears that the incorporation of design details is feasible if proper design procedures are employed and adequate sealing methods are utilized in the test. However, weight penalties are imposed on the overall pressure hull due to the addition of structural details. It was mentioned previously that the basic ring-stiffened cylinder has a W/D ratio of 0.52; the overall pressure hull, however, has a W/D ratio of 0.65. It is apparent that in order to achieve efficient pressure hulls, attention must be given to new concepts and approaches to obtain lightweight, watertight closures, joints, and penetrations.

Studies have revealed the importance of maintaining the integrity of a structure subjected to high-pressure water environment. The use of watertight metallic jacket is a possible method of overcoming this problem. This type of construction would permit cylinders or rings made of fiber-reinforced plastics to be placed side by side, not physically joined together, and would provide the major resistance to hydrostatic loading while the jacket would ensure watertight integrity, provide longitudinal strength, and prevent contact of sea water with the composite material.

This type of construction would permit the manufacturer to produce the primary elements in shorter, easier-to-fabricate sections. Construction would become a matter of merely placing the rings together and surrounding them with the metal jacket. Studies have been conducted along these lines. Hydrostatic tests with 1-ft diameter models have shown that a titanium jacket provides a feasible method of protecting GRP laminates. Studies to date have been limited to models having the basic configuration of a ring-stiffened cylinder. An effective stress of 100,000 psi was developed in these structures. Again, the primary mode of failure was due to the lack of shear strength in GRP materials. At one-half of the design collapse depth, the jacket was stressed to the yield of strength.

If it were possible to utilize the potential strength of GRP, the jacket would be required to undergo an extreme stress range due to the three-fold difference in elastic modulus between GRP and titanium. This could cause a fatigue problem. A high-modulus carbon-fiber composite with a titanium jacket appears particularly attractive since it would permit stressing the primary structural elements to an ultimate composite stress without overstressing the metallic jacket. The modulus of the carbon-fiber elements would be compatible with titanium. Likewise, the shear problem would greatly be reduced as to structural details, such as metallic reinforced openings and closures.

**c. Radial Fiber Shells.** Although the circular cylinder stands out as one of the most practical and convenient shapes for filament-wound pressure hull structures, it might not, however, be the shape that offers the highest resistance to shear type of failure. Doubly curved shells

such as spheroids and spheres would offer improved stability characteristics and associated improvements in shear levels. Also, these are
desirable shapes for small-sized vehicles.

Extremely encouraging results have been observed in tests of GRP
spheres fabricated by the UNIRoyal Company in which a unique fabrication technique is used to achieve radial orientation of each fiber. The
spheres are of a mosaic block construction very similar to the method
used to build igloos. Small blocks cut from cured, unidirectional GRP
plates are placed inside a mold with the fibers oriented in the radial
direction and are then impregnated with resin and cured to form
spherical segments. These segments are bonded together to form a
complete sphere. The observed strength-weight characteristics of these
shells have been more than double those obtained for the other GRP
shells.

Recent tests were conducted with spheres 3 in. and 11 in. in diameter
having a W/D ratio of 0.39. The 3-in. diameter sphere was tested with
a thin resin coating on the outer surface. It produced a collapse depth
of 45,000 ft. An 11-in. diameter sphere with the resin coating removed
so that bare ends of glass fibers were exposed to water pressure was
held for 45 days at a depth of 26,000 ft, then it was cycled 5,000 times
to 22,500 ft, and finally was tested to failure. The collapse depth was
56,000 ft. After the 45-day creep test, slight extrusions of resin along
the bond lines were noted. After the cyclic test where an original hairline crack of 2 in. grew only ¾ in. No other damage was observed.

The fabrication methods employed by UNIRoyal Company can
realistically be projected to larger diameter spheres. A 32-in. diameter
sphere was recently proof-tested at the Naval Ship Research and
Development Center to a pressure of 10,000 psi and then was subjected to a pressure of 9,000 psi for 30 hr.

The concept of radial fiber-GRP spheres appears to be very attractive for use as a flotation systems. The high-strength performance
of these spheres can be attributed to lack of shear and bending actions.
Also, due to the orientation of the fibers and the type of loading, the
fibers are in tension and therefore not susceptible to local buckling of
the individual fibers. These results serve to further demonstrate that
hull concepts and material disposition play a very important role in
realizing the full strength potential of fiber-reinforced plastic materials.

The introduction of a reinforced opening into a radial fiber sphere is
a very challenging problem. The material is shear sensitive in the
radial direction. The strength performance could be defeated by the

effects of the discontinuity. Solutions to this problem and the problems of water penetration and resistance to dynamic loading would lead to a lightweight primary pressure hull.

**d. Filament Wound and Shingle Shells.** Limited studies with filament-wound shells of double curvature such as spheres, oblate and prolate spheroid shells have given test results somewhat less than desired. To filament wind these structures, a helical winding pattern is generally used. In addition to being highly anisopropic and thus less tractable analytically, shells with crossed-over fibers have lower glass compaction, more resin-enriched regions, prone to glass failure at the crossover points, and have higher void content. New and unique methods of fabrication for doubly curved shells without crossed-over fibers are needed.

The use of a "shingle method" of fabrication appears to be very attractive, and work in this direction has recently been initiated by the Navy. The method is similar to a "building-block" procedure in which preimpregnated, pressure-compacted tiles of preoriented glass fibers are placed over a mold to form the pressure hull. The method offers the possibility of molding in lightweight GRP reinforcements around openings as well as a conceivable approach to fabricate doubly curved shells and nested spheres.

## D. Fundamentals for Growth and Profits

First, let us review fundamentals which affect market growth in RP and concern practically any type production or organization. In this era of explosive technological improvement, management has to maintain a strong technological base to provide the critically necessary information for creation of profits in present products, but more importantly the new products. The level and necessity of this technology is, of course, directly related to the company's type of business and competitive situation.

The task of producing high performance and economically sound products in any field (agriculture, building, aerospace, metals and plastics) are so complex that they require unique managerial arrangements for success. The broadest possible understanding of different disciplines are required. It includes the physical sciences and technologies.

Another important fundamental is our increasing commitment in Viet Nam and other important high priority government science and technology programs competing for federal funds and industry time.

Fig. 15-104. Surfaces of filament wound bazooka tubes are being examined by Taylor Corporation inspector as they enter curing racks.

In the competition of nongovernment programs, our free society permits us to direct our own efforts. However, establishing priorities becomes time consuming and laborious, since it involves interaction among many segments of society, including the scientist, engineer, market analyst, administrator, financier, and politician. All these facets are indispensible ingredients in order to make decisions which are balanced and reasonable.

The requirement to select among a variety of major technological advancements is a relatively new element in the business world. Also the time required for a new discovery to find practical application was usually measured in generations. A significant idea now advances from the laboratory to widespread use in less than a decade. In this environment those with education and skill in technology will carry growing responsibilities to keep up-to-date on changes and help impart to others an understanding of its nature and, most important, significance. Now that some of these changes are fairly well defined, the problem is one of using them most efficiently.

When reviewing modern trends in material technology it becomes obvious that the plastics industry has had and will continue to have a rapid growth. This total industry has had an average annual growth rate of 11% in comparison with 6.5% for the chemical industry and 3.5% for the gross national product (GNP). Predictions for the future have plastics moving at this accelerated rate. Overall growth expansion is much greater than population explosion.

Cost performance will continue to be more demanding as the products move into the inevitable larger volume markets which emphasize durability under various environmental conditions. Knowledge in the durability of composite structures will continue to expand with confidence so that they can find more acceptance in more nonstructural and structural applications.

Fig. 15-105. RP prepreg ready for fabrication and molding parts is continuing to be used. The target is to produce economically, fast curing lay-ups or mats which can be used in producing mass production parts, such as automotive parts.

In this view a molded part is being removed after a short cure. This U.S. Rubber Company's new Vibrin-Mat process was used.

## E. Marketing Considerations

Research and development makes it known, engineering and marketing makes it profitable. This statement encompases many facets of our business world such as material supply, production, patents, statistics, computer analysis, sales, promotion, and particularly management. It also concerns istelf with the more modern approach to profitable growth in either the commercial or military business organization. This philosophy provides the technology for new products and processes that will be the basis of future diversification of a company. Since we will observe an age of growing abundance in this country and are told that no major business recession will occur, the company progress is only limited by the skill and vision of its people. The raw materials of these people are ideas and ingenuity.

Market orientation of R&D is important to the growth of a company. Of course, there are those who would prefer to state "research and development orientation of the markets." Which comes first is irrelevant when new profitable products are sold. When no profit develops, or no saleable product is produced, then the usual arguments develop as to who should be controlling new products development— R&D or marketing. This situation resembles the one about which came first, the chicken or the egg.

Of course, the "no profit" situation can be caused by other factors such as company operating policies, company capabilities, and competitive situation. As an example, a company may have very limited R&D or marketing capability in regard to expanding use of RP in a completely different area. Other examples are those companies presently concerned with military efforts which generally are not organized to handle commercial prospects.

There are obvious misconceptions about the relations between market development and R&D in creating a new product, such as:

*1.* These functions are separate, compartmentalized tasks.

*2.* Their relation is sequential with research creating new products and then (and only then) market development determines their commercial markets.

*3.* The interaction between the two activities is only that short period of time necessary for research to inform and educate market development about the nature of the new product.

*4.* Market development activities have little or no effect on the conceptual and identification phases of new product development.

*5.* Research contributes little during the market development phases.
*6.* Marketing has no well defined relationship with the customers.

The activities of these two functions are not sequential with inter-action over a narrow period of time. They are, in fact, parallel with interactions both intimate and continuous throughout time. Inter-dependence and communications between the two functions is vital during all phases of developing a new product. The degree to which there has been a history of successful interactions between these two functions determines in large measure how quickly commercial values can be recognized. Product possibilities can be related to market needs only with mutual awareness by both parties.

New approaches to marketing show an increasing tendency also to go deep into the structure of a company. The companies that in-tend to grow or survive have already made the adjustment in the attitude recognized as marketing orientation. They carry market-ing's substance or information to and from the customer.

Perhaps the most important aspect to marketing is that there is more "talk" than "action." More often than not, managements of

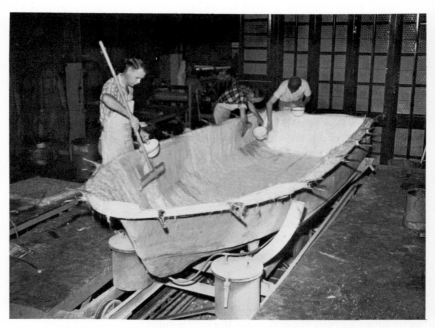

Fig. 15-106. The hand-layup system is being used to fabricate RP boat hulls. These parts can be cured by using room-temperature catalysts, ultraviolet cata-lysts, oven cure, autoclave, and others. The cured parts perform efficiently; water resistance, tough, decorative, streamline, etc.

companies do not recognize that this situation exists. In fact, sometimes this condition is recognized but not accepted, since management just does not understand marketing. This particular situation is very true with some of the companies producing RP parts, both the small and the large ones (54).

## F. Management Responsibilities

At this point, it may appear that this review has condensed information which is "old hat" or dogmatic. However, what has been reviewed will undoubtedly be repeated in years to come since they tend always to be present in business. They are basic problems definitely affecting the RP industry. They exist and actually aid those companies having the desire and ingenuity to be successful.

These facts can explain why substantial differences in the performance of individual companies exists. It also demonstrates the need and opportunity for improvement in the management of new product programs.

It is the rare product which succeeds without really trying. The first demonstration of a product's commercial utility usually rests with the company developing the product based on management coordination. At the other extreme, it can be said that the technical community can accomplish practically anything that is logically the next step in development or progress. The problem is that in most cases we cannot do them economically, politically, or socially, so management has to make the proper decisions to permit progress and minimize losses.

The RP industry, with all of its complexity, requires many different kinds of talent and the work of many people: those who create or design, others who make recommendations, those who conduct market surveys, those who make decisions, and those who implement the decisions.

Management must recognize technology as a major business force in this complex system. There is going to be more risk and more failure in decisions related to technology as to the direction of businesses. At the same time, competition will increase; life span of many products will be reduced; the time, money, and knowledge required to develop new products will increase; cost of products will decrease to greater operating efficiency; and many sound products will become obsolete by technological advances.

Probably the most important message to management is the fact that they must recognize the need for different kinds of leadership skill, dependent upon the current phase which the new material or product demands. Proper leadership through changes or supplement in personnel, organization, and procedures are necessary.

The RP industry, similar to the total plastics industry, in recent years has been involved in integration, mergers, and regrouping. At present, it appears that there will be much more of this action. For some markets, particularly the larger ones, the integration approach permits a company to go more efficiently from raw materials to end products. Acquisitions have also been a real boon for many organizations to expand in-house capability in a specific area. Companies who recognized the potential of RP in their infancy and prepared for expansion are still on the rise.

With these changes the independent RP processors face critical decisions in planning for growth. The independent processor working with all types of plastics who wishes to go it alone today finds himself hard pressed to decide what corporate strategy should be adopted to assure continued growth of his company.

One question uppermost in the mind of the owner is whether to continue independently or to join with another company. The answer is not a simple one. If the decision is to remain independent, the next question is one of resolving the right program for increasing volume to replace business lost to competition.

On the other hand, should the independent conclude it best to join forces with another company, many corporate, personal, and financial considerations are involved. Among the more important are keeping independent identity and the freedom to continue operating the company along lines which the owner has proved to be successful. What to do and where to turn under the conditions is truly the independent's dilemma.

In an effort to find a way out of the dilemma, W. H. Bingham of Hawley Products Co., itself an independent plastics processor of molded cellulose fiber components, recently conducted a study to learn what the outlook for the present and future position of the independent company might be in the plastics industry. The result indicated a number of critical decision areas which affect the corporate growth of the independent. They provide factual data which may be used to determine corporate strategy and solutions to the independent's pressing dilemma (50).

The decision making process is rendered even more complex by the added pressures generated by the plastics industry itself and the economy. The successful independent is daily made painfully aware of increasing demands for larger sums of money to maintain operations, to keep up with new materials and market changes, and to expand to meet growing markets.

Capital, in ever increasing quantities, is required to enlarge facilities, to modernize and add efficient equipment, and to attract and hold the best marketing, management, and technical talent and skills. Ever larger funds are required for market and product research and development to enable the independent to compete on a level comparable to that of larger corporations.

There are few independents today whose present business operations provide sales in sufficient volume and at a fast enough rate to generate the capital demanded for sustained growth comparable to the more than 11% annual rate enjoyed by the plastics industry. The alternative is usually debt financing, which, as most owners have learned, is limited and cannot always be obtained in sufficient amounts to meet short term demands or long term needs. Without access to large sources of funds, growth is restricted. Some 2600 independent plastics processors in the nation are confronted with these problems and they are all looking for a solution.

There is no question that there will always be a future for the independent plastics processor who wishes to go it alone. But, like materials manufacturers who have been forced to change their domestic corporate strategy radically because of violently changing conditions of world wide scope, so will the independent with foresight decide that he will have to change his own strategy if he plans to grow in our increasingly volatile national economic climate.

For those independents who are willing to share some of their independence with others to reduce their risks, the logical solution to the independent's dilemma is the "pooling of interests" concept.

Different management controls are used by companies to aid growth; they vary in accordance with size of company and product. Basically, they use the PERT approach. This Program Evaluation and Review Technique is now finding more use in commercial and government oriented managements. It develops successful new products and extends the realistic useful life of those in production. As most of us recognize, PERT sets up all factors which are required to perform the job from discovery to obsolescent. It provides through detailed planning phases such as: R&D, marketing and sales time schedule; sets up and coordinates all requirements; clearly defines responsibility; sets up and follows time schedules; and lists all costs and profits on a day-by-day basis. It makes a company identify all the action that has to be taken to develop new products. Many companies use the PERT approach, but do not identify or recognize it as such.

With all this organization, no management can survive without new products. Management must actively seek out and predict or anticipate demand. Passive actions are generally a waste of time and money, unless a captive type market condition exists. Keep in mind that the general trend originally was for the marketing people to reject more than 90% of R&D proposals on new products since no market existed for them. At present, the rejection rate in RP is close to 60%.

The obvious secret of business continues to be one of being in the right business at the proper time. Then if the companies unique characteristics are being properly oriented, profits can be sustained for the business life of the part. Remember that failures rarely occur in well managed and adequately financed companies. These companies have the skill and "desire" to stop development of a product anytime afer its conception when it starts to become a failure. The failure can occur back in the business analysis or the R&D stage.

### G. Expected Problems

Growth for RP has been reviewed. Associated with this growth are roadblocks which exist for certain companies. Many of these roadblocks must be overcome continually before composites are acceptable to industry for complete widespread use, similar to using sheet steel. The lack of complete confidence on the part of the designer can generally and rightfully be attributed to economics or reliability of design data. This reliability in primary structural applications is influenced by quality control evaluation procedures, particularly nondestructive types.

But then there are those designers who do not understand RP, due probably to time limitations. However, keep in mind that RP applications continue to grow and eventually RP data will be in all the handbooks, standards, and even college texts. In the meantime, effort to up-date and develop new specifications, standards, and handbooks are being continued by government agencies, industry, societies, and associations. A complete revision and expansion of the present handbook MIL-HDBK-17 (Plastics for Aerospace Vehicles) has been undertaken under the direction of a Service Working Group chaired by the Air Force. An Industry Advisory Committee has been organized to present the views and needs of industry. It has been asked to provide data that will be of value to the designer. New information to be included in the revised document will cover filament winding, joining and attaching, processing, and new resins and reinforcements (51,52).

Roadblocks for RP include:

*1.* Service data—There are RP's which can be used in production since they have reliable service data; then there are the new RP's which are in the R&D or preproduction phase. Mixing up these "RP's" can be damaging.

*2.* Safe market—Fabricators cannot consider any market safe.

Fig. 15-107. Chopped fiber glass is sprayed simultaneously with catalyzed resin onto a mold where a layer of glass fabric has been laid up and cured. The sabot is fabricated to military specifications for Westinghouse by Peterson Products, Belmont, California. Achievement of a glass-to-resin ratio of more than 42% without high loadings of costly glass fabrics represents a significant accomplishment, according to Westinghouse.

*3.* Economics—Cost reductions on new products tend to be non-existant.

*4.* Lost motion—Breakdown in communications between the customer and plastic manufacturer probably accounts for a large amount of lost motion and dollars. Perhaps another major cause is the pure sales approach within any industry which, in many cases, can delay technical progress. As an example, architects and builders desire factual data on products. However, their standards or codes identify only the composition of the end item, with no performance data. In most cases, the plastics were never subjected to engineering analysis. This situation is not new to the engineering community, where patience, time, and/or money resolves the problem.

*5.* Antique rules and codes—As reported by the architects, the industry is shamefully antique. It is composed of so many separate operations and trades that consideration of these factors is almost as important as the functional quality of the new material. No matter how ideal the functional qualities of a material perform, if union jurisdiction rules that it must be installed by tradesmen either untrained or unsympathetic, its quality become questionable. Also, building officials are charged, through codes, with responsibility for protection of the inhabitants and the building itself. Therefore, products must be acceptable to them. Success of codes often depends upon the discretion of enforcing officials. To guide officials in the evaluation of products, there must be plastics industry standards which keep pace with technological developments.

*6.* Outdating—Most new products eventually replace or encroach upon existing products in a sophisticated system of fabrication, formulation, and the like, built around the present product. Also new products can easily be replaced.

*7.* People—The character of people is changing: engineer, businessman, everyone. As an example, the profession of engineering is now undergoing the most drastic revolution in purpose, responsibility, and character that has occurred during its existence as a profession. Most practicing engineers do not fully realize what is happening. Although their profession is oriented toward the future, like most human beings they are disturbed by the rate of change and by the critical issues which have arisen. They want to feel that things are as they were, but this is futile and wishful thinking (33).

*8.* Business attitude—A different attitude or "climate" exists in how to operate with people in the commercial and government businesses.

*9.* Sales—Salesmen must be kept informed.

*10.* Statistics—Keeping pace with reliable statistics will always be difficult. However, in today's world and especially in this country, no responsible person in government or in business would attempt to make basic decisions without the most adequate factual support. However, the conditions we regard as indispensable today are of relatively recent achievement. Also, RP statistics are difficult to assemble.

*11.* Ideas—New ideas and innovations have to be examined.

*12.* Competition—There is a very important factor to consider in developing the market, a factor so common that we can fail to evaluate it properly. That vital factor is competition. It is a basic concept that can be easily overshadowed by a multitude of scientific and strategy theories, both sophisticated and down-to-earth types. Successful competition in today's new RP product economy requires increased involvement by top management to take positive action in what is to be done based on what others are doing. Competition comes from other plastics as well as other type materials.

The failure of a new product can logically be related principally to management, marketing, R&D, and/or manufacturing. Probably the reasons for most failures can be easily related to the fact that insufficient attention was paid to the market, the product was not understood, and/or competitors did not sit by.

Perhaps the major problem is one which is best resolved by continually up-dating industry on the progress being made in RP through reports, lectures, editorials, and other news media. The faults of materials known and utilized for hundreds of years are often overlooked; the faults of the new materials are often overemphasized. The news media is important to have people better understand these "faults."

## H. Machines

In addition to using some of the present available plastics machinery (Fig. 15-109), a challenge is the perennial problem of designing new machines and equipment to meet the product demands. A major development now occurring is the fast injection molding of reinforced thermosets as well as thermoplastics (53).

The new composites are on the threshold of a spectacular future, but the cost is high. But eventually these new materials are expected to be economically useful in commercial applications. This success

Fig. 15-108. Glass fiber reinforced-polyester resin railroad tank cars of different sizes, are being used in U.S. and other parts of the world to transport different liquids. Here is a tank car made with Scott Bader (England) polyester, being used in England.

will have to be accompanied by new concepts of design and manufacture of machines. Designs in metals can draw on a huge 100 year reservoir of knowledge and experience which, in many cases, has been compiled in engineering handbooks. RP can use only the knowledge gained since 1941. (28–30,43,54)

## I. Growth Rate of Plastics Industry

There are 400 reinforced plastics fabricators, a 78% increase over 1956.

Production of all plastic materials and resins has increased four-fold since 1953; RP increased four- to five-fold during this same period.

Hundreds of new plastic products and applications have been introduced in the past two decades; RP has a respectable position in new items.

The annual investment in plastic working machinery has double since 1960; with RP it has at least doubled.

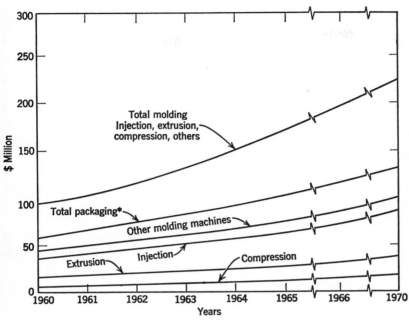

Fig. 15-109. Estimated United States machinery sales for all plastics, by major markets. Packaging machinery includes all categories: i.e., shrink wrapping, blister, heat-sealing, wrapping, testing, gluing, bag handling, etc. These data represent one-third of all types of packaging machinery.

Despite rising price levels, the average cost of plastic resins has declined about 30% in the past 6 years.

Of the 5700 United States companies in the plastics business, 2600 are independent processors.

In the past 10 years industrial production rose as follows:

Great Britain—35%.

United States—36%.

Western Europe—78%.

France—90%.

European Common Market—100%.

Germany—112%.

Italy—140%.

During this same period, plant expansion and modernization in terms of new machine tools installed was advancing far more actively in Europe than in the United States.

## J. Statistics on Size of U. S. Plastics Industry (1966)

It is estimated that with the 1966 production figure of almost 13 billion lb of plastics resins to be reached, industry will have established its 14 consecutive year of record breaking production. In 1956, production was 3.977 billion lb a 225% increase in just 10 years. Value of the plastics resins sold in 1956 was approximately $1.98 billion compared to the $6.5 billion estimated for 1966 (8). According to estimates of the Society of the Plastics Industry, Inc., there are in the U. S. more than:

5,700 companies who make plastics their business of which 50% are in the east, 34% in the midwest, 13% on the west coast and 3% elsewhere.

150 plastics materials manufacturers.

400 reinforced plastics fabricators, a 78% increase over 1956, of which 18% in the northeast, 10% in the southeast, 43% in the midwest, 11% in the southwest and 18% in the far west.

1,700 injection molders, a 68% increase over 1956.

300 extruders, a 25% increase over 1956.

900 compression molders, a 56% increase over 1956.

60 film and sheeting processors.

1,500 finishers of flexible films and sheeting.

1,500 finishers of rigid plastics.

20,000 injection machines, a 122% increase over 1956.

19,400 compression machines, a 31% increase over 1956.

175,00 employees.

## K. Factors That Make the Next 10 Years Extremely Promising

. . . . One factor is, RP with thermosets and thermoplastics. The elements of the future are already in place based on past and present performance, as well as what is in R&D. Effective exploitation of future opportunities is the key to the question of market penetration and profitability through RP. The first requisite for success is a recognition on the part of management that the function to accomplish this task is a major job. The evolution of new RP products is not an abstract business cycle. It goes in logical steps from concept through R&D and production to phase out or obsolescence (Fig. 6).

Growth areas include building and construction, boat, transportation, automotive, aircraft and missile, electronic, tank, pipe, ordnance, appliance, furniture, and data processing. Then there are products to be used in the most rapidly growing United States industries which are education, medicine and recreation.

While monumental technological breakthroughs are unlikely in the next decade, growth will continue to come through in steady incremental advances limited not by technology, but by economics. The real industrial breakthrough could occur when greater use of plastics is made in primary structural applications. Good basic and engineering understanding of RP, matching that practiced in metals, is developing and will provide more opportunities for application. In the meantime, RP utilizing stronger and higher modulus of elasticity fibers in a suitable matrix offer promise of a structural material with mechanical properties substantially better than those of metals. Military and space needs provide the impetus for research and development which in turn will follow the usual pattern of supplying commercial and industrial markets with new materials.

The major factors contributing to the growth record of RP have included the large investment in research and development, the industry's technical know-how and inquisitiveness, the intense competition among plastic companies, the large scale military and space demand, the broadening of markets through reductions in base material cost, the fact that many customers also are above average

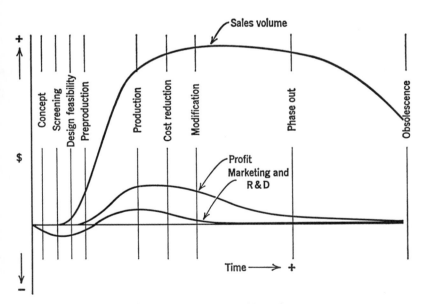

Fig. 15-110. Product life cycle.

growth industries, and the incentives created by a favorable rate of profits.

Increasing environmental requirements on earth, space, and the depths of the ocean are imposing high demands on materials that often cannot be met by any one material alone. RP can provide multipurpose characteristics which will aid in meeting these new demands. They also provide the means to mass produce quality parts in speciality machines.

The rapid accelerating growth of knowledge today is too often accepted as an inveitable result of the bounty of nature. These technical advances are very important; however, we can tend to forget that this knowledge and its use is principally gained if one is pushed.

## REFERENCES

1. The Age of Composites, *Reinforced Plastics & Composite World,* May-June 1967.
2. D. V. Rosato, Reinforced Plastics: Where Will They Go From Here? *Plastics World,* 24, **2,** Feb. 1966.
3. A. G. H. Dietz, Fiber-Reinforced Composites, SPE, March 1965.
4. R. Ripkin and J. Rivlin, Shell Theory, *Journal of Applied Mechanics,* p. 103-108, March 1963.
5. W. R. Dunnavant, Progress in the Development of Heat-Resistant Organic Polymers, 6, 4, p. 11, Apr. 1966.
6. D. L. Schmidt and R. C. Tomashot, Plastics in the Air Force, ML TDR 64-76, April 1964.
7. J. H. Freeman et al., Resins and Reinforced Plastic Laminates for use at 650°F, *SPE Transactions,* Apr. 1965.
8. K. H. Boller, Strength Properties of RP Laminates at Elevated Temperatures, WADC TR 59-569, Jan. 1960.
9. G. F. L. Ehlers, TGA Analysis of Polymers, ASD TR 61-622, Feb. 1962.
10. K. H. Boller and K. E. Kimball, Effect of Elevated Temperatures on Weight Loss and Flexural Properties of Three RP Laminates, WADC TR 59-216, Sept. 1959.
11. *Ibid.,* WADC TR 60-466, Dept. 1960.
12. *Ibid.,* ASD TR 61-482, Oct. 1961.
13. K. H. Boller, Tensile and Compressive Strength of RP Laminates after Rapid Heating, WADD TR 60-804, Feb. 1961.
14. K. H. Boller, Predicting the Strength of RP Laminates with Temperature Gradients, FPL Report No. 1881, Jun. 1961.
15. G. H. Stevens, Fatigue Test of Phenolic Laminate at High Stress Levels and Elevated Temperatures, FPL Report No. 1884, Aug. 1961.
16. K. H. Boller, Fatigue Characteristics of Two New Plastic Laminates, Reinforced with Unwoven "S" Glass Fibers, Under Cyclic Axial or Shear Loading, AFML-TR 66-54, Mar. 1966.
17. MIL-HDBK-17 Plastics for Flight Vehicles, Part I, Armed Forces Supply Center, Washington, D.C. 20025.

18. W. Lewis, Thermal Conductivity—Temperature Relationship for Nine Glass and Asbestos Fiber-Reinforced Aircraft Plastics, FPL Report No. 36, Aug. 1965.
19. G. H. Stevens, Effect of Thermal Cycling on Tensile and Compressive Strength of RP Laminates, FPL Report No. 37, Aug. 1965.
20. R. C. Tomashot and D. G. Harvey, Nuclear Radiation of RP Radome Material, WADC TR 56-296, 1956.
21. R. L. Keller, Nuclear Radiation of RP Materials, WADC TR 56-296, Sup. 1, Dec. 1959.
22. MIL-HDBR-23, Composite Construction for Flight Vehicles, Part 1, Armed Forces Supply Center, Washington, D.C.
23. D. V. Rosato, Reinforced Plastics—What They Can Do for You in the Next 10 Years, SAE, October 3–7, 1966.
24. E. W. Engstrom, Chairman, Executive Committee, RCA, speech to 1966 graduating class of Polytechnic Institute of Brooklyn.
25. R. L. Bisplinghoff, editorial, AIAA, June 1966.
26. A. G. H. Dietz, Composite Materials. ASTM Edgar Marburg Lecture, 1965.
27. Forging Military Aerospace Power. Air Force System Command Bulletin 1965.
28. D. L. Grimes, Why Develop New Composite Materials . . . Now. *Research/Development,* September 1965.
29. D. V. Rosato and C. S. Grove, *Filament Winding: Its Development, Applications and Design,* Interscience, New York, 1964.
30. D. V. Rosato, Reinforced Plastics; Where Will They Go from Here, *Plastics World,* February 1966.
31. D. V. Rosato, *Asbestos: Its Industrial Applications,* Reinhold, New York, 1959.
32. Building Construction: What's in It for Plastics. *Plastics World,* December 1965 and January 1966.
33. Science and Technology and the U. S. Department of Commerce, Background Memorandum, Dept. of Commerce, June 1966.
34. S. E. Tinkham, Cost Estimating for Profit. *Plastics World,* May 1966.
35. J. E. Sayre, Reinforced Polyesters—A Market Research Report. *Reinforced Plastics,* July-August, 1965.
36. Automated RP. *Plastics World,* September 1966.
37. Sandwich Panel Design Criteria. Building Research Institute Publ. 798, 1960.
38. Filament Winding—Tool of the Space Age. *Reinforced Plastics,* July-August, 1966.
39. T. A. Battaglini, Current Trends and Future Needs for Plastics in Computers. Paper presented at SPI National Plastics Conference, June, 1966.
40. G. R. Buck, Ammunition Packaging Design, *Plastics World,* June 1965.
41. J. D. Matlack, Plastics in Ammunition. Paper presented at SPI National Plastics Conference, June, 1966.
42. Processing of Plastics: Structural Integrity of Filament Winding. Paper presented Iowa State University Conference, April 29, 1966.
43. Filament Wound $1 Million R&D Contract Release. North American Aviation, Inc., June 23, 1966.

44. G. A. Rossi and J. H. Johnson, Composite Sandwich for Small, Unmanned Deep-Submergence Vehicles. ACME 65-UNT-2, May 1965.
45. D. V. Rosato and R. T. Schwartz, *Environmental Effects on Polymeric Materials*, Interscience, New York, 1968.
46. The All-RP Aircraft. Reinforced Plastics, March-April, 1966.
47. Composites Promise New Design Freedom. *Reinforced Plastics*, May-June 1965.
48. R. Reed, Polybenzimidazole and Other Polyaromatics for High Temperature Structural Laminates and Adhesives. AFML TR 64-365, Part I, Vol. 1, November 1964.
49. International Conference on the Mechanics of Composite Materials, Office of Naval Research, May 8-10, 1967.
50. W. H. Bingham, Roads to Growth: Independence or Merger. *Plastics World*, May 1966.
51. Plastics for Aerospace Vehicles. Military Handbook, MIL-HDBK-17, Armed Forces Supply Support Center, Washington, D. C.
52. Composite Construction. Military Handbook, MIL-HDBK-23, Armed Forces Supply Support Center, Washington, D. C.
53. Backing Industry Growth—Machinery. *Plastics World*, May 1965.
54. E. C. Bursk, A Rational for Marketing Growth. *Industrial Marketing*, June 1966.

# 16

## Other Materials

**Donald V. Rosato**
*Boston College, Boston, Massachusetts*

**Frank J. Riel**
*Whittaker Corp., San Diego, California*

## CONTENTS

# I. PLASTICS IN BUILDING AND CONSTRUCTION

## A. Introduction

The present and growing large market for plastics in building construction is principally due to its suitability in different environments. The versatility of different plastics to exist in different environments perhaps may be related to another characteristic; namely, ability to be maintenance-free when compared to the more conventional and older materials. This section will review the different parameters which are important in building construction and are related to different environments. The importance of environment-resistant plastics will be correlated with the amount presently being used with growth potential.

From a practical review, perhaps it can be stated that buildings and construction materials are exposed to the most severe environments, particularily when the long time factor is included. The environments include such conditions as temperature, ultraviolet, wind, snow, corrosion, hail, wear and tear, etc. Basically the following inherent potentials continue to be realized in different plastics:

Ease of maintenance
Light weight
Flexibility of component design
Combine with other materials
Corrosion, abrasion and weather resistance
Variety of colors and decorative appearance
Multiplicity of form
Ease of fabrication by mass production techniques
Total cost advantages (combinations of base materials, manufacture
    and installation)

Success in applying plastics has been based on a combination of factors; such as, adequate testing, keeping up-to-date on customer problems, product identification, quality control, establishment of engineering standards, approval of regulatory agencies, supervise installations, accurate cost and time estimation, organizational responsibility defined, meeting delivery schedule, development of proper marketing and sales approach, resolution of profit potential based on careful selection of application and acknowledge competition exists.

The functional attributes which permits its growth at an accelerated rate are reliability, acceptability, feasibility and economics. Field installations of the new products are now providing more of the necessary reliable data. The field tests continue to be the best approach in demonstrating acceptance.

The obstacles, limitations or disadvantages confronting acceptance of plastics are:

*1.* Service life versus legal risk—The architect and builder can appreciate the limited 10 to 20 year service test results but rarely can appreciate the more abundant zero to two year or accelerated weathering test results. Their present thinking is that plastic companies inherit their portion of risk.

*2.* Properties—Fire safety continues to be a major performance requirement. Creep and heat distortion are other important properties to be considered. A major deterent for the architect and builder is lack of common knowledge about plastics physical properties.

*3.* Cost—In no business is there more resistance to increase cost even if it represents true increase value.

*4.* Codes—The code problems are usually over emphasized. It is a recognized fact that obstacles do exist and many "heated" debates are already on the books and will continue to be on the books. The codes are important to society and must be recognized in plans and development programs for plastic building products. There are many examples of approvals such as pipe since 1965 as well as previous acceptance of paneling in 1959 by FHA on Sinclair-Koppers Company expandable polystyrene beads faced with asbestos cement or plywood.

*5.* Competition—In line with the sportsmanship approach or competitive business behavior, the entrenched steel, wood, concrete and other industries will logically continue to resist plastics acceptance and use all humanly available resources to fight plastics.

*6.* Aesthetics—The trend is to resist change in appearance so that plastic has to look like something else. In the minority cases where the beauty of plastic is accepted lower costs and more benefits have occurred.

*7.* Identification—To the nonplastic user and even certain plastic users, identification of over 18,000 plastics tends to be either misleading or confusing. Industry has just issued a bulletin on "Identification of Plastics in Building" outlining a course of action to resolve this problem. It suggests a voluntary uniform system of terminology and mark-eng, in which the first term is the trade mark, next is the generic name and last is the ASTM abbreviation regarding end-use product. This system was prepared by joint committees of the Society of Plastics Industry and the Manufacturing Chemist's Association. Companies involved in this project includes DuPont, American Cyanamid, Archer Daniels Midland, B. F. Goodrich and Dow Chemical.

*8.* Standards—Most buildings have never been subjected to thorough engineering analyses. Structural details have been controlled by tradition, precedent and judgment.

*9.* Performance data—Rather than make available principally sales type of data, the architect should review realistic and understandable technical data.

*10.* Consumer—General demand for traditional materials.

*11.* Labor—Generally sets-up problems but education on use of new plastics can be helpful.

In the meantime ideas for using plastic in building continues to vary in all proportions (Table 16-2). Quick disassembly embassies could be built to fit in with riot actions. Designers forecast spray-foamed homes during the October 1965 annual National Decorative and Design Show in New York City. It was described that entire rooms and furnishings molded-in-place would be both practical, appealing and survive environment.

## B. Applications

The largest market for plastics is building construction, which now uses approximately 25% of total U.S. plastic consumption. It is predicted that in 1966 alone, close to 3 billion pounds of plastics—$\frac{1}{2}$ billion worth—was consumed in building, with vinyls being the most widely used. Plastics are found in the established markets of wall covering, coating, electrical and heat insulation, flooring, paint, pipe and fitting, vapor barrier and window trim. An additional 3 billion pounds are estimated to have been used in building by the rest of the world. By 1970, consumption in U.S. is expected to rise to at least $4\frac{1}{2}$ or even up to 7 billion pounds (Table 16-3).

Government reports listed total building expenditure in 1964, as $86 billion, including $65.8 billion for new buildings alone. In 1965, new

TABLE 16-2.  Applications of Plastics in Building

| Exterior | |
| --- | --- |
| Adhesives | Vent stacks |
| Air support structures | Water proofings |
| Air vents | Weather strippings |
| Cables | Window panes |
| Caulkings | Window sash (prime and |
| Coating-metal, wood | storm) |
| Concrete forms | Wire insulations |
| Concrete mixes | |
| Curtain walls | **Interior** |
| Doors (prime and storm) | Acoustical panels |
| Expansion joints | Adhesives |
| Facings | Baseboards |
| Flashings | Cabinets |
| Gaskets | Ceilings |
| Glazings | Conduits |
| Grilles | Counter tops |
| Hardwares | Coverings |
| Illuminating panels | Decorative panels |
| Lighting fixtures | Drawers |
| Louvers | Ducts |
| Moisture barriers | Electrical fixtures |
| Mortar mixes | Floorings |
| Paints | Gaskets |
| Panels | Graphic arts |
| Pipes | Grilles |
| Railings | Hardwares |
| Rain system-gutters, | Insulations |
| downspout, etc. | Light diffusers |
| Roof edging, panels | Molding, trims |
| Safety and thermal glasses | Paints |
| Screens | Panelings |
| Sealants | Partitions |
| Sheathings | Pipe fittings |
| Shingles | Plaster backings |
| Shutters | Plumbing fixtures |
| Sidings | Railings |
| Signs | Sealants |
| Skylights | Shower stalls |
| Stuccos | Stair treads |
| Sun shields | Tanks |
| Swimming pools | Tile-floor, wall, ceilings |
| Tapes | Vapor barriers |
| Tool sheds | Wall coverings |
| Topping-walk, driveways | Wire insulations |

TABLE 16-3.  Construction Market (in Billions of Dollars) [a]

| Type of construction | 1950 | 1955 | 1960 | 1964 | 1965 [b] |
|---|---|---|---|---|---|
| Private | 26.7 | 34.8 | 38.1 | 45.9 | 47.2 |
| Residential buildings (non-farm) | 18.1 | 21.9 | 21.7 | 26.5 | 27.3 |
| New housing units | 15.6 | 18.2 | 16.4 | 20.6 | — |
| Additions and alterations | 2.4 | 3.3 | — | — | — |
| Nonhousekeeping | 0.2 | 0.3 | 0.9 | 1.5 | — |
| Nonresidential buildings | 3.9 | 7.6 | 10.1 | 13.0 | 13.4 |
| Industrial | 1.1 | 2.4 | 2.9 | 3.3 | — |
| Office buildings and warehouses | 0.5 | 1.3 | 2.1 | 3.2 | — |
| Stores, restaurants and garages | 0.9 | 1.9 | 2.1 | 2.4 | — |
| Religious | 0.4 | 0.7 | 1.0 | 1.0 | — |
| Educational | 0.3 | 0.5 | 0.6 | 0.7 | — |
| Hospital and institutional | 0.3 | 0.4 | 0.6 | 1.4 | — |
| Social and recreational | 0.2 | 0.2 | 0.7 | 0.5 | — |
| Others | 0.1 | 0.2 | 0.2 | 0.4 | — |
| Farm dwellings and construction | 1.5 | 1.4 | 1.3 | 1.2 | 1.2 |
| Public utilities (telephone, RR, electric, etc.) | 3.0 | 3.8 | 4.6 | 4.9 | 5.0 |
| Others | 0.1 | 0.2 | 0.3 | 0.3 | 0.3 |
| Public | 6.9 | 11.7 | 15.9 | 20.0 | 20.6 |
| Residential buildings | 0.3 | 0.3 | 0.7 | 0.8 | — |
| Nonresidential buildings | 2.4 | 4.2 | 4.8 | 6.2 | — |
| Industrial | 0.2 | 0.7 | 0.4 | 0.4 | — |
| Educational | 1.1 | 2.4 | 2.8 | 3.3 | — |
| Others | 1.0 | 1.0 | 1.6 | 2.4 | — |
| Military facilities | 0.2 | 1.3 | 1.4 | 1.0 | — |
| Highways | 2.1 | 3.9 | 5.4 | 7.2 | — |
| Sewer and water systems | 0.7 | 1.1 | 1.5 | 2.3 | — |
| Others | 1.1 | 1.0 | 2.0 | 1.5 | — |
| Grand Total | 33.6 | 46.5 | 53.9 | 65.8 | 67.8 |

[a] Additional cost for maintenance and repair: 1950—12.1, 1955—16.0; 1960—19.2, 1964—21.0 estimate and 1965—22.0 estimate.
[b] Estimates

building construction costs were $67.8 billion, with maintenance and repair estimates varying from $16 to $22 billion. Of a total 250 billion lb in building materials put to use in 1964, 2.4 billion lb were plastics; 138 billion lb, cement; 26 billion lb, steel; 13 billion lb, asphalt; 1.6 billion lb, aluminum; 31 billion board ft, wood; 7.7 billion, bricks; 2.1 billion sq ft, glass; and asbestos, copper and rubber. Plastics took a respectable small part of the Bureau of Labor's estimate of 48 to 55 cents figure used in every construction dollar for materials and equipment. Total construction expenditure is approximately 11% of the gross national product.

Residential building represents nearly 40% of the dollar value of all new construction. Each new home is said to offer a potential of an additional $3,000 for allied purchases, including plastics, during the first year of residence.

Plastics can be made to combine different desired characteristics or blend with other materials to produce useful composites. The major and most important growth of plastics is expected to be in the composite building shell of walls, roof, partitions and floors, now representing $\frac{1}{3}$ of all plastics used. They will serve three basic functions: structural, semistructural and nonstructural components. The least use of plastics is in structural members, even though many people superficially assume that building construction materials only encompass structural members. Major use is in nonstructural components, where plastics can complement or be joined with structures. Plastics provide many functional needs: insulation, durability, beauty, dimensional stability and corrosion resistance.

Growth will continue in established markets, such as flooring, coatings, decorative panels, sealants, interior finishes, siding, electrical and pipe. Extensive use of Dow Corning Corporation's and General Electric Company's silicone sealants in curtain walls this year (1967) is a typical example. New markets are developing: roofing, exterior walls, heat insulation and light transmission. Percentage consumption by application this year appears to be similar to last year 23% of total in surface coatings, 20% in flooring, 20% in wire insulation, 10% in heat insulation and vapor barriers, 9% in plywood and 8% in pipe. By type of plastic, consumption has been 27% vinyl, 16% polyethylene (PE), 12% phenolic, 10% alkyd and 10% styrene. Other reports show 210 million lb of phenolic and melamine went into plywood construction; 205 million lb of phenolic, polystyrene (PS) and PE into heat insulation and vapor barriers; 200 million lb of polyvinyl chloride (PVC), acrylonitrile butadiene styrene (ABS), etc. into pipe and fittings; 90 million lb of acrylic, polyester and PVC into glazing and skylights, and 70 million lb of melamine and phenolic into decorative laminates.

### 1. Walls

Maintenance-free exterior walls are growing in popularity. Solid or coated siding using PVC, acrylic, polyvinylidene fluoride ($PVF_2$) and polyvinyl fluoride (PVF) overcomes conventional wall shortcomings:

necessity of repeated painting, corrosion, moisture absorption, or denting. B. F. Goodrich Chemical Company has positive results from over 10 years testing of extruded PVC siding. Monsanto Company continues to expand its use of solid PVC siding. DuPont's PVF in the past year has vastly extended its use as a protective coating. Pennsalt Chemicals Corporation is extending the service life of $PVF_2$ covering to protect wood and metal siding. In addition, Rohm and Haas Company, a supplier of exterior facings for over 15 years has had wide acceptance in the non residential building markets.

Data assembled by Monsanto Company provide interesting correlation of plastics with competitive materials used for residential walls. Plastics were used in $1\frac{1}{2}\%$ of the $2\frac{1}{2}$ billion sq ft erected in 1964, and estimates are that 3–5% of 3 billion sq ft in 1970 will be plastic. Steel follows the same percentages. Brick and masonry will remain 29%. Wood will go from 33–30%, aluminum 23–25%, asbestos 9–8% and other materials will sink from 3–2%. With success in marketing strategy and costs, the plastic wall prediction for 1970 could be over 10%.

By a slight stretch of the imagination, a potential of one billion pounds of new business in curtain walls exists, without including the futuristic and popular shapes viewed at the New York World's Fair or in the Apollo spacecraft assembly building. Plastic facings of acrylic, PVC reinforced plastics, and foam cores of PS and polyurethane (PU) are now approaching wide acceptance.

### 2. Windows

After 10 years of service, PVC in window sash has definitely put itself in an established market. PVC is accounting for a sizable poundage in sliding tracks, meeting rails, jamb-liners, frames, weatherstrips and glazing beads. Some of the large wood window companies are now extruding and laminating PVC on their wood window parts. Even though the complete economically feasible all-plastic window has not been designed, plastic has penetrated this market. B. F. Goodrich Chemical Company estimates that 15 million pounds of rigid PVC were used for windows in 1964.

Unlike window sash, acrylic sheet is replacing glass in troublesome glazing areas. Its combination of breakage resistance and solar control is responsible for its success.

### 3. Floors

In the present soft flooring market of 8 billion sq ft per year, approximately 54% is for replacement. A total of 2.8 billion sq ft or close to 2.5 billion total lb of material includes $\frac{1}{2}$ billion lb of plastics. Rubber and asphalt yielded 1.4 billion sq ft. It is predicted that more PVC will be used if industry continues to significantly improve vinyl's resistance to burning and staining.

The total for hard surface, which includes synthetic fiber carpets, is an additional 2.7 billion sq ft. The 900 million sq ft of wood, stone and terrazzo will give way to plastic compositions, and there is a good possibility that polyester, epoxy and urethane will make substantial inroads. Tile with PVC grid and inlaid ceramic tile has a good market possibility, as it can be installed in much the same way as vinyl tile. An interesting innovation is development of tile using synthetic fiber carpet with vinyl backing.

**a. Vinyl Asbestos Flooring Compounds** (1). Numerous engineering projects exist to ensure that plastic products will perform satisfactorily in its natural (but destructive) environment. An example is the development of a stabilization system for vinyl asbestos compounds to meet different conditions such as heat stability. While this is a requirement for any vinyl stabilizer, the unique processing problems of these compounds require a type that will afford the proper lubricity and will not be the cause of tile imperfections such as blisters. In addition, today's high design standards demand a system which will protect the subtle color shades against heat degradation and provide a tile with the lowest possible water absorption after installation (Table 16-4).

The stability problems encountered with vinyl asbestos flooring are primarily due to the fact that these compounds consist of about 80% of inorganic fillers such as asbestos, calcium carbonates or talcs, and only 20% of binder, which includes vinyl polymers and plasticizers and stabilizers. By far, the material which predominantly controls the type of stability requirements which must be met is the asbestos filler.

As is well known to any compounder of vinyl asbestos formulations, the predominant visual sign of degradation is the development of blue color as the compound is heated. While there has been much speculation as to the reasons for this blue discoloration, it has been generally attributed to the presence of certain iron compounds which are present in the asbestos. The most efficient stabilizers which have been developed over the years have been materials which have had the ability

TABLE 16-4.  Water Absorption Effect of Different Stabilizer Systems in Vinyl Asbestos Flooring Compounds

| | | |
|---|---|---|
| Resin (15% PVAc) | | 40 |
| Limestone | | 90 |
| Asbestos 7R | | 45 |
| Santicizer 160 | | 12 |
| Drapex 6.8 | | 1 |
| $TiO_2$ | | 6 |
| Stabilizer | | 2 |

| Water absorption (% gain) 3 in. x 3 in. tile | Mark HH | Mark 225 | Mark 140 | Mark 178 |
|---|---|---|---|---|
| 1 day | 3.11 | 1.81 | 1.15 | 0.65 |
| 3 days | 3.38 | 2.50 | 1.97 | 1.56 |
| 7 days | 3.41 | 2.88 | 2.10 | 1.75 |

| Growth, cross-mill (%) 3 in. x 3 in. tile | | | | |
|---|---|---|---|---|
| 1 day | 0.78 | 0.47 | 0.16 | 0.08 |
| 3 days | 0.85 | 0.65 | 0.45 | 0.20 |
| 7 days | 0.87 | 0.71 | 0.67 | 0.24 |

Note:

| Polyol types | Nitrogenous types |
|---|---|
| Mark HH | Mark 140 |
| Mark 225 | Mark 178 |

to tie up or chelate these compounds, and, therefore, prevent them from forming the blue byproducts under the conditions of processing. The use of conventional vinyl stabilizer systems (barium-cadmiums or tins), has not proven successful in meeting the stability requirements.

Besides stability problems which can be seen to be the result of processing at high temperatures, there are also problems which are associated with the physical characteristics of these compounds. In order to insure the production of a tile which is free of imperfections, such as blisters and poor surface, it is necessary that the vinyl asbestos compound have excellent adhesion to the calender rolls. While this property can be controlled by processing conditions as well as formulation, the lubricating properties of the stabilizer are an important factor. In most cases, vinyl asbestos compounders desire stabilizers which are nonlubricating. This does not mean that lubricants or lubricating stabilizers are not used, but merely indicates the desire of the compounder to control the lubricity of his compound in his own way.

In addition to the problems encountered during processing, the formulator of vinyl asbestos compounds must be assured that his compound will perform well after its installation. VA tile manufacturers are constantly aware of the potential problem of dimensional stability of the tile after installation. This problem is associated with factors such as release of stresses and strains introduced during processing, as well as susceptibility to moisture. The latter problem is a most serious one, especially when one considers that a great deal of vinyl asbestos is installed below grade where moisture conditions are most severe. It is well known that VA compounds will absorb relatively high amounts of water, depending upon formulation composition, as well as processing conditions. This absorption of water leads to tile growth as well as curl and distortion of the product. This property is probably most severe because of the high surface areas present in these compounds, and is primarily due to the low binder content and high levels of large surface area materials such as asbestos, as well as the great porosity of the compound. While there is no question that all formulation ingredients contribute to water absorption, the stabilizer also has a pronounced effect.

The development of any stabilizer system must always include exhaustive testing of the effect it has on the water absorptivity of the compound. This property has probably become as important as the heat stability requirements of the compounds, especially since the VA stabilizers now available provide heat stability which is greatly superior to that obtained with stabilizers which were available a few years ago (Table 16-5).

Another problem mentioned before has been the prevention of blisters during the processing of the compound. This problem has been associated with air-entrapment during processing, evolution of $CO_2$ from carbonate fillers due to reaction with HCl evolved from degraded polymer, and many other factors.

**(1) Effect of Resin.** The effect of varying acetate content as well as the use of a homopolymer resin is not readily seen with the normal heat stability tests. Of course, under actual processing conditions, the use of lower acetate content resins or homopolymer resins will necessitate higher processing temperatures and will result in increased heat stability requirements. More interesting is the effect of acetate content on the water absorption characteristics.

**(2) Effect of Stabilizer.** The art of stabilization of vinyl asbestos compounds has advanced rapidly over the past four or five years and

TABLE 16-5. Water Absorption Effect of Varying Ratios of Asbestos to Limestone in Vinyl Asbestos Flooring Compounds

| | |
|---|---|
| Resin (15% PVAc) | 40 |
| Santicizer 160 | 12 |
| Drapex 6.8 | 1 |
| TiO$_2$ | 6 |
| Mark 140 | 8 |

| Water absorption (% gain) 3 in. x 3 in. tile | Asbestos 7R | (135) | Asbestos 7R Limestone | (90) (45) | Asbestos 7R Limestone | (67) (68) |
|---|---|---|---|---|---|---|
| 1 day | 2.06 | | 1.41 | | 1.16 | |
| 3 days | 3.06 | | 2.11 | | 1.85 | |
| 7 days | 3.08 | | 2.30 | | 2.05 | |
| | Asbestos 7R Limestone | (45) (90) | Limestone | (135) | | |
| 1 day | 1.15 | | 1.84 | | | |
| 3 days | 1.97 | | 3.64 | | | |
| 7 days | 2.10 | | 3.63 | | | |

| Growth, cross-mill (%) 3 in. x 3 in. tile | Asbestos 7R | (135) | Asbestos 7R Limestone | (90) (45) | Asbestos 7R Limestone | (67) (68) |
|---|---|---|---|---|---|---|
| 1 day | 0.26 | | 0.13 | | 0.14 | |
| 3 days | 0.67 | | 0.44 | | 0.41 | |
| 7 days | 0.91 | | 0.61 | | 0.59 | |
| | Asbestos 7R Limestone | (45) (90) | Limestone | (135) | | |
| 1 day | 0.16 | | 0.25 | | | |
| 3 days | 0.45 | | 0.75 | | | |
| 7 days | 0.67 | | 2.24 | | | |

has reached the point today where long term stability, as measured by the prevention of the typical blue color, is not a serious problem. Processors today are more concerned with the attainment of good initial color as well as the retention of it for as long as possible. Historically, the first successful vinyl asbestos stabilizers were lead compounds, with lead salycylate being an effective one. While these type stabilizers allowed processing of the early VA compounds, the colors obtained with them were generally pink rather than the more severe blue, and the danger of subsequent sulfide staining was always present. Immediately following these stabilizers, systems based generally on polyol compounds were developed and patented by stabilizer manufacturers. These materials were markedly superior to the older lead systems in the areas of initial color and control of initial color, and were greatly responsible for the ability of the vinyl asbestos compounder to produce the highly stylized products which are presently available. While these stabilizers met most of the requirements of the VA compound, the development of new stabilizers continued and resulted in the types of compounds which are presently being used by most manufacturers of VA tile. Patent applications on these materials are in the final stages of prosecution, and more detailed disclosure of their compositions can be made when they are issued. These stabilizers have met the requirements of stability, processing, low water absorption, and economy, and generally represent the most efficient systems available today. Work is, of course, being continued in this area, and will no doubt result in even more efficient and economical systems.

**(3) Effect of Asbestos.** The role of asbestos has been stressed throughout this paper, and it is evident that the stability of the compound is dependent on the type and concentration of it. Water absorption is also affected by the asbestos, with one important factor being the relative surface areas of the different fibers.

**4. Roofing.** With a combination of engineering, cost consideration and imagination, the expected market by 1970 could be stretched to $\frac{1}{2}$ billion lb principally in nonresidential buildings. Composite materials incorporating plastics are gradually evolving to meet various destructive environmental problems. As these are developed, they can be expected to sharply increase total plastics poundage in roofing.

Present yearly statistics show $2\frac{1}{2}$ billion sq ft of roofing in new residential homes, one billion in nonresidential construction, and equal quantities in renovation. PVC, PE, PS, PU, choroprene, polyisobutylene, reinforced plastics, PVF and $PVF_2$ coatings, films and sheets are being used to provide weather resistance, heat and electrical insulation, corrosion resistance, ease of maintenance and appearance. Use of chlorinated or chlorosulfonated PE are expected to continue to exceed each of the other plastics used. Moisture barriers, foam insulation, flashing, gutter, and drains are current applications.

The excellent sunlight and impact resistance of acrylic has expanded its use in large skylights, transparent geodesic domes and indoor sports arenas. A specialty application for acrylic was the new baseball stadium of the Houston Astros. The dome consists of 4596 skylights. This 9.5 acre stadium contains almost $7 million of plastics including acrylic panels, PVC weather stripping and coating of steel. An architecturally significant structure composed only of a concrete frame and acrylic sheet in-fills, is the Denver botanical gardens. Four by 12

ft panels using PVF film on the outside surface to provide additional
weather resistance have been used in the world's largest building at
Cape Kennedy. The NASA 52-story, 125 million cu ft building, with
many of these plastic panels on the side walls, will be the assembly
area for Saturn V rockets and the Apollo spacecraft. These 400 sq
ft of panels were hoisted to the roof by helicopter.

**a. Assessing Durability of Plastic Roofs** (2). In recent years a
large number of flexible roof coverings have been developed from
polymers and synthetic rubbers. These coverings are lightweight,
highly elastic, highly reflective, and easily cleaned of radioactive fallout. They are used mainly where more conventional roofing materials
may not be able to perform, as on roofs of unusual contour. Considerable interest is being shown in the properties of these new materials,
especially their durability. As roofs are directly exposed to solar radiation, their resistance to photo-oxidation, a measure of their durability,
is of prime concern.

Recently, a study was initiated at the NBS Institute for Applied
Technology (U.S. Department of Commerce) to determine the photo-
oxidation resistance of some plastics and to investigate the usefulness
of a recently developed colorimetric method of measuring photochemical degradation of polyesters. The results of this study indicate that the
colorimetric method studied should be a valuable means of rapidly
assessing the relative stability of polymeric coatings exposed to sunlight.

The colorimetric method is based on the reaction of $N$, $N$-dimethyl-
$p$-phenylenediame (DMPDA) with the photooxidation products that
form on the surface of a wide range of plastics. By determining the
amount of DMPDA that reacts with these products, the degree of
photo-oxidation of the plastic can be assessed. This method is more
sensitive than methods that involve the complete specimen, as both
photo-oxidation and the DMPDA reaction are surface reactions only.

Seven commercial coatings—five liquid-applied coatings and two
prefabricated sheets—were examined. The sheets were poly(vinyl-
chloride) (PVC) and poly(vinyl-fluoride) (PVF); the liquids were
acrylic emulsion (Ac), butyl-rubber emulsion (BR), chlorosulfonated
polyethylene solution (CSP), poly(vinyl-chloride-acetate) solution
(PVCA), and silicone rubber solution (SR). Of these, BR, PVC, and
PVCA were not specifically formulated for roofing use.

The liquid-applied materials were cured on glass strips into specimens 0.005–0.007 in. thick. Sheets of PVC and PVF, respectively

0.100 in. and 0.002 in. thick, were mounted on glass strips, also. Samples of each plastic were exposed to solar and carbon-arc radiation.

In the colorimetric method, a known amount of DMPDA in a benzene-methanol solution is placed in a container with the plastic specimen. The container is shaken for two hours, after which the specimen is removed.

During shaking, the DMPDA reacts with the plastic, changing the color of both the plastic and the solution. The irradiated specimens produce greater color changes than the unexposed specimens, with the colors ranging from yellow to brown to greenish brown.

Three techniques of judging the extent of the DMPDA reaction with a photooxidized plastic were found to be useful: (1) Determination of the amount of DMPDA reacted, (2) measurement of the DMPDA reagent solution color, and (3) measurement of specimen surface darkening.

In the first technique, samples of the reagent solution are diluted in methanol and a buffer, and treated with benzoyl peroxide. The peroxide oxidizes any unreacted DMPDA, causing the diluted solution to turn pink in color. The intensity of this color, determined by the absorbance at 520 m$\mu$, indicates the amount of DMPDA that was left in solution. The difference between the known amount of DMPDA originally in the solution and that left in solution is the amount that reacted with the plastic.

In the second technique, the change in the absorbance at 410 m$\mu$ of undiluted samples of the DMPDA reagent solution is measured. This indicates the amount of photooxidation products that dissolved in solution and reacted with the DMPDA.

In the third technique, color measurements with a tristimulus differential colorimeter are made of the specimens in three conditions of exposure and DMPDA treatment: (1) unexposed and untreated, (2) unexposed and treated, and (3) exposed and treated. The first condition gives a base value for comparison with the others. The difference between conditions 1 and 2, if any, is subtracted from the difference between 1 and 3 to show the effect of exposure alone. Average values of darkening were calculated and show a direct relationship to exposure time.

The three techniques showed good agreement in ranking the plastics as to degree of photooxidation. Assessment of the DMPDA reaction generally agreed with the amount of darkening caused by exposure. The seven roofing materials examined were generally rated in order of durability as follows, beginning with the least stable: PVCA, PVC, CSP, BR, Ac, SR, and PVF.

## 5. Pipe and Plumbing (3)

Pipe and plumbing fixtures have started on the road to providing the plastic industry with a large market for ABS, PE, PVC, polyvinyl dichloride (PVDC) and polyester (Table 16-6). Plastic pipe has become an increasingly active competitor of metallic piping. Its growth is the result of chemical resistance, ease of fabrication, low density, low cost and ease of handling. Like any other products, it has limitations such as temperature limitations for the thermoplastics and restriction to lower operating pressures for certain thermoplastics. The total U.S. pipe market is of the order of $4 billion per year, of which plastic piping accounts for only between 1 and 2%, indicating a significant potential.

Plastic piping is a good growth market for petrochemical products. It is expected that use of plastic piping in the United States will grow at a rate of 15% per year, twice as fast as the growth of the chemical industry itself. This market would undoubtedly grow at a faster rate if building codes are rewritten, or new standards adopted. Recently, there have been encouraging signs in this direction with code writing groups.

TABLE 16-6. Thermoplastic Pipe Production—(Millions of Pounds) [a]

|  | 1957 | 1961 | 1962 | 1963 | 1964 | 1965 est. | 1970 est. |
|---|---|---|---|---|---|---|---|
| ABS | 0 | 5 | 10 | 12 | 18 | 22 | 45 |
| Polyethylene | 35 | 43 | 49 | 59 | 58 | 64 | 95 |
| PVC | 6 | 15 | 18 | 30 | 43 | 56 | 130 |
| Rubber-modified styrene | 7 | 10 | 16 | 20 | 25 | 28 | 45 |
| Other [a] | 6 | 2 | 3 | 3 | 7 | 10 | 30 |
| Total pipe | 54 | 75 | 96 | 124 | 151 | 180 | 345 |
| Fittings | 5 | 8 | 14 | 16 | 18 | 20 | 50 |
| Total | 59 | 83 | 110 | 140 | 169 | 200 | 395 |
| Other Pipe [a] |  |  |  |  |  |  |  |
| Cellulose acetate butyrate |  |  |  |  | 0.3 | 0.3 | 0.1 |
| Polyacetal |  |  |  |  | 1.8 | 2.2 | 3.5 |
| Polyvinyl dichloride |  |  |  |  | 0.6 | 1.2 | 9.0 |
| Polypropylene |  |  |  |  | 0.2 | 0.3 | 15.0 |
| Other |  |  |  |  | 0.2 | 0.3 | 2.4 |
| Total |  |  |  |  | 6.9 | 10.0 | 30.0 |

[a] Source: Plastics Pipe Institute.

Plastic pipe sales in the United States for 1964 were estimated to be $100 million at the consumer level, or about 170 million lb. The market is expected to reach 500 million lb in the early 1970's, though future growth rate is dependent on increasing acceptance by code writing groups (Table 16-7).

Plastic piping is essentially a local business, as a result of high costs for shipping. Also, it is a simple matter for anyone to enter the business; equipment is relatively inexpensive, and complete technology is supplied by resin suppliers. Consequently, profit margins in the industry are low since the small operator with low overhead can keep prices at a low level.

While any plastic material, irrespective of its chemical composition and character, may be made into pipe or tubing, by far the greatest amount of pipe is made from thermoplastics which are adaptable to extrusion processes. Specialty pipe is made in small amounts from thermosetting materials such as phenolic and polyester, but commercial pipe is made from polyethylene, polyvinyl chloride, acrylonitrile butadiene copolymers, and acrylonitrile butadiene styrene types of "alloys." Specialty tubing in relatively small amounts is made of acrylates and acrylate copolymers, as well as other transparent materials.

In general, plastic pipe offers advantages over metal pipe because of its resistance to widely varying conditions, of environment, light weight, relatively low cost, ease and economy of installation, self-insulating characteristics, minimum solid-deposit tendency, and low frictional losses. On the other hand, plastic pipe usage is limited to a greater degree than metal pipe, as far as temperature and pressure are concerned. At this stage of development, there is a need for more sound design data on the mechanical and physical properties.

In large tonnage plants for electrorefining and electrowinning copper, manganese, nickel, and zinc, the problems of corrosion associated with sulfate electrolytes containing appreciable quantities of sulfuric acid were met in 1940 by utilization of lead pipe, lead linings on tanks, lead open channels or launders, lead pumps, and valves. In these plants, very large volumes are pumped and distributed to individual electrolytic cells. Lead was useful because it resisted corrosion as a result of the formation of insoluble lead sulfate on its surface, but with crystallizing electrolytes, any deposition of crystals in the pipe caused adherence to the inside surface and sooner or later restricted the flow through the pipe. It was difficult to clean the lead, and repairs were ordinarily made by chopping out a section of the pipeline, remelting the lead, and reforming the pipe.

**a. Polyvinyl Chloride Pipe.** A few years later, plastic pipe of various sorts came into experimental use. There was interest in these because they were lighter in weight, required less support, were less costly, and could be handled in much the same way as lead pipe, either by solvent joining or by welding. Polyvinyl chloride and polyethylene aroused the greatest interest. By 1950, particularly in manganese electrowinning, which went through a whole series of plant additions as a result of increased commercial demand for the electrolytic metal, each succeeding plant addition saw replacement of lead pipe in sizes up to 6 in. by rigid polyvinyl chloride, lead-lined launders by heavily resin-laminated plywood construction, lead manifolds by polyvinyl and polyvinyl chloride piping, and discharge and waste by polyethylene, often in lengths of 600 ft to a mile or more.

In the building of an electrolytic tin refinery in Brazil, metal piping of wide variety was not available on an economic basis. As a result, this entire unit involving aromatic sulfonate electrolytes was designed on the basis of PVC piping, PVC sheet-covered launders, PVC covered concrete deposition tanks, PVC valves and offtake lines as well as treatment tanks and pumping systems. The complete plant has been inspected every two years, and after four inspections needs no replacement save that caused by structural breakage when a lift truck was rammed into a portion of the piping system.

Similarly, in zinc electrowinning in nickel and electrorefining, plastic pipe, because it can handle crystallizing liquors, is corrosion resistant, light weight and easily supported and maintained, has replaced metallic piping almost entirely. Exceptions are heat-transfer mechanisms, such as coolers or heating sections, where the plastic pipe will not perform satisfactorily. In heating and cooling systems, the metals have been displaced by resin-impregnated carbon and graphite known as Karbate or Impervite, and by glass.

Following the performance of locally made PVC pigmented extruded pipe in the tin refinery in Brazil, locally made polyvinyl chloride pipe manufactured by a Colombian subsidiary of an American company was employed successfully in the original design of an electrolytic zinc plant in Bogota, Colombia. In this particular case metal piping was difficult to obtain, had to be imported, and was considerably more expensive than PVC. To all intents and purposes, all the piping in the plant for electrolyte solutions and water is PVC with PVC connectors, valves, manifolds, distribution systems, and collecting mechanisms as well as waste disposal pipe. Again, this installation was examined every two

TABLE 16-7. Plastic Pipe End Use—(Millions of Pounds)

| | Acrylonitrile-butadiene-styrene | Poly-ethylene | Polyvinyl chloride | Rubber-modified styrene | Other | Total |
|---|---|---|---|---|---|---|
| **1964:** | | | | | | |
| Water supply and distribution | 1.5 | 49.5 | 20.0 | 0 | 1.4 | 72.4 |
| Oil and gas production | 1.0 | 1.0 | 3.0 | 0 | 4.5 | 9.5 |
| Gas distribution | 3.5 | 0.4 | 3.0 | 0 | 0.3 | 7.2 |
| Electrical conduit | 5.0 | 2.0 | 4.0 | 10.0 | 0 | 21.0 |
| Sewer and drainage | 0 | 0 | 4.0 | 15.0 | 0 | 19.0 |
| Drain, waste, and vent | 7.0 | 0 | 1.5 | 0 | 0 | 8.5 |
| Industrial (process) | 0 | 0.5 | 5.0 | 0 | 0.5 | 6.0 |
| Miscellaneous (including inventory) | 0 | 4.6 | 2.5 | 0 | 0.2 | 7.3 |
| Total | 18.0 | 58.0 | 43.0 | 25.0 | 6.9 | 150.9 |
| **1965:** | | | | | | |
| Water supply and distribution | 1.5 | 54.0 | 23.5 | 0 | 1.5 | 80.5 |
| Oil and gas production | 1.5 | 1.3 | 4.0 | 0 | 4.9 | 11.7 |
| Gas distribution | 4.0 | 1.5 | 4.0 | 0 | 0.3 | 9.8 |
| Electrical conduit | 6.0 | 4.0 | 5.5 | 11.0 | 0 | 26.5 |
| Sewer and drainage | 0 | 0 | 6.0 | 17.0 | 0 | 23.0 |
| Drain, waste, and vent | 9.0 | 0 | 3.0 | 0 | 0 | 12.0 |
| Industrial (process) | 0 | 0.5 | 7.0 | 0 | 1.0 | 8.5 |
| Miscellaneous (including inventory) | 0 | 2.7 | 3.0 | 0 | 1.3 | 7.0 |
| Total | 22.0 | 64.0 | 56.0 | 28.0 | 9.0 | 179.0 |

1970: (Estimated)

| | | | | | | |
|---|---|---|---|---|---|---|
| Water supply and distribution | 2.0 | 68.0 | 55.1 | 0 | 7.0 | 132.1 |
| Oil and gas production | 2.0 | 4.0 | 8.0 | 0 | 8.0 | 22.0 |
| Gas distribution | 6.0 | 10.0 | 13.9 | 0 | 2.1 | 32.0 |
| Electrical conduit | 10.0 | 9.0 | 11.0 | 15.0 | 0 | 45.0 |
| Sewer and drainage | 0 | 0 | 12.0 | 30.0 | 0 | 42.0 |
| Drain, waste, and vent | 25.0 | 0 | 10.0 | 0 | 0 | 35.0 |
| Industrial (process) | 0 | 1.0 | 15.0 | 0 | 7.5 | 23.5 |
| Miscellaneous (including inventory) | 0 | 3.0 | 5.0 | 0 | 5.4 | 13.4 |
| Total | 45.0 | 95.0 | 130.0 | 45.0 | 30.0 | 345.0 |

years, and after the third two-year examination was still performing satisfactorily.

Meanwhile, in U.S. and Canadian plants of similar character, there has been extensive replacement of metal piping for circulation systems, distribution systems, manifolds, water systems, disposal lines, and the like.

The competitive effect on metal pipe, particularly steel, has been such that these industries have sought to protect their piping market by the acquisition of plastic pipe manufacturers, distributors, and the like. This has been as important in oil-country piping, where hundreds of miles of tubular goods are involved.

Rigid PVC pipe goes principally into the eastern market for processing industries, brewing, vinegar, chemical and other processing industries. The high-impact type is directed toward the western market for oil field, gas, and water piping.

Rigid PVC pipe competes in oil fields for the disposal of brine and for crude oil transmission; it is immune to galvanic corrosison and highly resistant to both salt water and crude oil. Rigid vinyl pipe is useful where soil is corrosive and paraffin accumulation on pipe walls is a problem for conventional pipe.

The installation of 15,000 ft of rigid vinyl pipe by a public utility company in 2 psi gas service lines was the start of large-scale use of rigid vinyl for such lines. Part of this pipe was pulled through metal lines which had failed; the remainder was buried directly. Results with both methods were good.

In another application, natural gas distribution services containing some 10,000 ft of rigid vinyl pipe were installed in Illinois by the Illinois Power Company. The system used ¾ in. pipe in home connections. The medium-wall pipe provided more impact strength than thin-walled pipe at little additional cost. The vinyl pipe was installed at depths below two feet. Variations in soil temperature permitted the pipe to be laid straight when required and made snaking the pipe, to allow for expansion and contraction, necessary only on the longer runs. Sand was hauled to the job and used for backfilling at points of connection to main lines, service risers, and wherever else necessary. This assured full support of the vinyl pipe at all joints to prevent sagging and consequent strain which might cause breakage. A 2 ft cross was welded to the steel house connection riser as a stabilizer to prevent twisting and to furnish support for the riser. The cross was buried below the surface of the earth where the solid ground holds it securely.

Irrigation and water service lines account for a significant portion of all rigid vinyl pipe produced. Utility companies install rigid PVC where they have to bring in water from distant sources; underground sprinkling systems are of rigid vinyl. In Florida, hotel swimming-pool piping was converted from metal to PVC to prevent saltwater corrosion. One hotel employed PVC in its air-conditioning water lines to prevent corrosion and also to save weight on top of the building. Rigid PVC pipe also has been installed in a 15 mile irrigation system in an avocado grove in California, replacing metal pipe which corroded rapidly when buried in continuously moist soil.

**b. Acrylonitrile-Butadiene-Styrene Pipe.** An important factor in rigid thermoplastic pipe is ABS pipe. ABS polymers are blends of resins and rubbers containing acrylonitrile, butadiene, and styrene. By 1957, over 8,000 miles of pipe fabricated from ABS materials had been installed in a wide variety of applications demanding corrosion resistance, impact resistance, and low overall cost. ABS has long-term working hoop stress in pipe of 1200 psi. The impact strength more than fills the requirements for the job. Its heat distortion temperature (under stress) has enabled it to be used in some applications at temperatures as high as 160–170°F. The chemical resistance has also been a factor. ABS plastics withstand deterioration in corrosive environments. Finally, the cost of installation and resulting overall favorable economics has played a role in bringing about this mileage record.

One 36,000 ft, 2 in. saltwater line had been operating successfully for six years. Perhaps there are refinery uses for salt water—for example, cooling water in those plants located near the ocean.

Of the more than 8,000 miles of ABS plastic pipe, over 3,000 miles had been used to transport natural gas. Much of this was in 2 in. thin-wall pipe carrying gas at pressures up to 50 psi to power irrigation pumps. In one domestic gas installation, supplying natural gas for a development of 200 new homes, the installed cost was less than that for steel. Here 4 in. mains and 1 in. and 1½ in. service lines were involved.

Since 1948, the Stickney Works of the Metropolitan Sanitary District of Greater Chicago has been replacing the thick-walled, non-ferrous piping on its 98 filters with ABS plastic pipe. By 1957, over 80,000 ft of plastic pipe handled waste from the west-southwest Chicago area, which includes not only a huge population but the stockyards as well. The lines carry the ferric chloride effluent (about 6–7% concentration) from the sewage sludge filters at room temperature and 16–20 in. vacuum.

A large water filtration plant has been using 2 in. ABS pipe to transport an activated carbon slurry. In this same plant, ¾ in. pipe is carrying 25% hydrofluosilicic acid at 60 psi and ambient temperatures. A 4 in. line carries ferrous sulfate solution.

In a rare earth extraction plant, 2 in. and 4 in. ABS lines have been operating since 1955 carrying dilute sulfuric acid and extracted salts at temperatures up to 140°F. In this same plant ¾ in. lines carry dry ammonia gas at 6 psi and room temperature.

Chlorine gas has been carried successfully in ABS pipe for as long as six years. Line sizes have varied from ½ in. to 3 in. in size and have operated at ambient temperature conditions with pressures as high as 80–90 psi.

ABS plastics have been developed with improved long-term hoop stress. This is the tensile value that counts in pipe. The long-term hoop stress is about 3,200 psi when the time to failure is plotted against hoop stress and extrapolated to 100,000 hr on a log-log plot. This is more than 2½ times the 1,200 psi Type 1 ABS.

Manufacturers of ABS plastic pipe and fittings (and their raw-materials suppliers) are eyeing the $250-million drain, waste and vent (DWV) pipe market, with the recent inclusion of an ABS/DWV Commercial Standard in the Basic Building Code of the Building Conference of America, Inc. The picture is not completely rosy, however, since most states have not given their official blessings to ABS pipe in DWV service.

**c. Other Plastic Pipe.** *1.* Polyvinylchloride drain, waste and vent pipe with an inspection port that simplifies cleaning and maintenance is now being extruded by Technical Machinery Corporation. In addition to the development of the inspection port, TMC's PVC pipe offers the lightweight, nonthreading, chemical-sealing benefits of plastic pipe. TMC's pipe can be extruded in any length or profile in sizes ½ in. O.D. to 4½ in. O.D. According to the firm, a pipe extrusion system with extruder take-offs, molds can be installed in less than 10 weeks at a cost of about $35,000 for 4½ in. O.D. pipe.

*2.* Rigid, vinyl pipe is replacing leaking metal pipe which carries water to housing developments in Saudi Arabian desert regions. According to the Arabian American Oil Company, desert salt has had a deleterious affect on metal pipe so that B.F. Goodrich Koroseal vinyl piping is now being installed as needed in the cities of Dhahran, Ras Tanura and Abqaiq. The vinyl pipe weighs only a fourth as much as its metal counterpart, ranges from ¾–2 in diameter, and attaches readily to the existing metal system or to vinyl.

**d. Plastic Pipe Testing Program** (4). The public health testing of plastic pipe by the National Sanitation Foundation developed out of research performed for the Plastics Industry by the Foundation, at the request of State Sanitary Engineers. This three-year research study completed in 1955 on thermoplastics proved the public health safety of plastic pipe for drinking water uses. Soon after the completion of the research, it was recognized by the plastics industry, public health and water works officials, and other governmental agencies that a program of evaluation and certification of plastics for potable water systems on a continuing basis was essential. At the outset the evaluation and certification program related solely to the toxicological and organoleptic evaluation of the plastic pipe. Later the physical qualities of plastics were included in the test requirements.

The National Sanitation Foundation is a nonprofit, nongovernmental, voluntary health agency. Its Headquarters are at the School of Public Health, University of Michigan, Ann Arbor, Michigan. Its fundamental purpose being research and education in the field of environment. The research studies, standards and programs of the Foundation are well recognized and accepted by both public health officials, manufacturers and users across the nation. It is fundamentally a public health organization and its standards and programs establish minimum public health requirements in many areas of activity.

An appropriate certification insigna (nSf) has been developed and copyrighted by the Foundation and is utilized to identify National Sanitation Foundation Approved plastic pipe and fittings for potable water use.

The nSf insignia must appear in the markings of approved plastic pipe at intervals not to exceed every 24 in. along the pipe. A typical marking on approved plastic pipe must include the following:

| Pipe size | Type material and des. stress | Pressure psi | Commer. stand. No. | Mfgs. trade name | Code for identif. of mat. | nSf seal |
|---|---|---|---|---|---|---|
| Example: | | | | | | |
| 2 in. | PVC1120 | 200 psi | CS256–63 | Fancy | A452 | nSf |

Before the nSf insignia can be used on plastic pipe by an extruder of pipe or a molder of fittings it is necessary that the basic thermoplastic materials (resins and/or compounds) produced by materials suppliers be tested to assure their public health safety and suitability from a design stress standpoint for pressure pipe application. Approved polyethylene compounds, for example, are required to contain small quantities of trace elements (innocuous chemicals) which may be identified spectrographically by the Testing Laboratory. This technique enables the Testing Laboratory to identify polyethylene pipe to which off-grade materials or unsafe ingredients may have been added.

Samples of plastic pipe and plastics materials are collected by the Testing Laboratory Staff from the pipe manufacturers plant or point of distribution, warehouses, or installation sites. All such product sampling is carried out on a random basis by the Testing Laboratory Staff at unannounced periodic intervals. Health officials, government agencies, and customers who have purchased plastic pipe, also submit samples of plastic pipe to the Testing Laboratory for identification and for routine testing.

The toxicological and organoleptic testing is performed on samples of aggressive drinking water which have been exposed to specific quantities of plastic to assure maximum extraction of chemicals from the plastic. The extraction exposures are conducted at temperatures of 100°F over a period of three days and then chemical and spectographic analyses are performed to determine the limits of chemical extraction into the drinking water. The limits of chemical contamination or extraction into drinking water are set forth in the Drinking Water Standards of the U. S. Public Health Service. The Drinking Water Standards, No. 956, 1962 Edition, is available from the U. S. Government Printing Office, Washington, D. C. All plastic pipe and fittings authorized to carry the nSf insignia are produced from thermoplastic materials conforming with the chemical limitations set forth in this Drinking Water Standards. The various tests are performed using the techniques and procedures set forth in Standard Methods for the Examination of Water, Sewage, and Industrial Wastes, 1960 Edition, as published by the American Public Health Association.

Since physical standards for plastics have not been established by the American Water Works Association, the Public Health and Industry Advisory Committees to the National Sanitation Foundation have recommended that the Commercial Standards of the U. S. Department of Commerce be utilized by the Testing Laboratory to establish the physical properties of plastic pipe. The ASTM tests set forth in the Commercial Standards for dimension and tolerances, quick burst, sustained pressure test (1000 hr), environmental cracking, and chemical resistance, are carried out by the technical staff of the laboratory.

In order to identify quality Drain-Waste-Vent pipe fittings, the National Sanitation Foundation in cooperation with the plastics industry, public health and user groups, established a certification program. DWV pipe and fittings are being tested and certified by the Testing Laboratory as complying with Commercial Standards CS-270-65 covering acrylonitrile-butadiene-styrene (ABS) plastic drain, waste & vent pipe and fittings, and CS272-65, for polyvinyl chloride (PVC). All NSF approved DWV pipe must be marked at least every 24 in. with the following insignia: (nSf-DWV). Each fitting must carry the same marking.

All such DWV pipe must be marked on two sides 180 degrees apart or spirally for easy identification at the point of installation. The plastic materials as well as the DWV pipe and fittings are collected by the Testing Laboratory Staff in the same manner as products for potable water applications. The ASTM Tests specified in Commercial Standards as well as additional tests agreed upon by the public health and industry advisory committees are performed by the Laboratory to permit certification and approval by the National Sanitation Foundation.

## C. The Architect Approach

Breakdown in communications between the building industry and plastic manufacturer probably accounts for a large amount of lost motion and dollars. Perhaps another major cause is the pure sales approach within any industry which, in many cases, can delay technical progress.

Architects and builders desire factual data on products. However, their standards or codes only identify the composition of the end item, with no performance data. In most cases, the plastics were never subjected to engineering analysis. This situation is not new to the engineering community, where patience, time and/or money resolves the problem.

It has been stated that architecture as a profession has often stood in the way of progress. Being a learned profession, it generally looked to the past for knowledge and inspiration. Although most people have an inherent resistance to change, there are always enlightened architects, builders and consumers who have the courage to overcome traditional beliefs and the foresight to anticipate new developmental trends.

Architects and builders do exist who foresee plastics as a major building material and represent a means to provide the building block or modular construction concept. The versatility of plastics permits developing single units containing water piping, electrical conduit, heating elements and other services. This building block approach has been used successfully in other industries, but, in most cases, developed due to government or military requirements. Many architects also see that plastics make possible the housewife's dream of a dust-proof construction.

The architect continues to look for a composite product that can be multifunctional. As an example in roofing, the product could perform a part or all of the functions. The roof has to provide structural integrity, temperature and sound insulation, vapor and moisture control, weather resistance, elastic qualities for change in weather, fire protection and aesthetic appeal. The present trend shows all the signs that plastic in film, foam, adhesive, transparent forms and reinforced will be required and used in these composites.

What the architect looks for in any new material has been expressed well by Jack D. Train, associate partner of Skidmore, Owings and Merrill, during the September 1965 American Institute of Architects and Society of Plastics Industry joint meeting at the University of Michigan. The first interest concerns the continuing search for practical, aesthetically pleasing and economically priced buildings. The materials or products are to provide new or better solutions to the myriad problems plaguing the construction industry. The second is that a complete and accurate account of each new material exist. The material is to fit within the manufacturing and installation practices of the present construction industry. The third is the assurance that architects are not left holding the bag when new materials do not perform satisfactorily. The economic situation as to who should be responsible represents a major problem area since legal suits can occur and architects lose prestige.

## D. Research in Plastic Building

From the practical aspect, the limited research now being conducted in building construction is from the materials or product manufacturer. This procedure has its limitations since it does not permit integrating the different disciplines existing in the building industry.

### 1. Academic

Now, progress in the field of research is taking place in various universities and colleges. As an example, Professors Albert G. H.

Dietz and Marvin Goody at the Massachusetts Institute of Technology and Professor Stephen C. Paraskevopoulos at the University of Michigan are actively engaged in directing research programs for the architects.

Professor Goody of MIT has discussed the present and future educational programs. The target is to develop architects with more practical knowledge of industry views and requirements. More architects will become directly involved in designing buildings through computers, building test models and conducting research on new concepts.

At MIT research studies continue on different structural supporting materials. As an example with the addition of 20% of polyvinylidene chloride in concrete the tensile and compressive strengths are increased by 100%. Concrete may be modified by the addition of natural or synthetic organic materials which significantly alter the properties of the concrete. In a series of tests the basic concrete mix was one part cement to 2.8 parts of fine aggregate and 3.2 parts of coarse aggregate to which the following materials were added, as 10 or 20% of the weight of the cement in the mix; styrene-butadiene, asphalt emulsion, epoxy, polyvinylidene chloride, polyvinyl acetate and acrylic. The preliminary results of the strength tests show that significant increases in strength occurred with the styrene-butadiene, polyvinylidene chloride, epoxy and acrylic additives whereas decreases in strength occurred with asphalt and polyvinyl acetate which had air content as high as 8–11%.

In another development mortars were studied based on work conducted in industry for the past decade. Dow Chemical Company and Rohm and Haas Company have made available latexes which are compatible with highly alkaline portland cement. Mortars commonly employed in masonry have good strength properties in compression and shear but are weak in tension. Consequently, masonry walls frequently have to be built considerably thicker than would be necessary to withstand only compression and shear because lateral loads such as wind and impact may cause bending stresses which exceed the low tensile strength of the mortar. If this could be increased, such walls could frequently be made considerably thinner than is customary.

Polymeric latex emulsions similar to those employed in modified concrete have been found to increase the tensile strength of mortars. This is particularly true of the polyvinylidene chloride and acrylic copolymers when added in approximately the same percentages as in the modified concrete. Acrylic and epoxy are also noted for having inter-bond adhesion with old substrates. Such modified mortars, applied similar to ordinary mortars, have been found to increase the tensile strength of brick walls to the extent that in instances houses have been built two stories high with brick walls one brick thick. The second floor and roof are supported by this brick structure.

At the University of Michigan programs sponsored by various plastic companies and the U. S. Department of State, Agency for International Development, are exploring principally the feasibility of using plastics for the resolution of housing problems in the underdeveloped areas of the world. The approach has been to use plastics as primary structural materials. The feasibility has been shown using paper and urethane foam sandwich, glass fiber reinforced polyester with urethane foam in umbrella shaped domes and glass fiber filament wound box shaped structures.

The urethane sprayed foam shell structure provides a low cost approach. Its shape permits the use of the foam even with its limitations such as low modulus of elasticity and creep. In the square umbrella-shell structure, different foam materials are combined with reinforced type plastics. The mass production sandwich technique of using foam core with paper skins developed low cost and quick erectable accordian and other type structures.

## 2. Industry

Industry research and progress is developed through different manufacturers, principally the large companies, and various trade and technical societies or organizations. Since the market potential exists for much more plastic use in building and construction, the time and money being spent in research and development is recognized by managements. By far the most time and money is being spent in obtaining service data on the effects of the plastics to environment. These test sites are located in practical all parts of world including on the surface, underground, underwater and in so called space homes.

An example of a program is the one set up in 1965. A basic research program on investigating the processes involved in the weathering of plastics is being undertaken at the National Bureau of Standards sponsored by the Manufacturing Chemists' Association, Inc. The ultimate aim of the project is to develop better methods of evaluating and predicting the weathering of plastic compositions under indoor and outdoor exposures. The research looks toward ways of increasing precision and reducing time needed for such evaluations. This project compliments a standards and certification program under development by The Society of Plastics Industry, Inc.

Various organizations and companies conducted extensive environmental service tests by statistically analyzing parts which have been put into service. Some organizations have designed and built homes specifically for the evaluation of new plastic applications. As an example, the NAHB Research Foundation, Washington, D.C. (non-government, profit making organization) stimulates development of new materials, equipment and construction methods for buildings. From 1956 to 1966 they have built six of these experimental homes. These houses are occupied by families (houses are rented) and subject to normal wear and tear. Periodic inspections are made by the Foundation personnel to check the structure.

The houses include various plastics such as; film coated plywood for roof, wall, batten, trim and soffit; aluminum window frame, casing and sash covered with PVC; vinyl floor; vinyl sheeting on gypsum wall; composite sandwich structural wall and roof using film, reinforced plastics and foam; vinyl faced ceiling tile; acrylic light diffusing panel; reinforced plastic decorative panel and kitchen cabinet; molded ABS doors and trim; vinyl covered railing; electric raceways; PE and EVA vapor barrier film; ABS, PVC, PE, and PP plumbing pipe and fitting; PVDC and PP hot and cold water supply lines; ABS gas pipe; fixtures such as bathtub, shower stall, vanity and even complete bathroom; and epoxy adhesives for mortars. With these new innovations these houses can have had FHA insured mortgages.

Studies continue to be conducted based on government and industry requests to the National Academy of Sciences—National Research Council through its Building Research Advisory Board (BRAB). Ad hoc advisory committees study materials, components and systems from the functional and technical points of view. There results can be used by industry to provide guidance for the establishment of specifications, codes and standards. As an example a study just initiated concerns underground heating and air-conditioning distribution systems for buildings. Foam insulations will be included in the evaluation. Now in progress for the National Bureau of Standards is a study examining the economic impact of performance codes and standards on various aspects of building. A study for the Federal Housing Administration concerns evaluation of a proposed test procedure for measuring flame spread in heating and air-conditioning ducts.

A BRAB study conducted with the National Bureau of Standards involves setting up performance characteristics for sanitary plumbing fixtures.

Plumbing Fixtures such as bathtubs, water closets, sinks, and showers have been in use for many years. However, only recently has it been recognized that there exist no practical means or criteria for the evaluation of improvements in existing fixture materials or configurations. To prepare such criteria, thorough investigation and detailed work analysis has been conducted. The work of a committee has included: identification and evaluation of essential functional and technical characteristics which are measures of performance for various fixture types; definition of existing, applicable test methods which may be used to ascertain the importance of these characteristics and their contribution to the level of performance; development of data and information through laboratory investigations and field studies as needed and development of new and needed test procedures with indications of the levels of performance attainable.

The Army Research and Development Laboratories, Fort Belvoir, Va. in September 1965 presented their latest report using rigid urethane plastic foam and honeycomb sandwich Army structures. Research has been conducted on fabrication, erection and testing of two foam plastics buildings in Greenland. The investigation was conducted to evaluate the feasibility of fabricating buildings in the field. It was concluded that it is feasible. This type of construction improves logistics by providing simplicity in fabrication with low shipping bulk and low unit cost.

A different approach in plastic applications concerns the Department of Defense. Under its military housing program field tests will be conducted for home builders. It is reported (1966) that DOD will build a few single family houses without venting of plumbing fixtures to test the findings of the Bureau of Standards that such vents in some cases are unnecessary. The military authorities can readily test new ideas since their buildings are on government owned land, free of all building codes.

## E. Codes

Codes have a responsibility to protect the public health and safety in building construction, yet, because of inadequate research and engineering facilities, code officials must rely upon past experience as a gage of performance. It is up to industry to prove that their products perform adequately and are quality products. Product standards will have to be provided even though a lack of performance engineering criteria for building construction exists. Therefore the plastics industry is faced with the need to determine end-use criteria before it can set performance standards. Some feel that the architects and builders should take a greater part in determining performance criteria.

It has been evident that the conservative nature of codes has definitely limited progress in the use of certain plastics principally due to "product standards"—where if it states cast iron is to be used, plastics just cannot be used. Then at the other end of the spectrum more "performance standards" are starting to be established.

An interesting development concerns what R. Wilson, field engineer for the National Fire Protection Association, explained in 1965 concerning the unnecessary and frightening community hazard in California. These hazards are based on the past six years experience. The privileged status for wood shingle and shake roofing permitted under state and local regulations constitutes major fire hazards to dwelling and community.

Then on another front, in New Jersey the state board of education has revised the school construction code to permit installation of acrylic windows in new school buildings. The purpose is to cut down on vandalism which in turn will save several hundred thousands of dollars annually due to replacement of glass windows.

### 1. Substitute Versus New Concepts

Architect E. H. Brenner of Lafayette, Indiana has stressed that fundamentally two approaches for using plastics exists. The most obvious and extensively described is that they are being developed as *substitutes* for existing building products. Because they are substitutes, they tend to receive opposition from all the entrenched interests. It would appear that the plastics developers could insure a better future for themselves were they to develop new procedures and new methods, and not merely substitute materials. Take as an example the Dow Chemical Company project in Lafayette. Dow has developed a method of spirally generating polystyrene insulated dome forms. These forms are relatively inexpensive but the resulting dome structure continues to be expensive based on the use of standard building practices. Scaffolding must be errected on the interior in order that the plastering sub-contractor can perform his work. The same procedure has to be followed on the exterior in order that the guniters, structural steel workers and the roofing people can perform their work.

But imagine the basic machine being programmed to move vertically and forming cylinders or to move horizontally forming tunnels of infinite length. It can also be programmed with adjustable arms to vary the distance of the machine head from the pivot point so that any conceivable geometric shape is possible such as hyperbolas and parabolic domes. All of this could be computerized, programmed, and field assembled in a very short time. Instead of feeding sticks manually to the machine, suppose the machine could generate its own building component, i.e., in a continuous extrusion. The material extruded might be of such a nature that simple exposure to the ultra-violet light from the sun could harden its exterior surface and eliminate the necessity for exterior coating. Perhaps the interior surface could be finished by the reaction of a chemical spray or gas which might make bright colored hues on the surface. Suppose the material forming the insulated shape could conduct electricity, perhaps in such a way that one could literally plug in a toaster anywhere in the wall. When all of these things are possible, then the architects will be limited in their enclosure of habitable space only by their talent and imagination.

These approaches are within the realm of possibility. The problems described are less difficult than putting a man on the moon. They would be less expensive to develop and return more to the developer in the form of profitable investment. Toilets that destroy waste without soil lines, furnaces that produce heat without conventional fuel, communication systems both visual and audio without wires, are all nearly marketable now.

## 2. Government Participation

As reported by the architects, the construction industry is shamefully antique. It is composed of so many separate operations and trades that consideration of these factors is almost as important as the functional quality of the new material. No matter how ideal the functional qualities of a material perform, if union jurisdiction rules that it must be installed by tradesmen either untrained or unsympathetic, its quality becomes questionable.

Some people agree that perhaps the federal government should become involved in order to provide the power to properly update the construction industry. Then there are those who believe that a permanent organization representing manufacturers, builders, consumers and government agencies needs to be established to channel private research efforts where they are most needed. They must keep in mind that the architects, builders and regulatory agencies have limited research capability to update the industry.

Regardless, building officials are charged, through codes, with responsibility for protection of the inhabitants and the building itself. Therefore products must be acceptable to them. Success of codes often depends on the discretion of enforcing officials. To guide officials in the evaluation of products there must be plastics industry standards which keep pace with technological developments.

## II. PLASTICS IN PACKAGING

### A. Introduction

Plastics in different forms provides the packaging industry with different environmental resistant materials which are useful and required. In 1966 the total value of consumer packaging material was approximately $10 billion, of which $2 billion was plastics. Since 1940 many new plastics particularly polyvinyl chloride and polyethylene, have caused the percentage of plastics used to go from less than 5 percent (total of $3 billion) to 20 percent in 1966. Typical new uses are shown in Figs. 16-1 through 16-7.

These plastics are used principally since they provide improved barrier and surface characteristics. The films particularly provide better barriers against the oil frequently found in food, as well as other oily or volatile substances and in improving their imperviousness to oxygen. Structural films, multilayered for performance not available from on film, have provided solutions to many of the more recent packaging problems.

Material combinations are frequently used to meet performance requirements and economy. The combination can be in laminated form, with or without plastic adhesives, or simply mechanical types, such as aerosol containers. Composite packaging examples include the following:

*1.* Collapsible tubes of plastics, paper and foil.
*2.* Shrink films with corrugated shipper trays.
*3.* Structural films to meet different environments:
   *a.* Biaxially oriented polypropylene films adhesively laminated

to cellophane to lower the temperature at which food pouches would otherwise crack.

   b. Polypropylene heat laminated with outer layers of medium density polyethylene to lower heat-sealing temperatures for bread-wraps.

4. Foams are wire-reinforced, bonded to molded outer shells to form sandwiches, metallized and used as decorative or functional package inserts for corrugated cartons.

5. Metal foils laminated to combinations of plastic and papers, forms pouches or cartons which may be hermetically sealed to hold vacuum.

6. Fiber-foil cans basically with metal ends and paper body use plastic, to provide different properties.

Review the section in this chapter on Films for details on properties and types. These films are used principally in the sheet form. However, two other forms are finding more applications, namely shrink films and those used in skin packaging. Shrink film, presently estimated to be less than 5% of the total film market, may be drawn down by heat to as little as 40% of its original dimensions, usually in a heat tunnel. They offer the user the advantages of a tight wrap without the high shrink force that can warp fragile products. Self-shrinking film of extruded PVC, which will conform to nonuniform shapes without the application of heat, will also find more widespread use. Tear strips will also become popular.

Skin packaging in a process in which a plastic film is heated and then drawn down around the product and a paperback or plastic backing by means of vacuum.

Rigid and semirigid plastics in forms such as bottles or boxes is not as widely used at the present time as films. They provide different desirable properties such as those of film, plus toughness and the capability to even be the shipping container. As more complete packaging units move into user plants, more use will be made of these plastics—even to the extent of substituting more of the metal and paper containers. The on-line forming, filling—to the shipping end of the production line will provide faster "total" production rates.

The typical containers to be produced in very large quantities will be oil cans, milk bottles, detergents, cosmetics, whiskey and, more important, products which at present cannot be packaged. The different plastics (provide different properties under varying conditions of environment) can be used in the various mass produc-

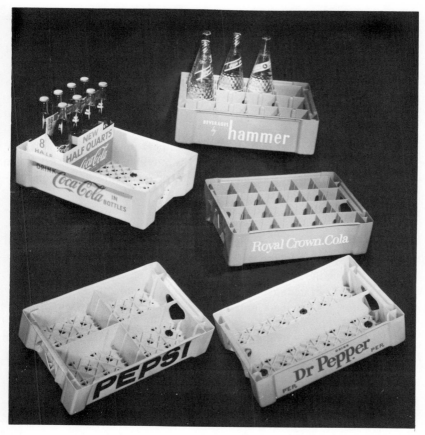

Fig. 16-1. Union Carbide's PE cases are available in different sizes; they are tough and usable for long periods of time, and are appealing to both the eye and environment.

tion equipment, such as blow molding, extrusion, injection, compression and thermoforming.

## 1. Current Trends

The containers and packaging production complex includes all or part of 40 manufacturing industries in the Standard Industrial Classification (SIC). Its 5,000 plants turned out a record volume of containers in 1964 estimated at $13.8 billion, compared with $8.7 billion in 1954. These values do not include packaging services such a contract packaging, drum reconditioning, engineering and design, and some "captive" packaging operations. After adjustment for price changes, the estimated annual rate of real growth averaged 4%, about equal to that of the national economy as measured by the gross national product (GNP).

Containers are one of the largest users of the Nation's raw materials output. They consume an estimated 50% of paper and paperboard, 95% of aluminum foil, 99% of cellophane, 96% of all glass except flat glass, and are the third largest users of steel after the automotive and construction industries. Containers play an important role in the economy since nearly all products moving in commerce require packaging to get them from their point of manufacture to the commercial, institutional, or household consumer.

Tougher competition, changing consumer demands, new merchandising techniques, and expanding technology characterize current conditions in the container and packaging industries. New materials and new concepts have been developed; some traditional containers have declined in poularity as newer ones have emerged. Significantly, despite patterns of change, ascending sales have continued.

Except for textile bags and wooden containers, the packaging industries have enjoyed sustained growth during the past decade. Especially high demand, in excess of 10% annually in sales, has been evident in plastics, aluminum, and fiber/foil containers and packaging materials, a trend likely to continue.

Output of containers and packaging is estimated to have reached a new record of $14.5 billion in 1965, on the basis of part-year results. This gain of 5% over 1964 was expected despite major but short-lived strikes in the glass container and metal can industries during early 1965. Continued buoyancy in the general economy may well push dollar volume in 1966 over the $15-billion mark for the first time. This 4% increase would fall short, however, of the back-to-back gains of 5% in both 1964 and 1965.

The standard—basically "old time" materials—and the new types provides the consumer markets with not only the traditional protection, durability and reasonable cost, but also convenience and attractiveness. Sales rise has been stimulated by the growing use of disposable containers and the development of new applications due to the availability of new materials, particularly plastics and plastic-paper combinations. The 2.2 billion pounds of plastics produced in 1965 just for packaging represents materials meeting these requirements. This includes 900 million lb in film (of which 80% is polyethylene, 6% is polyvinyl chloride and 5% is polypropylene). Blow molded

Fig. 16-2. Perforated nylon bags for boil-in-the bag foods and other packaging applications are being produced by M and Q Plastic Products, Freehold, N.J.

bottles are up to 300 million lb, with almost 95% being polyethylene. The 400 million lb for coatings includes 75% of polyethylene. Containers such as boxes and cups used up another 400 lb of which 90% was styrene.

For 1966 prediction was at least 2.6 billion lb of plastics. From the plastics industry's survey this amount was beyond the expectations as reported the previous year. Based on commercial and government reports concerning the total packaging/container industry the fastest growing segment of the industry will probably continue to be with plastic packages. Competition among the different material suppliers will continue at an expected higher rate.

The material consumption in 1965 was:

| | |
|---|---|
| Plastics | $1.5 billion |
| Paper and paperboard | 6.5 billion |
| Metal | 2.7 billion |
| Glass | 1.6 billion |
| Others | 2.2 billion |
| Total | $14.5 billion |

Over the past decade the production of paper and paperboard for use in packaging has grown at an average annual rate of 4.4%, for metals 2.5%, for glass 4.1% and plastic in excess of 5% The paper volume sales increase has been aided by its capability to combine with other materials such as plastics with resultant low cost composites. The metal containers expanded in certain fields such as motor oils and citrus fruits. New developments in glass technology has aided its growth. Plastics growth was due to its raw material reduction cost, improved production techniques, upgrading of quality control and its unique characteristics which have opened up new packaging markets.

Growing diversification of companies in the container and packaging field prevents analysis of the financial status of the individual industries. A sampling of major firms in the packaging complex reveals that earnings were nearly 5% net on sales of $5.3 billion, the best profit ratio since the 1958 recession. Data for 1965 are expected to show further improvement in the industry's profit position as a result of higher sales volume and strengthened prices. Expenditures on new plants and new equipment have also shown a tendency to rise recently providing the industry with a strong base to meet the broadened demands anticipated in the future.

## 2. Converted Flexible Packaging Products

Market shipments of converted flexible packaging products responded to the improving economic climate by advancing 6.4% in the first 9 months of 1965. An increase of 7.4% in commercial packaging more than offset the 13.9% decline in the low-volume military barrier and resale household bag category. Commercial packaging's upsurge was marked by a phenomenal 17.6% jump in laminated rolls and sheets which stemmed from unprecedented demand for polyethylene laminations and coatings with other materials except foils. Printed rolls and sheets, except laminated or coated structures, were up 7.8% over the same period, boosted by larger requirements from the food section, particularly for polyethylene wrapping materials.

Stepped-up purchases of polyethylene bags, pouches, etc. in the third quarter pushed 9-month shipments in this category 2.5% ahead of the 1964 period. Cellophane bags continued to decline, dropping 21.5% below the 9 month 1964 period.

## 3. Plastic Bottles (Blow-Molded)

Shipments of blow-molded plastic bottles in January-September 1965 reached almost 2 billion units, 152 million units or 8.4% above those of the 1964 period and approximately the volume recorded for the entire year 1963.

Slightly over three-fifths of total shipments in 1965's first 3 quarters went to the household chemicals market. The gain in this end use over the 1964 period was relatively small, 2.1%, compared with the 80.2% jump for the medicinal and health and the 9.4% increase in the toiletries and cosmetics end uses.

Polyethylene, which accounts for nearly all of the plastic resin used in plastic bottle manufacture, gained 11.1% in shipments by weight over the 9 months 1965/64. All other resins used climbed 39.5% for an overall advance of 11.7%, on a resin weight basis.

## B. Materials and Applications

### 1. Materials

Plastic continues to be used in larger quantities for packaging many different products, such as wearing apparel, liquid detergents, hot and cold drinks, oil, candy, medicines, cosmetics, jewelry, weapons, cakes, frozen foods, vegetables, bottle caps, delicate instruments, and astronauts. They provide combinations of various desirable properties such as transparency, attractive displays, air tight containers, noncorrosiveness, nontoxicity, ease of mass production, varying design shapes, toughnes, flexibility, resistance to environments and ease of handling.

Plastic are important materials being used in what could be referred to as the "old type packages." However plastics has made a major impact and has been responsible for developing packages for items which were never previously considered packagable. The principal materials being used are polyethylene (PE), vinyls, cellulose acetate, ethyl cellulose, polyvinyl chloride (PVC), styrene and reinforced plastics. These various materials are available in different forms such as film, vacuum formed, press formed, blow molded, extruded and foamed.

The PE film and extruded industrial and consumer plastic products continue to grow with projected prospects of doubling capacity within the next two years. Major advances are being made in developing the use of PE and other plastic in milk bottles and oil cans. The milk bottle industry is now starting in Europe.

Different type plastic drinking cups for the automatic vending machines continues to be a growing market. The use of either disposal or reusable food trays which initially start as containers for the same food continues to move at a slow rate but it is expected that potential growth possibilities exist for a vast market. Cups and dishes used for handling hot products are being made with single sheet and multiple foam sheets. The foamed type permits them to be handled with comfort. New materials are now being introduced which will continue to advance and produce new designed containers for hot drinks.

**a. Plastic Molding Compounds.** The raw material for molded parts such as film, tubes and rectangular boxes is available in different forms. Equipment to mold parts include injection, extrusion, transfer, and compression. Industry generally refers to equipment by its specific type such as extrusion equipment marther than just molding equipment.

The compounds used can be in the form of powder, small cubes, or other shapes. Various ingredients are generally included in these compounds in order to provide different properties or effects, such as solvents, plasticizers, stabilizers, flame retardants, colorant, antiblock agents, antistabic agents, antioxodants, fillers, catalysts, modifiers, and drying agents. Some of these terms are interchangable such as antioxidants to produce stability.

As an example polyethylene can be made to be more flexible at low temperatures by adding modifiers such as polyisobutylene or butyl rubber. Stabilizers are ingredients added to resins in order to maintain their chemical and physical properties during its service life or even before it is molded. When the polyethylene is exposed to air or moisture before molded it can be degraded due to oxygen contamination. In turn, it can result in poor extrusion processing properties and an abundance of "fisheyes" in the thin films. Antioxidants can be added to eliminate this problem.

This oxidation deterioration effect exists in most resin systems particularly the vinyl compounds. Antioxidants are added in amounts less than one percent by weight. They are capable of inhibiting or retarding the rate of oxidation. Vinyl antioxidants are generally phenolics such as hydroquinone, *tert*-butyl catechol and 2,6-ditertiary butyl-*p*-cresol. With a resin such as polyprophlene when compared to polyethylene, antioxidants are very necessary since it has a higher softening point and is used at higher temperatures. The PP when compared to PE is much more susceptible to oxidation at processing temperatures and therefore requires additional protection.

The antioxidants used for either resin are of the same general class; nickel organic complexes, synergistic phenol compounds, etc.

The plasticizers primary function is to soften or improve processing during molding and provide specific properties in molded parts. These relatively non-volatile compounds impart a permanent characteristic in the part. Most resins are plasticized by heat and pressure. Other additives such as solvents can behave as plasticizers but their effects generally disappear after processing or could develop new problems after processing.

With a resin the plasticizer allows a drop in processing temperature ranging up to 100°F for certain vinyl compounds. With thermosetting resins the dropoff is not significant. Without plasticizers most resins could not be processed into films, sheets and fibers. For the vinyls, cellulosic, and most of the thermoplastics the major types of plasticizers used are azelates, adipates, citrates, phosphates, phthalates, and stearates.

Solvent additives can be used to dissolve resins or compounded

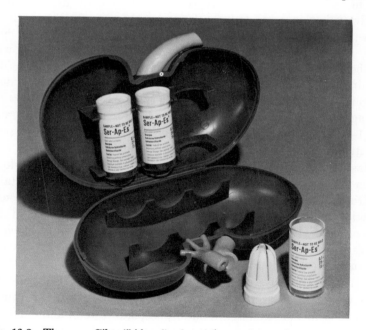

Fig. 16-3. The new Ciba "kidney" advertising package—for control of blood pressure—is a self-hinged polypropylene injection molded part. Bottle closures, of polyethylene, have a unique integral flexible tip which eliminates conventional cotton ball.

resins, as raw materials in the manufacture of resins, and permit certain resins to be processed. Individual solvents are rarely used. Combinations permit meeting final performance requirements for resin. Solvent formulations are generally developed based on both practical and technical experience. Important considerations in choosing solvents are based on other additives in compound, type of base resin, processing procedure to be used, solubility rate, evaporation rate, flammability characteristics, toxicity effect, cost, and degree of after-effects. Sometimes in order to meet specific part fabricating requirements the solvents can have a degrading effect after the part is in service. The solvents evaporation rate could take a long time with change in properties causing failure of part.

Preimpregnated fabrics or filament winding materials require that close controls be set up on quantity and uniformity of solvent collected when it is B-staged. The solvent content with directly effect the properties of a reinforced container or other part.

Various alcohols such as methyl, ethyl, and isopropyl are important solvents with most resins since they are technically useful and also relatively low in cost. Other solvents used are acetone (vinyls, cellulose, phenolics, acrylic, etc.) methyl ethyl petone (vinyl, epoxy, etc.), ethyl acetate, ethyl ether, benzene, toluene, and even water.

Other additives include many different fire retardants in order to eliminate combustion, control degree of flammability or degree of ignition temperature. The ultraviolet absorbers will protect plastics against damage due to the sun radiation. Small concentrations of 0.1–0.5% of metal complexes and other compounds per the patent literature provide a high degree of UV protection.

Plastics are generally good insulators or conversely poor conductors which results in their normally undesirable capability of retaining electrical charges. The amount of static charge is dependent on material composition, shape of part, climatic conditions, and location of part. Electrostatic build-up on thermoplastics is quick and causes problems such as attracting dust and dirt. Dirty packages obviously causes less sales appeal.

Antistatic additives used on the surfaces have limited applications since they can rub or wash off. The additives mixed within the compounds include amines, amides, phosphate esters, and salts. The amine type has (0.2%) proved to be exceptionally suitable in commercial polyethylene.

**b. Extrusion of Thermoplastic.** Extrusion machines continue to be developed and modified in order to meet their expanding needs.

Screw-type extrusion machines and their auxiliary equipment operate to give continuous production film and shapes with a wide variety of cross-sections. They can also be used for blow molding, preforming, or injection molding.

Auxiliary equipment consists of take-off devices such as adjustable speed conveyors, capstans, or squeeze rolls. Conveyor belts are sometimes used which can be made of polished stainless steel. Important auxiliary equipment involves cooling the extruded plastics. Means of cooling include heated or cooled air, controlled liquid tanks, liquid sprays, and cooled formed dies. In producing packaging film sheets constant-tension take-up reels are used in order to obtain control on film thickness and simplify collecting material.

In dry, hot extrusion process the plastic material is fed from a hopper into the machine screw. The process does not include a solvent in the plastic. Heat alone is used to soften the material. The process is the most popular based on large quantities of plastic consumption. A rotating screw inside controlled temperature zones of the machine cylinder heats and moves the plastic. The material is forced through a die orifice which has the approximate shape of the desired profile. Extruded material then goes through a cooling media and collected on take-off auxiliary equipment.

The extruder permits producing thin-walled films down to less than 1 mil in large diameters. Other machines such as calenders cannot produce these thin sheets. This thin film extruding equipment continues to open new possibilities in the field of packaging.

Machines are available which permit the direct use of powder mixes or dry blend without previous hot milling or granulating. Single and multi-screw machines successfully perform this operation. The materials used in commercial extruders include acrylic, acetate butyrate, cellulose acetate, ethyl cellulose, polyvinyl alcohol, polyvinyl butyral, polyvinyl chloride, polyvintylidene chloride (Saran polystyrene, polyethylene, vinyl chloride, silicone and tetrafluoroethylene resins.

There are different production techniques for producing films. As an example polyethylene film used for packaging can be made by blown-and-flat-film extrusion. They principally differ in the type of die used and method of cooling. In the blown technique a more uniform strength in all directions is achieved. The film is blown immediately after it passes the die. Blow up ratios of 2:1 to 3:1 provide best properties. In the flat technique relatively high orientation takes place in the machine direction. The flat film in wide widths are more easily controlled than slit blown film. Faster take off speeds

Fig. 16-4. Linear polyethylene ammunition containers are made to transport and store safely different size shells. PE is replacing a major portion of all cases presently being manufactured. Many millions of pounds per year are already injection mold parts which resist the outdoor and man-made rigid environments throughout the world. This swimmer is using two empty 81 mm cases to provide flotation.

of above 300 ft/min can be obtained with the flat technique. Take off speeds for blown film will range from 35 to 300 ft/min.

Film and sheet materials extruded are conveniently set up to supply several thermoforming machines which operate full time. Complete automatic forming machines can shape parts, cut out parts, and package such items as drinking cups, jewelry boxes, food containers, trays, etc.

**c. Vacuum Forming and Pressure Blowing Thermoplastic.** Transparent and semitransparent containers made from thermoplastic sheets have been used since the start of this century. The various techniques used for forming or drawing thermoplastics developed particularly since 1950 has caused increased demands for its use in many types of consumer goods. If desired the containers can provide direct contact with the consumer product and aid in stimulating its sales. This type of packaging has tremendous eye appeal, offers protection from soiling by handling, provides individual showcases, increases shelf life, and can also act as shipping containers.

They can be made in many varied shapes. The various forming techniques permit manufacture of parts individually or on mass production—continuous belt type production. The methods of forming principally thermoplastic sheet materials are identified by different names; such as, vacuum drawing, vacuum forming, vacuum or pressure snapback, slip-forming, pressure-forming, draping, blow-dieing, creasing, hydraulic-forming, and stretch-forming. Combination of these various techniques are used. Note that there are different advantages and limitations for these different techniques.

The types of sheet materials used include acetates, acrylics, butadiene-acrylonitrile-styrene, cellulose derivatives, ethyl cellulose, polystyrenes, and vinyls. Basically to draw thermoplastic sheets they must be heated to the drawing temperature just prior to and during the drawing cycle. The material can be heated on the mold plate or preheated on a hot plate, oven, or heated tunnel. Combinations of preheating with mold heating has its advantages particularly in production runs. The material when formed in the mold or die is held in position by some mechanical device such as clamps or pressurized hold-down plates. After drawn the sheet material must be cooled to harden. Frequently chill boxes, cold plates, or cool air systems are included in the forming equipment.

The temperature used to form sheets varies with material type, thickness, size and depth of draw. Other important factors include technique to be used and speed of operation. The most efficient temperature for a specific package is generally determined by a combination of drawing temperature previously experienced and experimenting. Too high a temperature may cause sags, heat-marks, or tearing. With too low a temperature wrinkles and fracture can occur.

Drawing temperatures of various materials ranging in thickness from 5 to 15 mils are as follows:

| Material | Temperature, °F |
|---|---|
| Acrylics | 240–325 |
| Butadiene-acrylonitrile-styrene | 225–325 |
| Cellulose acetate | 225–275 |
| Cellulose nitrate | 195–240 |
| Ethyl cellulose | 225–275 |
| Vinyl chloride acetate | 185–250 |

Vacuum forming methods use atmospheric pressure of air to force a heated sheet into a form. In the free blowing method the shaped plastic does not touch any solid surface. In the snapback method after the plastic is expanded a mole form to the desired contour is inserted. In turn the vacuum is released so that the plastic contracts and snapsback on the mold. This method permits forming reverse curves and difficult contours which could not be formed by other standard methods. In the vacuum-mold method the plastic expands against a mold surface. The mold surface contains small holes through which air can pass.

One of the oldest methods for forming sheet plastics consists of dropping a hot pliable sheet over a form. This dropping and hot bending method permits forming two-dimensional shapes over inexpensive constructed molds. In stretch-forming the hot sheet can be stretched and simultaneously put over a mold. This method can produce both simple and compound curvatures.

Cold blending of rigid thermoplastic sheets continues to be important since it is one of the simplest and fastest forming methods. They can be easily fastened to other materials such as metals or cardboard by means of metal or plastic fasteners or adhesives. Cold blending has limitation on the type of material to be used and degree of bending radii. Minimum cold blending radius for different plastics versus sheet thickness can be developed.

In regard to a summary on forming plastic sheets there appears to be more room for developing new methods of fabrication. This endless technique possibility exists since new plastic materials continue to be produced and new consumer products are being packaged.

**d.  Coatings and Finishes.**  Organic compounds are being applied to plastic and metal containers in order to provide improvements in appearance, resist environmental breakdown, easy handling containers, and lower cost products. Approximately 20% of the resins consumed by industry are used for coating materials in many different end items, such as, packaging, building, household and industrial appliances, transportation and clothing. In turn packaging consumes approximately 20% of these resins.

Continual consumer demands for more attractive and styled packages has caused plastic material suppliers to develop new coatings with high decorative and visual appeal. Selection of the plastic to be used usually depends on decorative and environmental requirements. Coated containers include beer cans, liquid containing tanks, and electronic packages.

Resins predominantally used are alpyds, allyls, coumarone-indene, acrylics, epoxies, ethyl cellulose, fluorocarbons, melamine, phenolics, polyamide, polystyrenes, silicones, styrene-butadiene, ureas, and vinyls. These resins are used alone or cross-blended with other resins. The resins are usually furnished in solvent systems or with certain resins such as vinyl in different forms of organic media dispersions. These higher solids content dispersions can be in nonvolatile (plastisol) suspension or in volatile (organosols) suspension.

The alkyds are principally used just in coatings and also the most widely used. Their ease of application, usefullness and low cost makes them useful. Epoxy systems are finding more applications since they inherently have desirable characteristics such as ease of adhering to substrate. Fluorocarbons are now being vacuum deposited on various metals and plastics containers which provides the expected environment resistance such as water repellent and salt spray. The polyamides are now also used to protect metal containers from weathering and chemical corrosion. When heat resistance is included in the coating requirement the silicones are considered. The urethane coatings are generally baked in order to provide maximum protection in such applications as electrical or outdoor packages.

The vinyls appear to be in a class of their own since they can be applied by many different techniques to metal parts before fabricated in different shapes. They are tough, flexible, provide good adhesion and are resistant to normal environments.

Major fuel resistant coating test programs have been in existence to permit handling gasoline and fuel oil in steel tanks. Coating systems employed in the past have been only partially successful in protecting the steel interior. They generally crack, peel or soften and expose the steel to corrosion. Excellent coatings were recently developed based on phenolic modified butadiene-acrylontrile copolymer. They have been field tested for over 21 months in tanks ranging in size from 5 to 1200 gallons. Damaged areas are easily repaired by using the same material. The air dry fuel resistant coating can be applied by spraying or slushing techniques.

**e. Foamed Plastic.** Growth continues in the use of foamed plastics in packaging using urethane, cellulose acetate, polystyrene, vinyl, polyethylene and phenolic. Other resins are being used in limited and generally special applications such as silicones, epoxy, and urea formaldehyde. Foam can easily be made into a package so that a "snug" fit exists around its content. These materials can provide a package which can be used for shipment, storage, display, and/or functional for such parts as dishes, instruments, medicine, electronics, bowling balls, and typewriters.

Plastics are made into light weight cellular foams ranging from flexible to rigid types principally by gas expansion. The gas can be put directly in to the plastic before the plastic solidifies. Reactant chemicals can be put in the plastic formulation which during polymerization will release a gas and produce the foam. The more popular technique used in producing foams, particularly urethanes, is to include in the plastic compound chemicals which will release gas during the application of heat. The chemicals decompose and produce gas. The blowing agents are generally toluene diisocyanate or polyethers.

The foam package can be made in production molds by using foamed-in-place technique or from foamed slabs. The foaming tech-

Fig. 16-5. Star-Vu Plastics, Ltd., is supplying a line of converted foam and other plastic products for the packaging of speciality products. The Hershey Chocolate Corporation is using 10 mil embossed thermofoamed sheet of foamed styrene to cushion its boxed candy.

nique can be defined briefly as a type of molding which involves putting a mixed liquid formulation into a cavity where simultaneous polymerization and gas generating reactance occurs. The mixture can be poured or sprayed into a cavity. The cavity is filled with a cellular-thermosetting plastic weighing from $\frac{1}{2}$ to 70 lb/ft³. Occasionally the outside container used to restrict the foam is retained as part of the package.

The technology of urethane foams has been developing at a fast rate since its inception during the early 1940's in Germany which was followed by U.S.A. development starting in 1950. This foam packaging material provides specific advantages. It insures firm support and restraint for the interior item by adapting itself to the item's complex contours. This characteristic greatly reduces or eliminates damage risks that exists in conventional packaging materials when handling special products.

In producing expanded polyethylene, polypropylene, and polyvinyl chloride the old foaming rubber technique is used. The plasticized rubber elastomer is treated with nitrogen in an autoclave under pressures of 1,000–5,000 psi. Essentially the same process is used with these plastics. Specially designed extruders can handle a mixture of polyethylene and a gas such as nitrogen. The material expands as it leaves the die.

Patents have now been issued in producing cellular polystryene. Foaming will take place with a mixture of resin and gasing agents when put under pressure. Gasing agents used are methyl chloride, propylene, butylene, or fluorocarbons. A wide range of properties can be obtained in foamed vinyls by just using carbon dioxide. These types of foam materials are now finding applications in the liquid and food serving container consumer markets.

Foam sheet made from expandable polystyrene beads is estruded in conventional equipment. This sheet material is relatively new and provides industry with a relatively low cost product with inherent thermal control characteristics.

**f. Energy Absorbing Containers.** Industrial and military test programs have developed honeycomb sandwich container structures to provide energy absorbing characteristics. Honeycomb readily lends itself to applications calling for the absorption of energy at a constant rate with no rebound. Materials used in constructing this structure have been of plastic, aluminum, and paper. Each of these materials provide some different and useful characteristics.

A construction with this energy absorbing property can be used in applications ranging from colliding containers to parachute supply drops. The energy absorbing capacity appears to be in direct proportion to the thickness, density and area under load.

**g. Transparent Packages.** Typical of some of the transparent plastics the acrylics have exemplified their use. The tough and attractive material has been successfully and continuously used for over a decade in diversified type containers such as demonstration models, display fixtures, displays for trade shows, instrument cases, vending machine compartments, appliance housings, canisters and jewelry boxes.

In merchandising and advertising, acrylic is a standard material for special cases where use is made of light-transmitting faces of internally illuminated sections. The weatherability of the acrylics in outdoor containers has been thoroughly established after more than twenty years of experience.

**h. Toxicity.** Health hazards and toxicity of plastic have been important considerations in certain type packages such as those for food, water containers, and biomedical implants. The universally used food container materials such as polyethylene are inert and do not cause problems. In regard to implants, various biomedical electrical devices are being used encased in plastics such as silicones.

Even though base resins may not be detrimental some of the additives can cause problems. Specification requirements have been developing in areas where toxicity could be detrimental such as infood packaging. The Food and Drug Commissioner has published in the Federal Register F.R. 7777, 1963, plasticizers which can be used in plastic employed with food packaging.

**i. Electronic Packages.** Plastic containers in the electronics industry continues to be used in large quantities. Applications include encapsulation of parts, integrated circuits, computer memory cores, and miniaturized circuit modules. Epoxy resins are predominantly used to provide combinations of services such as containers, insulators, resist environments, and insure that discrete electrical components are kept in their proper positions. Many different resins are used to package electronics and provide different electrical insulation properties to meet the varying requirements.

Integrated circuits have now become popular and has made a far greater impact in the electronics industry than transistors. Integrated circuitry is predominantly used with conventional electronics. Plastics provides bonding, insulation and packaging combinations in these circuits.

**j. Military Packaging.** Military packaging procedures continue to follow the defense standardization program. Many of our standard and high production consumer and industrial plastic packages are used. However they tend to make use of more reinforced plastics than what is commercially used in such applications as suitcases, tote boxes, and now what appears to be a potential big new product, namely transportable and underground fuel tanks. Military packaging with RP includes shipping and protecting such items as missiles, guns, instrument cases, permanent or long-life expected cases which will survive normal abuses and various climatic conditions, chemicals, propellants, and special foods.

Government specifications authorizing RP as one of the permitted materials in the construction of a container have been issued. Some of these specifications are:

MIL-C-4150 Case, Carrying and Storage, Shock and Waterproof
MIL-P-5806 Preservation and Packaging of Helicopter Rotor Blades
MIL-B-25305 Box, Shipping, Exterior, Rectangular, Reusable

The advantages as reviewed by the Air Force of containers made of RP over those of metal were claimed to be less weight and maintenance. They expect RP to be used in greater quantities in the supply system as improvements in fabrication techniques and materials are made.

The Army Electronics Command has stated that the excellent properties of RP render this material of great value for containers due chiefly to its corrosion resistance, high strength and light weight. Its major drawback is low stiffness but this is overcome in some cases by special design such as ribbed construction, honeycomb sandwich, and foamed interior support.

Army cases were previously made only of plywood, fiberboard or metal. The disadvantages of plywood are that it has to be protected against rotting in field use and in order to meet strength requirements it is necessary to be heavy and bulky. When metal cases are used they have to be protected against corrosion; however they are light in weight when composed of magnesium or aluminum.

Current Army Chemical Command strongly emphasizes that maximum preparedness with optimum material can be achieved in packaging with plastics. They are referring to all types of plastics such as vinyls, RP, etc.

The Navy has discovered that both RP and aluminum have shown to be feasible materials for large hermetically sealed containers. Aluminum is currently cheaper, lighter and more uniform in quality. However aluminum has low puncture resistance, it corrodes, and during an emergency it could become a critical material.

**k. Coloring Plastic.** Perhaps one of the more desirable characteristics of the plastic package is its availability in many different colors. The different plastics can be colored by different inorganic pigments, organic pigments or soluble dyes. Various methods of applying colors are available such as tumble-mixing dry powdered colorant with thermoplastics, ballmilling or attrition grinders with dry powdered thermosettings, and conventional mixing in liquid thermosetting resins with dry, liquid, or paste colors. With thermosets the liquid or paste concentrates are recommended. With certain plastics such as reinforced plastics the coloring can be incorporated only in a gel coat. The pigmented gel coating can be sprayed or brushed on a hot or cold mold surface before reinforced plastics is molded. During the resin curing cycle this gel coat becomes an integral part of the molded part.

Dry coloring is generally considered the least expensive coloring method. Competitive situations can not readily permit selecting the least expensive system versus the materials to be colored. Factors which cause cost variations are quantity of material to be used, type of material, color, range of color, and technique to be used for fabricating the end item. Colorant characteristics can also be related to specific performance requirements such as desired brightness, weather resistance, lightfastness, resistance to migration, heat resistance, alcohol resistance, and chemical resistance.

In order to produce a desirable color it generally requires the blending of different colorants. All individual colorants must be properly evaluated because each will tend to behave different when put in the same resin. The reactions during curing between colorants, catalysts, antioxidants, preservatives, and other ingredients will result in limiting what colorant can be used. This reaction problem is most prevalent when parts are compression molded.

The various manufacturers of colorants can provide the properties available based on the specific resins to be used. As an example with flexible vinyls they tend to become acidic during processing. There can be a reaction between colorants and other ingredients in the vinyls. Vinyls, as a rule, are processed at lower temperatures than other thermoplastics. The newer high temperature processed rigid vinyls are more difficult to color. When dry coloring extruded or injection molded polyethylene the colorant system has to provide easy dispersion. With custom molders using mixing equipment, such as ball mills, the colorant does not have to provide easy dispersion. The mixing equipment will permit colors to disperse much more readily.

There are resins which predominantly have their own color which is difficult to change or has limited color range. The epoxies, albaline phenolics and rubber blenck are usually gray, yellow, and brown.

## 2. Applications

**a. Bottles.** A total of 1,326,350,000 blow-molded plastic bottles were produced in the United States during the first half of 1965, according to 1966 statistics published by the U.S. Bureau of the Census. The figure on this fast-growing segment of the packaging industry represents a 10.7% increase over the 1,198,137,000 plastic bottles made in the same period last year.

Data is based on a manufacturers survey sponsored by the Plastics Bottle Division, Society of the Plastics Industry, Inc. The January-through-June amount represents totals submitted by companies manufacturing 90% of all plastic bottles made in the U.S.A.

The 1.3 billion aggregate encompasses production amounts for six end-use categories of the bottles:

| | |
|---|---|
| Household chemicals | 825,933,000 |
| Toiletries and cosmetics | 287,751,000 |
| Medicinal and health | 131,756,000 |
| Industrial chemicals and specialities | 42,164,000 |
| Food and beverage | 25,008,000 |
| Automotive and marine | 13,738,000 |

Actually, the Census Bureau report covered plastic bottle production for all of 1964 and the first half of 1965, but the figures for last year had been released previously. The 18-month total (January 1964 through June 1965) came to 3,741,949,000 plastic bottles.

The Bureau also disclosed information on the poundage of plastic resins used in bottle manufacture. In 1965's first six months, 127,348,-000 lb of resin were consumed. This total includes 113,311,000 lb of high density polyethylene, 11,074,000 lb of low and medium density polyethylene, and 2,963,000 lb of all other resins. During the same period last year, 113,067,000 lb of resin were used in plastic bottle manufacture. Breakdown of this total showed 99,438,000 lb for high density poly, 11,529,000 for low and medium density, and 2,100,000 for all other resins.

**b. Rigid PVC Containers.** A market explosion in the commercial usage of clear rigid polyvinyl chloride blow-molded bottles is underway. The first demonstration was the recent multimillion mail-sampling of the Colgate 100 mouthwash. Since then there have been literally hundreds of large-volume products tested in laboratories throughout the country. A great deal of test work is underway with many food products, but they have not yet been developed to commercialization. The reasons for the acceptance of clear rigid PVC bottles vary (5).

*(1) Permeability.* They can satisfactorily contain many products not now packageable in olefines (polyehtylenes and polypropylenes) because of permeability. The oxygen permeability factor for the various commercial PVC compounds ranges from 8–30 cc/24 hr/100 sq in./mil thickness. This is some 20–25% better than (less than) the rate for polyethylene (150–500 cc. for 0.96 and 0.92 densities, respectively). This low oxygen permeability allows for the packaging of oxygen-sensitive shampoos, hair-waving preparations, flavoring and odor ingredients that tend to oxidize, and, of course, for many food products that must be held in a low oxygen atmosphere.

In addition to its low-oxygen transfer, rigid PVC is suitable for packaging ingredients which permeate through polyethylene bottles— such as kerosene and pine oil which are both used widely in household cleaning liquids—and such other aliphatic hydrocarbons as cigarette lighter fluids. A table showing the packageability of organic liquids shows permeability spectrum of this material (Table (16-8) (6). This table does not accurately demonstrate the ability of PVC to

TABLE 16-8. Packageability of Organic Liquids (100% Concentration) in Rigid PVC

| Safely packageable | Unpackageable |
|---|---|
| Aliphatic and alicyclic hydrocarbons | Aromatic hydrocarbons |
| Some molecules containing trisubstituted carbon atoms | Halogenated hydrocarbons |
| | Ketones |
| | Aldehydes |
| Amides (aliphatic) | Esters |
| Alcohols | Molecules containing nitrogen (most) |
| Aliphatic ethers | Aromatic ethers |
| Organic acids | Anhydrides |
| Most inorganic liquids (including water) | Molecules containing sulfur (some) |
| | Molecules containing phosphorus (some) |

hold flavor ingredients. As can be noted, the esters are listed as being unpackageable, and this is valid if concentrated solutions are to be packaged. Commercially, however, the flavor and odor components are included in most products at only a fraction of one per cent and it was recently demonstrated that flavor ingredients—even esters—are not permeating through PVC when in dilute solution from.

Work in the Monsanto Camping Laboratories has shown that methyl salicylate in concentrated form swells and softens PVC bottles with rupture taking place in 1-24 hr (as is the case with other esters such as butyl acetate, ethyl acetate, ethyl formate, ethyl propionate, and heltyl acetate—Table 16-9).

Methyl salicylate tends to permeate through polyethylene, at a high rate also, but does not attack the polyethylene.

Alcohol when packaged in PVC or polyethylene permeates at a slow rate, and is considered "packageable."

It was originally estimated that solutions of methyl salicylate (this is oil of wintergreen, of course) in alcohol would permeate rather quickly, and we found with both vinyl and polyethylene that such predictions were valid for the concentrated (i.e., 80, 50, 25%) solutions, and that the vinyl was attacked.

However, when the concentration of methyl salicylate was reduced to 10%, with the same high weight loss being noted through polyethylene, there was very little methyl salicylate permeating through the vinyl bottle. At 1% concentration there was no measureable loss of methyl salicylate through PVC bottles, even when detection techniques such as chromatography were employed, and of course no swelling of the PVC bottle walls. Thus, at the commercially-used low levels, it is known that vinyls can package many flavor and odor components.

The reasons for this ponderous emphasis on dilute solution permeability results with methyl salicylate are that the mechanism at work implies that many, if not most, flavor ingredients will not pass through the PVC bottle wall, and that more work needs to be done on dilute solution permeability theory.

The significance of retention of flavor and odor ingredients is, of course, that rigid vinyls are satisfactory barriers for many products that to this date were not packageable in commercially practical plastics. So far as theory goes, Monsanto Company are wrestling with interfacial boundary reactions and other hypotheses, and propose soon to set-up special experiments to help us establish a reasonable explanation.

TABLE 16-9. P-Factors of 85 Organic Liquids in Monsanto Vyram Rigid Vinyl Determined for 0-oz Boston-Round Blown Containers[a]

| Permeant | Net contents, g | G/day/bottle loss | | P-factor (g/24 hr/100 in.³/mil) | |
|---|---|---|---|---|---|
| | | 73°F | 120°F | 73°F | 120°F |
| 1. Aliphatic hydrocarbons | | | | | |
| Cyclohexane | 77.8 | 0.0009 (E) | 0.013 | 0.10 (E) | 1.50 |
| Decane | 73 | (N) | 0.0026 | (N) | 0.30 |
| Decene-1 | 74 | (N) | 0.0035 | (N) | 0.40 |
| Dipentene (limonene) | 85.4 | 0.0004 (C) | 0.0029 | 0.05 (C) | 0.33 |
| 1-Ethyl hexene | 72.6 | 0.00012 (E) | 0.0060 | 0.014 (E) | 0.69 |
| Heptane | 68.4 | 0.00065 (E) | 0.012 | 0.075 (E) | 1.37 |
| Heptene-1 | 69.7 | 0.00063 (E) | 0.011 | 0.072 (E) | 1.25 |
| Hexane | 65.9 | 0.0015 (E) | 0.014 | 0.17 (E) | 1.60 |
| Methyl-cyclohexane | 76.9 | 0.0007 (E) | 0.0092 | 0.080 (E) | 1.05 |
| 3-Methyl heptane | 71.6 | (N) | 0.0059 | (N) | 0.67 |
| Naphtha | 64.3 | (N) | 0.0035 | (N) | 0.40 |
| Isopentane | 62 | 0.0006 (E) | (B) | 0.071 (E) | (B) |
| n-Pentane | 62.6 | 0.0023 (E) | (B) | 0.26 (E) | (B) |
| Tetradecane | 76.5 | (N) | 0.0018 | (N) | 0.21 |
| 2. Aromatic hydrocarbons | | | | | |
| Benzene | 87.9 | 15.8 (A) | 54.3 | 1,800 (A) | 6,200 (A) |
| Toluene | 86.6 | 17.5 (A) | 46.5 | 2,000 (A) | 5,300 (A) |
| o-Xylene | 88 | 10.5 (A) | 30.7 | 1,200 (A) | 3,500 (A) |
| p-Xylene | 86.1 | 9.65 (A) | 26.3 | 1,100 (A) | 3,000 (A) |
| 3. Halogenated hydrocarbons | | | | | |
| Carbon tetrachloride[b] | 159.4 | 0.075 (D) | 2.3 (S) | 8.6 (D) | 272 (S) |

| | | | | | |
|---|---|---|---|---|---|
| p-Chlorotoluene | 107 | 23.6 (A) | 85 (A) | 2,700 (A) | 9,700 (A) |
| Dibromomethane | 249.5 | 170 (A) | 301 (A) | 19,400 (A) | 34,500 (A) |
| 1,2-Dichloroethane | 125.3 | 89.5 (A) | 210 (A) | 10,200 (A) | 24,000 (A) |
| Dichloromethane | 133.6 | 105 (A) | (B) | 12,000 (A) | (B) |
| Fluorobenzene | 102.4 | 33.3 (A) | 96.5 (A) | 3,800 (A) | 11,000 (A) |
| 1,1,1-Trichloroethane [b] | 134.6 | 4.39 (A) | 26.3 (A) | 500 (A) | 3,000 (A) |
| Trichloroethylene | 146.6 | 45.6 (A) | 116.5 (A) | 5,200 (A) | 13,300 (A) |
| Trifluoro-1,1,2-trichloroethane [b] | 157.6 | (N) | (B) | (N) | (B) |
| $\alpha,\alpha,\alpha$-Trifluorotoluene [b] | 118.8 | 0.023 (N) | 0.24 (S) | 2.6 | 27.7 (S) |
| 4. Ketones | | | | | |
| Acetone | 79.1 | 109 (A) | (B) | 12,400 (B) | (B) |
| Cyclohexanone | 94.7 | 22.8 (A) | 82.5 (A) | 2,600 (A) | 9,400 (A) |
| Diacetone alcohol [b] | 93.1 | 1.58 (S) | 8.15 (S) | 180 (S) | 930 (A) |
| Methyl ethyl ketone | 80.5 | 123 (A) | 240 (A) | 14,000 (A) | 27,400 (A) |
| Methyl isoamyl ketone | 81.3 | 33.4 (A) | 79.8 (A) | 3,800 (A) | 9,100 (A) |
| 5. Aldehydes | | | | | |
| Benzaldehyde | 104.6 | 24.6 (A) | 105 (A) | 2,800 (A) | 12,000 (A) |
| Butyraldehyde | 81.7 | 127 (A) | v. high (A) | 14,500 (A) | v. high (A) |
| 6. Esters | | | | | |
| Butyl acetate | 86.5 | 36.8 (A) | 114 (A) | 4,200 (A) | 13,000 (A) |
| Butyl stearate | 85.5 | (N) | 0.0019 (N) | (N) | 0.22 |
| Ethyl acetate | 84.8 | 48.3 (A) | 138 (A) | 5,500 (A) | 15,700 (A) |
| Ethyl formate | 95.2 | 51.7 (B) | (B) | 5,900 (A) | (B) |
| Ethyl propionate | 89.6 | 32.4 (A) | 124 (A) | 3,700 (A) | 14,100 (A) |
| Heptyl acetate | 87.5 | 12.3 (A) | 30.7 (A) | 1,400 (A) | 3,500 (A) |
| Methyl acetate | 93.3 | 58 (A) | (B) | 6,600 (A) | (B) |
| Methyl benzoate | 108.7 | 13.2 (A) | 30.7 (A) | 1,500 (A) | 3,500 (A) |

*(continued)*

TABLE 16-9 (*continued*)

| Permeant | Net contents, g | G/day/bottle loss 73°F | | G/day/bottle loss 120°F | | P-factor (g/24 hr/100 in.³/mil) 73°F | | P-factor (g/24 hr/100 in.³/mil) 120°F | |
|---|---|---|---|---|---|---|---|---|---|
| Methyl salicylate | 118.2 | 4.8 | (A) | 24.6 | (A) | 550 | (A) | 2,800 | (A) |
| Pentyl acetate | 87.9 | 26.4 | (A) | 67.5 | (A) | 3,000 | (A) | 7,700 | (A) |
| Isopentyl propionate | 86.6 | 14.1 | (A) | 30.7 | (A) | 1,600 | (A) | 3,500 | (A) |
| 7. Nitrogen compounds | | | | | | | | | |
| Aniline | 102.2 | 3.5 | (S,D,F) | 11.5 | (A) | 400 | (S,D,F) | 1,320 | (A) |
| m-Chloroaniline | 122.3 | 1.14 | (S,D,F) | 26.3 | (A) | 130 | (S,D,F) | 3,000 | (A) |
| Diethylamine | 71.1 | 12.3 | (A) | 36. | (A) | 1,400 | (A) | 4,000 | (A) |
| 2-Dimethylaminoethanol | 88 | 1.57 | (S,D) | 4.38 | (A) | 180 | (S,D) | 500 | (A) |
| Formamide | 113.7 | | (N) | | (N) | | (N) | | (N) |
| Nitroethane | 139.2 | 17 | (A) | 59.5 | (A) | 1,940 | (A) | 6,800 | (A) |
| Nitromethane | 113.2 | 0.80 | (S) | 2.8 | (A) | 92 | (S) | 320 | (A) |
| t-Octylamine [b] | 77.2 | (N) | (D,F,S) | 0.17 | (C,F) | (N) | (D,F,S) | 19.4 | (C,F) |
| Isopropylamine | 69.4 | 36.8 | (A) | v. high | (B) | 4,200 | (A) | | (B) |
| Tetramethylenediamine | ≈100.0 | 15.8 | (A) | v. high | (A) | 1,800 | (A) | v. high | (A) |
| 8. Alcohols | | | | | | | | | |
| Allyl alcohol | 85.4 | | (N) | 0.01 | (C) | | (N) | 1.11 | (C) |
| Benzyl alcohol | 104.5 | (N,S) | (D) | 0.17 | (S) | (N,S) | (D) | 19.4 | (S) |
| n-Butyl alcohol | 81 | | (N) | 0.0017 | (C) | | (N) | 0.20 | (C) |
| sec-Butyl alcohol | 80.8 | | (N) | 0.0017 | (C) | | (N) | 0.20 | (C) |
| tert-Butyl alcohol [b] | 138.7 | | (N) | | (N) | | (N) | | (N) |
| Diethylene glycol | 144.7 | (N) | (C) | | (N,C) | (N) | (C) | | (N,C) |
| Ethyl alcohol | 78.9 | | (N) | 0.0047 | (S) | | (N) | 0.54 | (S) |
| Ethylene glycol | 111.5 | | (N) | | (N) (C) | | (N) | | (N) (C) |
| 2-Ethylhexyl alcohol | 83.4 | | (N) | 0.0008 | (N) | | (N) | 0.09 | (N) |
| Furfuryl alcohol | 112.8 | (N,C,F) | (D) | 0.027 | (C,F) | (N,C,F) | (D) | 3.1 | (C,F) |

| | | | | | |
|---|---|---|---|---|---|
| Glycerol | 147.4 | (N) | (N) | (N) | (N) |
| Heptyl alcohol | 81.9 | (N) | 0.00096 (E) | (N) | 0.11 (E) |
| Methyl alcohol | 79.6 | (N) | 0.0054 (S) | (N) | 0.62 (S) |
| Octyl alcohol | 143 | (N) | 0.001 | (N) | 0.11 |
| Isopentyl alcohol | 81.2 | (N,C) | 0.0014 (C) | (N,C) | 0.17 (C) |
| Phenol | 107.2 | (N) | 0.28 (S,C,F) | (N) | 32 (S,C) |
| Propyl alcohol | 138.6 | | 0.0026 | | 0.30 |
| **9. Ethers** | | | | | |
| Butyl ether | 76.9 | 0.0022 (C) | 0.0055 (C) | 0.25 (C) | 0.63 (C) |
| Methyl phenyl ether | 99 | 26.4 (A) | v. high (A) | 3,000 (A) | v. high (A) |
| Isopropyl ether | 72.6 | 0.0002 | 0.0041 | 0.02 | 0.47 |
| **10. Organic acids** | | | | | |
| Acetic acid | 104.9 | (N)(C) | 0.012 (D,S) | (N)(C) | 1.37 (D,S) |
| Caprylic acid | 90.8 | (N) | 0.0022 | (N) | 0.25 |
| Formic acid | 122.0 | (N) | 0.0037 | (N) | 0.42 |
| Hexanoic acid | 92.9 | (N) | 0.00088 (E) | (N) | 0.10 (E) |
| **11. Miscellaneous** | | | | | |
| Acetic anhydride | 108 | 0.77 (S,D) | 7 (B) | 88 (S,D) | 800 (B) |
| Dimethyl sulfoxide | 110 | 2.1 (A) | (A) | 240 (A) | (A) |
| Epichlorohydrin | 118 | 68.5 (A) | v. high (A) | 7,800 (A) | v. high (A) |
| Tricresyl phosphate | 116 | (N) | (A) | (N) | (A) |
| Water | 100 | 0.0055 | 0.04 | 0.63 | 5.65 |

[a] Code: (A) Liquid rapidly swells and softens bottle and rupture takes place from 1 to 24 hr. (B) Not tested due to low boiling point of permeant. (C) Bottle collapse. (D) Bottle distortion. (E) Value probably low due to lack of equilibrium (steady-state) permeation up to end of test period. (F) Discoloration. (N) No net weight loss after up to 77 days. Plus and minus fluctuations unrelated to permeation of test permeant. (S) Swelling and/or softening of bottle.

[b] Molecules containing trienbutited carbon atoms.

*(2) Clarity and Impact.* Permeability, clarity, and impact resistance are qualities dependent on the overall formulation of any rigid PVC compound. On the whole it can confidently be stated that as the formulation tends to be closest to 100% PVC that clarity and permeability are optimized, but that impact and processability are lowered. PVC's are very good on impact but present all manner of difficulties due to the extractability of such plasticizers.

The principal additive to the rigid PVC compounds that influences properties is the nature and amount of impact modifier. Increasing the impact modifiers—with modifications occurring at certain levels—lessens permeability resistance, and "whitening" resistance but improves impact resistance, clarity and processing. There is also a difference in all these properties dependent on both the amount and type of modifier.

The effect of these impact modifiers is complexly dependent on their own chemical identity and on their reaction with other additives. ABS, acrylics, chlorinated polyethylene and various other rubbers have been employed. In most cases, the larger the amount of the impact modifier the higher the impact. However, as the impact modifier increases it tends to make permeability as a potential problem. Furthermore, unless the index of refraction of the impact modifier approaches, or—for best results—is identical with that of the base polymer, clarity (haze) is appreciably lowered.

Returning to permeability problems with impact modifiers, the P-factor (g/24 hr/100 sq in./mil thickness) for water goes from 0.3 to 1.2 as the amount of ABS is increased. Such a change means that the contents loss of a 4-oz PVC Boston Round bottle containing water at 73°F and 50% RH will vary from about 0.8% per year to 3.6% per year. The lower weight loss is acceptable for most products, but the higher value of 3.6%—product change considerations aside—could mean running into difficulty with some products. Of course, in bottle sizes larger than 4 ounces the ratio of wall to volume is favorable, and there is a direct ratio in reducing the annual percent weight loss. Similarly—and conversely—the permeability problem is accentuated as the bottle size is decreased.

Oxygen is similarly affected by the impact modifiers. However, since the oxygen permeability is so low, an increase of three-fold does not usually alter the feasability of employing a PVC bottle. Oxygen values range from 8 to 30 cc/100 sq in./24 hr/mil thickness, and only some of the extremely oxygen-sensitive (or food) applications are affected by this 3–4 difference in oxygen permeability. It should be emphasized that even a P-factor of 30 is some fivefold less than that of high density polyethylene.

Polyvinyl chloride is an especially good material for retaining aliphatic hydrocarbons, and an observed twofold increase with increased modifiers (range of 0.1–0.2) does not appreciably change packageability.

*(3) Whitening.* One of the rather troublesome characteristics of polyvinyl chloride is the tendency for "whitening." This is the occurrence of a thin layer of white material present on the inner surface of a bottle after being conditioned at an elevated temperature for several weeks. It has been observed to occur at room temperature in a very few instances. Methanol has been observed to be one of the most potent materials to produce this "whitening." It is now felt that this "whitening" is the demonstration of the existence of a phase change. Plastics will tend to blush when flexed. In many cases this is a visual demonstration of an incompatible, or almost incompatible, phase being mechanically displaced. Methyl methacrylate modified-polymer bottles which blush extensively when squeezed but which blushing is removed when squeezed but which blushing is removed when the bottle is heated in water at 180°F.

Another possible explanation is that this whitening is surface crazing. When extruded acrylic rod or tubing is heated in a water bath, a circumferential ring of "spicules" or fine white crazing is developed at or near the surface of the rod. This white spicule formation is nothing more than the opening up of microscopic surface cracks by the swelling action of the water. This "whitening" (microscopic cracks that diffuse white light) of the acrylic rod can be removed by heating in an air atmosphere, as can the whitening with vinyl bottles. This whitening can also be scraped from the inner surface of PVC bottles to reveal the same degree of transparency as originally.

Such whitening has already produced shelf-life commercial problems during storage, when a naptha base household cleaning product was packaged in clear PVC bottles for a marketing test. In a short period of time (this particular material had an ABS modifier) that bottles turned milky and lost their original clarity to a degree that the container looked like a polyethylene bottle.

This whitening has been observed to occur with various liquid products during laboratory tests at both room and elevated temperature. One commercial mouthwash turned milky, in a bottle with an acrylic-modifier base, after several days at room temperature. Needless to say, this whitening is under intensive study and several experimental materials have tended to minimize or eliminate it.

Impact modifiers are used for the purpose of improving the impact resistance of PVC bottles. This area of impact resistance is difficult to define, for it involves many variables. In addition to such obvious factors as general bottle design, bottom design, and size, there are still unknowns such as: Tendency for orientation, crystallinity, internal thermal strains, etc.

**(4) Bottle Impact.** The traditional methods of measuring the impact strength of a material, i.e., izod strength, seems to bear no correlation with bottle impact failure. Flat sheet impact results, as tested with the Gardner Impact Tester or the Variable Height Impact Tester described by C. R. Newman in the Volume XI, V-2 of SPE "Development of an Impact Test for Evaluation of Weatherability of Rigid Plastics" also have only "purely coincidental" agreement with impact values as measured on bottles.

Tests continue to be in process for trying to establish means of measuring a physical property on the compound, and relating this to the finished bottle impact strength. Such techniques as high speed tensile testing, tensile energy-to-break, the installation of a transducer head in the bottle as it is dropped and other procedures are presently under investigation. The simplest and most direct method of evaluating whether a bottle has good impact properties is to fill it with water and drop it; unfortunately even such a simple test is fraught with many "Caution" and "Detour" signs.

The size and geometry of a PVC bottle have a large degree of control over its impact properties. For that reason Monsanto Company has settles on 17g, 4-oz Boston Round and 36 g, 17-oz "Coronet" bottles for our impact testing.

A statistically significant number of bottles are obtained so that a measure of the Estimated Mean Failure Height can be obtained. Even with this quantity it is difficult to predict the height at which no failure will occur. This is practically impossible to guarantee statistically.

**(5) Tests.** PVC bottles are tested at room (73°F) temperature and at 38°F after they have been filled with water at these temperatures and conditioned for 24 hr. It is found that freshly-filled bottles are not as good in impact, probably due to a stress being established in the bottle wall when the inside surface is affected by the water wetting only this inner surface, since it takes some time for even a thin bottle wall to come to a state of equilibrium.

Another quality which is somewhat troublesome, in that visual and instrumental interpretations are not in complete accord, is in the measurement of clarity. Among other techniques employed is a haze measurement (at 630 m$\mu$) otherwise done according to ASTM 1003.

Whitening is tested by filling the product into a container, and observing it visually during conditioning for 2 weeks at 120°F. Reference liquids can be used for judgment as to the whitening resistance of a bottle; namely such liquids as methanol, Pine-Sol, and a mouthwash.

On occasion it has been found that products cause collapse. This is very often a function of the product absorbing oxygen from the headspace, and producing enough of a pressure loss differential that the bottle walls are pulled in. The relatively low oxygen permeability of PVC does not allow this partial vacuum to come to equilibrium and thus prevent collapse. In many cases, this collapse problem can be avoided by proper container design and/or by the use of an inert gas in the bottle head-space.

**(6)  *Typical Bottle.*** The desired properties for a PVC bottle are listed in Table 16-10.

TABLE 16-10.  Requisite Properties for a Quality PVC Bottle

| Property | Target base value |
|---|---|
| *Impact* | |
| 4-oz Boston round estimated mean failure height—73°F | 11' Min. |
| 4-oz Boston round estimated mean failure height—38°F | 7" Min. |
| 17-oz Coronets estimated mean failure height—73°F | 8" Min. |
| 17-oz Coronets estimated mean failure height—38°F | 5" Min. |
| *Permeation—73°F—P-Factors* | |
| Hexane | 0.25 Max. |
| Water | 1.0  Max. |
| Oxygen (noncritical) | 30.0  Max. |
| Oxygen (critical application) | 10.0  Max. |
| Flexural modulus—psi | 360,000 Min. |
| Clarity (haze)—% | 5 Max. for super-clear |
| | 8 Max. for clears |
| Whitening—Pine-Sol—2 weeks at 120°F (preferable to employ, particular proprietary product) | Slight to moderate—Max. |

## C. Food Packaging

### 1. Types

(a) The Federal Food Drug and Cosmetic Act has listed which plastics can be used. Their reports tabulates synthetic polymers by several relevant categories of FDA criteria for safe use. Polyvinyl chloride as such appears among those polymers for which "Prior Sanctions Have Been Granted for Use as Films." The vinyl acetate copolymer appears in the same test; the vinylidene chloride copolymer is listed with those with prior sanctions, without explicit end-use. The list of materials containing polymers regulated as indirect food additives makes no direct reference to specific polymers. The precaution is added as these materials are regulated only for specific

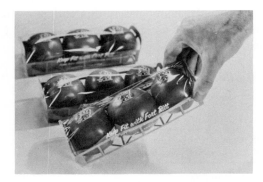

Fig. 16-6. Union Carbide polyethylene resin film offers advantages in packaging tomatoes, such as protection, extension of life, and attractive appearance.

uses—safety in other uses does not follow automatically (7) (Table 16-11.

(*b*) The use of PVC in the production of food packaging material has already gained essential significance in Europe. In the years to come, polyvinyl chloride will move into areas which thus far have been reserved for traditional packaging materials since this plastics integrates many qualities which are not equaled by other packaging mate-

TABLE 16-11.  FDA Criteria for Safe Use of Plastics

| Regulation subsection no. | Title | Basis for "safe use" |
|---|---|---|
| 2507 | Cellophane (as constituent or in coating) | No limits to extraction, or to content of homo-, copolymers |
| 2514 | Resinous and polymeric coatings (on metal substrates) | Limited extraction for total coating; no limit on homo-, copolymers |
| 2520 | Adhesives | Extremely low probability of migration, due to essentially no contact with food |
| 2524 | (Constituent of coating on) polyethylene teriphthalate film | Limited extraction for total coating; no limit on vinylidene copolymer; homopolymer not included |
| 2526 | Components of paper and paperboard in contact with aqueous and fatty foods | Limited extraction for total sheet or board, no limit on copolymers; homopolymer not included |
| 2545 | Textryls (nonwoven sheets) | Limited extraction for total sheet; no limit for acetate copolymer; homopolymer not included |
| 2569 | Resinous and polymeric coatings for polyolefin films | Limited extraction for total coating; no limit on homopolymer or copolymer content |
| 2571 | Components of Paper and Paperboard in Contact with dry food | No limits to extraction, or to contact of homo, copolymers |
| 2591 | Semirigid and rigid acrylic and modified acrylic plastics | As modifier, less than 50% of total formulation; limits to total non-volatile extractables, and to UV absorption of water, (8%, 50%) alcohol, and heptane extracts, for total formulation |

rials. However, it is of importance to anybody who is concerned with the question of packaging material. If, for example, sterilisation is required, PVC can not be used. Often there will be compromises if certain advantages of great value diminish the concern over other indisputable disadvantages (8).

The qualities which seemingly make PVC suitable for food packaging are low oxygen and water permeability; in connection therewith, a relatively good flavour barrier; glass-like transparency; non-toxic; sufficient impact strength and relatively low price.

Though the polymer has been known for 100 years, PVC did not gain technical and economical significance until the beginning thirties. Its significance increased year by year, and in 1964 there was a production of about 1.2 million tons in Western Europe which were contributed by the individual countries as follows:

|                              | 1964 (1,000 tons) |
| ---------------------------- | ----------------- |
| Benelux Countries            | 56                |
| Federal Republic of Germany  | 341               |
| France                       | 208               |
| Great Britain                | 178               |
| Italy                        | 290               |
| Norway                       | 25                |
| Austria                      | 17                |
| Portugal                     | 2                 |
| Sweden                       | 23                |
| Switzerland                  | 15                |
| Spain                        | 25                |

It is to be noticed that countries of relatively low production of PVC, e.g., Austria, may have a multiple per capita consumption quota of blown PVC for bottles as compared to important production countries like the Federal Republic of Germany.

Contrary to the situation within the U.S., there are no comparable production statistics of the individual European countries in the area of packaging, much less of synthetic packaging. A current effort has been undertaken to establish comparable foreign trade statistics at least for the area of the European Economic Community, and it is hoped that this goal will be achieved by 1970. On this basis, therefore, production statistics for the European Community shall be introduced. Therefore, one must refrain from making a statistical comparison. Detailed data concerning the Federal Republic of Germany is available.

The American processor has to realize that in the U.S. (which has about 65% of the population and thus 65% of the consumers of Europe) there is a uniform legislation and uniform practice of approval in the food packaging area. In Western Europe, with at least 17 nations of varying population and economic status, there are about as many separate, largely differing food laws. There are some countries in Western Europe, and even quite a number in Eastern Europe which, trusting upon the thoroughness of the German legislation, use it as the basis of their own laws within certain limits. However, uniform legislation still seems some time off.

European food packaging legislation is very different and somewhat confusing. Therefore, only the German regulations will be discussed thoroughly, whereas the situation in other countries shall be briefly examined.

Laws only set up the exterior frame work; specific regulations illustrate the factual situations. Such laws are based upon a common desire to protect the consumer. However, in some countries they haven't progressed beyond the traditional poison provision or a prohibition of certain dye colors. Other countries have enacted the most detailed specific regulations concerning formulations for making packaging material. Between these extremes, in countries like Great Britain (there has been a relatively complex memorandum of the Association of Plastic Industry in existence for years) there are recommendations and lists of products which have been published by industrial associations. This is also true for the Scandinavian countries, the Netherlands, Switzerland, Belgium and Luxemburg. Italy and some Eastern European countries use the German memorandum of the Federal Board of Health. Austria, on the other hand, takes a fundamentally different path and grants individual approvals for the finished package. As a consequence besides chemical identification, trade names are to be found in the state registers. Since the individual approvals are not substantiated, there are no basic guidelines on toxicity.

In France, approved plasticizers, stabilizers, and lubricants are fixed in lists, too. Approved as stabilizers are phenylindole, diphenylthiourea, epoxydized soybean oil, certain aminocrotonic-acid-esters and calcium-stearate, ricinoleate, lactate, silicate, carbonate, as well as some sodium combinations which, however, have no significance for application techniques. Organotin stabilizers are not yet allowed. An approval of other combinations can only be achieved by a very strict procedure. There is the impression that this law, even with due respect for the needs of accuracy and safety, must have very restrictive effects. For example, the following requirement seems entirely unrealistic:

"Substances which come into contact with foods must not give off any traces of elements which usually are not present in the foods."

## D. Plasticized PVC

Plasticizers, stabilizers, mold lubricants and other ingredients are required, all of which are fairly low molecular weight substances of varying compatibility with PVC which run the risk of migrating from the formulation. The migration of plasticizers has been thoroughly researched. The migration is considerable to such an extent that PVC containing plasticizers cannot as a rule be taken into consideration as packaging material for food.

In December, 1964, a recommendation dating back to 1960 was newly formulated by the German Federal Board of Health:

"The addition of plasticizers to high polymers in producing commodities for daily use (in the sense of sec. 2, No. 1 of the Food Law of January 17, 1936, lately amended by the Law concerning the Transition of Competency in the Area of Sanitation Laws of January 29,

Fig. 16-7. Paper packages treated with a fluorochemical stain repellant protect paper against stain from oil (being poured), grease, and water. (Courtesy of 3M Company.)

1964) is principally undesirable as long as there is the risk that plasticizers migrate to foods. Therefore, assuming unobjectionable toxicity reasons, considering necessary technical reasons, and pre-supposing unobjectionable odours and tastes, the application of softeners for aforesaid commodities of daily use is limited to."

The above regulation limits choice of plasticizer for use in compounds for the production of hoisting belts, beverage hoses, films, sheets and tubes.

Further limitations for the application of plasticizers and stabilizers were subsequently imposed for hoisting belts and beverage hoses.

For films, sheets and tubes the following monomeric plasticizers were approved—dibutylphthalate, di-2-ethylhexyl phthalate, di-*n*-hexylazelate, dibutylsebacate, acetyl-tri-2-ethylhexyl citrate, diphenyl-2-ethylhexyl phosphate, aryl sulfonic acid amides, and esters ($C_{12}$–$C_{20}$) of phenol and cresol. Polymeric plasticizers that can be used include adipic acid polyesters of 1,3-butanediol and 1,6-hexanediol and adipic acid polyesters of 1,3- and 1,4-butanediol (the free hydroxyl groups of which are acetylated).

The level of plasticizer must not exceed 35%. The most important plasticizers recommended in Germany are shown in the table, which at the same time presents a basis for comparison with the regulations of other European countries. Stabilizers and mold lubricants that are allowed in rigid PVC can also be considered for plasticized PVC, with the exception of organotin stabilizers.

Forecasts about the future demand for wine bottles in France have been made. The high wine consumption per capita of the population results in a PVC demand of 160,000 tons per year for wine bottles assuming the PVC bottle can capture this market. As to oil bottles, a demand of about 30,000 tons per year is estimated by 1970. Although there are about 20 companies of equal size in France which deal with the distribution of wine, it probably will be very difficult to expect all these companies to introduce PVC bottles.

However, there is a good opportunity for the packaging of slightly carbonated mineral water which is largely consumed in France. There are only two major producers, each having an almost equal share of the market. If one of the two should decide to introduce the PVC bottle, a considerable demand would arise, especially as the remaining producer sooner or later would have to follow that step. The demand in this case is estimated for about 60,000 tons per year.

## 1. Nontoxicity

If it is edible with impunity, any chemical or food product might be considered as safe within the framework of the Federal Register, U.S.F.D.A. However, chemicals which are non-toxic in administered controlled amounts are carefully studied by the U.S.F.D.A. with particular emphasis on the hazards of any mishandling by the nonprofessional (9).

Within the framework of Subparts E, F and G of the Federal Register, U.S.F.D.A., there is a delineation of both stabilizers, plasticizers and secondary comixtures for the impartation of certain technical processing and end-use property requirements.

In essence, the rulings of the USFDA in the matter of PVC compounds are predicted on a broad range view of the industry's control difficulties and the need to protect the general public against any and all unnecessary toxicological hazards. This latter point is their paramount purpose and I can see no reason for objection to their action.

The European attitude takes a somewhat opposing view. Here, extraction of specific stabilizers, including certain of the organo-tins, forms the guide line of food acceptance. Extraction tests and control under practical as well as theoretical use-conditions, therefore, become the basic factor of acceptance decision.

Thus we are confronted with opposed philosophies—one tempered to total general public protection, the other to an acceptance of industrial standards and tests for a particular market environment.

## III. PLASTICS IN TRANSPORTATION

Practically all types of plastics are used, and in many cases required, in all methods of transportation; such as, automotive, railroad, trucks, trailers, boats, submarines, aircraft and space vehicles. Figures 16-8 through 16-18 typify examples of applications. Throughout this book examples of plastic uses in these vehicles are reviewed. A major reason for its use is resistance to corrosion. Other reasons pertain to many different inherent characteristics which range from attractiveness to durability, mechanical strength or toughness to quick mass production techniques, etc. Different photographs are included in this section which highlight applications.

In regard to the automotive industry, consumption of plastics is increasing at a rapid rate. In 1965 about 30 lb of plastics were used per automobile in parts such as those shown in Table 16-12. It is

Fig. 16-8. Interior view of one of the attractive cars in the Westinghouse experimental mass transit railway system near Pittsburgh, Pa. Plastics, which are extensively used, are functional and attractive, and have a low maintenance. Parts include plastic seat shells and reinforced plastics one-piece curved window frames.

estimated that by 1970, 60 with a possibility of up to 100 lb will be used. This growth rate will occur if (1) overall cost reductions occur, (2) more data develops to show improvement in environment and service performance, and (3) relatively no weight increase is to occur (10).

The auto industry is continually increasing its demands for reliability and performance. Where plastics can help meet these demands their adoption will be rapid and they will aid the industry in the production of superior products for the future. The product and design engineer is taking a far more active role in controlling the use of materials than ever before considering price and properties.

During the past, plastics have been used in practically every conceivable area of the automobile. Increased usage of reinforced fiber glass materials has been evident in entire bodies and in components. Consumption of thermoplastic materials has risen in the decorative, as well

Fig. 16-9. The 1966 Ford Mustang uses tough Cycolac ABS plastics of Marbon Chemical for its sleekly styled instrument cluster (single molded part), full length console, and other parts.

as functional areas. Colored, vacuum metallized and plated plastics are used for decoration, E.G. polystyrene and ABS, acrylics for tail lights and blinker lights, vinyl for seat covers, urethane for insulation, polyolefin for floor pads, to name a few. Thermosetting materials are finding very wide use in those areas requiring temperature resistance and stability, such as under the hood applications. The improvements in finishing and metallizing have helped increase the use of plastics as well. Increased reliability of components has broadened the use of some of the electrical grades of both thermosetting and thermoplastic materials.

Reinforced plastic components should begin to find more and more use in the replacement field. This could include such items as fenders, hoods, etc. The development of a new primer surfacer for the reinforced plastic industry will undoubtedly increase the use of reinforced plastics in bodies and components.

Fig. 16-10. Instrument panel for the 1965 Cadillac is made of polystyrene thermoplastic glass fiber reinforced plastics. This large injection molded RP part has three components totaling 15 lb. (Courtesy of Fiberfil Inc.)

Large components, and perhaps entire auto bodies, may lie in the future for either thermosets or thermoplastics. In areas where volume is limited and the number of models is increased, the tooling advantages of plastics become evident. At present, there is an increasing number of special, medium volume cars in production and under consideration. This trend could increase the use of plastic car bodies.

## IV. PLASTICS IN SHOES

The footwear industry is a high volume market where billions of prices are made and assembled at a relatively high labor cost per shoe. The shoe market also is very style-conscious. Caught between a profit squeeze and demands for new styles, the industry is increasing its use of plastics and injection molding because of improved wear and economic factors such as molding hard PVC heels, compounding vinyl for soles, molding PVC shoe bottoms and injection molded, expandable PVC shot bottoms (11). (Figures 16-19 to 16-21 are typical examples.)

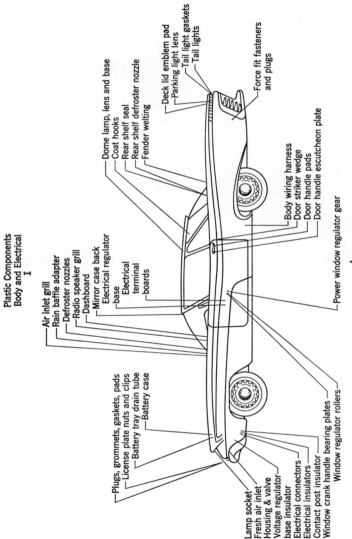

Plastic Components
Body and Electrical
I

Air inlet grill
Rain baffle adapter
Defroster nozzles
Radio speaker grill
Dashboard
Mirror case back
Electrical regulator
base
Electrical
terminal
boards

Dome lamp, lens and base
Coat hooks
Rear shelf seal
Rear shelf defroster nozzle
Fender welting

Deck lid emblem pad
Parking light lens
Tail light gaskets
Tail lights

Force fit fasteners
and plugs

Body wiring harness
Door striker wedge
Door handle pads
Door handle escutcheon plate

Power window regulator gear

Plugs, grommets, gaskets, pads
License plate nuts and clips
Battery tray drain tube
Battery case

Lamp socket
Fresh air inlet
Housing & valve
Voltage regulator-
base insulator
Electrical connectors
Electrical insulators
Contact post insulator
Window crank handle bearing plates
Window regulator rollers

A

Plastic Components
Body and Electrical
II

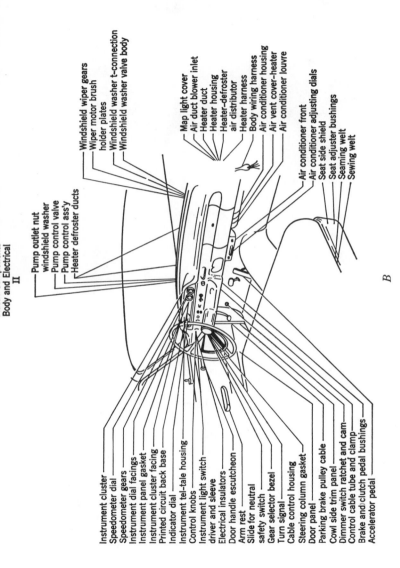

Pump outlet nut
windshield washer
Pump control valve
Pump control ass'y
Heater defroster ducts

Windshield wiper gears
Wiper motor brush
holder plates
Windshield washer t-connection
Windshield washer valve body

Map light cover
Air duct blower inlet
Heater duct
Heater housing
Heater–defroster
air distributor
Heater harness
Body wiring harness
Air conditioner housing
Air vent cover–heater
Air conditioner louvre

Air conditioner front
Air conditioner adjusting dials
Seat side shield
Seat adjuster bushings
Seaming welt
Sewing welt

Instrument cluster
Speedometer dial
Speedometer gears
Instrument dial facings
Instrument panel gasket
Instrument cluster facing
Printed circuit back base
Indicator dial
Instrument tel–tale housing
Control knobs
Instrument light switch
driver and sleeve
Electrical insulators
Door handle escutcheon
Arm rest
Slide for neutral
safety switch
Gear selector bezel
Turn signal
Cable control housing
Steering column gasket
Door panel
Parking brake pulley cable
Cowl side trim panel
Dimmer switch ratchet and cam
Control cable tube and clamp
Brake and clutch pedal bushings
Accelerator pedal

B

Fig. 16-11. *A:* Typical plastics parts shown in this automobile drawing include important electrical circuit devices. *B:* Automotive dash boards require extensive use of plastic electrical products, as shown in this drawing. (Courtesy of The Society of Plastics Industry, Inc.)

Fig. 16-12. Fiberglass tire being removed from vulcanizing press.

About 1955 the shoe industry learned that some plastics could be injection molded to make heels for ladies shoes. The significance must not be overlooked, for the industry learned that plastics could create strength and designs not available in wood. With experience, the industry then looked at injection molded heels for low cost casual shoes. To meet the requirements, semi-rigid PVC compounds were developed around a low molecular weight vinyl resin.

In the last few years, all satisfactory compounds have been in the Shore D hardness range of $60 \pm 5$ units and specific gravities of 1.35 to 1.45. Until about two years ago, plunger machines of almost every make and size were used to fill cavities ranging in number from 6 to 60. The current trend is toward two-stage machines, where the preplasticizer is either plunger or screw, or toward the reciprocating screw.

As the industry acquired experience, heels became larger and heavier, Today, PVC is used in large heels on higher quality shoes. Using vinyl lacquers, the industry learned to finish the heels in a broad range of colors. As a result, the PVC heel is better than the heel it replaced.

Fig. 16-13. Temperatures on the wing edges and certain spots on the fuselage of North American's giant XB-70A, No. 2 are expected to get so high at speeds of three times the speed of sound that about a ton of a special coating compound based on General Electric developed silicone resins is painted on wing edges and on the fuselage to offset the heat. Temperatures on the leading edges of the wings at top speeds are expected to reach about 600°F, which is high enough to melt solder.

The success of the vinyl heel led to the next big step—the injection molded PVC shoe bottom. This development evolved from a simple economic fact—the overall economics of the injection molded shoe bottom are better than those of the conventional sole because many finishing operations are eliminated. The smooth transition to this application is the result of the efforts of an SPI Committee which observed wear tests for two winters. From this study emerged this suggested guideline—when flexed at a rate of 100 flexes/minute at −20°F, the sole should have a minimum of 2000 flexes.

Footwear in the U.S. is a business with a retail value of almost five billion dollars, and a combined production of all types estimated at about one billion pairs in 1965. Plastics in general and PVC in particular have long appeared logical contenders as materials for many shoe components, and footwear has attracted increasing attention for PVC applications in the past ten years. It seemed a simple thing to replace some time-honored material with a better and less expensive material which can meet environmental service conditions (12).

Fig. 16-14. Since 1944 reinforced plastics have been used successfully in primary aircraft structures, such as fuselages and wings. The wings of this AT-6 airplane are made of a plastic sandwich: glass fabric polyester resin skins with cellular cellulose acetate core. The core was made up of basically square cross section bars, individually wrapped with the RP, layed out so that a flat core panel was produced. This type of construction permitted developing excellent bond between skins and core. This structure as well as others passed all the structural load and environmental requirements.

However, footwear is also a business that has been described as more a way of life than an economic sensibility, and this presented quite a tough challenge. The attraction of footwear has been a fatal one for several enthusiastic enterprises espousing PVC, and the traditions of shoe making and shoe merchandising proved as tough to crack as the best leathers they used. In the long run, PVC and the men who apply and merchandise it have proven equal to their task, and the cost and effort involved have been object lessons to the plastics industry.

For an understanding of the place of plastics in general and PVC in particular with respect to leather, it is, therefore, useful to recognize these three factors—raw material supply and uniformity, economics, and characteristics of finished goods. No matter how clever a case is made out for synthetics, leather will continue to have an

Fig. 16-15. Low cost, adaptability, fatigue elimination and appearance are qualities which explain the use of 92 lb of glass fiber polyester resin on every Piper airplane. In this photograph parts on display are the plastic wing tip tanks, prop spinner, engine cowl, wheel covers, rudder and fin tips, tail cone, passenger and luggage doors, and rear passenger cabin bulkhead. (Courtesy of Piper Aircraft Corp., Lock Haven, Pa.)

important appeal, and the plastics industry has done better by acknowledging this and working with the footwear industry along a path of progressive evolutionary change, rather thn revolutionary upheaval.

Rubber has also become an important staple material for footwear over the past 40 years, and its replacement by PVC is essentially a matter of economics and known, controllable physical properties. Rubber suppliers and users have considerable investments in machinery, equipment, trained staff, know-how and widespread consumer acceptance for their product. Most of the major rubber companies are also in the PVC business, so that their corporate policies based on profitable return for a given investment are factors in the progress of PVC in the shoe industry.

It is worth noting that until 1964 the official shoe industry statistics did not recognize canvas and rubber footwear as such. This has

Fig. 16-16. Paceship 32 is an R.P sailing craft manufactured by an old Nova Scotian firm which combines speed, weather resistance, and ease of handling.

Fig. 16-17. This 41 ft cabin cruiser, built by Hatteras Yacht Company, High Point, N.C., is constructed almost entirely of glass fiber polyester resin. The boat is virtually maintenance free.

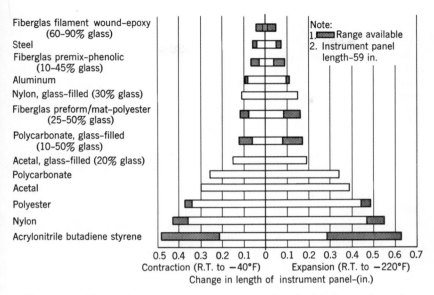

Fig. 16-18. Effects of temperature extremes upon length of instrument panels.

clearly distorted the true picture of shoe production since vulcanized footwear now amounts to 25% of the total of so-called conventional types of shoes and slippers consumed in the U.S. during 1965.

## A. Uppers and Linings

About 25 years ago, the commercial availability of high molecular weight vinyl resin made it possible for the coater to develop a new range of products for the shoe manufacturer. Well-formulated PVC coatings have proven to be functionally sound, and with their range of colors, embossings and print patterns have given the shoe stylist new design possibilities.

The shoe upper must be tough, flexible and dimensionally stable with good scuff resistance and flex fatigue qualities. Since vinyl uppers have found their best market in the price range of inexpensive women's cement shoes, compatibility with shoe cements is essential. PVC is applied to shoe uppers most frequently in the form of coated sateens, broken twills and drills.

## B. Insoles

Leather has been largely displaced as an insoling material by a range of sythetic and other treated materials, so that only a small

TABLE 16-12.  Automotive Applications

---

**NYLON**
Carburetor parts; coat hooks; clips and wire straps; radio speaker control knob; rear window track rollers; linkage bushings; side window channel brackets; distributor vacuum advance lines; breaker points; door lock striker; windshield wiper gears; dome light lenses; turn signal switcher; ash tray mountings; trim fasteners and clips; gears and bushings; venture tube for carburetors; fuel lines; skin on ball joint balls; seat belts; alternator insulator

**GLASS-REINFORCED NYLON**
Clutch throw out bearing; alternator coil form; hinge pins gas cap door; instrument coil spool; transmission thrust bearing; speedometer gears; windshield wiper gear; linkage socket; clips and fasteners

**ACETAL**
Carburetor parts; clips; name plate letters; clutch pedal bushing; horn wire contact plate; cushioning disks for hydraulic cylinders; keyhole cover plates; heater vacuum control gear rack; lower steering column bearing retainer; clutch idler bushing; lower shift tube collar bearing; venturi tube for carburetors; cigarette tray glide; radio tuner knob; lamp sockets; door jamb switch housing; courtesy lamp lens

**ABS**
Instrument clusters; kick panels; door panels; heater housings, ducting and related parts; headliners; arm rests; pillar covers; console housings and covers; garnish moldings

**POLYPROPYLENE**
Steering wheels; kick panels; side shields; accelerator pedal; window moldings; battery covers; clips; letters inserts; fuse box; electrical connectors; radio grills; steering column cover; air snorkel (directs air to carburetor); dome light lenses

**POLYETHYLENE**
Glove box; kick panels, side shields, powder backed carpeting; ball joint liners; headliners; windshield washer bottles; rear quarter and cargo panels in station wagons; spark plug wire harness; ducting; tire covers; spring spacers; inner door water shield

**REINFORCED POLYESTER**
Kick panels; heater housings, ducting and related parts; headliners; console housings and covers; radiator fan shroud; tonneau cover; radiator overflow tank

**GLASS-REINFORCED POLYSTYRENE**
Instrument panel supports

**VINYL POLYMERS**
Door and quarter panels; seat covering; heel pad; headliners; convertible top; welts and moldings; grommets

**ACRYLICS**
Rear light lenses; front turn signals; dial crystals and face plates; bezels; wheel cover insert; nameplates

**PHENOLICS**
Electrical components

---

Fig. 16-19. In Portugal, Delrin acetal resin recently made its debut in women's shoe fashions as both heel and lift. In the foreground, the molded heel with wood insert and lift await connection to the shoe like the one held in picture.

proportion of shoes under $20, retail are fitted with leather insoles. Good leather, well chemically treated is excellent for insoling but no match on a cost versus performance basis for suitable synthetics. Among these is a quality product consisting of porous PVC sheet bonded to a porous cellulose backing. For less expensive footwear—and it must be noted that the average retail price of all footwear including slippers and sneakers is less than $5 per pair—coated stock similar to that used for linings has been used as an insoling material.

## C. Rain Footwear

Slush molding of vinyl plastisols first became a commercial factor in the toy and electroplating industries after World War II, and about that time heat sealed transparent vinyl film overshoes for

Fig. 16-20. Insulated boots incorporated three PVC plastisols. The first two form the outer simulated leather surface. The third, slush molded, foams during cure to form an insulated lining. (Courtesy of FMC Corporation.)

women were being made. This footwear was of poor quality and served as a step to other things which were not always much better, such as dip molded footwear. For this a metal last was preheated, dipped in plastisol, had a coating gelled to the last and was then drained, fused and stripped from the last. The quality was still poor but here was the beginning of the large scale usage of PVC for footwear. These vinyl shoes were worn not over the foot but over other shoes purely as protection from wet weather and gave PVC the first opportunity to be walked on as an outer sole. Today outer soles account for the greatest use, in terms of total weight and value, of PVC in the footwear industry.

A patent granted to Mr. Sidney Porter, of Brampton, Ontario, for selective heating for slush molding in 1950 (he made his first slush molded shoe in 1946), was an important step in the burgeoning commercial use of PVC for footwear. Plastisols have continued to extend their place as a footwear material not only for protective rainwear, but also find a growing application as an outer soling material for casuals and slippers.

Fig. 16-21. A new tropical combat boot, considered by the Army to be the best footwear it has ever issued in wearability, traction, and foot comfort, has been officially adopted after ten years of testing. Costs have been reduced practically one-third. Replacing the welted sole, in use since 1944, are soles of Paracril Ozo, molded and vulcanized directly to the boot. The new sole material, a tough composition of nitrile rubber and PVC, was developed by the U.S. Rubber Company. These have been service tested in the U.S., Panama, Europe, Korea, and Viet Nam.

## D. Injection Molded Shoes

It has long been a dream of PVC salesmen to crack the footwear market with a shoe completely injection molded whereby pellets are converted into a satisfactory shoe in one shot with a total cycle time of a few seconds. There is nothing wrong with this basic premise and it is only a little more difficult to apply due to the high capital investment necessary for molds and machines; however, in all western countries with high average living standards it has been impracticable to persuade consumers and shoe merchandisers to accept such footwear except for limited end uses.

## E. Soles

In 1940 about 80% of outer soles were made of leather; the rest were mostly rubber or composition soles. By 1965 only about 20% of outer soles are of leather, the balance still being mostly of rubber or other compositions, with PVC also recognized as a substantial factor.

In 1945 the possibilities of heat sealing of vinyl soles were recognized and developed in Germany, where the original patents were taken out shortly after World War II. At that time PVC was not established as a soling material, and the formulation of an optimum combination of properties in respect of abrasion, flexibility, chemical resistance and ease of attachment was still being explored. It is estimated that during 1965, some 30 million pairs of PVC soles will be direct molded to shoe uppers and another 15 million pairs will have PVC soles cemented to them. The total of 45 million pairs has grown from just a few thousand pairs in 1959, and is about $4\frac{1}{2}$% of all footwear produced. This represents about 30 million lb of PVC, a fine measure of what has been achieved and an indication of the potential market yet to be developed in the footwear industry.

## F. Heels

The soles discussed so far, whether direct molded or cemented, are technically shoe bottoms, that is combination sole and heel units. It is significant that separate soft vinyl heels for men's shoes have not yet taken an important part of that market which is still largely the preserve of rubber. PVC heels are more difficult to trim and finish on existing shoe making equipment but once an economic ratio of value and price is reached, shoe factory resistance to this change will also give way.

Hard vinyl heels, mostly of medium height for women's semi-dress and casual shoes, have become big business over the past three years, and they are often molded and decorated to suit current dictates of fashion. At the present time, many heels appear to be made of stacked laminated wood are really made of PVC.

## V. ELECTRONIC AND ELECTRICAL DEPENDENCY ON PLASTICS

## A. Introduction

Plastics are essential in the present use and expansion for practically any electronic or electrical system. Different polymer structures are available to meet the many different environmental conditions; i.e., insulation resistance, flame resistance, arc resistance, corona, dielectric constant, volume resistance and many others. It can be said that if plastics did not exist to provide environmental protection, the electronic industry would not be capable of operating and civilization development would have been at an extremely low pace. Electronics performance and economics depend on plastics.

These plastics are now identified by groups such as organics, semiorganics, inorganics, semiconductors, pyrolites, stereoregular polymers, cross-linked thermoplastics, biopolymers, ion-exchange polymers, ladder polymers and ionic conducting plastics.

The annual U. S. 1965 plastics material market of $1 billion exists in components and systems, more than steel, aluminum and copper. The total raw materials consumed directly in electronics is estimated to be almost $1\frac{1}{2}$ billion. Total U.S. industry sales by the electronics industry was $18.4 billion. This insight in the industry can be related to the important role played by plastics so that the more sophisticated polymers now being developed, even with the higher costs, will have a dominate place in electronics. Their properties vary from improving environmental conditions of more heat resistance to performing more efficiently at cryogenic temperatures.

## B. Materials and Application (13)

Molecular structures of the many plastics provide arc resistance, break-down voltage, conductivity, corona, dielectric constant, dielectric strength, dissipation factor, flashover, insulation resistance, power factor, surface resistance, track resistance, volume resistivity, thermal shock resistance, noncorrosion, hemetic sealing, flame resistance, mechanical strength and others. Variations in the properties can occur based on factors such as filler content, processing, degree of flammability and environment.

The insulating value of plastics continues to be the most important electrical property. This is evident from the first applications in coil forms and plug connectors, to the time when polyethylene (PE) first became available in the U. S. The Defense Department required it all for wire and cable. Insulation makes possible multilayer boards, diodes and transistors to operate more efficiently so that now major changes are occurring in electrical appliances. Increased warrantees to colored television influences the choice of plastic insulated materials in order to obtain improved performance. Television lead wires with higher voltage require improved insulation.

At Bell Telephone Laboratories new developments have resulted in producing composite insulating substrates for data processing equipment. As operating frequencies have increased to handle the complex, high speed switching and data processing, microwave printed circuits have become of greater importance. In the past 15 years the substrates developed for production include fluorocarbon with glass cloth, styrene with glass mat and copperclad-polyethylene. Electically PE is outstanding but mechanically it has certain limitations. The new designed substrate by Bell is a composite which includes thermoset adhesive with polyester fibers, polyester insulating film and PE film.

In the mean time, irradiated polyolefin printed circuits are being developed to improve mechanical properties, toughness and temperature resistance. Parts are being used for different computers and missiles operating from low to high frequencies.

The largest single use of plastics in electronics involves wire and cable insulation with over $\frac{1}{2}$ billion lb of principally polyvinyl chloride, polyethylene and polypropylene (Fig. 16-22). PVC is important in building construction since it meets performance requirements, costs and provides flame resistance. In the area of coaxial insulation PE and PP are used since they are tougher and meet the more stringent electrical requirements. Union Carbide's PE foam insulation is used in large quantities. It is made up of 50% solids and uses a blowing agent which is blended into the PE particles.

Fig. 16-22. Wire and cable insulation in 1965 accounted for a half billion pounds of polyvinyl chloride.

Avisun is now (1966) developing a very tough and rigid PP foam in which the resin particles are coated with a blowing agent. As shown in Fig. 16-23, the sodium conductor with PE insulation is a major new development. Another major wire development is with Pennsalt's tough polyvinylidene fluoride ($PVF_2$). Memory cores and other black boxes in the computers can be reduced in size since this thinner insulator can be used.

A gap lies in the development of tougher, higher strength elastomers for sheath applications. Present developments show polyether-polyurethanes as superior materials. Although the price is higher than the polychloroprenes and other elastomers being used, its thinner wall could possibly offset the increased cost.

Heat-shrinkable insulating tubing continues to find more markets and applications in protecting electrical connections, leads, terminals and harnesses. The present $25 million market is expected to grow at an accelerated rate. Irradiated polyolefins represent 50% of this market. Various companies have extended its polyolefin products into modifications of skin-tight packaging and encapsulation. The silicone tubing products are also expanding in this area. Another important plastic, irradiated $PVF_2$, is a relatively new comer which provides unique combinations of different properties.

A more efficient thermal barrier system to protect communication

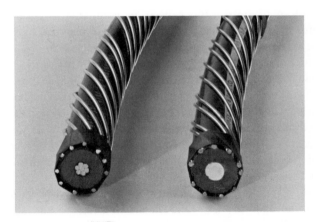

Fig. 16-23. Shown on the left is a conventional #4 stranded copper 15 kV concentric "Underground Residential Distribution" cable. On the right is an equivalent sodium cable produced by Simplex Wire and Cable Company, utilizing Union Carbide's new insulated sodium conductor. The electrical conductor core is produced by extrusion of a tube of polyethylene insulation which is simultaneously filled with sodium conductor.

cable cores from heat during cable manufacture has been introduced by Dow Chemical Co. The new foamable latex can be applied to metal or plastic tapes as shields or wraps for the cable core. The material provides an opportunity for greater latitude in choice of optimum extrusion temperatures, better bonding to adjacent materials and economic advantages.

Important are self supporting thin dielectric films of polyester, fluorocarbon, polystyrene and more recently polycarbonate to form the backbone of foil capacitors. To increase the capacitance of miniature units these films are required to be only a fraction of a mil thick. Supported films of parazylene are being coated in thicknesses of 0.01 mil directly on foils for experimental capacitors and special applications. In thicker form from 2–6 mils, the films of polyester, polycarbonate, fluorocarbon and polyimide are being bonded to parallel ribbons of copper foil to form "flat cable" constructions for flexible interconnections with improved thermal dissipation, simplified shielding and low mutual capacitants. Plastic materials are also being examined as potential thin filmed substrates less than one mil in thickness for integrated circuits. To date the major problem has been undesirable pinholes.

The telephone companies, particularly the Bell Systems, are using more acetal based on test results conducted to determine whether it retained its insulation resistance on aging. Test results were compared to those of hard rubber used in components having 40 year service life. Ultraviolet light exposure test at varying humidity conditions determined that hard rubber undergoes a more severe loss than acetal homopolymer or copolymer. Loss in acetal is not caused by lubricant, antioxidant or catalyst residues, but is due to surface crazing. Another Bell change concerns the use of polycarbobate (PC) to replace acrylic in the telephone finger wheel since it provides more resistance to impact and withstands more abuse.

Practically all types of plastics lend themselves to any conceivable method of fabrication. In fact, there is a healthy condition of competition between them. Ease of fabrication is combined with diversity in chemical, physical and mechanical environmental properties. Economical advantages are also significant in some of the applications, particularly the large-automated production runs for diodes and transistors.

Resins used include the old reliable phenolics to the modern and useful epoxies, urethanes, polycarbonates and others. A new general purpose phenolic has been developed to replace the headers in transistors presently using glass and metal. The Lamp Metals and Components Department of General Electric Co. product is now encapsulating solid state devices at less than ⅓ the cost. Durez Encap mineral filled and reinforced phenolic, alkyd and epoxy provides designers with combination encapsulating properties. The mineral-filled alkyd and epoxy have low dissipation factor of 0.01 at 60 cycles, high dielectric strength of 400 V/mil by the short method and 325 V/mil by the step by step method. The mineral-filled alkyd, besides being an electrical grade compound, also meets the requirements for being classified as a heat resistant compound and is recommended for high temperature applications where environmental temperature or operating temperature might rise to 300°F. Mineral-filled phenolic is being used to encapsulate nylon inserts or bobbins to give a chemical adhesion between the insert and encapsulant.

Alkyd is replacing phenolic distributor caps in automobiles and trucks, high temperature electronic applications with metallic inserts for tuner parts and connectors and encapsulation of fragile electronic components.

Plastic mechanical devices are important in electronic packages. Cost cuts ranging from 66–90% on electronic equipment hardware have resulted from using plastics such as polypropylene and acetal copolymer to replace metal in hinges, latches and handles.

Polyurethane potting system provides low-stress encapsulation with a 50% decrease in inductance change over epoxy systems. Polyester varnish film in phase coil insulation motors rated at 130°C class insulations. Fluorocarbons continue to find new applications where parts are subjected to extreme temperature ranges. The urea resin continues to be used to produce new attractive electrical housings, color-coded knobs and button controls.

New formulations of polyurethane prepolymers and epoxy resins permits meeting electrical coating requirements for printed circuit boards per MIL-I-46508A without pinholes. In out space, where protection is vital, astronauts wear space suits made with new high-temperature resistant fiber Nomex-nylon (DuPont). For the down-to-earth problem of insulating high temperature electrical equipment, Nomex in paper form is now available.

Relatively new plastics which will play important roles in electronic developments, in addition to those already listed, include Union Carbide's polysulfone, General Electric's polyphenylene oxide, Enjay's ethylenepropylene (EPM), Allied Chemical's chlorinated polyethylene and duPont's Surlyn A ionomer. Perhaps one of the newest innovations is Union Carbide's electrical conductor core produced by extruding a PE insulating tube and simultaneously filling it with a sodium conductor.

With advantages and use of any materials there are always problems to plague the industry. The most recent problem is being studied by the Denver Wildlife Research Center on developing rodent-proofing of communication wire. Dr. James J. Licari of Autonetics, a division of North American Aviation Inc. has been investigating the mechanisms of failure in microdiodes due to contaminants in plastics. In another propect the Air Force has determined that microorganisms similar to those that decompose fruits and vegetables have been found to destroy neoprene, fluorocarbon and other materials in missiles. So it appears these basically microscopic problems are developing what can be called the "purification era" requirement in plastics. (See section in this chapter on Biological Environment).

The sustained interest in plastics for future electronic applications is based, in part, on the far-ranging varieties of structures that can be imparted to them by chemical sythesis and applying them into electronic systems. This approach has already produced important and large usage of phenolics, epoxies, silicones, polyesters, PVC, PE, and others. With these many plastics being used, the importance of matching material for a particular application can develop interface problems. The interdisciplinary approach is important to follow in order to eliminate problems or logically develop more profitable products.

With the complexity of requirements, the criteria of reliability and performance are becoming more important considerations in industrial machinery, household appliances, power station equipment and other areas vital to our economy as they are in the aerospace and underwater applications. To some suppliers and fabricators this will mean sales of more highly refined and expensive plastics.

## C. Progress through Plastics

Plastics are essential in practically all electronic and electrical systems. Typical examples are shown in Figs. 16-24 through 16-29. These materials may perform insulative, magnetic, optical, environmental protection, structural and other functions. At a value of more than $300,000, these materials apear in applications ranging from insulators in cables and microwave circuits to electromechanical supports in coils and computer memories. Plastics have emerged as

Fig. 16-24. Joel Frados, editor of *Modern Plastics,* points out design feature of a 5 kV circuit breaker of the Glastic Corporation. The nonconductor parts of this unit are practically all glass filled polyesters.

dominant influences in improving existing products and developing new products.

Electronics is the science and technology which deals primarily with the devices which collect, process and transmit information in the form of electrical signals and either control machines or present the processed information to human beings for their direct use. Developments are evolutionary in nature. Radio and radar resulted from applying the principles to the previous knowledge of the telephone and telegraphy. Another step is now occurring in space communications. Plastics are considered one of the material technologies that has directly contributed to these advancements. Many important new devices are possible only through plastics such as coaxial cables, miniaturization and satellites.

Progress in advanced design has increasingly become a function of materials research. Historically, this has been reflected by changes in component size, configuration and characteristics. One phase has been the introduction of miniature and subminiature components. The concept of miniaturization has become more sophisticated with

Fig. 16-25. This cherry picker uses reinforced glass polyester buckets and arm to insure insulation of workers between high power lines and ground.

wire insulation and integrated circuits (IC). Thinner insulation is required to pack more wire in computor memories and other circuits. The integrated circuits, assembled in hybrid or composite multilayer boards, are in themselves components which contain the equivalent of two or more discrete components fabricated on or within a substrate.

## D. Markets

Since plastics permit electronic circuits to operate in all types of environments and electronics will become more useful to our way of life, its market grows. There is a trend for some of the electronic component manufacturiers to produce their own special or exodic materials. Some organizations have established internal facilities or captive suppliers. At the same time, plastic and chemical companies continue to enter the field of manufacturing components. As an ex-

Fig. 16-26. U.S. Electrical Motors, L.A., Calif., in 1966 introduced form wound insulation motors offering a broad range of protection against moisture, oils, chemicals, solvents, abrasion, mechanical fatigue, age embrittlement, heat, dielectric stress, and corona effects. Epoxy and polyester resins are used.

Fig. 16-27. Convenience, economy and good appearance are provided in this electrical baseway made from B.F. Goodrich Chemical Company rigid Geon vinyl (PVC). Installation is easy and quick. It permits flexibility in circuit layout and meets code requirements.

Fig. 16-28. In the assembly of the slip ring unit the circular insulators and separators are fitted over the shaft. The coefficient of thermal expansion of Taylor Corporation's grade of GEC-500 glass epoxy laminated plastic closely matches that of the metal in the tie rods, permitting a tight fit.

Fig. 16-29. Subminiature printed circuit card edge connector at left, and rack-and-panel cable connector at right, are precision molded from Union Carbide's polysulfone.

ample, one of these components is wire and cable which represents consumption of over $\frac{1}{2}$ billion lb of polyvinyl chloride (PVC) and polyethylene (PE).

A good example of present and future plastic growth is in transistors. Plastic encapsulated transistors, to be produced in the billions by 1970, will break the semiconductor cost barrier in consumer electronic product applications. This prediction was presented during the 21st annual National Electronics Conference (1965). Louis Lehner, of Motorola Semiconductor Products, Inc. has explained that plastic transistors, encapsulating germanium and silicone devices, will cost approximately 20 cents each. Silicone plastics will be at the 10 cent level. This change can be attributed to the new molding production technology which permits putting more into a single package.

Computers, space programs and home tape recorders consumed $100 million of plastic magnetic recording tape last year. By 1970, annual sales are expected to double. Expanded production of these tapes is now occurring at Celanese (Celanar polyester), DuPont (Mylar polyester) and Eastman Kodak (Durol cellulose acetate).

Tape recording is now the 4th major electronic home product, with television in first place, followed by radio and phonograph. All these are large users of plastics. It is interesting to note the tape market started during World War II. The first known practical use of modern tape was the German's secret weapon. Hitler's voice was heard "clearly" all over Germany—at the same time.

Printed circuit manufacturers can expect some gaping holes to be punched into their estimated $100 million annual market (of which 60% is for the military) as government development of integrated circuits moves ahead. However, the gap will be overflowing with more use of plastic materials in the new components and systems. Printed circuit board manufacturers are now concentrating on more specialized products, such as multilayer boards used with integrated circuits to operate at higher temperatures.

The Institute of Printed Circuits (IPC) reports that in the next few years the multilayer concept will have gained wide acceptance in electronic systems. Approximately 80% are now used in military or space systems. Multilayer printed wiring emerged as a solution to the problem of interconnecting miniature electronic components in more complex systems. However, at present, multilayer boards are not profitable to all in that business.

Another important outlet for plastics are the many different connectors. Forecasts place 1965 industrial and commercial connector sales at $300 million with 10–15% increase for next year. Diallyl phthalate (DAP) compounds continue to be one of the major plastics used.

Other component markets which use many different plastics include $385 million in transistors, the $1.1 billion in electromechanical devices such as switches and relays, the $335 million in resistors, the $372 million in capacitors, the $203 million in microcircuits and the $80 million in IC (next year IC will be $120 million). The Electronic Industries Association (EIA) totaled the 1965 component market at $4.5 billion.

As the $1.5 billion computer market continues to grow, the consumption of plastics will grow at a faster rate. Materials such as polyvinylidene fluoride (PVF$_2$), polyphenylene oxide (PPO), and polysulfone permit additional miniaturization and production of more reliable components. These materials provide more efficiency in operation under adverse conditions. Plastic components will continue to be used and, in some cases, to be manufactured by such computer manufacturers as IBM, GE, RCA Sperry Rand, Control Data, Honeywell, NCR, and Burroughs.

The telephone industry is a big user of plastics. Practically all installations use some type of plastic in overline and microwave circuits. There now exists 90 million telephones, with the rate of growth exceeding population growth. At present 46 telephones exist for each 100 people in U. S. as compared to 37 per 100 in 1952. This represents $40 billion in equipment which is held by approximately 2,500 companies; 81% by the Bell System.

### 1. Wire and Cable Insulation

Here is one of the largest single end item applications for plastics—over 1.2 billion pounds for 1967 in the United States for wire and cable insulation. This represents sales of at least $3 billion in plastics material and almost $3 billion to approximately 200 processors. But more important is the fact that consumption will double in six years and in the meantime certain machinery backlog orders have extended over a year. Almost 80% involves extrusion coating; 15% wrapping of film, tape or impregnated fibrous tape; and the remainder principally dip coating or the equivalent (14).

Due to their various environmental capabilities the 1967 expected annual rate of consumption is 520 million pounds of polyvinyl chloride (PVC) compound, 360 million pounds of polyethylene (PE), 230 million pounds of elastomers (principally butyl, SBR and neoprene) and 100 million pounds for the remaining materials (including polypropylene copolymers, fluoropolymers, polyimide and polyesters). Based on the present growth in consumption rate, by 1971 there will be more PE used than PVC. The average PVC compound consists of 50% resin, 25% plasticizer and the remaining 25% of different additives—mostly fillers, modifiers and stabilizers. Approximately $\frac{1}{3}$ of the PVC compound used by the wire industry is purchased as a compound. The remaining $\frac{2}{3}$ is compound by the processor (See Fig. 16-30).

PVC's major use is in building wire where fire resistance is of prime importance. It is estimated that 50% of the PVC goes into the building wire, 17% into communications, 13% into flexible cord, 8% into appliances and 12% for all other applications (principally automotive). Predictions are that the combined annual growth rate for these PVC applications during the next 5 years will be 7% per year.

The excellent electrical insulation properties of PE continues to make its use expand. At present 73% of PE consumption goes into communication wire, 22% into power cable, 3% into coaxial cable (principally foamed type in order to obtain better electrical properties) and 2% for all other applications. Since annual rate of growth in power cables is expected to be at 32% and communication wire at 12%, a crossover is predicted for 1972 when the major use for PE will be for the power line insulation.

The power, communication and other wire products using PE, PVC and elastomers represent large volume use of relatively low cost plastics insulation. Most of the other plastics used for wire and cable (e.g. polyester and polyimide) provides special properties for use in smaller, high performance wire applications. A commercial aircraft requires many miles of such special wires. Each Minuteman missile site uses thousands of miles of cables. More special wires goes into ships, submarines, missiles, weapons, space vehicles and computers.

**a. Apollo Disaster.** The importance of critical electrical wire insulation can be related to the findings of the Apollo U.S. Congressional Review Board concerning the January 27, 1967 fire disaster which took the lives of three astronauts. It charges specifically that the fire was caused by several arcs in wiring probably located near the lower left forward section where the Environment Control System (ECS) instrumentation power wiring goes into an area between the ECS and the oxygen panel. The Board had found numerous examples in the wiring of poor insulation, design and workmanship.

| Total in Billions of Pounds | | | | | | | |
|---|---|---|---|---|---|---|---|
| 1.0 | 1.1 | 1.2 | 1.3 | 1.5 | 1.6 | 1.8 | 2.1 |
| 1965 | 1966 | 1967 | 1968 | 1969 | 1970 | 1971 | 1972 |

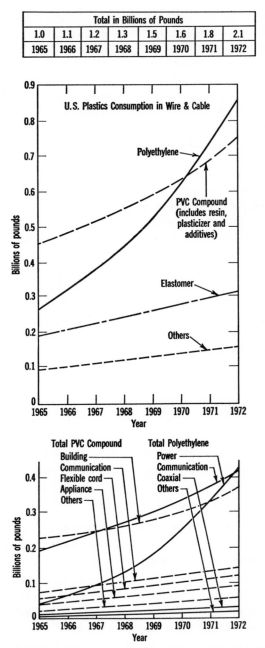

Fig. 16-30. U. S. plastics consumption in wire and cable.

The difficulties of pinpointing the blame are enormous. However these wiring problems with the lethal combination of 100% oxygen atmosphere, a repeated history of combustible materials of water-glycol spillage from the ECS, the 16 psi cabin pressure and a spark created an unnecessary hazardous condition. It was recommended by the Board that NASA and North American Aviation fully coordinate a more efficient program. Although the tragedy occurred, plastics which could have eliminated insulation breakdown, even with human negligence present, were available before the disaster.

**b. Wire Producers.** It is important to note that metal companies have been acquiring many of the independent wire producing companies. The largest independent wire producer now in the United States is Simplex Wire & Cable Co. Simplex produces many different types of wire and cable constructions. Other major independent companies tend to specialize in specific types of products, such as the TV camera cables produced by the Boston Insulated Wire & Cable Co.

The Essex Wire Corp. and Kaiser Aluminum & Chemical Corp. are the largest producers of building wire in the U.S. Both companies have plants at several locations. When reviewing the communications cable producers, there exists three major segments. Western Electric Co., the manufacturing arm of AT&T and General Cable Corp. are two of them. The third segment is made up of the "independent" producers, which include the Anaconda Wire & Cable Co., Ansonia Wire & Cable Co., Boston Insulated Wire & Cable Co., Brand Rex-Div. of America Enka, Essex Wire Corp., General Cable Corp., Okonite Subs. Ling-Temco-Vought Corp., Phelps Dodge Copper Products Corp., Plastic Wire & Cable Corp., Plastoid Corp., Superior Cable Corp., and Whitney Blake Co. By the end of this year capacity to produce telephone wire will be over 200 BCF (billion conductor feet).

Power cables are produced principally by organizations such as Anaconda Wire & Cable Corp., Essex Wire Corp., General Cable Corp., General Electric Co., Okonite Co., Phelps Dodge Copper Products Corp., Rome Cable, Simplex Wire & Cable Co., U.S. Steel Corp., Alcan Cable Corp., Alcoa, Kaiser Aluminum & Chemical Corp., Olin Conductors (Div. Olin Chemicals) and Reynolds Metals Co. These last five companies will continue to use larger quantities of aluminum wire while the others continue to use principally copper. Both copper and aluminum are now approved for use in power lines.

Using aluminum to replace copper in communication lines is now in high gear again and appears to be making the grade. In the past, corrosion of aluminum was the cause for unsuccessful developments. In defense of copper's position, mining specialists insist that there is sufficient copper ore to take care of the world demand for copper. However, domestic strikes, and foreign government control of the price and volume of copper exports have combined to keep the situation in constant turmoil. In addition to these reasons for expanding the use of aluminum, the more positive one is that at only $\frac{1}{3}$ the weight of copper it has 61% the conductivity.

The Nacon Corp., principally owned and managed by Union Carbide Corp. with Simplex holding the other interest, continues to advance the use of cable produced by the extrusion of a tube of PE insulation which is simultaneously filled with a sodium conductor. Sodium ranks third in electrical conductivity after copper and aluminum. Its resistivity and specific gravity are 4.88 and 0.97 with copper at 1.72 and 8.89; and aluminum at 2.83 and 2.70, respectively. The lower cost sodium power cables have a bright future even though certain problems exist.

The volume of cable for the coaxial or CATV (Community Antenna Television) market is relatively small when compared to communication lines. However, due to more critical performance requirements it presents an attractive market for the qualified manufacturers. Producers include Amphenol Corp., Anaconda Wire & Cable Co., General Cable Corp., Phelps Dodge Copper Products Corp., Plastoid Corp., Superior Cable Corp., Times Wire & Cable Co. and Viking Industries Inc.

**c. Communication Needs.** The growth of the market for wire in the telephone industry has held at a high level during the past several years and promises to be even higher in the future. The Rural Electrification Administration (REA), Washington, D.C. reports that the present capacity of the industry to produce cable products is insufficient to meet the needs of the independent telephone industry. REA borrowers project an average annual growth rate of $17\frac{1}{2}\%$ for the period 1965 through 1975. Unless additional cable capacity is provided, so reports C. Raymond Ballard, chief of Outside Plant Branch of REA, many of the independent company expansion and upgrading programs will be delayed.

The first specification for plastics-jacketed cables was prepared by REA in 1952. Since that time they have continued to recognize the importance of strong material and product specifications in terms of producing well-designed, low maintenance systems.

From a relatively low volume of plastics cables used in the early years of the REA telephone program, a large scale usage of plastics cable was initiated with the inception of the REA's buried plant program in 1957. By 1960 more than half of all construction was being placed underground. During this period they began to experience numerous failures of materials. A careful study of properties of plastic materials used in the cable designs at that time revealed that marginal or substandard PE was being used in many cases.

In 1960 REA issued its first specification, PE-200, for raw materials. During this same year REA introduced an inspection system where samples of the finished product from all construction projects were inspected for specification compliance through an arrangement with the Army's Frankford Arsenal. At the present time, REA has some 17 different specifications for plastics-insulated products used by this program. These specifications are in the form of joint evaluations by REA, the cable manufacturing industry, and the raw material suppliers.

It would appear that almost all materials utilized in REA wire and cable designs will be changed in the next two or three years. Serious shortages of copper in this country suggest the possible use of aluminum or copper covered aluminum conductors to replace the solid copper conductors presently used. Insulating materials such as polypropylene (PP), extra high molecular weight low density PE material, and a new family of high density PE's all hold great promise to improve cable designs. The importance of deriving improved mechanical properties in jackets suggests that high density PE jackets will become a standard within the next year.

By 1970 the Bell System expects to bury almost all telephone wire and cable that it installs in metropolitan areas. In most cases it will be unable to bury transmission lines by the conventional methods of digging a trench or plowing the cable into the ground. Tunneling underneath obstructions will be used to minimize restoration costs, avoid legal restrictions on cutting through major roads and creates only a minimum of traffic disturbance.

**d. AT&T Consumption and Business.** How Western Electric goes; so goes the world of wire and cable. They alone in 1965 used 94 million pounds of PE in wire. Christian Scholly of AT&T's Bell Telephone Laboratories reports that by the end of this year their volume will increase by 10 to 15%. Over 30 million miles of wire are now being coated annually for communications.

AT&T is providing the telephone industry with major new wire developments which will be a part of the new era of growth and innovation in telephone communications. AT&T is the country's largest corporation in assets ($31 billion); the largest employer (800,000). It has more customers (80 million) than any other corporation. While General Motors Corp. and Standard Oil of New Jersey sales may be higher, AT&T earnings surpass both. AT&T and its associated telephone subsidiaries annually spend three times the amount GM allocates for new facilities and equipment. In 1966, the AT&T figure was $4.2 billion.

**e. Status on Plastics. (1) Polyethylene.** With the advent of PE in the early 1940's (see Plastics World Report on 25 Years of Polyethylene, January 1967 issue, pp. 26 to 35), a new approach was taken to produce wire. PE provides excellent physical and electrical characteristics. Its low moisture pickup, ease of processing and low volume cost has made its use expand significantly. Modifications have been made to meet different requirements. As an example, carbon black compound ($2\frac{1}{2}\%$, by weight) provided the outer cable sheath with more resistance to ultraviolet rays.

Low density, high molecular weight PE is particularly noted for its processibility low dielectric constant, low dissipation factor and excellent electrical stability. In contrast, high density PE has longer chain molecules more tightly packed together which results in a harder material with higher tensile strength and higher dielectric constant (2.34 vs 2.27). REA specifications now require the use of HDPE in telephone wire because of improved mechanical properties when compared to LDPE.

Simplex, pioneer in PE for high voltage, has installed 138 kv cables. These VSP (Voltage Stabilized PE) submarine power cables are being used for installations such as off shore oil well drilling platforms. The VSP with its special additive provides superior electrical properties to LDPE. These cables are also being evaluated for much higher power lines.

A wide variety of PE has been developed for specific applications such as semi-conductive PE to replace fabric tape insulation in order to eliminate the problem of stress points in a cable caused by the tape lap. Cellular PE based on either low- or high-density polymers has improved performance in coaxial cable still further by providing lower dielectric constants than solid PE (1.5 and 1.7 compared to 2.27 and 2.34) PE with vinyl acetate improves stress cracking and low temperature properties. Crosslinked or vulcanized thermoset PE provides increased thermal properties and reduces environmental degradation and nearly the same electrical properties as are available in the regular thermoplastic PE. This year the consumption of these chemically crosslinkable compounds should be over 50 million lb with significant increases expected in the future.

Many plastics materials are being developed specifically for this expanding market. As an example, U.S. Industrial Chemicals Co. has just released nine new cross-linkable PE compounds specifically for wire and cable coatings. They have higher heat and stress crack resistance and broader electrical and chemical properties than conventional low, medium and high-density PE's.

A new high molecular weight LDPE tailored specifically for wire and cable insulation applications, is also available from Phillips Petroleum Co. Marlex TR-604MD provides long life in applications of high voltage primary insulation. This Type I, Class A, Grade 5 resin (ASTM D1248-65T) has a 0.917 density and 0.2 melt index. It exceeds specification requirements of IPCEA S-61-402 (NEMA WC-5-1961). A new low density foamable PE, Marlex TR-610 also from Phillips, provides insulation thickness ranging at least from 12 mils to $\frac{1}{4}$ in.

*(2) Polyvinyl Chloride.* Since its introduction in the late 1930's, PVC has been the workhorse for low voltage cables. In this country it has been practically restricted to 600-V lines. In Europe, due to lower cost and availability, PVC is used in service up to 36,000-V. Since World War II, with the target to save material, PVC has taken over many of the European products which previously used a rubber insulation. Plastics Wire and Cable Corp. has been a leader in developing the use of PVC for applications such as mining machine cables, THW (thermoplastic, heat resistant, water resistant) building wire and THW-N (nylon jacket) building wire.

PVC compounds are made in a broad spectrum of properties for use from 60° to 105°C in both wet and dry locations. Major advantages in the low voltage insulation field are its toughness; satisfactory insulating, outdoor weathering, and mechanical properties; attractive appearance; and inherent resistance to flame, ozone, corona discharges, oils, acids, and alkalies. These properties with other advantages, such as ease of handling and low cost, have made it take over the building wire field with the probability of making more inroads on rubber and elastomer insulated wire in the 600-V range.

Further improvements in resin, plasticizer and stabilizers will permit this compound to expand its usage in other areas, including cross-linkable PVC. An example of a special compound is Monsanto's conductive compound with a mineral filler to provide controlled electrical bleed-off.

For the latest information on plasticizers see *Plastics World,* August 1966, pp. 38–47. This year's plasticizer consumption for wire and cable insulation will be over the ¼ billion lb mark.

Stabilizers for wire and cable now total about 15 million pounds per year consumption. The majority are lead compounds because for electrical reasons they are the most practical and useful. It is known that heating PVC above 180°C will produce serious color change. Heat degradation occurs through duel mechanism of dehydrochlorination and oxidation. Under normal processing conditions, the former reaction (loss of hydrogen chloride) predominates. Since the MCl promotes ultimate degradation, it is necessary to remove or chemically combine this material as effectively as possible. When electrical properties are required, it is essential that this chemical combination not result in an electrolytic conductor, and it is necessary to combine the HCl into insoluble and nonionizable end products. Of all metals known, only silver, mercurous mercury and lead form insoluble chlorides. As a result, some form of reactive lead compound is the most suitable and practical source of HCl acceptor. Sometimes other compounds are used such as barium, cadmium, tin and sodium.

Newest from National Lead Co. in lead compounds are the XL family and Lectro 80. The lead chlorosilicate sulfates (or XL's) have built-in coatings on leads particles to provide improved interface between the stabilizer and PVC. The result is better dispersion and processing of PVC for fast automatic dry blending as well as improved electrical and moisture resistance. The Lectro 80 is the multipurpose stabilizer for dry blends. With this single inventory product, different PVC compounds can be prepared to provide low cost and low gravity performance.

Recent developments in barium/cadmium stabilizers are improving extrusion rates, surface characteristics and plant handling of compounds. Typical of these additives are R. T. Vanderbilt Co's Vanstay 4030 and HTE.

**(3) Elastomers.** At one time natural rubber had no competition in insulating or jacketing applications. Today, in the U.S., practically none of it is used with wire. It is still used in large amounts in Europe and Russia. The first replacements for rubber were the styrene butadiene (SBR) elastomers for low voltage applications in the early 1940's. By 1950 butyl rubber started to replace oil-base natural rubber in high voltage insulation. Now crosslinked PE is in the process of replacing butyl for many applications where flexibility is not a requirement. Ethylene propylene (EPM) will be replacing butyl where flexibility is required.

Neoprene continues to be used primarily as a cable covering or jacket material. Because of its high chlorine content, it provides insulation in very low voltage applications. It is capable of operating over a wide temperature range—as low as $-55\,°C$ when suitably formulated. Compounds are also used which operate up to $90\,°C$ or for a short time of a few hours at $260\,°C$. Neoprene provides good mechanical strength including tear resistance, flexibility and abrasion resistance; also, flame, oil and chemical resistance. Consumption this year is expected to be 80 million pounds for insulation.

For higher temperature operation, silicone rubbers have made their mark. They are presently the only power cable insulation which can carry a rating of $125\,°C$. For special applications it may be rated up to $200\,°C$ for short periods of time. These synthetic rubbers can be made tough for use in jacketing to resist abuse, even though there is some sacrifice in electrical properties.

At present, there is no single polymer to improve low-temperature flexibility without sacrifice of desirable electrical and physical properties. Compromises can be made in blends to improve an acceptable balance in characteristics. One of the newest consists of 60% high-molecular-weight polyisobutylene and 40% high-density ethylene copolymer.

Other elastomers being evaluated for special applications include urethane, ethylene propylene copolymer and terpolymer, and fluorinated hydrocarbon polymers. For more information on elastomers, see *Plastics World* "Report on Elastomers Perform and Prosper," April 1967, pp. 30–36.

**(4)** *Polypropylene.* When compared to PE, PP copolymer is extremely resistant to environmental stress cracking and has desirable lower dielectric constant and density. It also has higher temperature rating, toughness, crystallinity (harder) and softening point. The latest copolymers have rectified some of the problems experienced when only homopolymers were available. Low temperature properties and elongation have been improved.

The copper-poisoning (copper inhibits and degrades PP) has been improved by using special stabilizers in all types of PP. However based on work being conducted by different companies major improvements are occurring. As an example, Geigy's Chel 180 approximately doubles operating performance normally obtained in standard formulations. Present major reason for developing PP copolymer insulation is to produce defect-free telephone cables for REA. This action follows the work pioneered by U.S. Steel Corp. in using PP copolymer in a number of products.

**(5) Polyester.** There are three suppliers: DuPont's Mylar, 3M's Scotchpar, and Celanese Celanar. These products are largely used in the form of tapes. This material is particularly useful in high temperature resistant environments. In addition to excellent electrical, chemical and thermal properties, the tape material is transparent, flexible and tough. The film retains these properties from −60 to 150°C. Major uses are for primary insulation and shield insulation.

**(6) Polysulfone.** Produced by Union Carbide Corp. this product is a tough, abrasion resistant, high temperature insulation. It has been assigned a provisional temperature rating of 140°C by Underwriters' Laboratories. Because of its heat resistance and low cost it is expected to make some inroads in areas where flurocarbons are being used.

**(7) Polyimide.** Supplied only by DuPont in the form of their Kapton film, this polymer does not melt and only begins to char above 800°C. Successful applications range from −269 to 400°C. At room temperature its properties are similar to polyester. However, as the temperature changes, there is less change in stiffness than with polyester. Electrical properties remain nearly constant over the wide temperature range and frequency.

Wire insulated with polyimide or polyimide-fluorocarbon composite meets the new Navy rigid specification MIL-W-81381 (AS) for use in high performance aerospace electric systems. They provide effective insulation particularly in thin films, with the result that substantial savings in space and weight occurs.

**(8) Fluorocarbons.** Fluorocarbons do the job where the total system is expensive and requires extreme high reliability. They are characterized by extreme chemical inertness, do not burn and are thermally stable to at least 500°F.

**(9) Urethanes.** Big potential exists for urethane elastomers principally because fluorocarbon properties can be approached at a much lower cost. Most important properties are toughness, chemical resistance and good electrical behavior. They have not arrived, as yet, in large production orders but future success seems certain. Thanks to the development of raw materials for use in producing urethane foams, these elastomer types will have lower costs.

**(10) Ethylene Propylene.** These EPM's have been successfully introduced in high voltage insulation. For the low voltage and jacketing uses, ethylene propylene terpolymer (EPDM) has been developed. This year the fluorinated ethylene-propylene polymer have received from the National Fire Protection Association tentative interim approval for use with fixture wires operating up to 150 or 200°C. These polymers are designated by NFPA as PF, PGF, PFF and PGFF.

**f. Production Facilities on the Increase.** To meet the industry's present and future requirement for insulated wire production, increased production is now occurring in existing facilities and large new facilities are being built. Within six years output is expected to be at least doubled. A significant change is occurring at Western Electric where they are now purchasing more machinery from the machinery manufacturers to keep up-to-date on the latest technology. Previously they designed and manufactured most of their own plastic machinery.

Extruders will also have a wider choice of complete processing lines available. An example is the recent announcement by The Fellows Gear Shaper Company that they are now providing sales, engineering and service on all models of Scholemann twin screw extruders in the United States and Canada.

Another significant factor is that there is more than a one year backlog of orders for certain machinery. Delivery is particularly slow for certain types of complete systems.

Insulating 19–26 gauge telephone wire in $2\frac{1}{2}$ in. diameter extruder lines at 4,000 ft/min is now a way of life, with faster lines already on site. More of these lines are installing wire drawing machines in tandem with insulating equipment instead of using predrawn wire. Highly sophisticated electro-mechanical systems are used to control the many different operations. Building wires of 10–14 gauge using 6 in. diameter extruders are produced at 3000 ft/min with no print marks. If printing is required during extrusion then speeds are somewhat lower. The $4\frac{1}{2}$ in. diameter extrusion lines are more widely used with speeds in the 2000 ft/min bracket (12 and 14 gauge). A major trend is that more non-metallic sheath building wire will be produced. Both the insulation and jacket is made of PVC.

The state-of-the-art in extruder screw technology is advancing to meet higher output rates, increasing the quality control and processing efficiency of new poylmers. Changes are being made by processors, material suppliers, and machinery manufacturers. From Western Electric comes a new digital paper tape recording system to provide immediate and accurate information on temperature and pressure of the polymer at various points in the barrel of the machine. Work on various extruders show that obtaining scale-up data on a $2\frac{1}{2}$ in. diameter machine is satisfactory for 8 in. machine. Temperature and pressure action in an 8 in. is very similar to the $2\frac{1}{2}$ in.

In a similar vein, Monsanto has developed computer techniques for predicting flow behavior of both LDPE and HDPE at various temperatures. They have applied this computer program to the scale-up of special extruder screw designs. The company also uses computer technology to translate basic polymer knowledge into resins for specific applications.

Many plastics and machine suppliers provide inhouse test facilities for evaluating finished wire products. Union Carbide Corp. started concentrating in this area back during the 1930's. They have been a leader in this area with the probability that they continue to have more production inhouse test facilities than any electrical wire producer. During the past decades wire and cable industrial growth was achieved through the help of companies such as Union Carbide, B. F. Goodrich Chemical, DuPont, Monsanto, Phillips Petroleum, Eastman Chemical, U.S. Industrial Chemicals, Pennsalt, Dow Chemical, Dow Corning, General Electric and 3M. The plastics companies have conducted the necessary chemical and mechanical research and development programs, but more important is the unparalleled service back-up to the wire coating industry.

**g. Tape Wrapping.** Tapes are split between pressure sensitive (e.g., 3M, Permacel, Plymouth Rubber) and nonpressure (e.g., Extrudo Film Corp., Hercules Co.). Tape constructions can provide electrical and mechanical characteristics different than what are available with extruded insulations. As an example, tape is required for miniaturization. Fine wires cannot be handled on an extrusion line. They are also required to meet specific manufacturing demands. Extruding a plastics jacketing material directly around bundles of insulated wires can cause heat degradation of the insulated wires. Wrapping insulating tape around the bundles prior to the application of a jacketing material provides thermal protection.

The current polyester, PP, polyimide, fluoropolymer and other tapes make an extremely versatile group of products which can be used in many ways. Films and tapes are unique in their ability to conform to irregular contours in a fashion which cannot be matched with other forms of plastics. Also, these thinner films are much more efficient insulators than thicker sections because of higher voltage per mil required for breakdown to initiate. To achieve their higher insulation efficiency it is essential that the films be free of pinholes.

Laminated tapes, such as PP/polyester, provide a combination of low cost and excellent electrical properties for many applications. Donald Kingsley, manager of specialized marketing section at Extrudo, reports that experimental laminates include PP/glass paper, PP/spun bonded non-woven polyester fibers and PP/polyimide.

**h. Flat Cable.** Increasing demand for smaller, lighter weight, and lower cost electronic packages has expanded the use of flat flexible and printed wiring cables. They are used in missiles, rockets, and satellite systems; ground support equipment for defense; industrial computers; instrument and control systems; sensing and feedback equipment; telemetering and communication equipment. Manufacturing methods for the flat cables have been developed with varying degrees of success. The most successful involve the laminating and etching processes. Other processes include extrusion, printing, molding and vacuum deposition.

This year Alexander S. Basil, president of the Rockbestos Wire and Cable Co. introduced a line of flat cables. This is the first entry of a wire and cable producer into the flat cable market presently estimated to be $40 million/year. Average cable thickness is 3 mils using polyimide, fluorocarbon, polyester or PVC films for operation from $-100$ to $250°C$.

**i. Magnet Wire.** Another important area for plastics is in magnet wire for use in wound devices such as motors and transformers. Polyvinyl formals, such as Monsanto's Formvar, have been the workhorses of magnet wire since the early 1940's. This type resin is currently used in over 50% of all magnet wire insulation due to its toughness and adhesion. Other dip-coated resins are acrylic, epoxy, polyamide, polyester, polyimide, polyvinyl butyral, polyvinylidene fluoride-phenolic and urea-formaldehyde.

**j. Next Ten Years.** The activities and interests of the wire and cable producers ranges from fabricating their own plastic conduit, to setting up tandem and even triple extruders in wire production lines. More use is being made of underground installation of prewired conduits. PVC is used for the conduits.

Major strides are being made by machinery designers in order to operate at higher speeds. Mechanization includes more use of dry blending equipment and de-airing before extrusion. All this action will lead to higher speed fusing of plastics in wire coating.

Probably over 90% of today's insulated wire needs can be filled with standard plastics and machinery products. To make this knowledge more universally useful, the problem is to economically cross-fertilize different industries. If wire, plastics and machinery engineers are to reflect meaningful performance requirements, they must be kept up to date on available products and continually be up-dating specifications.

The never-ending task is now with the wire industry to provide narrower property limits than initially allowed in the accepted broad specifications. Properties to consider for streamlining are density, melt index, tensile and electrical characteristics, stress crack resistance, brittleness temperature, moisture absorption and carbon black dispersion.

REA forecasts that the consumption rate of insulated wires and cables in the next ten years will increase by as much as 400%. The manufacturing industry is presently expanding in a major way to provide new manufacturing capacities to meet these needs. At least seven new cable plants will be constructed during the course of this year. One of the smaller companies producing sophisticated wire and cable, the Plastoid Corp., is now completing a $1 million plant expansion. With an addition of 43,000 sq ft, a total of 219,000 sq ft will support an $18 million backlog. Sales for 1965 and 1966 have grown from $9 million to $14 million with earnings soaring. Executive Vice President E. H. "Bud" Cooper explains that the growth is the result of a realization of long term research and development efforts.

In revamping railway communications, large numbers of communication equipment will be required. Communication needs for defense are increasing at a rapid rate. Other organizations requiring more wire include the Municipal Signal Association, Bureau of Ships, Bureau of Mines, Federal Aviation Authority, Community Antenna Television Industry, and cable supplied abroad under AID programs.

### E. Growth with Electronics

U. S. Department of Commerce statistics show that the electronics market is growing faster than total U. S. industry. Plastics are also growing faster. Between 1958 and 1963 "valued added" by electronic component companies rose 78% from $1.4 billion to $190 billion. "Value added" is the difference between cost of products and the cost of materials used to produce them.

U. S. industry sales as reported by EIA in 1965 totaled $18.4 billion which includes $9.6 billion for defense and space, $5.0 billion for industrial-commercial, $3.1 billion for consumer and $0.7 for replacement. Total was $11 billion in 1960 with prediction of $21 billion in 1966 and $24 billion in 1970. Present sales (1966) are higher than last year's prediction, as was the case with plastics, due to the escalation of the Vietnam war, the continued rapid growth of computers, continued demand for color TV, and the steady increasing applications of a wide range of electronics in industry. The hot and cold war situation is causing the Defense Supply Agency to boost spending for electronics equipment by 20%.

Within the major segments of this industry pertinent facts directing growth are evident. The defense and space sales includes $2½ billion in research. Industrial-commercial electronics includes the equipment purchased by nonelectronic consumers, names automotive, pleasure boating, private aircraft and medical and educational institutions. Private aircraft potential is large but of course not nearly as large as what is now already in just one military airplane the F-111. Over 15% of the 1,500 being purchased accounts for electronics (at perhaps $1 million per aircraft).

It is reported that 25% of all engineers and scientists in the United States are employed by the electronics industry. There are approximately 6,000 to 7,000 firms active in electronics, up from 1,000 in 1947, with the rate to increase 5% yearly. The 20 largest producers in the industry have 50% of sales. Aerospace and automotive firms now have 25%, up from almost zero since World War II. An additional 15% originates with manufacturers of office equipment.

European electronic sales are also large. Total for 1965 was 7.2 billion with 1966 prediction at $8.0 billion. Major 1965 sales by country were $2.1 billion for West Germany, $1.7 billion for Great Britain, $1.5 billion for France and $0.7 billion for Italy.

## VI. Foams

The growth of plastic foams continues to be significant due to the inherent available properties and usefullness in different environments ranging from original to replacement parts in buildings, transportation vehicles, sports equipment, boats, underwater crafts, spacecrafts and others. Note that foamed materials are also referred to as cellular or expanded plastics. The environmental effects on foams can be recognized by the types of applications. This section will highlight typical uses.

In 1965 there were over 700 U.S. firms involved in the foam industry. They include oil companies, tire and rubber producers, textile mills, drug companies and nearly all of the major chemical companies. Hundreds of foams are on the market with many different characteristics (Fig. 16-31). Foams include slabs, preformed logs, sheets, rods, tubes, synthetics, choppings, netting tapes and particles. The foam-in-place types are liquids, beads, molding powders and plastisols. Foam mixtures are compounded to perform many functions, such as spraying ceilings. Vinyl plastisols using chemical blowing agents can be calendered, extruded, dip-coated or slush molded. There are at least nine basic raw material suppliers of polyols, ten of isocyanates, six of catalysts, three of surfactants, eleven of styrene monomer and five of styrene beads. With the quantity of basic materials increasing, new products continually develop. An example is Union Carbide Corporation's AFPI, which is similar to PAPI (polymethylene polyphenylisocyanate). The Upjohn Company, PAPI producer, is now examining the use of modified polymeric isocyanates for semirigid urethanes and to a limited extent in rigid urethanes. DuPont has developed a new inorganic foam system by treating colloidal alumina with small amounts of organic acids and their salts which varies in viscosity from liquid to paste form. Dow Corning Corporation has produced a new silicone cell control additive for flexible urethane foam which provides greater processing latitude. At a new plant in Kenton, Ohio, Hooker Chemical Corporation will produce Hetrofoam resins which are used to make inherent fire-retarded rigid urethane foam—no additive need be used to provide fire-retardance.

## A. Applications (15)

Formulators are able to control versatility of foams through varying the density (Fig. 16-32), cell geometry and size, strength-to-weight ratios, thermal and electrical insulation, mechanical flexibility or rigidity, corrosion resistance, color, processability, degree of adhesion to other materials and sound or microwave absorption. Parts can perform multifunctional use: insulation and load carrying, insulation and ease of application, or buoyancy and structural rigidity. For example, urethane foamed-in-place in a boat hull or hydrofoils

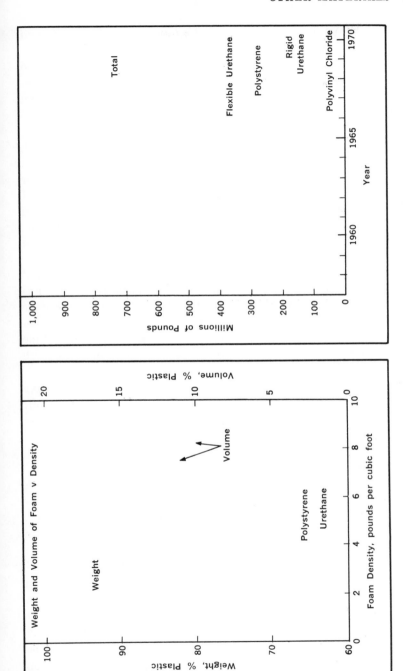

Fig. 16-32. Plastic foam consumption in U.S., growth and forecast, *Plastics World* survey.

Fig. 16-31. Weight and volume of foam vs. density.

makes the vehicles virtually unsinkable, reduces noise level and reduces structural vibration.

Similar to other materials, foams have limitations (16,17,18). No foam is fireproof but many of them can be made flame-resistant. Phenolics and silicones have excellent heat resistance but could crumble when subjected to vibrational stress. Many foams can be affected by solvents, but fluoronated types resist them.

Almost 45% of the total flexible foam produced in 1965, of which 70% is urethane, will be used in furniture cushioning and upholstery. To date, most of its use has been in replacement. Another major outlet is transportation which this year will account for 16% of flexibles (one-half PVC, the other half urethane) and 14% of rigid (urethane). They will be used mainly in automobiles for seating, crash pads, arm rests, carburetor air filters, sun visor pads, thermal and sound insulators, gaskets, and door panels.

Rigid urethane with fluorocarbon is recognized by tank car and trailer manufacturers to be the most efficient insulator. This immediate large market would permit refrigerated units increase storage capacity and probably also reduce weight. Use of foam insulation is also on the increase in refrigerated warehouses and pipes. Pipe insulation can be made by spraying, foam-in-place, or from slab stock and shaped stock

Other major uses for flexible foam in 1965 were in the competitive mattress product (16% of the total flexible foams and mostly urethane), clothing interliners for garments, shoes and accessories (5%), growing carpet underlay market (4%), packaging (4%), and wire and cable which now uses only pothethylene (5%), while polypropylene is being reevaluated.

In addition to the rigid foam going into the transportation market, major outlets include building and construction (30% of rigid production, with probably 20% in polystyrene and 10% urethane), packaging for cups and dishes (20%), appliances (20%) and marine (8%).

Roofing insulation, a big single potential for rigids, is now dominated by standard fiberboard, glass fiber and inorganic types. In 1964, this market was reported to be $36.0 million, with $15.6 million of glass fiber at 5¢ per board foot, $15.0 million of wood fiber at 4¢ and $5.5 million of rigid foam, primarily polystyrene at 5¢ and some urethane at 7¢. This year, 610 million sq ft are expected to be used at a cost of $61 million, and by 1970 may reach 710 million sq ft.

Fig. 16-33. Gerber Legendary Blades of West Linn, Oregon, uses Scott Paper Company's foam for protecting and cushioning their cutlery. The material is a flexible ester-type polyurethane foam which is permanently flocked with short, 1 mm, rayon fibers by means of an adhesive.

## B. Types of Foams

### 1. Urethane

Flexible urethanes continues to dominate the market. In the furniture and mattress business, it continues to replax latex foam, previously made of natural rubber and now predominantly butadiene-styrene. The combination of providing exceptional service and favorable price has made flexible urethane the standard.

The long range potential for rigid urethane indicates that it will equal polystyrene foam sales by 1970. Progress in the rigid has been slower than in the flexible for the following reasons: immediate large sales for flexible existed, markets for rigid foam were more expensive to penetrate, most of the industry's time and capital was spent on the immediately profitable flexible market, rigid has a higher cost and fewer sources for applying the foam (Fig. 16-34).

## 2. Polystyrene

Compared to other plastics, polystyrene foam is the construction industry's principal industrial wall and cold storage insulation. Total foam penetration in this huge market is comparatively small. According to the latest industry reports to help get a bigger share of this market, cost reductions have been brought about by production research that reduces polystyrene density without adversely affecting properties. Densities as low as $\frac{1}{2}$ lb/cu ft have been obtained with

Fig. 16-34. Insulating storage tanks in the temperature range of $-425$ to $250°F$ can easily be accomplished by using these boards from the Lacy Oil Tool Company of Long Beach, Calif. They are made up of a one inch or more thickness of a two pound density urethane foam manufactured by The Upjohn Company. The outside surface of these boards is bonded to glass fiber polyester resin laminates which make them weather and vandal proof.

more reasonable processing cost on bead forms. The lowest density for extruded sheets resulting in cost savings was at 1.6 lb/cu ft.

Even though rigid urethanes and polystyrenes are the present favorite for growth in building and construction, another new rigid foamable polymer could be developed to take their place. There are an infinite number of resinous compositions from which foams can be made, as all polymers can be expanded by a gas.

### 3. Polyvinyl Chloride

Flexible extruded foam of polyvinyl chloride ranging in density of 12–60 lb/cu. ft. consumed 22 million pounds in 1962, going to 45 million in 1965, and predicted at 100 million in 1970. One-third of the market is for automobile upholstery, since PVC foam can be sealed easily to vinyl surfacing sheet. Furniture accounts for another one-third, while one-tenth of the market is in wearing apparel, such as foam jackets and coats. The market developed largely to nonleaching plasticizers which permitted dry cleaning of the garments. With the growing potential in flexible PVC foams now developing in the ladies hand bag field, flexible urethanes are trying to enter this profitable business.

Until 1965, rigid PVC foams were never competitive with other foams, so that only approximately 4 million lb were consumed in 1962, growing to 8 million lb in 1965, and 24 million by 1970. New English and French processes are reported to produce foam on a large scale which will make it competitive with other rigid foams. This development could increase the predicted future potential in marine flotation, wire and pipe insulation and other applications.

Polyethylene foam markets will continue to grow and hold approximately 5% of the total flexible foam market. The high density nitrogen-filled type makes up the major portion. It is required in wire and cable electrical insulation because of its exceptional dielectric and strength properties. Growing competition again is with polypropylene foam. The low density type of PP, approximately 2 million lb in 1965, will have limited use in packaging, gaskets and practice golf balls.

### 4. Phenolic Foam

In the United States, the only large application for phenolic foam continues to be in the decorative floral market. Its open cell structure and low water absorption permits a large volume of water to remain with the flower holder. This type of foam is also used for insulation in Europe as it has particularly good fire-retardance and heat resistance.

## 5. Syntactic Foam

Microballoons, or spheres, ranging in diameter from 30 $\mu$ to 0.0004 in. of phenolic, urea, glass or silica combined with epoxy, polyester, phenolic or urea resin produces a unique syntactic foam. These high strength 8-50 lb/cu ft foams are used as void fillers in boats, cores for aircraft sandwich structure, refrigerator cores, microwave absorbers, high frequency communication antennas and deep submergence vessels.

## VIII. Films

In order to develop plastic applications which permit operation under different environments, one major form for these plastics is in film or sheet form. Industry generally identifies a film as being 10 mils or thinner, whereas sheets are thicker. Throughout this book reference and discussions have been made to the use of films. In Chapter I a rather complete table is included identifying the different plastics used and their properties, such as polyethylene, polystyrene, polyproplyene, polyvinyl chloride, urethane, cellulose acetate, etc. Typical applications are shown in Figs. 16-35 through 16-39.

Within recent history, polyethylene meant big sheets of a durable workhorse plastic, priced so attractively that it appealed to contractors as moisture proofing membrane under concrete building slabs; to farmers as silage covering, pond liners, and crop mulch and to converters and manufacturers as bag and liner materials of broad usefulness, largely on the less-than-glamorous side of packaging. If it had stayed right there, growing along with existing large markets, polyethylene would still be a large volume plastic (19).

After twenty years of somewhat prosaic usefulness, polyethylene is going into high-ticket display packaging and novelty areas in direct competition with fabric, foil, coated and high-finish paper and specialized variations on all of these. In several instances within the past year, it has met head-on and quickly displaced such long-established packaging methods as the blister pack, coming up with

Fig. 16-35. Polyethylene film used as liner between water and ground. (Courtesy of the Union Carbide.)

a more attractive and useful protective mass production package at as little as half the cost.

At the same time, the basic product that has represented the major use of polyethylene, sheeting, is itself undergoing a process of evolution and development toward greater physical strength, resistance to flaming and greatly lessened static properties. Its use as the basic material for other-than-disposable apparel and household items exist. This is an area of certain future growth, spurred by the development of taffeta embossed, printed and other specialized materials. Now barely into its third decade of development and evolution, polyethylene has this status and these prospects for further growth with the new look of embossed fabric patterns and printing colors of 20,000 shades, surface metallics as competitors for foil.

Taffeta-embossed polyethylene looks, feels, handles, draps and even sounds like fine woven fabric. Althouh known as taffeta in the trade, it more closely resembles the filmy lightness of hand, the smoothness and flexibility of chiffon. Despite the marked surface texture that gives embossed polyethylene its fabriclike qualities, its surface will take printing with extremely fine definition and no fuzzing. It is also amenable to all the printing, cutting, sealing and other processes by which bags, covers and other end-use products are made by converters and manufacturers in conventional polyethylene.

Fig. 16-36. This is the first manned jump using a plastic film parachute, on February 4, 1966, near Sioux Falls, South Dakota. This Raven Industries, Inc., development permitted Nick Piantanida to have a 360 degree rotation of the 37.5 ft chute in about 10 sec during the 5,000 ft drop. A nonwoven polypropylene fiber scrim laminated between two polyethylene films is used as the canopy material. The nonwoven scrime provides a floating lattice structure for optimum strength distribution and rip stop properties. Polypropylene yarns encased and sealed in a polyethylene sheath are used for shroud lines. Each shroud line is a continuous web extending from the harness attachment fitting to the canopy wing, over the crown to the opposite wing and down to the opposite harness attachment fitting. Two days later Nick made a record balloon ascent to 123,000 ft using a Raven 5,000,000 cu ft polyethylene film balloon.

In some of the largest sales areas for embossed polyethylene, the material has proved itself an substitute for woven fabric in disposable personal articles. Hospital bed pads, which bar seepage of blood or potentially infectious liquids into mattresses, and baby diapers that are comfortable and disposable are two of the best current and potential markets for taffeta embossed material, particularly in light pastel shades.

Some manufacturers of hard goods have been using polyethylene in tubular form for covering palletized hard goods, such as aluminum

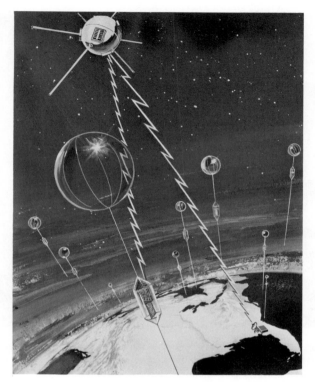

Fig. 16-37. Artists' concept of a proposed method of weather forecasting, involving up to 5,000 film balloons carrying sensing and radio apparatus. They would fit into the system of relaying data to satellites and ground stations. (Courtesy of G.T. Schjeldahl Company.)

that were once considered beyond the need of protection. These materials do not rust or corrode, but they are often compounded so that soot and other airborne contaminants can be a real problem.

## A. Coloring and Packaging

Colored polyethylene has long been a staple in limited selection due to the technical difficulties of shifting the extruder from one shade to another, limiting color to a relatively narrow range and specific order had to start at a minimum of 30,000 pounds. Color orders can now be filled for as little as 1000–2000 lb. The prices of colored polyethylene sloping downward, selection for exact color match can now be made from about 20,000 different shades.

Fig. 16-38. In a cold room where the temperature may be dropped to 60 degrees below zero, a scientist examines experimental sheets of a new cellophane developed by Olin Mathieson Chemical Corp.

The use of a widening selection of metallic polyethylenes in packaging, competing with foils, is doubtless going to follow the same marketing-evolution pattern that brought in metallics in the first place. Where the foils succeeded, so will the metallics; where the package catches the eye more effectively than the contents.

Metallic polyethylene has the quality look that lends itself to package upgrading, still retaining the physical advantages and the low cost of polyethylene. Techniques of production of bags and liners, of handling and particularly of sealing or closure are fully developed.

Skin packaging is far from new as a basic technique, but it has also been a developing art that has recently employed the latest in what is generally referred to as specification polyethylene film. Skin packaging has traditionally employed a paper backing board, coated with an adhesive, to which the film adheres under negative pressure and heat.

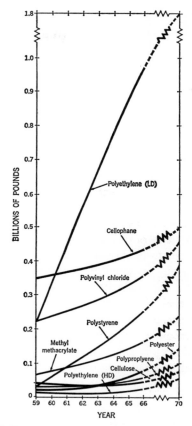

Fig. 16-39. Estimated U.S. consumption for film and sheet: **1966, 2.5** billion pounds; 1970, 3.7 billion pounds.

## B. Evolution of the Basic Product

At the same time that specialized, highly competitive forms of polyethylene have been coming into competition with other materials, all primary manufacturers have been working on improving the basic product for use in the fields where it has been dominant for the past twenty years.

Perhaps the most important in potential is the practical development of a high-strength material. This new copolymer type has more than twice the puncture resistance of conventional polyethylene, as well as greatly increased tear strength. It has much migher resistance to cracking at folds and seams than was formerly experienced, and puts polyethylene, which had just about every other qualification necessary, well in the running for single and multi-wall bags and similar containers, particularly for large-scale use with heavy, sharp pointed materials. There are also indications of significant economic benefits. Although the basic price for the high-strength material is necessarily higher at this point in its development, its increased strength will enable the user to reduce-thickness of material to the point where net savings can be effected in many applications. In addition, this new material (which is also available in colors and embossed textures) is going to put polyethylene in a better position against competitive materials such as woven fabrics.

The new antistatic polyethylene offers a double advantage to many users. It is much safer for the manufacturer who must package goods in areas where airborne dust or explosive vapors are a hazard. To the retailer, it means a package that will resist attracting dust during extended storage or display on open shelves.

Although polyethylene in general does not readily support flame, there are areas of use, particularly in hospitals and institutions where ultimate flame retardant characteristics are desirable. Until now, it has been difficult to get flame retardant qualities in polyethylene without sacrificing some of the material's other desirable qualities of pliability, broad color range, and low cost. The new flame retardant polyethylenes which retain these desirable characteristics are a breakthrough.

### C. New Fields of Application

Improvement of the basic product, development of new products to compete where competition was formerly impossible, are only part of the structure of polyethylene's present and potential stature. The desperately competitive market in which it has had to fight for life has led it into several fields of application in which use of the material as part of an integrated system, rather than direct product improvement, has made it useful and economically attractive.

An outstanding example of this is the wedding of the polyethylene liner and the infinite range of sizes and configurations of the corrugated container. Here is a situation in which two basic, universally-obtainable products compliment each other. The current market is one in which the separate polyethylene liner and the corrugated container most often come together at or near the point of use. There are several plans by large manufacturers to make the liner and the folded carton generally available as a factory-assembled package, cutting down the cost of insertion by the user. Food packaging, in which corrugated has made its greatest recent inroads, is the very area in which the combination shows some of its greatest promise.

At present, the poly/corrugated packaging combination exists as a strong competitor with metal and fiber drums and cans, lined or unlined, with the corrugated or other type container internally coated with polyethylene or protectives, and with plastic containers. Its rectangular shape alone gives it a competitive advantage over the cylindrical drum which packs and loads far less efficiently. It is also far lighter in weight. Its chief advantage is cost. Components are low in price, low enough to give one-time use (no cleaning, repairs, return charges) and still be sharply competitive. It is also no secret that corrugated containers in almost any size or configuration are at hand universally, or readily available. The same applies to the polyethylene liner. If standard sizes don't fit the container needed for a certain job, they can be run to fit.

There are a number of industrial products whose inherent nature and transportation patterns require the type of low-cost protection that polyethylene is best suited to give and at the same time need product identification/promotion that the product itself cannot possibly project, e.g., gypsum wall-board, or composition board, stacked on flatcars with only the thin edges visible. The flatcar, which may be 50 or more feet in length, is a natural for the continuous broad lengths of sheeting in which polyethylene is available. Skids and pallets of so-called unpackageable materials are now covered with clear or colored tubular polyethylene, sealed at one end to form a weather and contaminant-proof pullover cover and printed.

Another application in which existing materials are integrated to form a useful system is in color coding. A metals refinery, for instance, may produce a number of different alloys that are metallurgically distinct but look alike. An acre of these palletized ingots requires that an inventory be made by close scrutiny of the identifying labels on each skidload. Each alloy could be covered with a protective polyethylene bag of a distinctive color. Inventory could then be made by identifying the color of the covers.

In the market place, polyethylene has always had two basic appeals. It offers probably the lowest cost per job performed of any material, (in many cases including paper), and it sheds moisture. Its primary assignment has been protection for packaging. Regarded from both a current status and potential point of view, this means that conventional, improved and special new polyethylenes of all manufacturers are largely involved in containing goods, shedding moisture or other contaminants, and at the same time displaying and/or promoting products.

Polyethylene will doubtless continue to grow in uses where good packaging must also be inexpensive enough to be disposable without affecting product unit price adversely. Here polyethylene steps into the highly promising bulk milk and similar home dispensing consumer mass markets. It has also long been a staple in critical disposal jobs such as container liners for handling contaminated materials in hospitals.

### D. Types

Use of film and sheeting continually grows in consumption. Two and a half billion lbs, worth at least $1.5 billion in materials and $3 billion in processing and converting, will be put to use in 1967. In 1970, 3.75 billion lbs may very well be used (see Fig. 16-39).

Approximately 85% of the total consumption is of film less than 0.010 in. thick. Its major use is in packaging of produce, baked goods, meat, poultry, frozen foods, dry cleaning, etc. The next major market is industrial products such as magnetic tape, electrical insulation, photographic film, and pressure sensitive tape.

Plastic sheet—materials more than 0.010 in. thick—is used extensively in major growth markets: building construction, chemical processing equipment, appliances, electronics, transportation and agriculture. One major contribution of plastic sheet is resistance to both corrosion and weather.

ASTM defines film as an optional term for sheet having a nominal thickness not greater than 0.010 in. However, some companies and segments of industry separate film and sheeting at 0.003 or 0.006 in., depending on the industry. In the packaging industry where most of the material is less than 0.005 in., film is the term predominantly used.

Combining two or more plastics to form a film is becoming more popular in order to combine diverse advantageous properties. When discrete separate layers of plastics are joined together by an adhesive, heat or other method, the finished product is called a laminate. The term composite is presently used when 2 or more plastics are simultaneously extruded.

Some film producers have been hard-pressed to make a reasonable profit since the margin from resin cost to manufacturing cost and selling price has narrowed.

Much more profitable growth ahead, though, is envisioned for all levels of manufacture. This is due to continuing price stabilization, increased production rates, discount rates coping with competition and growing consumer markets that see economical and merchandising advantages in its use.

The present trend shows some slight cost increases. For example, cost of polyethylene has gone up. Extrudo Film Corporation announced a general increase in the price of its PE films. Increased 2¢/lb were its industrial, cloudy and multi-wall paper bag liner grade. Up 1½¢/lb is a medium priced, general purpose grade, while a premium quality, general purpose film went up ½¢/lb. Dow Chemical Company raised various packaging film ¼ to 1¼¢/lb with general purpose at 34¢/lb. Dow discontinued marketing industrial PE grades. Dow also brought about the first increase for polystyrene film in many years. Its general purpose and treated, or fog-resistant, grades went up 3¢/lb.

High density PE price increases of 1¢/lb have been announced by Celanese Plastics Company, Union Carbide, DuPont and Eastman Chemical.

## 1. Polyethylene

According to various U.S. industry sources, there are about a dozen companies who process more than half of all polyethylene film and sheeting. Practically all of these twelve are captive operations of resin or chemical producers. Of all the total producers, but about the first big fifteeen have annual sales below $5 million for resale to converters. There are about 100 film manufacturers and 15,000 film converters in the country.

Harry C. Byrne, general sales manager for the VisQueen Division of Ethyl Corporation, believes that this record PE sales year can be attributed to rapidly expanding use in bread bags, overwrap for numerous products, and in such agricultural jobs as reservoir and irrigation ditch lining, mulching, and greenhouse covering.

Two major growth areas are now developing, according to William J. Sachs, manager of marketing for Mehl Manufacturing Co., Packaging Sub. of Phillips Petroleum Co. More use will be made of the sophisticated PE films which have good clarity and can be used in higher speed production of industrial equipment. With the new PE copolymers more durability and serviceability will be obtained when compared to conventional PE.

A typical independent film producer is the Favorite Plastic Corporation. It will use 20 million lb of PE resin this year. Its flame-retardant type is now a big seller for use as receptacle liners in hospitals and other institutions.

Composites are of interest to consumer markets. Alfred Slatin, general marketing manager of Extrudo Film Corporation, sees PE-vinyl acetate copolymers as expanding the use of PE. These copolymers provide the higher strength required in packaging produce and frozen foods, also heavy duty shipping bags.

PE, as well as polypropylene and its copolymers, now competes with fabrics, foil and other large production products, according to Gering Plastic Co., a department of Monsanto Co. The motivating stimulant has been the availability of colored film in small order lots of 1,000 lb which can be matched to at least 20,000 shades, including metallics. Broader color selection now puts taffeta-embossed film well within the reach of every converter and manufacturer.

Although PE has been throught of as a major competitor to cellophane, it has not turned out to be. The reason: PE has been used in applications for which cellophane could never be considered, such as packaging fresh products, covering meat, poultry, frozen foods and dairy products.

### 2. Polypropylene

Since 1960, when commercial quantities of PP film became available in the U.S., this more versatile material has made significant sales advances. Pioneers in film were Avisun, Crown Zellerbach, Cryovac Div. of W. R. Grace Co., Extrudo (now part of Enjay), Kordite (now part of Mobil Oil Co.), and Hercules Inc.

Polypropylene film manufacture has been limited to far fewer producers than has been the case in PE, because of higher capital investment requirements and more sophisticated processing technology. Of the eleven or so packaging film producers in the business today, seven produce non-oriented film for bread, baked goods, textiles, fresh produce, etc. Four of the seven also compete with the remaining four companies who are strong in oriented PP manufacture. Oriented PP is sold for laminates and overwrap, but special types are made for shrinkwrap.

According to Roger F. Jones of Avisun Corporation, this latter market is undergoing the most vigorous growth. He estimates PP shrink film sales to increase three-fold by 1970. Overall, PP film should shoot to at least 75 million lb by 1970.

Film clarity has been a critical problem with PE and in many cases determines equipment construction, operating conditions and choice of polymer. With PP this problem is essentially non-existent but requires more sophistication during manufacture. Oriented PP also matches the mechanical properties of that old workhorse, cellophane.

PP provides combinations of characteristics desirable for food packaging: long preservation of freshness, high tear resistance, stiffness, and adaptability to existing wrapping machines. In 1961, consumption was $3\frac{1}{2}$ million lb; this year's expectation is 45 million lbs. Carl Setterstron, vice president of marketing for Rexall Chemical Co. predicts that by 1970 it may be over 85 million lb, between copolymer and homopolymer.

Different types of PP films are commercially available. Non-oriented cast film is used largely in hosiery bags, candy twist wrap, etc. It competes with low density PE even though its cost is higher.

Also available are uniaxially oriented film, though this is no longer considered to be a major factor in the market; unbalanced film; balanced biaxially oriented film, and heat-seat balanced biaxially oriented PP film.

The real growth potential is for oriented film. Hercules Inc. produces a grade with balanced biaxially oriented properties especially designed for shrink packaging. It operates well on most standard manual and automatic packaging equipment designed to provide impulse wire or other cut-off seals. Center-folded film is available for use on "L" bar sealers. Hercules BX 300 film for overwraps is a modified balanced biaxially oriented film. It operates on high speed automatic overwrap machinery and hand wrap equipment that provides folded or overlap seals where the film is heat sealed to itself. BX film is claimed to have unique stiffness which permits its use with minor modification on overwrap equipment designed for cellophane.

At present, the only commercial heat-set, balanced biaxial PP film is produced by Hercules, though Union Carbide and W. R. Grace both produce balanced biaxially oriented film. Because it is heat-set, the B 500 grade is unusually stable, having less than 1% shrinkage in any direction up to 248°F. This characteristic makes it useful in such applications as laminated pressure sensitive tape, graphic arts (book covers, for instance), and reinforced paper.

After its 44th year in the U.S., cellophane (cello) use has been growing at an annual rate of 3–5%. A large portion of the sales is in premium grades, which cost more than ordinary cellophane. Many different grades are available and, in most applications, they are coated with other plastics to extend durability and eliminate restrictions such as moisture sensitivity. At the present time, improved cellophanes are on the horizon.

### 3. Polyvinyl Chloride

PVC provides a film having clarity, shrinkability and stretchability. W. J. Vogel, general manager of the Plastics Division of Reynolds Metals, recently stated that it is the only material reflecting a steady high growth pattern among the flexible films. An estimated 45 million lb of PVC shrink film this year is anticipated. As for the future, Diamond Alkali management estimates a 400% rise in PVC packaging film by 1970.

### 4. Polystyrene

This film is important because of its low cost and availability in different copolymers. A major new outlet for oriented PS is high-speed production of thermoformed parts. An improved brown Polyflex oriented polystyrene sheet for packaging chocolate candy and cookies is now available from Monsanto Company's Packaging Division. Trademarked Polyflex 0401 brown, the sheet has a deep rich chocolate brown color which complements packaged candy and cookies. Uniform distribution of brown pigment in the sheet is expected to result in a consistently colored better quality formed part, according to the company. The colored oriented polystyrene sheet is 10–20% lower in cost than other plastic sheet materials used for the packaging of candy and cookies. Polyflex 0401 brown is available in thicknesses ranging from 0.005 in. and in rolls up to 60 in. wide.

### 5. Methyl Methacrylate

Methyl methacrylate has had an annual growth rate of 10 to 17%. Its weather resistance and optical properties are the chief reasons for its growing popularity in signs, lighting, and architecture. Major sources for sheet as well as molding material are American Cyanamid and Rohm and Haas. DuPont is a major supplier of monomer to companies who produce sheets, such as Cast Optics Corp., Div. of Escambia Corporation; Landover Div. of National Lead Corporation; and Swedlow Corp. Swedlow produces continuous cast sheet as well as the individual double-plate cast sheet.

Rohm and Haas has just extended its marketing interest from Plexiglas acrylic sheet and Kydex acrylic-PVC sheet to thin acrylic film, trademarked Korad. Korad-C, the first film grade available in the new series, is extruded in thicknesses down to 0.002 in. and in widths up to 50 in. Korad-C was designed specifically for press laminations of outdoor printed or decorative signs principally to eliminate deterioration caused by sunlight. The film can be laminated to rigid, calendered PVC sheet using the same conditions as for regular vinyl overlay film. It can also be laminated to other substrates such as cloth, paper, wood veneer, steel and other acrylic.

For detailed data on film and sheet, see *Plastics World* Film and Sheet Property and Price Chart, *Plastics World* Directory Issue, October 1966, p. 151.

The rate of development of new materials, higher than ever in the plastics industry in general, is translated into a nearly immediate effect on the film and sheet market specifically.

Resins continually leave the test tubes to go to market. At General Electric Co., polyphenylene oxide (PPO) and its modified phenylene oxide, Noryl, sheets are now in semi-production with expectations that commercial production will begin next year. Under development is PPO film for use as capacitor covers, cable wrap, and printed circuitry all of which require low creep, high modulus, operating temperature range from $-275$ to $+375°F$ and/or hydrolytic stability.

Union Carbide's polysulfone is now available commercially in sheet form. Rigid vinyl film and sheeting are also being produced by Union Carbide's Plastics Division in thicknesses from one to 40 mils and in clear or colored forms for packaging food, drugs, housewares and other items. The films are shrinkable but have high dimensional stability at normal use temperatures. The sheets can be vacuum-formed easily with short cycles.

Allied Chemical has made nylon film capable of enduring heat up to 400°F in autoclave and hydroclave bag molding.

A new high density PE resin for blow molding is available from Phillips Petroleum Co. It requires processing temperatures 20–30°F lower than other HDPE. According to Phillips, Marlex 6003 offers high impact resistance, high melt strength, meets FDA food regulation and has excellent processability. Saranex is the name of a new family of film made by Dow Chemical Co. said to combine the properties of saran with the sealable and machinable qualities of PE. It is said to be adaptable easily to use on conventional form-fill-seal equipment.

Hercules Inc. has introduced bioriented PP film specifically to overcome problems encountered on existing cellophane overwrap equipment, while Mobil Chemical Co. has another bioriented PP film to compete with cellophane.

Southwest Research Institute has a film which is made by using proteins from grain and synthetic amino acids. In tensile strength, it equals PE with heat stability raised to 550°F. This newly developed film flexible at −300°F and provides low water transmission with controlled range of air permeability. It is reported by SRI that the film should be economically practical.

More composites or laminates of plastics are being produced to provide tailor-made properties. Plasticized PVC film is coated with PE or saran to improve barrier property. Fresh meat packaged in this laminate has long shelf life since it is protected from the degradation action of oxygen, carbon dioxide, water vapor, etc. A phenoxy resin core coated with PE made by the Pollock Div. of St. Regis Paper Co. provides strength, gas barrier, and optical properties.

Film as thin as 0.00002 in. (0.02 mil) has been produced. Most of the commercial grades being used range from 0.0005 in to 0.005 in. for film (with tolerance of ±10%) and up to 0.375 in. for sheet. In the more sophisticated applications, such as electrical tape film, thickness tolerance is more rigid.

### 6. Polyimide

As reported by DuPont, a major breakthrough has developed with its Kapton polyimide film. This expensive product has rapidly moved from development only supplier. The major advantages of polyimide are space and weight saving, high dielectric strength, high radiation stability and high heat resistance—up to 900°F. The present major market is wire and cable insulation. United States railroad and aerospace industries use this ultra-thin insulation film for space-saving and its capacity to hold up at temperatures high enough to melt or decompose most conventional plastic materials.

## 7. Cellulosic

Even with new films taking over major segments of the market, the older cellulosic types like cellulose acetate continue to grow at an average annual rate of 4%. As some market losses occurred, gains in others developed due to improved compounds and better engineered end applications. As an example, cellulose acetate dominates in the video tape market.

## 8. Polyester

Here is a film with different combinations of characteristics, such as heat resistance, tensile strength up to 40,000 psi, and tendency to remain flat. Growth applications are in electrical insulation, magnetic tape, drafting film and packaging such as boil-in-the-bag packaging.

## 9. Fluorocarbon

These polymers in film and sheet forms are finding new applications in electrical, chemical and industrial equipment. DuPont is now in the process of promoting use of FEP-fluorocarbon resin in flat electrical-flexible cables and roll covers in printing plants. DuPont makes not only the film, but the end use roll covers, as well. With FEP, cables can be designed to meet new wiring concepts. For example, by using 5 mil thick FEP, Electro-Mechanism, Inc. is able to furnish the necessary 1,200 printed circuits wih zero defects in the Saturn V small distribution boxes.

A DuPont technical representative, Carleton K. Nicholson, recently reported that printers claim an increase in their production time as a result of smoother operations and less maintenance afforded by FEP roll covers. In addition, surface properties of the covers improved the printing quality. The roll covers are transparent, flexible plastic tubes placed around rollers and then shrunk up to 20% of their diameter by means of heat guns. The FEP is 0.020 in. thick and available up to 18 ft diameter.

## 10. Specialty Films

Diamond Alkali and others are examining the polyvinyl-fluoride ($VF_2$) market, possibly using dispersion paint systems. For 25 years,

DuPont has been the sole producer of this film; it is used principally for electrical insulation and chemical resistant protective covers.

Industry sales of ethylene-vinyl acetate (EVA) coplymers climbed from zero in 1964 to 5 million lb in 1965. John K. Moffett, director of plastics sales for U.S. Industrial Chemicals, believes a reasonable potential by 1970 is 50 million lb. Applications include products previously made of rubber; high pressure industrial hose, flexible bushings, appliance bumper caps, medical syringes, toys, gloves, etc.

Pennsalt Chemicals' polyvinylidene fluoride resin, which has FDA approval, is now going into food processing. For those who want to use sheet at temperatures up to 1,000°F, there are ceramoplastics, such as Molecular Dielectrics' glass-bonded mica trademarked Mykroy.

## E. Markets

Fresh produce, baked foods and soft-goods (hosiery, shirts, socks, etc.) are big consumers of transparent flexible packaging materials. From 160 million lbs in 1962, these products now account for approximately 400 million lbs.

Cheese is another big market. In 1963, over 1.5 billion lb of cheese were consumed in the U.S. Paper, film and foil were used in packaging 55% of it, while over 40% was wrapped in plastic films. Short term storage of 3 days uses moisture proof cellophane or Pliofilm. Polyvinyl dichloride (PVDC) film of B. F. Goodrich Chemical Co. and PVDC-coated cellophane (PVDC/Cello) film can hold the product longer. For still longer term storage laminates that will keep cheese fresh include Cello/PVDC/PE, Polyester/PVDC/PE, Nylon/PVDC/PE and a more complex sheet of oriented PP/PE/PVDC/Cello/PE. These composites provide different ranges in strength, moisture, sensitivity, air permeability and machine processing.

Reynolds Metals Co. recently pioneered the carton overwrap concept using clear, shrinkable film of plasticized PVC 0.0015 in. thick. This process could make inroads on the billion-pound corrugated paper market.

According to a Gering Plastics Co. report, colored PE received its large-scale start within the past decade as a packaging/promotion material for extremely bulky products. Fat-car loads of gypsum board and similar items were protected on their long journeys by colored PE wraps that were also printed with manufacturers' logos and product identification. Within the past few years, smaller bulk items such as high-grade aluminum ingots used the color wrap.

Recording discs for educational purposes are now being made from Vynatherm sheeting, a calendered unplasticized PVC product made by the Nixon-Baldwin Div. of Tenneco Chemicals, Inc. Additional applications envisioned are sales training aids, promotional sales messages, editorial matter for magazines and premiums.

Disposable plastic film-backed paper products designed as functional and attractive single-use items are a real boon to converters. PE and PP of about $\frac{1}{2}$ mil thicknesses are used. Ivan E. Becker of Extrudo Film Corp. has shown that the growth curve is virtually untapped—with unlimited potential. Three millions lbs of PE and PP were used in 1964 for the growing hospital market; $\frac{1}{4}$ million lb for bed pads (1.2 million in 1965), $\frac{1}{4}$ million lb in surgical towels, etc. A total 9 million lb market is expected next year. Baby diapers alone consumed 2.5 million lb of embossed PE film in 1964, 5 million lb in 1965, and are expected to rise to 11 million lb next year—to take care of at least 25 billion diaper changes annually. All of this is happening even with a present unit cost of 10¢ compared to a 4¢ reusable cloth diaper service.

Sinclair-Koppers Co. has been working aggressively with Liqui-Box Corp. in producing a relatively new milk container; the milk-in-bag and, in turn, the bag-in-box.

## F. Industrial Use

Calendered PVC sheet from 0.002 in. to 0.020 in. for building construction has a big potential. It is now starting to grow in both exterior uses (siding, facings, etc.) and interior uses (wall panels, ceilings, etc.)

Interleaving rolls of sticky, unvulcanized rubber for tire retreading is an upcoming use for PE film, such as Dow's Polyfilm 506, which is claimed to effect quick release.

Magnetic tape is a relatively old product which just keeps becoming larger, requiring premium grade tape. Annual tape sales volume is near $200 million with 40% in space programs.

Polyester and cellulose acetate are used in this country, but PVC is used in Europe. At present the electronic industry desires a base film which possesses the characteristics of present film but costs less. Since the plastics represent a significant cost of the base materials used, the lower cost would air them in penetrating new markets.

As companies are constantly developing more paper work, reproduction and storage retrieval is now a way of business life. Polyester films are finding new applications in this relatively untapped market. Products include engineering drawings, light-sensitive reproduction sheets and microfilm. They require the versatile film which possesses toughness and dimensional stability.

At the present time there is an important outlet for film through government procurement. The 2.75 in. rockets using extruded grain are wrapped with ethyl cellulose film as a flame retardant inhibitor (5 billion lbs. this year). Woven PP split film for 5 billion sand bags were recently procured just on one government order by Patchogue-Plymouth Co. Other purchase orders include those for expandable shelters. Polypropylene strapping for industrial packaging and shipping, introduced by American Viscose Div. of FMC Corp., is becoming a factor, competing strongly with metal strapping.

Balloon technology has been advanced with the help of polyester, PP and PE. High altitude research and extensive weather reporting has been accomplished with these lightweight, strong, tough films. Polyester films have also been very successful in new parachute designs. Other developments with film include inflatable space structures, inflatable satellites, gas filled doughnut shaped film for a soft moon landing, nylon/fluorocarbon film food package for astronauts, underwater shelters and aluminized/polyester film fire-resistant rescue blankets.

An interesting target for the film developer is application of a film by vacuum or static attraction to the outside of an automobile.

## G. Processing

The established processes used to produce film are extrusion casting, tubular (blown film) and calendering. Relatively new quick-forming, hot-melt resin systems used in packaging include Eastman Kodak's "Eastoflow," in which resin covers products located on a backing board, and Crompton and Knowles' "Liquifilm," in which products are nozzle-sprayed. Major developments are occurring in film-producing machines to provide fabricators quality-controlled material at high rates of speed. Of equal importance is the auxiliary equipment to produce film in different forms: tape, adhesive-coated, metallized and decorative types.

Film orienting equipment is becoming more sophisticated. Biaxial orientation greatly improves the strength of film. However, the only resins to appear so far exclusively as biaxially oriented are those whose properties in the unoriented form are inadequate to assure substantial markets. Polystyrene and polyester are such materials.

Other polymers, such as PE and PP, are improved considerably by orientation. Yet most PE on the market is still made by methods that do not take advantage of producing the most efficient film. The advantages are not required at present, as adequate properties exist for most uses. This is also true of PVC and cellulose, and partially true of PP. The only U.S. machine source for complete film orienting equipment from extruder to winder with single manufacturing responsibility is the Waldron-Hartig Div. of Midland-Ross Corp.

The Black Clawson Co. intends to pursue sales development efforts in the area of integrated equipment lines for conventional tubing, quality sheeting and heavy wall bag. This follows the introduction of its new scrap recovery pelletizing unit for the film and sheeting lines. To meet the growing composite market, a blown film die has been designed for production of multilayer film.

Another interesting approach is the computerized program for film extrusion which allows accurate prediction of cooling requirements as the extrusion machine operates. NRM Corporation's Richard Senn, vice president for sales, reports that a computerized program for film extrusion has been developed which allows accurate prediction of cooling requirements as the extrusion machine operates. With approximately 3,000 heat transfer calculations, integrated in one half hour, a customer is informed as to how to set up his equipment based on material used and output desired.

More resin and film producing plants are being built. A plant for the manufacture of PE film is being planned by Union Carbide Corporation. This plant will adjoin the firm's present facility in Wayne, N.J., which will continue to make PP film. Completion is expected in the fall of 1967. The new unit will be an extension of Union Carbide's PE film facilities in Cartersville, Ga. and Ottawa, Ill.

The new PVC plant being erected for the RC Div. of Hooker Chemical Corp., N.J. will start with 3 calenders (2 flexible and 1 rigid), and with near-future capacity of 5 calenders (3 flexible and 2 rigid). Farrel Corp. is scheduled to have 3 calenders operating by January 1967. To back-up this expansion, as well as growth in other markets, Hooker is building a new PVC plant based on a mass polymerization process licensed from Pechiney St. Gobain. The plant will have initial annual capacity of 60 million lb with future capacity of 120 million lbs.

A 200% expansion of Monsanto's Ligonier, Ind. plant is on stream. It produces clear meat trays thermoformed from Monsanto's oriented PS sheet. Union Carbide is building a PE plant with 500 million lbs a year capacity, the world's largest. The first stage, with 250 million lb capacity, will be on stream by late 1967.

DuPont expansion plans this year include more capacity for PE and ethylene-based polymers. Lushan Plastics Corp., subsidiary of Tenneco Chemicals, Inc. recently moved to a new 100,000 sq ft plant which will be the basis for extensive expansion. The product line will concentrate on unsupported vinyls, crystal clear vinyls and supported vinyl fabrics.

All in all, plastic film and sheet are moving ahead in high gear, accounting for a huge hunk of total plastics production.

# H. Standard Methods of Fire Tests for Flame Resistant Textiles and Films (Reprint)

**PREPARED BY NATIONAL FIRE PROTECTION ASSOCIATION INTERNATIONAL (NFPA NO. 701 — 1966)**

## 1966 Edition of No. 701

The 1966 edition is an extensive revision of the 1951 edition of the Standard for Flameproofed Textiles, NFPA No. 701. The change in title reflects the revisions made in the recommended test method so that synthetic textiles and plastic films can be tested as well as natural-fiber textiles.

## Origin and Development of No. 701

Requirements for flameproofing of textiles were adopted by the NFPA on recommendation of the Committee on Fireproofing and Preservative Treatments in 1938. These were amended in 1939, 1940, 1941 and 1951. This standard is now under the jurisdiction of the NFPA Committee on Fire Tests; the 1966 edition was prepared by that committee.

## Introduction

While it is not possible to make combustible textiles and films completely resistive to charring and decomposition when exposed to flame or high temperature, a degree of flame resistance can be achieved. Natural fiber textiles can be treated chemically to reduce their flammability and tendency toward smoldering, and synthetic fibers and plastic films can be formulated to be flame resistant, the flame-retardant chemicals being incorporated into the resin formulation. Both approaches may be necessary to impart flame resistance to materials in which natural and synthetic fibers are blended. The hazards introduced by combustible textiles may, of course, be avoided entirely where the use of such noncombustible fabrics as glass and asbestos is practical. It should be noted, however, that combinations of the noncombustible fibers with a relatively small percentage of combustible fiber will cancel the noncombustible effect.

Standards of flame resistance for theatre scenery, curtains, and furnishings in places of public assembly are commonly set by law. Flame-resistant fabrics are used in hotels, hospitals and similar occupancies in the interest of the preservation of lives and property from fire. Flame-resistant fabrics are also used as work clothing in industries where exposure to heat, open flames and flash fire is a possibility. Fabrics treated for flame and weather resistance are used for tents, awnings, tarpaulins, and other outdoor protective covering.

Flame-resistant synthetic materials, in the form of woven fabrics and plastic films, are used decoratively and for protective coverings. Many of these materials will soften and melt when exposed to heat and fire. They may also be subject to twisting, shrinking, dripping and elongation when subjected to fire conditions. Reinforced plastic films with flame-resistant qualities are used in air-supported structures. Transparent plastic films are often used as a temporary enclosure for greenhouses and for construction work.

An increasing range of flame-resistant treatments for natural-fiber materials is becoming available, and the selection of a particular treatment is governed by the intended use of the treated fabric. Treatments based on water soluble chemicals are generally the least expensive and most easily applied, but they are subject to removal by the leaching action of water in laundering, scrubbing, or exposure to weather. Some treatments may be impaired by the action of the solvents used in dry cleaning, and some may gradually lose their effectiveness under conditions of storage and use not involving dry cleaning or water leaching. Such relatively temporary treatments are suitable only where proper retreatment and renewal can be assured, or for decorations and other items which are used briefly and discarded. Situations where retreatment is uncertain or not feasible indicate the choice of one of the most durable treatments which are suitable for clothing and decorative fabrics. A number of these will withstand extensive laundering and dry cleaning, although they are higher in cost than the water-soluble type, and require professional application. For outdoor use, treatments have been developed which may be expected to remain effective for the useful life of the fabric under normal conditions of weather exposure. It should be noted, however, that painting or coating a treated or noncombustible fabric may impair its flame-resistant qualities unless the coating is itself flame resistant.

A number of other factors, which will vary in importance depending upon the end use of the fabric, must be considered in seleting a flame-resistant treatment. The effect on the appearance, texture, and flexibility of the fabric is often of primary concern. Some treatments may leave a fabric objectionably stiff, or it may become tacky at high atmospheric temperatures or brittle at low temperatures. Some flame-retardant chemicals are so hygroscopic as to dampen the fabric; others may effloresce to the extent of reduced effectiveness as well as unsightly appearance. Treatment may result in a reduction in strength of the fabric, and some flame-retardant chemicals may tend to deteriorate wood or corrode metal with which the treated fabric comes in contact. In all instances, the possibility of adverse physiological reactions in persons handling or otherwise exposed to the treated fabric must be considered by the manufacturer.

### Section 10. Scope

These requirements apply to flame-resistant materials which are used extensively in the interior furnishings of buildings and transport facilities, in protective clothing for certain occupations and situations, and for protective outdoor coverings such as tarpaulins and tents. However, the flame-resistant requirements are not dependent on the type of treatment, except that where durability to laundering or weathering is claimed, the fabric is tested for flame-resistance after being subjected to the applicable cleaning or exposure procedures.

These requirements apply to plastic films with or without reinforcing or backing, when used for decorative or other purposes inside buildings or as temporary or permanent enclosure for places of public assembly and buildings under construction.

When these materials are applied to surfaces of building or backing materials as interior finishes for use in buildings the test is to be conducted and the material classified in accordance with NFPA Method of Test of Surface Burning Characteristics of Building Materials, NFPA No. 255 (UL 723, ASTM E-84).

It is the intent of these requirements to provide tests to determine whether the flame-resistant textiles and films are comparatively difficult to ignite and whether it is comparatively difficult to propagate flame beyond the area exposed to the source of ignition. These performance tests do not necessarily indicate whether the material tested will resist the propagation of flame under severe fire exposure or when used in a manner which differs substantially from the test requirements.

Two methods of assessing flame resistance are described. Both methods will provide a comparison among textiles and films but do not necessarily indicate the behavior of a material in a large building fire or other conflagration. One test employs a relatively small sample and small igniting flame and is simple and convenient for general use. The other test requires a much larger sample and applies a more severe fire exposure which will more nearly approach severe fire conditions. The small scale test is commonly used to indicate susceptibility to flame spread from small ignition sources, and may also serve as a screening test followed by the large scale test.

## Section 20. Flame Resistance Requirements

### 21. Test Selection

All flame-resistant textiles and films shall be capable of complying with the performance requirements of either the small or the large scale tests or both. The authority having jurisdiction shall determine whether both the small and the large scale tests are required and this will generally depend on the purpose to be served or the nature of the materials tested. For those materials which show excessive melting or shrinkage by the small scale test, then the large scale test shall be considered applicable.

Textiles which are expected to retain their flame resistance through dry cleaning, laundering, water leaching, or weathering exposures should be subjected to the applicable procedures of Section 40 before being tested by either the small scale or the large scale flame test.

### 22. Small Scale Test

When subjected to the small scale test described in Section 31, a material shall not continue flaming for more than two seconds after the test flame is removed from contact with the specimen. The vertical spread of flame and afterglow (smoldering combustion) on the material, as indicated by the length of char or the measurement from the bottom of the sample above which all material is sound and in original condition, shall not exceed the values shown in Table 16-14.

Portion or residues of textiles or films which break or drip from the test specimens shall not continue to flame after they reach the floor of the tester.

### 23. Large Scale Test

When subjected to the large scale test described in Section 32, a material in single sheets or in folds shall not continue flaming for more than two seconds after the test flame is removed from contact with the specimen. The vertical spread of burning on the material in single sheets shall not exceed 10 inches above the tip of the test flame. This vertical spread shall be measured as the distance from the tip of the test flame to a horizontal line above which all material is sound and in original condition, except for possible smoke deposits. The vertical spread of burning on the folded specimens shall not exceed 35 inches above the tip of the test flame, but the afterglow may spread in the folds.

Portions or residues of textiles or films which break or drip from the test specimens shall not continue to flame after they reach the floor of the tester.

### Section 30. Flame Test Methods

### 31. Small Scale Test

(a) Five specimens of the material, $2\frac{3}{4}$ by 10 inches, shall be cut with their long dimension in the direction of the warp and five in

TABLE 16-14.  Permissible Length of Char or Destroyed Material—Small Scale Test

| Weight of treated fabric being tested ounces per square yard | Maximum average length of char or destroyed material for ten specimens inches | Maximum length of char or destroyed material for any specimen inches |
|---|---|---|
| Over 10 | $3\frac{1}{2}$ | $4\frac{1}{2}$ |
| Over 6 and not exceeding 10 | $4\frac{1}{2}$ | $5\frac{1}{2}$ |
| Not exceeding 6 | $5\frac{1}{2}$ | $6\frac{1}{2}$ |

the direction of the filling. Each lot of five shall be cut from at least four places in the sample separated sufficiently to give indication as to the uniformity of the flame-resistant treatment.

(b) The test specimens shall be conditioned in an oven, having forced air circulation with free air flow around each specimen, at temperatures of 140 to 145 degrees Fahrenheit, for durations of not less than 1 hour nor more than $1\frac{1}{2}$ hours before testing. Materials which distort or melt at the above indicated oven exposure are to be conditioned at 60-80 degrees Fahrenheit and 25-50 per cent relative humidity for not less than 24 hours. Specimens shall be removed from the oven one at a time and immediately subjected to the flame test described in Section 31(d).

(c) In conducting the flame test, the specimen shall be placed in a holder of metal which clamps each long edge of the fabric, leaving the ends free and exposing a strip 2 inches wide by 10 inches long. The holder and specimen shall be supported in vertical position within a shield 12 inches wide, 12 inches deep, and 30 inches high, open at the top, and provided with baffled vent holes amounting to 6 square inches distributed along the bottom of at least two sides. The shield shall have a door or sliding panel having an observation window of glass. Provision shall be made for moving the gas burner used in igniting the specimen into test position after the shield is closed. A rod attached to the base of the burner and extending through a slot near the bottom of one side of the shield will serve the purpose.

(d) The specimen shall be supported with its lower end $\frac{3}{4}$ inch above the top of a Bunsen or Tirrill gas burner, approximately 6 inches high and have a tube $\frac{3}{8}$ inch inside diameter, and with the air supply completely shut off, adjusted to give a luminous flame $1\frac{1}{2}$ inches long. The flame shall be applied vertically near the middle of the width of the lower end of the specimen for 12 seconds, then withdrawn, and the duration of flaming on the specimen noted. The burner shall be supported in a fixed position so that the barrel of the burner is at an angle of 25 degrees from the vertical.

(e) After all flaming and afterglow on the specimen has ceased, the length of char or material destruction shall be determined immediately. The length of char in this test is defined as the distance from the end of the specimen which was exposed to the flame to the end of the tear made lengthwise of the specimen through the center of the charred area in the following way: A hook is inserted in the specimen, on one side of the charred area, $\frac{1}{4}$ inch in from the adjacent outside edge and $\frac{1}{4}$ inch up from the bottom. A weight, which inclusive of the hook is equal to that specified for the fabric in Table 16-15, is attached to the hook. The specimen is then grasped on the opposite side of the charred area with the fingers, and raised gently until it supports the weight. The specimen will tear through the charred area until fabric strong enough to carry the load is reached. When it is not feasible to measure char, the material destruction can normally be judged as the measurement from the bottom of the sample to a horizontal line above which all material is sound and in original condition.

### 32. Large Scale Test

(a) The following method for conducting flame tests of materials employs a larger specimen and a larger test flame than are specified for the small scale test, Section 31. This method is also useful for investigating the flammability of fabrics when hung in folds.

(b) For conducting flame tests of fabrics in single sheets, a specimen 5 inches by 7 feet shall be used. For conducting flame tests of fabrics hung in folds, a specimen 25 inches by 7 feet shall be cut and folded longitudinally so as to form four folds, each approximately 5 inches wide, uniformly over the length (spacing about ½ inch).

(c) At least 10 specimens in single sheets and at least 4 specimens in folds shall be cut from each fabric. They shall be taken from as widely separated and symmetrically located sections as possible over the entire area of the sample of each fabric. One-half of the specimens of each kind shall be cut with the long dimension in the direction of the warp, and the balance of the specimens shall be cut with the long dimension in the direction of the fill.

(d) The test specimens shall be conditioned in an oven, having forced air circulation with free air flow around each specimen, at temperatures of 140 to 145 degrees Fahrenheit for durations of not less than 1 hour nor more than 1½ hours before testing. Materials which distort or melt

TABLE 16-15.  Tearing Weights—Small Scale Test

| Weight of treated fabric being tested ounces per square yard | Total tearing weight for determination of length of char pounds |
|---|---|
| 2 to 6 inclusive | 0.25 |
| Over 6 and not exceeding 15 | 0.5 |
| Over 15 and not exceeding 23 | 0.75 |
| Over 23 | 1.00 |

at the above indicated oven exposure are to be conditioned at 60-80 degrees Fahrenheit and 25-50 per cent relative humidity for not less than 24 hours. Specimens shall be removed from the oven one at a time and immediately subjected to the flame test described in Section 32(e).

(e) The apparatus for conducting the flame test shall consist of a sheet-iron stack 12 inches square transversely, 7 feet high and supported 1 foot above the floor on legs. The stack shall only be open at top and bottom and shall be provided with an observation window of wired glass extending the full length of the front.

(f) The single-sheet specimen is to be suspended vertically in the stack with its full width facing the observer so that the bottom of the specimen is 4 inches above the top of a Bunsen burner having $\frac{3}{8}$-inch diameter tube and placed on the floor below the stack. The gas supply to the burner is to be natural gas or a mixture of natural and manufactured gases having a heat value of approximately 800-1000 Btu per cubic foot. With a gas pressure of $4\frac{1}{4}$ inches (108 mm) of water, the burner is to be adjusted to produce an 11-inch oxidizing flame having an indistinct inner cone. The specimen is to be lightly restrained laterally with clamps and guide wires attached to its outer edges. For the folded specimen the conditions of test are to be the same as above except that it is to be suspended vertically with the edges of the folds facing the observer. The folds are to be spread apart about $\frac{1}{2}$ inch by means of guide rods inserted at the top and bottom ends.

The flame shall be applied vertically near the middle of the width of the lower end of the specimen in a single sheet, or to the middle of the width of the lower end of the middle fold of the specimen in folds. The position of the specimen relative to the test flame shall be maintained by guide wires attached to the outer edges of the specimen. The burner shall be supported in a fixed position so that the barrel of the burner is at an angle of 25 degrees from the vertical.

(g) The test flame shall be applied to the specimen for two minutes, then withdrawn, and the duration of flaming combustion on the specimen recorded. After all flaming and afterglow on the specimen has ceased, the length of char shall be determined. For purposes of this test, the length of char is defined as the vertical distance on the specimen from the tip of the test flame to the top of the charred area resulting from spread of flame and afterglow. For synthetic textiles and films the length of char is defined as the vertical distance from the tip of the test flame to a horizontal line, above which all material is sound and in essentially original condition.

## Section 40. Cleaning and Weathering Procedures

### *41. Application*

These procedures shall be applied to fabrics which are expected to retain their flame-resistant qualities through dry cleaning, laundering, weathering, or other exposures to water. The probable durability of a treatment relative to the life of the fabric is difficult to assess, but in general, flame-retardant treatments tend to be either very tenacious or quite easily removed. It is believed that such accelerated exposure tests as those described in this section provide sufficient testing to permit a reasonable appraisal of the durability of the treament (under the conditions for which it was designed) for the useful life of the fabric.

Each fabric shall be subjected to only those exposure procedures which are applicable to its intended use. It shall meet the flame resistance requirements of Section 20 after passing through the appropriate exposure cycles.

### *42. Accelerated Dry Cleaning*

(a) A sample of the treated fabric shall be agitated for 25 minutes in a suitable dry cleaning apparatus containing a solution of 1,000 parts perchlorethylene and six parts of dry cleaning soap. The volume of solution employed shall be in excess of that required to saturate the sample. The sample shall then be rinsed three times in pure perchlorethylene for periods of 5 minutes each, centrifuged and allowed to dry at room temperature on a horizontal screen. When dry the sample shall be pressed or steamed. The above procedure shall be repeated a total of ten times.

(b) In order to simulate the wet cleaning sometimes encountered in dry cleaning practice, the sample of treated fabric shall be agitated in perchlorethylene base solution, rinsed, centrifuged, and dried as described in the foregoing procedure. The sample shall then be placed on a porcelain, marble, or slate slab and treated with water containing 0.1 percent neutral soap at temperature of 90 to 100 degrees Fahrenheit. The fabric shall be kept thoroughly wet for 15 minutes. The sample shall then be rinsed for five minutes in water at 90 to 100 degrees Fahrenheit, centrifuged, and allowed to dry at room temperature on a horizontal ventilated screen. When dry the sample shall be pressed or steamed. The above procedure shall be repeated a total of ten times.

## 43. Accelerated Laundering

A sample of the treated fabric shall be washed in a 0.25 per cent solution of tallow soap of low titer dissolved in water not exceeding 50 parts per million hardness. A suitable automatic machine with a fixed operating cycle of approximately 28 minutes shall be used. The cycle shall consist approximately of a 12-minute washing in the soap solution at 125 degrees Fahrenheit, three 2½-minute rinsing periods, and a 3-minute extraction period, the remaining time to be allotted to inlet or outlet of the water in the machine. The sample shall be allowed to dry at room temperature on a horizontal ventilated screen, moistened, and pressed with a flat iron at a temperature of 275 to 300 degrees Fahrenheit. The above procedure shall be repeated a total of ten times. If the material is to be subjected to a special use more laundering may be required.

Where instructions for laundering a fabric are supplied by the manufacturer or finisher, those instructions should be followed in preference to the above procedure. This above procedure is intended to simulate ordinary home laundering practice. Commercial laundering is likely to be more severe, and commercial practices may vary considerably in the choice of detergents, temperatures, bleaches and sours, and in the mechanical wear imposed on the fabric. If the fabric will be subjected to commercial laundering in use, however, an attempt should be made to simulate a probable commercial procedure for test purposes.

## 44. Scrubbing

Certain articles of flame-resistant fabric not ordinarily washed by home or commercial laundering methods are sometimes scrubbed vigorously on one or both sides, applying laundry soap (or other detergent) and water with a stiff bristle brush. The fabric is then thoroughly rinsed with water and dried. Where treated fabrics are likely to be cleaned in this manner during their use, test specimens shall be subjected to flame tests after repeated cycles of scrubbing as outlined.

## 45. Accelerated Water Leaching

A sample of the treated fabric shall be totally submerged in a vessel containing tap water at room temperature for a period of 72 hours. The vessel shall have a capacity of at least 4 gallons of water. The water shall be drained from the tank and replenished at 24-hour intervals during the immersion period. At the conclusion of the immersion period, the sample shall be removed from the test vessel and dried at room temperature.

## 46. Accelerated Weathering

One of the two procedures described below shall be followed:

(a) The apparatus shall consist of a vertical carbon arc with solid electrodes 0.5 inches in diameter (1 cored electrode is used if the arc operates on alternating current) and uniform in composition throughout, mounted at the center of a vertical metal cylinder. The arc shall be surrounded by a clear globe of No. 9200 PX Pyrex glass 0.0625 inches thick or other enclosure having equivalent absorbing and transmitting properties. The electrodes shall be renewed at intervals sufficiently frequent to insure full operative conditions of the lamp. The globe shall be cleaned when carbons are removed or at least once in each 36 hours of operation. The arc shall be operated on 13 amperes direct current or 17 amperes, 60 cycles alternating current with the voltage at the arc of 140 volts. The specimens for test shall be mounted on the inside of the cylinder facing the arc. The diameter of the cylinder shall be such that the distance of the face of the specimen holder from the center of the arc is 14¾ inches. The cylinder shall rotate about the arc at a uniform speed of approximately three revolutions per hour. A water spray discharging about 0.7 gallons per minute shall strike each specimen in turn for about 1 minute during each revolution of the cylinder. Specimens shall be subjected to this exposure for 360 hours. They shall then be allowed to dry thoroughly at a temperature between 70 and 100 degrees Fahrenheit.

(b) The apparatus shall consist of a vertical carbon arc mounted at the center of a vertical cylinder. The arc is designed to accommodate two pairs of carbons, No. 22, upper carbons, and No. 13, lower carbons; however, the arc burns between only one pair of carbons at a time. The arc shall be operated on 60 amperes and 50 volts across the arc for alternating current or 50 amperes and 60 volts across the arc for direct current. The specimens for test shall be mounted on a rotating rack inside the cylinder and facing the arc. The diameter of the rotating rack shall be such that the distance from the center of the arc to the face of the specimen is 18¾ inches. The rack shall rotate about the arc at a uniform speed of about 1 revolution in 2 hours. No filters or enclosures shall be used between the arc and the specimens. Spray nozzles shall be mounted in the cylinder so that the specimens shall be exposed to wetting once during each revolution of the rack. Specimens shall be subjected to this exposure for 100 hours. They shall then be allowed to dry thoroughly at a temperature between 70 and 100 degrees Fahrenheit.

## Section 50. Field Test: Clamp Test

### 51. General

The following method for conducting flame tests of materials was designed for use on curtains and similar furnishings in place. It uses a vertical clamp, with attachment for supporting the candle, that enables a vertical edge or slit of the fabric to be placed in horizontal position for testing. The clamping of the material in the device will prevent spread of fire to portions of the material beyond the area exposed in the clamp. Due care must, however, be taken in any use of open flames in the presence of combustible materials.

### 52. Scope

These requirements supplement those provided in Sections 10-40 inclusive. This field test is intended to accomplish the same result as that achieved by flame tests in Sections 31 and 61, and the same general requirements apply.

### 53. Performance Requirements—Clamp Test

When tested by the method described in Section 54, a specimen shall not continue flaming for more than two seconds after the test flame is removed from contact with the specimen. The average length of char in three tests shall not be more than $2\frac{1}{2}$ inches for heavy ducks and drapery material, and not more than $4\frac{1}{2}$ inches for any material. By length of char is meant the length from the zero point on the scale to the point on the scale opposite the end of a tear through the charred area. This tear shall be made by hand with enough force to tear through the charred or scorched portion but not sufficient to break undamaged threads. Synthetic textiles and plastic films shall not be subjected to measurements for char length but shall be measured for the amount of sound material destroyed. Materials which break or drip flaming particles shall be rejected if the materials continue to burn after they reach the floor.

### 54. Test Method

(a) The test clamp, as illustrated, shall hold the portion of the curetain or other fabric to be tested at any convenient edge or slit. The candle shall be of paraffin and of $\frac{3}{4}$ inch norminal diameter. It shall be swung away from the fabric and the tapered portion allowed to burn away until a normal constant flame is reached. The wick shall bend to near the outer boundary of the flame and burn to a length that remains constant at about $\frac{5}{8}$ inch. The candle shall then be adjusted in its holder until the top of the wick is $\frac{1}{10}$ inch below the bottom edge of the fabric or zero point on the graduated scale. The candle flame shall be applied to the exposed edge of the fabric for 12 seconds. The tear shall be made by applying pressure by hand against the side of the specimen as mounted in the clamp.

(b) The clamp shall be made of duplicate pieces of sheet metal about $\frac{1}{16}$ inch thick, held with spring type paper clamps $1\frac{1}{4}$ inches wide. The candle holder shall be made of a $\frac{3}{4}$-inch hose clamp bolted to a window screen corner angle and hinged to the front clamp member with a brass hinge 2 by $\frac{1}{2}$ inches, the lower portion of one leaf of which is cut away to clear the paper clamp. The hinge and clamp support shall be mounted in such a manner that the clamp will swing against a stop when its center is directly under the middle of the 2 inches wide exposed lower edge of the specimen.

### Section 60. Field Test: Match Flame Test

### 61. Test Method

In conducting this test, a sample of the material shall be taken to a location where the test may be conducted safely. The sample shall be held in a vertical position and tested by application of a flame from a common paper match held in a horizontal position, $\frac{1}{2}$ inch under the sample, and at a constant location for a minimum of 15 seconds. Observations are made to determine that the sample does not ignite and spread flame over its surface after the match flame is removed. Materials which break or drip flaming particles shall be rejected if the materials continue to burn after they reach the floor.

**APPENDIX**

**Flame-Resistance Treatments**

*Decorative Textiles*

Hundreds of different chemicals have been used or tested for flame-retarding fabrics. Many proved reasonably effective flame-retardants, but only a few are in general use. Many chemicals are not suitable because of objectionable characteristics such as moisture absorption, change in color or deterioration of the fabric, deterioration under high-temperature drying or pressure, corrosion of metal in contact with the fabric, toxicity, requiring an excessively heavy weighting of the fabric to be effective, requiring difficult techniques in application, or being unduly expensive. Mixtures of two or more chemicals are usually more effective than the same chemicals used alone.

There are many proprietary flame-retardant preparations which vary greatly in effectiveness, cost and other factors such as tendency to absorb moisture. The purchaser should consult responsible testing authorities prior to purchase and use.

Many concerns specialize in the effective flame-resistance treatment of theater scenery, draperies and other fabrics, using standard flame-retardant chemicals. It is advisable to deal only with concerns of known reliability, or if dealing with an unknown concern, to have treated fabrics tested for adequacy of treatment.

Most of the treatments used are not resistive to water since the chemicals are water-soluble. A few have been developed that resist leaching action from exposure to weather, laundering, or dry cleaning.

Most of the treatments in use cause very little reduction in the strength of the fabric, but when subjected to higher than normal temperature and sunlight, some of the treatments cause decided loss in strength. It is often important that change in color and texture shall not be caused by the flame-resistant treatment of fabrics, and there are a number of treatments that will meet this requirement. Few of the treatments used contain chemicals that would cause poisoning or injury from handling of the treated fabric.

## Methods of Application

Water soluble flame-retardant chemicals may be applied by immersion of the fabric in a solution, by spraying, or by brushing. The objective is to deposit in the fabric the desired amount of the flame-retardant chemicals, measured in terms of percentage increase in weight of the fabric after treatment and drying, as compared with the original weight. As long as uniform treatment and the desired increase in weight are obtained, the particular method of application and the proportion of water used in the solution are unimportant. Good results may be obtained by dipping, spraying or brushing; the method selected is dictated by convenience and the character of the fabric to be treated.

Effective flame-resistant treatments may be obtained by the use of non-proprietary solutions of flame-retardant chemicals in water, without professional assistance, after some experience and testing of the results. The chemicals should be dissolved in clean water. Warm water and stirring will dissolve chemicals more quickly.

It is desirable to wash new fabrics containing sizing prior to treatment so as to secure proper absorption of flame-retardant chemicals. Commercial wetting agents may be added to the treating solution to increase penetration of flame-retardant ingredients.

When a piece of fabric is immersed, usually at room temperature, in a flame-retardant solution, the container must be large enough so that all the fabric is thoroughly wet and there are no folds which the solution does not penetrate, if too small tubs or tanks were used.

Care must be used in the wringing of the immersed material. If a mechanical wringer is used, more of the solution is likely to be extracted and a more concentrated solution may be necessary to obtain the desired weighting. Best results will be obtained if the articles can be dried in a horizontal position. Drying in a vertical position permits a certain amount of drainage of the solution, depending upon the wetness of the wrung articles. It is advisable to increase the weighting if horizontal drying is not feasible.

Where solutions are applied by brushing or spraying some skill is required for uniform application; repeated application may be necessary to secure the desired weighting.

It is difficult to treat cellulose acetate fabrics. Flame-resistance of fabrics may from proprietary synthetic fibers requires separate consideration, taking into account the effectiveness and suitability of the treatment for the given fabric.

## Formulas

The nonproprietary flame-retardant formulations described in the following are applied mainly to fabrics used for decorative or other purposes inside buildings. They are intended to provide protection against small sources of ignition such as matches, cigarette lighters, sparks, small coals, and smoldering cigars and cigarettes, and do not necessarily protect a fabric against flaming combustion under severe fire exposure, or when hung in folds or parallel strips. Renewal of the treatment is required after a certain time, and after every laundering, dry cleaning, or exposure to weather where the flame-retardant chemicals are subject to leaching by water. Where flame-resistance is required by law, it is common practice to require renewal of treatments at least annually.

Formulas are stated in terms of parts by weight and, also, where water is the solvent, in avoirdupois weight of chemicals and volume of water in United States gallons.

Formulas Nos. 1 to 5 are from Circular C455 of the National Bureau of Standards. (See References.) Formulas Nos. 6 and 7 are from York Research Corp. of Conn., Stamford, Conn. (New York: American Hotel Association, 221 West 57th St.). Research Report No. 8, March 3, 1947. 30 pages. Research Report No. 14, August 18, 1947. 30 pages.

## Formula No. 1:

| | | |
|---|---|---|
| Borax, $Na_2B_4O_7 \cdot 10H_2O$ ............ | 6 parts | 6 pounds |
| Boric acid, $H_3BO_3$ ............... | 5 parts | 5 pounds |
| Water ......................... | 100 parts | 12 gallons |

The fabric is steeped in a cool solution until thoroughly impregnated, then dried. Heavy applications by spray or brush are usually reasonably effective. Such applications may have to be repeated two or three times with drying between applications to obtain the desired degree of flame-resistance. The treatment has been used for many kinds of fabrics, including theater scenery. It is recommended for rayon. As in the case of most of the other formulas listed, care must be taken in ironing the fabric to avoid discloration by heat.

The treatment is effective in weighting from 8 to 12 per cent, depending upon the type of fabric. Hand-wringing the above solution from a fabric leaves a weighting of 10 to 12 per cent after drying.

**Formula No. 2:**

| | | |
|---|---|---|
| Borax, $Na_2B_4O_7 \cdot 10H_2O$ ............. | 7 parts | 7 pounds |
| Boric acid, $H_3BO_3$ ................ | 3 parts | 3 pounds |
| Water .......................... | 100 parts | 12 gallons |

The amount of water may be varied, and should depend upon the absorptive capacity of the fabric to be treated. For rayon and sheer fabrics, the same quantities of borax and boric acid may be used in 17 gallons of water. Loadings from 8 to 10 per cent of the weight of the dry cloth usually will be found effective. Hand-wringing the above solution from a fabric will give approximately these weightings. Fabrics so treated retain their flexibility and softness. They do not become dusty, feel damp, or lose their strength under ordinary conditions of use. The chemicals are nonpoisonous and do not promote the growth of destructive micro-organisms.

**Formula No. 3:**

| | | |
|---|---|---|
| Borax, $Na_2B_4O_7 \cdot 10H_2O$ .......... | 7 parts | 7 pounds |
| Boric acid, $H_3BO_3$ .............. | 3 parts | 3 pounds |
| Diammonium phosphate, | | |
| $(NH_4)_2HPO_4$................. | 5 parts | 5 pounds |
| Water ........................ | 110 parts | 13⅕ gallons |

This formula gives very satisfactory results both in flame-resistance and glow-resistance. It will be found effective in weightings of 7 to 15 per cent, depending upon the fabric treated. Hand-wringing the above solution from a fabric leaves weighting of about 10 to 12 per cent.

**Formula No. 4:**

| | | |
|---|---|---|
| Diammonium phosphate, | | |
| $(NH_4)_2HPO_4$ ............... | 7.5 parts | 7½ pounds |
| Ammonium chloride, $NH_4Cl$ ..... | 5 parts | 5 pounds |
| Ammonium sulfate $(NH_4)_2SO_4$.... | 5 parts | 5 pounds |
| Water ........................ | 100 parts | 12 gallons |

Either the solution can be applied directly to the cloth, or it can be used in making a starch sizing. The formula has been used for flame-resisting curtains and for cotton fabrics in general. The ammonium chloride and, to less extent, the ammonium phosphate, are hygroscopic; therefore this formula may not be advisable for flame-resisting materials exposed to dampness. The treatment is effective in weightings of 10 to 18 per cent, depending upon the type of fabric treated. Hand-wringing the above solution from a fabric leaves a weighting of about 16 to 18 per cent.

## Formula No. 5:

| | | | | |
|---|---|---|---|---|
| Ammonium sulfate $(NH_4)_2SO_4$... | 8 | parts | 8 | pounds |
| Ammonium carbonate, $(NH_4)_2CO_3 \cdot H_2O$ | 2.5 | parts | $2\frac{1}{2}$ | pounds |
| Borax, $Na_2B_4O_7 \cdot 10H_2O$ | 8 | parts | 8 | pounds |
| Boric acid, $H_3BO_3$ | 3 | parts | 3 | pounds |
| Starch | 2 | parts | 2 | pounds |
| Dextrin | 0.4 | parts | $6\frac{1}{2}$ | ounces |
| Water | 100 | parts | 12 | gallons |

The amount of water may be varied. The mixture should be applied at 86 to 100 degrees Fahrenheit. This solution is useful for many fabrics, particularly for laces and curtains, and is effective in loadings of 14 to 28 per cent, depending upon the fabric. Hand-wringing the above solution from a fabric leaves a weighting of about 28 per cent.

## Formula No. 6:

| | | |
|---|---|---|
| Diammonium phosphate $(NH_4)_2HPO_4$ | 100 | pounds |
| Water | 50 | gallons |

This solution, when applied by ordinary methods, produces a weighting of about 10 per cent, which is effective. It has superior flame and glow-retardant properties.

## Formula No. 7:

| | | |
|---|---|---|
| Ammonium sulfamate, $NH_4OSO_2NH_2$ | 80 | pounds |
| Diammonium phosphate, $(NH_4)_2HPO_4$ | 20 | pounds |
| Water | 50 | gallons |

This solution, when applied by ordinary methods, produces a weighting of about 15 per cent, which is effective. It is an efficient flame and glow-retardant agent. Some deterioration when heated; in drying and pressing, high temperatures should be avoided.

## Weather Exposed Textiles

Flame-resistant treatments for tents, awnings, tarpaulins and other fabrics exposed to the weather must be renewed at frequent intervals or must be of a special character combining water-retardant with flame retardant chemicals in order to prevent the leaching out of the flame-retardant chemicals in the course of time.

A wide variety of chemicals may be used for flame-resistant fabrics exposed to the weather. Many of the formulas used include chlorinated paraffin, chlorinated synthetic resins, or chlorinated rubber in combination with various water-insoluble metallic salts, plasticizers, stabilizers, synthetic resins, pigments, binders, mildew inhibitors, etc. Such mixtures are not water soluble and are used with hydrocarbon solvents, or are suspended in water emulsions. The effective application of such treatments calls for techniques and equipment ordinarily available only for factory processing. Application of flammable paint to these treated fabrics will present a fire hazard.

Weather resistant flame-resistant fabrics with and without striping are listed by Underwriters' Laboratories, Inc. These are comparatively difficult to ignite and do not propagate flame, even when in drafts, beyond the area exposed to the source of ignition, when used in single sheets (as in open awnings, tarpaulins, etc.) or in folds. Flameless or smoldering combustion which occurs on ignition may spread in folds, but in the case of single sheets does not extend beyond the area exposed to ignition. The treatment may be expected to remain effective under ordinary conditions of exposure for the useful life of the fabric. However, laundering will reduce the effectiveness of the treatment when so indicated in Underwriters' Laboratories, Inc.'s listings of individual fabrics.

### Noncombustible Fabrics

Noncombustible fabrics include those woven wholly from inorganic yarns, either glass or asbestos alone, or in combination with each other. Glass fabrics listed by Underwriters' Laboratories, Inc., for use as draperies are woven from glass yarns, which do not burn or propagate flame. Such materials cannot emit hazardous fumes if exposed to fire. Glass fabrics have many uses in addition to their use for decorative purposes; e.g., for matttress covers or as ticking for glass fiber-filled mattresses.

Asbestos fiber has relatively low strength, and cotton fibers are commonly used with asbestos to give asbestos cloth greater strength. Depending upon the amount of cotton used, such asbestos cloth may actually propagate flame. Fabrics woven from combinations of glass and asbestos fibers have satisfactory strength and are noncombustible. Any combustible fiber or combustible coloring or coating material, if used in sufficient quantity, may make a glass or asbestos fabric combustible.

## REFERENCES

Detailed information on the history, techniques of treatment and testing of flame-retardant textiles may be found in the following references:

NFPA Fire Protection Handbook (Boston: National Fire Protection Association) 12th Edition. 1962. 2,216 pp. Cloth, $17.50. (Section 6, Chapter VIII, Fire Retardant Treatments—Textiles and Fabrics, pages 6-117 to 6-125).

Sandholzer, Marjorie W., Flameproofing of Textiles (Washington, D. C. 20402: U. S. Superintendent of Documents). Circular of the National Bureau of Standards C455. August 23, 1946. 24 pp. 10 cents.

Ramsbottom, J. E. (Royal Aircraft Establishment). The Fireproofing of Fabrics (London: H. M. Stationery Office). Department of Scientific and Industrial Research publication. 1947. 128 pp. 2 shillings, 6 pence.

Little, Robert W., Flameproofing Textile Fabrics (New York: Reinhold Publishing Company). 1947. 432 pp. Cloth.

Church, James M., Little, Robert W., and Coppick, S., Evaluation of Flame-Resistant Fabrics. Industrial and Engineering Chemistry. Vol. 42, March 1950, pages 418-427. Contribution from National Research Council, Quartermaster Corps 27, Columbia University.

Textile Flammability Conference, October 2-3, 1962 (Boston: National Fire Protection Association). Proceedings of a meeting held in Boston under auspices of NFPA and U.S. Public Health Service. 48 pp. $1.

Symposium: Flammability of Textiles. American Dyestuff Reporter, June 10, 1963, pages 48-54. Proceedings of a meeting of the Metropolitan Section of the American Association of Textile Chemists and Colorists, New York, January 18, 1963.

Segal, Louis (Office of State Fire Marshal, California), Foam Rubber and Cotton Mattresses. NFPA *Quarterly*. Vol. 48, No. 2 (October 1954), pages 119-122. Discussion of ignition from smoking in bed.

Yockers, Joe R., and Segal, Louis (Office of State Fire Marshal, California), Cigarette Fire Mechanisms. NFPA *Quarterly*. Vol. 49, No. 3 (January 1956), pages 213-222.

Yockers, Joe R. (State Fire Marshal, California), Burning Characteristics of Fabric Clothing. NFPA *Quarterly*. Vol. 52, No. 2 (October 1958), pages 120-124.

Drake, George L., Jr., Science Making Progress in Imparting Flame Resistance to Cotton Textiles. NFPA *Quarterly*. Vol. 57, No. 1 (July 1963), pages 83-87. Report on work at USDA Southern Regional Research Laboratory, New Orleans.

Underwriters' Laboratories, Inc., Building Materials List (Chicago 60611: Underwriters' Laboratories, Inc.). Annual publication, with supplements bimonthly.

Listing of flame-retardant and noncombustible fabrics for tentage, awnings, draperies, decorations and other uses under ordinary conditions.

## Publications of Related Interest

NFPA Committee on Wearing Apparel, Standard for Classification of the Flammability of Wearing Apparel (Boston: National Fire Protection Association). NFPA No. 702. 1963. 20 pp. 50 cents.

Fire Protection Department, Underwriters' Laboratories, Inc., Standard for Flame Tests of Flame-Resistant Fabrics (Chicago 60611: Underwriters' Laboratories, Inc.). UL 214. First edition, August 1955, reprinted October 1960. 16 pp.

Rules and Regulations under the Flammable Fabrics Act (Washington, D. C.: Federal Trade Commission). Effective July 1, 1954, as amended to July 1, 1958, with text of act appended: 67 Stat. 111.

Flammability of Clothing Textiles (Washington, D. C. 20402: U.S. Superintendent of Documents). U.S. Department of Commerce, Commercial Standard 191-53, Revised August 23, 1954. 24 pp. 15 cents.

General Purpose Vinyl Plastic Film (Washington, D. C. 20402: U.S. Superintendent of Documents). U.S. Department of Commerce, Commercial Standard 192-53.

California Administrative Code, Title 19—Public Safety, Flame Retardant Chemicals, Fabrics and Application Concerns (Sacramento: California State Fire Marshal) Regulations, Subchapter 8, Register 60, No. 23. November 19, 1960, effective December 10, 1960, pages 169-188.

AATCC Research Committee RA 46, Fire Resistance of Industrial Fabrics (Box 886, Durham, S. C.: American Association of Textile Chemists and Colorists). AATCC Standard Test Method 34. 1952 (ASA L14.107-1961). 2 pp. Published in AATCC Technical Manual. 1962. $10.

ASTM Committee D-13 on Textile Materials, Standard Method of Test for Flammability of Clothing Textiles (Philadelphia: American Society for Testing and Materials). ASTM Designation D 1230-61 (American Association of Textile Chemists and Colorists Standard Method 33-1957. American Standard Association L 14.69—1963). Reprinted from Book of ASTM Standards, Part 10, 1963. 8 pp.

ASTM Committee D-13 on Textile Materials, Tentative Specifications for Fire Retardant Properties of Treated Textile Fabrics (Philadelphia, American Society for Testing and Materials). ASTM Designation D626-55T with editorial amendment July 1961. (Based on NFPA 701.)

U.S. General Services Administration, Textile Test Methods (Flame Resistance of Cloth: Method 5900, Horizontal: Method 5902, Vertical; Method 5903, Modified Vertical; Method 5904, Vertical, Field) (Washington, D. C. 20407; Business Service Center, GSA). Federal Specification CCT-T-191b. May 15, 1951. $1.75.

## British Test Methods

The following are publications of British Standards Association, 2 Park Street, London W.1. (In U.S. these should be ordered from American Standards Associa-

tion, 10 East 40th Street, New York, N. Y. 10016, for prices shown in parentheses.)
Flammability Test for Thin Flexible Materials. B. S. 476. Part 2:1955. 14 pp. 3 shillings (55 cents).
Method of Test for Flameproof Materials. B.S. 3119:1959. 8 pp. 3 shillings (55 cents).
Performance Requirements of Fabrics Described as of Low Flammability. B.S. 3121: 1959. 8 pp. 3 shillings (55 cents).
Tests for the Flammability of Fabrics. B.S. 2963:1958 and amendment, November 1959. 12 pp. 4 shillings (75 cents).
Performance Requirements of Materials for Flameproof Clothing. B.S. 3120: 1959. 8 pp. 3 shillings (55 cents).

## German Test Methods

The following are German Engineering Standards (DIN) of German Standards Association (Deutscher Normenausschuss-DNA), Berlin, W.15, Germany.
Clothing Protective Against Severe Flame Exposure. DIN 23325. April 1955. 4 pp.
Test of Plastic Film and Artificial Leather. One-sided flame exposure and swinging flame method. DIN 53382. October 1957. 2 pp.
Testing Incandescence Resistance of Plastics. DIN 53459. February 1962. 2 pp.
Test Methods for Decorative Laminated Sheets, Class A. DIN 53799. September 1960. 4 pp.
Combustibility of Textiles Tested on Vertically Suspended Specimens. DIN 53906. 4 pp.
Combustibility of Open Weave Textiles Tested on Horizontally Placed Specimens. DIN 53907. April 1961. 2 pp.

## VIII. ADHESIVES

### A. Review of Types, Properties, and Applications

Packaging, building, automotive, appliances and other major industries in the past year have required the development of new adhesives and new production facilities. Large building components and prefabricated buildings require more adhesives. The auto industry increased its use of adhesives. More adhesive primary structures are being produced in aircraft, ground transportation vehicles, aerospace systems and hydrospace vehicles (20).

The over and under ground vehicles take advantage of ease of fabrication, high-strength to weight ratio, smoothness, etc. characteristics. Builders envision the day when a complete house is put together without nails. In the meantime, more use is being made of adhesives for sealing of joints in curtain-wall type construction. Epoxy-polysulfide is used to bond cement to itself and other materials. Over 50 million lb per year of phenolic, melamine, and urea bonding resins go into chipboard and plywood sheets. Melamine and urea-formaldehyde adhesives for the wood industry this year will amount to over 200 million lb. Synthetic resins and casein adhesives are used in the expanding market of laminated structural timber beams. In metal construction, modified epoxies continue at a progressive rate to replace rivets and welds, principally because manufacturing costs are reduced, but also for other reasons such as multifunctional use of the adhesive, prevention of electrolytic corrosion, and simplification of assemblies.

The long range economic outlook for adhesive resins and modified starch adhesives is very impressive. The most important area of continued growth is packaging. The 1965 estimate shows up to $\frac{3}{4}$ billion lb of predominantly vegetable (55% of total—starch, etc.) and plastic resin (40% of total—primarily vinyls) adhesives were used in boxes, bags, labels, tapes, and other packaging applications. Since 1956, plastics has been taking a bigger portion every year. In 1944 it had approximately 20% of a total 400 million lb market. Automated packaging lines depend on these adhesives for speed and smooth operation.

Pressure-sensitive tapes and labels patented in 1930 by R. G. Drew (3M Company) have now in 1966 developed into a $260 million U.S.A. industry. They are comprised of synthetic and natural resin and rubber. The adhesive industry growth is due to many factors. There is no end in sight to new materials, new formulations, new product styling, new uses including the consumer "do-it-yourself" market. Progress will continue to be complex, as no one adhesive can meet the many diversified requirements. The total adhesive market this year is estimated to be approximately one-half billion dollars, including at least 35% plastic formulations. Typical types of adhesives are listed in Tables 16-16 and 16-17.

### 1. Future Adhesive

Modern plastic-based adhesives are essential at the present time but may be more important in the future. Product range from walking shoes to medical incisions; friction brake shoes to structures of aerospace of hydrospace vehicles; buildings to communication systems; containers for cosmetics to dehydrated food.

Plastic adhesives are being studied for use in surgery—muscle and

TABLE 16-16.  Chemical Types of Adhesives

There are many ways to classify adhesives. No single category is completely adequate for the industry users or producers; e.g., cure temperatures, pressure, adherends, gel formulation, end-products, cost, form, and chemical compositon. This latter category is the most logical and widely used.

| | |
|---|---|
| *Thermoplastic* | Polyvinyl alcohol |
| | Polyvinyl alkyd ether |
| Acetal | Polyvinyl butyral |
| Acrylate or methylmethacrylate | Polyvinyl chloride |
| Cellulose acetate | Polyvinyl methyl ethers |
| Cellulose acetate butyrate | Urethane |
| Cellulose nitrate | |
| Cellulose propionate | *Thermosetting* |
| Ethyl cellulose | |
| Ethylene-acrylic | Alkyd |
| Fluorocarbon | Casein |
| Polyacrylonitrile | Cyanoacrylate |
| Polyamide (nylon) | Diallyl phthalate |
| Polybutadiene-acrylonitrile | Epoxy and modifications |
| Polybutadiene-styrene | Furan |
| Polycarbonate | Melamine |
| Polyethylene | Melamine formaldehyde |
| Polyhydroxy ether | Phenol-formaldehyde |
| Polyimide | Phenol-furfural |
| Polyphenylene oxide | Polyester |
| Polypropylene | Polysulfide |
| Polystyrene and copolymers | Resorcinol-phenol formaldehyde |
| Polysulfone | Silicone |
| Polyvinyl acetate | Urea-formaldehyde |

*Formulations of blends or alloys*—thermosettings, thermoplastics, or thermosetting/thermoplastic—many combinations exist—popular blends are

| | |
|---|---|
| Epoxy-novalac | Polyamide-epoxy |
| Epoxy-phenolic | Polyimide-epoxy |
| Epoxy-polysulfide | Silicate-vinyl-phenolic |
| Epoxy-silicone | Silicone phenolic |
| Phenolic-butyral | Vinyl formal-phenolic |
| Phenolic-acrylonitrile | Vinyl butyral-phenolic |
| Phenolic-polyamide | |

lung tissue. Successful sutures have been made with both isocyanate-polyester cured with moisture and polyacrylamide-glyoxal.

Present and future industry can use adhesives as an important "building block" for composites, materials that are created by the assembly of two or more materials—namely, selected filler or reinforcing elements and compatible matrix binder to obtain specific character-

TABLE 16-17.  Adhesive Strength

| Type | Tensile lap-shear strength, psi |
|---|---|
| Alkyd | 1,000–1,500 |
| Acrylate | 800–1,200 |
| Casein | 10– 100 |
| Cellulose-nitrate | 50– 200 |
| Cellulose-vinyl | 300– 400 |
| Epoxy | 1,000–5,000 |
| Epoxy-novalac | 1,600–4,200 |
| Epoxy-phenolic | 2,000–3,600 |
| Epoxy-polyamide | 4,000–5,200 |
| Epoxy-polysulfide | 3,000–4,500 |
| Epoxy-silicone | 1,000–2,400 |
| Melamine-formaldehyde | 2,500–3,200 |
| Phenolic | 1,000–5,000 |
| Phelolic-butadiene acrylonitrile | 400–1,600 |
| Phenolic-neoprene | 2,500–3,500 |
| Phenolic-neoprene | 3,000–4,800 |
| Phenolic-vinyl | 2,000–5,300 |
| Polyacrylonitrile | 900–1,400 |
| Polyamide | 2,000–4,200 |
| Polyethylene | 900 |
| Polyimide | 1,000–2,600 |
| Polyvinyl-acetate | 50– 350 |
| Polyvinyl-butyral | 900 |
| Resorcinol-phenol formaldehyde | 1,800–2,000 |
| Silicone | 300–1,000 |
| Vinyl butyral-phenolic | 1,800–2,000 |
| Vinyl copolymers | 1,700–2,000 |
| Urea-Formaldehyde | 2,500–3,000 |
| Urethane | 4,000–9,000 |

This test represents only one of numberous tests that can be used for evaluation, control, etc. The tensile shear test with $\frac{1}{2}$ in. lap (ASTM) is predominantly used for strength control. These data are typical room temperature range of values based on bond line of 1–8 mils in thickness and bonding to different adherends. Note even though certain adhesives listed above may appear similar they will differ based on other properties—moisture resistance, peel strength, solvent resistance, temperature of application, etc.

istics and properties. They can be planned to provide a variety of speciality properties. Present and future homogeneous materials are unable to withstand all the pending environments and loads—temperature, moisture, corrosion resistance, stress, etc. Since adhesives are multifunctional, they will be very useful in these composites.

## 2. *Advantages*

Advantages of adhesives include efficiency in applications, reliability, compactness, high ultimate fatigue resistance, and aesthetic appeal. They combine parts which otherwise could not be accomplished by other techniques, for example, abrasive wheels, sandpaper, veneer furniture, packaging film laminated with other films or foil, bottle and can labels, and helicopter blades. Multifunctional uses stem from combinations of two or more capabilities, such as supporting high stress loads, electrical insulation or conductivity, moisture vapor barrier, corrosion resistance, or flexible matrix for adherends with different thermal expansion properties. When adhesives appear to be high in cost compared to competitive attachment methods, such as rivets, the completed assembly costs should be considered.

**Adherend or Substrate**—A body which is held to another by an adhesive.

Adhesive is a term which generally includes categories such as sealant, cement, glue, or paste—they all tend to be used interchangeably. As an example, a sealant can be considered a special adhesive requiring low porosity or permeability—generally it is flexible and is not required to provide high strength.

The fundamental aspects on nature of adhesion range from mechanical interlocking to the important theory of surface energy forces—where the surface chemistry may or may not be the principal controlling factor.

## 3. *Compounding*

Discovery of phenolic resins gave the plastic adhesive industry an important start in the beginning of this century. The next important growth step started in 1941 by the development of epoxy resins. Devoe and Reynolds Company and Shell Chemical Corporation independently produced these resins for the first time in U.S.A. In 1938 a liquid epoxy resin was developed in Zurich, Switzerland for preparation of dentures. By 1944 Ciba Limited, Switzerland, developed its Araldite epoxy adhesive. Then during the 1950's the adhesive industry started expanding its technology.

In the past few years with some of the old and new resins, compounds were developed to meet different requirements. As an example, if you have to bond underwater, modified epoxy systems are available. Or use the conductive adhesive solders in your electrical assemblies. If you want your supersonic aircraft bonded structure to withstand high temperature, the adhesives are now developed. Different adhesives can repair or seal your boat, repair a leaking pipe at home, or repair damaged jewelry.

Prior to 1941 adhesives were used largely in nonstructural applications. The development of structural adhesives, started in 1941, has been most fruitful for the industry. At that time, D. L. Grimes, then head of the Plastics Group in the Air Force Structures Laboratory, Wright-Patterson Air Force Base, with R. T. Schwartz, head of Nonmetallic Branch in the Air Force Materials Laboratory, met S. G. Saunders of Chrysler Corporation. Saunders had been working on an adhesive to be used in bonding glass to glass for automobile corner posts. Since his test facilities did not permit failure of bonds, he requested Grimes to conduct structural-failure tests with the equipment generally used to provide high test loads on aircraft structures. This turned out to be a major contributing factor in developing structural adhesives for use in aircraft and industry. Chrysler's Cycleweld adhesive was evaluated by the laboratory for specific use in bonding structures in place of rivets. Adhesives in film form are extensively used in present aircraft—examples Boeing 707 or Douglas DC-8 with over 6,000 sq ft each, Boeing 727 uses more, and C-141 airplane with over 10,000 sq ft. Over 1,000 lb is used in B-58 airplanes. More will be used on the Supersonic-SST aircraft. Many different modified epoxy and other structural adhesives continued to be developed since that time. Now, to retain strength but increase operating temperature from 350°F, polyimide and polybenzimidazole, among others, are being evaluated.

Silicone compounded adhesives have become useful because they remain rubberlike over a wide temperature range, but they are resistant to certain solvents (Fig. 16-41). New one-part systems cure on contact with moisture in the air. However, they have followed other resin adhesive growth patterns by developing markets based on their inherent characteristics. As an example, Dow Corning Corporation now produces at least 50 silicone sealants engineered for today's markets. General Electric Company's and other silicone adhesives are also numerous. Sealants are used in construction and manufacture of automobiles, marine products, safety glass, sinks, tubs, etc.

Silicone compounds include dimethylsilicone elastomers, polysiloxane, vinylalkoxysilanes, and cyanoalkylsilicone. The vinylalkoxysilane homopolymers can be used as plasticizers and modifiers for synthetic resins. They provide toughening and insoluble characteristics. Silicone pressure-sensitive tapes have been prepared using siloxane resin.

Our present dry bonds are possible by the individual or combination properties of the newer resins such as polyamide, acrylate, polyvinyl acetate, epoxy, polysulfide, and urethane. These plastics have been copolymerized or alloyed with other resins to provide properties required by different industries.

Resins such as polyimide, polysulfone, polyphenylene oxide, polybenzimidazole, and others now comint out of test tubes will provide more advanced adhesives for tomorrow. They will improve or simplify method of application, improve adhesion and increase heat resistance. These adhesives can be made compounds. They may also be formulated from combinations of synthetic or natural rubbers, modifying polymers, fillers, solvents, plasticizers, extenders, tackifiers, etc.

Fig. 16-41. G.E. Company silicone construction sealant is a high grade building adhesive type compound which requires no mixing since it is a one part system. Sealant flows at — 35°F, eliminating need for expensive warming.

### 4. Application Methods

Adhesives are generally applied in a low-viscosity fluid form to "wet" the adherend surface. The transition from fluid to the useful solid adhesive form is accomplished by polymerization, solution or solvent removal, or cooling of hot-melt. The polymerization systems, which have provided the most rapid technological progress, involve thermosetting resins, vulcanized elastomers and certain thermoplastic resins such as polymethyl methacrylate and cyanoacrylate esters. Adhesives are cured by heat, special catalysts for room temperature curing, or special activation such as light, oxygen or even defrosting. Systems with not external heating are required or desired for certain production runs. Formulations are available with resorcinal formaldehyde, unsaturated polyesters, methyl methacrylate, cyanocrylate esters, epoxies, and urethanes. All the polymerization reactions are usually exothermic so that bond lines may produce heats ranging from at least 90 to 400°F.

Thermoplastic and thermosetting adhesives are used in aqueous solutions and dispersions, and as solutions in organic solvents. Solution or latex systems contain adhesive composition in admixture of less than

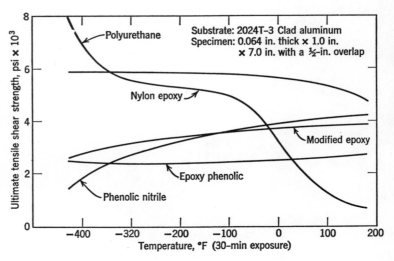

Fig. 16–42. Effect of cryogenic temperatures on different classes of structural adhesives.

50% with organic solvents or more than 50% with water solvents. To obtain over 50% it is necessary that at least a portion of the polymer be present in agglomerates of greater than colloidal sizes. Polyvinyl alcohol is an example of one of the most important water soluable adhesives. As a latex, the polymer is present in the form of globules existing as a discrete phase in an acqueous matrix. Acrylics, vinyls, epoxies, cellulosics, synthetic rubbers, and natural rubbers are the most readily used. Others, which are not considered major components, are polyvinyl butyral, polyvinyl acetate, and urea-formaldehyde.

Solvents most commonly employed include methylene dichloride, ethylene dichloride, glacial acetic acid, methacrylic acid, MEK, and diacetone alcohol.

An important consideration when using any solvent or solution system is to insure that the liquids are adequately removed.

Hot-melts are one of the most recent production developments. They are economical and provide processing simplicity. In hot-melt systems, all thermoplastic resins are used. Basically, all that has to occur is to soften the resin with heat. Upon cooling, it provides the adhesion. But

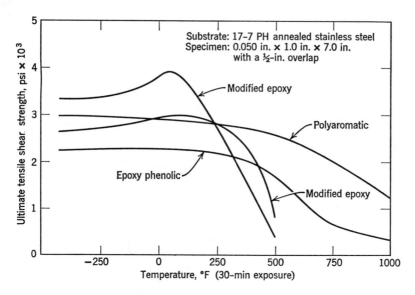

Fig. 16-43. Effect of elevated temperature on the different classes of structural adhesives.

higher strengths and more durability are available from the other systems.

Vinyl acetate polymers facilitate high-speed packaging labels. Ethyl cellulose and cellulose acetate butyrate hot-melts used in packaging to provide bonding and protection against moisture. Polyvinyl butyral and silicone hot-melt films are used in laminated safety glass. Extruded rope of ethylene polymers and copolymers, vinyl acetate polymers and polyamides make for fast production.

Compositions of hot-melts are usually a plasticized blend of low-molecular weight resins, such as coumarone-indene, alkyds, phenol formaldehyde, with high-molecular weight polymers, such as ethyl cellulose, polyvinyl acetate, polyethylene, polystyrene, butyl methacrylate, or polyisobutylene. Hot-melts are being produced to handle difficult jobs such as bonding to polyethylene. A typical formulation for PE contains 40–50% by weight of PE, 20–30% of isobutylene polymer, and 20–60% of a hydrocarbon resin.

## 5. *Internal Bond Line Curing*

Generation of heat within the bond to cure the adhesive is now being exploited, as are metal tapes and filaments thinner than one mil.

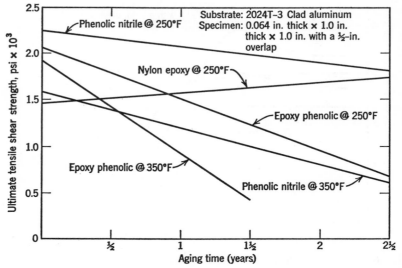

Fig. 16-44. Effect of long-time aging on the different classes of structural adhesives.

Electric heating in the bondline will speed the cure of strong adhesive joints. This type of curing is particularly useful in bonding materials having low thermal conductivity. In the conventional oven heating operations, relatively long curing cycles are required. Also, sections not needing will be heated unnecessarily and perhaps harmfully. Bondline temperatures of 350°F are reached within a few seconds. At 10 amperes, the power used is approximately 400 watts per square foot. Bonds 8 to 10 mils have been "wire cured." The expected maximum strength properties have been obtained in much less time than cures with conventional external heaters. Vinyl acetate maleate copolymer, cellulose acetate, PVC, and phenolic-neoprene adhesives have been cured within a second rather than the usual one half to many minutes. Modified epoxy adhesives (phenolic, polyimide, silica or others) are cured in one or two minutes rather than the usual three to six hours.

### 6. Factors Influencing Adhesive Selection

The choice of plastic-based adhesive subject to low stresses are almost unlimited. If high strength is required, the choice tends to be limited to the many polar compounds of high molecular weight formulations. In addition to stress requirements, many other variables are involved. There is no all-purpose adhesive for all types of design and service. Logic and economics (Tables 16-18 and 16-19) will determine the potential use of adhesive. If the adhesive is not available—and a good dollar market exists—it will be developed. On the other hand if an adhesive is developed ahead of the market—such as hot-melts for packaging—the industry will catch up.

Factors to consider are the adhesive form to be used for manufacture —unsupported or supported film, liquid, paste or putty, pellets in various shapes, powder or granule, rod or rope, tape or ribbon. Method of application varies: brush, extruder, flowing, gravity feed coater, immersion, knife coating, pressure gun, roller coater, spatula, spraying, and troweling.

Surface preparation for bonding is also an important consideration. Preparation varies according to the properties required. The usual nonstructural part may only require that no dust or dirt to be present) ; structural bonds may require special chemical etching on metal or milling on plastics. Surface treatments can selectively alter surfaces to obtain desired properties. As an example, polyethylene requires special treatments. The major treatment takes the form of energetic physical

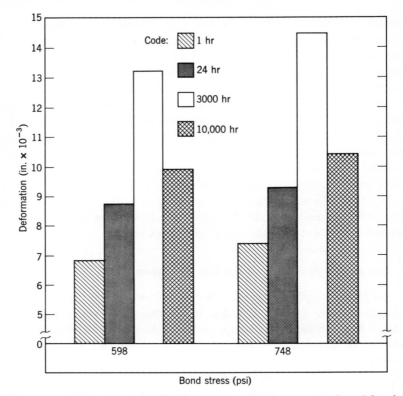

Fig. 16-45. Effect of varying bond stress on the creep properties of bonded 2024-T86 aluminum double overlap joint specimens using a nitrile rubber phenolic adhesive (2.0 sq in. overlap area).

processes which modify the nonpolar surface of the PE. Flame impingement and corona discharge methods are examples of these thin-surface treatments which involve surface chemical reactions.

Bonding tools and fixtures are generally required to obtain best results. For instance, a hot-melt production unit will provide or combine heat of fusion, apply the adhesive, maintain pressure contact, and prevent separation before set.

Probably the most important factor from the designer's requirement is effect of environment—temperature, humidity, etc. or tension, shear, peel, damping, etc. (See Table 16-20 and Figs. 16-42 to 16-45) Adhesives are available to meet different conditions. As an example they can join thermoplastic film and provide high peel strength. Bonded electronic parts can withstand shock and vibration. Reinforced plastics or metal bonds can perform in cryogenic ($-423°F$) to ultrahigh (over

TABLE 16-18.    Cost of Adhesive Components (Dollars per Pound)

| | |
|---|---:|
| *Plastics* | |
| Acrylic (emulsion, dry) | 0.40–0.45 |
| Butadiene-acrylonitrile | 0.45–0.53 |
| Butadiene-styrene resin | 0.28 |
| Casein | 0.15–0.20 |
| Coumarone-indene | 0.15–0.20 |
| Epoxy | 0.55–1.10 |
| Ethyl cellulose | 0.69 |
| Melamine-formaldehyde | 0.32–0.40 |
| Methyl cellulose | 0.69 |
| Phenolics | 0.25 |
| Polyamides | 0.60–1.60 |
| Polybenzimidazole (PBI) | 10.00–20.00 |
| Polyesters (unsaturated) | 0.31–0.47 |
| Polyimide | 12.25 |
| Polyurethane raw materials | 0.40–0.50 |
| Polyvinyl acetate emulsion | 0.29 |
| Polyvinyl alcohol | 0.57–0.58 |
| Polyvinyl butyral | 1.05 |
| Polyvinyl chloride | 0.16–0.20 |
| Resorcinol-formaldehyde | 0.90–0.95 |
| Styrene-butadiene rubber | 0.25–0.30 |
| Urea-formaldehyde | 0.13–0.20 |
| Urea | 0.05 |
| *Catalysts* | |
| Phenylenediamine | 1.10 |
| Tetraethylenepentamine | 0.56 |
| Triethylenetetramine | 0.49 |
| Hexamethylenetetramine | 0.22 |
| Borax | 0.03 |
| *Waxes* | |
| Montan wax | 0.22 |
| Paraffin | 0.15 |
| Polyethylene—LM | 0.27 |
| Glycerol | 0.29 |
| Ethylene glycol | 0.16 |
| Diethylene glycol | 0.15 |
| Tricresyl phosphate | 0.35 |
| Dibutyl phthalate | 0.26 |
| Dioctyl phthalate | 0.28 |
| Dioctyl adipate | 0.40 |
| Diethanolamine | 0.24 |
| *Fillers* | |
| Whiting | 0.01 |
| Bentonite | 0.10 |

*(continued)*

TABLE 16-18. (*continued*)

| | |
|---|---|
| *Fillers (continued)* | |
| Kaolin | 0.1–0.02 |
| Magnesia | 0.28 |
| Zinc oxide | 0.15 |
| Silica | 0.01–0.02 |
| *Solvents* | |
| Acetone | 0.08 |
| Cyclohexanol | 0.28 |
| Cyclohexanone | 0.33 |
| Ethyl acetate | 0.13 |
| Heptane/gal | 0.16 |
| Methylethyl ketone | 0.10–0.16 |
| Toluene/gal | 0.25 |
| Xylene/gal | 0.28 |

1200°F) temperatures, from vacuum to atomic blast pressures, and from dry to complete immersion in water.

Other important factors to consider are methods of testing and inspection. Procedures are available for conduction destructive static and dynamic tests. The nondestructive tests include tapping, ultrasonic, electrostatic, stub meter, x-ray and fluoroscopic.

## 7. Future

The market for adhesives will continue to be large and diversified. The greatest growth in the foreseeable future, as at present, is with the use of new plastic resins and modified starches. The continued growth will parallel the spontaneous development of new plastics. Every industry will have its own needs, its own specifications, and its own environmental requirements (Table 16-21). Typical parts are shown in Figs. 16-46 to 16-50)

Development continues on room temperature-setting systems with rapid addition polymerization of acrylic and vinylic monomer mixtures. For strength improvements, monomers being studied include acrylic

TABLE 16-19. Thermal Expansion

| Adhesive | in./in.-°F$\times 10^{-5}$ |
|---|---|
| Epoxy-polyamide | 3.2 |
| Nylon-polyamide | 3.2 |
| Polyurethane | 4.1 |

Fig. 16-46. After a uniform bead of sealant (adhesive) is applied to glass, windshield is lifted into place, supported on lower spacer blocks. Sealant allows effective seating of windshield with moderate effort, yet supports windshield weight when hand pressure is removed. The Dow Corning silicone compound is easy to apply since it does not have any limited shelf life.

TABLE 16-20. Strength of Polyimide Adhesives

|  |  | Tensile shear strength,[a] psi | |
| --- | --- | --- | --- |
| Temperature, °F | Time, hr | Unformulated [b] polyimide | Formulated [b] polyimide |
| 77 | — | 2500 | 2200 |
| 550 | 1 | 1800 | 1400 |
| 550 | 100 | 2200 | 1900 |
| 550 | 200 | 1800 | 1400 |
| 700 | 1 | 1400 | 600 |
| 700 | 10 | 1300 | 1100 |
| 700 | 24 | 1300 | 1200 |
| 700 | 60 | 0 | 1100 |

[a] Substrate tested was 17-7 PH stainless steel, phosphate etched. Bonds were formed at 575°F, under 200 psi pressure for 2 hr.
[b] Formulated material contains an antioxidant and various fillers; unformulated material is the straight polyimide.

Fig. 16-47. Different 3M Company sealers are used in the manufacture of aluminum windows, glass doors and curtain wall systems. Some adhere directly to the aluminum. With vinyl extrusion beads, types are available for use with either the soft or rigid vinyl glazing beads. The sealants do not affect the beads.

acid, methacrylic acid, maleic anhydride, itaconic acid, and itaconic esters. Ultimate strength developments involve blends of epoxy with acrylic or vinyls. The isocyanates, polyimides, PBI's, etc. will expand into more applications. Then new resins such as polyhydroxy ether, a thermoplastic, in the form of 100% solids with 1,000 psi tensile shear strength will find more use in high structural bond applications.

A new process for treating certain plastics so they can be joined strongly to other materials by adhesives has been invented at Bell Telephone Laboratories. The process also gives new insight into how materials stick together.

Many thermoplastics, including materials such as Teflon and polyethylene, can be treated by this new process. These plastics are difficult to "stick to" and cannot be bonded strongly to other materials by adhesives unless their surfaces are treated. Previously, surface treatments changed certain characteristics of the plastics, including such things as

TABLE 16-21.  Plastics in Adhesives

| Adhesive applications | Adhesive applications |
| --- | --- |
| Aircraft parts— <br>   aileron, bulkhead, door seal, firewall <br>   seal, floor, glass seal, instrumentation, <br>   integral fuel tanks, wing sections, skin <br>   sections, etc. | Electrical motor parts |
| | Electrical motor parts |
| | Electrical wiring harness |
| | Electronic components |
| | Encapsulation |
| Antenna masts | Envelopes |
| Army weapons | Expandable space structures |
| Automobile parts— <br>   vibration isolators, chrome trim, win- <br>   dow seal, door seal, mirror, etc. | Flexible tubing attachments |
| | Floor aggregate |
| | Floor panel |
| Baggage rack | Friction brake |
| Bathtub seal | Furniture |
| Battery parts | Glass joining |
| Boat parts | Granite joining |
| Book binding | Grinding and polishing wheels |
| Brank linings (trucks, etc.) | Helicopter parts— <br>   rotor blades, fuselage, etc. |
| Building parts— <br>   curtain wall, door, trim, prefabricated <br>   parts, window casing and caulking, <br>   etc. | Highway topping |
| | Honeycomb construction |
| | Hydrospace parts— <br>   paneling, seals, etc. |
| Buoys | Instrument lense |
| Cabin ceiling | Instrument panels |
| Cabinet | Instrument parts |
| Cargo container | Jewelry |
| Cartons | Knife blade handle |
| Cement and mortar repair | Label |
| Ceramic jointing | Lagging |
| Ceramic tile setting | Liquid hydrogen system |
| Chemical equipment liners and fittings | Liquid nitrogen |
| Cigar wrappers | Machine shop using double face tape |
| Clothing repair | Maintenance and field repairs |
| Communication antenna reflector | Marble joining |
| Construction parts | Marine parts |
| Consumer products | Masking tape |
| Countertop | Medical implant parts |
| Decorative paneling and laminates | Medical incision |
| Dental plates | Metal drum attachment |
| Dielectric heater filament condenser <br>   plate seal | Missile parts— <br>   insulation, structure, fin, electronic, <br>   etc. |
| Do-it-yourself repair kits | Model kits |
| Drain and gutter seals | Nonwoven fabrics |
| Electric conductor | OEM industrial maintenance and re- <br>   pair |
| Electric range duct | |
| Electrical cable | |
| Electrical insulation | |

*(continued)*

DONALD V. ROSATO AND FRANK J. RIEL

TABLE 16-21. (*continued*)

| Adhesive applications | Adhesive applications |
|---|---|
| Optical instrument parts | Signboards |
| Packages— | Skis |
|   bags, cardboard, plastic, metal, wood, | Solar cell |
|   etc. | Sound damping |
| Papers—special | Space capsule |
| Phonograph cartridge | Space vehicle— |
| Pipe fitting |   heat shield, structures, radome, etc. |
| Portable shelter | Sporting goods— |
| Potting |   fishing rod, golf club, tennis, etc. |
| Prefabricate structures | Steel strip coat |
| Printed circuit | Synchrotron, 12.5 billion volts |
| Printing plate | Tank treads—Army |
| Radome parts—foamed, | Telephone parts |
|   space frame, etc. | Textile operations |
| Refrigerator parts— | Thread—locking |
|   handles, seals, etc. | Thermal insulation |
| Repair techniques | Tile |
| Rocket motor insulation | Tool bit and holder |
| Roofing seals | Toy |
| Safety glass interlayer | Truck and trailer parts |
| Sandwich panels— | TV tube shield |
|   decoration, structures, flooring, etc. | Vinyl wall covering |
| Satellite parts | Wall partition |
| Sealing tapes | Wareguide tube |
| Sealing wax | Weather stripping |
| Shock absorbing pads | Wire and cable. |
| Shoes | |

tensile strength, color, and dielectric properties. The new process, however, does not alter the desirable chemical or physical properties of the plastics.

This process also makes it possible to print successfully on Teflon and polyethylene. Until now, Teflon could not be printed on successfully because its surface became badly discolored after exposure to surface treatment, thus obscuring the printing. (Printing is a form of adhering. Ink is the adhesive which "sticks" to the plastic.)

Drs. Ralph Hansen and Harold Schonhorn invented the new process. The two scientists found that by exposing a sample of thermoplastic to an electrically-activated inert gas, such as helium or neon, a tough

Fig. 16-48. This 60 ft diameter precision antenna operates at X-band frequency. Aluminum sandwich panels are used as the reflective surface. The sandwich structural panels are assembled with structural adhesives, usually nylon-phenolic compounds made into supported films using glass cloth scrim.

outer "skin" forms on the surface of the plastic. (This is somewhat like the skin that forms on paint when it is exposed to air.) This layer of tough skin makes an ideal surface for adhesive bonding. The result is an adhesive joint ten or more times stronger than possible with an untreated sample of the same plastic.

Until now, many scientists believed that weak adhesive joints were due primarily to weak interfacial forces between the thermoplastics and other materials. Drs. Schonhorn and Hansen have concluded that weak joints result primarily from a layer of weak material at the surface of these thermoplastics.

The two Bell Labs scientists now say that two conditions—complete

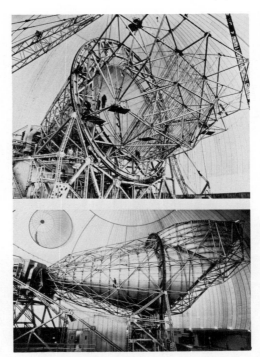

Fig. 16-49. A total of 500 contoured aluminum panels were used to fabricate the microwave reflective horn for the Bell Telephone Laboratory TELSTAR located in Andover, Maine. This is the Earth Space Communication Station, the U.S. relay station receiving signals from satellites and providing the U.S. and the rest of the world possessing ground stations with on the spot TV information. Whittaker Corporation designed and built the panels using structural adhesives.

interfacial contact and strengthening of the weak boundary layer material—are necessary to achieve maximum adhesive joint strength.

## B. Structural Adhesives

BY FRANK J. RIEL

### 1. Introduction

In any discussion of the effects of an environment on an adhesive, one must consider the behavior not only of the adhesive material itself but also the substrate to which the adhesive is bonded. Adhesive bonding

Fig. 16-50. Marine spacecrafts which carry out missions to Mars used adhesives in various parts; such as the G.E. Company silicone to bond 8,224 photovoltaic solar cells on the four paddles to aid in producing electrical energy during space flight and modified epoxy to bond the communication antenna dish.

is an old art, and there are adhesives which are designed to bond almost any of the materials we use in everyday life, to say nothing of the unusual materials being used in our modern, space age technology. There are adhesives for cloth, paper, cement, wood, aluminum, magnesium, rubber, plastics, synthetic fibers, shell, titanium, glass fiber reinforced plastics, cardboard, glass, ceramics, graphite, and even people. There are pressure sensitive adhesives, hot melt adhesives, solvent release adhesives, heat curing adhesives, room temperature curing adhesives, adhesives that release moisture during curing, and adhesives that cure by exposure to moisture. The interaction of various environments on all of these different types of adhesives bonded joints is a subject too broad for proper treatment in a single chapter. Furthermore, specialists best qualified to discuss the subject with one type of adhesive generally have little or no familiarity with many of the other types. Also, environments which are significant for one type of adhesive may be totally irrelevant to another type. For example, air at temperatures in excess of 500°F is a very significant environmental problem for adhesives designed for bonding of stainless steel. However, this condition is of no interest whatsoever for adhesives used for bonding paper, cardboard, and the like.

Because of these factors, it is necessary to limit the scope of this discussion, in terms of the adhesives types to be considered. To some extent, this limitation also limits and establishes the environments which are significant. In this chapter, we will restrict the presentation to the environmental effects on structural adhesives.

Structural adhesives may be defined as those which are used in association with structural materials, where significant load carrying potential is demanded from the bonded composite. This definition is not entirely satisfactory, however, since it is hard to establish what a significant load carrying capability may be. Perhaps it is more meaningful to think of structural adhesives as that class of special adhesives which has grownup with the modern aircraft industry, and find their major application in the bonding of thin sections of light weight, high strength materials such as aluminum, stainless steel, and glass fiber reinforced plastic composites. Applications for these materials in other industries, where the requirements for load carrying capabilities may or may not be severe, are developing. These are, however, special cases, and will not be discussed here, although some of the data to be presented may be of interest.

As previously pointed out, the effect of the environment on the combination of adhesive and substrate is the important factor, hence interactions and interfaces may be more important than bulk properties. In a typical adhesive bonded metal joint one can identify six separate regions, with different compositions (or gradations of compositions) and hence different properties. First, there is the bulk metal itself; second, there is the metallic surface; third, the surface coating on the metal (an oxide, hydroxide, carbonate, phosphate, etc.) ; fourth, there is an interfacial layer of mingled adhesive and substrate; fifth, there is an adhesive surface material; and finally there is the bulk adhesive itself. A given environment may attach this complex system at anyone of these regions, or all, and in all, any interaction leads to the destruction of the adhesive bond. In considering various environmental effects on adhesive bonded joints attempts will be made to point out the failure mechanism, when known.

## 2. *Applications*

In establishing the scope of this discussion, it has been decided to limit the adhesive systems to those suitable for bonding the following systems:

*Simple lap joints*
(1)  Aluminum
(2)  Magnesium
(3)  Steel
(4)  Titanium
(3)  Steel
(5)  Beryllium
(6)  Glass reinforced plastic composites

While it is possible to bond dissimilar metals to each other, it is not common practice to do so. While most adhesives are good electrical insulators, thus minimizing undesirable electrochemical interactions, there are other problems associated with differential expansion and strain incompatibility which make the practice generally undesirable. If such a joint is desired, its resistance to environment effects is at best that of the most susceptible member. In addition, under extreme humidity conditions there may be electrochemical interactions which accelerate the degradation processes.

Because of the relatively low shear and tensile strength of even the strongest adhesive systems, typical metal joints are almost always overlaps. Typical overlaps are from $\frac{1}{2}$ in. to many inches, or feet. The standard test specimen used for evaluating the properties of an adhesive consists of a $\frac{1}{2}$ in. overlap of 1 in. width. For experimental purposes, these specimens sometimes are fabricated essentially as single panels, using so called finger panels, or breakaway panels, for convenience. In other cases, panels up to 12 in. in width may be bonded at $\frac{1}{2}$ in. overlaps distances, and the panel subsequently cut into one inch wide strips. In evaluating environmental effects on an adhesive, one may expose either the uncut panel, the individual specimens cut from a panel, or the specimens fabricated in one inch wide strips. The military specifications which describe the test procedures for environmental exposures specify that the bond shall be fabricated from 9 in. wide panels, and one inch strips cut from each edge. The 7 in. wide panel, with freshly cut edges become the exposed test specimen. Many investigations, however, prefer to expose 1 in. wide freshly cut specimens, since this generally represents a more severe test.

Most adhesive systems are so designed, in terms of comparison and processing procedure, that the adhesive film joining the two metal sheets is thin, continuous, and relatively non-porous. While such a bond line is not always achieved, it is almost always desired. Because of this condition, attack by any environmental condition (except radiation) must be at the exposed edge of the joint, and must progress inward. Therefore, the geometry of the joint, and the condition of the edge surface become important factors. Because of the variety of shapes and configurations occuring in the actual assembly of an adhesive bonded part, it is seldom possible to design a representative test specimen, in order to obtain an estimate of the use life of the actual part when exposed to a given environment. Therefore, the usual practice is to select a very severe configuration, and base life expectancy projections on the date so collected. Generally, a 1 inch wide specimen, bonded to a $\frac{1}{2}$ in. overlap, and with freshly cut edges, is used as representatives of the most severe condition, from a geometrical standpoint, and is frequently used.

Practically all environmental exposure tests are conducted an panels in an unstressed condition. However since outdoor weathering tests, discussed elsewhere, indicate greater deterioration in stressed panels. This result is not especially surprising but in spite of the results, little attention has been paid to this condition.

*Sandwich Panels*

(1) Aluminum skin and core

(2) Aluminum skin and glass fiber reinforced plastic core

(3) Stainless steel skin and core

(4) Aluminum skin and balsa wood core

(5) Aluminum skin and paper core

(6) Glass fiber reinforced plastic skin and core

Sandwich panels, consisting of thin skins of metal (or reinforced plastic) bonded to honeycomb core material, basically will exhibits the same reaction with various environments as similar materials in simple metal to metal configuration. However, the basic geometrical difference between the bond lines of the two types of systems frequently results in a substantial increase in the rate of degradation. Assuming the core to be perforated and the edges unsealed, there is relatively free access of the environment to the entire bond line. Therefore, edge effects frequently are not as significant, and the geometry of the test specimen becomes less critical. This is not entirely true, however, since the adhesive generally will completely cover the inside surface of the skin, with a fillet formed around the core section adjacent to the skin. Under these conditions, the environment has access to the surface of the adhesive, and the interface between the adhesive and the core material, but the interface between the adhesive and the skin is exposed only at the external edges of the bond line. This condition may not be significant when a skin and core are of the same material, but it will be if they are different, as they frequently are.

Sandwich panels have certain environmental interactions which are independent of the adhesive system or structural materials if used. Most significant is the acquisition of water of condensation resulting from the changes in temperature and humidity.

## 3. Environments

**a. Elevated Temperatures.** Probably more effort has been expended on problems of high temperature resistance than on all other environmental conditions which are detrimental to adhesives. This in part, at least, is a result of the rather severe limitations of organic materials, in terms of heat resistance, as compared with the rapidly increasing high temperature requirements which have resulted from faster and faster aircraft, and the severe temperature profiles encountered by missiles and spacecraft (Tables 16-22 to 16-26).

Adhesives bonds can be destroyed by high temperature through three mechanisms. First the adhesive may melt, thus losing its adhesive strength. Second, it may dissociate, or de polymerize, thus being destroyed. Finally, it can interact with atmospheric oxygen, at some elevated temperature, and be destroyed by chemical oxidation. Thus the high temperature environment manifests itself in two ways, by thermal agitation and acceleration of the interaction of the adhesive and the oxygen in the air. Obviously, if the high temperature exposure occurrs in an inert atmosphere or a vacuum, the only effect of the heat is that of thermal agitation. However, air is such a common substance that practically all adhesive bonded parts exposed to high temperatures endure that exposure while in contact with some quantities of air. Therefore, unless otherwise specified, the high temperature exposures are assumed to be in air. Since the oxygen is the active ingredient, it follows that the severity of the exposure depends not only on the temperature of the air but also on the concentration of oxygen, which is determined by pressure. In addition, since we are dealing with an irreversible chemical reaction, time is important, and the extent of damage is determined by the time of exposure.

TABLE 16-22.  Effect of Extended 250°F Aging in Air on Structural Adhesives— Metal Substrate (21) (250°F tensile shear, psi)

| Aging period | 10 min | 0.5 year | 1.0 year | 1.5 year | 2.0 years | 2.5 years | 3.0 years | 3.5 years | 4.0 years | 4.5 years |
|---|---|---|---|---|---|---|---|---|---|---|
| Adhesive code | | | | | | | | | | |
| A | 2960 | 3620 | 3165 | 3190 | 3370 | 2260 | 1995 | 2010 | 3120 | 2960 |
| B | 1340 | 2110 | 2320 | 1680 | 2020 | 1670 | 1775 | 1700 | 1650 | 1960 |
| C | 1270 | 1260 | 1500 | 940 | 1240 | 1020 | 880 | 640 | | In test |
| D | 2000 | 1480 | 1340 | 1410 | 1170 | 760 | 940 | 700 | 780 | 765 |
| E | 360 | 1890 | 1050 | 2310 | 580 | 1470 | 1770 | 2160 | | In test |
| F | 2260 | 2350 | 2150 | 2300 | 2150 | 1450 | 1750 | 1810 | 2065 | 1880 |
| G | 1213 | 2250 | 2090 | 1830 | 1680 | 1035 | 2280 | 1670 | | In test |

Code:  A.  Bisphenol-A epoxy
  B.  Nylon epoxy
  C.  Epoxy-silicone-phenolic
  D.  Epoxy-phenolic
  E.  Vinyl-phenolic
  F.  Nitrile rubber-phenolic
  G.  Type F plus arsenic compound

TABLE 16-23.  Effect of Extended 350°F Aging in Air on Structural Adhesives (350°F tensile shear, psi)

| Aging period | 10 min | 0.5 year | 1.0 year | 1.5 year | 2.0 years | 2.5 years | 3.0 years | 3.5 years | 4.0 years | 4.5 years |
|---|---|---|---|---|---|---|---|---|---|---|
| Adhesive code | | | | | | | | | | |
| A | 1260 | 355 | 410 | 90 | 80 | 120 | No test | No test | 380 | 435 |
| B | 530 | Failed | | | | | | | | |
| C | 1220 | 390 | 470 | 190 | 340 | 290 | 350 | 295 | In test | |
| D | 1680 | 405 | 205 | 210 | Failed | | | | | |
| E | 80 | 440 | Failed | | | | | | | |
| F | 1520 | 1010 | 1205 | 870 | 890 | 640 | 410 | 440 | 560 | 475 |
| G | 550 | 1885 | 2080 | 1880 | 1730 | 1600 | 1500 | 1370 | In test | |

Code: See Table 16-22.

TABLE 16-24. Effect of Extended 250°F Aging in Air on Structural Plastics (250°F flexure strength, psi) (250°F modulus, psi $\times 10^{-6}$)

| Aging period | 10 min | 0.5 year | 1.0 year | 1.5 year | 2.0 years | 2.5 years | 3.0 years | 3.5 years | 4.0 years | 4.5 years |
|---|---|---|---|---|---|---|---|---|---|---|
| Laminate code | | | | | | | | | | |
| I | 39,700 (2.60) | 51,200 (3.01) | 50,600 (2.75) | 48,000 (2.87) | 47,700 (2.80) | 52,400 (2.94) | 48,000 (2.76) | In test | | |
| II | 58,900 (3.34) | 61,400 (3.58) | 54,200 (3.85) | 50,400 (3.62) | 35,200 (3.28) | 19,600 (2.42) | 20,100 (2.51) | 14,500 (2.16) | 11,700 (1.94) | 9,500 (2.00) |
| III | 66,900 (3.71) | 71,200 (3.95) | 59,100 (4.12) | 53,000 (3.73) | 52,800 (3.72) | 35,400 (3.40) | 38,000 (3.40) | 27,700 (3.09) | 20,300 (2.75) | 16,700 (2.85) |
| IV | 65,300 (3.68) | 66,500 (3.90) | 71,800 (4.46) | 56,100 (3.73) | 60,500 (4.00) | 53,600 (3.77) | 50,400 (3.58) | 56,500 (3.71) | 58,800 (3.71) | 58,200 (3.74) |
| V | 28,400 (2.94) | 27,100 (2.80) | 25,500 (2.59) | 27,100 (2.53) | 26,900 (2.53) | 25,000 (2.39) | 27,000 (2.54) | 28,700 (2.78) | In test | |
| VI | 17,700 (2.28) | 17,600 (2.33) | 16,400 (2.28) | 16,300 (2.00) | 17,500 (2.06) | 17,400 (2.14) | 17,700 (1.90) | 17,100 (2.13) | In test | |

Code:  I. Epoxy-novalac
II. Phenolic
III. Phenolic
IV. Silicone-phenolic (phenyl silane)
V. Silicone
VI. Silicone

TABLE 16-25.  Effect of Extended 350° Aging in Air on Structural Plastics (350°F flexure strength, psi) (350° modulus, psi$\times10^{-6}$)

| Aging period | 10 min | 0.5 year | 1.0 year | 1.5 year | 2.0 years | 2.5 years | 3.0 years | 3.5 years | 4.0 years | 4.5 years |
|---|---|---|---|---|---|---|---|---|---|---|
| Laminate code | | | | | | | | | | |
| I | 14,800 (1.48) | 44,500 (3.01) | 43,800 (2.53) | 44,200 (2.60) | 37,500 (2.43) | 22,300 (2.04) | 15,900 (1.13) | Failed | | |
| II | 56,900 (3.17) | 5,000 (1.63) | 1,800 (0.47) | 1,800 (0.47) | Failed | | | | | |
| III | 66,500 (3.62) | 1,700 (0.97) | Failed | | | | | | | |
| IV | 54,100 (3.41) | 49,900 (3.53) | 21,000 (3.40) | 4,400 (2.13) | 10,100 (2.35) | 2,300 (1.61) | 4,300 (—) | 2,800 (—) | 3,400 (—) | Failed |
| V | 21,000 (2.59) | 22,100 (2.53) | 23,400 (2.64) | 24,000 (2.57) | 22,700 (2.56) | 21,800 (2.49) | 21,800 (2.22) | 22,800 (2.55) | In test | |
| VI | 17,400 (2.37) | 18,900 (2.59) | 18,700 (2.56) | 17,900 (2.33) | 16,800 (2.23) | 17,600 (2.19) | 17,700 (2.16) | 18,300 (2.40) | In test | |

Code:  See Table 16-24.

TABLE 16-26. Tensile Shear Strengths at Room Temperature 10 Minutes at 300°F, 400°F, 500°F, 600°F, 700°F, 800°F, 900°F, and 1000°F (22)

(Comparison of Titanium Alloys Ti-8A1-1Mo-1V, Ti-6A1-4V, and 17-7 PH Annealed Stainless Steel, Tested in Air)

Adhesive Formulation: Resin: AF-A-121(31)-1,2
Carrier: Heat-cleaned 112 E-glass
Impregnation Procedure: Solution-coated with pyridine
Adherend: Ti-8A1-1Mo-1V; Ti-6A1-4V; 17-7 PH stainless steel, primed with solution
Surface Treatment: Phosphate etch at RT for Titanium alloys (2 min); standard phosphate etch for stainless steel
Cure Cycle: 1 hr at 600°F, 200 psi, cooled under pressure

| Test temp, °F | Time temp, min | Ti-8A1-1Mo-1V (No postcure) | | Ti-6A1-4V (No postcure) | | 17-7 PH Stainless steel annealed (No postcure) | |
|---|---|---|---|---|---|---|---|
| | | Tensile shear strength, psi | Type failure, % | Tensile shear strength, psi | Type failure, % | Tensile shear strength, psi | Type failure, % |
| RT | | 3360 | 90 | 3320 | 100 | 3540 | 100 |
| | | 3270 | 75 | 4080 | 100 | 3710 | 100 |
| | | 3360 | 90 | 4180 | 100 | 3760 | 100 |
| | Av. | 3330 | | 3860 | | 3670 | |
| 300 | 10 | 2740 | 60 | 3630 | 100 | 3340 | 100 |
| | | 2960 | 60 | 4000 | 100 | 2880 | 100 |
| | | 2930 | 60 | 3940 | 100 | 2850 | 100 |
| | Av. | 2870 | | 3856 | | 3023 | |
| 400 | | 2950 | 100 | 3750 | 100 | 3170 | 100 |
| | | 3210 | 100 | 3920 | 100 | 3270 | 100 |
| | | 3280 | 100 | 4310 | 100 | 2950 | 100 |

| Temp. | | | | | | | | |
|---|---|---|---|---|---|---|---|---|
| 500 | Av. | 3140 | | 3993 | | 3130 | | |
| | | 3000 | 95 | 3440 | 100 | 2860 | 100 | 100 |
| | | 2900 | 100 | 3650 | 100 | 2710 [a] | | |
| | | 2760 | 100 | 3800 | 100 | 3090 | 100 | 100 |
| 600 | Av. | 2880 | | 3630 | | 2887 | | |
| | | 2850 | 100 | 2410 | 100 | 2570 | 100 | 100 |
| | | 2690 | 100 | 2770 | 100 | 2580 | 100 | 100 |
| | | 2960 | 100 | 2760 | 100 | 2800 | 100 | 100 |
| 700 | Av. | 2833 | | 2646 | | 2650 | | |
| | | 1750 | 75 | 2110 | 100 | 2630 | 100 | 100 |
| | | 1750 | 75 | 2290 | 100 | 2510 | 100 | 100 |
| | | 1800 | 75 | 2120 | 100 | 2710 | 100 | 100 |
| 800 | Av. | 1766 | | 2173 | | 2617 | | |
| | | 1300 | 60 | 1490 | 25 | 1930 | 100 | 100 |
| | | 1040 | 40 | 1510 | 25 | 1930 | 100 | 100 |
| | | 1240 | 40 | 1430 | 25 | 1840 | 100 | 100 |
| 900 | | 1290 | 40 | 950 | 0 | 1430 | 90 | 90 |
| | | 1080 | 5 | 1210 | 5 | 1720 | 100 | 100 |
| | | 1030 | 100 | 1440 | 10 | 1590 | 100 | 100 |
| 1000 | Av. | 1133 | | 1200 | | 1580 | | |
| | | 1380 | 100 | 1382 | 100 | 1448 | 80 | 80 |
| | | 1358 | 100 | 1280 | 100 | 1374 | 80 | 80 |
| | | 1392 | 100 | 1428 | 100 | 1342 | 80 | 80 |
| | Av. | 1376 | | 1363 | | 1388 | | |

[a] Failed metal.

Note: All failures cohesive except where indicated.

Therefore, the natural environment encountered by adhesive bonded panels exposed to high temperatures is a combination of heat, and atmospheric oxygen, acting over the time of exposure. In another section dealing with specific adhesive systems, quantitative time temperature data are discussed.

The simulation of the high temperature environment appears, on the surface at least to be relatively simple. Most investigations evaluate adhesive bonds by exposure in an ordinary circulating air oven set at some predetermined temperature. While this procedure has produced much data, it should be recognized that it is important to assure free flow of air around each test specimen. Erroneous results may be obtained if specimens are stacked in such a manner that flow of air is restricted in any way. However, care must be exercised to prevent the direct impingement of a blast of hot air which might result in increased oxygen pressure around the part, or unusual agitation which results in an accelerated rate of degradation. If relatively long time exposures are being evaluated, that is, 100 hr or more, temperature control is very important. Temperature control to about $\pm 2°F$ is necessary for reproducible results. It follows, of course, that variations at various places within the oven must not exceed that limit.

With the precautions just mentioned, relatively reproducible test results can be obtained, and various adhesive systems can be compared for in their ability to resist high temperature. Such a test, however, is at best only a very crude simulation of the actual condition experienced in an actual part. First of all, of course, the bond geometry as pointed out in the discussion on test panels, is important, because oxidation attached at elevated temperature is an edge effect. If the adhesive system is melted or depolymerized at the test temperature, bond geometry is not significant. Assuming the degradation is oxidative, the pressure of air around the part and the velocity of air flow become important. In a typical actual part, such as the leading edge of an air foil, the aerodynamic heating resulting from high speed flights generally occurs at some altitude where the air pressure is less than sea level. This would suggest a condition less severe than a sea level oven exposure. However, those portions of the part subjected to the highest temperature generally are in areas where the flow of air is such that pressures considerably higher than ambient exist. In addition, flow patterns, the degree of turbulance, or lack there of, are factors which influence the rate of degradation.

Because of these factors, oven testing of adhesives for heat stability is only an aproximation of the actual usual environment. However, actual experience in bonded assemblies has revealed that the oven test procedure is not grossly misleading, and in all probability is a conservative but reasonable procedure.

One might assume that since most metals are relatively heat stable, compared to organic materials, the heat stability of an adhesive bonded joint is strictly a function of the adhesive, and independent of the nature of the substrate. This is not true, however, since certain metal surfaces appear to act as oxidation catalysts, which accelerate the degradation of the adhesive. Details of this problem are discussed later on.

In addition to the degradation effects produced by exposure of adhesive bonds and elevated temperatures, there may be harmful effects associated with long exposures at relatively mild temperatures, as in the region of the curing temperature of the adhesive. These changes are the result of additional curing of the adhesive, which may result in increased brittleness, hence reduced properties. This problem does not occur with all adhesive systems, but is a significant factor with some.

At the very high temperatures (3000–5000°F) generated by rocket engine exhaust gases, or by reentry conditions at supersonic speed, all organic materials dissociate by a complex process of pyrolysis thermal dissociation, oxidation, and volatilization. While adhesives may be used occasionally to join segments of ablative materials, the amount of adhesive exposed to the ablation environment is insignificant. The resistance of organic materials to the ablation environment is discussed elsewhere in this book, and will not be considered in this chapter.

Occasionally exposure of an adhesive joint to some elevated temperature will produce a void or blister within the bond line. Because most adhesives are very effective sealants, any volatile material entrapped in the bond line may, if heated sufficiently, generate sufficient pressure to fail the bond. This condition may occur at almost any elevated temperature, but generally will not occur unless the exposure is in excess of the cure temperature. The delamination may occur as soon as the part reaches same temperature. In this case, the combination of increased internal pressure, and decreased adhesive strength resulting from the increased temperature, results in a separation of the metal from the adhesive. In other cases, the void may appear only after some extended exposure at the test temperature. In the later case, the gradual embrittlement of the adhesive resulting from the extended curing condition may produce sufficient weakening of the joint to permit the development of a void area. Since extended curing conditions frequently produce additional volatile matter as a product of the polymerization reaction, a gradual increase in internal pressure contributes to the bond failure.

The appearance of blisters or voids after exposure of a bonded panel to elevated temperature is not necessarily an inherent characteristic of the adhesive being tested. Variations in processing conditions, errors in processing, improper surface treatments and many other factors may contribute to the development of voids. Hence, any such problems must be evaluated carefully, before conclusions are drawn regarding the ability of the adhesive to withstand the elevated temperature environment. As a matter of fact, it must be recognized that any evaluation of the ability of an adhesive to resist an given environment will be misleading unless every precaution is taken to insure that the test specimen is properly fabricated. It is never valid to draw conclusions based on the comparison of the strength retention of an exposed specimen with a control specimen, where the control specimen fails to exhibit the expected or published strength level. If the control properties are not right, the adhesive is different from that contained in a normal joint. Hence, conclusions in resistance to heat, solvents, moisture, etc., are not valid.

**b. Humidity.** Because of a natural desire to establish general elemental and climatic durability, adhesive systems have been subjected to a large variety of humidity tests. Both simulated environments and selected outdoor environments have been evaluated, using a variety of adhesive types and substrate materials. Although detailed test results are presented later on, certain general comments are of interest.

Most of the common structural adhesives are relatively inert to moisture, once they are fully and properly cured. Hence they provide excellent protection of the substrate material from excessive moisture, in so far as they form a continuous barrier between the metal surface and the humid atmosphere or condition. In this connection, however, it must be recognized that all organic films permit some finite passage of moisture, and hence are not absolute sealants against exposure of the metal substrate.

With a few exceptions noted later, deterioration of adhesive joints as a result of exposure to high humidity environments occurs at the interface between metal and adhesive. It invariably manifests itself as an edge condition, with the appearance of isolated areas of metal corrosion initiated along an edge of the bond line, and gradually progressing inward, as longer exposure times are experienced. Generally a freshly cut edge will be attached more quickly than the end of the overlap area, when a portion of the adhesive has been extruded from the bond line during the curing process. Once corrosion has commenced, it will spread out from the point of initiation, and eventually will destroy the entire bond. It is very common to observe that certain specimens within a given panel will be considerably more resistant to the initiation of corrosion than others. The test data scatter is always relatively great in any humidity exposure test, and values considerably lower than the controls will be found at one extreme, with some bonds resistant, and undamaged, at the other extreme. When a primer system is applied to the metal prior to bonding, it is very common to observe that the excess area past the overlap, which is coated with the primer, is uneffected by the exposure, even when there is extensive corrosion within the bonded area.

While the mechanism of destruction of an adhesive bond by an exposure to high humidity is not fully understood, some generalizations can be made. The humidity attack apparently consists of an initiation phase and a progression phase. The factors which govern the site of initial attack are not known, but it has been suggested that the physical surface condition of the metal may be such that certain minute discontinuties permit the initial entry of sufficient moisture to produce a small inclusion of liquid. For example, the surface of aluminum frequently contains small leaflets of metal which have been partially detached and pressed into the surface, probably by the shearing action of the rollers which form the surface as the metal is rolled into thin sheet form. The presence of such a surface condition can be detected by a careful microscopic examination of the failed area of an adhesive bond. Isolated small areas where tiny flakes of aluminum are adhered to the adhesive surface can be detected on many failed bonds. On very rare occasions the areas are sufficiently extensive that they can be seen without a microscope. Since the tensile strength of aluminum is considerably higher than that of the adhesive, it follow that the adhesive cannot pull bits of aluminum from the surface of the metal unless there are surface flaws. These flaws may provide the initial point of entry of a film of moisture into the bond line. Such a mechanism explains the erratic mature of the initiation steps, since the location of such a flaw at the cut edge of the bond line becomes a matter of chance. Once moisture has entered the bond line at the interface between adhesive and metal, propogation probably proceeds by an electrolytic process which is based on the concentration cell principle. This is the same process that produces pits when a metal corrodes. An area of the metal immersed in a liquid electrolyte, being exposed to less oxygen than the area of metal at the electrolyte-air interface becomes anodic, resulting in conversion of the metal to the cation. In the oxygen rich region oxygen gas is reduced to $OH^-$, the later diffusing into the electrolyte to produce the metal oxide. The net result is propogation of the oxidation reaction into the interior of the bond line, and progressive destruction of the bond.

The following observations tend to support the mechanism proposed above.

1. A relatively fluid primer, whose viscosity is such that it readily wets the metal surface, and presumably tends to fill in minor discontinuties will result in improved resistance to high humidity conditions.

2. Excessive surface etching, which tends to remove significant quantities of surface metal (hence reducing surface flaws) result in improved resistance to high humidity conditions.

3. An aluminum surface subjected to a polishing with a buffing wheel prior to standard etching and bonding will exhibit exceptionally poor humidity resistance. The smearing action of the buffing wheel produces an exaggeration of surface discontinuties, thus greatly increasing the opportunities for moisture penetration.

While less complete investigations have been conducted on other metals than aluminiu, it is likely that similar mechanisms contribute to the loss of strength of joints fabricated from steel, stainless steel, magnesium, and titanium. The rates of initiation and propagation are different, but the end result is similar.

There are a number of accelerated test procedures designed to assess the humidity resistance of adhesive joints. The water boil test is the simplest, and a six hour exposure in boiling water provides a relatively inexpensive means of obtaining a preliminary evaluation of moisture resistance. A more extensive procedure consists of a thirty day exposure in a salt spray cabinet. The salt spray test procedure is the same as that conventionally used for evaluation of paint films, and standard salt spray cabinets which operate in accordance with military specifications are commercially available.

More recently, the 120°F condensing humidity test has been adapted as a standard procedure, and is included in the current adhesive specifications (MIL-A-5090C and 25463).

Because of the importance of climate durability, extensive outdoor weathering of adhesive bonded panels has been conducted. While many companies have conducted such tests, to varying degrees of complexity, the most definitive work was performed by the Forest Products Laboratory, during the period of 1950 to present. This work was supported by an Air Force Contract and test sites were set up in Alaska, Arizona, Florida, and the Canal Zone. A variety of commercial adhesive systems representing all of the common classes, were evaluated, with both aluminum and stainless steel substrates. Both unstressed and stressed panels were exposed. Detailed data is presented in a later section of this chapter. However, certain generalization are of interest, as follows.

1. The most severe locations were these where relatively high humidities and warm temperatures were experienced.
2. Stressed panels deteriorated more rapidly than unstressed panels
3. Stainless steel panels were more resistant than aluminum panels.
4. Heat cured adhesive systems were more resistant than room temperature cured systems.
5. Using the better adhesives, unstressed bonded panels are relatively resistant to severe outdoor weathering conditions, although all panels eventually exhibited some strength losses.

**c. Organic Solvents.** Since all useful structural adhesives are organic polymers, they tend to be susceptable to attack by organic solvents. In this case, the degradation involves diffusion of the solvent into the bulk of the adhesive material with a subsequent weakening of its strength. Generally, the interface between substrate and adhesive is not vulnerable and no special interaction occurs at that location.

The organic solvents of main interest are those commonly found in aircraft and missiles, and generally fall in the classes of fuels, lubricants, hydraulic fluid, and anti-icing fluids. Military specifications call for 30 day soaks in JP4 fuel, iso alcohol (anti-icing fluid), hydraulic fluid (hydrocarbon). Practically all of the commercial adhesive systems exhibit a high degree of resistance to these fluids and it is not uncommon to observe 100% strength retention at the end of the test period. Therefore, there is little reason to be concerned over exposure to these common organic fluids.

However, some of the more effective solvents especially under conditions of elevated temperatures, may cause deterioration of adhesive bonded panels. Generally the temperature is important, and a system exhibiting relatively good resistance at some temperature may be attacked very rapidly at a temperature only 20 or 30° higher. Frequently an adhesive will exhibit solvent sensativity at about the same temperature that it suffers substantial strength losses. Solvents which are sufficiently high boiling to remain liquid at that temperature generally will destroy the bond. Exposure of most adhesive joints to ethylene dichloride, dimethylformamide, dimethyl sulfoxide, skydrol of Monsanto Company, and similar materials, will result in eventual destruction of the bond. The high temperature systems have the best resistance to solvents, and are relatively unaffected unless extreme conditions are experienced. Conversely, low or room temperature systems are most susceptable.

**d. Radiation.** Generally, radiation effect on adhesives are closely related to exposure to elevated temperatures. In many cases, for example, solar radiation, the total effect is that produced as a result of temperature increase. Other radiation effects may result in increased cross linking, with subsequent embrittlement. The radiation levels commonly encountered by structures in the space environment are not of sufficient magnitude to be harmful.

**e. Vibration, Fatigue, Shock.** One of the principle advantages of structural adhesives is their ability to absorbe shock and vibration exposures. Because of the elasticity inherent in most adhesive systems, they tend to dampen the propogation of vibration, thus preventing fatigue type failures. In addition, because of their ability to strain without failure, they tend to inhibit crack propogation. Because of there amorphous nature, they are not subject to work hardening, or the like, and retain their elasticity in spite of relatively severe shock and vibration exposures.

Military specifications describes a fatigue test, involving cycle tensile loads. Practically all adhesive systems which satisfy the tensile shear requirements established by the military specification are able to satisfy the specification fatigue requirements. Unfortunately, the standard test is of little value in predicting the fatigue life of an adhesive bonded assembly. Because of the complex nature of vibration stresses, the only practical approach has been to design and build the actual part, or a relatively complex simulation of the part, and subject it to the actual environment. Typical environments are sonic vibrations produced by jet engine blasts, mechanical vibration produced during the operation of very large rocket engines and various shock loads resulting from rapid acceleration of decelleration. In all of these instances, it is meaningless to think in terms of the vibration or shock resistance of an adhesive. The only meaningful consideration is the actual component design. While it is well known that designs using adhesive bonding are likely to be more resistant to fatigue or shock than designs which employ rivets or spot welded joints, in each case the actual part must be evaluated. A good design employing a rivet or fastener may be superior to a poorly designed part which is fastened by adhesive bonding.

A commonly used but controversial test of the ability of an adhesive to resist vibration is the peel test. This test consists of bonding two relatingly thin strips of metal together, and failing the specimen by peeling the panel apart in the manner one would separate two pieces of adhesive tape. The results of the peel test are expressed in terms of pounds required, per inch of specimen width, to separate the two strips. In some instances, special fixtures are employed to maintain a constant radius as the two panels are separated. The test frequently gives erratic results, and the values obtained have no value in terms of actual design limitations. However, the peel test does represent a good indication of the deforability of the adhesive, and in a general way, this property is indicative of shock and vibration resistance.

**f. Vacuum.** The increasing interest in space travel has resulted in an interest in the ability of all materials to withstand long exposure to very low pressure environments. ($10^{-6}$ to $10^{-12}$ torr) under conditions of very high pumping capacity. Any changes in a material resulting from this exposure obviously are determined by the vapor pressure of the material, and any appreciable vapor pressure will result in gradual evaporation. While certain common organic materials may contain plasticizers which are volatile at low pressures, structural adhesives generally do not contain such plasticizers. The other rigid requirements, especially elevated temperature and solvent resistance, have caused manufacturers to limit the content of their adhesives to relatively high molecular weight polymers, whose volatility is not significant. Consequently, exposures to low pressure are not harmful.

**g. Low Temperatures.** Exposures of adhesive joints to relatively low temperatures from $-20°F$ all the way to liquid hydrogen temperature ($-423°F$), may result in an immediate and drastic reduction in strength. This effect is the result of embrittlement caused by the decreased ability of the molecules to move or deform, within the polymer matrix. The magnitude of the effect is most pronounced with those adhesives which exhibit considerable ability to deform at room and moderately elevated temperatures. These materials have glass transition points at low temperatures and over a relatively small temperature range lose all elasticity, becoming very brittle.

Some of the adhesive systems specially formulated for extreme elevated temperature service exhibit relatively good performance at extremely low temperatures, because their glass transitions occur at relatively high temperatures. They are formulated to perform in the brittle condition, and while they are not very elastic at any temperature, they perform relatively well over a wide temperature range.

Recently some highly elastic adhesives have been made available, which exhibit good strength retention and elasticity at temperatures down to $-423°F$. These materials are based on nylon or polyurethane polymers.

A special problem of compatability of adhesives with a cryogenic fluid is that of sensativity to shock in contact with liquid oxygen. While direct exposure to liquid oxygen does not present a problem, any impact may cause local burning or detonation. This is not strictly a low temperature exposure, since the impact generates sufficient localized heating to initiate an oxidation reaction between the organic material and the high concentration of oxygen. The degree of sensitivity of the adhesive to this exposure seems to be a function of both the ease of oxidation of the adhesive and its ability to absorb the shock load without too excessive heat build up. Thus, a material which is very inert to oxidation, and is relatively elastic at liquid oxygen temperatures, will perform best. The only available organic polymer which is acceptable for use with liquid oxygen is Teflon. Other materials which are processable as adhesives are under development.

A standard test for evaluation of bulk organic material resistance to LOX impact has been developed. The test is strictly arbitrary, since actual shock values associated with field service are impossible to define. The test consists of impacting a sharp pointed instrument on a sample of the bulk adhesive at the level of 20 ft lb, while the specimen is immersed in liquid oxygen. Any failure in twenty specimens results in classifying the adhesive as not suitable for use with liquid oxygen. A failure is defined as any visual evidence of interaction between the adhesive and the oxygen, either during or after the test. Note that this test is run on the bulk adhesive, cast or formed into wafer shape test specimens, rather than a bonded specimen. Because of the indeterminant amount of amount of adhesive which might be exposed because of squeeze out from a bond line, the testing of the bulk material is considered as a more conservative test than an evaluation of the edge of an adhesive joint.

**h. Mixed Environment.** Since an adhesive bonded joint is hardly ever used under conditions of exposure to only one significant environment, the effects of combined environments become of interest. Surprisingly, very little work has been done in this area, with the exception of the rather special case of the combination of liquid oxygen and shock as noted above. Some work has been done in the field of sonic fatigue at reduced temperatures, but because of the importance of specimen design, no generalizations on adhesive performance can be made. Recently, some work has been done on salt spray exposure after aging at elevated temperature. As expected, aging which is in the temperature range where changes in ultimate strength can be noted produces decreased resistances to salt spray exposures. Considerable data exists in long time exposures to static loads at both room and elevated temperatures. In general, this data reveals that an adhesive will hold about 60–70% of its short time ultimate, when loaded for periods of up to 200 hr. At load levels in excess of 70% of ultimate, failure will occur at some shorter time interval. Some of the outdoor weathering tests conducted by Forest Products Laboratory, under Air Force sponsorship, included the exposure of stressed panels. As expected, the combination of both conditions generally resulted in greater strength losses than unstressed panels. In general, it can be expected that any condition causes a deterioration in bond strength, will, when used in conjunction with some other significant environment, may result in a faster rate of degradation than that observed with exposure to either of the environmental conditions by itself.

## 4. *Adhesive Systems*

It is outside of the scope of this discussion to present a detailed review of the various adhesive systems, and their overall characteristics. There are a number of books which discuss that subject in detail and the reader is referred to these sources for an extensive presentation of adhesive performance. However, for discussion purposes, it is useful to present in outline form the general classes of adhesives, plus a few very brief comments on their general resistance to environmental conditions (Tables 16-27 and 16-28). The most common structural adhesives fall into one of the following classes, based on chemical types.

TABLE 16-27. High Temperature Adhesives—Their Properties and Uses (23)

| Type | Ceramics | Polyaromatics | | Silicones |
| --- | --- | --- | --- | --- |
| | | Polybenzimidazoles (PBI) | Polyimides (PI) | |
| Performance Range | To >1000°F | 1000°F for short term; 450°F for continued use | 900°F for short term; 550°F for continued use | 900°F for short term; 450°F for continued use |
| Advantages | Excellent thermal stability and strength at pyrogenic temperatures | Good strength at very high temperatures | Excellent thermal and oxidation resistance; initial cure at 300°F with elevated post cure possible after jig removal | No volatiles given off during cure; good thermal stability |
| Limitations | Brittle, low peel strength; very high temperature cure required; difficult processing | Long, high temperature cures requiring special jigs and fixtures; volatiles released during cure; expensive | Bond strength above 1000 psi not usually possible at high temperatures; expensive | Low strength; long, high temperature cure; high cost |
| Forms available | Water slurries and metal wafers | Prepregs | Solution, prepregs and films | Asbestos prepregs |
| Applications | Metal bonding; some honeycomb constructions where shock in transition temperature range is minimal | Metal-metal bonding and honeycomb sandwich bonding | Metal-metal bonding; honeycomb sandwich bonding; filament winding | Some stainless steel bonding at elevated temperature |
| Specifications | None (see article) | MIL-A-5090D, Type IV; MIL-A-25463 | None (see article) | None (see article) |
| Typical Commercial Materials [a] | Pyroceram 45, 899, and 95 [b]; Metlbond X800 [c] | Imidite 850, 1850 [c], P-1101 [d] | H Film, Pyre ML [d] | SC-1013 [e] Metlbond 311 [c] |

| Epoxy-phenolics | Modified phenolics | Epoxies |
|---|---|---|
| 900°F for short term operation; continued use at 350°F | 350°F for short term; 250°F for continued use | 500°F for short term; continued use at 300°F |
| Good properties at moderate cures and low cost | Nitrile-phenolics have excellent aging properties and good peel strength | High versatility in tailoring properties, cure cycles and physical forms; no volatiles during cure; adheres to a wide variety of materials |
| Volatiles released during cure requiring pressure bonding. Bonds deteriorate at elevated temperature for exposure >200 hr | Suitable shear strength only within the transition temperature range | Not suitable much above transition temperature |
| Supported film and pastes | Calendered films; supported tapes; solutions | Powders, liquids, pastes, prepregs |
| Metal-metal bonding, sandwich construction and node bonding where volatiles can be tolerated | Sandwich construction; structural bonding where modest temperatures are expected | Bonding of all types of materials in many forms |
| MIL-A-5090D, Type II and III; MIL-A-25463, Type II and III, Class 2 | MIL-A-25463, Type I; MIL-A-5090D, Type I; some under MIL-A-13883A(ORD); MIL-A-1154B | Many meet: MIL-A-14042A (ORD); MIL-A-9067B; MIL-A-5090; MIL-A-8623A; some meet: MIL-A-25463, Type I and II; MIL-A-5090D, Type I and II |

(continued)

TABLE 15-27 (continued)

| Epoxy-phenolics | Modified phenolics | Epoxies |
|---|---|---|
| Aerobond 422, 430 [f], HT 424, 430, 431 [g], Dynabond 132 [h], Metlbond 302, 316, Narmco 2030-85 [c], Bondmaster M24B [l], Epon 422 [j], Hindux 1179A, 1197 [y] | Rubber phenolics: BR 200, 208 [g]; Cycleweld brake bonding adhesive K-83, H-2, H-2-J [t]; Plastilock, 608, 666 [u]; Pliobond HT [v], AF-32, 5930 [r]; Metlbond 402, 4041, 4021, 2105, 304, 305, 306 [c]; Raybond R-84015, R-81007, R-81001 [w]; Vinyl acetal phenolics: FM 47, 45 [g]; EC-147 [t]; Redux 775 [y]; Swedlow 371W [s] | Aerobond 500 [f]; BR-625 [g]; Helix Bonding Agent 393, Eccobond 76188 [k]; Epoxylite 5302, 5403, 850-9 [l]; Epocast 251/9029, 270, 271, 275 [m]; Homalite 345 [n]; Isochembond 811B [o]; Mareco 3446 [p]; AF 130 [r]; Metlbond 328, 329 [c]; Epon 914, 917, 929, 931 [j] |

[a] A partial list of commercial adhesives prepared from author's survey of over 200 adhesive manufacturers. [b] Corning Glass Works. [c] Narmco Materials Div., Telecomputing Corp. [d] E. I. du Pont de Nemours & Co., Inc. [e] Monsanto, Inc. [f] Adhesive Engineering Div. Hiller Aircraft Corp. [g] Bloomingdale Adhesives Dept., American Cyanamid Corp. [h] Convair, Div. of General Dynamics Corp. [i] Pittsburgh Plate Glass Co., Adhesive Products Div. [j] Shell Chemical Co. [k] Carl H. Biggs Co., Inc. [l] Epoxylite Corp. [m] Furane Plastics, Inc. [n] Homalite Corp. [o] Isochem Resins Co. [p] Mareco Products Div., Metachem Resins Corp. [r] 3M Co., Inc. [t] Chrysler Chemical Div., Chrysler Corp. [u] B. F. Goodrich Industrial Products Co. [v] Goodyear Chemical Div., Goodyear Tire & Rubber Co. [w] Raybestos-Manhattan Inc., Adhesives Dept. [y] Shurlock Bonded Structures, Inc. [s] Swedlow Plastics Co.

**a. General Purpose.** *1. Phenolic-Vinyl*—These systems are combinations of a heat curable pheonolic resin and a polyvinyl formal or butyral resin. They represent relatively standard products which have been available for at least 15 years. They are relatively tough but not elastomeric, systems, and require a full 350°F cure for optimum properties. They are relatively enert to most environmental conditions, and operate well over a somewhat limited temperature range (−60 to 180°F).

*2. Phenolic-Elastomer*—These systems consist of a mixture of a heat curable phenolic resin mixed with a synthetic elastomer. The elastomer generally is a nitrile rubber, although some older systems used neoprene. These systems produce relatively tough, elastomeric bond lines, when cured under pressure (about 100 psi) and at 350°F. They generally exhibit good all around resistance to environmental conditions over the temperature range of −65 to +200°F. Because of their high viscosity during cure, the bond lines are dense and non-porous. Consequently, they provide effective sealing of the joint, and are quite resistant to many conditions.

*3. Epoxy*—There are a great many different types of epoxy systems, and generalizations are not very accurate. Differences are due to both the resin type used, and the curing agent associated with the resin type. Most epoxy systems are liquids or pastes which are used as is (curing agent already added, heat cure required) or as two part systems, which require mixing just prior to use (room temperature or relatively low temperature cure). Epoxy systems, especially those cured at low temperature, in general exhibit marginal humidity, salt spray, and outdoor weathering resistance, especially if cured at room temperature. They usually have very limited high temperature resistance (150°F) unless specially compounded for that type of exposure. They tend to produce relatively brittle bond lines; hence show less resistance to fatigue, shock, vibration, and peel, than the elastomeric systems.

*4. Epoxy-Polyamide*—These systems are extensions of the epoxy systems when the curing agent is a low molecular weight polyamide resin containing excess free amino groups. These systems represent the best all around room or low temperature curing liquid and paste systems. However, they have the same environmental short comings as conventional epoxides.

*5. Epoxy-Nylon*—These systems are also an extension of the epoxy systems. However, they are solid film, heat curing materials, and in general exhibit unusually high strength, up to moderate temperatures (200°F). They have extremely tough, peel resistant characteristics,

TABLE 16-28. Low Temperature Adhesives—Their Properties and Uses (24)

| Type | Polyurethanes | Epoxy-nylons | Epoxy-phenolics |
|---|---|---|---|
| Performance range | −423 to 260°F | −423 to 180°F | −423 to 500°F |
| Advantages | High shear and peel str; adhere to wide variety of materials; room temperature cure is possible; low cost | Highest str in cryogenic range; light weight | Uniform properties; moderate cost |
| Limitations | Only useful up to 260°F; attacked by moisture | Moderate peel str; cannot be used at very high temp; high cost | Low peel str and shock resistance; require special surface preparation |
| Forms available | Two-part paste | Supported and unsupported films | Supported films |
| Applications | All types of structural bonding | All types of structural bonding | Large area metal-to-metal bonds sandwich construction |
| Commercial materials available [a] | APCO 1219, 1252 [b]; Flexane [c]; Mondur/Multron and Multranil [d]; Resin 7343/curing agent 7139 [e] | FM-1000, 1040, 1041, 1044 and BR-1009-8, 1009-49, 1040 [f]; AF 40 (primer 1956) [g]; Metlbond 400, 406 [e] | Aerobond 422, 430 [h]; HT 424, 430, 431 [f]; Dynabond 132 [i]; Metlbond 302, 316; Narmco 2030-85 [e]; Bond-master M24B [j]; Epon 422 [k]; Hidux 1179A, 11970 [l] |

| Rubber-phenolics | Vinyl acetal-phenolics | Epoxy-polyamides | Filled epoxies |
|---|---|---|---|
| −100 to 200°F | −423 to 200°F | −423 to 180°F | −423 to 350°F |
| None apparent for cryogenic uses | Low cost; fair prop at cryogenic temp; easy handling | RT cure; easy handling; low cost | Adhesion to many materials; easy handling |
| Restricted temp service range; low peel str at cryogenic temp | Low peel str at cryogenic temp; cures require jigs | Low peel str; cannot be used at very high temp | Very low peel str |
| Calendered film | Supported and unsupported film, solutions and solutions with powders | Two-part systems | Two-part systems |
| General purpose load bearing applications | Large area metal-to-metal bonds; sandwich construction | General purpose | Limited use |
| Rubber phenolics: BR 200, 208[f]; Cycleweld brake bonding adhesive, K-83, H-2, H-2-J[m]; Plastilock, 608, 666[e]; Pliobond HT[o]; AF-32, 5930[g]; Metlbond 402, 4041, 4021, 2105, 304, 305, 306[e]; Raybond R-84015, R-81007, R-8100[p] | FM 47, 45; HT-424-F, 488[f]; EC-1471[g]; Redux 775[l]; Swedlow 371 W[q] | Resiweld #4[r]; Narmco 3135[e] | BR-90, 92[f]; Epocast H-1169/985[a]; EC-1469[j]; Narmco 3147/7125, 3170/7133; Metlbond 406[e]; Lefkoweld 109[t] |

[a] A partial list of commercial adhesives available, prepared from author's survey of over 200 adhesive manufacturers. [b] Applied Plastics Inc. [c] Devcon Corp. [d] Mobay Chemical Co. [e] Narmco Materials Div., Whittaker Corp. [f] Bloomingdale Adhesives Dept., American Cyanamid Corp. [g] 3M Co., Inc. [h] Adhesive Engineering, Div. Hiller Aircraft Corp. [i] Convair, Div. of General Dynamics Corp. [j] Pittsburgh Plate Glass Co., Adhesive Products Div. [k] Shell Chemical Co. [l] Shurlock Structures, Inc. [m] Chrysler Chem. Div., Chrysler Corp. [n] B.F. Goodrich Industrial Products Co. [o] Goodyear Chemical Div., Goodyear Tire & Rubber Co. [p] Raybestos-Manhattan, Inc., Adhesives Dept. [q] Swedlow, Inc. [r] The H. B. Fuller Co. [s] Furnane Plastics, Inc. [t] Leffingwell Chemical Co.

and have outstanding retention of toughness at temperatures down to −423°F. Like most epoxies, they exhibit some degree of susceptibility to moisture, and hence are not outstanding in exposures involving high humidity.

**b. Special Purpose Adhesives.** *1. Epoxy-Phenolic*—These systems are blends of phenolic and epoxy resins, including a curing agent for the epoxy system. They were developed specially for high temperature (500°F) service, and perform well at that temperature, for both short and long time (200 hour) applications. They also exhibit excellent resistance to humidity, solvents, etc. They do not require excessive curing temperatures or pressures, but do exhibit an unfortunate tendency to produce frothy bond lines, due to release of volatiles, under conditions of low viscosity, during cure. The cured adhesive system is relatively brittle, and hence marginal in terms of fatigue, shock, and peel.

*2. Polimides and Polybenzimidazoles*—These systems are relatively new, and have not been fully evaluated. They have been developed primarily as ultra high temperature materials and are serviceable at temperatures in the 700–800°F range. They require relatively high curing temperatures (500°F) and produce brittle bond lines.

**c. Special Purpose—Low Temperature.** *1. Epoxy*—While most epoxy systems are not especially useful at very low temperatures, a few special formulations show some promise. These systems generally derive their low temperature characteristics from being mixed or associated with other polymers which do have good properties at low temperatures. Examples are nylon filled epoxies and bondable Teflon films used as carriers for epoxy systems.

*2. Epoxy-Nylon*—These systems, as previously discussed, exhibit excellent strength and elasticity at liquid hydrogen temperatures.

*3. Polyurethane*—Polymers based on the polyurethane structure, if properly selected, exhibit excellent low temperature properties and offer considerable promise for that application. Relatively mild curing conditions can be achieved, with proper selection of starting materials and curing agents.

Certain generalizations in expected performances of an adhesive system can be made regardless of chemical make up. They are:

*1.* An adhesive system generally is not serviceable at temperatures much higher than its cure temperature, and in some cases, to less than cure temperature. The phenolic-epoxy systems show the greatest deviation from this rule.

*2.* Room temperature curing systems generally are deficient in moisture resistance.

*3.* Heat cured systems (cure temperature 200–350°F) practically always have better all around properties (except high temperature resistance) than lower or higher temperature cured systems.

*4.* All high temperature adhesive systems are relatively brittle in the cured state, as compared to the conventional systems, and require curves in the range of 350–700°F.

*5.* High temperature adhesives tend to show fairly wide temperature ranges where as general purpose adhesives tend to·show drastic changes, with peak strengths over some relatively modest temperature range.

*6.* Solvent resistance and heat resistance are related, and these systems showing best heat resistance are generally inert to most solvents.

## References

1. S. Cohen, Stabilization of Vinyl Asbestos Flooring Compounds, SPE-RETEC, Argus Chemical Corporation, N.Y. (Sept. 1965).
2. National Bureau of Standards Offices of Technical Information and Publications, *Plastic Roofs* (Nov. 1965).
3. C. L. Mantell, Plastic Pipe Assumes Status, Vol. 24, No. 4, p. 42, Feb. 1966.
4. C. A. Farish, Report on Plastic Pipe Testing Program (July 1965).
5. J. Pinsky, Monsanto Co. for SPE-RETEC, New York City (Nov. 19, 1965).
6. M. Salame and J. Pinsky, Packageability of Rigid PVC, *Mod. Packaging,* April and May 1965.
7. G. W. Ingle, FDA of PVC, SPE-RETEC (Nov. 18-19, 1965).
8. K. Schultheis, Molded PVC in European Packaging, *SPE J.,* p. 60, (Feb. 1966).
9. D. M. Taylor, Practical Aspects of Non-Toxic Stabilization, SPE-RETEC, p. 45 (Nov. 18-19, 1965).
10. H. E. Chesebrough and V. P. Chrysler, *Reinforced Plastics,* p. 24 (Mar.-Apr. 1966).
11. R. J. McCutcheon, Molding of PVC Soles and Heels, SPE-RETEC, p. 20 (Nov. 18-19, 1965).
12. W. E. Cohn, Progress in PVC Molding in the Footwear Industry, SPE-RETEC, p. 28 (Nov. 18-19, 1965).
13. D. V. Rosato, Electronics Depend on Plastics, *Plastics World,* p. 22 (Mar. 1966).
14. D. V. Rosato, Plastics in Wire and Cable, *Plastics World* (June 1967).
15. D. V. Rosato, Plastic Foam Use Rises and Rises, *Plastics World,* p. 67 (Oct. 1965).
16. A Guide for the Spray-in-Place Application of Rigid and Semi-Rigid Urethane Foam, *SPI Bull.* (April 1965).
17. A Guide for the Poured-in-Place Application of Rigid Urethane Foam for Industrial Insulation, *SPI Bull.* (April 1965).

18. A Guide for the Application of Rigid Urethane Foam in the Transportation Industry, *SPI Bull* (April 1965).
19. J. Morrison, Workhorse Glamour Film; Polyethylene, *Plastics World,* p. 54 (Feb. 1966).
20. D. V. Rosato, Plastic-Based Adhesives, p. 40 (Aug. 1965).
21. S. E. Susman, Resistance of Structural Adhesives and Plastics to Extended Elevated Temperature Aging, *SAMPE J.,* 1.1, p. 22 (Feb/Mar. 1965).
22. *Structural Adhesive Bonding,* **(Appl. Polymer Symp 2),** Interscience, New York, 1966.
23. R. C. Kausen, Adhesives of High and Low Temperatures—Part I, *Mater. Design Engr.,* p. 94 (Aug. 1964).
24. R. C. Kausen, Adhesives of High and Low Temperatures—Part II, *Mater. Design Engr.* (Aug. 1964).

# 17

# *Summary Review*

**Dominick V. Rosato**
*Plastics World,*
*Boston, Massachusetts*

## CONTENTS

New plastics materials—and the ability to use them—have drastically altered the design of things. They have changed the shape, the form, the line of the office building, the factory, the home. New technology has changed the vehicles which speed over the earth's surface, under its waters, in the air and the space above it; the machines of production; the artifacts of the kitchen and the living room.

The designer of computer equipment must consider ease of maintenance, operator protection, circulation of air around the interior and other considerations which are part of the man-machine relationship.

Much of the same thinking is even reflected by the engineers who make missiles work under hostile environments.

Human efficiency definitely is affected by pleasure connected with the appearance of the equipment he uses. In the early days, we tended to find our block houses equipped with chaotic color schemes, varying heights of equipment packaging and comparatively cluttered consoles. But in more recent years we have become quite conscious of color schemes and uniformity of the packaging size and shape. Everything is cleaner, better organized and affords the crews more space to work in.

As reviewed throughout this book, plastics are a way of life—in all aspects. They are useful because of the major characteristic, namely, different plastics are available to meet the different environments. In order to obtain the total broad review on any one subject, material or part, refer to the index of this book. In this section different subjects will be reviewed which were not included elsewhere.

It should be evident that a publication, such as this two-volume book, is not just a reflection of sound work, but most important, a direct and significant bearing on the clarity and thoroughness of the

Fig. 17-2. Designer Pietro Belluschi, Dean of Architecture and Planning at MIT, in cooperation with George M. Ewing Co., architects and engineers, have incorporated different plastics in the new Rohm and Haas Philadelphia office building. Use of Plexiglas acrylic is extensive, includes light diffusers, paneling and kickplates.

thinking that is basic to carrying out the work. That is, the writing of an article over a course of a project activates ideas. These ideas can be directly useful in other projects. Also the work of others in regard to ones own work is important, particularly in the areas of problem solving and market development. So what happens is that a publication is a two-way communications channel that stimulates and inspires achievement. It is hoped that this two-volume book will provide these goals.

## I. PLASTICS CONSUMPTION AND ENVIRONMENTS

Throughout this two-volume book statistics and facts have been presented on the use of different plastic materials. These figures show the definite and pronounced growth in the use of plastics to meet the demands and requirements of different environments. As an example at the present time a large market exists for the polyolefins with no predicted limit to their future world demand (Table 17-1). Consumption is growing steadily with no prospect of leveling off during the next 30 years. The industry is faced with having to spend vast sums on

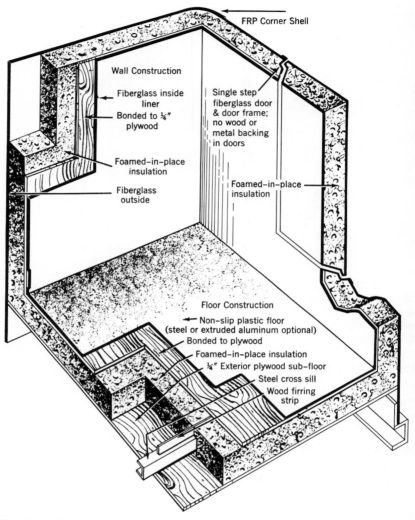

FRP Corner Shell

Wall Construction

Fiberglass inside
liner
Bonded to ¼″
plywood

Foamed–in–place
insulation

Fiberglass
outside

Single step
fiberglass door
& door frame;
no wood or
metal backing
in doors

Foamed–in–place
insulation

Floor Construction

Non-slip plastic floor
(steel or extruded aluminum optional)
Bonded to plywood
Foamed–in–place insulation
¼″ Exterior plywood sub–floor
Steel cross sill
Wood firring
strip

Fig. 17-3. Typical use of polyurethane foam-in-place insulation material used in a wall construction. (Courtesy of Johnson Co.)

new plants and in research and development by the manufacturers as well as end-users.

Within Chapter 4 on Weathering and elsewhere in these books, different aspects of weather-resistance for plastics are reviewed. An interesting analysis shows that approximately one-quarter of all plastics produced are subjected to outdoor weather environments. The products principally include those listed in Table 17-2.

Fig. 17-4. Vinyl wall covering is being used in the different rooms of the home. In addition to its attractiveness, it provides other advantages, i.e., withstand heat and steam in the kitchen and bathroom.

TABLE 17-1.  World polyethylene and polypropylene consumption

(1,000 long tons)

| | HDPE | | | LDPE | | | PP | | |
|---|---|---|---|---|---|---|---|---|---|
| | '65 | '70 | '75 | '65 | '70 | '75 | '65 | '70 | '75 |
| USA | 295 | 620 | 900 | 875 | 1500 | 2150 | 150 | 475 | 900 |
| Latin America | 10 | 45 | 100 | 85 | 220 | 400 | 3 | 40 | 100 |
| EEC | 125 | 290 | 450 | 420 | 900 | 1425 | 50 | 210 | 450 |
| EFTA | 60 | 130 | 200 | 275 | 540 | 800 | 30 | 150 | 320 |
| Other W. Europe | 7 | 25 | 50 | 40 | 90 | 150 | 3 | 20 | 50 |
| E. Europe | 20 | 130 | 350 | 110 | 540 | 1300 | 4 | 70 | 220 |
| Japan | 80 | 200 | 300 | 230 | 540 | 825 | 50 | 180 | 360 |
| Other | 58 | 180 | 400 | 255 | 670 | 1450 | 15 | 135 | 450 |
| World Total | 655 | 1620 | 2750 | 2290 | 5000 | 8500 | 305 | 1280 | 2750 |

HDPE—High density polyethylene
LDPE—Low density polyethylene
PP—Polypropylene

Fig. 17-5. Bird solid vinyl siding is manufactured by Bird & Son, Inc., East Walpole, Mass. Made of rigid polyvinyl chloride, it is extruded in two clapboard styles. One has two 4 in. clapboard exposures on the same panel (double-4 in.). The other has a single 8 in. clapboard exposure. Each comes in a standard length of 10 ft. Colors include white, green, and gray. Shown in white, double-4 in. siding.

## II. ARMOR—TACTICAL ENVIRONMENT

With the past and, more important, recent developments in the use of plastics armor for the soldier or policeman, tactical environments tend to deplete the effectiveness of the small-arms capabilities of the enemy more than ever in the past. In a tactical sense, the provision of armor is a two-edged sword. The United States, which is not unduly or critically penalized through wound casualties (as is the case with

Fig. 17-6. The Bird solid vinyl gutter system is manufactured by Bird & Son, Inc., East Walpole, Mass. Gutters, downspouts, and accessories of the system are made from rigid polyvinyl chloride. Shown with the system are Bird solid vinyl siding and Bird archiect Mark 25 asphalt roofing shingles.

less fortunate countries lacking adequate medical and hospital facilities), is vitally concerned with losses of men through death—accepting as an argument beyond question the premise that if men do get hit in battle, they should survive.

In those cases where armor forces the enemy to abandon the small caliber .225 ammunition which he can carry in large numbers, he becomes greatly penalized if forced to increase the caliber of his basic small arms to the caliber .30 size. The penalty in weight per bullet is a function of a cube law, and this penalty is enhanced since the basic weapon also weighs more, is more expensive to supply, and is more expensive to replace.

The provision of plastic-ceramic armor in certain tactical situations will force the enemy into even larger calibers, providing again an order of magnitude of additional problems (Fig. 17-13).

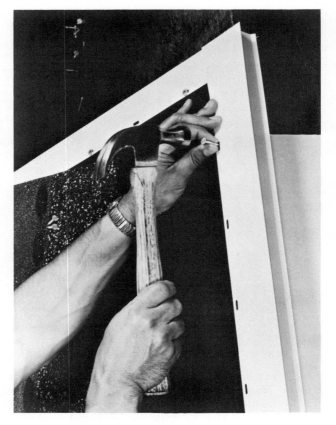

Fig. 17-7. Bird solid vinyl roof edgings are manufactured by Bird & Son, Inc., East Walpole, Mass. Made of rigid polyvinyl chloride, the product is available in four styles to accommodate various applications for both reroofing and new work. Shown is style "D" along the eave and style "G" along the rake edge.

Plastics composite armor is not "light" though it need not be so heavy as to be a prohibitive burden to the carrier. However, it is patent that a man can carry a 25-lb load (greater than the weight of such armor), at least 3 times as far as he can carry a 50-lb load. The point is that a natural penalty is imposed on the bearer of armor, but it is not necessarily of such a magnitude as to tie him down completely or restrict his area of operations unduly. Armor is not the panacea for military success without casualties. It is a tremendous step forward in protecting men in certain tactical environments from

Fig. 17-8. Prime window which combines rigid vinyl components with traditional wooden construction is the Malta Vinaline unit. Sash, weather-stripping and snap-in grids are made of B. F. Goodrich Chemical Company rigid Geon vinyl materials.

Fig. 17-9. Flexible plastic roofing was used on the terminal building at Dulles International Airport (Chantilly, Va.) as conventional materials would not withstand the expected large roof movements (about 8 in.).

Fig. 17-10. The roof of the terminal building at Dulles International Airport (Chantilly, Va.) is an example of a roof of unusual contour that was covered with a flexible plastic roofing.

mortal wounds and, in vehicular applications, from some disabling wounds.

The already widespread use of alumina armor provides a solid base for the acceptance of the lighter "new" plastics with ceramics, boron carbide and silicon carbide, and as these latter have several advantages in a weight sense, the scope of use of this type of armor will be enlarged in the future.

TABLE 17-2. Information on the Part of U.S.'s 14.68 Billion Pounds of Plastics Subjected to the Weather (1967 Estimates) [a]

| Market | Subjected to weather | | total plastics consumption, billions of pounds | percent of its market |
|---|---|---|---|---|
| | Billions of pounds | Percent of total plastics | | |
| Building and Construction | 1.2 | 8.2 | 3.9 | 31 |
| Packaging and Container | 0.6 | 4.1 | 2.8 | 21 |
| Electronics | 0.3 | 2.0 | 1.9 | 16 |
| Transportation | 0.3 | 2.0 | 1.0 | 30 |
| Pipe | 0.3 | 2.0 | 0.5 | 60 |
| Agriculture | 0.03 | 0.2 | 0.03 | 100 |
| Others (military, etc.) | 0.9 | 6.2 | 4.55 | 20 |
| Total | 3.63 | 24.7 | 14.68 | 24.7 |

[a] Usage is classified only once under major markets.

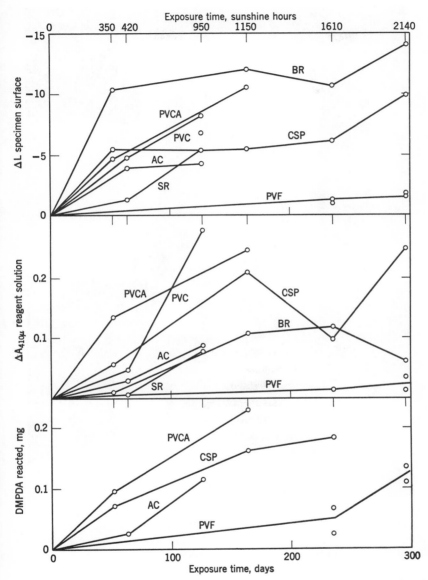

Fig. 17-11. The progressive photo-oxidation of plastic roof coverings exposed to sunlight was determined three ways: (top) darkening ($-\Delta L$) of the specimen surface, (center) change in absorbance ($\Delta A$) of the reagent solution at 410 m$\mu$, and (bottom) the amount of DMPDA that reacted with the exposed surface. The specimens were exposed to natural weathering conditions atop a building at the National Bureau of Standards in Washington, D. C.

Fig. 17-12. The screen, which separates the main living room and the dining area of the house, is made from random-length strips of Plexiglas acrylic plastic butt-cemented to form a rigid screen. Each strip was sandblasted to provide control of patterns of translucency and to impart surface texture.

Much of the credit for the evolution of ceramic armor belongs to the Natick Laboratories of the Army and the Army Material Research Agency at Watertown, Mass. These two entities—working in very close accord with each other and with an extremely cooperative and communications system with cognizant Navy, Marine Corps, Air Force, and other Army laboratories and commands as well as

Fig. 17-13. Helicopter gunner is provided with armor for the torso (front and back) and lower leg.

with industry—have spread the word among technical groups in what must be a model of unified cooperation on the technical level.

When one contemplates the vital importance attached to "materials" in today's modern warfare, where the deciding factors are often imposed by materials limitations either through weight or temperature performance, he can appreciate the problems inherent in translating technical breakthroughs into productive capacities.

For example, in all four services, there is an interest in protecting individuals in the air; in the Army, Navy, and Marine Corps, there is a deep interest in protecting tactical ground or water personnel; in all services, vehicle protection is highly desirable in certain ground and tactical water environments, and aircraft armor is a problem with all services (1–6).

## A. Plastics-Ceramic Armor

The combination of reinforced plastics with ceramics facing has been the latest development now in production to provide armor protection for flight crews and foot soldiers in Vietnam. Body armor components formed to the shape of the body, similar to the "Knights of Old," include chest, back, buttocks, groin and leg sections (Fig.

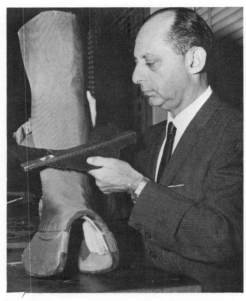

Fig. 17-14. Ed Barron of Army Natick Laboratories is in the process of developing lower leg armor with improved environmental performance for aircraft crew
chiefs and gunners.

17-14). As an example, the air crew's vest weighs 25 lb with a
front and back plate and those being considered for the infantryman
is 16 lb. While the situation today is by no means ideal in the sense
of furnishing absolute protection to individuals, judicious use of the
armor under specified combat conditions does furnish an appreciable
lessening of the risk to personnel.

In this construction, the outer ceramic material first tends to fracture or break-up a projectile. The inner RP provides an energy
absorbing media based on a theoretically shearing action of the
laminar material. Separately these two different materials would
not provide any protection against small arms. They only perform
when made into a well designed composite. Here is a synergistic system; the total effect is greater than the sum of the two effects.

Body armor is an area of tremendous importance and yet one presenting great problems from a comfort standpoint. It was during the
Korean War that $8\frac{1}{2}$ lb body armor for the infantry the first time
came into use by the American forces. Regarded initially by many
as too heavy to be acceptable, it came to be recognized during the
war that its life-saving potential could outweigh factors of weight

and discomfort. Armor is not the panacea for success without casualties. The armor now in production and being used is "lighter" in weight than those previously developed. True the "no weight" and "no space" occupying armor is desired. The composite offers the bearer more ease of operation and what was never before available with body armor, small arms protection.

Potential protection exists against 0.30 and 0.50 (12.7 mm) caliber armor-piercing ammunition or 7.62, $14\frac{1}{2}$, and 20 mm projectiles. Thickness of armor varies depending on the protection required. A typical construction for 30 caliber is $\frac{3}{4}$ in. thick and weighs 9 lb/sq ft. Ceramic is generally slightly less than one-half in thickness than the RP. Thickness of ceramic tends to match the diameter of the projectile. Comparative protection with other materials could be obtained using $\frac{1}{2}$ in. thick steel (22 lb/sq ft) or 18 in. thick oak.

Different reinforcements were examined for use in the RP. Woven glass roving (5 picks by 4 fill, 24 oz/sq yd) is the most efficient to date. It also happens to be readily available at low cost since it is used in the rather large and competitive industry of producing boat hulls. From 20 to 30% resin by weight of polyester resin is used. Other resins have different disadvantages, i.e., such as urethane good but more expensive, epoxy produces too good a structure.

A rather perfect match and bond has to exist between the RP and ceramic. Since it is difficult to provide repeatedly matched shapes of the body armor contoured ceramic, the RP is autoclave cured on the ceramic. The curing pressure of 100 psi results in the RP having a 30% resin content with a 1.8 specific gravity. Since flat ceramic parts can be reproduced sufficiently accurate, the RP is pressed cured more economically at higher pressures. It has 20% resin with 1.9 specific gravity. Bond of the two different materials is made with a urethane elastic adhesive in order to obtain the proper ballistic characteristics. The thickness of room curing adhesives is 20 mils; with heat cure it is 8 mils.

There are three qualified shielding ceramics used; alumina (aluminum oxide), silicon carbide, and boron carbide (Table 17-3). The common attribute of all ceramics for armor is their hardness; in fact, boron carbide is second to diamond. While weight-to-cost curves depend to some extent on the thickness required, the comparisons of weight versus ceramic are not linear. Preference would ge given to alumina on cost and to boron carbide on weight. In comparison, the cost of dual-hardness steels are so much less than alumina that the steel would win based on cost alone.

TABLE 17-3.   Ceramic Properties [a]

|  | Boron carbide (alumina) | Silicon carbide | Aluminum oxide |
|---|---|---|---|
| Defeating same projectile, at same velocity | Best protection | In between | Least protection |
| Specific gravity, g/cc | 2.51 | 3.09 | 3.5–3.94 |
| Availability | Limited | Limited | Very high capacity |
| Hardness, knoopscale | 2,800 | 2,700 | 1375–1690 |
| Costs | Highest | In between | Least |

[a] Ceramic only performs when used with the reinforced plastics.

Steel is not used in certain applications since weight savings is the important yardstick. Since ceramics are very brittle, they can only perform if properly backed up. So RP is used. In addition woven nylon fabric is used to cover the ceramic in order to provide a spall cover and protective shield against normal wear and tear.

Alumina is predominantly used since it is easy to mold or work and also the most readily available. Once boron carbide is processed into its hardened state, it is extremely difficult to grind and form. The high pressures and temperatures required for hot-pressing quickly destroy the useful life of its molds. Both alumina and silicon carbide can be "worked" in the green state under atmospheric conditions. A considerable latitude in shapes and sizes are available.

Cost of this armor is influenced by the type of ceramic used and method of molding. When preliminary production started cost for an aircrew's armor was $500.00. After a few months of production, costs were trimmed 30%, with indications showing that more cost reductions are now occurring.

### 1. Progress with Plastics

The origins of body armor are as old as man. Beginning with a rough tanned piece of leather stretched over a wood frame, man has tried to protect himself from enemy weapons. He progressed from leather to the ornate metal-formed medieval suits of armor. These disappeared gradually because of their weight and bulk, which restricted movement and, particularly, by loss of their protective characteristics against improving weapons.

Except for the steel helmet worn during both World Wars little or no armor for the foot soldier was available against small arms because of the heavy weight of materials. A flak protective vest, using overlapping metal plates in combination with cloth layers, was developed and used extensively by Air Force bomber crews. Doron insert body armor per Military Specification MIL-I-17368A (MC) used 143 starch oil sized woven glass fabric with 25% by weight of polyester resin. These approximate $\frac{1}{8}$ in. thick resin starved, poorly bonded designed laminates provided limited protection against fragments (not small arms). The other popular fragment protective wearing gear developed during the previous wars was a "nylon ballistic cloth" per MIL-C-12369D (GL). Twelve plies of 14 oz/sq yd of woven nylon cloth was held together loosely by means of polyvinyl butyral spot laminates or button-type stitching. The ballistic limit $V_{50}$ for these 12 layers of unbonded cloth is not less than 1,225 ft/sec in accordance with the Ballistic Acceptance Test Method for Personal Armor Material specified in MIL-STD-662. The $V_{50}$ ballistic limit is the impact velocity at which the probability of penetration of a material by a test projectile is 50%.

In order to conserve the energy of our combat forces through lightening the weight of these protective clothing, more recently, the Army Natick Laboratories developed a 5 lb body armor vest utilizing a needle-punched nylon felt. This fragment protective vest is reported to be almost as effective as the 11 lb Doron vest or the $8\frac{1}{2}$ lb nylon fabric vest (Figs. 17-15 and 17-16).

During the Korean War, a wound casualty survey team of the Army Surgeon General's Office found that 80% of those wounded or killed in action were casualties of grenade, mortar or artillery shell fragments. Faced with this need for protecting the foot soldier, the Army developed a fragmentation protective body armor vest which used plies of a specially developed ballistic nylon cloth. Large quantities of these vests were provided our troops in Korea. Data compiled by the SGO showed that the vest effected a 55% casualty reduction from fragmentation wounds or deaths. No materials were available to provide a significant degree of protection against small arms fire within a weight range that the soldier could wear without affecting his combat performance.

## 2. Current Progress

Since the Korean War, the Army has been actively engaged in an extensive materials research program aimed at obtaining lightweight

Figs. 17-15 and 17-16. FAIR EXCHANGE—The life saving armored vest worn by Warrant Officer Larry L. Benne, center, which stopped a Viet Cong .50 caliber bullet fired into his helicopter, was replaced by a new, improved model at the U.S. Army Natick (Mass.) Laboratories. Brigadier General W. M. Mantz, left, commanding general of the Laboratories, where military body armor is developed, made the presentation as Colonel C. T. Riordan, deputy commander, holds the fragmented bullet. Benne, returned from Southeast Asia duty, is assigned to the 5th Infantry Division, Mechanized, at Fort Carson, Colorado. His home is in Chamois, Missouri.

protective armor materials against small arms fire. Under the direction of the Army Material Command, related agencies have participated in this research. Prime responsibility for research and development of protective combat clothing is within the mission area of the U.S. Army Natick Laboratories, Natick, Mass. a field agency of AMC. They also are responsible for procurement of body armor and preparation of specifications to meet Vietnam requirements. The Army Materials Research Agency, Watertown, Mass. and Frankford Arsenal, Philadelphia, Pa. are involved in materials research. The development and Proof Services and Ballistic Research Laboratories, Aberdeen, Md. provide ballistic tests and vulnerability data.

Picatinny Arsenal, Dover, N.J. furnishes technical assistance in developing production techniques, bonding ceramic to RP and RP requirements; also ballistic confirmation tests. The office of The Surgeon General, Washington, D. C. provides medical support regarding priority areas for protection and casualty data. Aviation Materials Command, St. Louis, Mo. has been responsible for designing, developing and procuring Army Aircraft armor.

The Army has taken the lead in this field, not because they are better qualified, but because of their vital need. Over 90% of personnel in Vietnam are Army. It all began in 1965 when increasing ground-to-air small arm bullet wounds among the helicopter crews was drastically multiplying, "flak-vests" were found to be unsatisfactory, and no standard armor would provide proper protection.

New concepts in armor have always been a major drawback. The composite idea has been around for some time, but only four years ago when Goodyear Aerospace Corp. (Phoenix) presented a specific construction did progress develop. Principally under Army in-house and industry contracts, an advancement in the state-of-the-art occurred. Perhaps one of the most important individuals in this program are Edward R. Barron of the Army Natick Laboratories and George R. Rugger of Picatinny Arsenal. Within $2\frac{1}{2}$ years they were able to expedite the design development and production of this composite armor now being used in Vietnam.

A variety of composite armor materials have been developed recently. These include the composite of a ceramic facing bonded to reinforced plastics and a dual-hardness steel (very hard steel bonded metallurgically to a softer steel). For the first time the promise to provide the foot soldier with genuine bullet-proof protection may become a reality (Fig. 17-17).

With the increased military activity in Vietnam and the accompanying intensive use of supporting Army helicopters, it soon became apparent that these aircraft and their crews were vulnerable to small arms fire from the ground.

To provide adequate and immediate protection, AMC assembled a team of experts from its concerned agencies to visit Vietnam in February 1965, and they took several conceptual models for trial evaluation. These included front, back, and leg armor. These early tests showed ready acceptance by the users. As a result, 500 sets of a flat type RP-ceramic chest protector were shipped to Vietnam

Fig. 17-17. Torso armor subjected to projectile impact: left view shows result of two impacts traveling at 2,550 ft/sec on impact; right view is after five impacts at 2,550 ft/sec and one at 2,700 ft/sec. No projectiles went through the armor.

where local facilities were used in designing and fabricating a suitable carrying system for the armor. This chest protector when used with the armored seat provided excellent torso protection for the pilots. It was also worn by the gunners and crew chiefs. Immediately upon the team's return to the U.S., AMC directed production and procurement of quantities of protective armor for aircrewmen. There are now over 15,000 aircrew composite armor vests currently being used.

Flat type chest protectors with carriers were provided. These were fabricated under AMC contract with Aerojet General Corp., Azusa, Calif. Tooling for the anatomically curved, better fitting armor was also initiated. Since last year, requirements were received from Vietnam for additional aircrew protective armor units. Original manufacture and procurements were by Goodyear Aerospace Corp., Akron, Ohio; Norton Company, Worcester, Mass.; UNIRoyal Co., Mishawaka, Ind.; and Coors Porcelain Co., Denver, Col.

Additionally, the Chinook helicopter Program Manager placed a requirement for front, back, and leg armor so that Chinook units departing the States would have the armor with them upon arrival in Vietnam. These items were being provided on schedule.

The Army aircrewman's protective armor system now available consists of a nylon/cotton cloth type carrier or vest with large envelopes or pockets at the front and back. The curved armor panel is inserted into these pockets. Thus the carrier can be used for either a front panel only or for both panels. The front panel armor is worn by pilots and copilots, as the aircraft seats are already armored. The front and back panel sets are worn by crew chiefs and gunners. The cloth carrier has a fragmentation protection padded shoulder with adjustable slide loops and a quick-release for emergency removal. The major break-through occurred in production when curved composites were made into full size curved vests to cover the front or back. Previously, size limitations existed since ceramic parts could only be made in approximately 6 in. by 6 in. flat sheets. In turn a tile arrangement was used which provided weak sections between the tiles.

Leg armor is now being evaluated in theater for crew chiefs and gunners. This armor is semiarticulated, curved thigh and lower leg unit, covering the front and sides of the leg. At its side is a foot support extension resting on the aircraft floor. The extension takes the weight off the legs in much the same way as a metal band or stirrup is used with a plaster cast. Latest design of the aircraft seat using the composite reduces weight from 165 to 135 lb with expectations that it can be further reduced to 105 lb.

Using the new composite material, Natick Laboratories has designed an experimental infantry type armor vest to protect against small arms fire. Its use at the outset is intended for perimeter defense, security, and patrol personnel, and for drivers and troops riding in vehicles along roads where ambush may be encountered. Wider use of the new infantry vest will depend upon results of the field evaluations and wearer acceptance.

Documentary evidence has been obtained showing the need and usefulness for the new composite armor. For example, the aircraft hits and losses in UH-1 helicopters was found to be about one half as frequent when used. The armor has stopped many projectiles and different blunt fragments from shells and other explosives.

Looking beyond the war, the composite armor will provide important peacetime uses. Law enforcement officers, bank guards and peace missions can use them (Fig. 17-18).

Over and beyond the past capability of providing protection through body armor against fragmentation weapons, these relatively lighter weight armor materials have become available which will stop bullets. For the first time we can speak of "bullet proof" vests and be factual. However, research and development programs continue to provide the soldier with even lighter weight, improved protective measures and more mobility by means of new composite designs.

Fig. 17-18. The M. C. Gill Corp., El Monte, Calif., "Little Joe" shields made of reinforced plastics composite provide protection to police and law enforcement officers. The officer looks through a slot protected by a 3 in. thick acrylic prism. Official tests show that the new shields will stop a .44 magnum bullet fired from 10 ft distance. A one inch thick shield will stop a 30-30 rifle bullet from 25 yd.

Armor composites manufacturers and potential producers include the following:

Aerojet General Corp.
AVCO Corp.
Carborundum Co.
Cincinnati Testing Lab.
Falcon Research Co.
Gates Rubber Co.
Goodyear Aerospace Corp.
Materials Research Lab.
North American Aviation Inc.
Norton Co.
Philco Corp.
Reflective Laminates Inc.
H. I. Thompson Fiber Glass Co.
Thompson-Ramo-Woolridge Inc.
UNIRoyal
Whittaker Corp.

Ceramic manufacturers include:
American Lava Corp.
AVCO Corp.
Brush Beryllium Corp.
Brunswick Corp.
Carborundum Co., Refractories Div.

Coors Porcelain Co.
Frenchtown Ceramics
Kennametal, Inc.
National Beryllia Corp.
Norton Co.
Western Gold & Platinum
Reinforced plastics manufacturers include:
American Acrylic Corp.
Atkins & Merrill, Inc.
Coast Manufacturing and Supply Co.
Geonautics, Inc.
Lewcott Chemicals and Plastics Corp.
Reynolds Metals Co.
Russell Reinforced Plastics Co.

## B. Flyers' Head Protection

Helmets use nylon-phenolic instead of glass polyester or epoxy laminate, polystyrene foam, vinyl foam, urethane foam and polycarbonate eye shield instead of acrylic. This new helmet exhibits greater impact energy dissipating characteristics than other military helmets. It also provides resistance to penetration by ballistic fragments, not present in other military crash helmets. Abraham L. Lastnik, plastics technologist, Army Natick Laboratories, who has been in charge of this development, provided the pertinent information on this subject (5–15).

The Army's new helmet has the same configuration as the Navy's APH-6 and Air Force HGU-2A/P helmets. Increased protection was achieved by making its shell of laminated nylon fabric instead of laminated glass cloth. Impact energy attenuation was further increased by lining the shell with $\frac{1}{2}$ in. thick, 4.5 lb/cu ft, expanded polystyrene.

Subjected to two successive impacts of 160 ft lb in the same area, there was no evidence of bottoming, nor were accelerative forces in excess of 300 G measured on an instrumented headform. Duration of impacts were not less than 6.0 msec. The glass cloth helmet impacted with only 100 ft/lb imparted 300 and 600 G, with duration of impacts not exceeding 4.0 msec.

This helmet also uses a vinyl slow-recovery foam interliner and urethane resilient foam pads to provide proper fit. An injection molded polycarbonate eye shield, rather than the more conventional acrylic shield, is being evaluated since improved protection can be obtained. It resists shattering on impact and fragmentary blows, can be optically clear or tinted, and is already produced at $\frac{1}{2}$ the cost.

Studies conducted by the U.S. Board for Aviation Accident Research show that 97% of all Army aircraft accidents are theoretically surviveable. An air accident is defined as "surviveable" if the crash forces involved are within the limits of human tolerance (50–150 G transverse to the spine) and any portion of the inhabitable area of the aircraft is not collapsed sufficiently to impinge upon or crush vital areas of a person seated in a normal position. It is in this category of accident that a protective helmet can play the most significant role.

Army aviation accident reports during a 42-month period indicated that helmets prevent and reduce severity of head injuries. The accidents studied involved 1,259 persons, of which 991 did not wear helmets and 268 did. Fatal head injuries were sustained by 5.9 and 1.1 percent of each group, respectively.

The standard helmet for Army aircraft crewmen is similar to helmets worn by the pilots of the Navy and Air Force. Their crash protection is provided by a hard rigid shell made from glass cloth laminated with polyester or epoxy resin and lined with $\frac{1}{4}$ in. thick, crushable, expanded polystyrene. To add to the head protection of the aircraft crewman, and have him accept the new helmet with a minimum of testing and subjective controversy, the Army decided to retain the configuration of the standard helmet and increase the crash protection by using improved energy-dissipating materials (Figs. 17-19 and 17-20).

### 1. Materials of Construction

The appearance of the newly developed Army flight helmet is similar to that of the standard. Both contain impact energy-absorbing liners made of expanded polystyrene plastic, integral communications equipment, visor housing and visor; however, the shell of the new helmet is made of laminated nylon fabric. The outside dimensions of the nylon helmet are slightly larger than those of the glass helmet because of the greater bulk of the nylon structure. The weight of both is about the same. Based on performance, the nylon shell was found to be considerably more durable.

Early impact studies with the Army's combat vehicle crewmen helmet (tanker's helmet) indicated its excellent impact energy-dissipat-

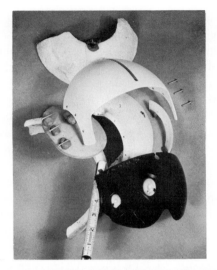

Figs. 17-19 and 17-20. Unassembled and partly assembled protective helmet shows nylon phenolic reinforced plastics helmet with polystyrene foam, vinyl foam, and urethane foam liners, and polycarbonate eye shield.

ing properties as compared with the standard glass fabric flight helmet. Its shell structure also provides greater resistance to penetration by ballistic fragments. The tanker's helmet absorbs great quantities of energy. Highspeed motion pictures reveal excessive transient deformation in the impact area. This localized deflection of the helmet shell could cause head injury. Transient deformation is the deflection of a material under an impact load and the rapid recovery when the load is removed. This deformation is of extremely short duration.

The shell of the combat vehicle crewmen helmet is made of multilayers of nylon cloth laminated with from 15 to 18% by weight phenol formaldehyde and polyvinyl butyral modified phenolic resins. An investigation of this lamina and of laminae with increased resin concentration provided Natick Laboratories the following information about its energy-absorption properties:

Resin concentration has no significant influence on a laminate's ability to resist penetration of ballistic fragments (Fig. 17-21).

The energy absorbed by a laminate increases with increased resin concentration.

Resin content in excess of 40% increases the weight of the lamina without significantly affecting the flexural modulus (Fig. 17-22).

Resin content of 35–40% was selected for the shell of the improved protective nylon helmet. The shell is made of 9 plies of ballistic nylon extending from the crown to the brow line and around the helmet, and feathering to four plies at the edge of the ear sections. (Fig. 17-23) This structure, with between 35 and 40% resin content, will resist penetration, resist deflection; and, as a result of its flexural characteristics, absorbs some impact forces and distributes the residual forces over a large surface area.

Irreversibly crushable foamed plastic (4.5 lb/cu ft expanded polystyrene, nominally $\frac{1}{2}$ in. thick) is used as the energy-absorbing liner. The irreversible crushing of the liner absorbs impact energy and thereby attenuates the impact forces before they reach the head. The head

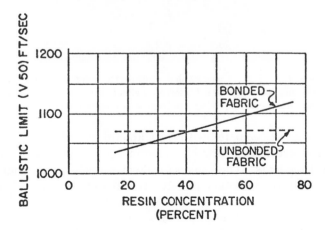

Fig. 17-21. Effect of resin concentration on ballistic limit of nylon fabric laminate (9 plies).

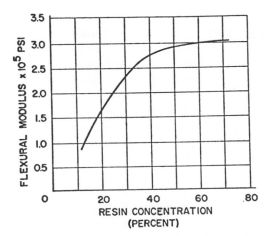

Fig. 17-22. Effect of resin concentration on flexural modulus of nylon fabric laminate (9 plies).

is, therefore, subjected to a lesser impact force than is impinged upon the helmet.

The interliner, considered an integral component of the sizing system, is made of $\frac{1}{4}$ in. thick slow-recovery material (6 lb/cu ft expanded

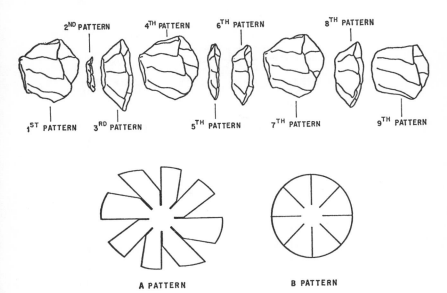

Fig. 17-23. Preform assembly for flight helmet. Exploded view of assemblies of nine patterns to make helmet preforms.

polyvinyl butadiene acrylonitrile plastic blend). Although this material is not suitable for providing protection against high-level impact it is satisfactory as a shield against the bumps and buffeting of combat operations. The slow-recovery characteristics of the interliner will preclude damage of the crushable liner caused by continuous exposure to low-level impact.

A resilient material, such as expanded latex or urethane, is at best a comfort feature. Soft resilient pads of various thicknesses are adhered to the interliner in order to adjust the size and fit of the helmet.

## 2. Performance Data

Impact tests on the nylon helmet were conducted with a drop type of apparatus. (Fig. 17-24). A 16.3 lb mass with a 1.9-in. radius impacting surface drops onto a free-swinging hollow headform assembly made of cast magnesium alloy weighing 13 lb. An accelerometer,

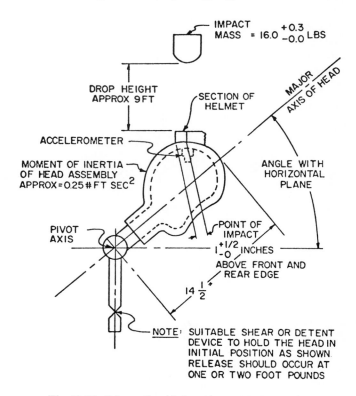

Fig. 17-24. Schematic of helmet impact test appartus.

mounted on the inner surface of the headform directly below the point of impact, is connected to an oscilloscope that records acceleration as a function of time. The helmet, with visor housing and visor removed, but with the guide tracks in place, is mounted on the instrumented headform. The impactor is then dropped from predetermined heights to obtain the desired impact forces and velocities. The resulting acceleration time traces on the oscilloscope were photographically recorded.

Resistance to fragment penetration was evaluated by the standard ballistic acceptance test for Army personnel armor material (using the $V_{50}$ ballistic limit value). The $V_{50}$ ballistic limit is the impact velocity at which the probability of penetration of a material by a test projectile is 50% (Fig. 17-25). The projectile used for this evaluation is designated as a caliber .22 T37 (17-grain) fragment simulator that has a hardness of Rockwell C30-2.

The feasibility of the new improved flight helmet was first explored by comparing the impact-energy attenuation characteristics of molded nylon shells (made in the same molds as the standard glass flight helmets) and the glass helmet. Both helmets were then impact tested in accordance with the military specification for the Navy pilot's helmet APH-6.

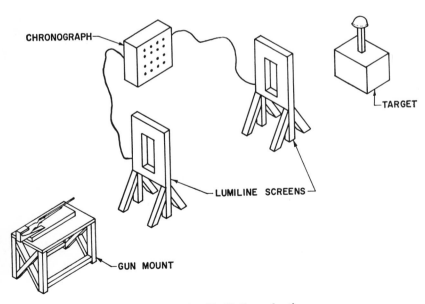

Fig. 17-25. Schematic of ballistic evaluation range.

When subjected to two successive impacts of 100 ft/lb in the same area, the nylon helmet showed no evidence of "bottoming." No accelerative forces greater than 130 G were transferred to the instrumented headform. Similar impacts on the glass helmet imparted 300 and 600 G's, respectively. The time duration of the impacts ranged from 6 to 11 msec for the nylon helmet and from 2 to 4 msec for the glass helmet. Bottoming is a phenomenon occurring during the impact or crushing of energy-absorbing systems when input energy is transmitted to the sensing element with little or no attenuation.

By adjusting the mold dimensions to account for the greater bulk of the nylon laminate structure, large as well as smaller nylon helmets (designated as large and medium size) were made. Both the large and medium size helmets were impact tested in four areas (front, rear, left, and right sides). The results show that the difference in size does not significantly effect impact-energy attenuation characteristics (Table 17-4).

The same test procedure was used by the Snell Memorial Foundation to measure the helmet's impact-energy attenuation characteristics. Two successive impacts were made on the helmet in each of the four areas situated on a locus of points from 1 to 1½ in. above the horizontal plane described by the front and rear edges of the helmets.

From the data obtained it shows the peak acceleration recorded. The differences in impact-energy attenuation among the sites was negligible (about 20 G difference in each impact series). The uniformity of these results reveals the consistency in the design and construction of the nylon helmet (Table 17-5).

Data are available showing characteristic acceleration time curves for three successive impacts on the front of a nylon helmet (without the visor assembly) at 144 and 160 ft-lb, respectively. The first impact on each generated forces in the instrumented headform of less than 230 G; the second impact on the same site generated forces of 300 G or less. The third 144 ft-lb impact generated a force of 300 G; the third 160 ft-lb impact caused the helmet to bottom and generated

TABLE 17-4. Peak Accelerative Forces in G's Imparted by One 100 ft-lb Impact

| Impact site | Regular size | Large size |
|---|---|---|
| Front | 63.2 | 66.0 |
| Rear | 57.2 | 61.9 |
| Left side | 89.8 | 85.8 |
| Right side | 81.8 | 87.0 |

TABLE 17-5. Peak Accelerative Forces in G's Imparted by Each of Two Successive 144 ft-lb Impacts

| Impact site | First impact | Second impact |
|---|---|---|
| Front | 230 | 250 |
| Rear | 220 | 250 |
| Left side | 210 | 230 |
| Right side | 220 | 230 |

forces in excess of 400 G. The duration of all the G forces, except those that caused bottoming, were at least 6 msec (Fig. 17-26).

Projections on the surface of a helmet would normally be expected to be areas of energy concentration upon impact; therefore, particular emphasis was given to the effects of impact on the molded nylon visor guides. One of these projections (about $\frac{1}{4}$ in. high and $\frac{1}{2}$ in. wide) was impacted with 144 ft-lb of energy for six successive impacts. None of these impacts generated more than 300 G in the instrumented headform. This is in sharp contrast to the results when metal guides are used as on older Army and Navy flight helmets.

Metallic projections are relatively inelastic and are sources of energy concentration, whereas the nylon visor guides attenuate the energy. The first impact on the nylon guides undoubtedly has its energy absorbed by compression of the nylon. The second impact exhibits a decrease in energy absorption; the guide is probably

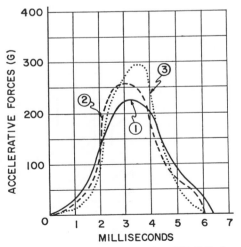

Fig. 17-26. Helmet impact test. Three successive 144 ft-lb impacts on the front center of a nylon helmet.

approaching its ultimate compression point; the next two impacts absorb progressively more energy. This unexpected occurrence is probably caused by the breaking up of nylon material. The final two impacts show a progressive increase of G forces as the nylon fragments further approach their ultimate compression point (Fig. 17-27).

The average areal density of the helmet shell is 17.86 oz/sq ft of surface. Because the ballistic limit is a function of areal density, the helmet was evaluated as two structures, each with a different areal density. Density was not determined experimentally, but was calculated to be 19.65 oz/sq ft in the crown and 13.10 oz/sq ft in the ear sections. The $V_{50}$ ballistic limits of these structures were thus found to be 1163 and 1045 ft/sec, respectively. Areal density is the weight per unit area, a measure for comparing the relative effectiveness of armor materials.

Various animal and package-cushioning studies have shown that the duration of acceleration as well as the maximum acceleration, may be related to the degree of injury of damage incurred. The threshhold of head and brain damage cited in terms of peak acceleration and duration of impact varies among investigators; each investigator appears to establish damage criteria based upon the specific grouping of the literature he may have examined.

A study to determine the relationship that may exist between peak acceleration, rate of acceleration, duration of acceleration and kinetic energy absorbed by the head, concludes, within the limits of the study, that there is a positive relationship between peak acceleration,

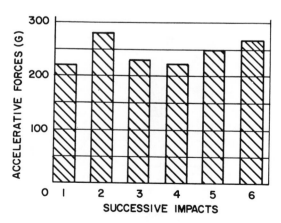

Fig. 17-27. Helmet impact test. Accelerative forces resulting from successive 144 ft-lb impacts on projecting visor guides of a nylon helmet.

rate of acceleration and duration of acceleration. It further concludes that the measurement of peak acceleration gives sufficient information to evaluate the protective characteristics of headgear. Whether the protective criterion of a helmet is peak acceleration itself or a combination of peak acceleration and duration of acceleration, the Army's nylon flight helmet will exhibit more impact-energy attenuation capabilities than other military helmets now being used.

## III.  AIRCRAFT

Over the years innovations in aircraft have given rise to more new plastics development and have kept plastics industry profits at a higher level than any other major market principally since they can meet different environmental conditions. Virtually all plastics have received the benefit of the aircraft industry's uplifting influence. In 1967 $\frac{1}{2}$ billion or 50 million lb of practically all conceivable top quality plastics are used to provide cost advantages and improvements on flight system performance. Now an average of 5% of plane's weight is plastics. This percentage is expected to double or perhaps triple in the next decade.

The chief challenge to the plastics industry is not in pounds of plastics needed but rather in the translation of polymer development technology into production line know-how. The aircraft industry is geared to pay high prices for plastics with exceptional properties— as high as hundreds of dollars per pound with up to ten-fold cost increases for fabricated parts—plus additional dollars to conduct continual testing and evaluation to insure safety of aircraft operation.

As an example, commercial development of the Boeing-SST will cost $4-$5 billion (Fig. 17-28). Estimates of the world market are as high as 600 SST's by 1980. SST will sell for about $50 million when it enters airline service in the mid-'70's. Ultimately, Boeing could obtain at least $30 billion in sales. Present design of this 675,000 lb "take off weight" airplane includes the use of more than 12,000 lb of plastics. Approximately 6,000 lb of heat resistant polyimide-glass fabric honeycomb will be in the wing sandwich panels, 3,000 lb of plastics in the passenger area, and still more in other parts—including baggage compartments, gaskets, seals, carpets, thermal insulation, windows, radomes, avionics black boxes, and electrical wiring.

The use of plastics in aircraft continues to expand. In most applications, they are required to meet rigid environmental performance requirements. Because of this factor, most of those used are the more

Fig. 17-28. Scale models of the new Boeing supersonic transport (SST) design reveal details of the 1,800 miles/hr airliner as it would appear in supersonic flight (top) and subsonic flight (bottom) for landing and takeoff. This SST weighing 675,000 lb is already designed to use over 12,000 lb of plastics that will endure extreme environmental conditions of temperature, load, and electrical insulation.

expensive plastics since they provide exceptional performance. For those plastics material and fabricating companies in this business, return on investments is excellent.

Present indicators show that a ball park figure of 5% of the airplanes' weight represents the use of plastics. Some heavier planes use 1–2% with lighter planes at 20%. Keep in mind that the weight of these plastics are lower than practically all the other materials used; specific gravity of plastics ranges from 1 to 2. Estimated consumption for 1967 is 50 million pounds or $1½ billion with practically every conceivable type plastics used to some degree. The reinforced plastics composites predominate; 50% of the plastics used is reinforced plastics (RP). It has always been difficult to estimate or approximate plastics consumption in aircraft since the industry has never developed data on consumption of materials on the weight basis. Educated marketing analysis have been conducted in order to obtain the above estimates. As described in this section, the multitude of parts range from the fluoropolymer seals, fillers and lubricants to polyimide RP and stretched acrylic.

## A. Aircraft Industry Growth

The aerospace industry—the nation's largest industrial employer (1,350,000) and with a product mix encompassing aircraft, missiles, space vehicles, electronic systems and varied supporting equipment— had sales of $23.8 billion during 1966. Aircraft accounted for 50% of this industry's revenue. A new high, this was 15% above the previous record of $20.8 billion set in 1964 and 32% greater than in 1961. The war effort in Vietnam has played an important role in the industry's recent expansion, creating a strong demand for military aircraft and helicopters (Table 17-6). Civilian demands have also increased, notably for jet aircraft. Volume would have risen even more but for widespread delivery delays. With both labor supplies and production facilities proving inadequate, shipments of engines and other com-

TABLE 17-6. Aircraft Defense Budget Plan Fiscal years 1966 and 1967 [a]

(Millions of Dollars)

| Fiscal year | Procurement | | Research, development, test, and evaluation | |
|---|---|---|---|---|
| | 1967 | 1968 | 1967 | 1968 |
| Army | 1,202 | 769 | 114 | 116 |
| Navy | 3,463 | 2,560 | 335 | 280 |
| Air Force | 5,685 | 5,782 | 711 | 740 |
| Defense agencies | — | — | 12 | 10 |
| Total | 10,350 | 9,111 | 1,171 | 1,145 |

[a] Subject to increase.

ponents have fallen behind schedule. In consequence unfilled orders have risen sharply. Backlog is now approximately 150% of sales.

In terms of annual airframe weight delivered, military purchases predominated since 1948 to 1964. Since 1965 civilian purchases have had a slight edge. According to Karl G. Harr, Jr., president of the Aerospace Industries Association, the years ahead show a favorable and mature growth with demand for commercial aircraft one of the primary contributors.

### B. Military and Commercial Demands

Military demands upon the aerospace industry are heavy at present. The Vietnam conflict has called for greatly increased production of helicopters and aircraft as well as a buildup of engine and spare parts output. Aircraft losses in Vietnam were estimated to be running at an annual rate of $1 billion early in 1966, while the use of spare parts was at a $200 million rate. Among the aircraft now in production are the F-4 Phantom, the A-6 tactical bomber, and the C-141 cargo transport, all of which are being used extensively in Vietnam.

Additional numbers of A-7 tactical aircraft are also being procured for Vietnam use. Scheduled for production during fiscal 1968 is the C-5A, an enlarged transport. This plane, which will be in operation in 1969, has a capacity of fifty-six tons and will handle the loads of four C-141's. Orders are also being placed by the Air Force for the FB-111 strategic bomber and by the Air Force and Navy for their versions of the F-111 tactical aircraft. All of these planes make extensive use of plastics

The major types of aircraft which will add to production during the next 5 years include the supersonic transport (SST), supersized cargo transport with passenger transport version (Fig. 17-29), and possibly vertical lift transport.

### C. Why Use Plastics?

In many cases, aircraft requirements could not be met without plastics. Primary reasons for use are functional, cost savings, ease of installation and maintenance, freedom from corrosion, fire resistance, and durability (Table 17-7). They can be termed functional, meaning that some property of the plastic material (mechanical, physical or electrical) makes it desirable for a particular application. A typical example is electromagnetic transparent windows or radomes and also

Fig. 17-29. Jumbo jet for 1970 to be used by TWA is Boeing's 747 StarStream jet. This 340 ton plane with a wing span of 195 ft makes extensive use of plastics, such as in the insulation, sandwich core, practically all of the 2 deck interior, eleven lavatories, and electronic circuits and control boxes.

electronic gear. With increased use of electronic equipment in present day aircraft, this application is expanding. The use of optically transparent plastics in windshields, canopies and other glazing areas is another example of their functional use. Low K-factor of urethane foam, silicone and polyimide require them in the different thermal environments.

Adhesives have made it possible to make lighter metal structures without the use of rivets that give nonhomogeneous stresses and interfere with surface smoothness (Table 17-8). As an example, the design environment, weight, and performance goals of the B-58 required an efficient, multipurpose structure. Specifically, the structure had to provide aerodynamically smooth surfaces, serve as fuel tank insulation, contain large quantities of fuel, support high stresses, and withstand high fuel pressure, severe acoustic noise, and induced thermal stresses. Essentially the entire surface of the B-58 is aluminum bonded panel construction which performs all the required functions. It has the lowest structural weight to gross weight ratio of an airplane the Air Force flies today.

Many aircraft parts can be fabricated at lower cost and faster than

TABLE 17-7. Lockheed Aircraft

| Material | F-104 | P-3 | XH-56A |
|---|---|---|---|
| ABS | | Ducting, trim | Ducting, cockpit liners, covers |
| Acetal | | | Antenna standoffs, rollers |
| Acrylic | Canopy | Windows | Canopy |
| Alkyd | | | |
| Epoxy | | | |
| Fluorocarbon | Bearings | Bearings, rub strips, insulation blankets | Wire insulation |
| Nylon | | Tubings | Harness strips |
| Phenolic | | Electrical, high temp. applications | |
| Polycarbonate | | Ducting, trim | Ducting |
| Polyester | | | |
| Polyethylene | Tubing | Tubing | |
| Polypropylene | Electrical, shrink sleeving | Electrical, shrink sleeving | |
| Polystyrene | | Air grilles, trim | |
| Urethane | Seat head rest | | Foams, coatings, elastoms |
| PVC | Tubing | Tubing | Tubing |
| Silicone | Ducting | Ducting | |
| Polysulfide | Fuel tank, cockpit sealing | Fuel tank, cabin sealant | Sealing for corrosion prevention |
| Glass Fiber-Polyeston | Antenna enclosures | Radomes, ducting trim, electrical radio antenna covers | Covers, pans |
| Glass fiber-epoxy | Radome— Filament wound | ECM radomes, doppler radome | Antenna covers, fairings, wing, tail panels (structure), wing tips, sponsons |

with other materials. Complicated-shaped parts usually fall into this category. A typical example is an air inlet duct for a jet or turboprop engine. These are usually designed with complex, compound curved shapes for aerodynamic reasons, and may be difficult and costly to form in metal, requiring several subassemblies (Fig. 17-30).

Another reason for using plastics is that, depending on type of loads and part configuration, higher strength-to-weight ratio can be realized with plastic composites compared to metal. As new materials are further developed (such as higher modulus glass, graphite and boron

TABLE 17-8.  General Dynamics F-111

(Total weight of airplane is 60,000 lb)

| Glass Reinforced Plastics | | |
|---|---|---|
| Resin system | Number of parts | Weight per plane, lb |
| Phenolic | 150 | 300 |
| Epoxy | 250 | 640 |
| Polyester DAP | 1 | 160 |
| Silicone | 3 | 10 |
| Polyimide | 2 | 2 |

Approximately 40% of the parts are structural and 60% are nonstructural. Typical applications include: nose radomes, wing radomes, antenna covers, wing tips, fairings, hot air ducts, air scoop, engine inlet panels, battery box, fuselage panels.

| Thermoplastics | | |
|---|---|---|
| Material | Number of parts | Weight per plane, lb |
| ABS | 10 | 15 |
| Polycarbonate | 50 | 70 |
| Nylon | 160 | 25 |
| Teflon | — | 25 |

Typical applications include: cabin console fairing, electronic covers, clamps for hydraulic lines, wire coverings, cold air ducts, sliding surfaces, compass housings.

| Other Plastics | | |
|---|---|---|
| Material | Weight per airplane, lb | Typical applications |
| Adhesive-high temp., epoxy novolac | 550 | Bonding metal sandwich panels |
| Adresive-general purpose-epoxy | 35 | Semi-structural and non-structural applications |
| Potting compounds (epoxy-aluminum or glass beads filler) | 80 | Fairing core details; fillers in GRP parts; bonding inserts in sandwich panels |
| Urethane foam | 15 | Insulations |
| Glass core | 35 | Sandwich panels (Navy radome) |
| Glass reinforced molding compound | 15 | Fairings; pilots grip stick; air deflectors |

Fig. 17-30. Lear Jet Corporation's plane uses approximately 5%, by weight, of plastics (parts include ABS window trims and cabinets, urethane insulation, and RP radome).

fibers, and improved resin matrices) this factor is becoming increasingly important.

Aero Commander, a division of Rockwell-Standard Corporation, is the only airframe manufacturer building light twin-engined aircraft specifically for business in all three propulsion categories:  piston, turboprop and pure jet.  The Aero Commander Line has a world wide reputation for their performance.  "If it weren't for plastics, the Jet Commander and all other business aircraft, for that matter, would be entirely different aircraft," said Don Long, Aero Commander chief engineer.  "We just couldn't offer the utility to cost ratio in executive aircraft that we do now if there were not a wide range of plastics for use in our aircraft.  Developmental and manufacturing costs would be considerably higher resulting in a greater initial cost to the customer as well as higher maintenance costs," Long added.

But the use of plastics at Aero Commander doesn't begin or end at the Jet windshield, far from it.  Besides over 500 parts fabricated from plastics for the various models of Aero Commanders, plastic tooling is a vital manufacturing technique at Aero Commander.  "Many more manufacturing hours would be added to each unit if plastic tooling was not used," said Lee Bush, plant manager.

### D.  Interior Practically All Plastics

Similar to other past and future planes (Fig. 17-31), the uses of plastics in Douglas commercial aircraft have increased steadily over the past years.  The developments in thermoplastic sheets have made

Fig. 17-31. Here is the interior of Boeing's 747 jet being designed for TWA with the interior practically all plastics of many different types from thermosets and thermoplastics.

this particular type of material extremely attractive in terms of economy and weight savings. The interiors of DC-8's and DC-9's are made of acrylonitrilebutadene-styrene (ABS) and polyvinyl chloride (PVC). Major plastic interior and structure parts are RP.

Typical examples of the utilization of plastic materials are as follows: metalized ABS reflectors in the ceilings of DC-9 aircraft, covered by extruded acrylic diffusers; ABS thermoformed washroom structures; ABS overhead passenger service panels: ABS-PVC laminate window trimmings and thermoformed polycarbonate ducting halves. Additional uses include radomes which employ large plastic panels on the undercarriage of the DC-9 and nearly all interior for the passenger and crew cabins. *Ninety-nine per cent of the cabin interior as viewed by a passenger is plastics.*

## E.  Significant Developments

Applications of plastics are now rather extensive and will continue to grow. They have been in use since the beginning of aircraft. The earliest wings were covered with cellulose nitrate-doped fabrics. Phenolic resin woods were used for structural parts. Milestones in the development of acrylic for glazing, polyethylene for radar cable insulation, glass fiber-reinforced polyester resin laminates for radomes, adhesive bonded structures, and special eslatomers for tires occurred during World War II.

As expected foams such as urethanes are extensively used for sound and thermal insulation, as well as filling space. The commercial history of rigid urethane foam dates back to the 1940's when Germany needed strong aircraft wing tips and rudders—needed them fast and in the face of great materials shortages. The promise that rigid urethane foam would be the key to rapid production provided the incentive for a high priority crash-development program.

For wire insulation, polytetrafluoroethylene is principally used in all aerospace systems for this purpose up to 500°F. For example, over 212 miles of TFE-coated wire is used in the B-70 but a gap exists between 500 and 1,000°F where ceramic insulation is used, and flexible insulating material is needed in this temperature regime.

## F. Reinforced Plastics Composites

One of the most significant developments is in the reinforced plastics (RP) industry where its application goes into primary structural elements of modern-day aircraft (Table 17-9). In the past several years great strides have been made toward introducing glass and boron RP into actual primary structural applications. Significant cost and weight savings have been shown through the use of RP. North American Aviation has proceeded as far in this field as proposing two development aircraft systems to the services. One was the OV-10A all-glass reinforced plastic airplane proposed to the Navy and the other was a YAT-28 all glass fiber airplane proposed to the Air Force. Even

TABLE 17-9.  Grumman Aircraft

| | Reinforced plastics, glass-epoxy, lb | | ABS and Polycarbonate, lb | Other plastic, lb |
|---|---|---|---|---|
| | Primary | Secondary | | |
| A-6A—Intruder | 200 | 500 | 400 | 300 |
| E-1B Tracer | 800 | 300 | 10 | 200 |
| E-2A Hawkeye | 1200 | 600 | 200 | 400 |
| F-111—TFX | 500 | 600 | 100 | 400 |
| Gulfstream | 150 | 400 | 400 | 300 |

though neither of these proposals were accepted at the time, they were the forerunners in the field of aircraft system development and technology in this area. The near future will undoubtedly bring greater primary structural applications and the possibility of a complete airframe structure fabricated of reinforced plastics.

Prior to World War II, the principal uses of RP in planes were for secondary and non-structural uses, such as pulleys, control cable conduits, fairings, and fillets. In most instances these parts were machined from high presure molded paper, cotton, or asbestos, phenolic laminate stock shapes, such as sheet, rod or tube. The first use of airborne glass RP radomes is believed to have occurred in 1943 with the equipping of B-17 bombers with retractable hemispherical radomes. Subsequently, other World War II vintage aircraft were equipped with radar and radomes. These radomes were usually appendages which protruded from the aircraft fuselage, since they were not anticipated in the original aircraft design. With the advent of high speed jet aircraft, it was mandatory that radome design be integrated with airframe design to give low drag characteristics. An example of a "faired-in" radome is the nose radome for the F-100 fighter aircraft. Here the lower portion of the radome also forms the cowling for the air intake. Another example is the "chin radome" for the B-70 aircraft. Here the radome forms the lower section of the nose of the aircraft, hence the "chin" designation.

At about the same time that glass polyester laminates were being adopted for use in radomes, these materials were also being used in development of fuselage and wing structures for aircraft. This pioneering work performed at Wright-Patterson Air Force Base included design, fabrication, static testing, assembly, and flight testing of an RP fuselage for the BT-15 airplane and wings for the AT-6C airplane. The BT-15 airplane was a two-place, low wing cantilever monoplane of the basic trainer class. The AT-6C was an advanced trainer airplane, very similar in appearance to the BT-15.

The fuselage for the BT-15 was of sandwich construction, having RP faces and a balsa wood core. Fabrication of the fuselage was completed on November 7, 1943, static tests were conducted November, 11–15, 1943, and flight testing was performed on 24 March 1944. On a strength/weight basis, the RP fuselage was 50% stronger than the aluminum fuselage and 80% stronger than the wooden fuselage then in service. The wings for the AT-6C airplane were also of sandwich construction, consisting of glass fabric polyester laminate skins, and a core consisting of strips of cellular cellulose acetate wrapped with polyester impregnated glass fabric. Fabrication of the first RP wing was completed on May 31, 1945. Several additional wings were fabricated and static testing was successfully completed on September 10, 1946. The RP wings were successfully flight tested for over 1,600 hr.

The most recent aircraft off the assembly line is the F-105 of Fairchild-Hiller Corporation with an approximate gross weight of 36,000 pounds. It utilizes some 350 RP parts including a filament wound nose radome, vential fin and antenna cover. In the Caravelle 3,300 lbs of RP are used. The bodies of new Sub-Aviation helicopters are, for their larger parts, made of RP. Plans at Bellanca are to build an all RP 4-passenger high-performance plane. See Figs. 17-32 through 17-36 for other typical developments.

## G. Aircraft Development Delayed

More R&D programs in plastics are developing. These multimillion dollar programs of the past, present and future continue to be major assets. However, from a military aspect, R&D's efforts have been lagging since the Korean War. As an example, if more work had been conducted on the new very high strength and modulus reinforced plastics the present F-111 fighter-bomber-reconnaissance aircraft

Fig. 17-32. The Cherokee of Piper Aircraft Corporation makes extensive use of reinforced plastics parts, as shown above, as well as of other plastics in other sections.

Fig. 17-33. The Sikorsky CH-53A transport helicopter makes use of reinforced plastics in most of its structural members such as this cockpit canopy–uses prepreg of glass fabric with epoxy resin.

Fig. 17-34. The Grumman E-2A Hawkeye 24 ft rotodome (radar dome rotates at 6 rpm) and four vertical stabilizers are made of reinforced plastics. They provide structural efficiency, radar transmission, resistance to ocean corrosiveness, and ease of maintenance.

Fig. 17-35. One of the first large scale production uses of an ultarviolet energy source for curing Ferro-Cordo UV-sensitive prepreg molding materials turned out to be a success in 1967, according to officials of Pan American World Airways. Here are highlights of Pan Am's experience: improved mechanical properties; excellent dimensional stability; controlled accuracy of parts; substantial overall cost savings; faster, controlled cures; considerably lower tooling costs; more design flexibility. The reinforced plastic components made by Pan Am protect the walls and upholstery in a Boeing 707-321C passenger aircraft when it is converted to cargo hauling. In addition, the sidewall panels protect the plane windows and allow sunlight to filter through and provide enough light for loading operations.

could be 3000 lb lighter in weight, which in turn would give it more "striking power."

The Vietnam war must be a headache for the Pentagon planners of military aircraft. After a decade of peace spent on the development of intercontinental missiles and supersonic fighters and on arguments whether or not manned bombers should be abandoned, they find when a war comes along that the most effective aircraft for tactical support of Army helicopters and ground forces are a modified light airplane for use by the forward air controllers, a transport developed in the 1930's for airline use adapted for ground-attack missions by the installation of three side-looking rapid-fire guns, and the B-52 of the Strategic Air Command, which has to fly over a thousand miles each way to accomplish its battle-area mission.

Fig. 17-36. General Electric Company's Evendale, Ohio, plant is designing, fabricating, and testing gas turbine jet engine parts–all first stage air compressor assemblies. Glass and boron reinforced plastics stator vanes, compressor blades, and integral blades/disks assemblies are the major parts being developed with plastics.

Practically all the more-useful airplanes for purely tactical missions were developed before the Korean War. The first replacement, scheduled to go into combat this year, is an attack type converted from an advanced trainer. The only suitable mission for the supersonic attack and fighter aircraft of the Air Force and Navy is the essentially strategic one of bombing the ports of entry in an attempt to plug the enemy supply pipeline at its source.

After about five years of "war," attrition has reached the level that many types of the older aircraft will have to be phased out and replaced. The DOD has already announced several competitions for design studies of new types. Practically all these studies make extensive use of plastics in order to meet operational requirements.

## H. Advances

Technological advances in any area, military or commercial, are necessarily geared to the materials available (Table 17-10). Engineers have learned that metals can be strengthened by oxide dispersion to allow a very significant increase in operating temperatures. They

TABLE 17-10. Fairchild Hiller Aircraft Parts

| | |
|---|---|
| Fairings | Polyester glass |
| Doors (wheel, access) | Vinyl phenolic |
| Windows * | Acrylic |
| Interior trim | Vinyl |
| Carpets | Nylon |
| Ducts | Polyester/glass |
| Trailing edges, wing,[a] movable surfaces | Polyester/glass |
| Wing, tips | Polyester glass |
| Stabilizer, tips | Polyester glass |
| Fin, tips | Polyester glass |
| Glare shields | Acrylic |
| Fairleads | Phenolic cotton |
| Placards | Acrylic |
| Handles | Acetal, butyl, styrene (ABS) |
| Knobs | (ABS) |
| All surface leading edges [a] | Bonded honeycomb adhesive-epoxy |
| Foam fuel tank baffles | Isocyanate foam Polysulfide rubber |
| Insulation, sound proofing | Vinyl foam |
| Electrical, black boxes | Polycarbonate |
| All fuselage panels are of metal to metal bond [a] | Epoxy |
| Plenum chambers | Polyester glass or rubber |
| All movable surface panels are metal to metal bond [a] | Epoxy |
| Water methanol tank | Polyester/glass |
| Radome | Polyester glass fabric |
| Ice shield | Fiberglas polyester resin |

[a] Denotes structural parts; others are nonstructural

have also shown that new plastics composite materials of metalloid fibers in organic binders promise great weight savings with a gain of strength and stiffness. Fibers under consideration include high modulus glass, boron, carbon, silicon carbide, and boron carbide. Various programs have demonstrated the high payoff potential in the form of flightworthy hardware. Presently the composite materials technology is directed toward filling specific needs. General Electric Company's Evendale plant is testing gas turbine engine items—all first-stage compressor assemblies. Boron and glass reinforced stator vanes, compressor blades and integral blade/disc assemblies have been fabricated and are being tested. Whittaker Corporation/Bell Helicopter Company has undertaken the design, fabrication, and test of a UH-1F helicopter tail rotor section. An aeroelastic rotor blade specimen—a full-scale section of a UH-1F helicopter tail rotor—has been designed, fabricated and tested. It is 25% lighter and 36% stiffer than a similar aluminum piece. In addition, main rotor root end attachments and a main rotor spar section have been designed which will be tested soon. North American Aviation is responsible for designing, fabricating and testing a wing box beam representative of the T-39 configuration. One beam has been static tested and a second beam will be fatigue tested.

General Dynamics has tested two experimental demonstration items which represent the attachment and mid-section of the F-111 horizontal tail. This piece has a titanium fitting, boron-epoxy face sheets, glass-epoxy spars and an aluminum honeycomb core. It possesses a 350-lb weight savings potential for the F-111 tail. A 16% weight reduction was effected by simply replacing the aluminum skin on the F-111A air deflector door with a composite skin. All of these programs are in the early research and development phases—no boron composites are involved in the operational F-111A at this time. It has been computed that a weight saving of 3,000 pounds in the F-111A, if sheets of a boron composite material were used in place of titanium. However, it would take 2 years or more to make such a change.

## I. Boeing

Of the 727, Boeing's 170,000 lb jet, 435 lbs of RP go into such parts as the navigational and guidance external control systems. Their resistance to sonic fatigue has enabled them to stand up for thousands of hours where metal parts would have failed in a few hours of service. An example is the tail cone of the 727. This is the cone at the extreme aft end of the aircraft, between the horizontal stabilizers. RP's show excellent damping characteristics in areas of high sonic vibration.

The low elasticity of plastics make them useful in areas where they are designed to take the usual aerodynamic pressures, but where they will flex under unusual loads. Examples are engine inlet ducts and wing leading edges, wing-to-body fairings and the fin-tip fairings at the top, forward corner of the vertical stabilizer. Most of the sides of the vertical stabilizer also are of RP. Rudder seals are composed of RP covered with a metalized coating.

In the nonstructural area, the strength and rigidity of over 1500 lb of plastics have made them useful in interior decorative panels. Such parts are integrally pigmented or painted to achieve the desired appearance. To overcome damage caused by severe impact loads in the cargo area, Boeing has developed a special lightweight plastic laminate. Other applications of the nonstructural type are various substructures such as partition panels and junction boxes, air conditioning ducts and protective covers for electrical wire bundles.

As most aircraft producers report, Boeing continues to emphasize that plastics provide cost savings because they can be shaped faster and with greater ease than metal parts. Their light weight holds an advantage over metal for some uses, resulting in a lighter aircraft with correspondingly greater load capability. This approach is putting more RP and plastics in Boeing's smallest jet liner, the 737, which is scheduled for delivery late this year (108,000 lb).

RP will be used on the 737 in areas such as empennage trailing edge panels, rudder, elevators, control tabs and the tail cone. Designers also have specified it for fuselage and wing-to-fuselage fairings, air conditioning bay doors and wing leading edge access panels, and nose wheel doors. The use of RP parts has reduced construction man hours for these parts by as much as 50% and the parts are up to 34% lighter than the metal assemblies they replace.

Since the first use of RP assemblies in 1961, hundreds of pounds and thousands of dollars have been saved on the Boeing 727. For the new Boeing 737 the first use was on the rudder. Skins of RP sandwich were fastened to metal spars and ribs. Engineers were able to reduce the number of ribs and eliminate the aft spar. Tests proved the structural integrity of the new rudder. Its simple construction reduced manufacturing costs nearly 70% in relation to the sheet-metal rudder assembly cost. The same technique was used on the elevator assemblies with similar success. Redesign of the elevator and aileron control tabs, to use fiber glass sandwich construction, allowed a reduction in skin thickness—a weight-saver. It also cut manufacturing costs 50% for producing tough, corrosion-resistant assemblies.

Certain areas of the 737 will be subjected to high temperatures due to thrust reverser action and exhaust from the aircraft's auxiliary power unit. Here it was necessary to provide temperature resistance for the fiber-glass details used in these areas. By using a high temperature resistant resin in the fiberglass sandwich engineers came up with the desired results. The parts have the same weight and cost saving advantages as well as excellent heat resistant qualities.

The same high temperature resistant RP sandwich also will serve in other areas. Air conditioning bay access doors, located forward of the main landing gear must withstand extreme sonic and dynamic stresses as well as high temperatures during thrust reverser action. The use of metal in this area was not practical from the weight and cost standpoint while RP more than met the designers requirements. The same is true for the tailcone, hinged flap, and certain wing access panels.

The single-stage operation in molding plastic exterior components proved so successful Boeing process engineers developed a single-stage process for the fabrication of 737 interior appointments (partitions, panels and hatracks). The development of a fire resistant polyamide (nylon) fiber, processed into the honeycomb core for the sandwich, was a primary factor in the economic success of this program.

Further developments provided a means of applying decorative surfaces to the sandwich during curing. In addition, panels with textured surfaces and sound-reducing characteristics can be manufactured by this single-stage method.

RP materials also are used in areas of the 737 normally not seen by the passengers. One of these is the cargo or baggage compartment. The materials used in this area must withstand constant pounding from suitcases and containers, yet be light, fire resistant and repairable. The use of RP cargo liner will reduce costly operational delays due to the ease of maintenance and reduction of service damage which requires repair prior to takeoff.

The Boeing 707 jetliners now use RP material in the nose radome and on certain fairings and antennas. Plans call for extensive use of the material on the giant Boeing 747 jet transport.

## J. SST (Supersonic Transport)

Design plans at Boeing for their 300-passenger SST, to be commercially flying in eight years, will use over 10,000 sq ft of a sandwich construction. Titanium skins are supported by a glass fiber-polyimide resin core. The core construction has been designed to withstand temperatures of 450–500°F. A polyimide adhesive will be used to bond the plastic core to the Titanium.

Fuel for the SST will be carried in wing and body tanks sealed by a rubber-like fluorosilicone elastomer. This material will withstand the blistering temperatures caused by the aircraft's friction with the air at supersonic speed. Until recently, good sealants would last only 7500 hr under such punishing conditions. Just before submitting its proposal to the Federal Aviation Administration last year in the final round of the U.S./SST competition, Boeing tested a new fluorosilicone elastomer to meet these rugged requirements. By 1970, Boeing expects other advanced sealants—such as perfluoroalkyltriazine—to be available. Between 1000 and 1500 lb of sealant will be used per airplane.

Although the skin of the SST in flight may reach temperatures of 450°F, Boeing plans to keep the aircraft's fuel below 140°F by use of a lightweight fluorocarbon or fluorosilicone insulation. This material will be troweled, putty-like, onto the inside walls of the fuel tanks. To cut weight, spherical glass beads or other light-weight fillers may be added to the insulation. In some cases, the insulation may be applied as low-density foam. A polyimide-resin foam also is being considered.

Seals, compounded of advanced materials, will be used extensively on the SST. Those subject to flexing, such as door seals, will be made of a silicone material reinforced with temperature-resistant fabrics. Stationary seals, as well as hydraulic and fuel-line seals will be made of fluorinated rubber.

In a search for materials for the SST, the high temperature polymer research activities initiated in the early 1960's were reviewed to select promising resin systems. The silicones were eliminated as being too weak, even though they were resistant to high temperature; the phenolics, phenyl silanes, diphenyl oxides, and polyarylene ether phenols were rejected as being not resistant enough to temperature; and polybenzimidazole was too difficult to process as well as being inferior in temperature resistance to the polyimides. Screening of resins was merely the first step. Techniques for manufacturing laminates and sandwich structures had to be investigated and practical procedures had to be developed for the production of large complex parts. Formulations of polyimide resins were tested in early 1963 as adhesives, honeycomb core impregnating resins, and as laminating resins. The investigations of resin formulations and associated resin developments were then followed by many hours of testing to establish properties and reliability

In most cases properties improved with initial temperature aging, because of the familiar phenomena of continued curing of the resin, and then dropped to some continuously maintained strength level. The behavior of resins depends upon initial molecular structure, formulation techniques, resin additives, and manufacturing processes. It was found that laminates using some polyimide resins can exhibit acceptable strength properties after 1000 hr of conditioning at 550°F but, when conditioned for 5000 hr at 550°F, the strength value dropped to zero. These characteristics demand that material engineers, with the support of stress engineers, conduct extensive testing under controlled parameters in order to intelligently evaluate each contributing variable. This philosophy was implemented early in 1963 with the poly-imide resins and the current status insures engineering that heat stability, structural reliability, and service life can be expected for RP composites in the projected supersonic transport environments.

## K.  Lockheed

In addition to Lockheed's major program on the SST, it is involved in other major new aircraft developments, all considering different types of plastics. The world's largest aircraft, the Air Force C-5A, is scheduled for its flight in June of 1968 with deliveries in late 1969. The Lockheed-Georgia Company is building this super subsonic jet. It will make extensive use of plastics. Meeting the C-5A structural weight goals requires the use of advanced structural materials and new concepts in the application of these materials.

RP laminates and sandwich panels are to be employed extensively in fairings and primary structure, especially where sonic pressures are greatest. Honeycomb material represents the most efficient structure in many areas. Major honeycomb use includes the nose radome, wing leading edge, wing trailing edge flaps, engine nacelles and pylons, cargo doors, landing gear fairings, troop compartment floor and aft fuselage panels. Honeycomb sandwich is also used in the wing tips, fixed wing trailing edge structure, pressure bulkheads, and wing-to-fuselage fairings.

Experience with honeycomb in the C-141, where some 6000 sq ft of $\frac{3}{4}$ in. thick material were used, provided much helpful information on sonic fatigue resistance and sealing aspects of glass fabric-plastics honeycomb structures. By way of comparison, the C-5A has the equivalent of 25,000 sq ft, or more than half an acre, averaging 1 in. in thickness distributed throughout the airframe.

## L.  Seals and Gaskets

The cruising speed of the supersonic transport was set not by its structural components, nor by the power available in the design of its engine system, nor by economic considerations—although all of these have a bearing—but by the life temperature limits of the non-metallics on board. The same consideration has a devastating effect on plans for advanced military aircraft—Mach 3 is pretty much the limit and even a long-life Mach 3 aircraft is slightly beyond reach.

In addition to the obvious metal, aircraft has the not so obvious thousands of elastomers in dozens of applications from O-rings to structural sealants. It has adhesives, flexible connectors and tires, lubricants and greases, and all kinds of coatings. And all of these components are temperature-limited and those limits are currently in the 400–600°F regime.

The problem is not only that they break down immediately— though this can be true in some advance concepts—but that sustained and continued use at these temperatures cuts into their operational life. The target is to get these organics to live in the environment. They are extremely difficult to eliminate or to replace with the higher-temperature material families. Elastomeric seal and gasket materials are extremely important because of the extent of their use and the high reliability required.

There are thousands of sealing devices in any high-performance aircraft, buried in the fuel, lubricating, hydraulic, pneumatic, and air-handling systems. These are both static and dynamic seals. Advanced supersonic designs call for elastomeric seal materials capable of performing at temperatures up to 1,200°F and beyond and at pressures up to 5000 psi.

Elastomers used as insulation in electrical systems on Mach 3-plus aircraft must operate in the 1000°F-plus range. Metallic and ceramic alternates have been used with limited success but totally lack the requisite flexibility or ease of fabrication and usually impose a weight penalty.

If high temperature alone were the standard, many of the problems probably would not be as severe. But all of these systems operate over a temperature range and it is the low end, far below zero, coupled to the higher ranges that makes the game so rough.

In many areas the penalties will just have to be accepted. For instance, there is not much hope for high-temperature tires, and hence the wheel well has to be cooled. But sealants cannot be cooled.

Other compromises are possible because of the subsystem itself. Even though the engines operate at higher and higher temperatures, there is a replacement factor. The lubricants can be replaced after every flight—or, in the extreme case, run through once and removed.

## M. Problems in Using More Structural Plastics

In the nonstructural applications, the airplanes practically depend on the use of plastics—examples include seals, insulation, electronics and interior trim. On the structural side, RP has made extensive

inroads but it is targeted that much more will eventually be used due
to different advantages. Roadblocks which are gradually disappearing
for plastics include insufficient standardization, design data, and reliable data. Material reliability and processing limitations exist since
small production runs are made. Government sponsored research programs continue to be in progress to develop improvements in these
areas.

The modern designer must cope with a strong interaction between
new ways of construction and new methods of calculating their
strength. Occasionally the theorist using filamentary construction
indicates the direction for structural design, but, as a rule, the details
of the evaluation of the strength of new structures are worked out
completely only after the vehicles have been flown.

## N.   Filament Wound Structures

Techniques for applying filament winding to the design and construction of aircraft lifting surfaces is being developed by the Columbus Division of North American Aviation, Inc., under a $1 million
contract with the Air Force Materials Laboratory. Aerojet-General
Corporation's Von Karman Center is the major subcontractor. This
two-year effort, to be concluded in May 1968, is one of several being
funded by the Air Force to reduce the whole family of advanced composite materials and processes to production practices. The North
American/Aerojet program is oriented toward the eventual automated
production of aircraft wing and tail load-carrying surfaces.

Charles Tanis, Air Force Material's Laboratory program director,
reports that this program is not merely substituting a new material
for older ones. Rather, emphasis is on designing a wing so the S-994
glass-reinforced plastic is used to its best advantage and the aircraft's
operational stress levels. In practice this means alligning the fibers in
directions where stresses occur with a mandrel-type machine; the
continuous fibers become the strength ingredient of structural spars,
ribs and skin. "Building" a wing by the winding technique will be at
lower cost and easier than conventional manufacturing methods. Static
and dynamic tests are to be conducted on half-length wing sections
developed under the same program. They will have 3 times the
strength and $\frac{1}{3}$ the weight of an all-aluminum wing.

Goodyear Aerospace Corporation has a development contract with
the Army and Navy to produce design data and structural parts.

These programs will basically use present available materials and processing techniques.

## O. Government–Industry Cooperation

Plastics use can be related to the basic aircraft industry philosophy of safety standards and costs. Four things are unique to the economy of the aviation industry. Three of these factors are: the degree of federal regulation, the high cost of handcraftsmanship even on an assembly line, and the value of parts reduction. The one final factor is cutting ownership costs. The cost of aircraft ownership has increased in direct proportion to the ability of a federal agency to regulate the manufacture, operation and end use. Federal regulation is one of the cost increasing factors unique to aviation.

It is the belief of many within the aviation industry that had the automotive industry been regulated to the degree and with the same intent that the Federal Aviation Agency has engaged itself in aviation, the automobile would not exist in its present form and the cost of ownership would be prohibitive. However, as with other industries such as the railroad, government participation is required in order to develop the aircraft industry.

In all fairness to the FAA, it should be stated that it was never the purpose of the FAA to increase the cost of aircraft ownership or reduce the size of the nation's fleet of civil aircraft. This resulted, however, because of a directive of the U.S. Congress that this agency is to act in such a way as to assure the public of the highest degree of safety which aviation industry can be expected to attain. Any regulation by a force outside a firm's direct influence will increase the cost of development and manufacturing, and the greatest, most unpredictable contribution to this cost occurs in the exercise of human judgment on what is considered safe.

## P. Future

While monumental technological breakthroughs are unlikely in the next decade, growth will continue to come through in steady incremental advances limited not by technology, but by economics. The real breakthrough will occur when more use of plastics is made in primary structural applications.

The next five or ten years will see the application of more plastics to such aircraft as commercial jets, military counterinsurgency and medium-high performance aircraft requiring extremely good weathering and humidity resistance. Improvements in structural efficiency and performance are nearly directly proportional to those improvements in the modulus of elasticity of the composite. The composite stiffness properties can be improved both through the matrix material and the fiber material. As we progress into the ten-year range, applications of plastics' temperature resistance up to 600 and 700°F will be required.

The most influentual factor in aircraft's plastic future will be the designers. At this time the materials and process people, and the fabricators are considerably ahead of the designers in the state of the art. The greatest opportunity for progress is in the established industries. These industries are dominated by their past. Any new material, to succeed, must be substantially better. The present growth trend, in spite of these odds, makes plastic's future look very bright.

## IV. VACUUM METALLIZED PLASTICS

Metallized plastics have made major inroads in large markets previously reserved to metals or plated metals. Aluminum is principally used but cadmium or zinc are more economical for thick coatings. New stationary and continuous coating processes will expand the use of many different coatings on different plastics and in different forms for use in different environments, i.e., electrical insulation, packaging of food, tough automotive parts, hardware appliances, outdoor store displays and others.

Coated plastic fibers and fabrics are finding more use in insulation and decorative applications. Heat reflecting glass now produced by sandwiching a metallized transparent plastic film between glass panes will be used in windows. Also magnetic tapes may potentially be produced by continuous vacuum coating in the future.

It is reported that over 550 production facilities in U.S.A. coat more than 2 billion plastic parts per year at approximately 3 cents per square inch of surface. Progress in plastic coating can perhaps be compared to the U.S.A. market for high vacuum hardware. In 1964 sales were $68 million with sales expected to double by 1975. Products to be processed will be in the billions of dollars.

## V. CERAMIC PLASTICS (16)

Adaptation of available heat-resistant materials, namely ceramics, to conventional structural components of hypersonic weapon systems has generated a new philosophy in materials technology. These ceramic materials demonstrate outstanding thermal and chemical stability, but their brittle nature often becomes a limiting factor in their use. Solid state research is currently revealing factors important to the strength behavior of brittle materials. However, the problem of fabricating large complex aerodynamic shapes from these materials is ever present.

The strength behavior and the other mechanical properties of a brittle material are related to the microstructural traits, and they in turn are related to the processing technique. The effects of microstructure on the strength of polycrystalline oxide systems have been investigated by many. Their results did not agree nor did they include variables of processing. The present state of ceramic processing is insufficient to provide a controlled microstructure. As a result, the forming techniques incorporated for a particular material system establishes the potential utility.

A forming technique utilizing a low temperature-low pressure approach normally associated with plastic molding compounds has been exploited for the forming of ceramic materials for aerospace structural applications. The basic material system is composed of an electrical grade alumina in a silicone matrix which is formed into a close-tolerance green body. This tolerance is observed throughout the final sintering operation at 2500°F. The plastic molding process offers two main advantages over conventional ceramic forming processes: (*1*) low temperature-low pressure (325°F–300 psi) forming, and (*2*) the ability to machine the component with conventional tooling to close tolerances prior to sintering. Processing variables, sintered microstructure, and mechanical test data are discussed.

The formation of a complex structural component utilizing the refractory ceramic materials is generally accomplished by pressure forming, followed or coupled with a sintering operation. Aerospace structures of interest include radomes, leading edges, and other hardware components. Considerable effort has been expended on a variety of techniques for forming alumina ceramic shapes for these applications, because sintered alumina exhibits the highest fracture strength of the refractory oxides.

The key to a low temperature-pressure plastic-molding process is the organic binder and its compatibility with the ceramic filler. The silicone family of resins have this compatibility. In addition the resin system must have the following:

*1.* Sufficient plasticity to flow during molding cycle.

2. Proper set in the mold allowing easy removal of the formed body without distortion.

3. The resin must outgas properly during presinter yet retain sufficient strength to maintain dimensional stability throughout the firing operation.

The silicone resins have demonstrated resistance to high and low temperatures, inertness, unusual surface properties, and release, or antistick properties. The silicones have found numerous applications in conjunction with ceramic materials due to these inherent characteristics. A siloxane resin has been developed capable of adaptation to the silicone—ceramic system. Alumina, which is inert and has a melting point in excess of 3700°F, was selected as the filler material. The $Al_2O_3$ utilized is an electronic grade material. The particle size is not extremely critical although the data generated herein was obtained using $-200+325$ mesh particles. The alumina was calcined above 900°F prior to mixing.

## A. Molding

The $Al_2O_3$ particles are mixed with the siloxane to form a silicone-ceramic molding blend. A catalyst to aid in the curing of the resin and a mold release agent are added to the mixture. The mixture may contain from 1 to 30 wt% of the siloxane resin, 99 to 70% of the $Al_2O_3$ filler, a small percentage of PbO as the catalyst, and calcium stearate as the mold-release agent. The siloxane $Al_2O_3$ ratio is established from the requirements of the plastic molding process. Consideration is given to the component size, expected flow range, molding temperature, and molding pressure. The mixture is allowed to dry and then granulated in preparation for the plastic molding operation.

Preforming is recommended for most plastic forming procedures utilizing thermoplastic molding systems. The preforming operation offers the following advantages:

1. The ability to weigh a predetermined charge.
2. Much easier to handle, less bulk.
3. Simpler to preheat using the high-frequency generator.

The granular silicone-alumina molding material is preformed under ambient temperature conditions at pressures of from 3000 to 5000 psi. The preform configurations are dependent upon the shape of the final molded component. Upon the application of pressure, bulk volume is reduced by 10 to 30%. Pressures in excess of 500 psi are not desirable for preforming because of the possibility of delamination upon heating.

Preheating of the thermoplastic preforms prior to molding offers the following advantages:

*1.* Shorter mold cycle
*2.* Better flow characteristics
*3.* Increased homogenization of resin-particle mixture
*4.* Reduced forming costs.

The importance of the preheat cycle on the strength characteristics of the molded component was determined with a high-frequency generator (70–100 Mc). Silicone compounds usually require longer preheat time in the high-frequency equipment than other organic plastics due to their low dissipation factors. The silicone-alumina preform slabs are preheated only until they have the consistency of putty. This occurs when the internal temperature is between 120° and 180°F which corresponds to 90 to 180 seconds in the high-frequency generator. The preheated material is transferred directly into the mold cavity for plastic forming. Control of the preheat cycle is of utmost importance because the thermoplastic material will lose its flow characteristics if overexposed to heat and will form superficial blisters.

The silicone-alumina preforms are formed utilizing either transfer- or compression-molding techniques. The transfermolding process is favored because of the advantages offered by the preheat cycle.

Efficient production practice requires removal of the molded component from the hot mold after the shortest allowable press cure cycle which will produce a blister, crack, warp-free rigid part. Molding time is related directly to the thickness of the component. Problems arise from having the molding temperature too high or too low. Increasing the molding pressure increases the density of the sintered component.

One of the primary objectives of the molding technique is to form a configuration with close dimensional tolerance. The silicone-alumina molded component can be machined in the green state with conventional tools prior to presintering.

## B. Sintering

The presintering of the molded component involves the conversion of the silicone resin system into silica. The decomposition rate of the silicone resin is related to the size and thickness of the molded component. A normal cycle involves heating to 950°F over an extended time period to ensure removal of all volatiles prior to conversion to silica.

The parts retain their precise shapes without special furnace fixtures. The extended presintering cycle assures outgassing at such a rate that no bloating occurs, and that enough strength is imparted to the body during the silicone decomposition to insure dimensional stability.

## VI. PLASTICS BEARINGS, GASKETS, PACKINGS AND SEALS

Excessive use is made of many different plastics in bearings. Different combinations of properties are available to permit meeting different functional requirements, ranging from self lubricating to operating in extreme high or low temperatures. Plastics are also used as composites; in combination with metals and other materials. Inherent properties which can be changed by varying the plastics and be useful include low coefficient of friction, corrosion resistance, light weight, color, intricate design, low cost, etc.

Gaskets, packings and seals made of plastics, similar to the bearing comments, find use in many different applications.

## VII. PLASTIC GEARS

The main plastic gear materials are: acetal, nylon, polycarbonate, modified polystyrene, and filled phenolic. Other materials are used such as phenoxy and different reinforced thermoplastics. The advantages in their use are numerous; however there are some limitations which must be considered in designing with plastics. Full knowledge of the properties of the contemplated material as related to the intended gear environment must be known (19).

Plastic gears have been used extensively in commercial applications. In many cases they have been found to be functionally superior to their metal counterparts, and produced at lower manufacturing and operating costs. Successful results have been achieved with plastic gears in: speedometers, windshield wipers, cameras, clocks, appliances, business machines, power tools, small gasoline engines, lawn sprinklers, can openers, slide projectors, pumps, and counter components.

In specific commercial application, a plastic material has been used for gears in an inboard marine engine, which provided an economical gear-driven accessory group. The selection was made because of the material's corrosion resistance and its resistance to petroleum products at temperatures in the vicinity of 180–185°F. The use of a thermoplastic gear material in an electric can opener, to replace a canvas-based phenolic gear (machined), provided a cost savings of 25%. Plastic gears used in a valve drive were satisfactory under load at an operating temperature of 180°F. They yielded good fatigue resistance, low friction, and strength while providing an economical unit. In other applications such as chart drives and indicators, the economies of injection molding made possible the production of intricate, precisely dimensional parts at a lower cost than machined gears. Utilization of plastic gears in business machines is widely practiced. Here the low wear factor, quietness of operation, and economical production are the main reasons for their selection.

## VIII. TEMPERATURE CONVERSION TABLE

| °F | °C | °K | °R | °F | °C | °K | °R |
|---|---|---|---|---|---|---|---|
| 0 | —18 | 255 | 459 | 1300 | 704 | 977 | 1759 |
| 50 | 10 | 283 | 509 | 1350 | 732 | 1005 | 1809 |
| 100 | 38 | 311 | 559 | 1400 | 760 | 1033 | 1859 |
| 150 | 66 | 339 | 609 | 1450 | 788 | 1061 | 1909 |
| 200 | 93 | 366 | 659 | 1500 | 816 | 1089 | 1959 |
| 250 | 121 | 394 | 709 | 1550 | 843 | 1116 | 2009 |
| 300 | 149 | 422 | 759 | 1600 | 871 | 1144 | 2059 |
| 350 | 177 | 450 | 809 | 1650 | 899 | 1172 | 2109 |
| 400 | 204 | 477 | 859 | 1700 | 927 | 1200 | 2159 |
| 450 | 232 | 505 | 909 | 1750 | 954 | 1227 | 2209 |
| 500 | 260 | 533 | 959 | 1800 | 982 | 1255 | 2259 |
| 550 | 288 | 561 | 1009 | 1850 | 1010 | 1283 | 2309 |
| 600 | 316 | 589 | 1059 | 1900 | 1038 | 1311 | 2359 |
| 650 | 343 | 616 | 1109 | 1950 | 1066 | 1339 | 2409 |
| 700 | 371 | 644 | 1159 | 2000 | 1093 | 1366 | 2459 |
| 750 | 399 | 672 | 1209 | 2050 | 1121 | 1394 | 2509 |
| 800 | 426 | 699 | 1259 | 2100 | 1149 | 1422 | 2559 |
| 850 | 454 | 727 | 1309 | 2150 | 1177 | 1450 | 2609 |
| 900 | 482 | 755 | 1359 | 2200 | 1204 | 1477 | 2659 |
| 950 | 510 | 783 | 1409 | 2250 | 1232 | 1505 | 2709 |
| 1000 | 538 | 811 | 1459 | 2300 | 1260 | 1533 | 2759 |
| 1050 | 566 | 839 | 1509 | 2350 | 1288 | 1561 | 2809 |
| 1100 | 593 | 866 | 1559 | 2400 | 1316 | 1589 | 2859 |
| 1150 | 621 | 894 | 1609 | 2450 | 1343 | 1616 | 2909 |
| 1200 | 649 | 922 | 1659 | 2500 | 1371 | 1644 | 2959 |
| 1250 | 677 | 950 | 1709 | 2550 | 1399 | 1672 | 3009 |

| °F | °C | °K | °R | °F | °C | °K | °R |
|------|------|------|------|------|------|------|------|
| 2600 | 1427 | 1700 | 3059 | 3300 | 1816 | 2089 | 3759 |
| 2650 | 1455 | 1728 | 3109 | 3350 | 1843 | 2116 | 3809 |
| 2700 | 1482 | 1755 | 3159 | 3400 | 1871 | 2144 | 3859 |
| 2750 | 1510 | 1783 | 3209 | 3450 | 1899 | 2172 | 3909 |
| 2800 | 1538 | 1811 | 3259 | 3500 | 1927 | 2200 | 3959 |
| 2850 | 1566 | 1839 | 3309 | 3550 | 1954 | 2227 | 4009 |
| 2900 | 1593 | 1866 | 3359 | 3600 | 1982 | 2255 | 4059 |
| 2950 | 1621 | 1894 | 3409 | 3650 | 2010 | 2283 | 4109 |
| 3000 | 1649 | 1922 | 3459 | 3700 | 2038 | 2311 | 4159 |
| 3050 | 1677 | 1950 | 3509 | 3750 | 2066 | 2339 | 4209 |
| 3100 | 1704 | 1977 | 3559 | 3800 | 2093 | 2366 | 4259 |
| 3150 | 1732 | 2005 | 3609 | 3850 | 2121 | 2394 | 4309 |
| 3200 | 1760 | 2033 | 3659 | 3900 | 2149 | 2422 | 4359 |
| 3250 | 1788 | 2061 | 3709 | 3950 | 2177 | 2450 | 4409 |

## IX. SELECTION OF PLASTICS

The large increase in the number of sophisticated plastics, and the fine points of their capabilities, place a greater responsibility on the product designer who must specify the materials that are suitable for the application. Subsequent economic analyses will determine which of these materials will be selected for production (20).

In general, it must be remembered that selection of the proper material requires analysis of the good points and the weak points of each material considered for the job. No one material will possess all of the qualities desired but none of the weak qualities. Undesirable characteristics must be compensated for in the product design.

There is a workable elimination approach to the selection of the right plastics material which will narrow the field to a limited choice. In this case, the final material selection problem becomes one of field testing under actual use conditions to prove the endurance and stability of the product.

In designing, consideration must be given to all environments to which the item is subjected. It is extremely important that the proper design criteria be utilized when plastic materials are being considered for use. Directly related to the design criteria are certain material characteristics that are most important because of the long term storage and temperature requirements. As an example for some plastics it very well may be the limiting factor in their use. When a material is subjected to a load an initial deformation or creep will occur. With time this deformation becomes constant and is referred

TABLE 17-11. Types and Properties of Plastics Bearing Materials (17)

| Material | Advantages | Disadvantages |
|---|---|---|
| Nylon | High abrasion resistance, toughness and reliability; good conformability; reduces vibration | Absorbs water and has low thermal conductivity and high thermal expansion |
| Acetal | Very low friction coefficients which are same for both static and dynamic conditions; inexpensive; resists water and most solvents | Low heat resistance; generous clearances required |
| Fluorocarbon | Excellent resistance to heat, water and chemicals; very low friction coefficients; easily filled to provide special properties | Relatively expensive; low thermal conductivity and high expansion; some types cannot be molded |
| Phenolic | High resiliency and resistance to severe shock and impact; low wear rates | Absorbs water; low thermal conductivity in large sizes |
| Chlorinated polyether | Excellent dimensional stability; high water and chemical resistance | Bearing properties not as good as most other plastics |
| Polycarbonate | Close tolerances and good dimensional stability; good resistance to heat and impact | High coefficient of friction |
| High-molecular-weight polyethylene | Excellent impact resistance and good wear properties | Relatively difficult to fabricate |

to as cold flow. Creep characteristics are influenced by the applied stress and temperature. With regard to plastics, thermoplastics are more subject to creep than thermosetting materials (21). This cold flow example is reviewed in various sections of this book. The contents of this book actually provides industry with many, if not most, of the important parameters to consider when designing or evaluating the variables which can develop with plastics.

## X. CHRONOLOGY OF PLASTICS

1820   Era of synthetic organic chemistry starts

1820   Hancock invented prototype of modern rubber processing mill.

1823   Liebig and Wohler made isomerism of cyanates and fulminates.

1825   Faraday discovered benzene and hydrocarbon isomerism.

1826   Aniline discovered.

1826   Faraday provided basis for elastomers or synthetic rubbers development by establishing the empirical formula $C_5H_8$ for natural rubber.

1828   Dumas explained Etherin Theory where organic compounds are additional products of ethylene.

1828   Wohler produced urea from ammonium cyanate.

1830   The Radical Theory explained where radicals are capable of separate existence.

1831   Earliest decription of styrene reported.

1832   Liebig and Wohler decribe the benzoyl radical.

1833   Liebig and Dumas explained that organic chemistry is the chemistry of radicals.

1834   Liebig first isolated melamine.

1835   Pelouze nitrated cellose.

1835   Regnault prepared vinyl choride.

1839   Goodyear discovered vulcanization of rubber.

1844   Connection broken between organic and inorganic compounds.

1845   Bewley design extruder for gutta-percha tubes.

1845   Hoffmann obtained aniline and benzene from coal-tar.

1845   Nitration of cellulose first described.

1845   Schonbein nitrated cellulose in the presence of sulfuric acid.

1847   Berzelius made first polyester.

1847   Nitration of benzene occurred.

1848   Wurtz discovers amines and their relation to ammonia.

TABLE 17-12.   A Summary of Gasket Materials (18)

| Material | Max service temp, °F | Properties |
|---|---|---|
| Rubber (straight) | | |
| Natural | 225 | Good mechanical properties. Impervious to water. Fair to good resistance to acids, alkalis. Poor resistance to oils, gasoline. Poor weathering, aging properties |
| Styrene-butadiene (SBR) | 250 | Better water resistance than natural rubber. Fair to good resistance to acids, alkalis. Unsuitable with gasoline, oils and solvents |
| Butyl | 300 | Very good resistance to water, alkalis, many acids. Poor resistance to oils, gasoline, most solvents |
| Nitrile | 300 | Very good water resistance. Excellent resistance to oils, gasoline. Fair to good resistance to acids, alkalis |
| Polysulfide | 150 | Excellent resistance to oils, gasoline, aliphatic and aromatic hydrocarbon solvents. Very good water resistance, good alkali resistance, fair acid resistance. Poor mechanical properties |
| Neoprene | 250 | Excellent mechanical properties. Good resistance to nonaromatic petroleum, fatty oils, solvents (except aromatic, chlorinated or ketone types). Good water and alkali resistance. Fair acid resistance |
| Silicone | 600 | Excellent heat resistance. Fair water resistance; poor resistance to steam at high pressures. Fair to good acid, alkali resistance. Poor (except fluorosilicone rubber) resistance to oils, solvents |
| Acrylic | 450 | Good heat resistance but poor cold resistance. Good resistance to oils, aliphatic and aromatic hydrocarbons. Poor resistance to water, alkalis, some acids |
| Hypalon | 250 | Excellent resistance to oxidizing chemicals, ozone, weathering. Relatively good resistance to oils, grease. Poor resistance to aromatic or chlorinated hydrocarbons. Good mechanical properties |

| Material | Temp. (°F) | Properties |
|---|---|---|
| Viton fluoroelastomer | 450 | Can be used at high temperatures with many fuels, lubricants, hydraulic fluids, solvents. Highly resistant to ozone, weathering. Good mechanical properties |
| **Asbestos** | | |
| Compressed asbestos-rubber sheet | To 700 | Large number of combinations available; properties vary widely depending on materials used |
| Asbestos-rubber woven sheet | To 250 | Same as above |
| Asbestos-rubber (better addition process) | 400 | Same as above |
| Asbestos composites | To 1000 | Same as above |
| Asbestos-TFE | 500 | Combines heat resistance and sealing properties of asbestos with chemical resistance of TFE |
| **Plastics** | | |
| TFE (solid) | 500 | Excellent resistance to almost all chemicals and solvents. Good heat resistance; exceptionally good low temperature properties. Relatively low compressibility and resilience |
| TFE (filled) | To 500 | Selectively improved mechanical and physical properties. However, fillers may lower resistance to specific chemicals |
| TFE composites | To 500 | Chemical and heat resistance comparable to solid TFE. Inner gasket material provides better resiliency and deformability |
| CFE | 350 | Higher cost than TFE. Better chemical resistance than most other gasket materials, although not quite as good as TFE |
| Vinyl | 212 | Good compressibility, resiliency. Resistant to water, oils, gasoline, and many acids and alkalis. Relatively narrow temperature range |
| Polyethylene | 150 | Resists most solvents. Poor heat resistance |

TABLE 17-13.  Packing and Sealing Materials (18)

| Material | Max service temp, °F | Important properties |
|---|---|---|
| Rubber (straight) | To 600 | Mainly used for ring-type seals, although some types are available as spiral packings |
| Rubber composites | | |
| Cotton-reinforced | 350 | High strength. Chemical resistance depends on type of rubber used; however, most types are noted for high resistance to water, aqueous solutions |
| Asbestos-reinforced | 450 | High strength combined with good heat resistance |
| Asbestos | | |
| Plain, braided asbestos | 500 | Heat resistance combined with resistance to water, brine, oil, many chemicals. Can be reinforced with wire |
| Impregnated asbestos | To 750 | Environmental properties vary widely depending on type of asbestos and impregnant used. Neoprene-cemented type resists hot oils, gasoline and solvents. Oil and wax-impregnated type resists caustics. Wax-impregnated blue asbestos type has high acid resistance. TFE-impregnated type has good all-around chemical resistance |
| Asbestos composites | To 1200 | End properties vary widely depending on secondary material used |
| TFE | To 500 | Available in many forms, all of which have high chemical resistance |
| Carbon-graphite | 700 | Good bearing and self-lubricating properties. Good resistance to chemicals, heat |
| Organic fiber | | |
| Flax | 300 | Good water resistance |
| Jute | 300 | Good water resistance |
| Ramie | 300 | Good resistance to water, brine, cold oil |
| Cotton | 300 | Good resistance to water, alcohol, dilute aqueous solutions |
| Rayon | 300 | Good resistance to water, dilute aqueous solutions |

TABLE 17-14.  Properties Chart: Gear Materials, Injection Moldable (19)

| Property | Units | Poly-carbonate | Polyamide (6/6) | Acetal | ABS polymer |
|---|---|---|---|---|---|
| Impact strength (per in. of notch) | ft lbs | 12–16 | 1.0–3.6 | 1.4–2.3 | 207–10.0 |
| Tensile yield strength | psi$\times 10^3$ | 8–9 | 8.5–11.8 | 10.0 | 2.5–9.0 |
| Tensile modulus | psi$\times 10^3$ | 345 | 260–400 | 410 | 100–410 |
| Elongation | % | 75 | 60–300 | 15–75 | 10–140 |
| Flexural strength | psi$\times 10^3$ | 13.5 | 8–14 | 14.1 | 3.6–13.5 |
| Flexural modulus | psi$\times 10^3$ | 340 | 210–410 | 410 | 240–450 |
| Compressive strength | psi$\times 10^3$ | 12.5 | 7.2–13 | 18 | 2.5–11.0 |
| Compressive modulus | psi$\times 10^3$ | 345 | — | — | 200–370 |
| Heat distortion temperature | °F (264 psi) | 270–280 | 150 | 212 | 165–225 |
| Heat resistance (continuous) | °F | 250–270 | 270–300 | 185–250 | 140–250 |
| Coefficient of thermal expansion | °F$\times 10^{-5}$ | 3.9 | 5.55–8.33 | 4.5 | 3.33–7.22 |
| Thermal conductivity | BTU/hr/ ft²/°F/in. | 1.35 | 1.52–1.70 | 1.61 | 0.41–2.52 |
| Volume resistivity | ohm-cm | $1.7\times 10^{17}$ | $4.5\times 10^{13}$ | $6\times 10^{14}$ | $10^{13}$–$10^{16}$ |
| Dielectric constant | (60 cycles) | 3.17 | 4.0–7.6 | 3.7 | 2.7–4.8 |
| Dielectric strength (ST ⅛ in.) | volts/mil | 400 | 385 | 465 | 310–410 |
| Power factor (60 cpm) | | 0.0009 | 0.014–0.05 | 0.004 | 0.004–0.034 |
| Arc resistance | sec | 120 | 130–140 | 129 (burns) | 71–87 |
| Water absorption 24 hrs | % | 0.15 | 1.5 | 0.4 | 0.1–0.3 |
| Rockwell hardness | | M80–R118 | R108–R118 | M94–R118 | R30–R118 |
| Flammability | | self-exting. | self-exting. | slow burning | slow burning |
| Specific gravity | | 1.2 | 1.14 | 1.425 | 0.99–1.10 |
| Mold shrinkage | in./in. | 0.005–0.007 | 0.012–0.030 | 0.015–0.035 | 0.003–0.008 |
| Color possibilities | | unlimited | limited | limited | limited |

TABLE 17-15.  Gear Materials—Application Comparison (19)

| Material | Recommended use | Material properties | Limiting factors |
|---|---|---|---|
| Acetal | Maximum fatigue life requirements<br>Varying humidity conditions at elevated temperatures | High tensile strength<br>High impact strength<br>Very high fatigue resistance<br>Creep resistant<br>Low moisture absorption<br>High chemical stability [1]<br>High heat resistance<br>Wear resistant<br>Low coefficient of friction | None of significance |
| Nylon (polyamide 6/6) | General purpose gears when dimensional requirements are not critical | High tensile strength<br>High impact strength<br>Good fatigue resistance<br>Extremely wear resistant<br>Extreme toughness<br>Low coefficient of friction | Poor dimensional stability [b]<br>High moisture absorption<br>Low heat distortion temperature |
| Polycarbonate | High impact, intermittent loads (not suitable in cyclic stress applications)<br>Light loading applications | High tensile strength<br>Very high impact strength<br>Extremely creep resistant<br>Very low moisture absorption<br>Very high dimensional stability [b]<br>High heat distortion temperature<br>High heat resistance | Low fatigue resistance |
| Polystyrene [2] (modified) | Light load, low temperature applications | Very high impact strength<br>Creep resistant<br>Very low moisture absorbtion<br>Very high dimensional stability [a] | Low fatigue resistance |

| | | | |
|---|---|---|---|
| Phenolic (fabric filled) | Heavy duty, large size gears | Very high tensile strength<br>High impact strength<br>Good fatigue properties<br>Extremely creep resistant<br>High dimensional stability<br>Very high heat distortion temperature<br>Very high heat resistance<br>Wear resistant | Lack of versatility in design when molded |
| Nylon-glass filled<br>Polycarbonate-glass filled | | | |

Glass reinforcement improves the physical and mechanical properties. Of particular interest is the high increase in heat distortion temperature and reduction in moisture absorption of Nylon which improves these limiting factors of the unfilled material.

a Varying humidity conditions.
b Limited data available.

TABLE 17-16. Advantages and Limitations of Plastic Gears (19)

| Advantages | Limitations |
| --- | --- |
| Economy in manufacture (injection molding) | Low load carrying capacity |
| | Low high-temperature-limit |
| Light weight | High coefficient of thermal expansion |
| Ability to dampen shock or vibration | Low accuracy of manufacture |
| Operation with little or no lubrication | |
| Low coefficient of friction | |
| Low wear factor | |
| Silent operation | |
| Resistance to corrosive chemicals | |
| Less critical tolerance requirements | |

1850 A. P. Critchlow developed shellac compounds molding daguerreotype cases and started plastic molding in the U.S.A.: Prophylactic Brush Co., Florence, Mass. (and continues to be in business).

1859 Butlerov decribed formaldehyde polymers.

1859 Chlorination of rubber produced hard plastic.

1860 Berthelot and de St. Gilles prepared hydrolysis of esters.

1860 Greville Williams isolated isoprene by the dry distillation of natural rubber.

1862 Baldwin's compression mold patented.

1862 Display of Parkesine in London.

1865 Parke's main patent for Parkesine process.

1865 Schutzenberger acetylated cellulose.

1866 Berthelot synthesized styrene.

1868 Celluloid, first pyroxylin plastic (Hyatt).

1870 Establishment of Hyatt's Albany Dental Plate Co. (later to become Celluloid Manufacturing Co.).

1870 Hyatt's basis celluloid patent issued.

1872 Baumann reported polymerization of vinyl chloride.

1872 Bayer reported reaction between phenols and aldehydes.

1872 'Celluloid' registered as trademark by Hyatt.

1872 Hyatt Brothers patented first plastics injection molding machine.

1873 Caspery and Tollens prepared various acrylate esters.

1878 Hyatt introduced first multicavity injection mold.

1879 Francis Shaw Ltd. produced the first commerical screw type extruder in England.

1879 Gray granted patent for first screw extruder.

1879   Polymerization of isoprene into rubber occurred.

1880   John Royle & Sons, Inc. produced the first commercial screw type extruder in the U.S. (processed rubber tubing).

1880   Kahlbaum polymerized methylacrylate.

1884   Chardonnet produced first artifical silk.

1884   Holzer isolated urea-formaldehyde condensation products.

1886   Bayer described constitution of benzene.

1890   John Royle & Sons, Inc. produced the first screw type extruder for wire and cable rubber insulations.

1892   Cross and Bevan developed viscose silk.

1892   Shaw Insulator Co. founded in Newark, N.J.

1894   Cross and Bevan produced industrial process for manufacture of cellulose acetate.

1897   Euler made isoprene synthetically.

1898   Ehrlich introduces organometallic compounds.

1898   Einhorn described polycarbonates.

1898   Haskel invented rubber-wound-core ball (typical present-day golf ball).

1898   Pechmann probably first to report on polymer from diazomethane in ether.

1899   Continuous cellulose nitrate film first made by casting on a polished drum.

1899   Kipping began research into organo-silicon compounds.

1899   Kritsche and Spitteler patented casein plastic and established Galalith.

1899   Smith published patent on phenol-formaldehyde composition.

1901   Rohm awarded doctorate for his thesis on acrylate polymers.

1901   Smith discovered alkyd resins by reaction of glycerol and phthalic anhydride.

1904   Kipping's investigation of silanes was the basis for the development of silicone chemistry.

1905   Miles prepared secondary cellulose acetate.

1907   Aniline rubber accelerators produced.

1907   Tech-Art Plastics Co. (Loando Rubber Co.) molded first phenolic plastics compound.

1909   Baekeland granted his "Heat and Pressure" patent for phenolic resins.

1909   Cold molded bitumin, phenolic and cement-asbestos introduced.

1911   Burton developed process for petroleum cracking.

1912   First emulsion polymerization patent applied to isoprene.

1912   Klatte synthesized vinyl chloride and vinyl acetate from acetylene.

1912   Ostromislenski patented polymerization of vinyl chloride.

1915   First production of synthetic rubber (methyl rubber).

1916   R. Kemp applied for patent on structural reinforced plastics elements; patent 1,393,541 issued in 1921.

1918   John patented urea-formaldehyde condensation resins.

1919   Casein introduced.

1919   Eichengrun produced cellulose acetate molding powder.

1919   Percy B. Crossley developed glass-bonded mica.

1920   Era of polymer chemistry synthesis starts.

1921   Eichengrun designed modern injection molding machine.

1921   Rayon introduced commercially.

1922   Staudinger began work on macromolecules.

1922   R. Kemp's patent 1,435,244 on producing an all reinforced plastics airplane.

1923   Polysulfide introduced commercially.

1924   Casein introduced commercially.

1924   Polyvinyl alcohol discovered and prepared.

1925   Nitrocellulose lacquers introduced commercially.

1926   Alkyd introduced.

1926   Analine-formaldehyde introduced in U.S.

1926   Eckert and Ziegler marketed plastics injection molding machine.

1926   Fisher-Tropsch catalyst developed.

1926   Shaw Insulator Co. invented transfer molding in order to provide a solution to a critical thermoset compression molding problem involving a firing pin for use by US Navy. This giant step in molding permitted over 150 worldwide licenses to use the process. It can be said what Ford gave to the automobile, Shaw gave to plastics.

1927   Cellulose acetate introduced commercially.

1927   Polyacrylate introduced commercially.

1927   Polyvinyl chloride introduced in U.S.

1928   Carothers started his research on polymers and polymerization.

1928   L. E. Shaw patented transfer molding.

1928   Urea formaldehyde introduced commercially.

1928   Urea-formaldehyde molding powder (Beetle) introduced commercially.

1928   Vapor-phase cracking introduced commercially.

1928   Vinyl chloride and vinyl acetate copolymerized.

1929   British Plastics Federation founded.

1929 Industrial research on styrene and polystyrene initiated in Germany.

1929 Urea-formaldehyde introduced.

1929 Shaw Insulator Co. produced first (24 cavity) automatic unscrewing mold (produced thermoset mechanical pencils). Pinpointing gating was started; more recently this type gating was applied to injection molding.

1930 Injection molding of polystyrene started in Germany.

1930 Polysulfides introduced by Thiokol Corp.

1930 Semon plasticized polyvinyl chloride.

1931 Bauer and Hill separately began investigating esters of methacrylic acid.

1931 Carothers described condensation of polymers.

1931 Carothers discovered neoprene.

1931 DuPont manufactured an elastomer based on chloroprene, named DuPrene, later renamed neoprene.

1931 Hyde began research on organo-silicon polymers.

1931 Initiation of ICI research leading to high pressure polyethylene.

1932 Buna N (acrylonitrile-butadiene) and Buna S (styrene-butadiene) developed in Germany (based on World War I preliminary developments).

1932 M. W. Perrin and J. C. Swallow, ICI of England, recommended work be conducted on the effect of high pressures in chemical reactions.

1932 DuPrene (neoprene) was commercially produced at DuPont's Chambers Works, Deepwater, N.J.

1932 Polyester developments occur.

1932 Screw pre-plasticization in injection molding patented.

1933 Crawford devised commercial synthesis for methyl methacrylate.

1933 ICI produced a minute amount of solid polymer of ethylene during research into the behavior of certain gases under extreme pressures.

1933 Ellis patented unsaturated polyester resins.

1933 Ethyl cellulose introduced commercially.

1933 Norddeutschen Seekabelwerke AG Patent on extruded film.

1933 Polyamides developments occur.

1933 Research on styrene monomer and polystyrene began at Dow Chemical Co.

1934 Fawcett and Gibson polymerized ethylene under high pressure.

1934 Polyvinyl chloride introduced commercially.

1935 Ethyl cellulose introduced in U.S.

1935 Ferngren and Kopitke built first modern hot-melt blow-molding machine (later Plax Corp.).

1935 Henkel made melamine-formaldehyde resins.

1935 Plasticized PVC introduced in U.S.

1935 Polysulphide elastomers became commercially available.

1935 Staudinger proposed three phase addition polymerization process.

1935 Troester produced first extruder designed for thermoplastics.

1935 Vinyl butyral introduced commercially.

1935 Vinyl polymer developments occur.

1936 Acrylic introduced in U.S.

1936 Name was changed from DuPrene to neoprene (name used generically) December 11, 1936.

1936 Polystyrene introduced commercially.

1936 Polyvinyl acetate introduced in U.S.

1937 Automatic compression molding introduced commercially.

1937 Butadiene-acrylonitrile (Nitrile, Buna N) and Styrene-butadiene (GR-Buna S) introduced in Germany (1940 in U.S.).

1937 Imperial Chemical Industries Ltd. Patent 471,590 on high pressure polyethylene.

1937 Polyamide introduced commercially.

1937 Polyurethanes first produced.

1937 The Society of the Plastics Industry was incorporated.

1937 Vinyl copolymer introduced commercially.

1938 Cellulose acetate butyrate introduced.

1938 Clement D. Shaw patent covering molding of thermoplastics and thermosets, including automatic injection.

1938 Colombo and Pasquetti constructed twin-screw extruder for plastics.

1938 Melamine introduced commercially.

1938 Nylon (polyamide).

1938 Observations of polytetrafluoroethylene (PTFE) were made.

1938 Plax started commercial blow molding of acetate and styrene.

1938 Polyethylene development occurs.

1938 Polymerization of caprolactam occurred (nylon 6).

1938 Polystyrene or styrene.

1938 Polyvinyl acetal introduced in U.S.

1939 First patent (in Germany) on epoxy.

1939 Melamine-formaldehyde introduced.

1939 Polyvinylidene chloride introduced commercially.

1939 Styrene based plastics became commercial.

1939   Based on the submarine cable requirement, ICI erected a plant with a 200,000 pound per year capacity. Ethylene for the plant was then made by dehydration of alcohol.

1939   Submarine cables with PE from the ICI plant to be used in linking England and France were not installed until after World War II. With the start of the war, all PE was immediately used for flexible high frequency cables in ground and airborne radar equipment. Plant capacity was expanded to meet war requirements.

1939   First significant marketing effort in the U.S. by DuPont resulted in first commercial use of PE in this country. Coaxial cable insulated with polyethylene was installed by Bell Telephone between Baltimore and Washington in 1940. It is still in use today.

1940   The first PE prepared by Union Carbide Corporation, independent of ICI, was polymerized by high pressure synthesis in a continuous tubular process by Dr. C. L. Strother, Tonawanda Laboratory. This PE, compared to that of ICI, had a higher flow point and much narrower distribution of molecular weight. Britain's was not satisfactory by itself so it was combined with polyisobutylene.

1940   Union Carbide, when examining ICI's PE in regard to its electrical properties, considered it useful primarily in film form.

1940   Polyethylene introduced commercially.

1940   Production of polyvinyl chloride in England.

1941   Butadiene copolymer introduced commercially.

1941   Rubber Reserve Co. (U.S. Government) initiated synthetic rubber industry of U.S.A.

1941   Society of Plastics Engineers founded.

1941   Urethane-polyester type introduced in Germany.

1941   Whinfield and Dickson invented polyethylene glycol terephthalate (Terylene).

1942   Dow Corning made silicone industrially.

1942   Plax first blow molded polyethylene bottle.

1942   Polyester introduced commercially.

1942   At the request of the U.S. Navy's Bureau of Ships, DuPont erected a 1-million pound plant in Belle, West Virginia based on the licensed ICI process.

1942   Union Carbide's pilot plant permitted the Navy to give a similar production contract to Union Carbide. The plant was built in South Charlestown, West Virginia with initial capacity of 1.4 million pounds per year.

1942   I. G. Farben, Germany began PE manufacture on a small scale.

1942   Extrusion equipment available in U.S. could only operate at low and high temperatures permitting use of low and high molecular weight PE. Useful experience had been gained in handling PVC in long barrel and high capacity machines.

1942   Production of polyethylene started.

1943   Castan's patent issued on epoxy.

1943   Fluorocarbon introduced.

1943   Pilot plant production started of PTFE.

1943   Polyisoprene introduced in U.S.

1943   Urethane-polyester amide introduced in England.

1945   Cellulose propionate introduced.

1945   First squeeze-spray bottle.

1945   Tetrafluoroethylene introduced commercially.

1946   Organosols and plastisols introduced commercially.

1946   Polyurethane elastomers introduced.

1946   Shaw Insulator Co. molded the first polyethylene hinges, advancing state-of-the-art in using rubber self-hinge closures and developed first thermosetting major mold automation design.

1946   Shaw Insulator Co. provide first major mold automation design. A Matam Corp. iron handle revolutionized the iron handle business. Prior process involved slow, split cavity thermoset compression, manually-operated presses. New process used transfer pots, primary and secondary ejection, side cylinders etc,

1947   DuPont initiated research program of polyformaldehyde.

1947   Epoxy introduced commercially.

1947   Polyacrylates introduced in U.S.

1948   Chlorotrifluorethylene introduced commercially.

1948   Process for extruding polyethylene onto paper was developed by DuPont. Widespread application of this knowledge did not come until 1953, suggesting a complicated technology for the resin supplier and the coater.

1949   Keaton brothers developed automatic screw transfer press.

1949   Vinyl ether developments occur.

1949   Allylic introduced.

1950   Chlorosulfanated polyethylene (Hypalon) introduced by DuPont

1950   First large scale production started of Teflon (PTFE).

1952 MacDonald established conditions for production of commercial polyformaldehyde.

1952 Urethane introduced commercially.

1952 Demand for PE increased to such a degree that PE licensing policies were broadened by court order. Result of anti-trust judgments in U.S. courts against ICI and Du Pont was the compulsory licensing of the ICI master patent to other important U. S. companies.

1953 Ziegler made polyethylene using organo-metallic catalyst.

1953 Phillips Petroleum Company made patent application for HDPE in January.

1953 K. Ziegler of the Max Planck Institute in Germany patented in November and announced PE could be produced without the use of pressure to produce HDPE. Organo-metal catalysts were used. Linear PE was produced as opposed to the branched polymer obtained by the ICI high pressure process.

1954 Professor G. Natta of the Italian Istituto di Chimica Industriale del Politecnico announced the discovery of a stereoregulated polypropylene which he termed "isotactic" PP. The Ziegler and Natta discoveries provided the world with new forms of PE and other polyolefin materials.

1954 Eastman Chemical Products, Inc. was the third LDPE manufacturer in the U. S. with first shipment in November.

1954 In U. S. American Telephone and Telegraph Co., approved use of PE coated wires for the first transatlantic telephone cable to Europe.

1954 *cis*-Polyisoprene (synthetic rubber) was synthesized.

1954 Polyurethane or urethane introduced in U.S.

1954 Ziegler produced polyethylene without pressure.

1955 Phillips Petroleum Co. disclosed its new process of polymerizing ethylene under low pressure.

1955 Polypropylene introduced commercially.

1956 Fluoroelastomers introduced.

1956 Plant scale production started of high density polyethylene.

1956 Schnell published results on polycarbonates.

1957 Polycarbonates developed commercially.

1957 A. Keller of the University of Bristol in England announced a new concept of crystallinity and crystallization. Single crystal-like thin flakes of PE showed a regular, rhombohedral shape and gave perfect crystal patterns in X-ray and electron deflection.

1957    Hercules Incorporated first producer of HDPE in the U. S. via Ziegler process, including UHMWPE.

1957    Urethane-polyether type introduced in U. S.

1959    Chlorinated polyether introduced commercially.

1959    Polycarbonate introduced commercially.

1959    Polyformaldehyde introduced commercially.

1960    Isotactic polymer developments occur.

1961    Vinylidene fluoride introduced commercially.

1962    Phenoxy introduced commercially.

1962    Polyallomers introduced commercially.

1962    Polyethylene copolymer EPR introduced commercially.

1964    Ethylene-vinyl acetate introduced.

1964    Ionomers introduced commercially.

1964    Polyimide introduced as a fabricated product.

1964    Polyphenylene oxide introduced commercially.

1965    Methylpentene introduced commercially.

1965    Parylene introduced commercially.

1965    Polysulfone introduced commercially.

1966    Bartsch golf ball patent for single molded golf ball (Princeton Chemical Research).

1966    Phosphophonitrilic resin introduced commercially.

1967    Sohio (Vistron) introduced methacrylonitrile.

## XI. PICTURE REVIEW ON IMPORTANT PLASTIC APPLICATIONS AND FUTURE GROWTH

### A. General Review

Throughout this book important applications and future growth for different plastics or polymers are reviewed. These plastics permit resisting or extending the life of a part when it is subjected to an environment. Subjects not reviewed in the book which have merit, are highlighted in this section. Also in this section are statements concerning machinery and craftsmen which participate in the important growth of plastics in this exciting age of vast developments and changes.

Growth of the new plastic applications to perform in the different environments will continue to be dependent on the new concepts of design of machinery. Design in metals can draw on a huge 100 year reservoir of knowledge and experience, which in most cases, has been compiled in engineering handbooks. However it is important to keep in mind that metals and other nonplastic materials will continually confront problems in order to be used in the new applications. These new applications will always confront our society.

Progress will also be related to the craftsman in order to ensure that new and replacement parts, using plastics, will survive the environment. True the trend for the past few centuries has been to reduce or eliminate craftsmen, but the fact remains that they will always be required. They may be called by some other name, such as technician, but they will be important to train and educate in the use of these plastics.

## B. Future Growth—Dependent on All Size Companies

From a business stand-point, it is generally stated that a growth of an industry is always dependent on all types and sizes of businesses, ranging from the large corporations to one man "plants." Each has its place in society and the industrial community. More has been written on the large organizations and companies with an individual or single type operation. In this section a review will be presented

Fig. 17-37. Facing panels of jade grey Plexiglas acrylic plastic were used to create this custom designed facade for the North Grove Elementary School in Greenwood, Indiana.

Fig. 17-38. Asbestos-cement facing sheets bonded to urethane core form the exterior walls of this cupola atop 3-story manufacturing facility. Same type of curtain wall panels were also used on top 2 floors of this cement block and steel structure. Panel surfaces are virtually self-cleaning, require no painting and minimum maintenance. (Courtesy Hooker Chemical Corp.)

based on the concepts by William H. Bingham of Hawley Products Company, St. Charles, Illinois on the subject of:

The small molder's dilemma—independence or merger? Critical decision areas effecting corporate growth of independent plastics processors

There is scarcely a well-operated, privately owned independent plastics processor today who does not feel jilted by the ever increasing number of supplier and customer companies, as well as other firms,

Fig. 17-39. The transparent Plexiglas acrylic plastic dome is a beacon for business–especially at night when it is brightly illuminated.

Fig. 17-40. Two story experimental structure made from paper skin polyurethane foam board. (Courtesy of Union Carbide.)

Fig. 17-41. More plastics are being used in building and construction.

moving into segments of the plastics industry which he serves. As the trend intensifies competitive conditions, the independent who wishes to go it alone finds himself hard pressed to decide what corporate strategy should be adopted to assure continued growth of his company.

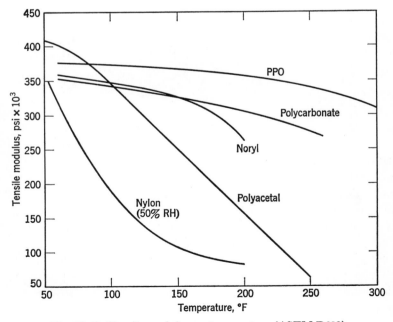

Fig. 17-42. Tensile modulus vs. temperature (ASTM D638).

Fig. 17-43. Dome shaped buildings are now being built using polystyrene boards by the Dow Chemical Company spiral generation technique. Boards are heat bonded in a continuous pattern which produces the dome shape. Sections cut from the dome can be made into doors, connecting halls going from dome to dome. These domes are self supporting, requiring no internal or external support during or after manufacture. It also provides its own insulation and other advantages. (Courtesy of Dow Chemical Company).

One question uppermost in the mind of the owner is whether to continue on independently or to join with another company. The answer is not a simple one. If the decision is to remain independent, the next question is one of resolving the right program for increasing volume to replace business lost to competition.

On the other hand, should the independent conclude it best to join forces with another company, many corporate, personal and financial considerations are involved. Among the more important are keeping independent identity and the freedom to continue operating the company along lines which the owner has proven to be successful. What to do and where to turn under the conditions is truly the independent's dilemma.

The decision making process is rendered even more complex by the added pressures generated by the plastics industry itself and the economy. The successful independent is daily made painfully aware of increasing demands for larger and larger sums of money needed,

Fig. 17-44. Workmen (craftsmen) are heat-bonding in a continuous pattern polystyrene boards to produce dome shaped structures. The Dow Chemical Company material and process called "spiral generation" are being used in this view as well as the next two views.

not only to maintain operation, but to keep up with new materials, market changes and to expand and keep ahead, or just even with the parade.

Capital, in ever increasing quantities, is required to enlarge facilities, to modernize and add efficient equipment, and to attract and hold the best marketing, management and technical talent and skills. Ever larger funds are required for market and product research and development to enable the independent to compete on a level comparable to those of larger corporations and competitors.

There are few independents today whose present business operations provide sales in sufficient volume and at a fast enough rate to generate the capital demanded for sustained growth comparable to the more than ten percent annual rate enjoyed by the plastics industry. The alternative is usually debt financing, and as most owners have

Fig. 17-45. Model of clustered PS dome shaped medical clinic now being built in Lafayette, Indiana (1966).

Fig. 17-46. Section cut from the central medical clinic dome will interconnect with smaller dome and form connecting rooms.

Fig. 17-47. This is an example of machinery aiding plastics in developing a new application. Complete automated systems are now being set up to produce milk bottles. Bottles improve handling properties, reduce breakage, etc., and will also become more economical to use. (Courtesy of Waldron-Hartig.)

Fig. 17-48. More plastics are now undergoing extensive service tests to evaluate all the environmental conditions. Here is a typical house designed and constructed under the direction of the NAHB Research Laboratory of Rockville, Md. This house built in 1966 includes new ideas for all types of materials, including different plastics.

Fig. 17-49. Different type structures are being designed with plastics. Here the University of Michigan, under the supervision of Professor Stephen C. Paraskevopoulos, and in collaboration with Wyandotte Chemicals Company, there has been designed and built for service tests umbrella-shaped roof components made with sprayed polyurethane foam.

learned, is limited and cannot always be obtained in sufficient amounts to meet short term demands or long term needs. Without access to large sources of funds, growth is restricted. Some 2,600 independent plastics processors in the nation are confronted with these problems and they are all looking for a solution.

One popular recommendation for those companies who wish to buck the competitive trend is "specialization." Some have specialized in process and others have specialized in markets. Either method, or a combination of both, has helped many firms. But, when sales and profits are hitched to one or two special processes and/or markets, the lone plastics processor sometimes finds that expansion is difficult to achieve because the business often remains restricted to rather narrow and often limited markets.

It is apparent that something more than specialization is needed by the independent to tap broader growing markets if he is to share and participate more successfully in the large and challenging future which lies ahead in the plastics industry.

Fig. 17-50. Here is an example of the progress being made in the present and future use of plastics in the new office buildings. Architects and engineers have incorporated different plastics in the new Rohm and Haas Philadelphia office building. Use of Plexiglas acrylic is extensive, includes light diffusers, paneling, and kickplates.

The fundamental underlying question then for which the independent is seeking an answer to the future is that of first determining the proper course of action which will allow the company to successfully meet competitive conditions and assure future growth. Once this question is answered, the independent can decide whether or not to go it alone or ride the merger trend.

In an effort to find a way out of the dilemma, Hawley Products Company, itself an independent plastics processor of molded cellulose fiber components, conducted and completed a study to learn what the outlook for the present and future position of the independent might be in the plastics industry. The end result indicated a number of critical decision areas which effect the corporate growth of the independent. They provide factual data which may be used to determine corporate strategy and to develop solutions to the independent's pressing dilemma.

The study is based on an analysis of the data published by the U. S. Department of Commerce in "Current Industrial Reports" showing "Shipments of Selected Plastics Products," beginning with the year 1960 through the latest available data for 1964.

Fig. 17-51. Industrial plants, such as the nitric acid plant in Belgium, will make use of more plastics to meet severe environments. Reinforced glass fiber-polyester resin translucent panels from International Filon Products Assoc. are used in this plant as walls, and cooling tower.

The figures are the most authoritative information available which indicate the trends in the pounds and dollar shipments of plastics products produced, and the types of materials used by approximately 2,600 independent processors annually in the nation. Authoritative as these figures are, it is most difficult for the government, or any other source for that matter, to precisely separate the operations of the independent from captive activities down to the precise number of pounds or dollar amounts. It is recognized that there may be some discrepancies, but the information is the most reliable available, and provides a reasonably good measure of the independent's operations.

Fig. 17-52. Here is a major change in the centry old steel building bridge process; this recently built bridge uses plastics coating and interlinner in its steel cable construction. This development is the present joint program of Bethlehem Steel Corporation and DuPont.

TABLE 17-17.  Molded Plastics Products Types (Dollar Shipment Trends)

| Type of plastics products | Millions of dollars | | | | | Percent increase or (decrease) | |
|---|---|---|---|---|---|---|---|
| | 1960 | 1961 | 1962 | 1963 | 1964 | Amount | Percent |
| Industrial | *614* | 576 | 671 | 793 | *845* | 231 | *38* |
| Packaging and shipping containers | *184* | 294 | 379 | 420 | *504* | 320 | *174* |
| Consumer and commercial | *176* | 229 | 246 | 304 | *361* | 185 | *105* |
| Laminated sheets, rods, and tubes | — | 207 | 215 | 232 | 259 | — | — |
| Construction | 381 | 187 | 205 | 226 | 322 | — | — |
| Foamed | *112* | 149 | 182 | 228 | *259* | *147* | *131* |
| Dinnerware, tableware and kitchenware | *98* | 122 | 135 | 139 | *147* | 49 | *50* |
| Other | *55* | 72 | 115 | 167 | *175* | *120* | *218* |
| Total | *1,620* | 1,836 | 2,148 | 2,509 | *2,872* | *1,252* | 77 |

ᵃ Includes laminated sheets, rods, and tubes.

Fig. 17-53. Roadbed ballast stabilized by DuPont neoprene sheets are being used by the Japanese National Railways. These elastomeric sheets are made into continuous membranes.

TABLE 17-18. Molded Plastics Products Types (Percent of Dollar Shipments)

| Type of plastics products | Percent to total millions of dollars | | | | |
|---|---|---|---|---|---|
| | 1960 | 1961 | 1962 | 1963 | 1964 |
| Industrial | 38 | 31 | 31 | 32 | 29 |
| Packaging and shipping containers | 11 | 16 | 18 | 17 | 18 |
| Consumer and commercial | 11 | 13 | 12 | 12 | 13 |
| Laminated sheets, rods, and tubes | — | 11 | 10 | 9 | 9 |
| Construction | 24 [a] | 10 | 10 | 9 | 11 |
| Foamed | 7 | 8 | 8 | 9 | 9 |
| Dinnerware, tableware and kitchenware | 6 | 7 | 6 | 5 | 5 |
| Other | 3 | 4 | 4 | 7 | 6 |
| Total | 100 | 100 | 100 | 100 | 100 |

[a] Includes laminated sheets, rods, and tubes.

Fig. 17-54. Sheets of neoprene, placed beneath the railbed in unstable areas, are bonded together to form a continuous waterstrip. Sheets reduce maintenance on ballast above soft, wet subsoil.

The Bureau of Census recognizes the problem by stipulating that "the survey excludes all plastic products specifically assigned as primary products to other industries, such as converted flexible packaging, boats, toys, sporting goods, luggage, etc., and captive production by companies which do not recognize the plastics operation as a separate establishment." Put another way, the data indicates, insofar as possible, trends in the volume of business produced solely by the independent plastics processors in the United States.

Let us now orient the independent plastics processor within the total plastics industry. Review the tables in this section. Note these

Fig. 17-55. The present aerospace programs make use of many different plastics to perform important functions in "extreme" environments. This book provides information on many of these different applications and their effects in these environments. Here is an artist concept where plastic research and development programs are using different plastics for use in space vehicles, platforms, and escape systems.

data represents that portion, only, of the plastics pertaining to the independent processor which, as expected, use plastics subjected to many different environments.

The critical decision areas effecting the corporate growth of independent plastics processors which have been presented furnishes basic information upon which to plan corporate growth strategy and offers aid to the independent deciding what the solution is to the dilemma of whether to remain an independent or join forces with other companies.

A wide choice of growth objectives are established in the charts for the independent who wishes to continue going it alone. They enable him to make his own decision as to the rate and the potential volume of business desired; and to decide on the choice of product categories, markets and geographical areas which will get him to his goals. Once the objectives are selected, the independent can then develop immediate and future plans for reaching the targets.

The decision as to which objectives the independent should select as a goal for accomplishment depends upon a number of factors. They

Fig. 17-56. Artist sketch of LEM (Lunar Excursion Module) which will land men on the moon uses plastics which will not out-gass (during flight in space where interior environment will include $\frac{1}{3}$ atmospheric pressure and all oxygen) and perform required functions of mechanical, electrical, and heat insulation. (Courtesy of Grumman Corp.)

are the rate at which the independent wants to grow, his position in the industry category he is now serving, and whether the company is in a position to program and provide the resources for what is required to reach the objectives selected.

It is quite clear from the trends shown in the charts, however, that the independent who wishes to successfully compete and grow in the future and expand at the dynamic rate of the total plastics industry must broaden his operation to include the five basic processes. Otherwise, the chances are that the company may be left behind in the market place by remaining an independent operation.

There are two solutions for the independent who wishes to bring the five basic processes together for growth accomplishment. Whichever solution one wishes to adopt, the underlying philosophy for each is based on preserving the identity of the independent.

It is a commonly accepted fact within the plastics industry that the most successful way to operate a plastics processing operation is on a relatively small, compact, independent basis, each basic process located

Fig. 17-57. Now returning to earth, plastics will make more inroads where parts are subjected to under and above the earth. Here is a Western Electric communication control center at the Goddard Space Flight Center, Greenbelt, Md. Extensive use of plastics is made in many different electronic and electrical applications.

in strategic geographical areas and more or less isolated from the other, and preferably managed and operated under separate roofs by people well established and experienced in the particular process. It is, for these reasons, highly desirable that the maintenance of independent management be insisted upon in each of the two solutions.

The first solution, then, is rather obvious. The independent who decides to expand more totally into the plastics industry can do so on his own by taking the necessary steps to expand his own process and facilities and, in addition, acquire the other four basic processes, each of which should be established in separate facilities and with the necessary organization to operate them independently.

The problem, however, of combining markets, materials and processes by this route into a coordinated growth directed effort would more likely than not be most difficult for many present day independents to accomplish alone because they are just not big enough in size.

The financial, technical, marketing and organizational assistance required, the special business services and talent needed, and the

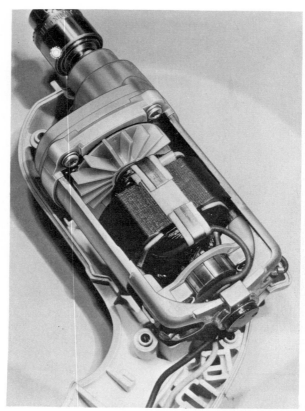

Fig. 17-58. Another down-to-earth growth area is in the appliance industry. This electric motor drill makes extensive use of Fiberfil reinforced glass fiber-thermoplastics in the electrical system: insulator, fan, etc.

company structure itself, would probably not permit achievement commensurate with the requirements demanded to reach the pre-established growth goals. Today's and tomorrow's business complexities call for access to larger resources and broader experiences.

The second solution is more practical. It proposes that the independent gather together a group of independents who agree that the best way to grow in the future is to unite their forces through a pooling-of-interests, but to continue to operate separately. Each member of the group should be carefully selected, represent each of the five basic processes, and have proven histories of running successful and established businesses. This proposes a company framework which could be developed into a strong, national concern.

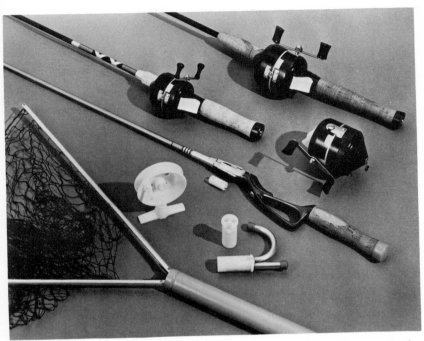

Fig. 17-59. Down-to-earth: fishing gear continually makes use of more plastics.

Time alloted to this talk will not permit going into the details to describe how such a company structure should be set up. There is a type of corporate concept, however, which fits the requirements and has many times been proven successful in other industries. It is well suited to pooling-the-interests of independent plastics processors and, at the same time, satisfies the growth requirements brought out in the study, including the provision for corporate resources and services to accomplish the task.

It is possible to design such a structure in a manner which would furnish each of the members of the group with long range equity capital, long range marketing on a national scope, long range R & D in market, product, process and materials, combined purchasing advantages, personnel recruiting and training, labor, legal and other types of benefits and services which are made available today in the larger corporations.

There are many advantages for the independent to consider in pooling interests with a group of selected successful processors. A few of the major ones are described as follows:

Fig. 17-60. For the ever-growing plastic markets are clothing and sporting equipment. Plastic surf boards, by Ventura International Plastics, is one example which requires rigid structural and water resistant properties, as well as beauty.

## 1. Financial Advantages

1. An opportunity is provided to solve personal estate problems and to participate in future growth through capital appreciation.
2. Access is given to institutional and public capital markets both for long term borrowing and for equity capital for the following:
   a. Expanding facilities and modernizing equipment
   b. Development market, product and process diversification
   c. Employing specialized administrative, marketing, technical, manufacturing, executive and organizational talent

## 2. Management Advantages

1. The independent owner is able to remain as top executive of his business, with incentives to expand the company further, and with access to the necessary capital.
2. Members of the independent's organization, including top executives, may look forward to better job security, better promotion

Fig. 17-61. Gary Player wins with Shakespeare Fiberglas Wondershafts.

opportunity, incentives to attract and hold talent, and the opportunity to develop and remain in the business.
3. Specialized talent and assistance is made available in all professional business areas.

## 3. Advantages of Flexibility

The markets and the materials available for the processing of plastics products are in a constant state of revolution. The changes that take place in both areas are rapid and at a rate that can wipe out a

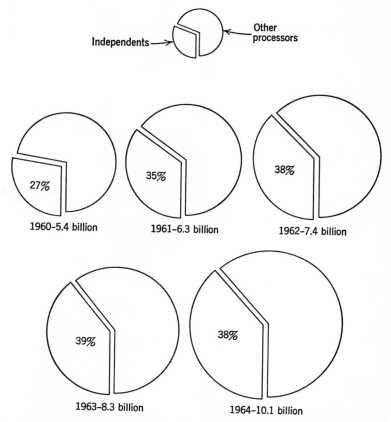

Independents →     ← Other processors

27%
1960–5.4 billion

35%
1961–6.3 billion

38%
1962–7.4 billion

39%
1963–8.3 billion

38%
1964–10.1 billion

Fig. 17-62. Independent plastics processors consume more than one-third of total plastics materials produced.

substantial amount of business overnight. This could be fatal to the independent working alone.

The five basic processes, on the other hand, are in a state of evolution. It is doubtful as to whether any one of them will change radically from their fundamental concept or be entirely replaced. Improvements and modifications, it is anticipated, will come gradually. Consequently, rapid transfers may be made from one process to another as changes in the market or in materials require such moves in order to retain the business for the group. At the same time, immediate steps can be taken to develop other new business for the member of the group whose company is temporarily and adversely affected.

The group who pools their interests thus enjoys a degree of insurance

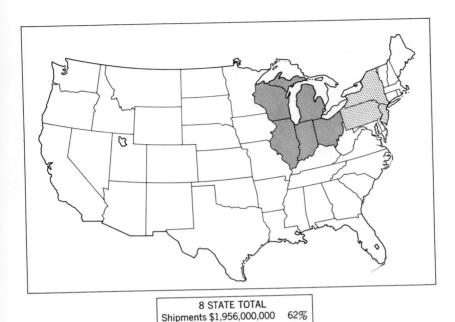

| 8 STATE TOTAL | |
|---|---|
| Shipments $1,956,000,000 | 62% |
| Processors 1,473 Firms | 56% |

Fig. 17-63. Geographical concentration, independents and shipments. Eight state total: shipments, $1,956,000,000....62%; processors, 1,473 firms....56%

and flexibility in that processes may be shifted from failing products, or markets, or obsoleted materials, to other more desirable products or markets and to newer materials. Meanwhile, resources are available which can be tapped to reorientate the independent division which is affected by failing business into other markets and products suitable to the particular process.

## 4. SUMMARY

Most successful independent processors have achieved their position by many years of hard work and by reinvesting most of their profits in the added equipment and facilities needed for normal growth. Each processor has succeeded in creating a valuable asset, but they now find themselves with all their eggs in one basket, a basket that is primarily plant, equipment, and goodwill, and not very liquid.

It is logical to believe that many independent processors, who want to remain as independent operators of their businesses, but who are finding that corporate growth is difficult to achieve without access

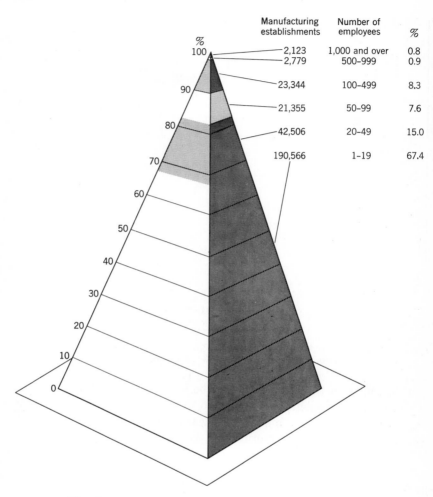

Fig. 17-64. Industrial market for molded plastics products.

to the operational advantages of a larger concern, will consider more seriously than ever before becoming a member of a group in a strong concern. The reasons can be fairly well summarized.

Every independent processor recognizes the market and industry conditions which must be met in order to achieve dynamic future growth. Each is likewise aware that the prevailing industry trend is toward consolidation and mergers, and that competitive and economic

TABLE 17-19. Molded Industrial Products Types (Dollar Shipment Trends)

| Type of plastics products | Millions of dollars | | | | | Percent increase or (decrease) | |
|---|---|---|---|---|---|---|---|
| | 1960 | 1961 | 1962 | 1963 | 1964 | Amount | Percent |
| Transportation equipment | | | | | | | |
| Motor vehicles | 89 | 100 | 138 | 162 | 176 | 87 | 98 |
| Aircraft | 35 | 29 | 26 | 24 | 31 | (4) | (11) |
| Missiles | 24 | 31 | 47 | 56 | 47 | 23 | 96 |
| Other | 10 | 10 | 12 | 18 | 13 | 3 | 30 |
| Total | 158 | 170 | 223 | 260 | 267 | 109 | 69 |
| Electrical and electronic equipment | 100 | 102 | 118 | 135 | 138 | 38 | 38 |
| Household and commercial | | | | | | | |
| Air conditioners | 7 | 8 | 8 | 7 | 10 | 3 | 4 |
| Refrigerators and freezers | 41 | 36 | 37 | 45 | 47 | 6 | 15 |
| Other major appliances | 28 | 34 | 39 | 46 | 49 | 21 | 75 |
| Small appliances | 18 | 25 | 30 | 40 | 40 | 22 | 122 |
| Total | 94 | 103 | 114 | 138 | 146 | 52 | 55 |
| Office machines and equipment | 14 | 16 | 21 | 20 | 21 | 7 | 50 |
| Gears, bearings, bushings, and cams | 15 | 16 | 16 | 22 | 22 | 7 | 47 |
| Other [a] | 233 | 168 | 179 | 217 | 251 | 18 | 8 |
| Total | 614 | 575 | 671 | 792 | 845 | 231 | 38 |

[a] Includes other components, housings, accessories and industrial products not specified by kind.

pressures will continue to mount. While each processor knows his ability to compete in his own market, he also realizes that capital is a limiting factor in expansion and growth.

There is no question but what there will always be a future for the independent plastics processor who wishes to go it alone. But, like material manufacturers who have been forced to radically change their domestic corporate strategy because of violently changing conditions of world wide scope, so will the independent with foresight decide that he will have to change his own strategy if he plans to grow in our increasingly volatile national economy.

While the self-initiated, self-created, self-financed and self-managed

TABLE 17-20.  Molded Industrial Products Types (Percent of Dollar Shipments)

| Type of plastics products | Percent to total millions of dollars | | | | |
|---|---|---|---|---|---|
| | 1960 | 1961 | 1962 | 1963 | 1964 |
| Transportation equipment | | | | | |
| Motor vehicles | 14 | 17 | 20 | 20 | 21 |
| Aircraft | 6 | 5 | 4 | 3 | 4 |
| Missiles | 4 | 5 | 7 | 7 | 6 |
| Other | 2 | 2 | 2 | 2 | 1 |
| Total | 26 | 29 | 33 | 33 | 32 |
| Electrical and electronic equipment | 16 | 18 | 18 | 17 | 16 |
| Household and commercial | | | | | |
| Air conditioners | 1 | 1 | 1 | 1 | 1 |
| Refrigerators and freezers | 7 | 6 | 6 | 6 | 6 |
| Other major appliances | 5 | 6 | 6 | 6 | 6 |
| Small appliances | 3 | 5 | 4 | 5 | 5 |
| Total | 16 | 18 | 17 | 17 | 18 |
| Office machines and equipment | 2 | 3 | 3 | 3 | 2 |
| Gears, bearings, bushings, and cams | 2 | 3 | 2 | 3 | 3 |
| Other [a] | 38 | 29 | 27 | 27 | 29 |
| Total | 100 | 100 | 100 | 100 | 100 |

[a] Includes other components, housings, accessories and industrial products not specified by kind.

methods that once lead to significant business success will never be outdated, they have lead many to their present quandry. For those independents who are willing to share some of their independence with other to reduce their risks, the logical solution to the independent's dilemma is the pooling-of-interests concept.

## XII. THE PLASTICS AGE

As is evident from the contents of this publication (two volume book) many different plastics have in the past and will continue in the future to meet the ever lasting and different environments. Plastics

TABLE 17-21.  Pounds of Resin Types Used in Molded Products

| Type of resin | Millions of pounds | | | | | Percent increase or (decrease) | |
|---|---|---|---|---|---|---|---|
| | 1960 | 1961 | 1962 | 1963 | 1964 | Amount | Percent |
| *Thermoplastic* | | | | | | | |
| Polyethylene | 253 | 633 | 922 | 1,043 | 1,267 | 1,014 | 401 |
| Styrene and copolymer | 379 | 463 | 531 | 657 | 768 | 389 | 103 |
| Vinyl and vinyl copolymer | 262 | 396 | 498 | 590 | 688 | 426 | 163 |
| Cellulosics | 43 | 79 | 85 | 82 | 117 | 74 | 172 |
| Polypropylene | 20 | 40 | 54 | 83 | 115 | 95 | 475 |
| Acrylic | NA | NA | 31 | 93 | 35 | — | — |
| Polyamide | NA | NA | 20 | 26 | 34 | — | — |
| Other | 99 | 158 | 119 | 108 | 91 | (8) | (8) |
| Total | 1,056 | 1,769 | 2,260 | 2,682 | 3,115 | 2,059 | 195 |
| *Thermosets* | | | | | | | |
| Phenolics | 184 | 187 | 215 | 234 | 252 | 68 | 37 |
| Diisocyanates and polyurethanes | NA | NA | 79 | 99 | 140 | — | — |
| Melamines | 61 | 64 | 73 | 91 | 93 | 32 | 52 |
| Polyester resins, including diallyl phthalate | 73 | 80 | 73 | 88 | 90 | 17 | 23 |
| Urea | 28 | 28 | 32 | 30 | 33 | 5 | 18 |
| Other | 77 | 88 | 29 | 30 | 34 | 43 | 56 |
| Total | 423 | 447 | 501 | 572 | 642 | 219 | 52 |
| Total | 1,479 | 2,216 | 2,761 | 3,254 | 3,757 | 2,278 | 154 |

is as important to society as are other materials such as iron, aluminum, copper and others. Forecasts have been made that shows the volume consumption of plastics will be greater by 1985 than any other material; iron which is now in first place will move down to second place. Immediately after the 21st century starts the weight consumption of plastics will be in first place (22–26).

Both the plastics and environmental test conditions tend to appear complex. In the case of plastics the situation can exist due to what appears to be a condition of many new material types. Not long ago, all plastics had an organic backbone and could be classified reasonably well as thermoplastic or thermoset. Now we include in our discussions

TABLE 17-22.  Percent of Resin Types Used in Molded Products

| Type of resin | Percent to total millions of pounds | | | | |
| --- | --- | --- | --- | --- | --- |
| | 1960 | 1961 | 1962 | 1963 | 1964 |
| *Thermoplastic* | | | | | |
| Polyethylene | 17 | 29 | 33 | 32 | 34 |
| Styrene and copolymer | 26 | 21 | 19 | 20 | 20 |
| Vinyl and vinyl copolymer | 18 | 18 | 18 | 18 | 18 |
| Cellulosics | 3 | 3 | 3 | 3 | 3 |
| Polypropylene | 1 | 2 | 2 | 3 | 3 |
| Acrylic | NA | NA | 1 | 3 | 1 |
| Polyamide | NA | NA | 1 | 1 | 1 |
| Other | 7 | 7 | 4 | 3 | 2 |
| Total | 72 | 80 | 81 | 82 | 82 |
| *Thermosets* | | | | | |
| Phenolics | 12% | 8% | 8% | 7% | 7% |
| Diisocyanates and polyurethanes | NA | NA | 3 | 3 | 4 |
| Melamines | 4 | 3 | 3 | 3 | 3 |
| Polyester resins, including diallyl phthalate | 5 | 4 | 3 | 3 | 2 |
| Urea | 2 | 1 | 1 | 1 | 1 |
| Other | 5 | 4 | 1 | 1 | 1 |
| Total | 28 | 20 | 19 | 18 | 18 |
| Total | 100 | 100 | 100 | 100 | 100 |

such identifications as organics, semi-organics, inorganics, copolymers, crosslinkables, ladder polymers, stereoregular polymers, pyrolites and the usual thermoplastics and thermosets. These terms do not confuse or distort facts which the plastics specialist knows. Like the medical doctor or metal specialist, if someone has an environmental problem with a plastic product—make sure the plastics expert or specialist is consulted. Also compare the situation with a legal problem; get the proper type lawyer for the problem at hand. Regardless the real problem is to do the best possible in analyzing the environmental condition; environments can be either controllable or uncontrollable. When they are uncontrollable, statistical evaluation and other techniques are to be used.

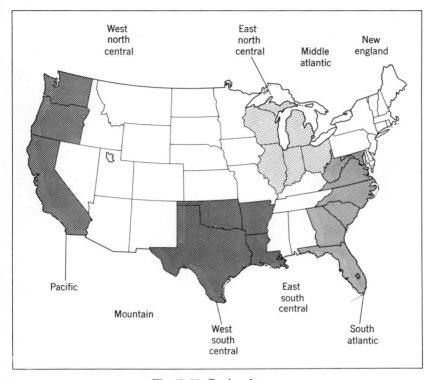

Fig. 17-65. Regional areas.

In the past we have had many important eras, such as the Stone Age, the Iron Age and the Industrial Age. All these steps throughout the past centuries have advanced the knowledge and economical growth of mankind. We are now entering the next step: the Plastics Age (see Table 17-28).

The materials revolution, which has been taking place since 1940, has clearly shown that the major technical developments occurred in plastics. Redesigns and new product developments now put more plastics in use than any other material. In fact different surveys show that the plastics technology will have more effect in the future developments than any other category, such as high strength metals, automatic assembly, solid state components, integrated circuits, computer-aided design, lasers, cryogenics, and atomic energy. These categories are in their order of importance with plastics being the most

TABLE 17-23.   Molded Product Dollar Shipments (Geographic Area Trends)

| Regional division [a] | Millions of dollars | | | | | Percent increase or (decrease) | |
|---|---|---|---|---|---|---|---|
| | 1960 | 1961 | 1962 | 1963 | 1964 | Amount | Percent |
| N.E. | 219 | 333 | 331 | 353 | 394 | 175 | 80 |
| M.A. | 395 | 606 | 674 | 774 | 852 | 457 | 116 |
| E.N.C. | 635 | 875 | 1,053 | 1,182 | 1,258 | 623 | 98 |
| W.N.C. | 66 | 76 | 93 | 124 | 171 | 105 | 159 |
| S.A. | 92 | 143 | 189 | 242 | 291 | 199 | 216 |
| E.S.C. | 17 | 49 | 66 | 128 | 182 | 165 | 971 |
| W.S.C. | 38 | 54 | 69 | 90 | 92 | 54 | 142 |
| M. | 5 | 7 | 8 | 4 | 8 | 3 | 60 |
| P. | 153 | 175 | 214 | 247 | 262 | 109 | 71 |
| Total | 1,620 | 2,318 | 2,697 | 3,144 | 3,510 | 1,890 | 117 |

[a] N.E., New England; M.A., Middle Atlantic (3 states); E.N.C., East North Central (5 states around Chicago); W.N.C., West North Central; S.A., South Atlantic; E.S.C., East South Central; W.S.C., West South Central; M., Mountain; P., Pacific.

TABLE 17-24.   Molded Product Dollar Shipments (Percent by Geographic Areas)

| Regional division | Percent to total millions of dollars | | | | |
|---|---|---|---|---|---|
| | 1960 | 1961 | 1962 | 1963 | 1964 |
| N.E. | 14 | 15 | 12 | 11 | 11 |
| M.A. | 24 | 26 | 25 | 25 | 24 |
| E.N.C. | 39 | 38 | 39 | 37 | 36 |
| W.N.C. | 4 | 3 | 4 | 4 | 5 |
| S.A. | 6 | 6 | 7 | 8 | 8 |
| E.S.C. | 1 | 2 | 2 | 4 | 5 |
| W.S.C. | 2 | 2 | 3 | 3 | 3 |
| M. | — | — | — | — | — |
| P. | 10 | 8 | 8 | 8 | 8 |
| Total | 100 | 100 | 100 | 100 | 100 |

TABLE 17-25.  Number of Independent Processors by Geographic Areas

| Region | 1960 | 1961 | Percent increase or (decrease) | |
|--------|------|------|--------|---------|
| | | | Amount | Percent |
| E.N.C. | 692 | 746 | 54 | 8 |
| M.A. | 701 | 727 | 26 | 4 |
| P. | 353 | 378 | 25 | 7 |
| N.E. | 309 | 343 | 34 | 11 |
| W.N.C. | 131 | 145 | 14 | 11 |
| S.A. | 116 | 142 | 26 | 22 |
| W.S.C. | 73 | 76 | 3 | 4 |
| E.S.C. | 34 | 40 | 6 | 18 |
| M. | 29 | 33 | 4 | 14 |
| Total | 2,438 | 2,630 | 192 | 8 |

TABLE 17-26.  Percent of Independent Processors by Geographic Areas

| Region | 1960 | 1961 |
|--------|------|------|
| N.E. | 13 | 13 |
| M.A. | 29 | 28 |
| E.N.C. | 28 | 28 |
| W.N.C. | 5 | 6 |
| S.A. | 5 | 5 |
| E.S.C. | 1 | 2 |
| W.S.C. | 3 | 3 |
| M. | 1 | 1 |
| P. | 15 | 14 |
| Total | 100 | 100 |

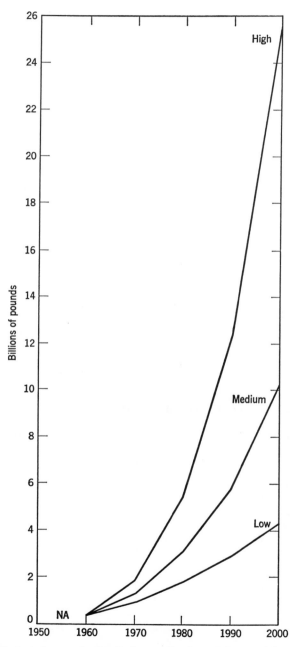

Fig. 17-66. Projected use of polyethylene and other olefins, moldings, and extrusions. Sources: Resources for the Future, Inc.

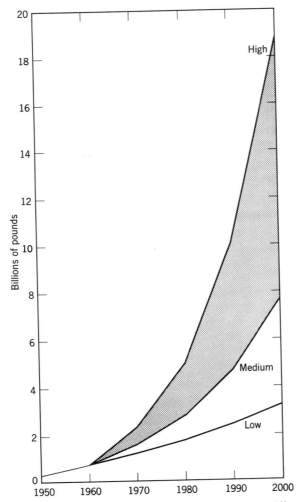

Fig. 17-67. Projected use of styrene and copolymers moldings.

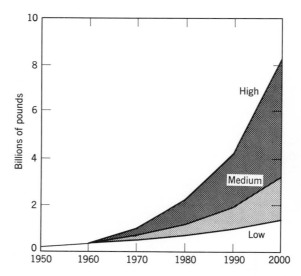

Fig. 17-68. Projected use of vinyl and vinyl copolymers moldings and extrusions.

TABLE 17-27.   Average Annual Dollar Shippments of Independents

| Region | Year | Average dollar shipments |
|---|---|---|
| N.E. | 1960 | $709,000 |
|  | 1961 | 972,000 |
| M.A. | 1960 | 563,000 |
|  | 1961 | 834,000 |
| E.N.C. | 1960 | 917,000 |
|  | 1961 | 1,173,000 |
| W.N.C. | 1960 | 508,000 |
|  | 1961 | 527,000 |
| S.A. | 1960 | 792,000 |
|  | 1961 | 1,009,000 |
| E.S.C. | 1960 | 505,000 |
|  | 1961 | 1,231,000 |
| W.S.C. | 1960 | 516,000 |
|  | 1961 | 704,000 |
| M. | 1960 | 171,000 |
|  | 1961 | 210,000 |
| P. | 1960 | 433,000 |
|  | 1961 | 462,000 |
|  | 1960 | 664,000 |
| Total Average | 1961 | $882,000 |

TABLE 17-28. The Plastics Age: Estimated Annual World Consumption of Different Materials

| Year | 1970 | 1980 | 1985 | 1990 | 2000 |
|---|---|---|---|---|---|
| Population, billions | 3.7 | 4.6 | 5.0 | 5.6 | 7.0 |
| Synthetics | | | | | |
| Plastics | | | | | |
|   Million tons | 27 | 105 | 240 | 420 | 1700 |
|   Kg/person | 7.3 | 23 | 48 | 7.5 | 243 |
|   Million cu. meters | 23.4 | 91 | 205 | 365 | 1480 |
|   Liters/person | 6.3 | 20 | 41 | 65 | 212 |
| Syntretic rubbers | | | | | |
|   Million tons | 5.5 | 11.5 | 16.0 | 23.0 | 44.0 |
|   Kg/person | 1.5 | 2.5 | 3.2 | 4.1 | 6.3 |
|   Million cu. meters | 5.8 | 12.0 | 17.0 | 24.0 | 46.0 |
|   Liters/person | 1.6 | 2.6 | 3.4 | 4.3 | 6.6 |
| Man-made fibers | | | | | |
|   Million tons | 7.2 | 13.0 | 17.0 | 24.5 | 46.0 |
|   Kg/person | 1.9 | 2.8 | 3.4 | 4.4 | 6.6 |
|   Million cu. meters | 6.0 | 11.0 | 14.2 | 19.5 | 38.0 |
|   Liters/person | 1.6 | 2.4 | 2.8 | 3.5 | 5.4 |
| Total synthetics | | | | | |
|   Million tons | 40 | 130 | 273 | 467 | 1790 |
|   Kg/person | 11 | 28 | 55 | 83 | 256 |
|   Million cu. meters | 35 | 114 | 236 | 490 | 1564 |
|   Liters/person | 9.5 | 25 | 47 | 73 | 224 |
| Metals | | | | | |
| Iron | | | | | |
|   Million tons | 560 | 900 | 1130 | 1400 | 2250 |
|   Kg/person | 151 | 196 | 226 | 250 | 321 |
|   Million cu. meters | 72 | 115 | 145 | 179 | 287 |
|   Liters/person | 19 | 25 | 29 | 32 | 41 |
| Aluminum | | | | | |
|   Million tons | 11.3 | 32 | 55 | 90 | 250 |
|   Kg/person | 3.0 | 7.0 | 11 | 16 | 36 |
|   Million cu. meters | 4.2 | 11.9 | 20 | 33 | 93 |
|   Liters/person | 1.1 | 2.6 | 4.0 | 5.9 | 13 |
| Copper | | | | | |
|   Million tons | 6.2 | 9.2 | 10.0 | 13.5 | 20.0 |
|   Kg/person | 1.7 | 2.0 | 2.0 | 2.4 | 2.9 |
|   Million cu. meters | 0.7 | 1.0 | 1.1 | 1.5 | 2.2 |
|   Liters/person | 0.2 | 0.2 | 0.2 | 0.3 | 0.3 |
| Zinc | | | | | |
|   Million tons | 5.0 | 7.2 | 8.7 | 10.4 | 15.0 |
|   Kg/person | 1.4 | 1.6 | 1.7 | 1.9 | 2.1 |
|   Million cu. meters | 0.7 | 1.0 | 1.2 | 1.5 | 2.1 |
|   Liters/person | 0.2 | 0.2 | 0.2 | 0.3 | 0.3 |

(continued)

TABLE 17-28 (*continued*)

| Year | 1970 | 1980 | 1985 | 1990 | 2000 |
|---|---|---|---|---|---|
| Population, billions | 3.7 | 4.6 | 5.0 | 5.6 | 7.0 |
| Total metals | | | | | |
| Million tons | 582 | 948 | 1204 | 1514 | 2535 |
| Kg/person | 157 | 206 | 241 | 270 | 362 |
| Million cu. meters | 78 | 129 | 167 | 215 | 384 |
| Liters/person | 21 | 28 | 33 | 38 | 55 |
| | | Natural Products | | | |
| Natural rubber | | | | | |
| Million tons | 2.5 | 2.6 | 2.7 | 2.8 | 3.0 |
| Kg/person | 0.7 | 0.6 | 0.5 | 0.5 | 0.4 |
| Million cu. meters | 2.7 | 2.7 | 2.9 | 3.0 | 3.2 |
| Liters/person | 0.7 | 0.6 | 0.6 | 0.5 | 0.5 |
| Natural fibers | | | | | |
| Million tons | 21.5 | 30.2 | 35.0 | 41.5 | 60 |
| Kg/person | 5.8 | 6.6 | 7.0 | 7.4 | 8.6 |
| Million cu. meters | 18.0 | 25.0 | 29.0 | 34.5 | 50 |
| Liters/person | 4.9 | 5.4 | 5.8 | 6.2 | 7.1 |
| Total natural products | | | | | |
| Million tons | 24.0 | 32.8 | 37.7 | 44.3 | 63.0 |
| Kg/person | 6.5 | 7.1 | 7.5 | 7.9 | 9.0 |
| Million cu. meters | 20.7 | 27.7 | 31.9 | 37.5 | 53.2 |
| Liters/person | 5.6 | 6.0 | 6.4 | 6.7 | 7.6 |
| | | Total | | | |
| Million tons | 646 | 1111 | 1515 | 2025 | 4388 |
| Kg/person | 175 | 241 | 303 | 361 | 627 |
| Million cu. meters | 134 | 271 | 435 | 662 | 2001 |
| Liters/person | 36 | 59 | 87 | 118 | 286 |

[a] Metric ton equals 2204.6 lb.
[b] One kg equals 2.2 lb.

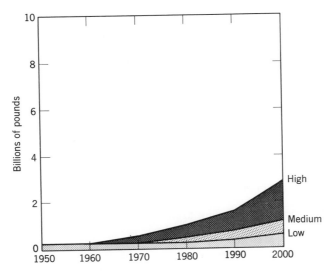

Fig. 17-69. Projected use of phenolics moldings.

significant and atomic energy the least to effect new developments. These factors provide the reason for the Plastics Age—with the capability of plastics, or polymers, to survive in different environments providing one of the important basic characteristics.

## REFERENCES

1. S. J. Kennedy, "Boots, Clothing, Body Armor for Vietnam," *The Review,* Defense Supply Assoc., pp. 41-139 (March/April 1966).
2. J. K. Taussig, Jr., "Ceramics for Defense," *Ordnance,* pp. 292-294 (Nov.-Dec. 1966).
3. Army Natick Laboratories Body Armor Fact Sheet, 1967.
4. N. L. Reed, "New Materials for the Modern Army," *Army Digest,* pp. 42-45 (Oct. 1966).
5. A. L. Lastnick, "A Crash & Ballistic Protective Flight Helmet," Aerospace Medical Assoc. Sci. Mtg. Conference, April 1966, Las Vegas, Nev.
6. D. V. Rosato, "Armor," *Reinforced Plastics & Composites World* (July-Aug. 1967).
7. "Army Aviation Helmet Experience." Rpt. HF4-61 U.S. Army Bd. for Aviation Accident, Ft. Rucker, Ala.
8. "Ballistic Acceptance Test Method for Personnel Armor Materials," MIL-STD-622, June 1961.
9. A. A. Bezrah, "Level and Priority of Protective Requirements," presented at in-process review Army aircraft crewmen's helmet. QMR&E Comd Natick, Mass., Sept. 1961.
10. "Helmet Flying HGU-2A/P," MIL-H-26671A, Mar 1961.

11. "Helmet Pilot's Protective Type APH-6," MIL-H-22995, no date.
12. "Helmet Combat Crewmen," MIL-H-43059, Feb. 1962.
13. A. L. Lastnik and J. W. Gates, "The Effect of Resin Concentrate on Physical Properties of a Laminated Structure for a Crash and Ballistic Protective Helmet," Clothing br series rept. no. 29, Clothing & Organic Materials Div. QMR&E Comd. Natick, Mass., Apr. 1962. Presented at Personnel Armor Symposium U.S. Naval Res. Labs. Wash. DC 4-5, Oct. 1961.
14. R. C. Nelson, J. F. Alexander, H. J. Montoya, and W. D. Van Huss, An Investigation of Various Measures Used in Impact Testing of Protective Headgear," *J. Sports Phys. Fitness,* **4** (2) SP-102 (June 1964).
15. G. G. Snively and C. C. Chichester, "Safety in Racing," Research Grant No. RG-6094 Natl. Inst. of Health, U.S. Pub. Health Serv.
16. J. E. Burroughs and H. R. Thornton, "Refractory Aerospace Structural Components by Plastic Molding Process," *Ceramic Bull.,* **45,** 2-187 (Feb. 1966).
17. R. J. Fabian, "Plastic Bearing Materials," *Matl. Design Engr.,* p. 90 (Mar. 1964).
18. R. J. Fabian, "Materials for Gaskets, Packings and Seals," *Matl. Design Engr., Manual No. 165* (Dec. 1959).
19. J. Nardone, "Plastic Gears," PLASTEC Report 16, July 1964.
20. J. H. DuBois, "Plastic Materials Selection," *Plastics World,* **23,** 10, 52 (Oct. 1965).
21. D. V. Rosato and C. S. Grove, *Filament Winding,* Interscience, New York, 1964, p. 171.
22. R. Houwink of Wassennar, Netherlands, presentation at the World Chemical Engineering Congress, Mexico City, Mexico, Nov. 1965.
23. *Modern Plastics,* pp. 98-100 (Aug. 1966).
24. *Kunststoffe,* **36** (Aug. 1966).
25. D. V. Rosato, Plastics Panel presentation, Society of Plastics Engineers, Newark Section Meeting, May 19, 1966.
26. D. V. Rosato, "The Impact of New Machinery in '76," Society of Plastics Industry, New England Conference, Oct. 7, 1966.

# AUTHOR INDEX, VOLUME II

Numbers in parentheses are reference numbers and indicate that the author's work is referred to although his name is not mentioned in the text. Numbers in *italics* show the pages on which the complete references may be found.